ELEMENT	SYMBOL	ATOMIC NUMBER	ATOMIC WEIGHT
Molybdenum	Mo	42	95.95
Neodymium	Nd	60	144.27
Neon	Ne	10	20.183
Neptunium	Np	93*	(244)
Nickel	Ni	28	58.71
Niobium (Columbium)	Nb	41	92.91
Nitrogen	N	7	14.008
Nobelium	No	102*	?
Osmium	Os	76	190.2
Oxygen	O	8	16.0000
Palladium	Pd	46	106.4
Phosphorus	P	15	30.975
Samarium	Sm*	62	150.35
Scandium	Sc	21	44.96
Selenium	Se	34	78.96
Silicon	Si	14	28.09
Silver	Ag	47	107.880
Sodium	Na	11	22.991
Strontium	Sr	38	87.63
Sulfur	S	16	32.066
Tantalum	Ta	73	180.95
Technetium	Tc	43	(99)
Tellurium	Te	52	127.61
Terbium	Tb	65	158.93
Thallium	Tl	81	204.39

ELEMENTS

ELEMENT	SYMBOL	ATOMIC NUMBER	ATOMIC WEIGHT
Platinum	Pt	78	195.09
Plutonium	Pu	94*	(244)
Polonium	Po	84*	210
Potassium	K	19*	39.100
Praseodymium	Pr	59	140.92
Promethium	Pm	61	(145)
Protactinium	Pa	91*	231
Radium	Ra	88*	226.05
Radon	Rn	86*	222
Rhenium	Re	75	186.22
Rhodium	Rh	45	102.91
Rubidium	Rb	37*	85.48
Ruthenium	Ru	44	101.1
Thorium	Th	90*	232.05
Thulium	Tm	69	168.94
Tin	Sn	50	118.70
Titanium	Ti	22	47.90
Tungsten	W	74	183.86
Uranium	U	92*	238.07
Vanadium	V	23	50.95
Xenon	Xe	54	131.30
Ytterbium	Yb	70	173.04
Yttrium	Y	39	88.92
Zinc	Zn	30	65.38
Zirconium	Zr	40	91.22

Boldface type is used for elements most frequently occurring in the discussion of the physical world. An atomic-weight in parentheses is an approximate value for the isotope of longest known half-life. An asterisk denotes a radioactive element. Elements 43, 61, 85 and 93–102 are synthetic. See also the Periodic Table, pp. 392–393.

THE STUDY OF THE PHYSICAL WORLD

NICHOLAS D. CHERONIS
Brooklyn College

JAMES B. PARSONS
University of Chicago

CONRAD E. RONNEBERG
Denison University

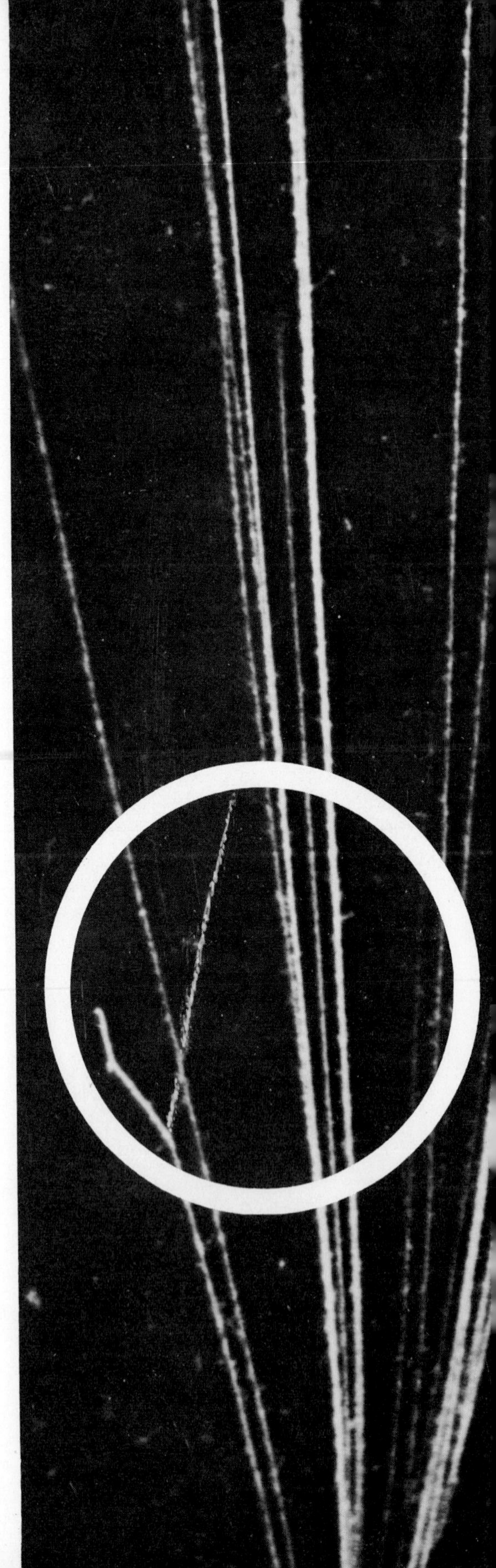

HOUGHTON MIFFLIN COMPANY

The Riverside Press Cambridge

THE STUDY OF THE PHYSICAL WORLD

third edition

The Riverside Press
Cambridge, Massachusetts
Printed in the U.S.A.

PREFACE

THE THIRD EDITION of this work, based on the general plan of the earlier editions, has been completely reorganized and rewritten. The main changes in organization are based on suggestions from the many teachers who have used the book over the last fifteen years, as well as the continued teaching experience of the authors. One of the principal changes is a reduction in the amount and kind of subject matter covered. A deliberate effort has been made to treat fewer topics more intensively so as to gain in depth without losing sight of the integrating links between the physical sciences.

As in earlier editions, the subject matter is drawn from astronomy, chemistry, geology, and physics. As before, the treatment is quantitative rather than qualitative in that no attempt is made to avoid difficult topics merely because they are difficult, or to sidestep the use of elementary mathematics. Indeed, the chapter on mathematics has been somewhat expanded. Nor has there been an attempt simply to "survey" the areas of the physical sciences; rather, the aim has been to select important facts and principles, and the theories which help to correlate and explain them, so as to give a clear understanding of the methods of science, as well as its major accomplishments. Even though there has been considerable reduction in the variety of topics covered in the four main areas, there is still an abundance of material to provide a course for a full year. It is our belief that these changes will permit greater flexibility and easier adaptation of the text to local teaching situations.

Notable features of the present edition are the following:

1. Reduction in the amount of factual material, with greater emphasis on principles and their applications.

2. A more thorough treatment of radioactivity and nuclear energy, with emphasis on potential peacetime uses.

3. Chemical transformations of matter are presented from the modern electronic point of view, including the Brönsted concept of acid-base reactions. The chapter on polymers (resinoids, fibroids, and elastomers) does not merely describe; it relates the useful properties of polymers to their molecular structure.

4. Energy is discussed largely from the modern point of view, as heat, electricity, and nuclear energy. The concept of fields of force about electrical charges has been extensively used to give a deeper insight into electrical phenomena. In view of this emphasis, much conventional descriptive material has been omitted. It is felt that the majority of students who reach the level at which this text is used will find facts of themselves of less permanent use and value than the principles and theories which interrelate and explain the facts.

5. The materials on geological processes and earth history have been unified and correlated, and placed in the early part of the book. This has been found psychologically desirable, since few students have been introduced to the earth sciences in high school.

6. A deliberate attempt has been made throughout the book to emphasize the social implications of all science and to point out that accumulated scientific knowledge alone, without vision, free play of ideas, wisdom, and social responsibility, will not solve the tremendous problems that face our society.

As in the previous editions judicious use has been made of chapter summaries, study exercises, and suggestions for further reading. It is felt that the special effort made by teachers to motivate students toward assignments which involve reading from original sources aids in extending the development of students' mental horizons and should be encouraged. With this in mind, some suggested readings from original sources have been included. Another feature new to this edition is the listing of a number of paperbound books in the sciences; these are all titles of real merit, readily available through a college bookstore, and it is hoped that the student may thereby be encouraged to build up an inexpensive science library of his own.

For almost thirty years the authors have been working with the organization of materials in the teaching of science for general education. Over this period the emphasis has considerably shifted from the "survey" organization to the present selective-content scheme, in which a smaller area is covered intensively so as to give reasonable depth in understanding. A second desirable trend is to supplement the usual lecture demonstration with some specially constructed laboratory experiments to be performed by the student. This is an area which still calls for development and experimentation.

Credit for the improvement of the volume belongs primarily to those who have used it in their classes. The authors are especially anxious to acknowledge the suggestions of the following persons for their aid in preparing the first and second editions: Dr. John R. Ball, Department of Geology, Northwestern University; Mr. Don Carroll, Illinois State Geological Survey; Mr. Ross Rollins, Boston Geological Society; Drs. Henrietta Freud, William Colburn, Glenn W. Warner, Phillip Constantinides, Sebastian Durban, J. Colin Moore, R. R. Hancox, W. L. Groenier, John A. Schaad, H. R. Voorhees, A. L. Burlingame, and Professors M. I. Meyer, C. G. Fawcett, Norman Hedenberg, W. H. McLain, H. C. Wilson, and W. T. Weis, all of the Chicago City Colleges; Dr. Thomas R. Ernest of the Thompson Manufacturing Company; Dr. Theodore A. Ashford of Saint Louis University; Professors William E. Morrell, College of General Studies, Robert H. Baker, Chairman, Department of Astronomy, and Harold R. Wanless, Department of Geology, all of the University of Illinois; and Mr. W. T. Bradley, who read the entire manuscript. The authors especially wish to acknowledge the great help given by Dr. M. D. Engelhart, Director of Examinations, Chicago City Colleges.

They further wish to express their sincere appreciation to all those who have assisted in any way with this third edition: Professors Verne Booth of the Department of Geology and Homer Jacobson of the Department of Chemistry, Brooklyn College; Drs. Peter Crager and Irving Slutsky, Harlan T. Guest, and Theodore Phillips of the Chicago City Colleges; Professor Edgar M. Collins and Dean Parker N. Lichtenstein of Denison University; Professor Henry L. Yeagley of the Department of Physics, Pennsylvania State University; and Professor Norman N. Holland of the Massachusetts Institute of Technology. Finally, they wish to acknowledge the generous help given by Irene Cheronis and Florence L. Ronneberg in the preparation of the manuscript and in the correction of the proof.

THE AUTHORS

TABLE OF CONTENTS

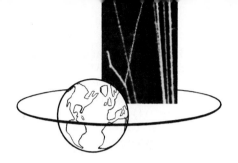

1

PRELUDE TO SCIENCE

A HUNDRED YEARS AGO, before our modern technological society emerged, knowledge of the forces operating in nature and knowledge of the structure of matter were not regarded as indispensable, even for the well-educated individual. Most people could function adequately in the society of that era without such knowledge. People of that period were largely dependent upon themselves for most of their food, clothing, fuel, and transportation. The person who aspired to a position of leadership was educated in the literature and art of Greek and Roman antiquity with a mere smattering of mathematical knowledge of the world in which he lived. Today we live in an interdependent, complex society very different from that of a century ago. Meaningful living today calls for many complex skills, techniques, specialized vocations, synthetic textiles, medicines, foods, and fuels, and is dependent upon many time-saving and labor-saving devices and a host of scientific gadgets, now commonplace, which operate on cheap electricity. These are products of modern science. The well-educated person today, therefore, must have an understanding of the physical sciences and their effect on today's world.

To illustrate the dependence of our mode of life on the physical sciences, consider what would happen if gasoline and other liquid fuels became unavailable within the next few days. The reserves of these processed fuels would soon be exhausted and every machine operating on gasoline or similar fuel would be stopped. Automobiles and trucks would disappear from the streets and highways, airplanes would vanish from the sky, tractors could no longer be used to till the farms, many industries would shut down, and even our railways would have to stop functioning. There would soon be economic, social, and governmental chaos.

It should be pointed out, however, that modern science also represents potential dangers to mankind. We now have, for example, the problems brought by the atomic and hydrogen bombs. These weapons are applications of our modern knowledge of nuclear energy for purposes of destruction. Yet at the same time the potentialities of nuclear energy for the good of mankind are fantastic. It is man who must choose how nuclear energy is to be used. Procedures in science recognize no real difference between the way atomic bombs were developed and the way the new antibiotic wonder drugs were obtained from molds: only the objectives were different. No one knows the number of human lives that have been saved by the antibiotic penicillin, but a nuclear bomb and penicillin equally represent end-products of scientific thinking — they are not science itself. Science is purely a mental construct.

The choice as to how nuclear energy, for example, is to be used in the future must be made by man, who is often unpredictable. It may please some of us to say that man represents the highest form of animal life, but man's body in certain respects is inferior to that of many animals. He is weaker physically, has poorer eyesight, hearing, and sense of smell than many members of the animal kingdom. The average span of life of quite a number of animals exceeds the traditional "threescore years and ten" for man. Many animals live where conditions of temperature make human life impossible. How then did man attain a position of dominance on the earth? The answer is both easy and difficult. Man is more intelligent, and his intelligence has resulted, with the passage of time, in the accumulation of knowledge, customs, and practices forming great cultures which have been transmitted from generation to generation and which have continually changed and improved to meet new conditions by the process of trial and error and by the process of reflective thinking.

Culture in this context includes knowledge, belief, art, morals, law, custom, and any skills or habits acquired by man as a member of society. Man is what he is today because of his culture, a heritage from the past. The beginning of our modern western culture or civilization is for convenience divided into a number of stages: (1) Eolithic or Dawn Stone Age, (2) Paleolithic or Old Stone Age, (3) Neolithic or New Stone Age, (4) Bronze Age, and (5) the early cultures of Egypt and Mesopotamia. The essential element in the evolution of these various cultures was time. The Eolithic cultures existed about a million years ago; the Paleolithic about a hundred and fifty thousand years ago. The Neolithic cultures date back about fifteen thousand years, and the Bronze Age to about 4000 B.C.

It is natural to inquire why these cultures changed so slowly, especially during the early stages of civilization. There are three main reasons: (1) the lack of a system of writing; (2) the empirical method of obtaining new knowledge; and (3) man's own attitude toward nature or his own environment.

Because of the lack of a system of writing, the advances of one generation could be passed on to the succeeding generation only by precept and example, often a very unreliable and uncertain process. Writing came into use in Egyptian civilization about 3000 B.C. J. H. Breasted, the great student of early Egyptian civilization, has emphasized the tremendous importance of this development:

> The invention of writing and of a convenient system of records on paper has had a greater influence in uplifting the human race than any other achievement in the career of man. It was then and is now more important than all the battles ever fought and all the constitutions ever written.[1]

The empirical method of accumulating knowledge depends upon fortunate observation. Thus, the superiority of copper or bronze over flint as a material for making vessels, scrapers, and knives lies in the fact that copper can be shaped by hammering, drawing, or casting, whereas flint can be shaped only by chipping. Yet this information undoubtedly came to primitive man very slowly as a result of working with the metal. Similarly, some early observer noted that the seasons could be related to the height of the sun in the heavens at midday, and that the time that elapsed from new moon to new moon was about thirty days. Upon these observations, early man based a division of time into the month and the year. In this way all early cultures slowly accumulated knowledge.

The dawn of our present civilization began in early Egypt along the Nile and in

[1] J. H. Breasted, *Ancient Times* (Boston: Ginn and Company, 1935), p. 66.

ancient Babylonia and Chaldea along the Tigris and Euphrates rivers. Here, in regions of great fertility and mild climate, two civilizations, based largely upon an agricultural economy, arose almost simultaneously. Intellectual advances were largely the result of empiricism and accident. Often these advances resulted from the necessity of overcoming some difficulty in connection with making a living. For example, the planting of crops is dependent upon the seasons. It became a very practical problem, therefore, to know when to plant the wheat crop. The calendar, with a year of three hundred and sixty-five days based upon the apparent movements of the sun, was perfected in Egypt as early as 4241 B.C.

The empirical method of extending knowledge, though slow, accomplished a great deal. The ancient arts of tanning leather and of making glass, the use of natural dyes, the making of boats, the spinning of high-quality textiles from wool and camel's hair, are examples of skills of high order. Even before 2000 B.C., the practical arts were highly developed by the people living in the valleys of the Nile, Tigris, and Euphrates. They traveled in large ships and in vehicles; they had beds and chairs, exquisite jewelry, combs, rouge, hats, shoes, and razors. The Egyptians used $3\frac{1}{7}$ as the value of π. A more precise value of this constant was not known until the time of Archimedes (287–212 B.C.). These early peoples also devised units for coinage, for mass, length, and capacity. They worked out the elements of arithmetic and made the beginnings of geometry.

Fundamentally, the character of the culture of any nation will depend on the extent to which its people have been able to make nature contribute to their physical well-being. Primitive man had virtually no control over his environment, though he early attempted some control. Historically, man has tried to control his environment and to enrich his culture by three different methods: the practice of primitive religion; the practice of magic; and finally, the practice of science.

PRIMITIVE RELIGION

Primitive man tried to put every aspect of his world into one coherent pattern. Natural events, social problems, even the individual's sense of moral responsibility were all, he thought, related. Thus primitive man could understand a crop failure or a famine as a punishment for some social or personal act. This quite naturally led to a personification of natural forces within the environment. Primitive religions are all characterized by a great multiplicity of gods. There was a god to control the growth of the crops, others to control hunting, fishing, the rains, and the like. The entire period needed for the planting, growing, and harvesting of crops, for example, was broken with many religious holidays to do honor to the god of the crops so that he would be moved to reward his followers with bountiful harvests. While this approach to understanding his environment enabled primitive man to see *every* event as part of a great environmental picture, it gave him no control over any particular event.

THE FUNCTION OF MAGIC

Man's first attempt to control his environment for his own betterment was through the use of magic, a practice still widely followed. There are even yet many agriculturists who insist that the proper time to plant potatoes is during the first dark of the moon after Good Friday. Magic serves psychologically to relate each individual to the larger world-picture; magic also offers the apparent possibility of physical control of the environment. Magic was a way of looking at the world which resulted in the elimination of fear of an environment that was not understood. It should not be difficult for us to conceive of people who never carried on any activity, such as building a home, starting on a journey, treating an illness, or cooking a meal, without first going through a ritualistic ceremony in the belief that, if the ceremony was correct, success was insured. After all, though we no longer believe that magic will control our environment, we still use magic psychologically to relate ourselves personally to larger natural forces or historical traditions. Such practices as carrying a rabbit's foot or hanging a horseshoe over a door to bring "good luck" are still widespread. We still launch ships with a ceremony which includes breaking a bottle of wine over the prow to start them off on a successful career. Many a banquet is marked by drinking a toast to an honored guest. These are but modern relics of ancient magic; it still offers us, in a sense, comfort.

ORIGIN OF SCIENCE

Both primitive religion and magic were important parts of all early cultures. Science was relatively unimportant or unknown among early peoples. It appeared much later, but it has become increasingly important until now it is the most important single force in modern culture. Science is a method of thinking and an attitude toward life and environment that more than any other single factor is responsible for the changes that have occurred in our manner of living during the past century. The significance of science can be pointed out by calling attention to the increase in the average life-span of human beings. It is said that the average span of human life during the Middle Ages was twenty-one years; by 1780 this had increased to twenty-six years; by 1825 it was thirty years; by 1850, forty years. The figure has continued to increase with the progress of science. The figures of the Office of Vital Statistics, U.S. Department of Health, Education and Welfare, for the present century are especially striking.

1900	47.3 years
1910	50.0 years
1920	54.1 years
1930	59.7 years
1940	62.9 years
1950	68.2 years
1955	69.5 years

This increase in the average span of life is due to scientists working principally in the fields of chemistry, physics, medicine, sanitation, agriculture, and engineering. Workers in these varied fields have evolved the modern methods of sanitation, the knowledge and methods of control of diseases, the present understanding of adequate diets, and the better and more abundant food supplies, which have increased the life expectancy for all.

The beginnings of science are obscure. It is safe to say that science began when individuals became curious about events and began to collect, study, and record facts concerning them. Slowly the conviction arose that natural events are not the same kind of thing as social and personal events. If nature acts regularly, then it becomes possible to make predictions of certain natural events and thus attain a measure of control over nature. To many primitive peoples, an eclipse of the sun was an awesome event. But Babylonian astronomers made a record of eclipses they observed. In time this record enabled them to predict eclipses because they found that these phenomena did not occur erratically, but at regular intervals of eighteen years and ten or eleven days. The division of the year into twelve months, the seven-day week, the division of the day into twenty-four hours, the hour into sixty minutes, and the minute into sixty seconds, we owe to these early Babylonian astronomers.

Science made but very slow progress until the rise of Greek culture, when Greek thinkers demonstrated the power of scientific thinking. The credit for first extensively employing the scientific method belongs to the Greeks. A combination of circumstances made Greece the home of a civilization dominant for a thousand years. The cultures which developed around the eastern Mediterranean gradually moved northward and westward. By 1200 B.C. highly developed cultures were established on many of the islands, and on the mainland around the Aegean Sea. Historians refer to these cultures as the Cretan, the Minoan, and the Mycenaean. Into these civilizations migrated vigorous barbarians from the north, and from this mixture of stock Greek civilization gradually developed. It began to flower about 600 B.C.

Greek civilization differed in many ways from the civilizations that had developed in the valleys of the Nile and of the Tigris-Euphrates rivers. These were composed of great masses of homogeneous peoples held together by strong centralized governments. The mountainous character of Greece resulted in the development of many small independent city-states. These small city-states never became burdened with institutionalized religion and a priestly class interested in the *status quo.* The Greeks gained distinction by participating in the duties of a government of thinking citizens. The mark of intelligence came to be curiosity in all activities of human life. Thus the Greeks became interested in knowledge, not because of its utilitarian value, but for its own sake and for the personal satisfaction attained in seeking knowledge. They became interested in *all questions* and in *all phenomena.* The inclination to inquire, to discuss, to argue, to discover relations, became a passion. They set up criteria for testing the validity of reasoning – the laws of logic. In short, the important contribution of the Greeks was their conviction that the universe followed, not whims and choices, but laws understandable by man. Without this fundamental concept, there could be no science. During the period of about five hundred years (600–100 B.C.), the Greeks made more striking advances in the field of the natural sciences than had been made in all of previous recorded history, and set a record that was not to be equaled until the seventeenth century of our era.

The contributions of Greek scientists make an imposing list. Thales (*ca.* 580 B.C.) visited Egypt and was impressed by the empirical rules used for land surveying. From these rules Thales derived certain axioms and postulates which became the basis for geometry. From these relatively few axioms and postulates it was possible to deduce an immense number of consequences by *logical reasoning processes alone.* Pythagoras (*ca.* 550 B.C.) extended the work of Thales in geometry. He gave the first proof that the square of the hypotenuse of a right triangle is equal to the sum of the squares of the other two sides. The Greeks tackled the problem of the constitution of matter. Later in this volume, we shall study Dalton's atomic theory in connection with chemistry and find that the concept of atomism – that all matter is composed of small particles called atoms – goes back to Democritus (*ca.* 420 B.C.). This concept has had a tremendous influence on the thinking of man.

The greatest of the ancient scientists from the standpoint of his influence on human thought was Aristotle (384–322 B.C.). His ideas were destined to influence the pursuit of all knowledge to the present time. Aristotle, the son of the court physician of King Philip of Macedon, was an exceedingly well-endowed and talented individual, whose keen mind was thoroughly schooled under the famous Greek philosopher Plato. He was associated with Alexander the Great, first as tutor, and then as a recipient of financial support for his school of science.

Aristotle made many lasting contributions to human thought and science. One of his most important contributions was to point out clearly the meaning of the *inductive method* of advancing knowledge. This method requires first facts, and then more facts as a basis for the extension of knowledge. He pointed out the dangers of trying to advance knowledge by reasoning processes divorced from the world of sensory experiences. At the same time Aristotle emphasized that science results only from the proper utilization of factual material. He therefore formulated the principles of sound reasoning and thus was the creator of formal logic.

In creating certain fields of study, such as zoology, embryology, and physiology, Aristotle was unusually successful. In other fields (for example, astronomy and physics) his efforts came to naught; he failed because he did not always follow his own *modus operandi:*

We must not accept a general principle from logic only, but we must prove its applicability to each fact; for it is in facts that we must seek general principles, and these must always accord with facts, from which induction is the pathway to general laws.

The reputation of Aristotle, great even in his own day, increased with time. During the revival of learning in Europe following the early medieval period, the science of Aristotle and his laws of logic grew in prestige until they came to represent absolute truth. Aristotle was considered right in all matters. It is ironical that Galileo and Copernicus and other workers who were partly responsible for the second great appearance of the scientific spirit were frequently persecuted by those in authority who insisted on the absolute truth of some of the wrong conclusions of Aristotle from the first great appearance of the scientific spirit.

No story of Greek science is complete without mentioning Archimedes (287–212 B.C.). Archimedes was a modern, seventeen hundred years ahead of his time. He was unusually successful in applying the principles of science to the solution of practical everyday problems. Furthermore, he expressed important ideas in the concise language of mathematics. He proved that the value of π was greater than $3\frac{10}{71}$ and less than $3\frac{10}{70}$. He discovered the laws concerning pulleys, the lever, and hydraulic screws, and stated the law of floating bodies. To him we owe the concept of density. His method of attacking a problem was truly scientific. He isolated a relatively small problem, studied it experimentally, drew his conclusions, and then checked them by experiment. This greatest scientist of the modern type in the ancient world was killed by a Roman soldier after the conquest of Syracuse in southern Italy in 212 B.C.

Science in Alexandria. Greek influence in the advance of knowledge was at its height from 700 B.C. to A.D. 200, though not always in Greece itself. Alexandria in Egypt became the intellectual center of western civilization about 300 B.C. and continued dominant until about A.D. 400, even during the period when the center of government was in Rome. The Roman genius lay in the field of law and in solving the practical problems of government. The Romans built excellent roads, aqueducts, and public buildings, but contributed little to the advancement of science. From the center of Grecian learning in Alexandria, however, notable contributions to knowledge continued to come. Hipparchus (*ca.* 140 B.C.) discovered the precession of the equinoxes and calculated the distance to the moon and the moon's diameter with an accuracy that is surprisingly close to the values we accept today. Euclid wrote his geometry in Alexandria. Eratosthenes (*ca.* 225 B.C.), while librarian of the great museum in Alexandria, satisfied himself that the earth was essentially spherical and even determined its circumference. His value differed from the present accepted value by less than half of one per cent, a truly remarkable achievement.

The outstanding Alexandrian scientist, in his influence on human thinking, was the astronomer Claudius Ptolemy (A.D. 127–151). His great work, the *Almagest,* is really an encyclopedia of astronomy. It was in this work that he expounded the geocentric conception of the universe. This is the conception that the earth is the center of the universe, and that the moon, Mercury, Venus, and the rest of the planets travel in circular orbits around it. This conception had also been taught by Aristotle. The geocentric conception of the universe came to be referred to as the *Ptolemaic system.*

We have written of the achievements of the Greek scientists. But they had certain weaknesses that should be pointed out. The Greek scientists often failed because they were content to rely too much on intuition or reasoning processes alone. They seldom stopped to verify their theories and conclusions experimentally. This was partly because the Greek citizen placed experimental work on a par with manual labor, which was reserved for slaves. The Greeks were also reluctant to experiment because they saw in natural laws a *telos,* an over-all purpose or ultimate end. Thus they tended to think experimenting with details less important than reasoning about the ultimate end. The Greek period, in spite of its defects, represents the first flowering of the methods of science. An exceedingly large number of fundamental ideas which form an important part of our culture, we owe to the Greeks.

The Decline of Learning. The thousand-year period following A.D. 400 was almost entirely devoid of scientific advances. It is the early part of this period which is often referred to as the Dark Ages. The learning of the Greeks would have disappeared but for the guardianship of knowledge by the scholars of the eastern Roman Empire centering in Byzantium, the Arabs, and the Mohammedans. The empire of the Arabs flanked the Mediterranean as far west as Gibraltar and Spain. The only significant scientific advances, largely in the fields of mathematics, optics, and chemistry, were made by the Arabs. The major intellectual force during this long period was the Church. Fortunately, however, manuscripts of the contributions of the Greek philosophers and scientists were preserved in monasteries. About A.D. 1200, the philosophy and teachings of Aristotle came to be accepted by the thinkers of the Church and were reconciled with the teachings of the Church fathers. The leading exponent of this fusion was Thomas Aquinas (*ca.* A.D. 1260), whose greatest work was the *Summa Theologica.* This fusion movement is referred to as *scholasticism.* Most of the great university centers of Europe — Paris, Florence, Padua, Pisa, and the like — were fostered by the Church and in all of them the ideas of Aristotle exerted a tremendous influence. As has been explained before, the notions of Aristotle in the physical sciences were often erroneous; nevertheless his prestige was so great that for more than a thousand years his mistaken conceptions often hindered advances in science.

MODERN SCIENCE

The second flowering of the scientific method is associated with the names of Copernicus, Kepler, Galileo, and Newton at the time of the Renaissance. The Renaissance, a complex social, religious, economic, and scientific reorganization of the nations in western Europe, resulted from a broader mental outlook as a result of the diffusion of learning through the new art of printing and the stimulus to industry and commerce resulting from the exploitation of the wealth of the New World and the Indies following the voyages of discovery by Columbus, Magellan, and many others. There were many material, moral, and intellectual factors which developed simultaneously to result in the great unfolding of the human spirit which is called the Renaissance. The development of science during this period was a very important part of the whole movement.

The state of science at the beginning of the sixteenth century is indicated by the fact that the motions of the heavenly bodies were still interpreted by the Ptolemaic or geocentric conception of the heavens — the earth was the center and controlling force in the universe. Copernicus (Poland, 1473–1543) advanced the heliocentric or sun-centered conception of the solar system. But the forces, social, religious, and governmental, of his day were so opposed to change that Copernicus did not dare publish his ideas until he knew he was about to die. John Kepler (Germany, 1571–1630) went on to express the motions of the planets in precise and comprehensive laws which established our present conception of the universe. But the first great protagonist of modern science was Galileo (Italy, 1564–1642). He was a giant intellectually, a man of the world, an engaging and effective teacher, a resourceful experimenter, a practical mathematician, endowed with a crusading spirit for the cause of science. His insistence on the immutability of facts often brought him into serious difficulties with the authorities of his day. His ability to heap scorn and ridicule upon those who could not forsake the ideas of Aristotle and Ptolemy helped to establish the methods of science, but meant for him a stormy career. His fame spread through Europe and has

Fig. 1–1 *Galileo Galilei, 1564–1642.* (*Brown Brothers*)

not diminished with time. It can truly be said that Galileo started science on the path down which it has moved to the present day.

It is impossible to discuss modern science without frequent reference to Sir Isaac Newton, who possessed one of the best minds of all time. Newton was born the year Galileo died (1642), and from early manhood until his death in 1727 was continuously in the service of society as an investigator and teacher in England's great University of Cambridge, and as Master of the Mint in London. His contributions to thought were enormous: he founded mechanics – the basis for all the physical sciences, originated the science of optics, and extended enormously the techniques of mathematics. But most important of all, he popularized the methodology and philosophy of modern science, based on the premise that all nature is governed by orderly laws which are understandable by man.

In the realm of philosophy one often reads of Newtonian science. This reached its apex of development during the nineteenth century. Toward the end of the nineteenth century, scientists achieved measuring techniques vastly more precise than any known previously. Then just at the dawn of the present century there occurred the discovery of X-rays and radium. These discoveries, little understood at the time, and the ability to make very accurate measurements, initiated the train of events which was to culminate in the atomic bomb of 1945. This event was a triumph of the post-Newtonian physical science, the science of relativity and quanta, of Einstein, the Curies, Rutherford, Compton, Lawrence, Bohr, and many others whose discoveries led directly or indirectly to the development of nuclear energy. The contributions of each of these scientists will be presented later in this volume.

The broad sweep of science has very briefly been described here. Much of the work of this volume will be concerned with unfolding the story of the physical sciences. Reference will be made many times to the scientists mentioned in this chapter, in connection with their contributions to the history of science and their part in developing the outlook that we have toward nature today and the method of thought that we call scientific. A preliminary discussion of the nature of scientific thinking is a subject for the next chapter.

SUMMARY

1. The early cultures of man changed very slowly for three reasons: (*a*) the lack of a system of writing; (*b*) the empirical method of obtaining new knowledge; and (*c*) the lack of a scientific attitude toward nature.
2. Historically, man's effort to control his environment to advance his personal well-being has been along three different lines: (*a*) the practice of primitive religion; (*b*) the practice of magic; and (*c*) the use of science.

3. Early man personified as gods the forces in nature which he did not understand. Primitive religion had for its object the control of nature for the benefit of man, through ceremonies pleasing to the gods.
4. The early widespread practice of magic was based on the conviction that desirable events are the result of the proper practice of certain ritualistic exercises.
5. The first important advance of science which resulted in significant changes in culture occurred in Greece and in Alexandria, Egypt, during the years 500 B.C. to A.D. 200. Some of the outstanding scientists of this period were Thales, Euclid, Pythagoras, Aristotle, Archimedes, Hipparchus, Eratosthenes, and Ptolemy.
6. Some important contributions of Greek science were: (*a*) the discrediting of magic and superstition by emphasizing the notion of an orderly nature; (*b*) the glorification of reason; (*c*) the formulation of laws of logic; (*d*) the necessity of tolerance; (*e*) the development of certain important branches of mathematics, especially geometry and trigonometry; and (*f*) an attitude of mind that resulted in an effort to understand all phenomena in nature.
7. The principal shortcoming of Greek science was a too great dependence upon intuition and reasoning divorced from experiment.
8. The second flourishing of science occurred during the Renaissance in Europe, and is largely associated with the work of Copernicus, Kepler, Galileo, and Newton.
9. The present period of rapid growth of science — the third — began in the twentieth century. This period is associated with such recent scientists as Einstein, the Curies, Rutherford, and Bohr. This is the age of quantum theory and nuclear science.

STUDY EXERCISES

1. Neolithic stone man fashioned many tools and weapons of flint, which was relatively easy to chip into shape and which took a high polish. These tools and weapons were a vast improvement over the crude granite tools and weapons of Paleolithic stone man. Did this transition occur slowly — during many generations — or rapidly? Was it largely the result of a process of trial and error or the result of experimentation? Discuss.
2. Many familiar utensils, tools, jewelry, and the like, are now being made of various plastics instead of the wood or metals formerly used. These plastics were hardly known thirty years ago. Was this largely the result of a process of trial and error or the result of deliberate experimentation? Discuss.
3. When Cortez (A.D. 1520) with a relatively small army, equipped with firearms and artillery, conquered the Aztec nation in Mexico, he found a civilized nation. The Aztecs, however, knew nothing about the wheel and its applications. List as many devices as you can that the Aztecs did not possess because of their lack of knowledge of the wheel. By what process may the concept of the wheel have come into our culture?
4. All the individuals listed below made significant contributions to the advancement of human thought. For each, give the time in which he lived, his country, and his important contributions: Euclid; Pythagoras; Aristotle; Archimedes; Ptolemy; Copernicus; Kepler; Galileo; Newton.
5. List as many differences as you can which show how the modern scene — your environment — differs from that familiar to your grandparents. How do you account for the differences?
6. Stone Age man could transmit accumulated knowledge from one generation to another for the most part only by word of mouth or example. List the methods that are now available for the preservation and transmission of knowledge. How many of these methods are relatively recent applications of scientific principles?
7. There are a number of reasons that motivate men to perform the work necessary to make new discoveries, such as (*a*) the desire to satisfy individual curiosity: (*b*) the desire for monetary returns; (*c*) the desire to help their fellow men; (*d*) the wish to receive the acclaim of their fellow men, and so on. Which of these motives have predominated

in the lives of those individuals who have made unusual contributions to the total sum of human knowledge?

8. Give examples of the practice of magic as a guide to human behavior. Why do people continue to practice or believe in magic?
9. Contrast magic and science.
10. Human behavior is often guided by submission to some "authority." Give examples. Does this process favor or hinder scientific thinking? Discuss.

FOR FURTHER READING

1. TAYLOR, F. S., *The March of Mind.* New York: The Macmillan Company, 1939.

   Chapters I, II, and III discuss the beginnings of science, the role of primitive religion, magic, and science in early cultures, and the science of Greece.
2. SARTON, GEORGE, *A History of Science.* Cambridge, Mass.: Harvard University Press, 1952.

   Treats in a thorough manner the Oriental and Greek origins of science. Points out the very considerable achievements of the ancients.
3. RAMSPERGER, A. G., *Philosophies of Science.* New York: Appleton-Century-Crofts, 1942.

   Chapter II treats of the significance of Aristotle especially during the years preceding the Renaissance. Chapter III treats of the emergence of modern science during the Renaissance.
4. Paperback: FRANKFORT, H., *Before Philosophy.* Penguin, 65¢.

   Can be read with pleasure and profit by everyone. It deals with the beliefs, attitudes, and culture of the early Egyptian and Babylonian civilizations and traces the beginnings of systematic inquiries of man as to his environment and his strange universe.
5. Paperback: WADDINGTON, C. H., *The Scientific Attitude.* Pelican, 35¢.
6. Paperback: MALINOWSKI, B., *Magic, Science and Religion.* Anchor, 95¢.
7. Paperback: SINGER, C., *From Magic to Science.* Dover, $1.65.
8. Paperback: FARRINGTON, B., *Greek Science.* Pelican, 65¢.

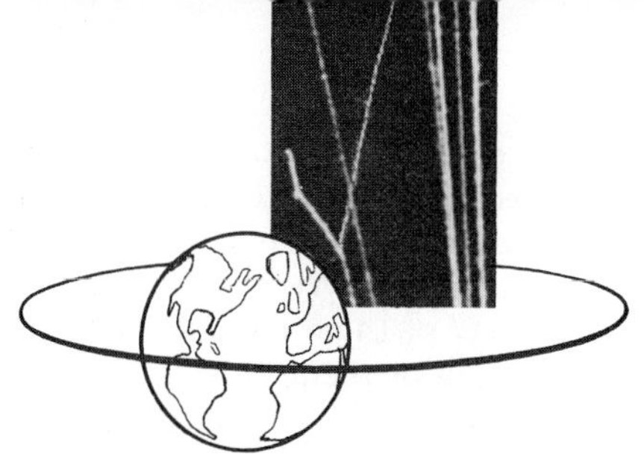

2

THE TOOLS OF INQUIRY

MANKIND CAN ADVANCE only by converting more of the unknown into the known. Newton, in the twilight of his life, wrote: "I seem to have been only like a boy playing on the seashore, and diverting myself in now and then finding a smoother pebble or a prettier shell than ordinary, while the great ocean of truth lay all undiscovered before me." Newton, by an almost fanatical adherence to the principles of the scientific method of thinking, laid the foundation for our present-day conception of the universe and made the modern physical sciences possible. Lagrange, an eminent French mathematician, paid this tribute to Newton: "Newton was the greatest genius that ever existed and the most fortunate, for we cannot find more than once a system of the world to establish."

What, then, is this scientific method which has led to so many discoveries? It consists in the intimate union of experiment and theory; it is both deductive and inductive in its processes. It differs from the empirical method in that the experiments are not made at random, but are guided by reason. Furthermore, the reasoning processes are always linked to objective facts by experiment. Scientific thinking is not a stilted process that must follow certain prescribed steps. Furthermore, it actually follows different patterns in different areas of human activity. Thus the scientific procedures of astronomers may differ markedly from those used by electronic engineers or workers in the social sciences. Since scientific thinking follows no set procedure or formula, it can only be described in terms of certain aspects which are found to be present.

ASPECTS OF SCIENTIFIC THINKING

Thinking is a response to the recognition of a need or problem, which may be envisioned vaguely or completely. It is characteristic of a true scientist always to aim to get as precise a picture as possible of the nature of any problem requiring solution. This is always a part of the planning stage. In particular, the modern scientist tends to break a problem into a number of smaller problems of simpler solution. In many situations a problem may be so involved and complex that the only hope of solution is to delimit it. The successful solution of the smaller parts of the problem permits a gradual solution of the whole.

After recognizing the nature of a difficulty or problem, the second step is to assemble all possible objective facts pertaining to it. This must be done without bias or preconceived notions which may unconsciously cause the accumulation of only certain facts and the disregarding or overlooking of other facts. It is impossible to overemphasize this aspect of scientific thinking. Every fact must be accepted as it stands, irrespective of any desire to make it fit into a larger pattern of thinking. It is dangerous to rationalize too soon while collecting the facts necessary to solve a problem. This was one of the reasons for the failures of many of the followers of Aristotle. They worshiped human reason and authority, and thus were not able to see, or at times disregarded, certain troublesome facts. The true scientist must accept all facts even though he does not understand their significance. It is a common experience with scientists that in connection with some problems there is such a paucity of fact-material that it is necessary to devise and conduct experiments for the deliberate purpose of acquiring a body of fact-material to use in solving the original problem. Here it is necessary to bring out clearly the meaning of the term *objective evidence*. When facts concerning a given problem can be accumulated by different independent experimenters and described similarly in terms of some scheme of measurement, they can be said to be *objective*. Facts described in terms of individual opinion without resort to quantitative measurement and critical evaluation by other independent thinkers are frequently subjective and unreliable.

SCIENTIFIC LAWS

A frequent third step in scientific thinking is to aim to systematize and classify the factual material by some logical process. This means discovering relationships and interrelationships within a mass of factual material. This procedure often ends in a generalization which is referred to as a *scientific law*. A scientific law is merely *a concise statement of some uniform mode of behavior* that has been shown to be true from the study of an array of facts pertaining to a certain phenomenon. We are actually familiar with many of these laws, though we often do not think of them as laws. For example, the ratio of the circumference to the diameter of any circle is a constant number, 3.14159. . . . This is a generalization deduced from a study of the facts pertaining to many circles, and no one has yet discovered a circle for which this ratio departs from the value given above. This simple example, incidentally, illustrates the economy of effort, mental and physical, that results from a knowledge of scientific laws. Imagine, now, that we did not have this law of the circle. A tinsmith is to make a round tank with a certain diameter. He will need to know the length of the circumference. Without the law of the circle, he would have to trace out a circle on the given diameter and then actually measure the circumference with a measuring tape. This would be a time-consuming operation, and the result could not possibly be as accurate as the simple procedure of finding the product of the diameter multiplied by 3.1416.

While classification of facts in some rational scheme is frequently necessary and desirable, it must also be pointed out that the ability to classify may be quite sterile in outcomes. Nearly every science in its development at one stage or another became static because it was content with mere classification, and became largely a descriptive science. This has been true at various times, for example, of chemistry, bacteriology, medicine, botany, and geology.

Scientific laws differ from man-made laws in that they refer to phenomena in nature beyond the control of man. Any legislative body can, for example, change the speed limit on a public highway, but for that same legislature to attempt to change the numerical value of π would be a meaningless procedure.

Two distinct kinds of scientific law can be recognized. Some scientific laws describe phenomena which are invariably found to hold true. That is, certain causes predictably lead to certain effects. We may assume that such laws are always true — that there are no exceptions. Examples are the laws of Charles and Faraday, of which we shall learn in later chapters. But there are also probability laws. That is, a given set of circumstances will *usually* lead to certain results with a certain probability. But probability is not certainty. We shall find that there are many probability laws in science. Thus water when cooled to the freezing point will probably freeze. But we can never be certain. It is not uncommon for water at the freezing point to supercool and remain a liquid.

Scientific laws also differ in their origins, and we can distinguish between *rational* and *empirical* laws. The latter laws are generalizations based upon a body of experimental or observational facts. The reliability of the law then depends entirely upon the acceptability or precision of the facts. Rational laws, on the other hand, apply to some ideal or perfect situation and are arrived at by some rational logical process. Thus the statements, "The whole is equal to the sum of its parts," and "The ratio of the circumference of any circle to its diameter is 3.141592+," are rational laws. They were never discovered by direct experimental methods. The discovery of rational laws may even precede actual experimentation.

Induction. The phase of logic involved in finding general laws from a study of assembled facts is called *inductive reasoning,* and is of special importance in experimenting science. It is characteristic of the physical sciences that these generalizations are often expressed in the precise symbols of mathematics. Thus, the generalization concerning the circle given above can be expressed,

$$\frac{\text{C(ircumference)}}{\text{D(iameter)}} = \pi = 3.1416\ldots$$

It is especially important that inductions from a mass of facts be demonstrably true by experiment. Hence, generalizations cannot be accepted until verified by ample observation and experiment. They will be accepted as true only so long as no new facts are discovered which cause the law to be questioned.

Deduction. Scientific laws are important because they result in an economy of time and effort for all who apply them. A science is well along the path toward usefulness when a large number of laws have been formulated. Many of the practical problems of life can be solved by the mere application of these laws. This is the phase of logic called *deduction* — the application of a general law or principle to a new situation. Thus, someone may raise the question of the relationship between the hypotenuse and the two legs of a right triangle. The answer can be found in more than one way, by making use of certain broad generalizations which are a fundamental part of geometry. Deduction is the reasoning process employed when we proceed from previously systematized and accepted knowledge. There can be only one criterion as to the correctness of any conclusion reached by deduction — experimental verification. As has been stated before, many of the conclusions of the Greek scientists and philosophers were erroneous. Their conclusions were reached by reasoning alone with no final verification by controlled, deliberate experimentation. In short, scientific thinking frequently begins and ends in experimentation.

CONTROLLED EXPERIMENT AND THE STATISTICAL APPROACH

The discussion of the scientific method in the preceding paragraphs has of necessity been from the point of view of a "first look." It is important, however, to emphasize that experimentation with suitable controls in order to gain the new factual materials needed to solve many problems cannot always be employed. For example, in astronomy, geology, and some phases of chemistry and physics, because the distances, dimensions, and forces are either too large or too small to measure, other scientific techniques must be employed. The same is true for the biological and social sciences where controlled experimentation is difficult; one cannot experiment under fully controlled conditions with biological and social units (plants, animals, people).

When controlled experimentation is not feasible, the *statistical method* employing certain *probability laws* is used. An illustration is the science of life insurance. It is impossible, for example, to predict the life-span of a particular person thirty years of age. Yet on the basis of length-of-life studies involving a group as large as 100,000 individuals of age thirty, and employing the mathematical methods of statistical analysis, the average life-span of the average person of age thirty has been determined quite accurately.

Probability laws based upon statistical analysis of large bodies of observed facts are actually a large part of modern science. The observed facts are classified on the basis of the relative number of occurrences of certain kinds of events. By inductive processes, then, generalizations are formulated which will permit predictions to be made for future situations involving the same kind of phenomena with a degree of certainty. We shall find later that in chemistry, for example, many of the laws concerning atoms and molecules are probability laws.

WORKING HYPOTHESES

The work of a scientist does not stop with the induction and the application of general laws. He wishes to move from the known to the unknown. He is not only interested in a concise statement of *how* things behave; he is even more interested in *why* they behave as they do, what things are causing the uniformity he has observed. This leads frequently to a fourth step, one of the most important in scientific thinking – the formulation and testing of *working hypotheses.* An hypothesis is merely a working "guess" as to what invariably makes certain *causes* lead to certain *effects.* An hypothesis is of little value unless it can do what it is designed to do, that is, *explain* clearly and completely. Hence an hypothesis should be tested experimentally, or if that is impossible, then the hypothesis should account for and explain all the known facts. For example, if the scientist hypothesizes the existence of an invisible particle, he must go on to look for *evidence* that such a particle in fact exists. This testing procedure links the hypothesis to reality and may confirm the hypothesis or it may contradict it. If it contradicts, the hypothesis must be discarded in favor of another tentative explanation to be similarly tested. It often happens that a part of an hypothesis must be modified while the rest remains unchanged. The new or modified hypothesis must again be subjected to the test of experiment. This interplay of experiment with reasoning is the essence of the scientific method.

SCIENTIFIC THEORIES

Only when an hypothesis has stood the test of many experiments designed to check it, does it attain the rank of a *theory.* The theories explain the facts and principles of science. They tie apparently unrelated observations together and enable us to see the connections between them. This is one of the important functions of any theory. In brief, theories explain past observations. Later, we shall see that many phenomena of the universe are organized around the theory and law of gravitation; of chemistry, around the modern atomic and electronic theories of the elements; of heat, around the kinetic molecular theory.

The most important function of a theory is to open the way to further advances of knowledge by suggesting new experiments or fields for research. The average person often does not realize that most significant discoveries now being made are the result of the application of theories which, strangely enough, may not be permanent in themselves. People who pride themselves on being "practical" sometimes are inclined to heap scorn on theory and theorists, but this is from a lack of appreciation of the true significance of a scientific theory. One of the greatest medical advances of recent decades was the discovery of insulin. Insulin is the hormone supplied to the blood by the pancreas, the lack of which causes diabetes; and this hormone was predicted to exist twenty-five years before its discovery. Similarly, a working hypothesis was all that Edison had to guide him when he was doing the experimental work which led to the perfection of the electric light bulb. We are to learn later that it was the electromagnetic theory of radiation devised by Clerk Maxwell, the English scientist, that pointed out the possibility of the existence of radio waves, which later were experimentally proved to exist by the German scientist Hertz, and which Marconi still later used for wireless communication. Among the outstanding developments of modern chemistry are synthetic rubber and synthetic textile fibers superior to natural rubber and fibers. They are possible because of the application of a theory concerning the behavior of what the chemist calls *unsaturated molecules* and their linkage together by a process called *polymerization.*

Theories usually are in a state of flux and improvement. Occasionally new facts are discovered which cast doubt upon the validity of an accepted theory. In case a theory does not harmonize with new facts, however insignificant, it is the theory that is modified or even discarded. The reason this is not more generally realized is that one seldom hears of the working hypotheses that were invented, tested against the known facts, and discarded because they were found wanting. The only theories we usually hear about are the successful ones.

A theory, moreover, must be the *simplest* theory that will account for *all* the facts. This principle, known as Occam's Razor, was originally stated: "Entities must not be multiplied unnecessarily." Occam was a British scholastic philosopher (d. 1347) whose ideas greatly influenced the science of the Renaissance. The principle of Occam simply means that the scientist should not introduce anything not absolutely necessary to explain the phenomenon he is working on. In its most general form, this concept is called the Principle of Sufficient Reason: if alternative beliefs are possible and if there is no "sufficient reason" to prefer one to another, none should be preferred. For example, if the known facts can be explained either by saying that the sun is at the center of the solar system or by saying that the earth is, and if there is no sufficient reason for preferring one explanation to the other, both explanations must coexist pending the discovery of further facts. This principle, though essentially an aesthetic criterion, is the cornerstone of scientific skepticism. It accounts for the beauty and elegance of scientific reasoning, and the concept of what makes a "sufficient reason" is the most basic assumption the scientist makes. The greater simplicity of one theory over another, for example, would be "sufficient reason" for accepting the simpler theory and excluding the other.

SCIENCE AND MATHEMATICS

Mathematics occupies a unique position in science, for it is the language of science. Science without mathematics is impossible, and the use of mathematics to express scientific statements is constantly increasing. The physical sciences are most mathematical, the biological sciences are becoming more mathematical, and there is plenty of evidence that the social sciences are moving in the same direction. One reason for the universality of science is that it is based upon mathematics, which is a universal language among the learned people of all nations. Mathematics expresses in a few symbols (or abbreviations) a large amount of information; to express the same thing in words would in many cases require several paragraphs. The meaning of this concise symbolism is so important in science that Chapter 11 is devoted to its fuller discussion.

SCIENCE AND CHANGE

A true science is never static. The truths of one generation become the stepping-stones to new truths in a succeeding generation. Matter, for example, was once considered indestructible, but now we know that matter often disappears, as such, with the simultaneous appearance of some form of conventional energy. Changes in concepts must come as a result of new discoveries. It often happens that progress is slowly made in science as a result of successive approximations. Some measurements with a certain precision and certain conclusions then follow. When more precise measurements are made, it is frequently necessary to modify previous conclusions. This procedure often leads to a more refined law or theory. Absolute and unchanging truth is a rarity in science.

SCIENCE AND REALITY

An important characteristic of many scientific hypotheses is the creation of imaginary objects or processes which cannot be directly perceived or demonstrated. For example, atoms, molecules, and electrons are hypothetical constructs, inferred to be as they are only through events or phenomena which they serve to explain. In some cases, such hypothetical objects may be later discovered and proved to exist. Thus vitamins were originally proposed as hypothetical substances to explain nutritional disorders; later, they were isolated, their structure determined, and they are now made synthetically. We shall find that many hypothetical objects or processes are a part of the mental construct we call science. Hence reality for science is *that system of concepts which serves to correlate and predict the data of experience.*

SCIENCE AND THE UNKNOWN

A most important aspect of science is that it is so frequently concerned with the unknown – the discovery of new truths, facts, and generalizations. Scientists today are intensely concerned with such questions as the cause of cancer, the thickness of the ice sheet over Antarctica, the nature of the center core of the earth (is it solid or liquid?), the possible uses of rare metals such as rhenium, titanium, and zirconium, the height of the atmosphere, the effects of atomic radiation on human heredity, the possibility of space travel to the moon, and many other such problems. Thousands of scientists are engaged in this type of research. Their support and the costs of their research require many millions of dollars annually. Society and governments make these funds available. Why is this being done? There is only one answer: science is a powerful force in our culture. This book will be largely concerned with a treatment of modern physical science and with the many applications of scientific method. As more and more people learn the nature of modern science, we may hope for more and more efficient use of science the world over.

SUMMARY

1. Scientific thinking is often a very complicated process. Usually some or all of the various steps listed below are followed, though not necessarily in the same order.
   a. Recognition of a problem or difficulty.
   b. Collection of a large mass of facts pertinent to the problem, by observation and experimentation.
   c. Systematization and organization of the fact-material to make possible the induction of generalizations or scientific laws.
   d. The application of the generalizations to new situations, by deduction.
   e. The elaboration and testing of tentative working hypotheses to devise reasonable explanations of laws and facts.
   f. The evolution of tested and accepted hypotheses into working scientific theories.
   g. The use of scientific theories to serve as a framework for the organization of a body of knowledge and to point the way to further discoveries.

2. Logic, both inductive and deductive, is a necessary part of scientific thinking, but all conclusions must be tested by experiment.
3. Induction is the process of deriving a generalization from a mass of fact-material.
4. Deduction is the process of applying generalizations to new problems; i.e., to work out a solution of a particular difficulty by reasoning from some accepted generalization.
5. Mathematics is a necessary part of science, serving as a universal language and as an aid to thinking.

STUDY EXERCISES

1. What is the distinction in meaning of the following terms: *fact, knowledge, science, art, feeling?* Give examples.
2. What is the distinction between a scientific hypothesis and a scientific theory? Discuss.
3. Sometimes the campaign orator or the newspaper columnist speaks scornfully of theories. Is this always justified, or does it reveal a lack of appreciation of what is meant by scientific thinking? Discuss.
4. Discuss two of the important functions of theories in scientific thinking.
5. After each of the following, mark *T* if you consider the statement true; *F,* if you consider it false; D, if you consider it doubtful.
   a. The discovery of general laws and theories is one of the important objectives of science. ....
   b. If one learns the laws of science, it is not necessary to know facts. ....
   c. The study of inanimate objects has no social significance. ....
   d. If one memorizes the summaries in the text, he learns science. ....
   e. The most important objective of science is to gain knowledge so that it may be applied to the service of man. ....
   f. All hypotheses can be experimentally tested. ....
   g. A theory is a hypothesis which has been repeatedly tested and found to agree with the phenomena which it serves to correlate and explain. ....
   h. The most important reason for studying science is to obtain an insight into a method of thinking and acquire if possible the scientific attitude. ....
   i. All hypotheses are elaborated first by deduction without reference to facts. ......
   j. A natural law is a constant mode of action in nature. ....
6. Place a number to indicate the order in which the following steps are frequently followed in scientific thinking:
   .... Invention of working hypothesis.
   .... Definite recognition of a problem.
   .... Induction of scientific laws from a body of organized fact material.
   .... Collection of a mass of fact-material by observation and experimentation.
   .... Testing of working hypotheses which often lead to acceptance of scientific theories.
   .... Further application of scientific theories to discover new relationships and make new discoveries.
7. What constitutes a "sufficient reason" to a modern scientist?

FOR FURTHER READING

1. FEIGL, HERBERT, and MAY BRODBECK, eds., *Readings in the Philosophy of Science.* New York: Appleton-Century-Crofts, 1953.
   See especially: "Nature and Function of the Philosophy of Science," *by May Brodbeck;* "The Scientific Outlook: Naturalism and Humanism," *by Herbert Feigl;* "The Logic of Modern Physics," *by P. W. Bridgeman;* "Physical Theory and Experiment," *by Pierre Duhem.*
2. RAMSPERGER, A. G., *Philosophies of Science.* New York: Appleton-Century-Crofts, 1942.
   Chapter X discusses scientific knowledge; Chapter XII, the nature of scientific laws; Chapter XIII, measurements in science. The volume includes an excellent bibliography.
3. RUSSELL, BERTRAND, "The Place of Science in a Liberal Education," page 36 in *Readings in the Physical Sciences,* by H. Shapley, H. Wright, and S. Rapport; New York: Appleton-Century-Crofts, 1948.
4. Paperback: CALDER, R., *Science in Our Lives.* Signet, 35¢.
5. Paperback: CONANT, J. B., *On Understanding Science.* Mentor, 50¢.
6. Paperback: SULLIVAN, J. W. N., *The Limitations of Science.* Mentor, 50¢.

3

A FIRST LOOK AT THE EARTH

FROM OUR EARLIEST CHILDHOOD we are told that the earth is round and that it belongs to a small family of planets revolving about the sun called the *solar system.* Yet there is very little in our everyday experiences to suggest any of these notions. The earth appears, even from an airplane, as a flat pancake traversed by winding streams and broken up by valleys, ridges, and mountains. We do not apprehend earth's curvature as a visible fact. Only on rare occasions when we find ourselves on a clear dark night looking upward at the myriad shining dots which stud the vault of heaven do we wonder about the earth as a part of the vast spectacle overhead. A very large part of what we know about the shape, size, and motions of the earth in relation to the outer universe we learned between the ages of seven and seventeen as factual information without critical discussion or so-called proofs. Scientific education is a slow process. Much of it involves learning the same things over again, but each time learning them better or acquiring a greater depth of knowledge. The object of this chapter is to give a critical discussion of our notions about the earth and the world we live in.

SCIENTIFIC FACTS

The first essential step in scientific study consists in careful observations leading to an assembly or accumulation of facts. By facts, we mean data of experience or actual realities *which can be confirmed by the observations of others.* Thus, when we say that the statement "Living things come from seeds or eggs" is a fact, we indicate an actual reality which can be confirmed by direct observation. A large number of scientific facts – for example, the so-called scientific facts as to the shape, size, and motions of the earth on which we live – cannot readily be verified by direct observations. Indeed, direct observations may lead us to confusion, for often things are not what they seem to be at first glance.

That things are not always what they seem is illustrated by our view of the sky overhead. During the day it appears as a blue film, spherical in shape and meeting the earth at a line called the *horizon.* On this blue film the sun appears to rise in the east and set in the west; the next day the sun is seen to rise in the east again. When the sun sets, a countless multitude of bright points called *stars* appear in the sky. The stars also rise in the east, pass across the sky, and set in the west. The same stars appear in the east again the next evening. Most stars appear as shining points of light; this light is unsteady, and hence stars are said to twinkle. There are nine bright celestial objects, however, which shine with a steady light and whose movements are different from those of the other stars. Although traveling daily, like the other stars, from east to west, their *relative* position among the stars in the sky also changes from day to day, so that, as the months pass, most of them appear to be at the same time moving slowly from west to east and, after undergoing a reversal of their motion, from east to west. Inasmuch as these heavenly bodies do not appear to keep their positions among the other stars, they are called *planets* (wanderers).

The most obvious conclusion from these observations is that the sun together with the whole firmament to which the stars appear to be attached revolves about the earth once every twenty-four hours. Indeed this was the view held by both the learned and the man in the street until some three hundred years ago. It is common knowledge now that the earth rotates once a day on its axis and as a consequence, everything about it — the sun and the stars — seems to be moving past it as though on a gigantic merry-go-round. The fact that one star — the North Star or Polaris — appears to move scarcely at all in the northern sky, is offered as evidence of the diurnal (daily) rotation of the earth on its axis. The North Star lies almost directly over the north pole, in line with the earth's axis of motion, and so gives the impression of not moving, while stars in its vicinity seem to move around it in circles. Thus the rotational motion of the earth on its axis is not an *observable* but an *inferential* fact, a conclusion which we draw to explain observable phenomena. One of the main tasks of science is to construct models or conclusions by deduction or induction which are in agreement with observations.

The Reality of Scientific Facts. The picture of the earth and the changes of matter and energy occurring upon it and the relation of our planet to the outer uni-

TABLE 3–1

FACTS ABOUT THE EARTH

PROPERTY	DESCRIPTION AND VALUE
Planet	Member of a family of sun and 9 planets and 31 moons
Shape	Oblate spheroid
Size	
Mean radius (r)	3958.82 miles, or 6371.23 kilometers
Mean diameter ($2r$)*	7917.64 miles, or 12,742.46 kilometers
Circumference ($2\pi r$)	24,875.126 miles
Volume ($\frac{4}{3}\pi r^3$)	259,000 million cubic miles, or 1.08×10^{27} cubic centimeters
Mass	6.78×10^{21} metric tons, or 5.975×10^{27} grams
Density (M/V)	5.517 grams per cubic centimeter
Rotational motion	Once daily
Orbital motion	29.80 kilometers per second
Shape of the earth's orbit	Ellipse
Eccentricity of the earth's orbit	0.01674
Mean distance to the sun	92,870,000 miles

* The equatorial diameter is 7926.68 miles (12,756.78 kilometers) and the polar diameter 7899.98 miles (12,713.82 kilometers); the equatorial diameter is nearly 27 miles greater.

verse, which will be presented in this volume, may confuse the student as to the meaning of reality in science. For example, the earth is pictured as an oblate spheroid about 8000 miles in diameter spinning upon its axis as it revolves with its eight sister planets about the sun. Further, this sun-planet, or solar system, is only an infinitesimal part of a large disc-like congregation of stars called the Milky Way or Galaxy whose diameter is such that light at a speed of 186,000 miles per second requires 100,000 years to traverse it. The solar system lies near the edge of this disc and revolves about the center at a speed of about 170 miles per second; that is, the whole Galaxy rotates about its center once in 200 million years.

Turning from the macrocosm to the microcosm, the student is confronted with a number of imaginary constructs which cannot be directly perceived or demonstrated by the senses. For example, *atoms, molecules,* and *electrons* are *hypothetical objects perceived only through events or phenomena which they serve to explain.* Although atoms and molecules are considered to be imaginary objects, we will give their precise diameters and their characteristic properties as if they were objects that could be handled at will, measured, and weighed.

Science, then, deals first with natural phenomena directly perceived by the senses, and secondly with objects and phenomena not directly perceived. Therefore, scientific facts (i.e., reality) comprise all the models and concepts which have been constructed to explain, correlate, and predict the data of experience.

Table 3–1 summarizes certain facts about the earth. The purpose of the discussion that follows in this chapter is to obtain an understanding of the evidence from which these facts are derived.

THE EARTH AS A PLANET

Figure 3–1 shows a diagrammatic representation of the solar system; it represents the nine planets which revolve about the sun. These planets, accompanied by thirty-

Fig. 3–1 *The sun and the planets.*

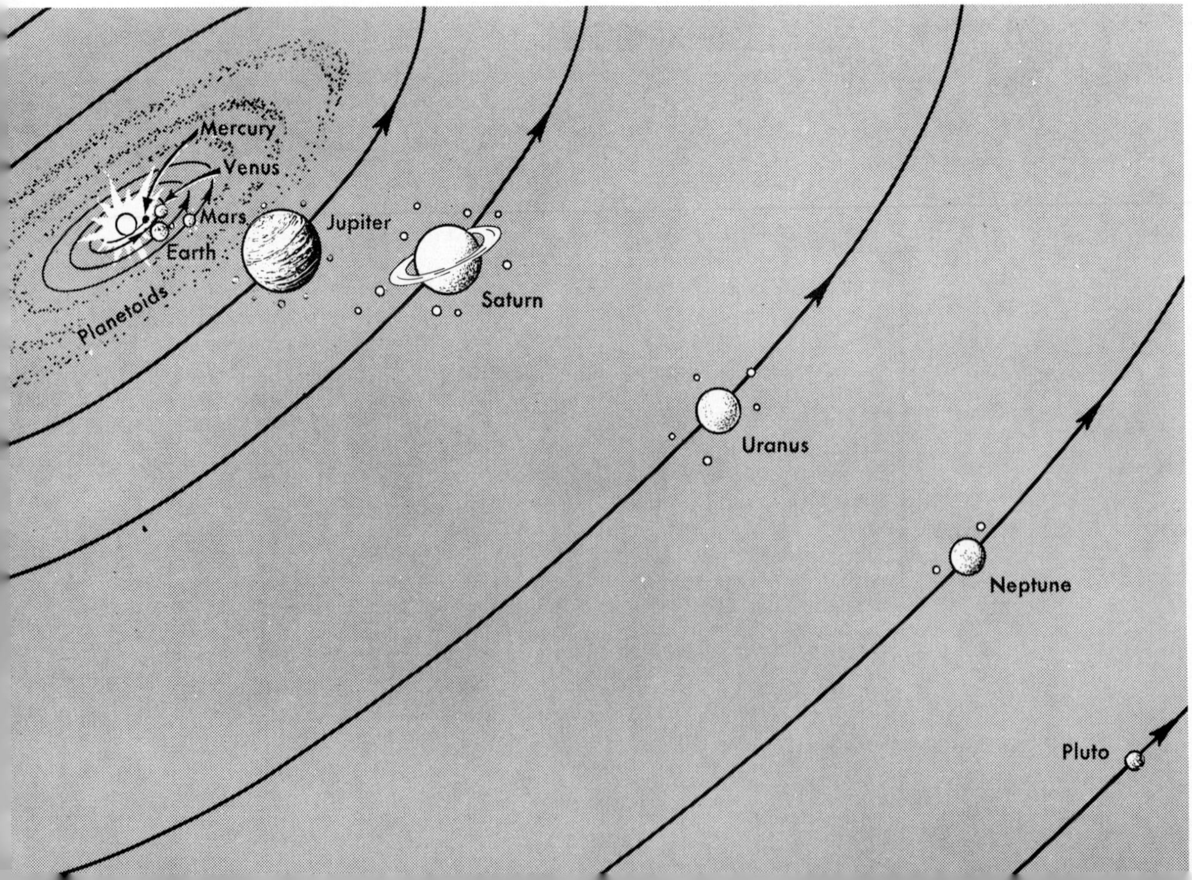

one moons, together with several thousand small planets, called planetoids, some comets, and an immense number of meteors, make up the solar family. To this family we may add now the man-made satellites which at the present writing revolve about the earth.

Information about planets and the sun has accumulated from ancient times through observations with the unaided eye and through more systematic study with the instruments of modern astronomers. The stars viewed through a telescope appear like tiny points of light because of the tremendous distances which separate us from them. Even the nearest star (Proxima Centauri) is 4.5 light-years away; that is, light emanating from our nearest stellar neighbor traveling at a speed of 186,000 miles per second requires 4.5 years to reach us. On the other hand, most of the planets viewed through the telescope appear as clear discs and their satellites or moons are clearly discernible.

In size, the earth in relation to the other planets is just average, neither the smallest nor the largest. It belongs in the subfamily of inner and smaller planets which are closer to the sun. The outer planets, with the exception of Pluto, are larger. The distances which separate us from our nearest neighbor planets seem great even in these days of rocket speeds of several thousand miles per hour. We are about 2 light-minutes away from Venus if we travel toward the sun, and about 4 light-minutes away from Mars, the first planet we will meet if we travel away from the sun. Even with the man-made satellites traveling at a steady speed of 18,000 miles per hour, it would take us more than three months to reach Mars and find out whether it is inhabited by a species of intelligent, energetic beings similar to those upon earth.

The observable motions of the sun and stars, as pointed out earlier in this chapter, follow a somewhat regular pattern of motion from east to west. The planets also move, but with variable speeds and in complex paths. Generally, each planet moves first from east to west with variable rate; then at intervals it stops, and moves for a brief time eastward, before taking up the westward direction again. In other words, planets as viewed from the earth occasionally exhibit *retrograde motion*. The reasons for the presence of curves and loops in the apparent paths of planets will be explained in a later chapter. Suffice it for the present to indicate that the planets, like the earth, rotate on their axes and revolve about the sun, the time required to make a complete revolution increasing as the distance from the sun increases. For example, the earth completes its revolution in one year, Mercury in 88 days, Mars in 687 days, Jupiter in 11.9 years and Pluto in 248 years.

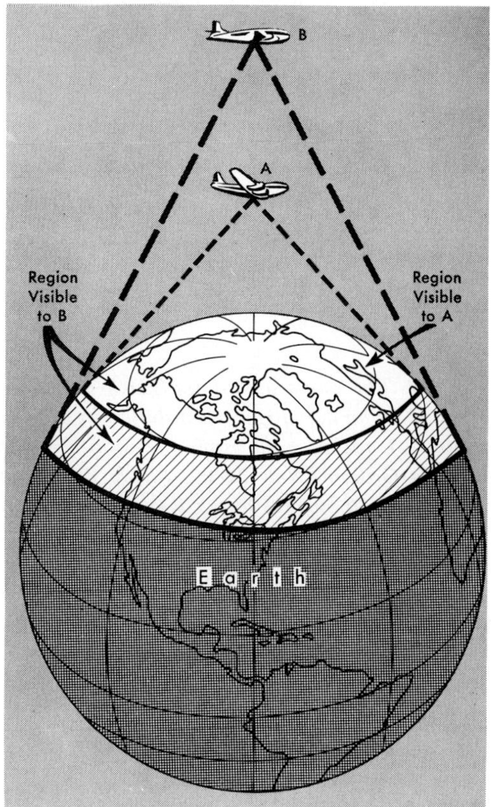

Fig. 3–2 *A proof of the curvature of the earth.*

SHAPE OF THE EARTH

The shape of the earth is defined as that of an oblate spheroid. Roughly, it can be

Fig. 3–3 *Another proof of the curvature of the earth. The earth casts a circular shadow, as seen in a partial eclipse of the moon.* (Sky and Telescope)

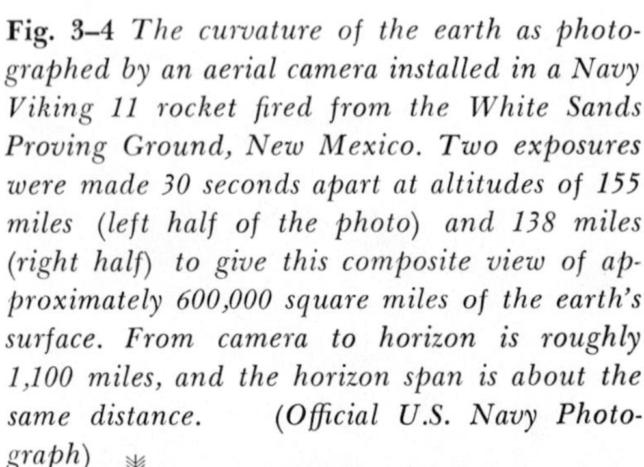

Fig. 3–4 *The curvature of the earth as photographed by an aerial camera installed in a Navy Viking 11 rocket fired from the White Sands Proving Ground, New Mexico. Two exposures were made 30 seconds apart at altitudes of 155 miles (left half of the photo) and 138 miles (right half) to give this composite view of approximately 600,000 square miles of the earth's surface. From camera to horizon is roughly 1,100 miles, and the horizon span is about the same distance. (Official U.S. Navy Photograph)*

compared to an orange bulging a bit about the middle and compressed a bit at the top. The evidence for the sphericity or curvature of the earth may now be presented.

The first evidence which may be cited is the area visible to an observer as he ascends to higher altitudes in an airplane or a balloon. Consider, for example, the two airplanes *A* and *B* in Figure 3–2. If the earth were flat, all would be equally visible from *A* and *B* and the visibility would be limited by the observer's power of vision. But if the earth were curved, then the region visible from airplane *B* would be greater than that visible from airplane *A*. The experience of observers is that from an altitude of 1000 feet the radius of visibility is limited to about 40 miles, but at an altitude of 40,000 feet the radius of visibility is about 250 miles.

The second observable piece of evidence for the sphericity of the earth was first advanced by Aristotle, whose arguments were essentially those which we employ today. The shadow of the earth, seen upon the moon during a lunar eclipse, when the earth is between the sun and the moon (see page 22), is essentially circular, as the photograph reproduced in Figure 3–3 shows. The diameter of the earth's shadow is, of course, several times larger than the apparent diameter of the moon.

Additional support is offered by the experience of watching a ship traveling away from us. At first, the whole ship is in sight, but after some time only the upper parts of the ship — the funnel and the masts — are visible. The ship, as it goes away, gradually vanishes, the lower part disappearing first. If the earth were flat, the ship would become smaller and smaller, but would remain wholly visible, though the outline might be blurred. But if the earth is curved, the gradual disappearance of the receding ship is explained.

Finally, the most direct proof of the curvature of the earth is shown in the photographs of the earth's surface made during stratosphere flights and by means of cameras attached to V–2 bombs and other more recent guided missiles. Figure 3–4 shows the curvature of the earth as photographed from a rocket.

SIZE OF THE EARTH

Reference to Table 3–1, page 19, which summarizes the facts about the earth, shows that all the data as to its size can be derived by means of the formulas given in the first column, in parentheses. For example, if we know the radius, we can calculate all the other relations, such as diameter, circumference, area, and volume. Actually, the method employed is to determine first the circumference by measuring the length of a degree of arc. The method is essentially the same as that employed by Eratosthenes (librarian of the great museum and library at Alexandria, 273–192 B.C.) by the angle of the sun's elevation. His result for the circumference of the earth was about 24,500 miles, a surprisingly close approximation to the modern value of 24,875.126 miles.

The principle of the method is illustrated in the following example: Two cities, *A* and *B*, are situated 690 miles apart, as indicated in Figure 3–5. The linear distance has been accurately measured by means of a chain used in surveying. Observers at these two cities agree to take observations on a certain star at the same time, say 10 P.M. on June 29. Observer at *A* points his telescope at the star agreed upon, which is directly overhead. At the same moment, observer at *B* points his telescope at the same star and measures the angle a_1 formed by the line to the star, *BD*, and the vertical, *CBZ*, which is the direction taken by a plumb line. Now, the lines *CAE* and *BD* are in effect parallel, since they both point to a star so far from the earth that the departure from exact parallelism cannot be measured. Since the two lines are parallel, the two angles a_1 and a_2 are equal. The value of angle a_1 in the present example was found to be 10° of arc. The linear distance for 10° is 690 miles, and therefore the length of 1° of arc is $\frac{690}{10}$, or 69 miles. The circumference is then found by multiplying the linear distance of 1° of arc by

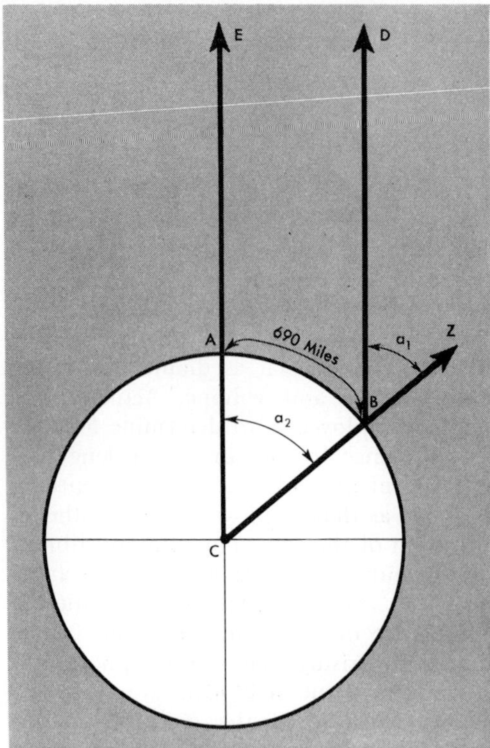

Fig. 3–5 *Measuring the earth's circumference. Method used by Eratosthenes, 235 B.C.*

360; hence the earth's circumference is

$$69 \times 360 = 24{,}800 \text{ miles.}$$

The length of a degree of arc is not the same in various parts of the earth, since the earth is flatter near the poles. The difference, however, is not very great: about 69.4 miles at the pole, and 68.7 at the equator. The equatorial radius is calculated as 3963.34 miles while the polar radius is 3949.99 miles, a difference of 13.35 miles. The mean radius and diameter and other data on the size of the earth are given in Table 3–1, page 19.

MASS, VOLUME, AND DENSITY

By the term *mass* is meant the quantity of matter, which is measured in pounds or grams; the *volume* designates the amount of space occupied by a body, and is measured in cubic feet or cubic centimeters; the term *density* designates the ratio of the mass divided by the volume of a body, and expresses *the amount of mass in one unit volume.* The density of water is 1 gram per cubic centimeter at 4° C.; the density of iron is 7.8 grams per cubic centimeter, and therefore any volume of iron is 7.8 times heavier than an equal volume of water. The method by which the mass of the earth is measured is discussed in a subsequent chapter. The value obtained for the earth is 6×10^{21} metric tons, or 5.97×10^{27} grams. For comparison, a ton may be taken as 1×10^{6} grams. An average sun or star represents about 1×10^{32} grams, while the largest star is estimated at 1×10^{35} grams. The volume of the earth is obtained from the formula for the volume of a sphere $(V = \frac{4}{3}\pi r^3)$. The value obtained is 259×10^{9}, or 259,000 million cubic miles, or 1.08×10^{27} cubic centimeters. The density, M/V, is obtained by simple division:

$$\frac{5.97 \times 10^{27}\ \text{g}}{1.08 \times 10^{27}\ \text{cm}^3} = 5.517 \text{ grams per cubic centimeter,}$$

or about 5.5 times that of water.

ROTATIONAL MOTION

Our examination of the earth has given us some definite knowledge about its form and size and also the methods by which this knowledge can be checked. It is now desirable to examine the facts indicating that the earth moves.

Our everyday experience does not give any direct observable evidence of this motion; instead, it is the sun and the other heavenly bodies that appear to move. The sun appears to rise and set, causing an alternation of day and night. The stars, if watched for a few hours, appear to slide, so to speak, upward overhead or downward to the horizon. In order to explain this apparent behavior we can make two assumptions. First, we can assume the obvious hypothesis, long held to be true, that the sun and the stars are attached to the inner surface of a huge celestial sphere which turns around daily. Second, we can propose what is today assumed to be true, that the earth rotates on its axis in twenty-four hours and thus exposes alternately each of its hemispheres to the sun.

This second hypothesis raises a question that should be answered before we examine the evidence in its favor. If the earth is moving, we may well ask, why are we not aware of its motion? The answer is simple. By *motion* we understand the change of position of an object with reference to another. If the earth moves, everything on the earth moves with it; unless there were a reference object that did not move, or else moved along with a different speed, we could never perceive this motion. The motion of an automobile or a train is known by the passenger because of the vibrations and jerks, and the sight of objects which are passed on the way. If the vehicle could be made to run without any vibration, and if there were no windows, the passenger would be unaware of motion.

EVIDENCE FOR ROTATION

The earth is assumed to turn about on an imaginary axis which passes through the earth itself and reaches the surface at two points called the *poles*. The line of midpoints on the surface of the sphere between the north and south pole is the *equator*. If we stick a colored pin or spot of paper on the equator of a small globe spinning on its axis, then move the spot upward or downward to various positions nearer one of the poles, and finally put it on the pole itself, it will be evident that the spot travels its greatest distance at the equator, the lengths of its revolutions become shorter as it approaches the pole, and when on the pole it does not travel at all, but simply rotates upon its own axis. Now, if we were to attach the base of a pencil to the globe, so that the point of the pencil aimed out straight from the globe and met a piece of white cardboard held within its reach, the pencil would draw a straight line when affixed to the equator, and a series of smaller and smaller circles as it approached the pole.

If we are right in assuming that the earth rotates on its axis, then stars observed directly overhead at the equator should appear to move in straight paths, but those observed near the poles should seem to have circular courses. By using a camera, the equivalent of the pencil in our experiment with the small globe, allowing several hours for each exposure, we can show that this is true. In Figure 3–6 are photographs of typical "star trails."

Photographs such as those in Figure 3–6 constitute evidence which must be considered in connection with all other evidence bearing on the motions of the earth. The best proof for the earth's rotation is an experiment first performed by Foucault in

Fig. 3–6 *Star trails around the pole* (*left*) *and at the equator* (*right*). (*Yerkes Observatory photograph*)

Paris in 1851. This experiment, when first performed, was "front page news" the world over. The principle of the demonstration can be understood if we carry out a simple experiment with a heavy pendulum supported from the ceiling by a wire of such length that the pendulum bob just grazes the top of a table. A pin is attached to the lower end of the pendulum to trace a path in a layer of fine sand. The trace left by the swinging pendulum indicates its plane of swing. If, while the pendulum is swinging, the table is slowly turned, the pin will cut new traces in the sand to indicate the circular motion of the table top. The plane of swing of the pendulum thus serves as a means for indicating the motion of the table top. For his experiment, Foucault used a wire two hundred feet long fixed to the dome of the Pantheon at Paris. When set in motion, his pendulum left a new mark in sand at each swing, and the veering was clockwise. This apparent veering clockwise is accounted for by the rotation of the floor (*counterclockwise*) under the plane of the vibrating pendulum. If the earth did not rotate, the stylus would have continued to trace the same groove on the sand. This experiment has been repeated many times. In the southern hemisphere the apparent deviation is counterclockwise or opposite to that in the northern hemisphere. At the poles the rotation would be a complete turn, or 360° in twenty-four hours.

There are still other facts which cannot be adequately explained on any basis other than the assumption that the earth rotates on its axis, making a complete turn once in twenty-four hours. The student will find references to some of these other proofs in the list of suggested readings. The direction of the rotation is from west to east; the speed of the rotation is greatest at the equator. This is obvious since a given point at the equator travels 25,000 miles in twenty-four hours, a little more than 1000 miles per hour, while a point in the United States travels only about 15,000 miles, at the rate of about 600 miles per hour in the same length of time. The rotation of the earth on its axis, once every twenty-four hours, produces the apparent revolution of all heavenly bodies around the earth in the same time. Hence the early notion of the hollow celestial sphere, with the heavenly bodies attached to its inner surface, rotating each day around an axis – the celestial sphere axis. It should be noted, however, that the celestial sphere appears to move in the direction opposite to the motion of the earth; the sun and the stars appear to rise in the east and to set in the west, because the earth rotates from west to east.

ORBITAL MOTION

While rotating on its axis once every twenty-four hours, the earth at the same time is assumed to move around the sun in a path called its *orbit*. This motion is called the *orbital revolution* of the earth.

Actual observations do not show that the earth travels around the sun; they make it appear that the sun moves among the stars. If we observe the sun at noon, once a week for a year, we note that during the spring the sun climbs higher in the sky each day, until about the end of June, when it begins to descend toward the south, reaching, about the end of September, the same noonday height that it had in the spring. As winter approaches, the sun moves to a lower and lower point until the end of December, when it begins to climb northward toward us again. In the spring, which is the end of the year of our observations, the sun reaches the same noonday height as it had when we started. This shifting of the sun's position marks the divisions of the year that we call the seasons. (This topic is further discussed in Chapter 4.)

There are a number of ways to prove that this phenomenon is really caused by the revolution of the earth around the sun. The simplest is to select a particular bright star and note its position with reference to two of its neighbors which appear to be farther away in space. In order to record exact positions, we can take a photograph of this group and label each star by arbi-

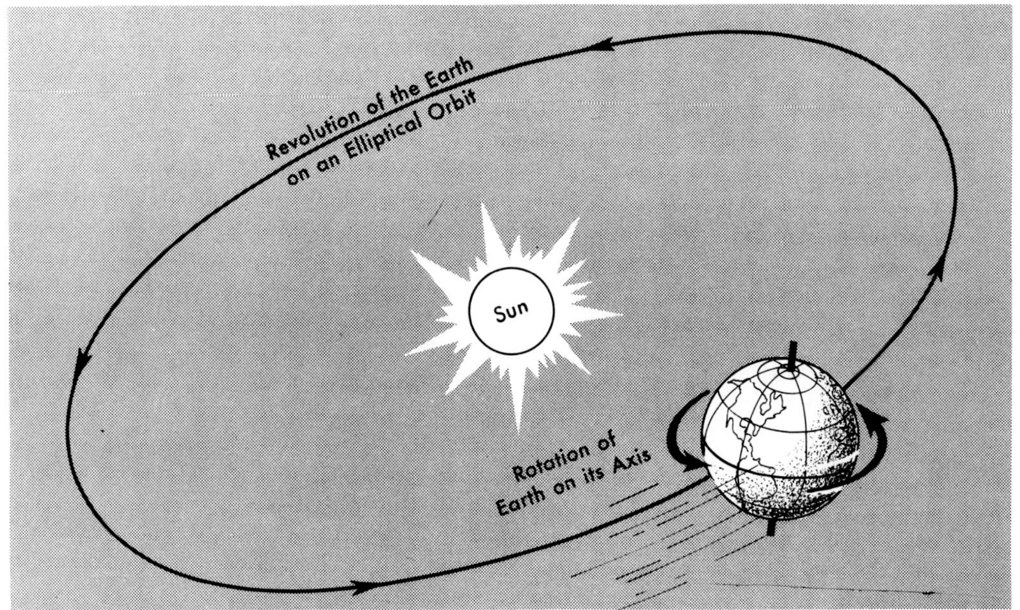

Fig. 3–7 *The earth's rotation on its axis and orbital revolution around the sun.*

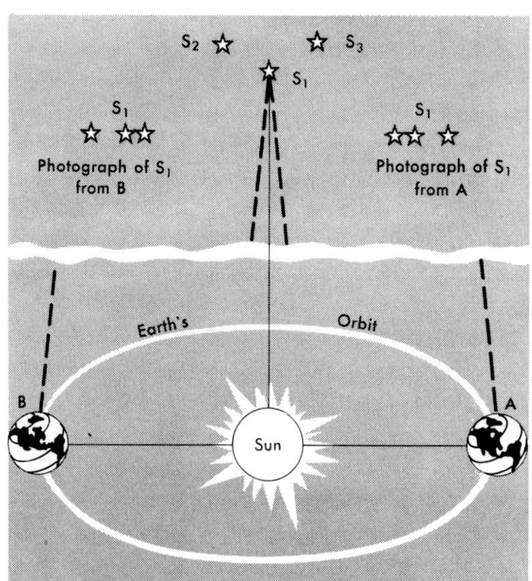

Fig. 3–8 *Determining the parallax of a star. Star S_1 is seen closer to S_2 or S_3 according as it is viewed from the opposite points A and B in the earth's orbit.*

trary symbols S_1, S_2, S_3. If the earth does not move around the sun, the star S_1 will remain always in the same direction from us and will appear always in the same position with reference to stars S_2 and S_3. But if the earth revolves, as is shown in Figure 3–8, the star S_1 will appear in January in different positions, with reference to the stars S_2 and S_3, from those in June. When the star S_1 is sighted from position A in January, it appears closer to S_2 than S_3. Six months later, the earth is in position B, and when star S_1 is observed, it now appears closer to star S_3 than S_2.

This change in position of objects against a distant background due to the motion of the observer is called *parallax,* and the apparent shift of the near stars in relation to the faraway stars is called the *parallactic displacement.* Aside from their use as evidence for the orbital motion of the earth, parallactic displacements are used to measure the distances of the nearer stars.

THE EARTH'S ORBIT

As stated above, the path which the earth follows in its revolution is called the *earth's orbit.* Since the earth returns annually to a given point, the form must have a shape roughly circular. If we determined the distance to the sun at different times in the year, say every month, and if the distance from the center (sun) to the orbit (earth) remained the same thoughout, then the orbit would be a perfect circle. But since the distances measured in January and June are found to differ by about 3 per cent, we arrive at the conclusion that the earth's orbit deviates slightly from a circle. The difference is so small that if one draws a circle so that the center is closer by 3 per cent to the right side than to the left, the eye cannot distinguish it from a perfect circle.

The form of the earth's orbit is an *ellipse.* An ellipse is a curve with two points within called *foci,* instead of a center as in the circle. The two positions are shown diagrammatically in Figure 3–9. The sum of the distances from any point on its circumference to the two foci is a constant. In Figure 3–9, the curve represents an ellipse of which the foci are F_1 and F_2. The midpoint C is called the *center.* The diameter AB which passes through the two foci is called the *major axis,* and the diameter DD' which is at right angles to AB is called the *minor axis.* If we represent half of the major axis by a and half of the distance between the two foci (line F_1C or F_2C) by c, then the ratio $c/a = e$ denotes the eccentricity of the ellipse. The distances $F_1P + F_2P = F_1P' + F_2P'$. The less the eccentricity of the ellipse the smaller the extent of deviation from a perfect circle; therefore, a perfect circle may be defined as an ellipse of zero eccentricity. The eccentricity of the earth's orbit is 0.016.

Fig. 3–9 *Diagram of an ellipse. For explanation, see text.*

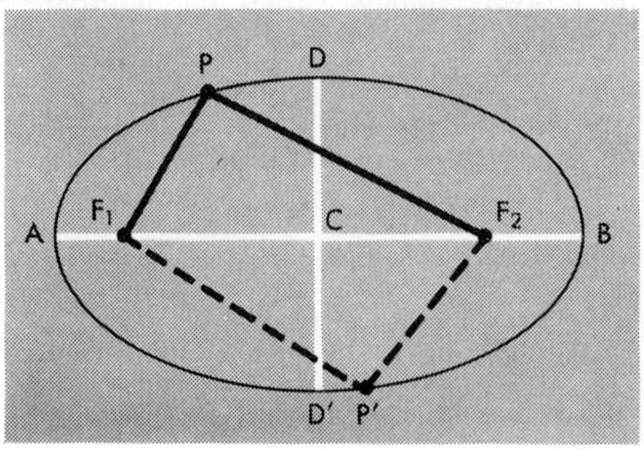

Since the earth's orbit is elliptical and not a perfect circle, with the sun occupying one of the foci, it follows that there will be a position which will be closest to the sun. This position is known as the *perihelion.* At the point opposite the perihelion, the earth is farthest from the sun. This position is known as the *aphelion.* The line joining aphelion and perihelion, passing through the foci, is the major axis of the orbit. The positions are shown diagrammatically in Figure 4–4, page 37.

The greatest distance of the earth from the sun is 94,500,000 miles, or 152,200,000 kilometers, while the least distance is 91,500,000 miles, or 146,900,000 kilometers; the difference between perihelion and aphelion is in the neighborhood of 3,000,000 miles, or 5,000,000 kilometers. The mean, or average, distance of the earth from the sun is 92,870,000 miles, or 149,450,000 kilometers. The sun, when photographed from the perihelion and aphelion, shows a difference in size. Figure 3–10 shows a comparison of the two photographs by superimposing one-half of the view taken from the perihelion on one-half of the view obtained from the aphelion. The earth is found at the perihelion on January 3 or 4, and at the aphelion on July 3 or 4.

While considering these basic scientific facts and theories of the earth, we should bear in mind that our present views are the product of several thousand years of slow development. Though the present picture was developed more systematically and with greater precision since the time of Copernicus, we should not forget that some of the ancients formed essentially correct ideas about the shape, size, and motions of the earth. Eratosthenes' calculation of the circumference of the earth was about 250,000 stadia. Although we do not know the exact distance of a stadium, it is believed to have been 517 feet. This would give 24,500 miles for the earth's circumference, a figure which, as we have seen, is remarkably close to 24,875 miles as calculated by modern

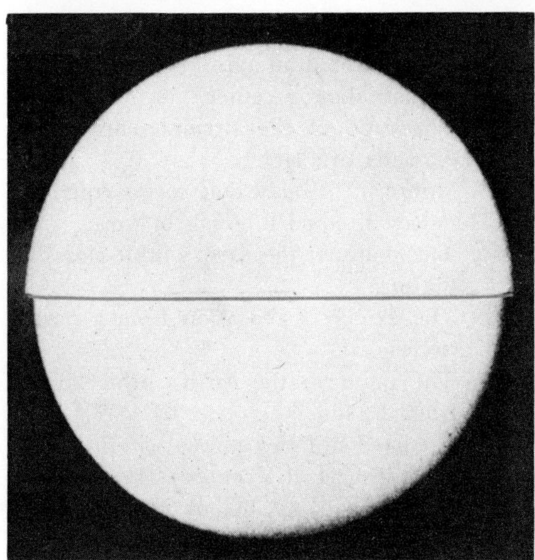

Fig. 3–10 *Sun's apparent size at perihelion (top) and at aphelion (bottom).*

methods. The problem of the motions of the earth is more difficult, and yet both the rotation and the orbital motion were advanced as hypotheses in antiquity, though they did not gain wide and permanent acceptance since instruments for accurate observations were lacking. The earth's rotation on an axis was advanced by Heracleides, and the earth's revolution about the sun by Aristarchus. Unaided by a telescope, Hipparchus, one of the most brilliant of the ancient astronomers, discovered the eccentricity of the earth's orbit. Whether the earth moved in this orbit, as Aristarchus had proposed, or the sun, as everyone else believed, must have been an open question to Hipparchus for some time. If the earth revolved, he finally reasoned, there should be a parallactic displacement of the stars. Like a true scientist, he made observations to discover whether there was any such displacement, and failing to find any with the instruments he possessed, he came to the conclusion that the earth was at the center of a circle about which the sun revolved.

After this analysis and a critical discussion of the facts about the earth, we shall consider in the next chapter the motions of the earth in greater detail. There are two reasons for this further consideration. First, the rotation of the earth is used to measure time. Second, the alternation of the seasons – spring, summer, autumn, winter – is intimately related to the motion of our "average planet."

SUMMARY

1. Scientific facts comprise all data of observable phenomena, together with the non-observable but hypothetical models and concepts which have been constructed in order to explain, correlate, and predict the data of experience.
2. The earth belongs to a family of heavenly bodies known as the solar system. It is one of the planets which revolve about a star known as the sun.
3. The appearance of ships when moving away from a stationary observer, the shadow of the earth on the moon during a lunar eclipse, and photographs of the earth's surface during stratosphere flights are proofs of the earth's curvature.
4. The circumference of the earth is 24,875 miles; its mean diameter 7917 miles, and its density 5.5 grams per cubic centimeter.
5. The earth rotates upon an axis which passes through two points called the poles.
6. Photographs of "star trails" at the equator and at the poles and the Foucault pendulum experiment are accepted as evidence of the earth's rotation.
7. The earth rotates from west to east with a velocity of about a thousand miles per hour at the equator.
8. The earth's rotation produces the apparent east-to-west motion of the sun and stars.
9. The earth revolves around the sun in an elliptical orbit, making a complete revolution in one year.
10. The shift of the nearby stars among the faraway stars as viewed from the earth at different times, called the parallactic displacement, is a proof of the earth's orbital motion.
11. The orbit of the earth is an ellipse; in an ellipse the sum of the two distances from any point on its circumference to two points within the curve, called foci, is a constant.

12. In the earth's orbit the sun occupies one of the foci; the other focus is an imaginary point in space.
13. Perihelion is the point on the earth's orbit closest to the sun, and aphelion the point most distant from the sun.

STUDY EXERCISES

1. Describe the appearance of the portion of the sky in which Polaris is situated to an observer: (*a*) at the equator; (*b*) at the north pole.
2. Describe and explain the apparent daily motions of the following heavenly bodies across the sky: (*a*) sun; (*b*) moon; (*c*) stars; (*d*) planets.
3. To account for the daily motion of the sun and stars, we can make three hypotheses: (*a*) there is a celestial sphere which holds the sun, moon, and stars, and which is turning; (*b*) there is an eastward rotation of the body upon which we live; (*c*) both the body upon which we live and the sphere move. Discuss briefly how each assumption fits the facts.
4. Give evidence to support the following: (*a*) The earth is an oblate spheroid. (*b*) The earth rotates on its axis. (*c*) The earth revolves about the sun. (*d*) The earth is not a perfect sphere.
5. Twelve of these technical terms are referred to in the definitive phrases below. Identify them by letter in the margin.

A. aphelion	H. perihelion
B. retrograde motion	I. pi (π)
C. satellite	J. radius
D. density	K. rotation
E. eccentricity	L. circle
F. motion	M. ellipse
G. orbital motion	N. uniform motion

   1. The ratio of the mass of an object to its volume.
   2. A geometrical figure that has all points of its surface equidistant from the center.
   3. A change of position of an object with respect to another.
   4. The apparent motion of a planet, first westward, then eastward, then again westward.
   5. Motion about an axis.
   6. Motion about a center.
   7. The ratio of the circumference to the diameter of a sphere.
   8. Motion of a body that covers equal distances in equal intervals of time.
   9. The point in the earth's orbit closest to the sun.
   10. The extent of deviation from a perfect circle.
   11. The point in the earth's orbit farthest from the sun.
   12. A curve with two points within (called foci) instead of a center as in a circle.
6. In the following, a list of observations is given. Place after each statement: *A* if the observation helps to prove that the earth is spherical in shape; *B* if it helps to prove that the earth rotates on its axis; *C* if it helps to prove that the earth has orbital motion; *X* if the observation proves none of these three statements.

   Observation:

   a. Smoke tends to go upward. ....
   b. In traveling from Chicago to Florida, new stars come into view. ....
   c. Freely falling bodies actually fall a little east of the point directly underneath the original point of support. ....
   d. At an altitude of a thousand feet the region visible to the observer is less than at two thousand feet. ....
   e. The sun always travels westward. ....
   f. Fixed-camera photographs at the equator show star trails as straight lines, but at the poles the trails are circular. ....
   g. There are twelve new moons in a year. ...
   h. Photographs of distant stars taken in January show relative displacement when taken again in July. ....
7. Two cities, *A* and *B*, are situated 2075 miles apart. At each of these cities simultaneous observations are taken on a distant star which is directly overhead at *A*. The observer at *B* notes that his line of sight to the star makes an angle of 30° with his plumb line. Calculate from these data (using the method of Eratosthenes) the length of the circumference of the earth. Draw a diagram to illustrate your solution to this problem.

FOR FURTHER READING

1. PAYNE-GAPOSCHKIN, CECILIA, *Introduction to Astronomy.* New York: Prentice-Hall, 1954.
   An excellent college textbook on astronomy. Rotation and revolution of the earth are discussed in Chapter II.
2. DUNCAN, JOHN CHARLES, *Astronomy.* New York: Harper and Brothers, 1955.
   A college textbook on astronomy. The discussion of the rotation and revolution of the earth will be found in Chapters 3 and 5.
3. Paperback: VERRILL, A. H., *The Strange Story of Our Earth.* Premier, 35¢.
4. Paperback: MATTERSDORF, L., *A Key to the Heavens.* Premier, 35¢.
5. Paperback: EDITORS OF SCIENTIFIC AMERICAN, *The New Astronomy.* Simon and Schuster, $1.45.
6. Magazine Article: "Planets from Palomar Observatory," *Scientific American,* February, 1953.
7. Magazine Article: "The World We Live In: The Starry Universe," *Life,* December 20, 1954.
   Discusses the solar system and the planets. It also contains material on galaxies, stars, and theories of the universe that will be useful in connection with Chapters 16, 17, and 39 of this text. Illustrated with eleven black-and-white and fifteen color photographs.

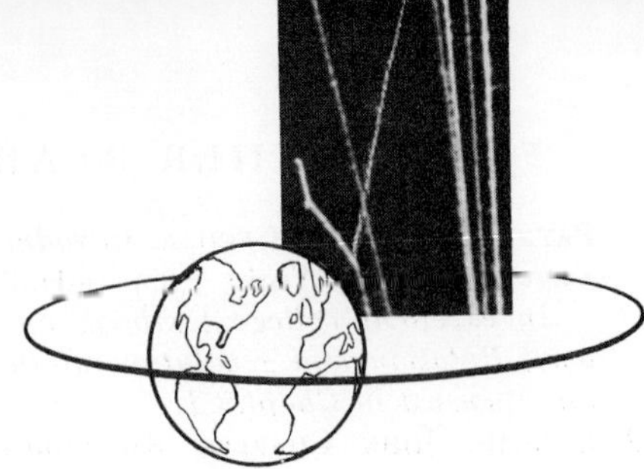

4

THE CONCEPT OF TIME

THE CONCEPT OF TIME is difficult to comprehend because, unlike matter, it cannot be held in our hands and observed with our eyes. By *time* we usually mean *the interval between events.* If our day is full of doing things, time "flies" and the day appears short. If we have little to do and the day is dull, time "drags" and the day seems unusually long. Time, as understood in that sense, is not measured by clocks and watches but by our minds and is called *psychological time;* it is a vague and subjective concept with no definite standard of measurement except the events which come to our consciousness. For an absolute *standard of time* it is necessary to choose an event that recurs at regular intervals. The event which rigorously fulfills this condition is the apparent revolution of the celestial sphere, caused by the rotation of the earth, and this event has been used from remotest antiquity as a measure of time. An object like a star or the sun directly overhead in the sky is chosen as a reference point. The interval between the initial observation and the return of the heavenly object to the same point is called a day; hence the measurement of time is based on motion – one complete rotation of the earth. To measure time accurately, then, it is necessary to have a system for locating a reference point in the sky.

CIRCLES OF REFERENCE ON THE CELESTIAL SPHERE

In the last chapter it was pointed out that the earth's rotation causes an apparent daily rotation of the sun and stars, and that it early led to the notion of the celestial sphere with the heavenly bodies attached to its inner surface rotating each day around on an axis. Though we know that this notion is not correct, we will make use of it in order to develop a system of locating the exact position of a heavenly body.

The celestial sphere is assumed to rotate on an axis which touches the surface at two points, the north and south celestial poles. Since the apparent revolution of the celestial sphere is due to the earth's rotation, the celestial poles are the points where the earth's axis of rotation prolonged in space would pierce the celestial sphere. Similarly, the plane of the earth's equator prolonged outward touches the celestial sphere at a circle called the *celestial equator.*

If we suspend from a string a small weight which tapers downward to a point, the arrangement is called a *plumb line.* If we imagine the plumb line to extend upward in the sky until it touches the celestial sphere, the point is called the *zenith.* The other end of the plumb line, extended to the invisible part of the sphere directly opposite the zenith, reaches what is called the *nadir.* If we draw a great circle around the celestial sphere midway between the zenith and the nadir — 90° from each of them — it is called the *horizon.* In Figure 4–1, *Z* represents the zenith and *NESW* is the horizon. The term *horizon* in everyday speech means the imaginary boundary line where the sky meets the earth, and therefore depends on the landscape. To distinguish between the two the latter is called the *visible horizon.*

In order to locate any point on the celestial sphere, vertical circles are drawn from the zenith at right angles to the horizon and through the nadir. We can draw as many circles as we wish, so that any point in the sky can have one of these circles passing through it. In order to obtain a reference circle, we choose the north-south great circle which passes through the celestial poles known as the *meridian* circle. In Figure 4–1 the meridian is *NZS.* The points where the meridian intersects the horizon are the *north* and *south points,* while midway between them are the *east* and *west points.* The east-west great circle passing through the zenith 90° from the meridian is the *prime vertical.*

To locate a heavenly body in the sky, we find the vertical circle passing through it, and then measure the number of degrees between it and the horizon. It should be noted that we are measuring the arc of a circle and not a straight line, and therefore we must express it in degrees. In order to locate the star *A* in Figure 4–1, we note that it is situated on the vertical circle *ZX,* which of course can be prolonged to pass through nadir and then to zenith. The arc *AX* in degrees expresses the angular elevation of star *A* above the horizon, or the *altitude* of the star. The arc *SX* is called the *azimuth* and expresses in degrees the position of the star, westward, measured from the south point of the meridian.

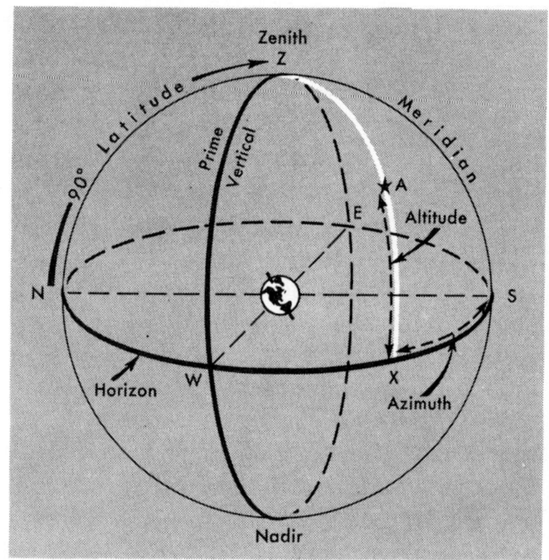

Fig. 4–1 *Horizon system of coordinates.*

The altitude of Polaris at the equator is nearly zero, that is, it is almost on the horizon, while at the north pole, it is nearly overhead and therefore, has an altitude of nearly 90°. The angular distance of any point on the surface of the earth, north or south from the equator, is called its *latitude.* The latitude at the equator is chosen as zero; latitudes north of the equator have positive values from zero to +90°; those south of the equator, negative values from 0 to −90°. For any city in the United States the altitude of Polaris can serve to measure the latitude. The angular distance east and west from a reference point is the *longitude;* and the meridian passing through Greenwich, England, is taken, by convention, as the zero reference point. Longitude is often expressed in hours, minutes, and seconds instead of degrees. Thus, 360° = 24 hours, 1 hour = 15°, and hence 1° = 4 minutes of time. West of Greenwich is expressed as positive (+) and east as negative (−).

SOLAR TIME

Having obtained a method of locating a heavenly object accurately, we can follow its apparent motion from day to day. Since the rotation of the celestial sphere is dependent upon the rotation of the earth, we take the interval required for one complete rotation as a basis for the measurement of time. Therefore, the sun is selected and observed through a transit telescope. This is a special type of telescope mounted on an axis east and west, so that it can follow the meridian of the place at which the telescope is mounted. The eyepiece is provided with special and delicate apparatus to record exactly when the sun crosses the thin line across the field of view which designates the meridian. The transit is observed and the time is recorded. The next passage of the sun will occur when the earth has completed one rotation. The interval between two successive passages of the center of the sun through the meridian is called a *true solar day.* The day is divided into twenty-four hours, each hour into sixty minutes, and each minute into sixty seconds.

The solar days vary slightly in length owing to the variation in the orbital speed of the earth. When the earth is at the perihelion, or closest to the sun, it travels faster, and when it is at the aphelion, it travels slower. In order to eliminate the situation of having the noon oscillate, it has been found convenient to adopt a solar day, which is invariable, by making a simple adjustment. The average of the lengths of all the solar days in the year is taken and called the *average* or *mean solar day.* Thus, the sun is made to be at the meridian at mean noon; all mean solar days are equal. *One mean solar second is 1/86400 of a mean solar day; this is the fundamental unit of time. All ordinary clocks are constructed on the basis of mean solar seconds.*

TIME ZONES

It is quite obvious from the definition of mean solar time that what we call noon here is not noon two hundred miles west or east of us. The local apparent noon changes as a person travels east or west. In order to avoid the confusion which would result if each town and city had its clocks adjusted to the local apparent noon, it has become necessary to adopt a system of keeping the same time in certain zone areas, each of which is about a thousand miles in width. The time zones in the United States and eastern Canada, shown in Figure 4–2, are as follows:

1. *Atlantic,* which includes the region located east of a line running east of 68° west meridian; this zone is not used in the United States;
2. *Eastern,* which includes the region located east of a line running from Cleveland to the western boundary of Florida;
3. *Central,* which includes the region west of the Eastern line to the western boundaries of the Dakotas, Nebraska, Kansas, Oklahoma, and Texas;
4. *Mountain,* which includes the regions extending from the Central line to the Rockies;
5. *Pacific,* which includes the region west of the Rockies.

In addition to the four zones of standard time that are used in the United States, most large metropolitan centers adopt daylight saving time during the summer; this is one hour earlier than standard time. Central daylight saving time, therefore, is the same as Eastern standard time.

For world-wide reckoning, the longitude east or west of Greenwich (see page 33) is employed. For each 15° (360°/24 = 15°), east or west, there will be an hour's difference in time.

If a traveler starts from New York and proceeds west, he must set his watch back an hour for every fifteen degrees of longitude, or roughly one thousand miles, because the earth is moving eastward. If he takes an airplane westward, he will apparently lose one day if he goes around the earth. To simplify matters for travelers, by international agreement, a change of date is made at the 180th meridian from Greenwich. This line is in the Pacific Ocean, and a traveler going westward jumps one day when he crosses what is called the International Date Line. If an airplane or ship traveling westward arrives at the date line on the evening of June 10, it changes the date as it crosses the line to June 11. Simi-

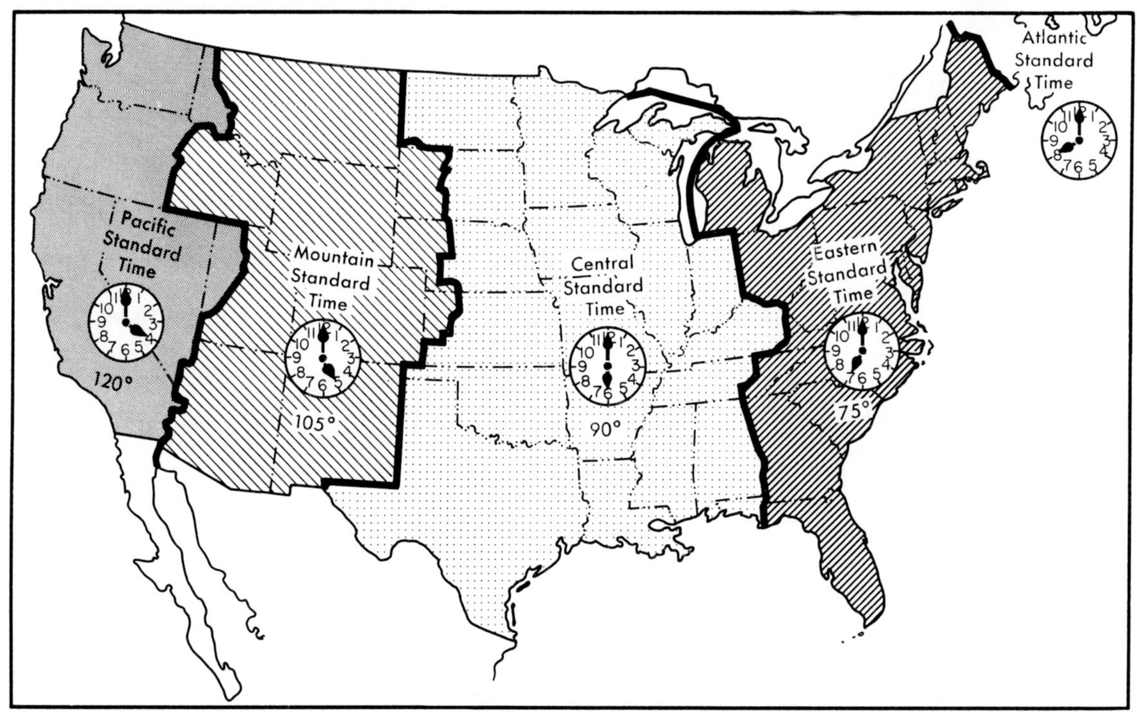

Fig. 4–2 *Time zone map of the United States. (Zone boundaries are established and modified by the Interstate Commerce Commission.)*

larly, if one travels eastward and arrives at the date line on the evening of June 10, the date is changed to June 9.

ATOMIC STANDARD OF TIME

The absolute standard of time must be an event that recurs at regular intervals; and as discussed in the preceding sections, the rotation of the earth has been used as this invariable event. However, by the beginning of this century it had become apparent that fluctuations in the earth's period of rotation take place sporadically, though the causes for this are not as yet definitely known. For example, in 1870 the annual period of rotation was 1.6 seconds fast and in 1900 0.6 seconds slow as compared with periods of rotation over long intervals of years. In addition, errors in astronomical observations, together with the difficulties encountered in calibrating and checking the pendulum clocks which are used in observatories as secondary standards of time, prompted scientists to investigate other natural events which have an *invariable period.* As a result of these investigations atomic clocks have been developed which are based on the invariant frequencies of the vibration of atoms and molecules (see Chapters 22 through 25). The *Spectroscopic Servo Clock* used in the National Bureau of Standards (Washington) is based on one of the vibration frequencies of *ammonia molecules,* while the atomic clock of the National Physical Laboratory (England) employs one of the vibration frequencies of the *cesium atoms.* A precision of one-billionth of a second is possible by the use of these atomic clocks.

THE SEASONS

The alternation of the seasons — spring, summer, autumn, winter — is familiar; its explanation is related to the motions of the earth and may be considered at this point because the seasons from the very beginning have been used by men as points of demarcation in the reckoning of time.

The earth is assumed to turn about an imaginary axis which passes through the earth itself and meets the surface at the two poles. We can place a small globe representing the earth at a distance from an electric light bulb representing the sun. The axis on which the globe turns is so arranged that the light from the bulb strikes it in a direction perpendicular to its axis. The plane containing the earth and the sun is called the *plane of the ecliptic.* Since our model earth's axis is perpendicular to the plane of its orbit, it makes with the ecliptic an angle of 90°. If the real earth's globe were to rotate on its axis at this angle and to revolve slowly about the sun, we should have conditions over most of the earth vastly different from what they are at present. At a latitude of 40–45°, which is about midway between the equator and the north pole, the sun would rise always in the same place in the east, climb in the sky at 45° and set exactly twelve hours after sunrise; hence, day and night would be of equal length. The climate would be an everlasting spring. At the pole the sun would always be at the horizon, never rising and never setting, but making a complete round every twenty-four hours. Each place on earth would have approximately uniform year-round general weather conditions.

Now, suppose we tilt our model globe representing the earth 23.5° so that it makes with the ecliptic an angle of 66.5°. Then the variations of the seasons, the inequality of day and night in our latitudes, can be explained. If we incline the north pole of our model toward the sun, we will obtain an idea of the position of the earth during the summer at our latitude. The day is almost fifteen hours long. The north pole is continuously illuminated as the earth rotates; the illuminated portion is a circle of 23.5° from the pole, called the *Arctic Circle.* At the southern hemisphere, which is tilted away from the sun, the reverse conditions exist. The days are short; at about 40°–45° south there is daylight for about nine hours. The south pole, and the territory of a circle 23.5° from it, is enveloped in a long night. If we incline the north pole of our model away from the sun to the same degree, it is obvious that we will have exactly the opposite conditions in each hemisphere from those described above — summer in the southern hemisphere and winter in the northern hemisphere. If we tilt the model to the right or to the left to the same degree (23.5°) as before, we obtain the approximate positions of the earth in the spring and fall. With this rough illustration in mind, the

Fig. 4–3 *Relation of vernal and autumnal equinoxes to the ecliptic and the celestial equator.*

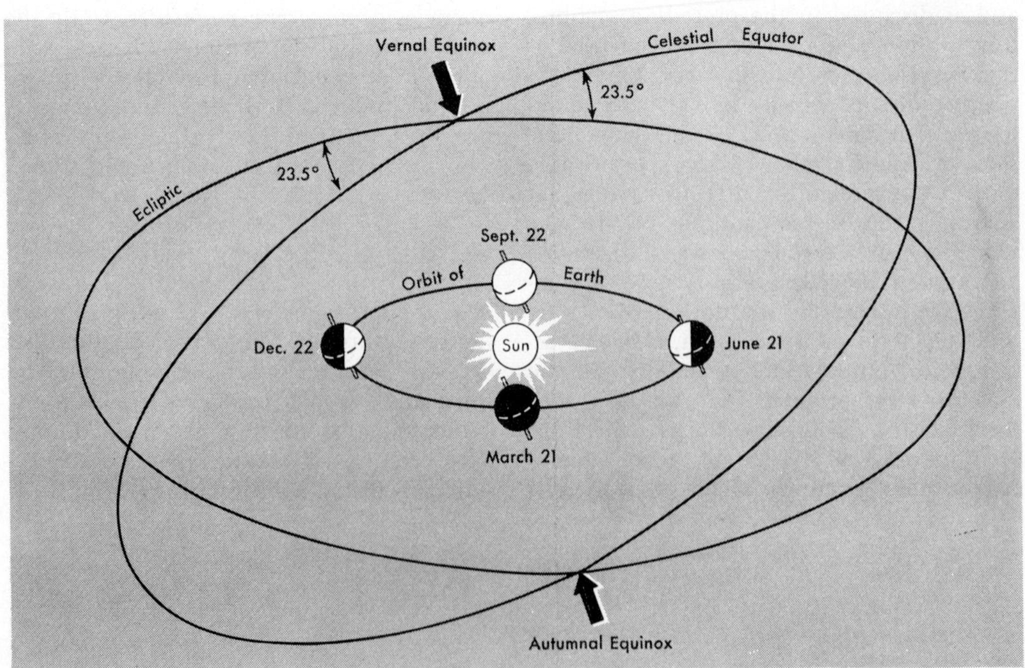

alternation of seasons can be considered in greater detail.

Refer to Figure 4–3. As previously noted, the plane of the ecliptic is the plane determined by the sun and the earth. If this plane is projected outward until it intersects the celestial sphere, it will form a great circle called the *ecliptic.* A little reflection will show that this circle is related to the earth's orbit, since this circle marks the apparent path of the sun among the stars in the course of a year. It will be also recalled from previous discussion that the celestial equator is the circle which the earth's equator marks on the celestial when projected outward from the earth until it intersects the celestial sphere. The ecliptic intersects the celestial equator in two points (situated opposite to each other) at an angle of 23.5°; these points are called the *equinoxes.* These are the points where the sun apparently crosses the equator, moving northward on or about March 21 (the *vernal equinox*) and southward on or about September 22 (the *autumnal equinox*). Midway between the equinoxes – that is, ninety degrees from each other on the ecliptic – are points called *summer* and *winter solstices.* These represent the two positions of extreme declination of the north pole toward and away from the sun.

Consider the position of the earth on the vernal equinox, referring to Figures 4–3 and 4–4. The axis of the earth is perpendicular to the line of light between the sun and the earth. The sun is at the horizon at both north and south poles; at the north pole it is rising after the long Arctic night, and at the south pole it is about to set after a long Antarctic day. Since the axis of the earth is perpendicular to the plane of the ecliptic and hence is not turned toward or

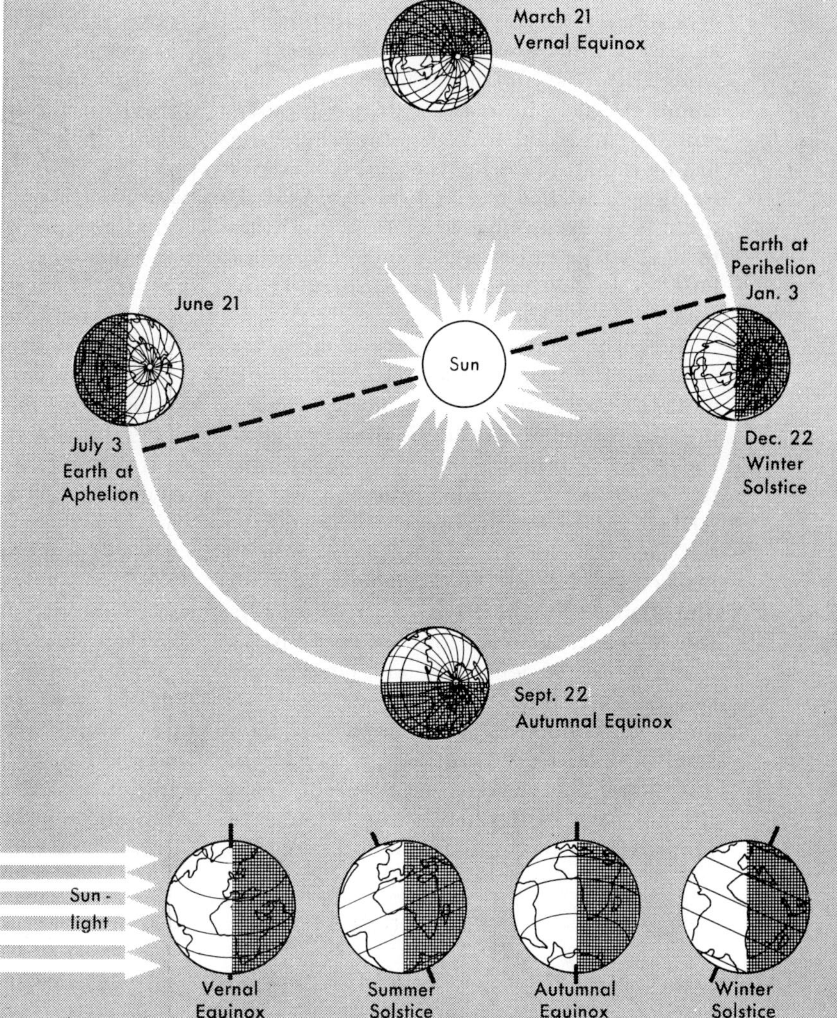

Fig. 4–4 *Position of earth at various seasons. Position of sun displaced to show more clearly that the aphelion and perihelion distances are different. (The dates for the equinoxes and solstices are not fixed; each varies as much as a day from time to time.)*

away from the sun, night and day are equal everywhere on earth. The position of the sun at noon as measured by the meridian altitude varies from 0° at the poles to 90° at the equator. In the United States at about 42° north (New York or Chicago), the meridian altitude of the sun is 48°.

Beginning with the vernal equinox, the length of the day in the northern hemisphere increases while in the southern hemisphere it decreases; as the length of the day increases, the meridian altitude of the sun also rises; in other words, the sun rises to a higher and higher position at noon. Since the rays become more nearly perpendicular and the heat is received for longer periods, the weather is generally warmer. When the summer solstice arrives on June 21, the north pole (see Figure 4–3) is turned toward the sun; the length of day in the northern hemisphere at about 40°–45° latitude is fifteen hours, while in the southern hemisphere at a corresponding latitude the length is nine hours — and the season is winter. In the northern hemisphere the amount of heat, for reasons already pointed out, has increased to the point where the loss by radiation during the nights becomes smaller than that received by day, and so there is an accumulation of heat from day to day which causes a rise in temperature familiar in the hot spells of July and August.

After the summer solstice the noonday altitude of the sun decreases, and the length of day decreases, until at the autumnal equinox the meridian altitude is the same as at the vernal equinox: 48°. The conditions on September 22 are the same as those described above for March 21. In the northern hemisphere, the advance of fall is marked by decrease in the length of days and increase in the length of nights. The sun moves to a lower and lower point at noon. Since the length of daylight has decreased and the rays of sun strike at an angle, the amount of heat gained becomes smaller than the amount lost by radiation, and hence the weather becomes colder in the northern hemisphere while the reverse holds true in the southern hemisphere. On December 22 the conditions are the reverse of those described for June 21. In the United States the length of day (40°–45° latitude) is about nine hours. Above a latitude of 66.5° north there is no daylight at all, and south of 66.5° there is no night at all. After the winter solstice, when the northern hemisphere is inclined away from the sun, the revolution of the earth in its orbit brings it on March 21 to the position of the vernal equinox from which we set out on our seasonal journey. Unlike the passage of seasons at the middle latitudes, conditions in the equatorial regions do not change appreciably during the year. Strictly speaking, there are no seasons at the equator; and day and night are of about equal length throughout the year.

THE CALENDAR

The reckoning of time over long intervals is made in terms of the year. Generally the year may be defined as the time required for the earth to complete one revolution in its orbit about the sun. More precisely, it is the time included between two successive arrivals of the sun at the vernal equinox. This is called the *tropical year,* and its length is 365.2422 mean solar days.

The subdivision of the year into months and weeks and the system of keeping account of the years was developed early and was based on the motion of the moon. The phases of the moon have always been of great interest. Since the moon completes its revolution (with reference to the sun) in 29.5 days, there are 12.4 lunations, or intervals between new moons, in a year ($12.4 \times 29.5 = 366$ days). It was this which gave rise to the division of the year into twelve months.

When Julius Caesar revised the calendar, the year was assigned 365 days, and every fourth year 366 days. This implied that the tropical year contains 365.25 days, while in reality it has 365.2422, or 0.008 of a day shorter. As a result, with the passage of one thousand years the Julian calendar had an error of eight days. In 1582 the date of the vernal equinox had shifted from March 21 to March 11. In that year, Pope Gregory XIII changed October 5 to October 15, dropping ten days. To prevent further displacement, it was decreed that the rule of adding one extra day every fourth year should be followed except in the case of those century years whose number is not divisible by 400. Thus, A.D. 1700, 1800, and 1900 were not leap years while 2000 will be a leap year. The Gregorian calendar is used by practically all the Christian nations. The Jewish and Mohammedan calendars are based on the lunar month.

Reform of the Calendar. Improvements of the present calendar have been proposed from time to time. The reform most often proposed is to add one month and thus have thirteen months of twenty-eight days each, with New Year's Day not assigned to any month. The leap-year rule would have to be retained, and the extra day assigned between June 28 and July 1. In the proposed reform, all days and dates are fixed; the first of every month would fall on Sunday, and the last Saturday in a month would be the twenty-eighth. All months would be alike, and no new calendar would be required for each year. Changes of custom and practices, however, are slow, and such calendar reforms may not take place for many years.

SUMMARY

1. Time is the interval between events; as ordinarily understood it is psychological time, measured by the events which come to our consciousness.
2. The measurement of time as used in science is based on one complete rotation of the earth on its axis and with respect to the sun. More recently, the vibration frequencies of atoms and molecules are being introduced as a standard of time.
3. The measurement of time involves the accurate location of a celestial body. Circles of reference on a hypothetical sphere are used in one system of location.
4. The point directly overhead, as shown by a plumb line, is called the *zenith.* The great circle which passes through the celestial poles and the zenith is the *meridian.*
5. The interval required for one complete rotation of the earth with the center of the sun as reference point is a *solar day.*
6. A *mean solar day* is the average of all the solar days.
7. The standard unit of time is 1/86400 of a mean solar day and is called one *second.*
8. Owing to the rotation of the earth, noon varies over various places. There are four time zones in the United States; each covers about a thousand miles in width and differs by one hour.
9. *Latitude* is the angular distance north and south of the equator on the surface of the earth. *Longitude* is the angular distance east and west of Greenwich, England.
10. The earth's axis is not perpendicular to the plane of its orbit, but is inclined at an angle of 23.5°. This is the cause of seasonal variations.
11. The *ecliptic* is a great circle formed on the celestial sphere by the outward projection of the plane made by the earth and the sun. The two points at which the ecliptic intersects the celestial equator are the *equinoxes.* The *solstices* are the two points in the ecliptic where the sun is farthest from the equator.
12. The *tropical year* is the time included between two successive arrivals of the sun at the vernal equinox.
13. The calendar is the method of reckoning time over long intervals. There have been several reforms of the calendar now used.

STUDY EXERCISES

1. Explain the term *time* as employed in everyday speech and as used in science.
2. Assume that you leave for London from Idlewild Airport, New York, on July 7, noon, Eastern Daylight Saving Time, and that the airplane travels with an average speed of 275 miles per hour with no stops. What time (Greenwich) will you arrive at London? (The air distance from New York to London is 3450 miles.)

3. Assume that you take off from New York on July 10, 1:00 P.M., Eastern Standard Time, for the Philippines, with stops of one hour each at Chicago, Kansas City, and San Francisco airports. Assume also an average speed throughout of 250 miles per hour. Give the date and time (local) of arrival at San Francisco and Manila. (The air distance from New York to San Francisco is 2570 miles; from San Francisco to Manila, 7800 miles.)
4. Give a concise definition of each of these terms:

longitude	mean solar day
latitude	meridian
aphelion	vernal equinox
perihelion	winter solstice
altitude of a star	International Date Line
tropical year	Standard Time Zone
solar day	uniform motion

5. Make a drawing of the celestial sphere. On the basis of your drawing, explain: zenith, altitude of a star, horizon, meridian, ecliptic, celestial equator.
6. Show by a diagram the earth at vernal and autumnal equinox, and at summer and winter solstice. Show that the southern hemisphere has summer weather during December; that on June 21 the sun shines twenty-four hours at the north pole; that the sun shines twenty-four hours at the south pole on December 21; and that the equatorial regions have no seasons.
7. Consulting a map, determine the longitude and latitude of the following: International Falls, Minnesota; San Francisco, California; Portland, Maine; Miami, Florida; and the town in which you are attending school. Express the longitude both in degrees and in hours, minutes, and seconds.
8. Describe the seasons the American continent would have if the earth's axis were perpendicular to the plane of its orbit.
9. Identify the following universities: (*a*) latitude +42°, 03′, 27.2″; longitude +5 hours, 40 minutes, 41.84 seconds; (*b*) latitude +52°, 12′, 53.3″; longitude −0 hours, 00 minutes, 22.77 seconds.

FOR FURTHER READING

1. PAYNE-GAPOSCHKIN, C., *Introduction to Astronomy*. New York: Prentice-Hall, 1954.
   The rotation of the earth and the seasons are discussed on pages 33–44; time, on pages 52–57.
2. DUNCAN, J. C., *Astronomy*. New York: Harper and Brothers, 1955.
   The celestial sphere is discussed in Chapter 1; time, on pages 73–78; and the seasons, on pages 110–115.
3. BAKER, R. H., *An Introduction to Astronomy*. New York: D. Van Nostrand Company, 1957.
   For the celestial sphere, see Chapter 2; for time, the seasons, and the rotation of the earth, Chapters 3 and 4.
4. Magazine Article: "Atomic Clocks," *Journal of Applied Physics*, XXII (1951), 1365.
   An excellent but highly technical article. See also Bulletin 33–17, published by the United States Bureau of Standards.

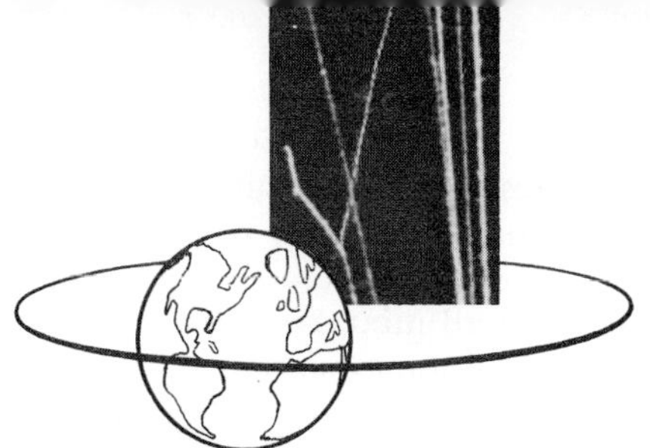

5

A CLOSER LOOK AT THE EARTH

STAGNANT, stationary air is a rarity. As every householder knows, heated air rises toward the ceiling, often carrying dust from the floor to deposit on walls, especially behind radiators. Cold air enters through any opening or collects near the floor. In the winter, moisture frequently condenses on cold windowpanes as frost. All this is evidence of the movement of invisible air in accordance with well-known physical laws. These same processes occur on an enormous scale in the atmosphere over the entire earth. Instead of little currents of air, there are immense masses of air, often miles in depth, moving hundreds and thousands of miles and transporting many millions of tons of water to fall again as dew, frost, rain, hail, or snow.

This complex circulation of the atmosphere over the earth is the cause of all weather and all climate. The atmosphere also is responsible for the continuous processes of change on the earth's surface. These are entirely absent, for example, on the moon. The day-to-day changes are called *weather;* the long-period changes, including those of the seasons, are called *climate.* The cause of weather and climate is found in the tilting of the earth's axis, in the direction and amount of the rays of the sun (insolation), and in the broad general movements of the atmosphere found in the wind belts. Weather often has tremendous influence on the way we live. A knowledge of climate is necessary, therefore, to understand past history, human and geological, and to account for the various types of civilization over the face of the earth. In this chapter the changes that occur in the atmosphere and their effects will be studied.

THE ATMOSPHERE

The geographer's globe gives an incomplete picture of the earth. It does not show the gaseous envelope, the *atmosphere,* which surrounds our planet. The atmosphere is one of the three divisions of the earth; the other two are the *hydrosphere* and the *lithosphere.* The hydrosphere, or "water-envelope," covers about 71 per cent (143 million square miles) of the earth's surface in the form of oceans and seas. The

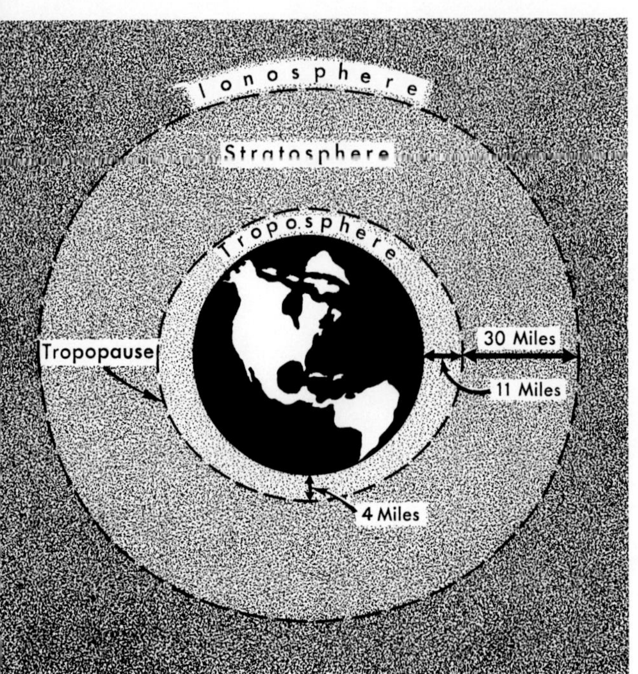

Fig. 5–1 *The divisions of the atmosphere.*

hydrosphere fills the depressions in the surface of the solid sphere, the depth of these depressions in some points being as much as six miles. The lithosphere, or "stonesphere," comprises the solid portion of the earth. Those parts which rise above the sea are known as continents or continental masses. The surface of the lithosphere is not smooth like that of the hydrosphere, but is marked with hills, valleys, and mountain ranges. The highest peak is nearly six miles above sea level and hence the maximum difference in the elevation of the earth's surface, above and below sea level, is about twelve miles.

We are always conscious of the earth and water which constitute our environment. The presence of air is less obvious. Does it, for example, have weight? It is quite easy to demonstrate in many ways that air has mass. A deflated inner tube from a tire can be weighed, then inflated with air and weighed again; the increase shows that air has weight. Other properties of air can be mentioned. It is odorless, tasteless, and colorless; it is not usually felt unless one moves rapidly through it. Like all gases, it can be compressed and expanded.

The term *air* is used to designate the mixture of gases which compose the atmosphere. Air, like all mixtures, does not have the same composition everywhere. It is common knowledge that air in certain regions contains less moisture than in others, and the composition of air at sea level differs from air at high altitudes. Refer to Table 5–1. Inspection of the table shows that two gases, nitrogen and oxygen, make up most of the air. Nitrogen and oxygen are elementary substances or elements. (The name *element* is applied to pure substances which cannot be broken down by ordinary methods, such as heating, into simpler substances.) Oxygen is directly used in the vital processes of animals, while the chief effect of the nitrogen is just to dilute the oxygen. Carbon dioxide results from a combination of the elements carbon and oxygen. It is produced by the breathing of animals and burning of fuels and is constantly being removed from air and used as food by growing plants. Water occurs in air, either in the form of vapor or as clouds or fog in minute droplets or even minute crystals of ice. The amount of water varies at or near the surface of the earth from small amounts in hot, arid regions to about 5 per cent in the very moist regions. The final component of air, dust, is an impurity carried by the wind. The number of dust particles is usually high in industrial centers and may reach two hundred thousand or more per cubic centimeter of air. Dust particles furnish nuclei for the condensation of water vapor, and by scattering light, help (in normal concentrations) to give the sky its characteristic blue appearance.

The mass of the atmosphere in a given volume varies as one climbs a mountain or flies upward in an airplane; the air becomes gradually "thinner" as the altitude increases. The fact that one has difficulty in breathing at high altitudes shows that the amount of oxygen is less than at the surface of the earth. About one-half of the total mass of the atmosphere lies within the first 3.5 miles. Only about 15 per cent of the to-

TABLE 5-1

COMPOSITION OF AIR

COMPONENT	WEIGHT of 1 liter at 0° C. and 1 atmos.	PER CENT [1] by volume dry air	PER CENT [2] by volume moist air
Nitrogen	1.250 g	78.09	77.2
Oxygen	1.429 g	20.95	20.8
Rare gases	.....	0.93	0.92
Carbon dioxide	1.977 g	0.03	0.03
Water [3]	.....	0.0	1.2
Dust particles [4]	.....	.....	.....

[1] Relatively constant to elevation 12 miles.
[2] Variable depending on amount of water vapor.
[3] Varies up to 5 per cent. [4] Variable.

tal mass of air exists above an altitude of ten to eleven miles. The lower region is known as the *troposphere* and the upper region as the *stratosphere*. The troposphere extends about eleven miles high at the equator and about four miles at the poles. It is a region of continuous circulation of the gaseous components, and is characterized by clouds, fogs, rains, lightning, wind, air currents, with wide fluctuations in temperature. The stratosphere usually begins at an altitude of about seven miles. In contrast to the troposphere, it is a region of eternal quiet, with a constant temperature (about –55° Fahrenheit in the latitude of Chicago), free from dust, storms, and clouds. The earlier knowledge of the stratosphere was obtained by sounding balloons carrying automatic recording instruments. Since 1931, stratosphere flights have been made by the use of special balloons. The first, by Auguste Piccard, reached a height of 52,000 feet. The highest altitude so far attained by man is slightly over 100,000 feet by Dr. David Simons in 1957. Dr. Simons was in a sealed capsule carried by a huge balloon. At his highest altitude, 99 per cent of the earth's atmosphere was beneath him. The air pressure outside the capsule was only about 7 millimeters of mercury. Normal atmospheric pressure is 760 millimeters of mercury. Figure 5–1 shows the extent of troposphere and stratosphere.

The stratosphere becomes thinner toward the outer space until it merges with traces of gases that exist in the spaces between the planets. One method used in estimating the

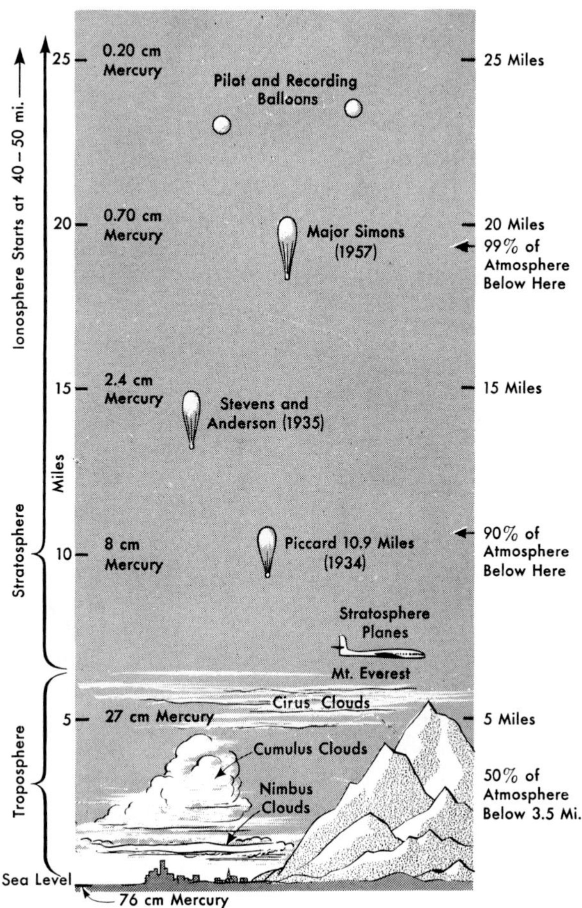

Fig. 5–2 *Important facts relative to the troposphere and stratosphere. (Adapted from H. E. White,* Classical and Modern Physics. *Copyright 1940, D. Van Nostrand Co., Inc., Princeton, New Jersey.)*

height of the atmosphere is observation of meteors, or "shooting stars." Meteors which enter the earth's atmosphere are solid matter ordinarily varying in size from that of a pinhead to that of a walnut. Since they move with very high velocities, they create tremendous friction as soon as they enter the region in which air is present. They heat up, therefore, until they become incandescent, and thus visible, as they fall toward the earth. Meteors usually become vaporized before they reach the troposphere and very rarely reach the ground. If the same meteor can be seen or photographed by two observers stationed a few miles apart, it is possible to determine the actual height by triangulation. Meteors usually appear at heights of less than one hundred miles, but some meteors have been observed at heights close to two hundred miles. This shows that even at these heights some air exists. Observations of the Aurora Borealis show that the rare gas helium exists up to a height of five hundred miles above the surface of the earth.

It should be realized, however, that at heights much above twenty-five miles the gases of the atmosphere are in an extremely rarefied state. Even at altitudes of five miles the air is so rare that the lungs cannot absorb a sufficient quantity of oxygen to support human life. For this reason all aviators seeking high altitudes must have tanks of compressed oxygen to maintain life. For the same reason airplane engines at high altitudes must be equipped with compressors (superchargers) to compress the air before it enters the engine intake.

The region above the stratosphere, at an elevation of about fifty to sixty miles above the earth, is called the *ionosphere* and contains a large amount of ozone, or active oxygen gas. The lower part of the ionosphere (elevation of fifty miles) is the Kennelly-Heaviside layer, named after the scientists who first hypothesized the existence of such a region. The gases in this region have a very high electrical conductivity and are of great importance in radio broadcasting. Radio waves from broadcasting stations travel in all directions. The presence of electrically charged gaseous particles in this Heaviside layer causes the radio waves to be reflected back to the earth. By thus confining them to the earth, the Heaviside layer makes long-distance radio reception possible. The complete breakdown of overseas radio communication occasionally observed for two- or three-day periods has been associated with sunspot activity, at which time it is believed that gaps appear in the Kennelly-Heaviside layer and the radio waves pass out into space.

ATMOSPHERIC PRESSURE

If a person dives to the bottom of a swimming pool, he feels *pressure* because of the weight of the water above him. In the same way the air of the atmosphere exerts pressure upon the objects at the earth's surface, because of the weight of all the air above that surface. Pressure means force or weight per unit of area. The weight of the atmosphere above each square inch of surface is usually about 15 pounds. Hence, atmos-

Fig. 5–3 *Principle of mercury barometer.*

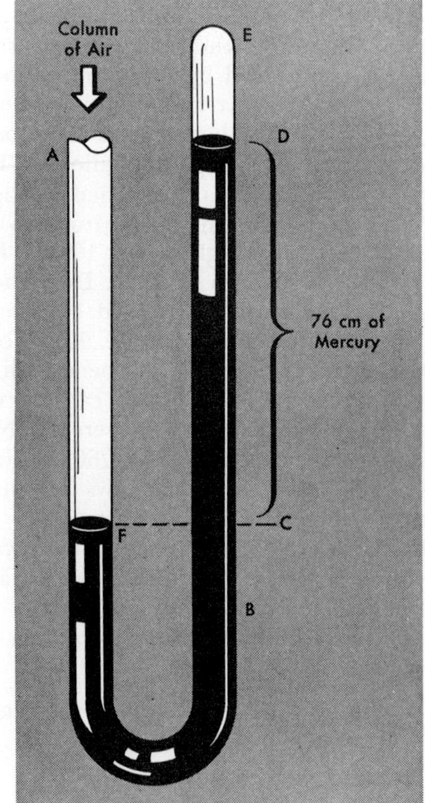

pheric pressure is said to be 15 pounds per square inch (15 lbs/in^2).

This pressure was long overlooked and methods for measuring it were not developed until the seventeenth century. The common mercury barometer, however, clearly demonstrates the existence of air pressure. For example, a U-shaped glass tube with a closed arm about a yard in length can be filled with enough mercury to extend somewhat beyond the turn. (See Figure 5–3.) The tube can then be raised to a vertical position. It will be observed that the level of the mercury in the closed column falls but it does not empty. At sea level, the height of the mercury column will be about 76 centimeters or 30 inches. What supports this mercury? Why doesn't it continue up the left tube until the two mercury columns are at the same height? Above the surface *F* rests a column of air which extends to the top of the atmosphere. It is the weight of this air that pushes at *C* on the column of mercury *CD* on the right side of the closed tube (Figure 5–3). For this reason, the height of the mercury column in the right arm rises and falls as the pressure of the air changes. The height of a mercury column in a mercury barometer, then, directly indicates the pressure of the air, and we often express atmospheric pressure in inches or centimeters of mercury. Another experimental type of the mercurial barometer is shown in Figure 5–4.

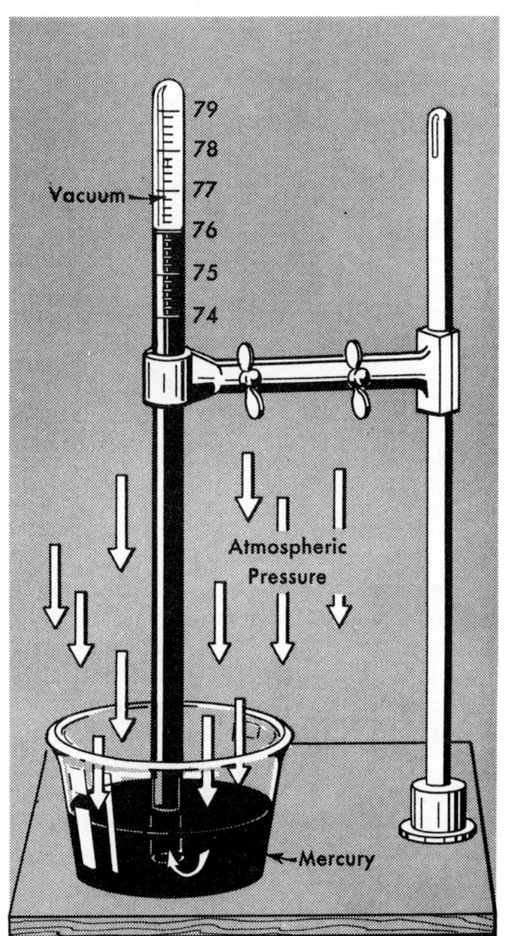

Fig. 5–4 *Mercurial barometer (experimental type).*

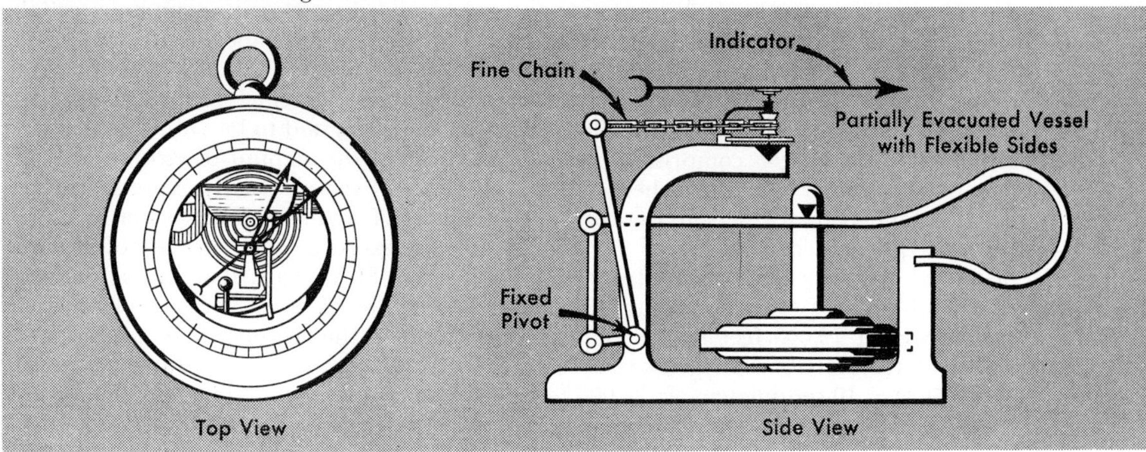

Fig. 5–5 *Essential parts of an aneroid barometer.*

Fig. 5–6 *Aneroid barometer. (Central Scientific Company)*

TABLE 5–2 RELATION BETWEEN BAROMETRIC PRESSURE AND ALTITUDE

ALTITUDE in feet	BAROMETRIC PRESSURE	
	In inches	In centimeters
0 = sea level	29.9	76.0
1,000	28.9	73.2
2,000	27.8	70.7
3,000	26.8	68.0
4,000	25.8	65.7
5,000	24.9	63.5
10,000	20.6	52.5
15,000	16.9	43.0
20,000	13.8	35.1
24,000	11.8	30.0

A more convenient type of barometer to use is an aneroid, shown diagrammatically in Figure 5–5. The small chamber with flexible sides is sealed after partial removal of the air. The movement of one side of the chamber, as a result of changing air pressure, is communicated by a suitable mechanical system to the indicating dial. The markings on the instrument are established by reference to a mercury barometer. (See Figures 5–5 and 5–6.)

Barometers are used for measuring altitudes. Table 5–2 lists barometric pressure at different altitudes. From the table it is clear that for each inch of decrease in pressure in the lower levels of the atmosphere the elevation increases approximately one thousand feet. A barometer which is calibrated to read altitude directly and which is extensively used in airplanes is called an *altimeter*. Since oxygen comprises approximately one-fifth of the atmosphere at sea level, it follows that a person absorbs oxygen at a pressure of one-fifth of 76 centimeters or about 15 centimeters. Inspection of the table shows that the pressure of the atmosphere at 10,000 feet is 52.5 centimeters, and therefore the oxygen pressure is about $50/5 = 10$ centimeters. At 24,000 feet the oxygen pressure is $30/5 = 6$ centimeters of mercury. At this oxygen pressure a person soon becomes unconscious. The oxygen pressure may be increased by adding pure oxygen to the air, but even with an atmosphere of pure oxygen a person becomes unconscious in an open airplane at an altitude of about 45,000 feet. The difficulty is overcome by sealing the airplane and increasing the air pressure or by using a mask with oxygen from a tank.

ATMOSPHERIC MOISTURE

Water vapor in the air plays a very important part in all the weather and climates of the earth. Water left in an open vessel evaporates. In a closed vessel, however, the amount of water vapor that will be absorbed by the air is limited for any given temperature. Air which has absorbed all the water it can is said to be saturated. A direct measure of the amount of saturation is the pressure of vapor, usually expressed in millimeters of mercury. Thus water at 25° C. (77° F.) exerts a vapor pressure of 23.8 millimeters. This means that water placed in a closed chamber will evaporate until the pressure in the chamber reaches 23.8 millimeters. The air is then saturated and is said to have a relative humidity of 100 per cent at 25° C. If this air is now heated to 40° C., it is capable of taking up more water vapor. The air is then said to be unsaturated.

Air which is nearly saturated at ordinary temperatures is said to be humid. Air with little or no moisture is said to be dry. The rate of evaporation from the surface of the skin of our bodies depends upon the relative humidity. Since the evaporation of perspiration from the skin produces a cooling effect and cooling by evaporation of water proceeds more rapidly in dry air, we feel uncomfortable in weather which is both warm and humid because evaporation of perspiration proceeds very slowly or not at all. Thus, a temperature of ninety degrees in a humid climate can be nearly unbearable, but not especially uncomfortable in a dry climate.

Water vapor in warm air will not remain as vapor if the air is cooled, because the air reaches the saturation point for the new, lower temperature. Further cooling results in condensation of water vapor as liquid water or *dew*. The temperature at which a sample of air begins to form water condensate is called the *dew point*. The determination of the dew point, then, is a convenient way to determine how saturated the air is with water vapor.

It is customary to describe dry or humid air in terms of its relative humidity, that is, the ratio of the amount of water actually present — indicated by its dew point — to the amount that would be present in an equal volume of saturated air at the same temperature. An equivalent definition is the ratio of the pressure of water vapor present in a sample of air to the vapor pressure in a saturated sample at the same temperature. It is important to note that the relative humidity of a given sample of air decreases with a rise in temperature and increases with a drop in temperature. The relative humidity alone does not indicate the amount of water present. This depends upon both the temperature and the relative humidity. Thus air at 0° C. may be saturated — have a relative humidity of 100 per cent — but the actual vapor pressure is very low — only 4.6 millimeters. On the other hand, air at 90° C. and fully saturated has a vapor pressure (of water) of 525.8 millimeters. Even at 50 per cent of saturation, the pressure of the water vapor (0.50×525.8 mm $= 262.9$ mm) at 90° C. is very much greater than for the sample of cold air. Thus, warm humid air, even if not saturated, contains much more water vapor than cold dry air.

Another very important distinction between dry and moist air is their relative densities. Particles of water vapor (called molecules) have less mass than particles of oxygen and nitrogen, the principal components of air. The replacement of particles of oxygen and nitrogen by particles of water vapor means a decrease in density. Thus a liter of air at 30° C. saturated with water vapor weighs about 2 per cent less than a liter of dry air at 30° C. This is one reason why atmospheric pressures in the tropics are always less than in cooler regions. This results in mass movements of the atmosphere toward the equator.

MOVEMENTS IN THE ATMOSPHERE

The atmosphere is a huge circulation system deriving its energy ultimately from the sun. Either locally or over large areas the air becomes heated, expands, falls in density, and starts to rise and move just as warm air rises above a radiator. The amount of heating of an air mass depends upon a number of factors, such as the direction of the sun's rays, the relative lengths of day and night, both of which depend upon the inclination of the earth's axis and its rate of turning on its own axis. (See Figure 5–7.)

Of the energy from the sun which strikes the earth, some heat energy is reflected out into space, some is absorbed and re-radiated out into space, while a part of the energy stays absorbed, raising the temperature of the land, air, and water. *The average temperature of all the climates over the entire earth does not sensibly change.* Hence, over a long period of time, the amount of heat received from the sun must be very nearly balanced by the heat lost to outer space. Otherwise, the earth as a whole would be either heating up or cooling down.

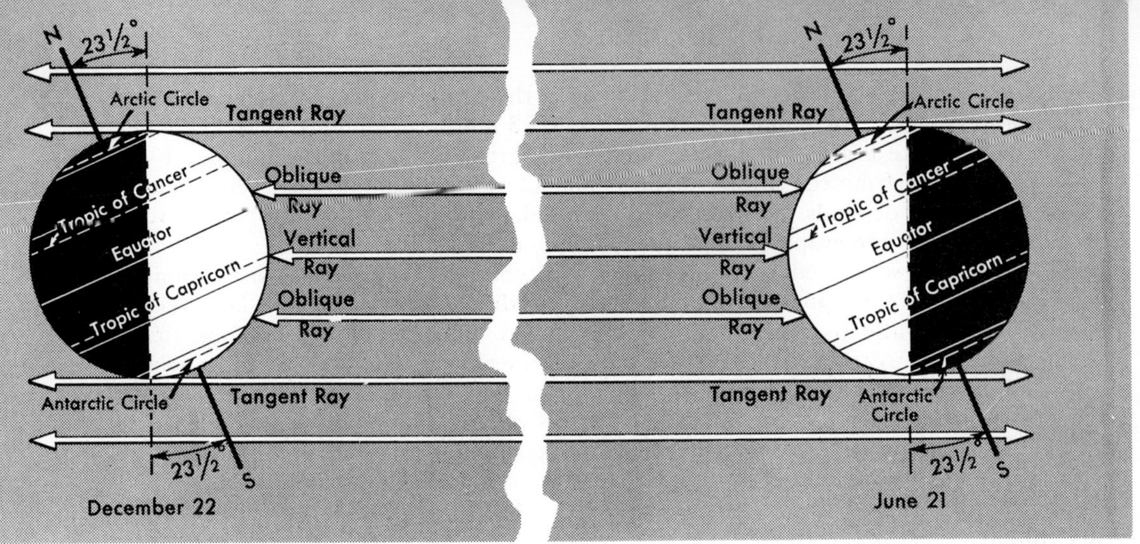

Fig. 5–7 *The heat received from the sun in any region depends upon the latitude and the time of year.*

THE SOLAR CONSTANT

The amount of energy received from the sun at the outer limit of the atmosphere on a surface perpendicular to the sun's rays is remarkably constant – about 1.94 calories per square centimeter per minute. It is slightly greater about January 3 or 4, when the earth in its orbit is at perihelion and slightly less about July 3 or 4, when the earth is at aphelion. The total amount of energy received by the earth is thus truly enormous. An area of one square mile of the earth's surface receives energy from the sun at the rate of 800 million calories per second, which is equivalent to 4,690,000 horsepower. It is this energy which is responsible for the weather, for the formation of fossil fuels as coal, for growing vegetation and the maintenance of life.

DIFFERENTIAL HEATING OF EARTH'S SURFACE

The geometry of the earth with respect to itself and to the plane of the ecliptic results in different amounts of energy being received over like areas of surface, these differences in the local rate of heating or cooling being related to latitude and the season. Thus, Figure 5–8 shows that the amount of heat absorbed per unit of area in a given amount of time is considerably greater at the equator than at the poles for two reasons: first, because the sun's rays are much more concentrated at the equator; and second, because the path through the atmosphere is much shorter than near the poles and less heat is absorbed by the atmosphere. The effect of the tilting of the earth's axis with respect to the ecliptic is another important reason for the differential heating of the earth's surface. During the summer season, for example, temperatures in the northern hemisphere are significantly higher than those in the southern hemisphere. Six months later this condition is reversed. (See Figure 5–9.) If the axis of the earth were perpendicular to the ecliptic and the sun's rays, the length of the day would everywhere be the same and the amount of heating and cooling of the earth's surface would be approximately constant. Then there would be definite zones of climates along the parallels of latitude from the equator to the poles. The mean temperature at any locality would remain approximately the same. But, for the reasons given above, the amount of *insolation* (heat energy received from the sun) over the earth continuously fluctuates and the result is the seasons.

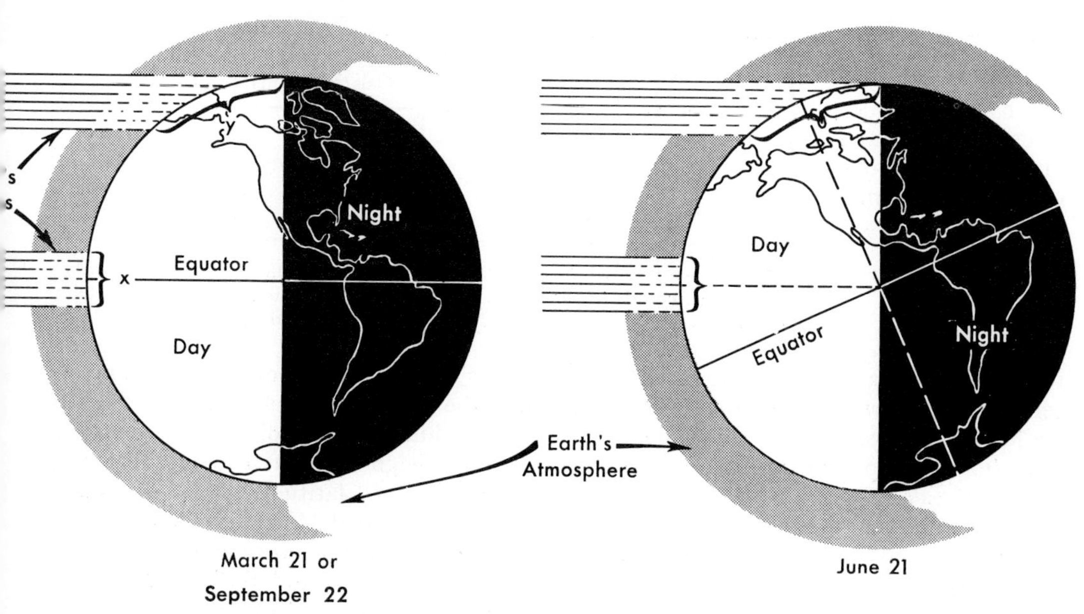

Fig. 5–8 *Variation of rate of heating of earth's surface with latitude.* *(Redrawn from G. T. Trewartha,* Introduction to Weather and Climate, *McGraw-Hill Book Co., Inc.)*

These differences on a world basis are shown in Figure 5–9. This figure merits close study. Note that the region of maximum heating varies with the time of year. On June 22 (the summer solstice) and on December 22 (the winter solstice) the rays of the sun strike the earth perpendicularly at latitudes 23.5° north and 23.5° south, respectively. The heating effect for these latitudes is then at a maximum – about 600 calories per square centimeter per day. But on March 21 and September 22 the sun's rays are striking perpendicularly at the equator. At that time the daily insolation of the earth is at a maximum in the latitudes near the equator – again about 600 calories per square centimeter per day. Note also that during the period from Oc-

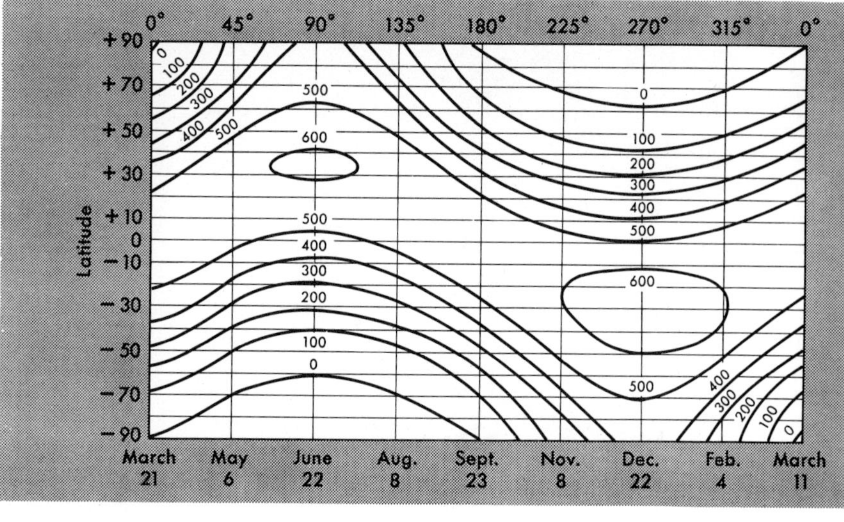

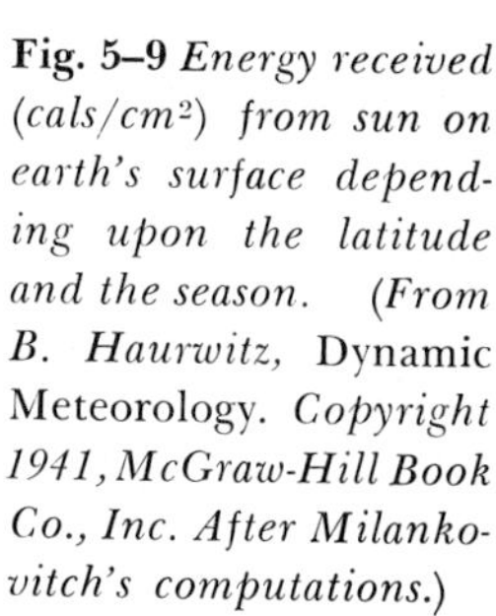

Fig. 5–9 *Energy received (cals/cm²) from sun on earth's surface depending upon the latitude and the season. (From B. Haurwitz,* Dynamic Meteorology. *Copyright 1941, McGraw-Hill Book Co., Inc. After Milankovitch's computations.)*

TABLE 5–3

HEAT BUDGET AND CAUSE OF HEAT TRANSPORT FROM LOWER TO HIGHER LATITUDES (AVERAGED)*

LATITUDE	HEAT RECEIVED (Cals/cm²/min)	HEAT LOST (Cals/cm²/min)	SURPLUS OR DEFICIT
0° (Equator)	0.339	0.300	+ 0.039
30°	0.297	0.283	+ 0.014
60°	0.193	0.245	− 0.052
90°	0.140	0.220	− 0.080

* Compare J. Gilluly, A. C. Waters, and A. O. Woodford, *Principles of Geology* (San Francisco: W. H. Freeman and Co., 1952), p. 100; or B. H. Haurwitz, *Dynamic Meteorology* (New York: McGraw-Hill Book Co., 1941), p. 102.

tober through early March no heat is received in the north polar region. Similarly, no heat is received in the south polar region during the period from April through August of each year.

The actual temperature of any region depends not only upon the rate of heat received but also upon the rate of heat lost by radiation into outer space. These two rates are seldom actually equal, though their averages are. It is true that in low latitudes more heat is received than is lost — the day is generally longer than the night — and in high latitudes more heat is lost than is gained. This is brought out in Table 5–3. These data indicate that the air masses in the tropics would continuously *rise* in temperature unless there were some compensating cooling effect. The circulation of air masses provides this cooling effect. The air near the equator expands because it is less dense. Thus a column of air near the equator must weigh less than a column of cooler air in northern latitudes, say, a thousand miles to the north. The result is that the cooler air from the north moves down toward the equator, and the warmer air at the equator is pushed up and then toward the poles. Thus a huge circulation process is set up: warm air flows toward the poles and cool air flows toward the equator. (See Figure 5–10.) The cooler air coming in from the north prevents a continually rising temperature near the equator.

There is a second reason for the existence of these huge circulating air masses in the atmosphere. Near the poles more heat is lost by radiation than is received. (See

Fig. 5–10 *Generalized movement in air cells over earth in northern hemisphere.*

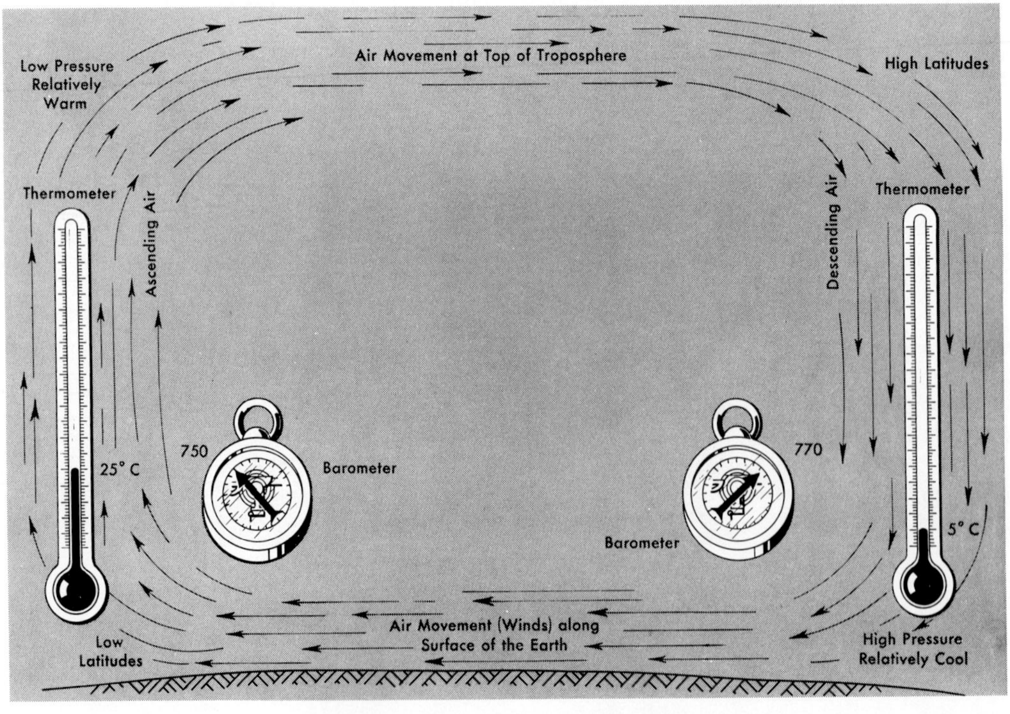

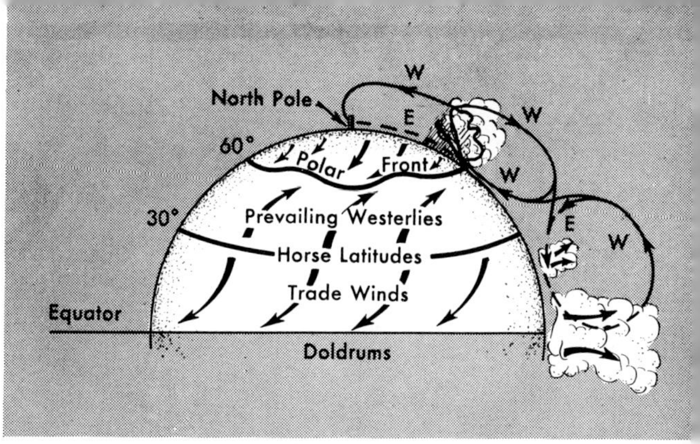

Fig. 5–11 *Air mass circulation over the earth from equator to poles. (Redrawn from* Climate and Man, *1941 Yearbook of the U.S. Department of Agriculture.)*

Table 5–3.) Hence regions near the poles would be continually getting colder unless there were a compensating heating effect. The relatively dense air in the northern hemisphere over the polar regions moves south. It is replaced by warmer air from more southerly latitudes. (See Figure 5–11.) This warmer air travels north along the earth's surface until it hits a polar front of denser air when it rides up over the polar front but continues moving poleward. It eventually sinks again to bring heat to the polar regions.

Thus, there is a continuous movement of enormous air masses to form three huge, more or less vertically circulating cells of air, which go around the earth. The boundaries of these cells are characterized by certain surface characteristics of the atmosphere described by three terms, the *doldrums,* the *horse latitudes,* and the *polar front.* The doldrums are the regions of relatively calm winds near the equator. Here, warm tropical air is rising. The horse latitudes are about 30° north and 30° south latitudes, also characterized by relatively calm winds. Here, warm equatorial air is descending to the surface of the earth, some to flow toward the equator and some toward the poles. A polar front is a region of very unsettled weather where moisture-laden tropical air meets a denser, cooler air mass from the polar region.

EFFECT OF EARTH'S ROTATION

If the earth did not turn on its axis, these air-mass movements would be in a generally north-and-south direction, as shown in

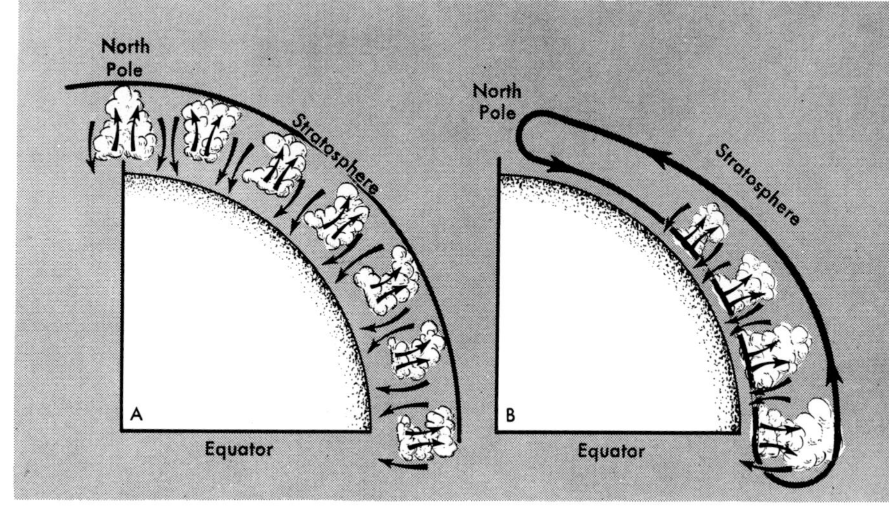

Fig. 5–12 *A. The circulation of the atmosphere which would exist were a non-rotating sphere heated uniformly at the equator. B. Circulation of atmosphere if the earth were a non-rotating sphere heated principally in low latitudes. (Redrawn from* Climate and Man, *1941 Yearbook of the U.S. Department of Agriculture.)*

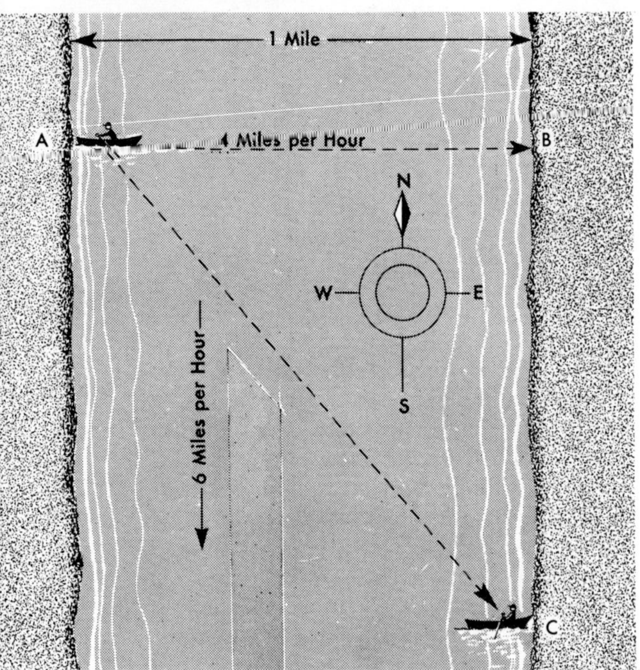

Fig. 5–13 *The law of independence of motions.*

Figure 5–12, but the earth does rotate and this rotation changes the north-south wind direction. Figure 5–13 shows why this is a necessary consequence of the "law of independence of motions." The rower starts from *A* to row eastward to *B*. If the body of water is a lake, the rower will reach point *B*, one mile east of *A*. His eastward speed of 4 miles per hour means that he will be rowing fifteen minutes. If, however, this is a stream flowing south at the speed of 6 miles per hour, the rower will take fifteen minutes to cross it, but he will land at point *C*, $1\frac{1}{2}$ miles south of *B*. This follows because his motion relative to the stream and the motion of the stream itself are *independent* of each other. The result is that he rows four miles east and six miles south. The distance traveled along the diagonal is

$$\sqrt{1^2 + 1.5^2} = \sqrt{3.25} = 1.8 \text{ miles.}$$

The law of independence of motions applies to the surface winds of the earth. A point on the equator, rotating with the earth, moves eastward at the rate of about 1000 miles per hour. At latitude 45° north, a point on the earth moves eastward about 700 miles per hour. The surface winds originating in the horse latitudes must therefore travel both south and west, or from a generally northeast to a southwest direction. That is, as these winds move south, the eastward velocity of the surface of the earth increases and the winds acquire a westerly direction with respect to the earth. These winds blowing obliquely toward the equator are known as the *trade winds.*

The winds traveling northward from the horse latitudes, warm, moisture-laden tropical air, move into latitudes where the eastward motion of the surface of the earth is continually decreasing. The surface winds must therefore travel eastward and also northward, or from southwest to northeast. These winds are the *prevailing westerlies.* In general, they are found between latitudes 30° north and 60° south. (See Figure 5–11.)

The pressure profile for the northern hemisphere is shown in Figure 5–14. Note that the polar regions have relatively high atmospheric pressure and that the pressure gradually decreases from the Arctic region to about 60° north latitude. Then, it gradually increases to about 30° north latitude, when the pressure again starts to decrease as the equator is approached. Thus, there is a trough of low pressure about 0° and 60° north latitude and ridges of high pres-

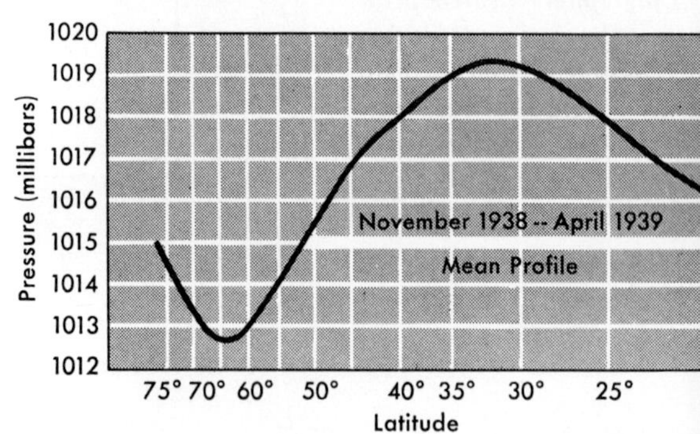

Fig. 5–14 *Pressure profile in northern hemisphere. (Redrawn from* Climate and Man, *1941 Yearbook of the U.S. Department of Agriculture.)*

sure about 90° and 30° north latitude. The troughs of low density occur because at these points the air is relatively warm and is also heavily laden with moisture (moist air is *less dense* than dry air).

AIR MASSES

As a result, then, of differences in insolation and in the amount of moisture in the air, and because of the earth's rotation, the local weather over large portions of the earth's surface is always changing with the movement of huge masses of air, 500 to 1000 miles across, and as much as five miles in depth. Thus, there are often tropical masses of warm, moisture-laden air moving in a generally southwest to northeast direction over the United States. This air comes from either the Pacific or the Gulf of Mexico in the prevailing westerlies, which bring warmer temperatures and moisture. There are also continuous movements of relatively cold polar air masses from Arctic regions flowing south into the United States, bringing cold, dry, crisp weather. Where a cold mass meets a warmer mass, a polar front forms, causing stormy weather, rain, hail, or snow, depending upon the local conditions at the time. Sometimes the line of contact is so sharp that there results a so-called "line squall" with heavy precipitation and high winds.

These huge air masses are always in rotation. The masses of air moving north in the northern hemisphere rotate counterclockwise. The cold, high-pressure air masses moving in an easterly and southerly direction rotate clockwise. As a general rule, masses of air about an atmospheric "low" rotate counterclockwise in the northern hemisphere, but clockwise about an atmospheric "high" (Figures 5–15 and 5–16). These air masses may be as much as a thousand miles in diameter and move about 500 to 700 miles per day. They are to be found over any continental land mass.

Air masses with high pressures move horizontally toward regions of lower pressure. The air in a high also is cooler and more dense than the warmer air in a low, so that, whenever a polar front meets a low, it rolls underneath the low and displaces it upward.

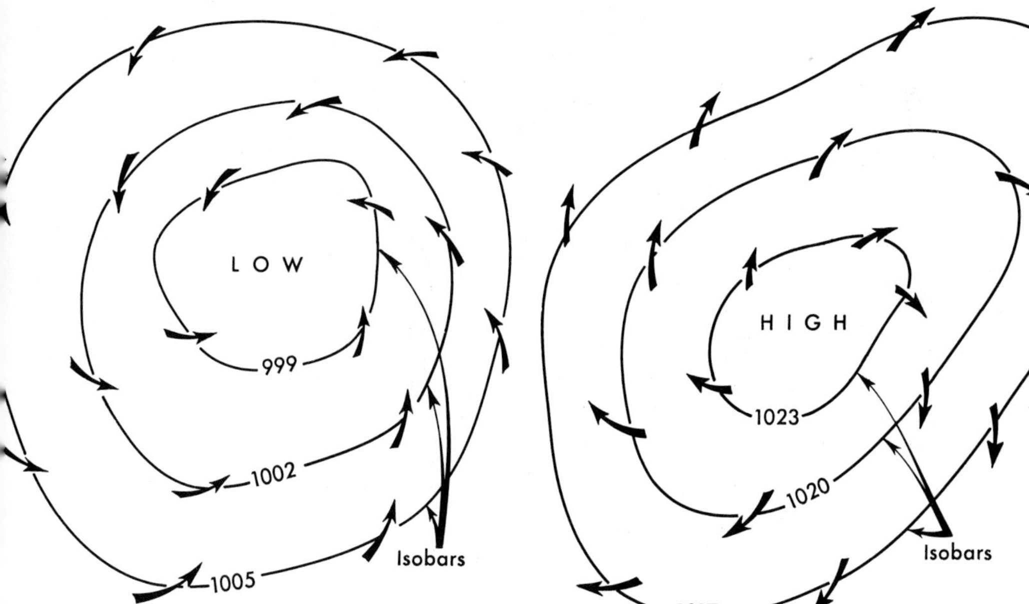

Fig. 5–15 *Isobars of a low in the northern hemisphere.*

Fig. 5–16 *Isobars of a high in the northern hemisphere.*

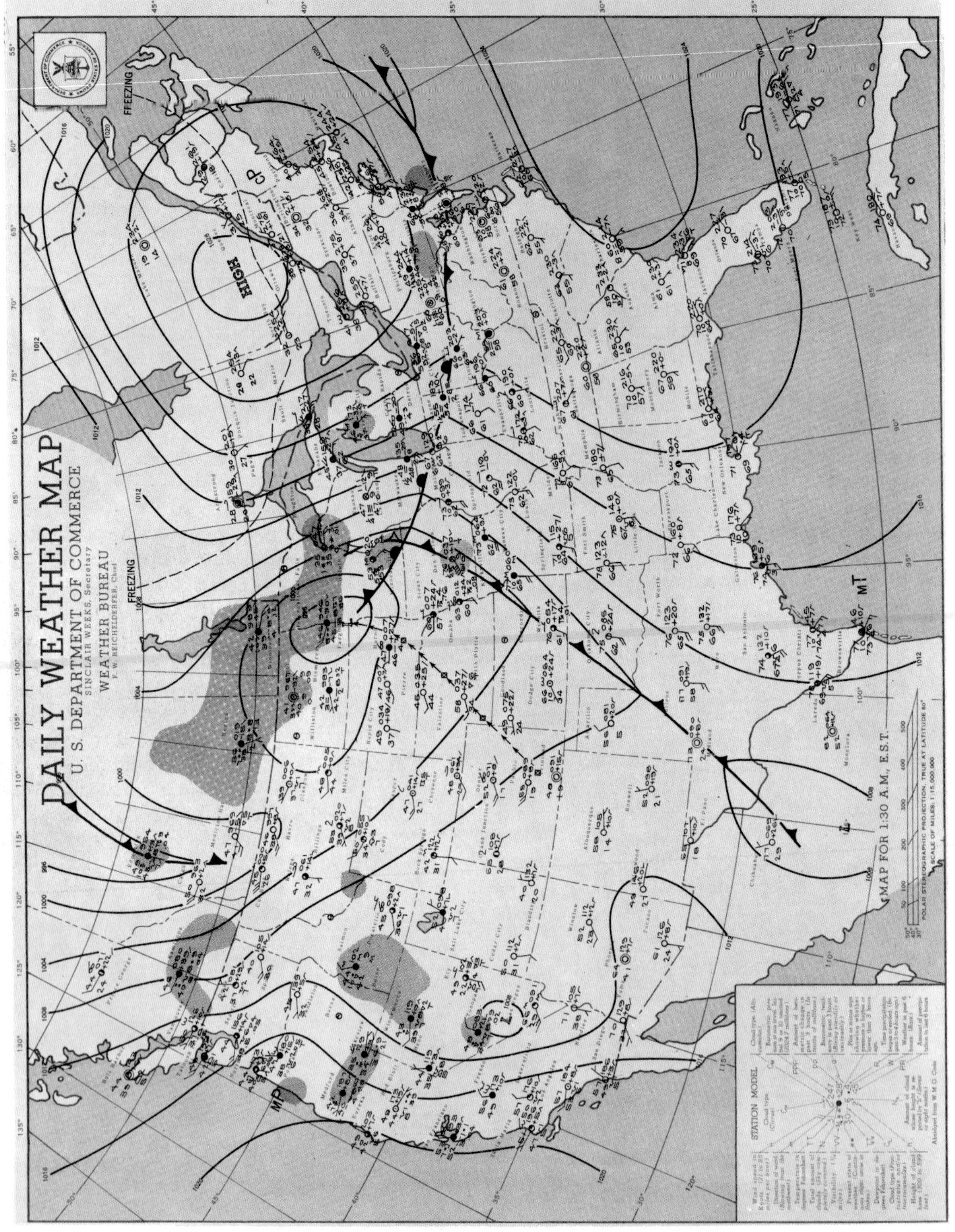

Fig. 5–17 *Daily U.S. weather map for May 11, 1956.* **(*U.S. Weather Bureau*)**

The zone of contact is always marked by cloud formations, and frequently by precipitation or very unsettled weather or storms.

WEATHER SERVICE AND WEATHER MAPS

Complex societies require services which are absent in simpler societies. Many activities in modern society are influenced by changing weather. Thus agriculture, our modern communication systems, our rail, highway, and air transportation systems, our public utilities, and many other activities need to anticipate weather conditions as much as possible. To them, the functioning of the United States Weather Bureau is one of the most important of our governmental services.

A typical daily twenty-four-hour forecast of the weather for the nation is based upon a daily weather map as shown in Figure 5–17. The meanings of the various terms and symbols used on this map are shown in Figure 5–18. Note that the weather map for May 11, 1956, gives much of the detail pertaining to local weather conditions over the entire United States. These data include the temperature, pressure in millibars,[1] the wind directions and speed, the humidity, and the amount and form of precipitation. The solid lines are *isobars,* which connect all places of equal pressure, outlining the atmospheric lows and highs. The map indicates that the winds are clockwise around a high but counterclockwise around a low.

To get the weather events for May 11 in proper perspective, it is necessary to know the movements of the air masses over the entire North American continent and surrounding oceans, as shown in Figure 5–19. This sequence shows that the huge air masses characterized by high pressure move generally eastward or southeastward 500 to 700 miles per day. Thus, the high pressure mass centered southwest of Hudson Bay on May 10 has moved to the south of Hudson Bay on May 11, a movement of 600 miles to the southeast. Atmospheric lows, on the other hand, move eastward or northeastward at a similar rate. Notice, for example, that the path of a low which was centered over eastern Colorado on May 10 moved north and eastward until it was located in Labrador on May 13. During all this time it traveled in a trough between atmospheric highs.

The edge of a polar high as it travels east and south is called a polar front. The temperatures on the north side of a polar front

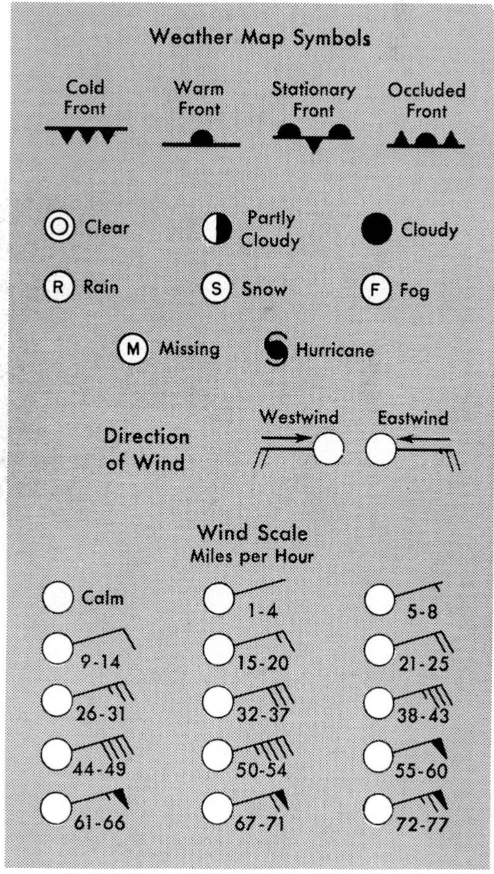

Fig. 5–18 *Symbols and terms used in connection with weather maps.*

[1] The height of the mercury column is often given in millibars. The relations to the pressure in atmospheres or inches or centimeters of mercury are as follows:

1 atmosphere = 76 cm mercury = 29.92 inches mercury = 1013.2 millibars; or, 1000 millibars = 0.9869 atmospheres = 75.0 cm mercury.

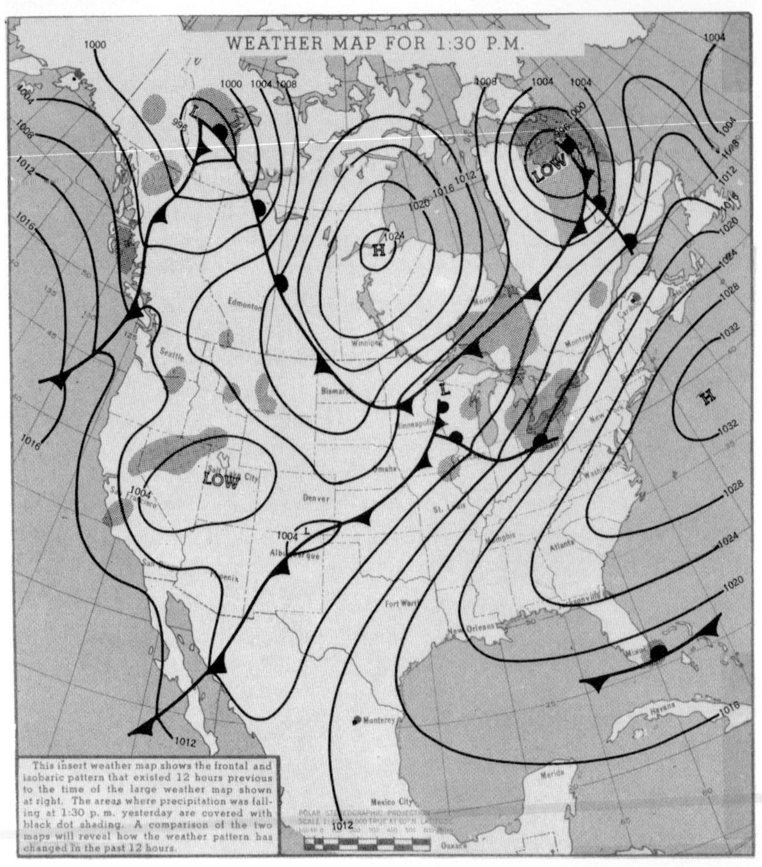
WEATHER MAP FOR 1:30 P.M.
This insert weather map shows the frontal and isobaric pattern that existed 12 hours previous to the time of the large weather map shown at right. The areas where precipitation was falling at 1:30 p.m. yesterday are covered with black dot shading. A comparison of the two maps will reveal how the weather pattern has changed in the past 12 hours.
LOW
H
LOW
H
Edmonton
Winnipeg
Seattle
Bismarck
Minneapolis
Omaha
Salt Lake City
Denver
Albuquerque
Phoenix
St. Louis
Memphis
Atlanta
Fort Worth
New Orleans
Miami
Havana
Monterey
Mexico City
Montreal
New York
Washington
POLAR STEREOGRAPHIC PROJECTION

May 10, 1956

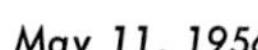

May 11, 1956

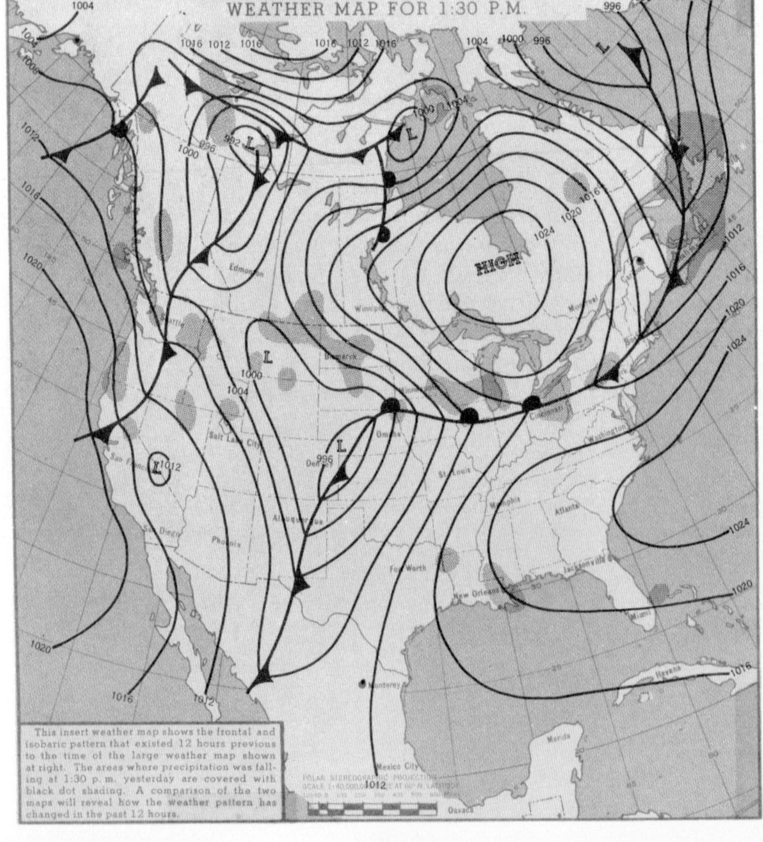
WEATHER MAP FOR 1:30 P.M.
This insert weather map shows the frontal and isobaric pattern that existed 12 hours previous to the time of the large weather map shown at right. The areas where precipitation was falling at 1:30 p.m. yesterday are covered with black dot shading. A comparison of the two maps will reveal how the weather pattern has changed in the past 12 hours.
HIGH
Edmonton
Winnipeg
Seattle
Bismarck
Omaha
Salt Lake City
Denver
Albuquerque
Phoenix
San Diego
San Francisco
St. Louis
Memphis
Atlanta
Fort Worth
New Orleans
Jacksonville
Miami
Havana
Monterey
Mexico City
Montreal
Washington
Cincinnati
POLAR STEREOGRAPHIC PROJECTION

May 12, 1956

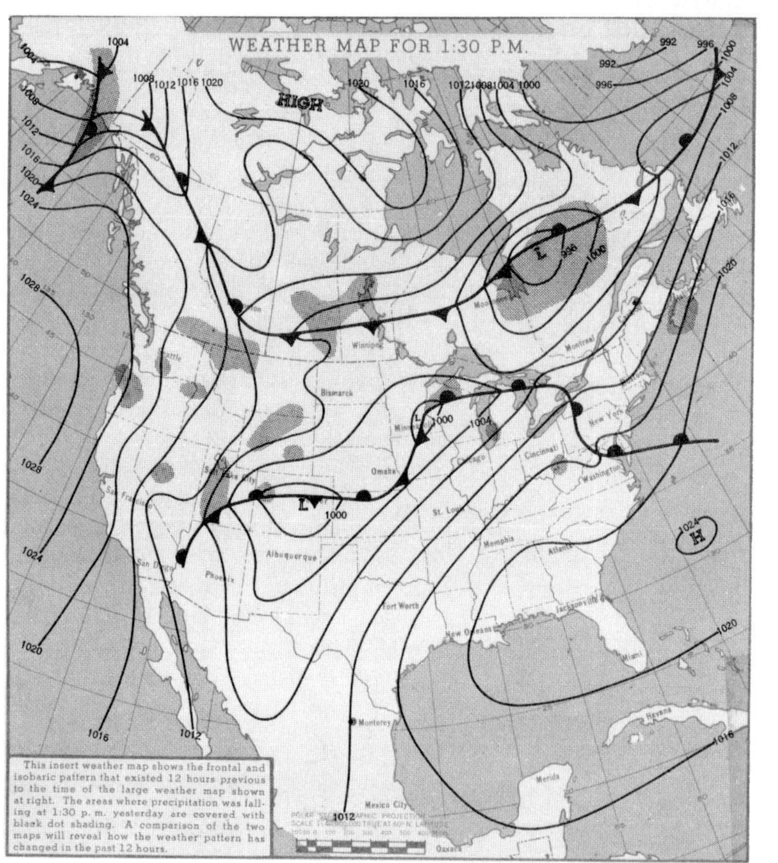

May 13, 1956

Fig. 5–19 *This sequence of weather maps shows the movement of air masses over North America for May 10, 11, 12, and 13, 1956.* (U.S. Weather Bureau)

are always lower than on the south side. Thus, on May 11 the temperature at Syracuse was 39° F., but 63° at Richmond. The polar masses, as we have seen, originate in the polar regions and carry very little moisture, while the air masses responsible for the lows usually originate in the Gulf of Mexico or the Pacific, have relatively high temperatures, and carry a great deal of moisture. With the information given in weather maps as shown in Figures 5–17 and 5–19, and using these principles, experienced meteorologists can make twenty-four-hour predictions of the weather with a high degree of certainty. Thus, the forecast for Washington, D.C., for Friday, May 11, 1956, reads, "Considerable cloudiness with the highest (temperature) around 73° today and the lowest about 57° tonight; Saturday partly cloudy and warmer." At that time, Washington was in the zone of contact of a polar front traveling southeast and a mass of humid warmer air from the southwest. The forecast predicted that during the night a part of the polar mass would pass over Washington with a predicted low temperature of 57°. By the next day, however, this would be replaced by warmer, more humid air from the southwest bringing warmer weather and clouds. By that time the center of the high could be expected to be over the Atlantic Ocean.

CLIMATIC REGIONS IN NORTH AMERICA

Climate is the average of weather conditions over a considerable period of time for any region. A region acquires a distinctive climate-character because of the dominating influence of one or more of the following factors:

1. The effects of latitude.
2. The effects of the seasons.
3. The effects of the wind belts.
4. The effects of adjacent oceans.
5. The effects of mountains.
6. The effects of altitude.
7. The effects of moving polar or tropical air masses.

There are, for example, about seven distinct climatic regions in the United States, and they are still instrumental in determining the kind of economic activity that prevails in different sections. These climatic regions are as follows:

1. Marine west-coast continental, as in Washington and Oregon on the ocean side of the Coastal Range.
2. Mediterranean, as in much of California.
3. Desert, as in parts of California and Nevada.
4. Steppe or dry region of grasslands, as in northern Texas and eastern Colorado.
5. Humid continental with long summers, as in Missouri, Illinois, and the Middle Atlantic states.
6. Humid continental with short summers, as in Minnesota and Maine.
7. Humid subtropical, as in Louisiana and Mississippi.

The climatic features of these regions are quite different and distinct. Each has many advantages and disadvantages, and all contribute to the varied character of the United States.

This account of the principles of weather and climate is necessarily brief, but it is enough to enable the reader to pursue this fascinating topic further if he wishes.

SUMMARY

1. The atmosphere is the gaseous envelope that surrounds the earth. The water covering the earth constitutes the hydrosphere. The lithosphere is the solid portion of the earth.
2. The lower part of the atmosphere is called the troposphere; the upper, the stratosphere.
3. Changes in weather are caused by air movement and occur only in the troposphere. The thin air in the stratosphere is largely stationary.
4. Nitrogen and oxygen make up the bulk of the gases of the atmosphere, the rest being small amounts of water vapor, rare gases, and carbon dioxide. The atmosphere also contains many dust particles.
5. Nitrogen and oxygen are elementary substances, or elements (substances which cannot be decomposed by ordinary methods).

6. The height of the atmosphere is estimated by the scattering of sunlight and by the observation of meteors or "shooting stars."
7. The gases of the atmosphere have mass and hence exert pressure. The atmospheric pressure at sea level may be expressed as: 1 atmosphere, 76 centimeters of mercury, 29.92 inches of mercury, or 1013.2 millibars. The pressure decreases with altitude.
8. The barometer is an instrument for measuring atmospheric pressure and is also used for measuring altitude.
9. Ordinary air usually contains a certain amount of water vapor. The amount of water vapor required to saturate air depends upon the temperature and increases with a rise in temperature.
10. The temperature at which water vapor in air becomes saturated and starts to condense is called the dew point.
11. Relative humidity is the ratio of the amount of moisture present in the air to the amount required for saturation. The relative humidity is 100 per cent at the dew point.
12. The heat received by the entire earth from the sun is essentially constant.
13. The heat received from the sun is partly reflected out into outer space, partly absorbed and then retained by the earth, and partly absorbed and then re-radiated out into space.
14. Because of the earth's rotation and the inclination of its axis, the heat absorbed by the earth in equatorial regions is slightly greater than the amount of heat lost by radiation. The reverse is true in polar regions. This results in the movements of huge air masses which cause weather.
15. Movements of air masses are winds. The various kinds of winds are related to the rising of the air in the equatorial regions and its settling down at the polar regions. The wind belts are: the doldrums, the trade winds, and the prevailing westerlies.
16. Water vapor, depending on atmospheric conditions, precipitates as clouds, fog, dew, frost, rain, snow, and hail.
17. The term *weather* denotes the prevailing state of atmospheric pressure, temperature, wind direction and velocity, humidity, cloudiness, and precipitation.
18. An air mass is a widespread body of air approximately homogeneous in its horizontal extent and having the properties of the regions over which it has remained for some time.
19. The air masses of importance for the weather of North America are the cold polar (continental polar and maritime polar) and the warm tropical air (continental tropical and maritime tropical).
20. The various air masses, with the characteristics of their sources, move as a result of the general atmospheric circulation and become modified by the region over which they pass and determine its weather conditions.
21. A front is the surface which marks the boundary between a cold and a warm air mass. Cold fronts displace warm air, and warm fronts ride over cold air.
22. The pressure fields (highs and lows) generally move from west to east. The lows move counterclockwise in the northern hemisphere, and the highs clockwise. Lows generally are associated with cloudiness and precipitation, and highs with light winds and clear skies.
23. Weather forecasting is accomplished by observations at six-hour intervals at many stations over the United States, which identify and report the various air masses, their movements and their relation to each other, and the location and movement of the fronts.
24. *Climate* is the term for general weather conditions obtaining in a region over a relatively long period of time.

STUDY EXERCISES

1. On a day when the temperature was 32° C., the air had to be cooled to 20° C. to reach the dew point. The saturation pressure for water at 32° C. is 35.6 millimeters. It is 17.4 millimeters at 20° C. What was the relative humidity?
2. The altitude of Pike's Peak, Colorado, is 14,109 feet above sea level. Consult the data for barometric pressure in this chapter and

estimate the barometric pressure at the top of the peak, (*a*) in centimeters of mercury, (*b*) in inches of mercury, (*c*) in millibars. Measuring from the top of Pike's Peak, what is the weight in grams of the column of air recorded as cylindrical with a base area equal to 1 square centimeter and reaching to the zenith?

3. Fill in the following table:

	Tropo-sphere	Strato-sphere
Approximate fraction of total mass of atmosphere		
Begins at height (miles above the earth)		
Ends at the height known by measurements (miles above the earth's surface)		
Characteristic regional conditions		
Approximate temperature of region		
Approximate composition		

4. Describe the changes that would occur in the weather and climates of the earth if the axis of the earth were to become perpendicular to the ecliptic.
5. Give examples of the law of independence of motions. How can this law be used to account for the directions of the trade winds and the prevailing westerlies in the northern hemisphere?
6. By referring to the weather maps shown in Figures 5-17 and 5-19, describe the weather that probably prevailed in your community on May 12, 1956.
7. On a certain day the barometer read 73 centimeters of mercury. What would be the pressure in (*a*) inches and (*b*) millibars?
8. The expression, "It's not the heat but the humidity that bothers," is frequently heard. What is the basis for this phrase?
9. In general, when there is a severe rainstorm as the result of the arrival of a polar front, does the moisture that is precipitated originate in the high or the low? Explain.
10. In general, during rainstorms, will the heaviest rainfall be on the north, east, south, or west side of the low which is responsible for the rain? Explain.

FOR FURTHER READING

1. Haurwitz, B., *Dynamic Meteorology.* New York: McGraw-Hill Book Co., 1941.

   The effect of incoming and outgoing radiant energy is discussed in Chapter 5. The general circulation of the air is discussed in Chapter 13.
2. Blair, T. A., and R. C. Fite, *Weather Elements.* Englewood Cliffs, N.J.: Prentice-Hall, Inc., 1957.

   General circulation of atmosphere is discussed in Chapter 8; air masses and air fronts in Chapter 9; climate and world weather, in Chapters 15 and 16.
3. Taylor, G. F., *Elementary Meteorology.* Englewood Cliffs, N.J.: Prentice-Hall, Inc., 1954.

   An excellent elementary presentation of the science of meteorology.
4. Trewartha, G. T., *An Introduction to Climate.* New York: McGraw-Hill Book Co., 1954.

   Part Two gives an excellent presentation of world climatic types.
5. United States Department of Agriculture. *Climate and Man — Yearbook of Agriculture,* ed. G. Hambridge. Washington, D.C.: U.S. Government Printing Office, 1941.

   A very readable presentation of weather and climate. Topics such as climate as a world influence, the scientific approach to weather and climate, with full accounts of climatic data for the United States, are admirably covered.
6. Paperback: Sloane, E., *How You Can Forecast the Weather.* Premier, 35¢.

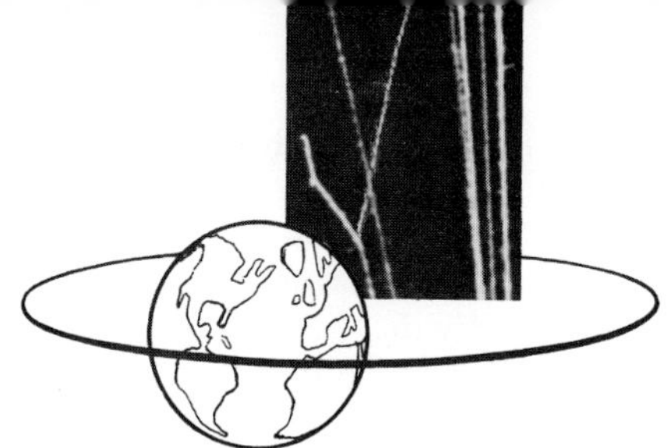

6

THE CHANGING LITHOSPHERE

THE FACE OF THE LAND as seen from an airplane in the spring or summer gives a glimpse of the vast panorama of life. Ridges covered with trees alternate with broad green blankets of cultivated fields. This is the silent world of plants on which the noisy life of man ultimately depends. The basic occupation of any society is to produce enough food even before any other cultural endeavor can be considered. The production of food, whether it is wheat, corn, fruit, vegetables, or meat, is based on the cultivation of plant life in soils. The presence of good soils therefore becomes the foundation of any society, be it relatively primitive or highly industrialized.

Soils are popularly considered as static masses of inorganic material, even by some farmers. They are, however, essentially dynamic bodies of nature which acquire properties in accordance with the forces that act upon them. Soils contain not only fine and coarse particles of inorganic matter but also organic compounds and living plant and animal matter, such as fungi, bacteria, or worms. They also contain water and gases. A system such as this, exposed constantly to the climatic variations described in the preceding chapter, is obviously in a state of constant change. The most important factors which determine the nature of a particular soil are the parent material, the climate of the region, and the nature of vegetation past and present that has become associated with it. The parent material of all soils, the gray-red soils of the deserts, the black soils of the warm moist regions, the gray-brown soils of the cool moist regions, or the red soils of the rain-soaked tropics, was originally the same — the rocks of the earth. Soil genesis begins with the breakdown of rocks into smaller and smaller fragments as a result of complex changes included under the term *weathering*. To understand soils, then, we must consider the composition and structure of rocks.

THE ROCKS OF THE EARTH

If we dig or drill into the soil, we shall first pass through the true soil (topsoil) composed of fine-grained mineral matter associated with organic particles (humus), then through coarser and coarser particles with less and less organic matter, until we eventually reach solid rock known as *bed-rock.* The upper zone, which varies from a few inches to several hundred feet and is known collectively as *mantle rock,* can be seen in deep cuts or at the banks of streams. In some places the mantle rock consists of the same materials as the bedrock, a fact indicating that it was derived by crumbling and decay of the bedrock beneath. In other places the mantle rock is quite distinct from the bedrock; this indicates that the mantle rock has been detached from rocks in other places and transported by such agents as streams, glaciers, wind, or gravity. Sometimes the mantle rock is absent and the bedrock is exposed. Such exposures are called *outcrops.* These are common on slopes of steep valleys and mountains, on cliffs that face seas or lakes, and in the channels of swift streams. The appearance of most exposed or outcropping rocks does not at first examination present many features which would be of aid to the beginner in their classification and study. For example, we may choose the texture or appearance of rocks as a basis of classification and by this means subdivide them into coarse-grained, fine-grained, and glassy. This, however, does not give us much information, and we are therefore obliged to employ the composition and mode of formation of rocks, besides their texture, as a basis for classifying them.

MINERALS

Examination of most rocks through a magnifying glass will disclose that they are composed of individual particles packed very closely together. Usually the shape and color of the individual particles are not the same throughout, which shows that rocks contain more than one ingredient. In other words, they are aggregates of different things. The small individual particles which are packed together to make the

Fig. 6–1 *Mantle rock and bed rock near Fairmount, Illinois. (Illinois State Geological Survey)*

Fig. 6–2 *Granite (Hornblende). Rockport, Massachusetts.*

rocks are called *crystals;* occasionally a small sample of a rock will have throughout the same kind of crystals. The individual crystalline particles are called *minerals,* which may be defined as naturally-occurring pure materials or substances each of which has a fixed chemical composition, distinctive physical properties, and a characteristic crystalline structure. For example, from a piece of granite (Figure 6–2) it is easy to separate the following minerals: (*a*) white or gray crystals of *quartz;* (*b*) buff-colored crystals of *feldspar;* (*c*) dark crystals of *mica.* Each of these minerals has definite properties such as density, melting point, and solubility, and each has a definite chemical composition. Quartz, for example, has a density of 2.65 grams per cubic centimeter and melts at 1470° C. Its solubility in boiling water (100° C.) is 0.03 per cent. Its chemical composition is 46.72 per cent of the element silicon and 53.28 per cent of the element oxygen.

Quartz is called a compound substance or *compound.* Silicon and oxygen are called *elements.* For the present, we shall define elements as elementary substances which cannot be made from other elements by chemical means. A more detailed study of elements and compounds is given in Chapters 20–25. It suffices for our present purposes to say simply that rocks and most objects found in nature are usually *mixtures* of *pure substances,* and these pure substances are mostly compound substances or compounds. Mixtures differ from compounds in that they are not the same throughout (not homogeneous) and do not have a constant composition. For example, various kinds of granite have different proportions of quartz, mica, and feldspar. On the other hand, pure quartz, no matter what its source, contains always the same ratio of silicon to oxygen.

Fig. 6–3 *Minerals found in granite: (top) Quartz crystals; (center) Feldspar (Orthoclase); (bottom) Mica pegmatite. (U.S. Geological Survey)*

THE ABUNDANCE OF ELEMENTS

Silicon and oxygen are two of the 92 naturally-occurring elements which cannot be separated into simpler substances by ordinary chemical or physical means. Most of the elements are rare. About one-half of the rocky crust of the earth is made up of feldspars; *orthoclase* or potassium feldspar contains 45.9 per cent oxygen, 30.3 per cent silicon, 14.1 per cent potassium, and 9.7 per cent aluminum. Water contains 88.9 per cent oxygen and 11.1 per cent hydrogen. And as stated above, quartz, a widely distributed mineral, is a compound of oxygen and silicon. The important conclusion, therefore, is that only a few elements are abundant in the outer surface of the earth, and of these, oxygen and silicon are the most abundant. Figure 6–4 shows diagrammatically the relative abundance of elements in the crust of the earth and indicates that most elements are exceedingly rare. Fewer than twelve elements comprise 99 per cent of the earth's crust.

As the diagram shows, oxygen and silicon are the most abundant. The amount of these two elements is very nearly the same as in feldspars. Oxygen is not only the most abundant element in the outer veneer of the lithosphere, but also exists (combined with hydrogen) to the extent of 88.9 per cent in water and (in the free state) to the extent of about 21 per cent in the gases of the atmosphere. It should be noted that in the atmosphere it occurs in the free elementary form, but in both the hydrosphere and the lithosphere it is in combination with other elements. Table 6–1 shows the composition of the earth's crust and also the composition of the hydrosphere, the atmosphere, and the earth's crust combined. It should be realized that this table refers

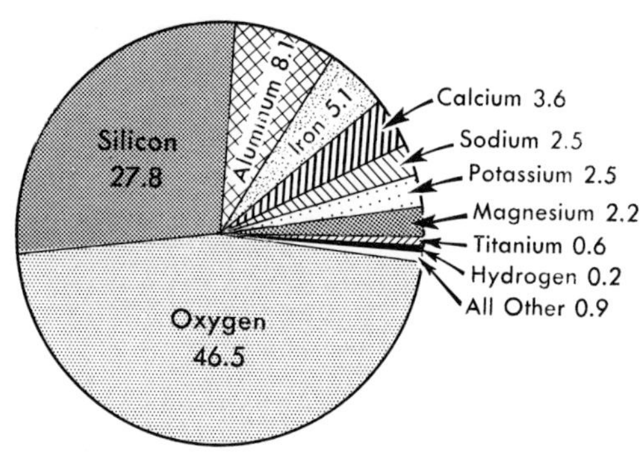

Fig. 6–4 *Percentage composition of the earth's crust.*

only to the known portions of the earth, which do not exceed ten miles in depth. The composition of the earth as a whole, though not known directly, appears to be vastly different and is discussed at the end of Chapter 8.

The number of elements is usually given as 92, although recently ten elements have been synthesized, increasing the number to 102 (as of 1957). A list of all the elements will be found inside the front cover. Those in boldface type are to be especially noted, as they occur often in the discussion of the physical world.

TABLE 6–1 COMPOSITION OF THE EARTH'S LITHOSPHERE, HYDROSPHERE, AND ATMOSPHERE

ELEMENT	COMPOSITION OF EARTH'S CRUST	COMPOSITION OF EARTH'S CRUST, HYDROSPHERE, AND ATMOSPHERE
Oxygen	46.5%	50.0%
Silicon	27.8	25.8
Aluminum	8.1	7.3
Iron	5.1	4.2
Calcium	3.6	3.2
Potassium	2.5	2.3
Sodium	2.5	2.3
Magnesium	2.2	2.1
Titanium	0.6	0.5
Hydrogen	0.2	1.0
All others	0.9	1.3

CLASSIFICATION OF ELEMENTS

The names of the elements, like the names of animals and people, follow no general rule. Those known in antiquity were not many: copper, carbon, gold, iron, lead, mercury, silver, sulfur, and tin. The other elements were discovered after the seventeenth century, with the exception of a few discovered by medieval alchemists. Elements are named after colors (iodine), odors (bromine), countries (gallium), and so on. Their symbols as employed today are useful abbreviations, and the beginner is encouraged to learn this simple shorthand for the most important elements. For example, it is easier to write *I* than iodine. Similarly, *Cl* is used for chlorine. Sometimes the symbols are derived from the Latin or Greek word for the same elements. For example, *Na* from the Latin *natrium* signifies sodium, and *Ag* from the Greek *argyros* indicates silver. It should be emphasized that symbols and formulas are a shorthand method of notation; knowledge of the symbols alone is of no particular value, but they are extremely useful in describing transformations of matter.

The elements are usually classified into *metals, nonmetals,* and *inert gases.* The basis for this classification is certain common characteristic properties. It should be pointed out that the term *properties* may indicate such *physical* properties as color, density, solubility, crystal structure, taste, luster, and hardness, or *chemical* properties — the behavior of a particular substance toward other substances. For example, iron rusts in moist air and gold does not. The rusting of the one and the absence of rust in the other are chemical properties of iron and gold. A certain group of substances, including acids, is generally used to test the behavior of other substances; these are called *reagents.* For example, copper foil looks almost the same as gold foil; the easiest way to differentiate them is by the action of nitric acid, which dissolves copper but leaves gold unaffected. During the process of observing a chemical property, some of the matter being studied is changed into

TABLE 6–2

CLASSIFICATION OF ELEMENTS

PROPERTIES	METALS	NONMETALS	INERT GASES
Characteristic state	Hard solids	Gases or brittle solids	Gases
Density	High	Low	Lowest
Melting point	High	Low	Lowest
Metallic luster	Present	Absent	None
Ductility, malleability	Good	Poor or none	None
Conductance of heat or electricity	Good	Poor	Poor
Chemical behavior towards oxygen	Most metals combine to form oxides	Most nonmetals combine to form oxides	Do not combine

other quite different forms of matter. This kind of change is called a *chemical change.* In a *physical change* the kind of matter persists unchanged, though its state may be changed; in a chemical change the *original kind of matter disappears and new and different kinds appear in its place.*

The division of elements into metals and nonmetals came very early. It was noted that iron, copper, silver, and gold are heavy and possess metallic luster, ductility, and malleability, whereas sulfur, carbon, chlorine, and oxygen are light and have none of these characteristic metallic properties. Consequently the elements were arranged in these two groups. When, later, the rare gases of the atmosphere — helium, neon, etc. — were discovered, it was found that these elements did not combine with others to form compounds; hence they were called inert gases and placed in a group by themselves. The classification is not a very sharp one, for many elements possess both metallic and nonmetallic properties. On the other hand, it should be realized that classifications are man-made devices to facilitate study, and that in nature we meet usually with gradual transitions from one extreme to another, whether it be day and night or oxygen and iron. Table 6–2 summarizes the characteristic properties of the three groups of elements.

TABLE 6–3

COMMON MINERALS

MINERAL	ELEMENTS PRESENT	CHEMICAL NAME
Simple Minerals:		
Quartz	Silicon, oxygen	Silicon dioxide
Hematite	Iron, oxygen	Iron oxide
Magnetite	Iron, oxygen	Magnetic iron oxide
Calcite	Calcium, oxygen, carbon	Calcium carbonate
Pyrite	Iron, sulfur	Iron sulfide
Complex Minerals:		
Feldspars: Orthoclase	Silicon, oxygen, aluminum, potassium	Potassium-aluminum silicate
Ferromagnesians:		
Pyroxenes	Silicon, oxygen, calcium, iron, magnesium	Calcium-iron-magnesium silicate
Micas	Silicon, oxygen, potassium, aluminum, hydrogen	Potassium-hydrogen-aluminum silicate
Olivine	Silicon, oxygen, magnesium, iron	Magnesium-iron silicate

Fig. 6–5A *Asbestos, a hydrated magnesium silicate. Lowell region, Vermont. (U.S. Geological Survey)*

Fig. 6–5B *Poorly formed galena (lead sulfide) crystals. Lucky Boy Tunnel, Gunnison County, Colorado. (U.S. Geological Survey)*

THE COMMON MINERALS

Several hundred minerals are known, but most of these are not very common. The bulk of the known part of the lithosphere is composed of a few complex minerals (see Table 6–3).

Inspection of the table shows that a simple mineral is usually a compound of oxygen with another element and hence is called an *oxide.* If the oxide is that of a metal, like iron oxide, it is a *metallic oxide;* if the oxide is that of a nonmetal, like silicon dioxide (quartz), it is a *nonmetallic oxide.* If the lower part of Table 6-3 is examined, it will be seen that the complex minerals may be regarded as complex compounds of silicon or *silicates* derived by the combination of the nonmetallic silicon dioxide with one or more metallic oxides. For example, a feldspar, which contains the elements silicon, oxygen, aluminum, and potassium, may be regarded as a complex silicate containing silicon dioxide together with the metallic oxides of potassium and aluminum. Likewise, pyroxenes are composed of silicon dioxide and the oxides of calcium, iron, and magnesium. It should be understood that the names *feldspars, pyroxenes, micas* refer to groups of minerals which are closely related.

MODE OF FORMATION OF ROCKS

Close examination of various rocks discloses two general types. In the first type the crystalline structure indicates that they were formed by solidification of molten matter which originated within the earth. The crystals of one mineral may be large, those of another smaller, and those of a third may be squeezed together in spaces left between other crystals, indicating that these were the last ones to form and filled the spaces that were left. Such formation is known to occur today in many volcanoes of the world where streams of lava, originating deep in the *crust* of the earth, flow out and slowly cool to form rocks. These rocks, on account of their mode of formation, are called *igneous.* The molten matter may rise from the depth of the earth to higher levels and cool slowly before reaching the surface, forming *intrusive* igneous rocks; those that form near or on the surface from lava issu-

Fig. 6–6 *Sedimentary beds of limestone. This picture is of Mississippian limestone and was taken a short distance south of East St. Louis, Illinois.* (*Illinois State Geological Survey*)

ing from volcanic vents are called *extrusive*. The most common example of igneous rock is granite, which forms the core of many mountains. As we have seen, even a superficial examination shows that it is a mixture of crystals of quartz, mica, and feldspar.

The second group of rocks shows many layers, with the individual particles more or less compact. Shells and imprints of sea animals, if present, indicate that these rocks were formed by deposition of sand, mud, and other sediments in the seas and lakes. Sandstone, shale, and limestone are the characteristic rocks of this group, called *sedimentary* rocks. From these two general types of rocks arises a third, originally either igneous or sedimentary rocks but since altered by high pressures and temperatures within the crust of the earth. Since they have been altered, they are called *metamorphic* rocks. An example of this class is slate, formed from shale.

COMMON IGNEOUS ROCKS

The most important igneous rocks and their general characteristics are listed in Table 6–4. The coarseness of the crystals of granite indicates that the rock crystallized very slowly from the molten mass of minerals. If the molten mass had been near, or had flowed upon, the surface, the rate of cooling would have been rapid and the resulting rock would have very fine crystals or even a glassy appearance. Hence the inference is drawn that granite must have formed at great depths where the insulating effect of the overlying rocks permitted slow cooling and therefore differentiation of its various minerals in large crystals. Rhyolite has approximately the same composition as granite, but was formed from molten rock at or near the surface. The relatively rapid cooling results in a fine-grained rock which has small crystals. When the cooling has been very rapid, the rock is composed entirely of glass and is called *obsidian*. Both granite and rhyolite are light in color, since they contain light-colored feldspar and quartz. Gabbro and basalt contain no quartz and an excess of ferromagnesian minerals and for this reason are dark. Diorite and andesite contain an intermediate amount of silica, much feldspar, and some ferromagnesians.

The granites are found in the Rockies and in practically all mountain systems; large rhyolite flows are found in the Yellowstone region. Andesites occur in many places in Colorado, Arizona, Nevada, and neighboring states. Basalt, on cooling, forms characteristic columnar structures and is found in many regions.

TABLE 6–4

COMMON IGNEOUS ROCKS

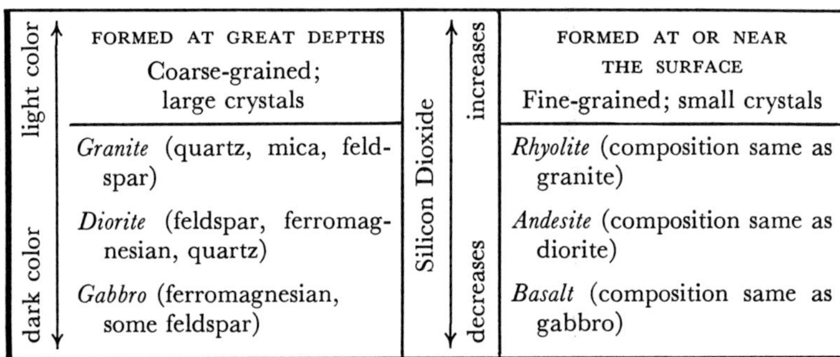

light color ↑	FORMED AT GREAT DEPTHS Coarse-grained; large crystals	Silicon Dioxide ↑ increases	FORMED AT OR NEAR THE SURFACE Fine-grained; small crystals
	Granite (quartz, mica, feldspar)		*Rhyolite* (composition same as granite)
	Diorite (feldspar, ferromagnesian, quartz)		*Andesite* (composition same as diorite)
dark color ↓	*Gabbro* (ferromagnesian, some feldspar)	decreases ↓	*Basalt* (composition same as gabbro)

Fig. 6–7 *Gabbro (Hornblende), an igneous rock. Salem Neck, Massachusetts.*

Fig. 6–8 *Diabase porphyry, an igneous rock. Cape Ann, Massachusetts. (Ward's Natural Science Establishment, Inc.)*

COMMON SEDIMENTARY ROCKS

Sandstones, conglomerates, and shales are familiar sedimentary rocks formed by deposition of the broken fragments and debris of older rocks. Under the combined effect of the atmospheric forces, solid rocks are constantly crumbling to smaller fragments, which are being continuously transported and deposited as sediment. These changes have been going on continuously from the remote past down to the present. Water evaporates from the oceans, lakes, and streams, and the vapors or clouds are swept far inland by winds, to fall eventually as rain or snow. Then the long journey of this surface water through the soil and through flowing streams begins – a process which continues until the water reaches the sea again, but now carrying with it a vast amount of suspended debris and dissolved minerals; the suspended material eventually settles and later hardens to form sedimentary rocks. Wind and glacial ice also act as transporting agents of broken rock which is dropped and accumulated as sedimentary deposits.

Sediments accumulate from minerals carried in solution, or from broken rock material, such as gravel, sand, silt, and clay. The coarse sediments are dropped first, and therefore the usual deposits as we proceed outward from the shore of a sea or lake are gravel, coarse sand, fine sand, and fine clay. This order may be disturbed by the shifting of the sediments through wave action or by lowering or elevation of the sea level, so that fine material may alternate with

TABLE 6–5

COMMON SEDIMENTARY ROCKS

SEDIMENTARY ROCKS	NATURE OF UNCONSOLIDATED SEDIMENTS
Conglomerate and breccia	Gravel (pebbles or boulders)
Sandstone	Sand grains (quartz)
Shale	Clay (mud)
Limestone (limestone, marl, chalk)	Limy mud, calcareous sand, shell fragments
Chert, flint	Finely divided silica which may have been deposited from solution
Coal	Plant remains

Fig. 6–9 *Banded and faulted sandstone, an example of sedimentary rock. Buffalo Gap, South Dakota.* (*Ward's Natural Science Establishment, Inc.*)

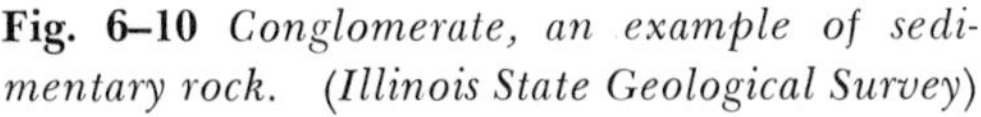

Fig. 6–10 *Conglomerate, an example of sedimentary rock.* (*Illinois State Geological Survey*)

coarse. This gives the outstanding characteristic of sedimentary rocks – the *stratified* structure. The *strata* or layers vary in thickness, color, texture, or composition. Each stratum is separated from the one above and below by a plane which is called the stratification plane, and it represents a change in some character of the sediment. As the beds increase in thickness, the pressure of the overlying beds compresses the lower beds, making them more compact. As the beds sink, water slowly passes through the pores and deposits from solution calcium carbonate or silica or iron oxide, which thus act as cementing material. Figures 6–6, 6–9, and 6–10 show various types of sedimentary rocks. Table 6–5 lists the most common sedimentary rocks and the character of the sediments which were involved in their formation. The dissolved material is discharged, or is precipitated, by changes in temperature and pressure or by chemical reactions of the solution. Marine life removes calcium from the water to form shells, which are later deposited as sediments. The sediments from broken rock material are chiefly transported by running water and drop to form horizontal or nearly horizontal layers when the velocity of the stream diminishes.

COMMON METAMORPHIC ROCKS

All metamorphic rocks were originally igneous or sedimentary, but have had their original character changed by high temperatures and enormous pressures within the earth's crust. Around the borders of igneous intrusions older rocks are baked, hardened, and altered. The changes are more intense in the immediate vicinity of the zone contacting the igneous mass, and less so away from it. For example, limestone, when it is intruded by an igneous mass, changes from a dull rock to brilliant snow-white marble. The organic material in the limestone is expelled, and the fine grains of calcium carbonate recrystallize into larger crystals. The heat may also be produced as a result of the rock movements to which deeply buried rocks are subjected by the weight of the overlying rocks. Pressure may also be exerted on rocks that are not deeply buried by the folding of strata into arches as a result of *diastrophic movements,* which include the displacements of one part of the lithosphere with respect to another. In metamorphism of this kind the rocks are deformed, stretched, and compressed; pebbles are elongated; crystals are rotated or re-formed (recrystallized) so as to lie with their long axes in the direction of least pressure and offer minimum resistance.

Both igneous or sedimentary rocks may be altered into *slates, schists,* or *gneisses.* The slates, formed chiefly from shales, break easily along planes parallel to the elongation of the rock; the crystals which form during the alteration of the original rock are very small. Slate is a fine-grained, low-grade metamorphic rock; that is, it is produced by comparatively low increases of temperature and pressure. Higher temperatures and pressures produce (from shales or slates) coarser-grained rocks called schists. Thus, in schists, the tiny mica flakes of slates become large enough to be seen readily by their flashing. Gneisses are high-grade metamorphic rocks; they are characterized by a coarsely foliated structure called *banding.* Gneisses from sedimentary rocks have had much feldspar and quartz injected along the foliated planes by igneous solutions derived from molten material at greater depths. The banding of granite gneisses is due to a shearing movement after the crystallization of the mica but before the complete solidification of the granite. This shearing oriented the mica flakes, causing a type of banding which is discontinuous.

Fig. 6–11 *Specimen of folded schist, a metamorphic rock. Bennington County, Vermont. (U. S. Geological Survey)*

Table 6–6 lists the common igneous and sedimentary rocks and the metamorphic type to which they are usually altered. It should be noted that the first conversion of limestone and sandstone results in marble and quartzite. Quartzite is no longer porous, and the fractured surface does not reveal the grains of the original rock. Pore spaces have been eliminated by enlargement of the sand grains through precipitation of silicon dioxide from solutions which

TABLE 6–6

COMMON METAMORPHIC ROCKS

IGNEOUS AND SEDIMENTARY ROCKS	METAMORPHIC EQUIVALENT
Granite	Granite gneiss
Rhyolite	Rhyolite schist
Andesite	Hornblende schist
Basalt	Biotite schist, chloride schist
Shale	Slate, mica schist, gneiss
Limestone	Marble
Sandstone	Quartzite
Bituminous coal	Anthracite, graphite

seep through rocks. Both quartzite and marble on further alteration may give rise to schists.

WEATHERING AND EROSION

Soil comes from rocks through the complex changes included under the term *weathering,* whereby rocks break down to smaller and smaller fragments. These changes are noticeable along the surface of bedrocks and joints and the cleavage planes of the feldspars; the presence of soft, loose, and discolored material is evidence of the decay of the rocks. The changes, though very slow if measured by the span of a human lifetime, nevertheless are extensive. No matter how strong the solid rock or how permanent the hills and mountains may appear, all slowly crumble to fragments which are constantly being moved away toward the sea. This continuous alteration of the face of the earth by the crumbling of rocks and transportation of the debris is called *erosion.* The wind, streams, subsurface water, glaciers, and the sea are the important agents involved in the transportation of the debris; the processes are usually referred to as *wind erosion, stream erosion,* and so on. In most of these processes considerable fresh material is transported along with weathered material. Weathering, however, enormously increases the rate of erosion and hence is one of the most important factors of general erosion.

Fig. 6–12 *Exfoliation in granite. Northwest of Grouse Lake Yosemite Quadrangle, California.* (*U.S. Geological Survey*)

The changes and factors involved in weathering are complex and need not be considered in detail. They may be divided into the physical action of *disintegration* to particles of smaller size and the chemical action of *decomposition* in which the complex minerals of the rocks are broken down into simpler substances. Both of these actions occur at the same time, although one may predominate over the other because of local conditions. In arid regions mechanical disintegration is more pronounced, and in moist regions chemical changes predominate.

DISINTEGRATION OF ROCKS

All rock masses contain cracks called *joints,* formed by diastrophic forces such as uplift, warping, and the like, which are discussed in detail in Chapter 8. Stresses are developed in the rock masses which enlarge the joints and eventually shatter the large rocks into fragments. These stresses can be divided for the purpose of discussion into physical and chemical.

The physical stresses are primarily due to changes in temperature and pressure. Heating by day and cooling by night produce changes in rocks somewhat similar to those resulting by the sudden heating or cooling of glass. Also, when the temperature falls below 0° C., the water in the pores and cracks of rocks freezes and exerts considerable pressure, since it expands about one-eleventh of its volume. The effect is more noticeable in porous rocks, such as shales and sandstones, whose pores account for 10 to 25 per cent of their volume. Repeated freezing and thawing near the edges of cliffs and in mountaintops disrupt and dislodge small and large blocks of rock.

The effect of changes in pressure is best seen on granite rocks such as those of Yosemite Valley. These granites were formed deep within the crust of the earth under high pressures. Removal of the overlaying rocks by erosion released the pressure, thereby causing "splitting" or "shelling off," with the shell forming concentric to the surface. The process is called *exfoliation,* and an example of it on a large scale is found in the white granite rocks of Yosemite National Park.

Aside from the disintegrating effects of changes in temperature and pressure, rocks are cut and slowly broken down by the small particles of rock which are blown by the wind. As discussed in the previous chapter, the velocity of the winds varies. Light breezes move with a velocity of ten to fifteen miles per hour, strong breezes with a velocity of thirty to forty miles per hour. As the gaseous mass travels over the surface of the earth, it removes large quantities of earthy material, dust, and even particles of sand. In this manner, particularly during the summer and in periods of drought in semiarid regions, large quantities of soil are removed from the land, giving rise to dust storms. Though the heavier particles of sand are not transported very far, they are blown over rocks and erode their surfaces through *abrasion.* This "sandblast" action is more noticeable in arid and semiarid regions, where it sculptures the rocks into grotesque forms, pinnacles, needles, and table rocks.

CHEMICAL DECOMPOSITION

A piece of iron exposed to moist air ultimately crumbles to a soft powder called *rust.* Chemical examination of the new substance shows that it consists of a mixture of iron oxides, part of which contains water (or is *hydrated*) and some iron carbonate. In other words, the rusting of iron is a chemical combination between the iron and three of the gaseous or vaporous components of the atmosphere: oxygen, water, and carbon dioxide. The process, then, may be described as *oxidation, hydration,* and *carbonation.* In exactly the same manner as the hard iron changes to flaky rust, the minerals in the hard rocks undergo chemical combinations with oxygen, carbon dioxide, and water. The iron silicates in such minerals as mica and other ferromagnesians combine slowly with oxygen and water to form yellow or brown stains of iron oxide on the rock. Finally, the rock is pulverized to soil; thus the red, brown, and yellow colors of soil develop. Another agent aiding in the chemical alteration of rocks is the acid action of ground water. As rainwater falls from the atmosphere to the ground, it dissolves some carbon dioxide to form carbonic acid. The amount of acid in ground water is further increased from the organic acids produced by the decay of plant and animal matter. The minerals of the rocks in the upper part of the lithosphere are continually being subjected to this acid action of ground water. Carbonic acid combines with metallic oxides, yielding such carbonates as potassium carbonate and calcium carbonate. Since a number of these carbonates are soluble, ground water carries away many minerals in solution and thus produces pits, holes, cracks, and caves, chiefly in regions composed of limestones and marbles.

The chemical decomposition of rocks is accompanied by mechanical effects due to the increased volume of the changing rock. For example, as a piece of granite undergoes chemical weathering, the feldspars on the surface and along the cleavage planes and grain boundaries are changed chemically to kaolin or clay; in this process there is an increase in volume (nearly 100 per cent) causing crowding of the grains and hence a chipping off of the rock mass into small granules. The chief end-products of the decomposition of a granitic rock containing quartz, potash, feldspar, and black mica are broken granules of quartz, iron oxides, clays, and potassium carbonate. The broken quartz granules mixed with varying amounts of iron oxides make up the sands of the seashores and the soils.

A number of other factors assist in the disintegration and decomposition of the rocks, though to a smaller extent. The roots of plants grow into cracks and crevices and push rocks apart. Animals, such as earthworms, ants, and rodents, burrow into the soil and loosen it. Bacteria are very abundant in soils and on bare rocks. Decaying plants produce carbonic acid and other acids which attack the rocks. Man speeds up erosion by excavating road cuts and tunnels, by mining, and by cultivating the land. The breaking of the sod, the clearing of brush and timber, and the destroying of forests by fire and lumbering have permitted rapid erosion.

It should be realized that all these actions are modified by variation in climate, in topography, and in the resistance of the rock. It is this *differential erosion* that has produced the many landscape features that tourists travel far to see. The deserts present an awe-inspiring spectacle of bare vertical cliffs sculptured in many patterns and colored in many hues. In humid regions the decomposition of rock proceeds more rapidly than in arid regions, resulting in the familiar rounded hills with smooth slopes, covered in most places by soil and vegetation.

SOIL DEVELOPMENT

As noted in the preceding discussion, the parent material in soil development may consist of a variety of materials. It may be solid bedrock or eroded material transported and deposited by winds or glaciers. The alteration of the parent material involves further complicated chemical reactions beyond those already outlined. The complex mineral groups containing aluminum, silicon, and oxygen – chiefly the feldspar group– become slowly altered chemically and give rise to clay minerals. This alteration proceeds at a steady rate. For example, if in a young soil – that is, a soil 10,000 years old – the clay in the first six inches of the soil is found to be about 20 grams per 100 grams of parent material, then the amount of clay formed annually is 0.0002 grams. As the upper part of the mantle has sufficiently decomposed to yield some plant nutrients, some of the virile plants (weeds and grasses) take root.

The soil during this stage is still immature, but, as plant matter grows and decays, the amount of organic matter increases. As the plant roots grow they become factors in changing the primary minerals. If the roots are able to remove from a complex mineral some element which serves the plant as a nutrient, then the plant becomes an agent in the alteration of that mineral. Further, the roots in growing contribute carbon dioxide to the soil. As plant material increases, its destruction by bacteria also increases so that the products of organic decomposition accumulate in the soil. The bacterial action may be so high that the black organic matter of a well-developed soil may never accumulate. For example, the soils of many tropical areas support dense vegetation, but the bacterial action due to the temperature is so rapid that the organic black humus (partially decayed organic matter) of the cool and temperate soils never accumulates – the bacteria completely destroy humus as rapidly as it is formed. Thus, tropical soils are not black, but red, because of the lack of humus and the presence of oxidized iron; these are *latosols.*

In moist, cool climates the immature soil, with its continuous cycle of plant growth and decay combined with bacterial action, loses all except the most insoluble particles

Fig. 6–13 *Soil profile, McLennan County, Texas. Note the "horizon" between the friable top layer of clay loam and the layer of coarse, heavy clay below it.* *(U.S. Department of Agriculture, Soil Conservation Service)*

Fig. 6–14 *An example of gullying, common in over-grazed or dry areas.* (*U.S. Geological Survey*)

of the parent material (such as quartz and some feldspars) and becomes *mature.* Generally, mature soils are in layers, distinctly varied in color, texture, and consistency, called *horizons,* with bedrock beneath the lowermost layer. All the soil materials from the surface down to a point where the properties remain uniform are termed the *soil profile.* The thickness of a profile may vary from several inches to several feet. The organic matter diminishes with depth in the various profiles.

Thus the factors which determine the type of soil are the parent rock material, the vegetation that grows on the soil, the climate, and the age of the soil. If the parent rock material was granite, the soil in the initial stages will be rich in clay minerals from the weathering of feldspars, iron oxides derived from the mica, and grains of unchanged quartz. If the climate is cool and moist (temperate climates of the United States), the organic matter increases and dark soils rich in humus develop. Moisture in the presence of humus removes by solution iron and aluminum oxides and deposits them in lower parts of the profile. In the tropical countries the development of dark soils does not occur because of the absence of humus. Further, abundant rainfall removes many of the water-soluble plant nutrients and causes a concentration of iron and aluminum compounds, thus creating soils which yield poor crops, a condition found in many areas of Brazil and India.

Even the rich, well-developed soils of our country are never static but dynamic; they form a changing body — a layer in which complex chemical, physical, and biological activities are constantly going on. Unwise cultivation and grazing leads to the washing away of the topsoil, followed by gullying and extensive erosion, and eventually to farmland incapable of supporting vegetation. For this reason the conservation of soil by preventing and checking soil erosion is receiving wide attention.

Fig. 6–15 *The organic matter which supports vegetation diminishes with soil depth; hence an eroded soil yields poorly or not at all.* (*U.S. Department of Agriculture, Soil Conservation Service*)

The first step in a program of soil conservation is to establish waterways for the drainage of the run-off water after heavy rains and to seed these waterways with grasses so as to prevent the formation of ditches and gullies. The farmland, whether it is hilly or even ground, may be terraced with the terraces sloping toward the waterways, thus checking erosion while permitting complete use of the land to raise crops. Another method of combatting erosion is to leave strips of land unplowed and uncultivated. In areas where the slope is great, and hence the rate of erosion is rapid, it is best to raise a cover crop of grasses as a protecting layer against erosion. Trees and shrubs judiciously planted in areas where the rate of erosion is rapid also help to conserve the soil.

The importance of soils to the welfare of the community cannot be overemphasized. In many parts of the world, even in America, one finds districts of agricultural well-being right next to regions of abject poverty and squalor. The poverty and squalor are not necessarily due to the laziness or incompetence of the inhabitants, but may be attributed to the infertility of the soil. Actually, this infertility may stem from the practices of early settlers who, finding a virgin soil beneath the huge forests which they cleared away, and knowing that there was plenty of land and an apparently eternal frontier to move on to, did not worry about conservation. Today, with the population increasing rapidly, and even though science has helped make each acre more productive through the selection of seed and the use of fertilizer, soil conservation continues to be one of the most urgent problems that confront our national community.

SUMMARY

1. The parent material for all soils is the earth's rocks.
2. As a result of changes included under the term *weathering,* rocks break into smaller and smaller fragments. Ultimately, through complex chemical changes, rocks form a mixture of fine, inorganic particles consisting of clay minerals (alumino-silicates), quartz (sand), feldspars, oxides, and other compounds of the elements. This mixture is the basis for soils.
3. In addition to fine, solid, inorganic particles, mature soils contain organic matter (humus), bacteria, fungi, water, and gases. The factors determining the nature of soils are the parent material, the climate of the region, and the nature of past vegetation that became associated with it.
4. Unwise cultivation causes the erosion and depletion of soil. Measures can be taken to conserve soil.
5. Most rocks are aggregates of minerals. Minerals are naturally-occurring compounds of the 92 elements.
6. Elements combine with each other in constant ratios to form compounds.
7. Ten elements comprise 99 per cent of the outer part of the lithosphere. Oxygen and silicon comprise 75 per cent.
8. The most common minerals found in rocks are quartz, feldspars, and ferromagnesians.
9. Rocks are classified according to their mode of formation into *igneous, sedimentary,* and *metamorphic.* Igneous rocks are formed by solidification of molten magma. Sedimentary rocks are formed by the deposit and consolidation of sediment in shallow seas. Metamorphic rocks are produced from both sedimentary and igneous rocks by the combined effects of heat, pressure, and the intrusion of molten matter during crustal movements of the earth.
10. Through the combined effect of temperature changes and the chemical action of the atmosphere, rocks undergo changes included under the term *weathering* and break down into smaller and smaller fragments called the mantle.
11. Erosion comprises all the processes including weathering, whereby rocks are broken into mantle, which is transported and deposited, ending ultimately as sediment deposited in the sea.
12. Since the production of all foodstuffs is based on the cultivation of plant life, good soils are the foundation of society and the prerequisite to any cultural endeavor.

STUDY EXERCISES

1. Define the following terms: mature soil; soil profiles; igneous rock; sedimentary rock; metamorphic rock; mantle; weathering; erosion; elements; compound; mineral; soil horizon.
2. Indicate the reasons which account for the existence of tropical soils without appreciable organic matter, despite the huge tropical plant growth. Contrast these with soils of the moist temperate zones.
3. Describe how it is possible to:
   a. distinguish between a rock and a mineral.
   b. tell by examining an outcropping rock formation whether it is igneous or sedimentary.
   c. tell whether an igneous rock was formed at great depths or shallow depths.
   d. tell whether a certain lava flow consists of basalt or rhyolite.
   e. distinguish whether a sample of rock is metamorphic or igneous.
4. What is the difference between quartz and sand? If the formula of quartz is expressed by $(SiO_2)_n$ would you expect several samples of pure quartz from various parts of the world to yield the same formula on analysis? Explain.
5. Make a table of the principal igneous, sedimentary, and metamorphic rocks, including name of rock, its chief minerals, and characteristics (e.g., texture, appearance, mode of formation).
6. Mark *I* if the material is an igneous rock; *S* if it is sedimentary rock; *M* if it is a metamorphic rock; *F* if it is a feldspar; *FM* if it is ferromagnesian mineral, and *N* if it is none of these.

.... granite	.... bituminous coal
.... limestone	.... andesite
.... schist	.... anthracite
.... marble	.... orthoclase
.... conglomerate	.... basalt
.... shale	.... gabbro
.... slate	.... gneiss
.... asbestos	.... quartzite
.... quartz	.... rhyolite
.... sandstone	.... diorite

7. Name the sedimentary rocks described here and give their metamorphic equivalents.
   a. Formed by consolidation of sand particles.
   b. Formed from shells of marine animals.
   c. Formed from extremely fine particles of clay.
   d. Formed from buried vegetable material.
   e. Formed from consolidation of coarse particles such as pebbles.
8. Briefly discuss:
   a. Stages and processes in the formation of mature soils in temperate climates.
   b. The importance of good soils to a community.
   c. Causes of soil erosion and measures for controlling it.
   d. Whether the use of soils in our country has been guided by the best possible available scientific information.

FOR FURTHER READING

1. GILLULY, J., A. C. WATERS, and A. O. WOODFORD, *Principles of Geology.* San Francisco: W. H. Freeman and Co., 1954.
   Minerals and rocks are discussed in Chapter 5; soils, in Chapter 6.
2. GARRELS, R. M., *A Textbook of Geology.* New York: Harper and Brothers, 1951.
   See Chapters 9, 11, and 12 for rocks and minerals.
3. LONGWELL, C. R., A. KNOPF, and R. F. FLINT, *Physical Geology.* New York: John Wiley and Sons, 1948.
   Rocks and minerals are discussed in Chapters 12 and 13 and in Appendixes A and B.
4. MATHER, K. F., and S. L. MASON, *Source Book in Geology.* New York: McGraw-Hill Book Co., 1939.
   An excellent collection of original papers. See especially: Arduino, "Origin of Marble and Dolomite," *p. 76; Dermarest,* "The Volcanic Origin of Basalt," *p. 90; Hall,* "Marble from Limestone in the Laboratory," *p. 158; Sedgwick,* "The Metamorphism of Sedimentary Rocks," *p. 222; Bunsen,* "Genetic Relations of Igneous Rocks," *p. 381; Dana,* "The Origin of the Mineral Constituents of Igneous Rocks," *p. 416; Fouqué and Michel-Levy,* "The Artificial Production of Feldspars," *p. 494.*
5. Paperback: RAPPORT, S., and H. WRIGHT, *The Crust of the Earth.* Signet, 35¢.
6. Paperback: PEARL, R., *How to Know the Minerals and Rocks.* Signet Key, 50¢.

7

THE EROSION CYCLE

THE LAST CHAPTER dealt with the continuous alteration of the face of the earth by the crumbling of rocks and the transportation of the debris by winds, streams, subsurface water, glaciers, and the sea. These agents of erosion tend to sculpture the face of the land and then to reduce it to sea level. Long before systematic studies on water erosion were made, man recognized its effects, for he sang, "The waters wear the stones; thou washest away the things which grow out of the dust of the earth." [1] The object of the present chapter is to study one set of forces – known as the erosion cycle – which are constantly at work changing the lithosphere.

EFFECTS UPON THE LITHOSPHERE

We have seen that, by the processes summarized under the term *weathering,* rocks are disintegrated and decomposed into smaller and smaller fragments called the *mantle,* which is moved slowly to lower levels. The forces that accomplish the transportation of the debris are generated by the sun and the earth. As discussed in Chapter 5, energy radiated from the sun is responsible for the movement of the atmosphere. Unequal heating of the earth by the sun causes differences in temperature, which in turn give rise to differences in pressure, generating winds. The winds transport the moisture evaporated from seas and from land surfaces, and this moisture is later precipitated as rain and snow to form streams and glaciers. Thus, the processes of weathering and erosion can be traced to the forces originating from the sun and acting upon the earth. In addition, the force of gravity within the earth (Chapter 14) acts on all objects on its surface and tends to move everything from higher to lower levels. This tendency is greatly increased by running water, which transports the weathered rock debris and also wears away bedrock. Glaciers and subsurface water also contribute to this general process of erosion, while the movements of the waters of the seas erode the margins of the land and distribute the debris transported by the streams to the sea floors. Through the continuous action of these agents, the higher portions of the earth's crust are worn away or graded, and hence the combined process is called *gradation.*

The processes grouped under gradation would long ago have obliterated all land surfaces above sea level but for opposing forces within the earth which tend to build

[1] Job 14:19.

up land. Diastrophic forces operating from within the earth cause the elevation of previous sea floor to high plateaus and mountains, and may vary from gentle warpings and depressions to violent crustal movements characterized by extensive crumpling and breaking of the rock strata. The internal forces of volcanism are responsible for the formation and movement of the molten rock masses which rise upward to fill cracks and fissures in the rock strata and build high volcanic peaks and lava plateaus.

THE GEOLOGICAL CYCLE

The changes outlined in the preceding section are based on evidence most of which is directly observable. The effects of the agents of gradation can be seen in operation. The sidecuttings of its banks by a stream can be seen over a period of years — even, occasionally, from one day to the next. In the short span of a lifetime it is possible to observe the sculpturing effects of a stream. The transporting and gouging of rocks by glacial ice is also directly observable. The effect of the internal forces is best seen in active volcanic areas where repeated outpourings of molten rock are still piling up successive layers into mountains. Examination of the rock strata of many lofty mountains, including Mount Everest, discloses that the crumpled and buckled rocks on their summits are sedimentary and were formed in what were once shallow seas. The evidence that marine sedimentary strata form large areas of our present continental masses is very extensive.

Evidence obtained by many workers through observations accumulated over many years and through analysis and reasoning reveals a cycle of geological changes in which the high portions of the land masses are constantly eroded and the material transported by streams is dumped into the seas to form deltas, coastal plains, and continental shelves. Thus shallow seas begin to encroach on and cover much of the land. In the past they were far more extensive than they are today. An abundance of evidence indicates that these shallow seas have spread over the land and retreated time and time again. As the debris accumulates in the shallow sea floors, these areas become eventually zones of weakness (page 124) and are slowly uplifted and warped or crumpled to form new highlands. There again follows a long period of erosion during which the agents of gradation attack the new highlands to form gravel, sand, mud, and soil, which are carried away and deposited in shallow seas to form new sedimentary layers. Looking back over the past history of the earth (Chapters 9 and 10) we discern a rhythm in the cycle of geological changes, which consists of long periods of erosion and gradation of the continental masses, followed by shorter periods of crustal adjustments, uplifts, mountain building, and movements of molten rock.

FORCES OF GRADATION

It was shown in the preceding chapter that weathering is an important part of the general process of erosion. Winds, ground water and running water, glacial ice, and sea waves are important agents of erosion because they not only transport the debris but also exert considerable abrasive action on rock material. In addition to these agents, the constant slow downslope movement of the mantle, called *creep,* and the less frequent but more rapid movements known as *landsliding* should be included under the processes of gradation.

WIND EROSION

In addition to its weathering effect, the atmosphere acts as an agent of erosion through the effects of the winds. The abrasive "sandblast" action of wind-borne particles of sand against the surfaces of rocks has already been mentioned. The wind also acts as an agent of transportation by rolling the heavier sand particles and carrying in suspension the lighter sand and dust parti-

Fig. 7–1 *Example of wind erosion. The Navaho twins, Punch and Judy, in Utah.* (*U.S. Geological Survey*)

cles. Dust caught in an upward current is carried over great heights and transported to great distances; dust from the explosion of volcanoes has been observed to travel around the world. The dust eventually is deposited as a fine-grained sediment called *loess*. Vast areas of Europe, Asia, and North America are covered with deposits of loess; it forms in masses of varying thickness without horizontal stratification, and sometimes forms high bluffs in valleys. Many deposits of loess are found in the Missouri and Mississippi valleys. The Chinese deposits of loess are several hundred feet thick and constitute the best soil of China.

Another transportational effect of wind is the migration of hills of sand, known as *dunes*. The force of the wind pushes the particles of sand and carries them a short distance. The process is repeated, and in due time the entire dune will migrate. The growth of a dune begins with an obstacle such as a brush or a stone which breaks the force of the wind; in time a heap of sand grains accumulates and continues to grow. In humid regions, dunes form usually on shores where there is abundance of sand and wind blowing inland. The Indiana dunes from Gary to Michigan City along the coast of Lake Michigan offer an example of these conditions. The wind blows the sand particles in successive layers so that they are deposited parallel to its direction. As the sand grains are blown over the crest, the windward side becomes less steep than the lee side. The surface of the dune is covered with ridges similar to ripple

Fig. 7–2 *Sand dune in Saudi Arabia.* (*Standard Oil Company, N.J.*)

marks. As the dune migrates, it buries trees and other vegetation in its path. The invasion of fertile regions by dunes, therefore, requires checking by man. Dunes generally vary in height up to a hundred feet, but under rare conditions, as in Africa, they may attain a height of five hundred feet.

GROUND WATER

The water that is discharged by the clouds in the form of rain always seeks a lower level and eventually finds its way back into the ocean. After each rainfall, part of the water runs off into streams; some is re-evaporated, while another part, referred to as *ground* or *subsurface water,* sinks into the earth. Thus, the mantle rock and bedrock down to a certain depth contain considerable amounts of water. The amount of ground water has been estimated to be sufficient to submerge all the continents one hundred feet deep. This figure is only approximate, but it indicates the extent of the circulation of the hydrosphere within the outer part of the lithosphere. The amount of water in various rocks depends on their porosity or open spaces left in the arrangement of mineral particles. The open space between particles varies from 1 per cent, as in compact, crystalline rock, to 30 per cent in very porous sandstone. As the water descends, it finally reaches a level where all mantle rock or bedrock is saturated with water, and this internal surface, or interface, is known as the *water table.* The water that lies between the water table and the earth's surface is often termed *vadose* water. The water table tends to follow the general contour of the land and generally rises after heavy rainfalls. Ground water first descends until it reaches the water table, and from there it follows the general direction of run-off water at the surface. The movement of ground water is very slow. It may vary from a few feet to a few hundred feet per year and depends primarily on the permeability of the underlying rock. This flow follows the path of least resistance, usually along cracks and fissures, through the most permeable zones to emerge at lower levels.

EMERGENCE OF GROUND WATER

When the water table intersects the surface of the land, water emerges as seepage or springs, usually on a hillside or in a valley. Springs also form at the base of rock masses or layers permeable to water, such as sandstone or limestone. The emergence of ground water in the form of springs has an important effect on the level of streams and fresh water lakes. If the water table sinks below the bottom of the streams or lakes (as in times of drought) these eventually become dry. In regions where springs are not found, wells are bored into the ground to a point below the water table. The bottom of the well should be in a permeable rock, in order that it may replenish itself rapidly. Deep wells from which ground water rises in a continuous flow to the surface are called *artesian wells.* The conditions for artesian wells are illustrated in Figure 7–3. A permeable layer such as sandstone lies between impervious rocks

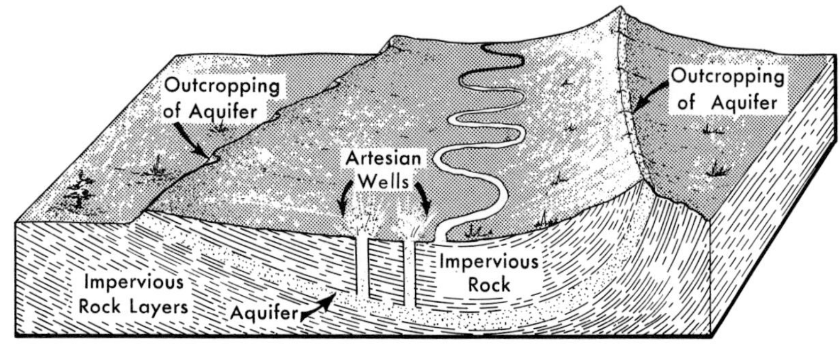

Fig. 7–3 *Conditions necessary for artesian wells.*

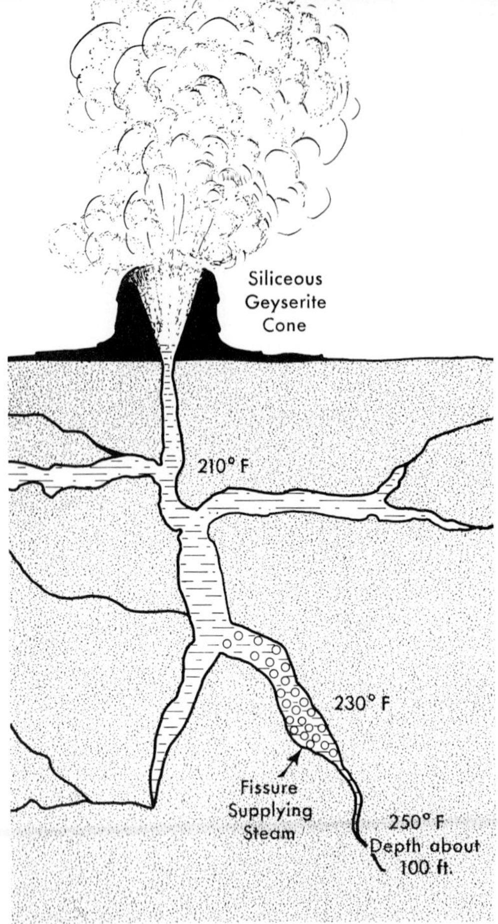

Fig. 7–4 *Conditions necessary for the existence of a geyser.*

Fig. 7–5 *A geyser in eruption: Old Faithful in Yellowstone National Park. (National Park Service)*

such as shale, which are inclined, and water may enter at the outcrops of the sandstone. The water moves through the sandstone slowly, which thus forms a water conductor, or *aquifer,* of an artesian well. If a hole is bored at some point, water will rise to the surface owing to the difference in elevation between the outcrop and the point of boring.

Water emerging from springs in certain localities is hot, ranging in temperature from 100° to 200° F. The hot springs in Arkansas and in Yellowstone Park are among the best known *thermal* (or hot) springs in this country. In such regions there are masses of hot igneous rocks (which have not yet cooled off following their solidification) which heat the ground water before it emerges at the surface. In the Yellowstone region certain hot springs become turbulent and at regular intervals throw a jet of water and steam up in the air, and then subside for periods ranging from minutes to hours. Such springs are called *geysers.*

The condition necessary for a geyser is essentially a hot spring having an irregular tube which causes poor circulation of the waters. The irregular geyser tube extends downward nearly vertically into a region of hot rock. The tube is filled with water from the surrounding rocks. The water in the lower part of the tube is heated above 212° F., but does not become steam, because of the pressure of the column of water above. Finally, the temperature rises to such a point (about 250° F.) that steam is formed, even under the great

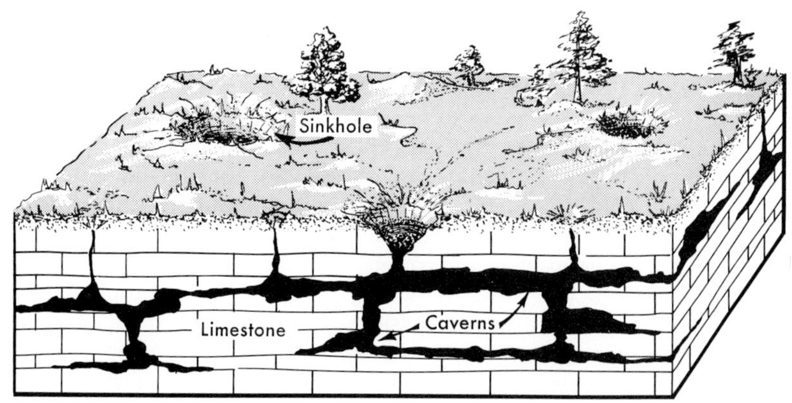

Fig. 7–6 *Solvent action of ground water.*

pressure. This pushes up the column of water, and some of it spills over at the top and thus reduces the pressure. A part of the superheated water flashes into steam and an eruption follows.

SOLVENT ACTION OF GROUND WATER

In falling to the earth, rain absorbs carbon dioxide, oxygen, and other gases. Organic acids are added to it as it passes through the soil, and increase its solvent power. As it seeps through the rocks, it is heated, and its solvent power is further increased. Therefore, as it circulates through the rocks, it dissolves the most soluble minerals, increasing the porosity, and eventually produces a crumbling effect. For example, the cementing material in many sandstones is calcium carbonate, which is slightly soluble in water containing carbon dioxide; water passing through outcrops of such sandstones dissolves the calcareous cement, causing the rock to break into loose sand. A part of the dissolved mineral matter is deposited elsewhere, and another part is discharged into streams and is ultimately carried to the sea. Some of the less soluble minerals are deposited in the seas or lakes, and the more soluble salts accumulate through the constant evaporation of water and give the characteristic salinity to sea water.

The solvent effect of ground water on limestones has produced *caves* and *sinkholes*. The water passing through cracks in limestones enlarges them, in time producing channels, tunnels, and chambers which, when connected with the surface, are called caves. A number of remarkable caves are known in the United States. In the Mammoth Cave, in the limestone region of Kentucky, there are several hundred miles of galleries and passageways connected by chambers, lakes, rivers, and waterfalls.

DEPOSITION BY GROUND WATER

Water, as it circulates, deposits or precipitates part of the mineral matter that it carries. Thus it may deposit calcium carbonate or silicon dioxide in the cracks of rocks. Hot *magmatic* waters, which are residual fluids from the solidification of great

Fig. 7–7 *A concretion of geode.*

bodies of molten rock matter, contain metallic compounds in solution which are deposited in cracks or fissures. Such deposits are known as *mineral vein* deposits. The majority of the metals, including lead, zinc, and copper, are extracted from compounds which are obtained from vein deposits.

The deposition by ground water around some nucleus, such as a small object like a fossil or a mineral particle, gives rise to rounded irregular bodies called *concretions*. Sometimes cavities are filled with crystal deposits, usually of quartz or calcite and pointing inward. Such forms, called *geodes,* occur in many rocks; often they are found as large pebbles which when broken disclose the cavity with well-defined crystals. The best known examples of deposition by water are formations of *stalactites* and *stalagmites* in caves. When water containing carbon dioxide passes downward through a limestone formation, it dissolves a quantity of calcium carbonate as calcium bicarbonate. On reaching the roof of the cave, some of the water evaporates and gives up some of its carbon dioxide, with the result that part of the calcium carbonate is deposited; when the drops of water fall to the floor more calcium carbonate is deposited by the same process. As a result, long icicle-shaped stalactites extend vertically downward from the roof of the cave, and similar, but usually thicker, stalagmites extend up from the floor.

Occasionally ground water deposition becomes an exchange of matter, in that one substance may be dissolved and an equal amount of another deposited. Such an exchange is known as *replacement.* By this process, buried trunks of trees and bones of animals often become slowly petrified. The organic material is dissolved and simultaneously a mineral, usually silica or calcite, is deposited. The petrified forests of Arizona and Yellowstone Park, the petrified bones of dinosaurs, and some deposits of metallic compounds are examples of replacement. Thus, by solution and redeposition, ground water exerts a metamorphic effect upon the rocks.

Fig. 7–8 *Stalactites above and stalagmites below. Great Onyx Cave, Kentucky. (U.S. Geological Survey)*

Fig. 7–9 *Petrified tree trunks.* (*U.S. Geological Survey*)

RUNNING WATER

By far the most important agent operating to modify the shape of the land is running water. Together with the natural movement of the mantle from higher to lower levels under the force of gravity, stream erosion sculptures the land, wears away the hills and mountains, and transports the weathered and eroded debris to be deposited at lower levels in the form of *bars, fans, flood plains, deltas,* and *marine sedimentary layers.*

The amount of precipitation in the United States varies from about eight inches annually in arid regions such as Nevada to about forty-eight inches in temperate or moist regions such as Virginia. As previously noted of the total precipitation, about a third forms surface run-off water. This usually collects in small gullies or *rills,* which unite to form large gullies or *rivulets;* these in turn converge and, augmented by ground-water run-off in the form of seeps and springs, finally form a definite system of channels called a *stream system.* Each stream, large or small, excavates a valley, which it occupies. The main stream with its tributaries forms a river system that resembles a tree, the trunk emptying into the sea, the branches, twigs, and leaves extending inland. The streams of the whole system are engaged in erosion and deposition. They lengthen their courses in a headward direction as they erode. The process of stream development is slow if measured in terms of human generations; nevertheless, the evidence is convincing. Continuously the material of the upland moves downward under the force of gravity and is washed away; the ridges and hills are lowered, and the final result tends to be a featureless level surface called a *peneplain* (almost a plain) . In time, the region may be uplifted again, and thus the cycle of erosion may begin anew.

Fig. 7–10 *Erosion in a river bank. Turkey Run State Park, Indiana.*

STREAM EROSION

The process of erosion by a stream is accomplished by (*a*) the *hydraulic action* or force of the moving particles of water against the mantle, (*b*) the *transporting action* due to the ability of the moving water to pick up and carry away the mud, silt, sand, pebbles, and even boulders, (*c*) the *abrasion* effected on bedrock by the load of the stream, and (*d*) the *solvent action* of water on the rock. The hydraulic action is most noticeable in flat-floored valleys along the curves where the banks consist of thin horizontal layers of unconsolidated sediments. The force of water as it swings around the curves dislodges and carries away the rock mantle. As the water of the stream system flows through gullies, ravines, and valleys, it picks up weathered earth and rock material and through these exerts a constant grinding action against the rock of the floor and the sides. The sand grains, pebbles, and boulders driven by the force of the moving water scrape and scour the bed of the stream and thus excavate and widen the stream channel. Finally, though water reaching the stream from the tributaries and through the ground carries already dissolved matter, it exerts a small but definite solvent action on the rock and mantle of the bed and banks.

The erosive power of the stream depends on a number of factors such as the velocity of the flow, the volume of water, the load of the stream, and the shape and gradient of the channel. The first two, however, are the most important.

The velocity is determined to a great extent by the gradient or slope of the stream bed and its shape. The steeper the slope, the greater the velocity and consequently the greater the hydraulic and abrasive action. If the velocity is doubled, the abrasive power is increased at least four times. This becomes apparent if we consider that in doubling the velocity we double the number of particle bombardments against the rock per unit time and also double the force of such bombardment. With greater velocity larger fragments are picked up, also increasing the erosive power. Therefore, the abrasive power usually varies between the square and the sixth power of the velocity.

The volume of water in streams varies with the rainfall. In the spring, when snow melts in the mountainous regions, and after heavy rainfalls, many moderate streams become raging torrents with enormous destructive power. The increased volume of water not only increases the transporting capacity of the stream, but also the velocity of the water and consequently its transporting power. Thus, the velocity and the volume of water determine the transporting power of the stream.

The mode of transportation of the stream load can be observed by watching the flow of water near the bank of a rapid stream. The fine, lighter particles may be carried in suspension without a great tendency to settle to the bottom. The heavier particles of sand and the pebbles are rolled and dragged along the bed of the stream. Since the bed is seldom uniform, the sediment is carried along jerkily; the boulders and heavy pebbles cause a deflection of the moving water, producing eddies and upward currents. As they tend to reach the bottom of the stream, the particles are picked up and carried forward, or they may fall to the bottom and remain there until they are dragged, rolled, or thrown upward again.

The erosive power of streams may be visualized by considering the load that the Mississippi carries to the sea. It has been estimated that this river discharges annually into the Gulf of Mexico 2×10^{13} cubic feet of water, containing about a hundred and fifty million tons of material in solution and four hundred million tons in suspension. Since the Mississippi River system drains an area of about 1,200,000 miles, the basin is reduced by one foot every eight thousand years. As the land is lowered, the rate of erosion decreases due to the lessening of the slopes and hence of stream velocity. However, if we take the above rate of erosion (denudation) as an average for all the rivers of the United States and also consider that the average elevation is two thousand feet, we find it will take sixteen to eighteen million years, more or less, to reduce the land to sea level or base level if no crustal movement intervenes. Though this rate may seem slow, it is regarded as rapid from a geological standpoint.

TRANSITORY FEATURES

As the river system develops, a number of features, such as falls and rapids, may arise, which, though they may be transitory as far as geologic time is concerned, are regarded as permanent by most human beings encountering them. Whenever a stream flows from harder to softer beds of rock there is differential erosion: the softer beds are cut away at a faster rate than the more resistant ones farther upstream, and thus there will develop a series of *rapids.* As the erosion proceeds, the rapids become steeper and finally a waterfall may result. Waterfalls may be also formed by other geological conditions. For example, a glaciated valley is deepened more than the valleys of the tributary streams, and after glaciation, falls develop at the junction. In the same manner, falls may develop at the junction of tributary streams if the main valley is eroded at a faster rate.

The Niagara Falls were formed in the wake of the last glacier's retreat about 25,000 years ago when Lake Erie spilled out and over a ready-made cliff of horizontal beds of unequal hardness formed during a previous erosion cycle. The bedrock at the falls is of dolomitic limestone, about eighty feet in thickness, with weaker shales and sandstones underneath. The softer beds are eroded more rapidly, leaving the harder capping limestone projecting outward, and over this the water plunges. The process of undercutting is accelerated by the spray of the falling waters until the weakened projecting shelf breaks away in blocks and falls below. In this manner there is a constant recession of the falls which has been measured quite accurately for the past hundred and fifty years. According to the figures, the recession amounts to about three feet per year. By this type of recession, the falls have moved back seven miles, forming a gorge of that length. The Niagara limestone in this re-

Fig. 7–11 *Trenton Falls, New York. Waterfalls may be caused by differential erosion, when the softer beds of rock over which the stream flows are cut away at a faster rate than the harder beds. (U.S. Geological Survey)*

gion is not horizontal, but gradually dips southward at the rate of 35 feet per mile. When the falls, now 160 feet in height, have retreated another two miles, they will be about 90 feet high. Eventually they must disappear, when the water in the river below the falls is at the same level as the Niagara limestone itself. Thus, the apparently permanent Niagara Falls are but a brief episode of geological history.

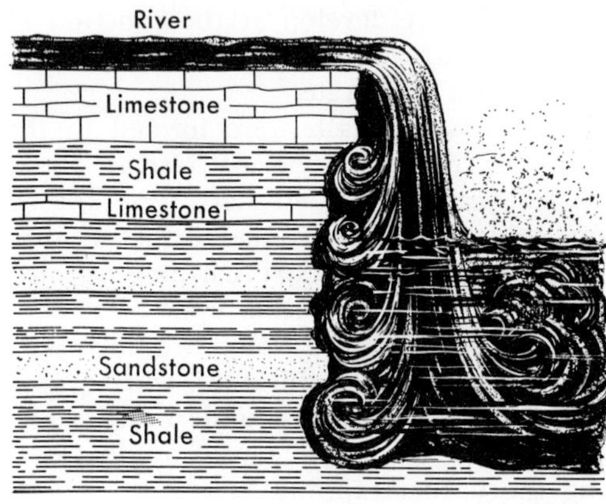

Fig. 7–12 *Diagram of Horseshoe Falls, Niagara, showing structure and strata.* (*After U.S. Geological Survey*)

STREAM DEPOSITION

When the velocity or the volume of a stream is diminished, a corresponding diminution of transporting power occurs, and therefore a part of the load is deposited. This happens many times in the life of a stream, and the resulting river sediment is called *alluvial deposits* or *alluvium*. Such sediments accumulate usually at the foot of hills and mountains, and in stream channels, flood plains, and deltas.

When the velocity of the stream is checked or slackened as a result of an abrupt decrease in gradient, as when a stream flows from a mountain into a plain, a part of its load is dropped in the form of an alluvial *fan-shaped* deposit. As the sediment accumulates, the fan radiates outward from the mouth of the stream and is much thicker close to the place where the velocity is first checked. Huge fans have been built at the base of mountains with steep slopes.

During the low-water stage, streams tend to drop part of their load within their channel to form *bars*. Some of the bars are carried away during the high-water stage, but others may remain permanently and may grow sufficiently to choke up the channel with deposits. The stream then overflows and cuts new channels which in turn become choked, thus giving rise to an intricate pattern of a *braided* stream consisting of a network of shallow channels.

During high water, a stream may overflow its banks and deposit silt, sand, and mud on the *flood plain* over which it runs. As the river widens its valley and ranges laterally in greater and greater curves, it deposits material along the inside of the curves and erodes the bank on the outside, with the eventual result that flood plains are built on both sides of the stream. That part of the Mississippi flood plain which lies between Cairo, Illinois, and the Gulf of Mexico is about six hundred miles long, forty to sixty miles wide, and twelve thousand square miles in area.

As the flood plain becomes higher on either side of the stream, deposition occurs during highwater mark along the sides of the channel where the velocity of the water is checked as the stream overflows its banks. In this manner, the flood plain develops ridgelike deposits at the border of the stream, which are known as *natural* levees and which offer some protection from seasonal floods.

Another type of alluvial deposit occurs at the mouths of streams as they enter the sea or a lake. The velocity is checked and the load drops to the bottom, gradually building successive layers of alluvium which grow to a shape resembling an inverted Greek letter Δ, and hence are called *deltas*. The stream, as described in the preceding paragraphs, chokes up its channel, spills over, and forms new channels, which in turn become choked, thus giving rise to many channels across the delta, and through

Fig. 7–13 *An alluvial fan. Emerald Lake, British Columbia.* *(Geological Survey of Canada)*

these it continues to build new alluvial deposits farther out in the sea.

Deposition of alluvium is important to man. Two of the oldest civilizations grew up along the river banks of the Nile and the land enclosed by the Tigris and the Euphrates. The reasons are not hard to find. The land that is a mile or two away from the banks of the Nile is a desolate desert. Yet in a small strip of land on either side of the Nile there exists even today the most dense population of the world. The land can support that population, thanks to its fertility, for the river brings from equatorial Africa a deposit which is extremely fertile. Long systems of canals irrigate and flood the land, so that it is possible under the subtropical sun to raise three or four crops a year. The river system with its valleys, tributaries, and flood plains has been the cradle of mankind.

GENERALIZED CYCLE OF EROSION

From the preceding discussion it is possible to construct an hypothetical cycle of erosion in order to obtain a better picture both of the cycle for stream valleys and of the cycle for regions. These two cycles are related, but one deals with the valley occupied by the stream and the other with the area drained by the stream and all its tributaries. Further, it should be pointed out that these two generalized cycles as outlined here are for a humid or moist climate; the stream valleys and the sculpture of the land in arid and semiarid regions (receiving five to twenty inches of rain annually) present a different picture. Whereas in moist regions there is an abundance of rolling hills of fine-textured mantle covered by vegetation, in dry regions the land is extensively gullied with an abundance of bare, steep, rocky slopes, accumulated taluses, and a discontinuous coarse mantle often devoid of vegetation (badlands). Whereas in moist regions chemical weathering is dominant, in dry regions mechanical weathering predominates. As a consequence, in the arid or semiarid regions gullies are more numerous, many streams are intermittent, the waters of permanent streams are turbid, and all streams are subject to sudden floods. In some of these regions, as in Libya, wind, not water, sculptures the face of the land.

Fig. 7–14 *Contrast between landscape of moist and arid regions.*

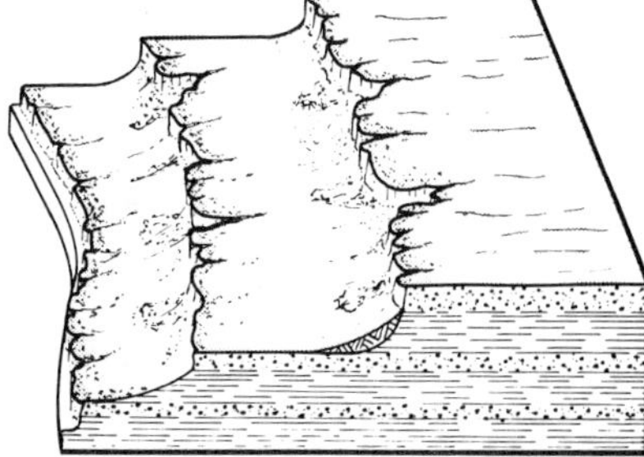

Fig. 7–15 *V-shaped valley. Canyon of the Yellowstone River.* *(U.S. Geological Survey)*

Fig. 7–16 *Valley in early maturity with flood plain. Silverton, Colorado.* *(U.S. Geological Survey)*

EROSION CYCLE OF VALLEYS

We can begin with a land area which has been uplifted to a moderate height in a moist climate. With the rainfalls, the rills and rivulets run along depressions forming gullies. Adjacent gullies slowly form connecting chains which gradually develop into valleys. The stream valleys go through a series of changes which, for the purpose of characterization, are classified as *young, mature,* and *old.*

In *youth* the stream channel occupies virtually all of the valley floor, the banks rising directly on each side of the channel. The banks may be high or low, steep or gentle, according to the hardness of the rock, the relief, and the climate. The cross profile of most young valleys is V-shaped. The dominant type of stream erosion during early youth is downcutting. Since the gradient is steep, swift rapids and falls may develop along the crooked courses of the youthful streams. The canyons of the Colorado and the Yellowstone are examples of young stream valleys on a large scale.

In *maturity* the stream channel does not occupy all of the valley floor but is bounded on one or both banks by a level flood plain of small or great width. The development of the flood plain is due to the meandering of the stream and the decrease in gradient and consequent decrease in downcutting. As the erosion of the stream is directed toward the sides of the valley, the stream begins to meander from one side to the other so that steep bluffs occur on both banks. With increasing maturity, the flood plain becomes broader and the stream assumes the shape of sweeping curves.

As *old age* sets in, the net downcutting action of the stream has ceased and erosion is confined to valley widening. The higher portions of the plain which follow the stream banks constitute natural levees.

This cycle may be interrupted at any stage by geological changes. For instance, crustal movements may increase the gradient of an old region, thus rejuvenating the stream. The rejuvenated stream inherits a meandering course from the earlier erosion cycle but again deepens its valley, re-

Fig. 7–17 *Region in late maturity with meandering stream. Trout Creek, Yellowstone National Park.* (*Josef Muench*)

developing a V-shaped cross profile; this winding V-shaped stream is said to exhibit entrenched meanders and may be bordered by terraces, remnants of an old flood plain The meandering of the San Juan River in southeastern Utah affords a good example of entrenched meanders. Some rivers through mountainous regions have kept their courses during the elevation of mountains, and their banks are used by man as routes to travel.

EROSION CYCLE FOR REGIONS

In *youth* a region is imperfectly drained. The upland is dominant in the topography of the region. Its superficial features may result from one of various causes, all unrelated to stream erosion, such as continental glaciation, volcanism, the draining of a huge lake, or the elevation of a portion of a shallow sea floor like that of Hudson Bay. The divides between streams are generally broad and there may be lakes or marshes on these divides. During youth a stream system develops an increasingly large and complex network of tributaries so that less and less uneroded land remains between the valleys.

In *early maturity* a region is almost perfectly drained, a maximum proportion of the area is in slope, and divides are reduced to narrow belts not always broad enough for the construction of upland divide roads. During *maturity* the valleys of a region become broader and the drainage of their floors thus becomes less perfect. The remaining uplands decrease in height, ruggedness, and extent.

With *old age* the remaining uplands are eroded by the tributaries and there is a gradual decrease in the height of the hills until the region is reduced to a *peneplain,* a plain of low relief very gently rolling, with a few resistant remnants of the former highlands called *monadnocks,* after Mount Monadnock in New Hampshire. This featureless plain is imperfectly drained and may include marshes or lakes, frequently of the *oxbow* or crescent type.

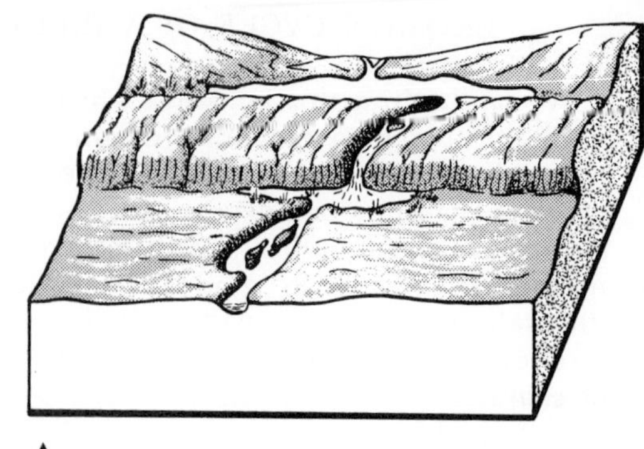

Fig. 7–18 *Diagrammatic representation of the erosion stages of a region.* (*Brooklyn College, Department of Geology*)

A. *In early youth the region has lakes, waterfalls, and rapids.*

B. *By middle youth the lakes are gone, but falls and rapids persist along the narrow incised gorge.*

C. *Early maturity brings a smoothly graded profile without rapids or falls, but with the beginnings of a flood plain.*

D. *Approaching full maturity, the region has a flood plain almost wide enough to accommodate the meandering stream.*

E. *Full maturity and old age are marked by a broad flood plain and freely developed meanders.*

The terms *youth, maturity,* and *old age,* then, indicate stages in a hypothetical erosion cycle; the time involved and also the stages are profoundly altered by the climate and by the nature of the rocks of the region. Moreover, the two erosion cycles, though related, are not necessarily the same. For example, the valleys may be in early maturity and the region may be very young, or vice versa. Table 7–1 gives a summary of the two erosion cycles.

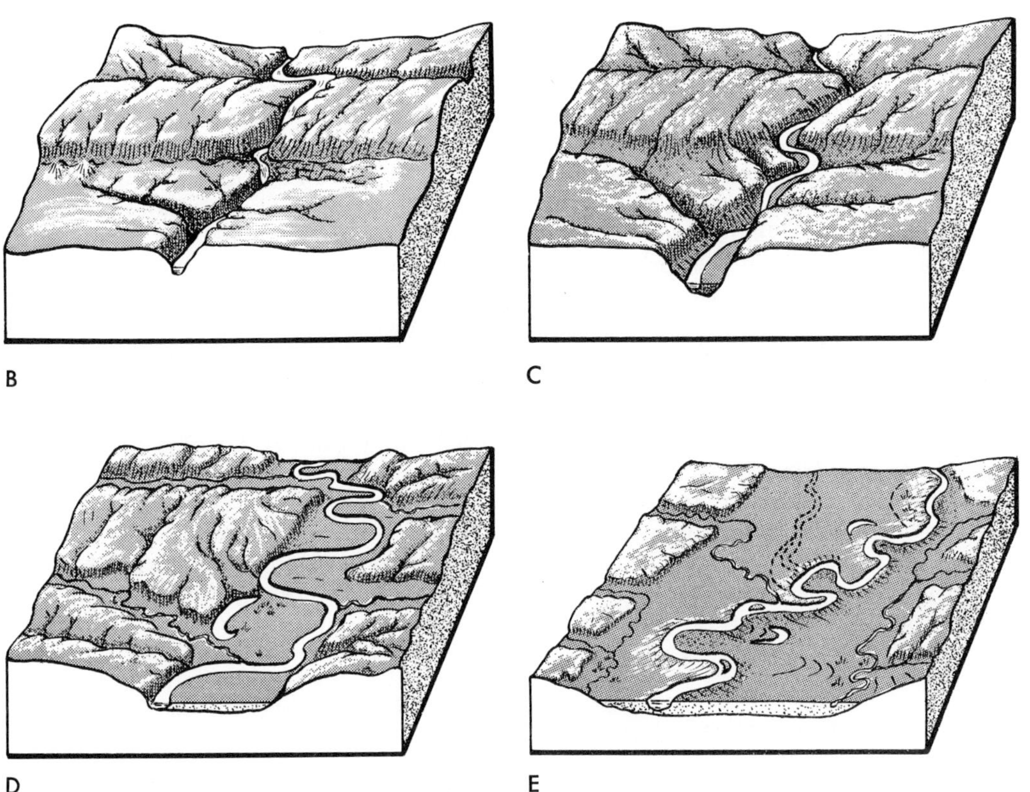

TABLE 7–1 SUMMARY OF EROSION CYCLES FOR STREAM VALLEYS AND REGIONS (MOIST CLIMATE)

CHARACTERISTICS	YOUTH	MATURITY	OLD AGE
Stream Valleys:			
Shape	Mostly V-shaped with steep walls; channel occupies all valley floor; falls and rapids	Broad with flaring sides; meandering channel does not occupy all valley floor; development of flood plain	Gentle slopes with broad flood plain; meandering channel bounded by low plains
Type of erosion	Mostly downward; high gradient	Lateral; gradient diminished	Valley widening in a peneplain
Regions:			
Drainage	Imperfect	Nearly perfect	Imperfect
General features	Broad divides; few and short tributaries	Narrow divides; numerous and well-developed tributaries; flood plain begins	Trend toward featureless plain; few tributaries; very broad flat valley floors

SNOW AND ICE

The weathering effects of freezing water were considered in the preceding chapter. There is a constant wedging action on the mantle rock and the outcropping bedrock. Similarly, when the rivers freeze, a wedging action at the sides and bottom occurs. When the ice begins to melt in the spring, many boulders encased in ice float downstream. However, the erosional and transportational effects of ice in frozen rivers or on lake shores are not as significant as those resulting from large masses of ice in motion. Huge moving ice masses, called *glaciers,* are the chief agents of erosion in high mountains and in the Arctic zones, as in Alaska and Greenland. There is abundant proof that much of the present topography of Illinois, Wisconsin, and the Northeast is due to large glaciers that flowed several times over these regions in the past.

FORMATION OF GLACIERS

In high altitudes snow remains the year round. The snow line in the Alps is about 8500 feet above sea level; in Alaska it is 5000 feet; in Greenland 2000 feet. When snow falls, it is flaky and dry, but when it accumulates, it becomes compact. Under the effect of pressure of the layers above, each snowflake partially melts and refreezes, acquiring a granular texture like small particles of hail. In time, by successive changes, snow many hundreds of feet thick is finally converted into compact ice by its own weight. When it begins to move under its own weight, it becomes a glacier.

When the ice attains a great thickness and the slope is steep enough, it begins to spread slightly outward and mostly downward. If the land is fairly horizontal, vertical pressure at the center of the ice field spreads the ice in all directions and makes an *ice cap* or *ice sheet*. Greenland is covered with such an ice sheet 700,000 square miles in area and 8000 feet in thickness at the center. The Antarctic continent is buried under a larger ice cap, covering more than five million square miles. When the gradient is steep, as in the valleys of high mountains, the sheets of ice move downward and are called *valley glaciers.* Glaciers of this type are found in the Alps, Caucasus, and Himalayas. The most important in the United States are those of Mount Rainier, Mount Shasta, Mount Hood, and Crater Lake. Valley glaciers are usually one to two miles long, and move about one foot a day. The rate of motion – which in the winter is about half of the summer rate – is faster in the middle than at the sides or bottom, since the friction against the valley walls and floor impedes motion. Because of the slower movement of the sides, tension develops which results in cracks that widen to form chasms called *crevasses.*

Many theories have been proposed to account for glacial motion, of which only one will be briefly mentioned. It is assumed that under the great pressures from above and behind, the ice crystals at points of greatest compression melt and the water produced refreezes after undergoing a slight relative change in position. As the valley glaciers move downward, there is melting and evaporation. The water flows into crevasses which may lead into subglacial channels.

Fig. 7–19 *A valley glacier. Tanana Glacier, Alaska. (U.S. Geological Survey)*

Fig. 7–20 *Section of foot of Valdez Glacier, Alaska. (U.S. Geological Survey)*

Ultimately the water from the melting of the glacier emerges in the form of streams or lakes beyond the ice. If the rate of melting exceeds the rate of supply of ice by snowfall at the head, the glacier recedes, and when the supply exceeds the melting, the glacier advances. Occasionally the two rates will approximate each other, and the glacier appears to be stationary. When glaciers end in the sea, as in Greenland and Antarctica, huge blocks of ice break off and float away as *icebergs.*

GLACIAL EROSION AND DEPOSITION

The glacier acquires a load of rock debris as it moves. Mantle rock falls from the valley sides or is plucked away from the cliffs and edges. These pebbles and boulders become embedded in the bottom ice and so become the chief tool of glacial erosion. As the glacier moves, a part of the load, by constant grinding, is reduced to powder. The sides of the valley are scoured and ground out. In many places the grinding action produces scratches, grooves, and smooth surfaces. The boulders deposited by glaciers show similar polish and scratches, called *striae.*

Prolonged glacial action changes a youthful V-shaped valley into a U-shaped one, since the sides are eroded as rapidly as the bottom. In the glaciation of a valley that has tributaries, the main channel is eroded to a lower level because of the greater volume of ice. When the ice recedes, the tributary valley is left hanging high above the floor of the main valley, and is hence known as a *hanging valley.* The Yosemite Valley has hanging tributary valleys whose streams plunge as much as eleven hundred feet or more down to the floor of the main valley. The plucking and shearing action of glacial ice produces on the upper ends of practically all glaciated valleys amphitheater-like shapes called *cirques.* In the high latitudes, glaciated valleys may be partially submerged by the sea to form vertical-walled valleys whose floors are hundreds of feet below sea level; these are called *fiords.*

When glaciers melt, a heterogeneous mass of rock debris, ranging from clay to huge boulders, is deposited. The name applied to such deposits is *glacial drift.* The material dropped directly by the glacier is known as *till.* Material carried by the glacial stream and deposited farther along is known as a *glacio-fluvial* deposit. Ridges of till deposited by glaciers at their sides or at their ends are known as *moraines.*

As the glacier moves, it deposits irregular heaps of excess load which accumulate at its borders. When the ice melts, these irregular ridges, called *lateral moraines,* are

Fig. 7–21 *Typical U-shaped valley. Tenaya Canyon, Yosemite Valley.* (*U.S. Geological Survey*)

left at the sides. At the end of the glacier, where the melting may proceed for a long period at the same rate as the advance, considerable till is dropped and forms ridges called *terminal moraines.* Ridges of this type may be deposited by material which is pushed by the front of the advancing glacier. These ridges may be quite high, but are not wide unless formed by great slowly-retreating ice sheets, when they become as much as twenty miles in width.

Streams from melting glaciers carry considerable amounts of a flour-like suspension of pulverized rock, sand, pebbles, and boulders, and deposit such glacio-fluvial material beyond the terminal moraines, in

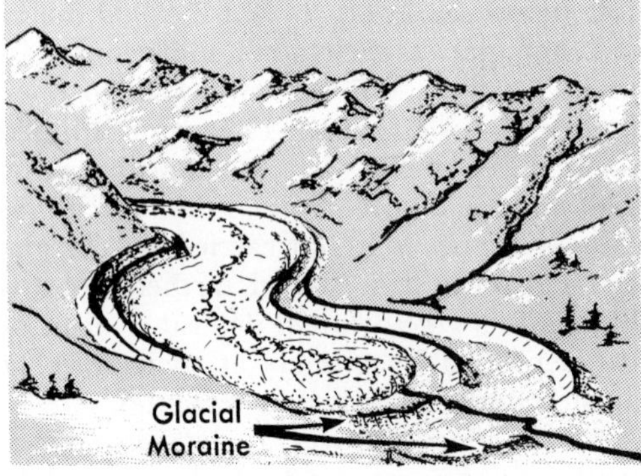

Fig. 7–22 *Glacier leaving a moraine.* (*After U.S. Geological Survey*)

shapes much like the alluvial fans. Many such fans may coalesce to develop an *outwash plain.* Other characteristic deposits of glacial streams are winding ridges of sand and gravel known as *eskers,* many of which resemble railway embankments. These ridges are formed by subglacial streams flowing beneath the ice.

ICE AGES

In Illinois, Wisconsin, and other states, several layers of glacial drift are found separated from each other by thin deposits which indicate soil and vegetation of warm climates. From a study of these layers there are assumed to have been four different advances and retreats of the huge ice sheets in recent geologic history. These are named the Nebraskan, Kansan, Illinoian, and Wisconsin advances.

Study of glacial striae made in many parts of North America, of the alignment of moraines, and of other evidence, indicates that the ice originated outside the Arctic regions, in three main centers. One originated in Labrador on the coast of Hudson Bay, one west of Hudson Bay, and the third in the Rocky Mountain area of Canada and the northernmost United States. From these three centers, ice sheets radiated, covering most of the North American continent from the lower part of Illinois northward. The extent of the huge ice sheets may be realized from the dimensions given for the Greenland ice sheet. It is estimated that the ice sheet at its maximum covered four million square miles of the North American continent. In Europe similar ice sheets covered most of the northern countries. This subject will be discussed again in Chapter 10.

THE SEA

The sea (ocean) occupies about 72 per cent of the earth's surface. Its shallow margins, which can be considered as parts of the continents, are the ultimate depository of the sediments of eroded material from the higher portions of the continental masses. It is the reservoir in the water cycle and furnishes the major part of the water vapors that fall upon the continents as rain and snow. It also acts as a reservoir for a considerable amount of heat received from the sun. The amount of heat absorbed by water is retained for far greater periods of time than that absorbed by rocks and the soil. Great currents from the equatorial zones move warm water to northern latitudes and make the climate milder. Similar effects, though to a smaller degree, are produced by large lakes. The water during the summer months is heated, and during the winter as the water on the surface reaches 39° F., or 4° C., it becomes heavier and sinks, thus bringing warmer water to the surface. This in turn heats air passing over the surface and exerts an influence on the atmospheric temperature of the surrounding regions.

At the same time the sea is an energetic agent of erosion. By the pounding action of the waves and the constant action of the waters on the shores the sea aids the other gradational agents in eroding the continents. By receiving and distributing the sediments brought in by the streams it becomes the gigantic ceramic factory for the production of the sedimentary rocks which today form a large part of the outer shell of the continents.

The average depth of the sea is two and one-half miles. It should not be thought, however, that this depth is attained within a few hundred feet of the land. Evidence from soundings and other oceanographic measurements indicates that the first twenty to a hundred miles out in the sea are shallow, with a depth seldom exceeding 500 to 600 feet. This shallow portion of the sea is really an inundated margin of the continent and is called the *continental shelf*. The continental shelves are widened partly by continuous erosion of the shoreline and partly by the deposition of sediments which are carried outward to its edge by sea currents. The shelves slope seaward at an average rate of about 10 to 15 feet per mile to a depth of about 600 feet, where the depth increases rapidly (200 to 300 feet per mile) to the floor of the sea basins, which are marked by rises and deeps.

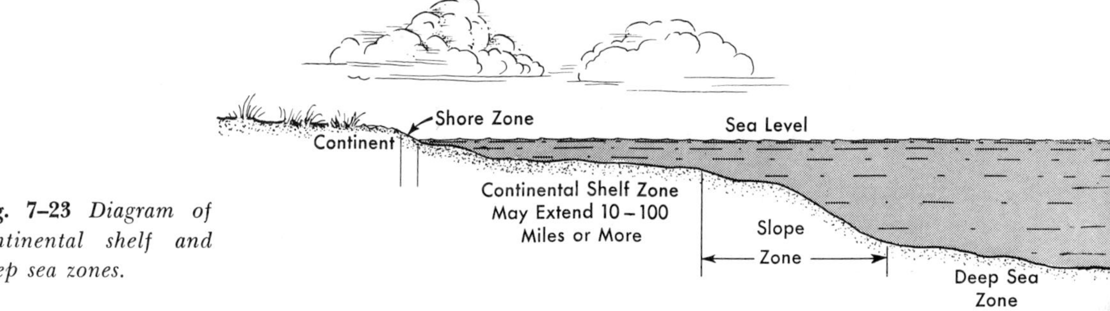

Fig. 7–23 *Diagram of continental shelf and deep sea zones.*

Some of these rises and deeps consist of plains and valleys probably produced by currents and of mountains formed by warping, faulting, and submarine volcanic action (see Chapter 8). The greatest deeps adjoin regions of recent mountain building, areas which appear to have gone down as the mountains arose. Two great deeps are in the Pacific Ocean: one, off the coast of Japan, is approximately 36,000 feet in depth; and the other, near the Philippine Islands, is about 35,500 feet. The great Atlantic deep is about 31,500 feet and is located off Puerto Rico. It appears that these great deeps of six miles below sea level correspond roughly to the highest mountains of from 5 to 5.5 miles above it.

The continental shelves and the shorelines have changed many times in the geologic past as the ocean basins have alternately shallowed and deepened. When the basins shallowed, the water spilled over the continents until as much as 50 to 60 per cent was under water. As the basins deepened, withdrawal of the water took place and the continental shelves were exposed until the next submergence. As it will be shown in a subsequent chapter, this alternation has occurred repeatedly over the geologic ages, and even now some shelves are undergoing slow elevation and others subsidence.

WAVES AND CURRENTS

Winds blowing over the surface of the sea keep it in constant agitation to a smaller or greater degree. In the relatively shallow waters of the continental shelf the formation of *waves* by winds is very common. Waves are formed by frictional action of the wind on the surface of the water and are pushed forward in rapid succession. As the waves approach shallow water, their lower part drags on the bottom and is retarded, while the upper portion is propelled forward with undiminished velocity. This produces a shortening of the distance between crests (wave length) and an increase in height of the crest and depth of the trough. Finally the crest rolls over and forms foamy *breakers,* dashing the water forward on the shore.

The water of the breaking wave which piles up on the shore returns to the sea in the form of a current along the bottom and under the incoming waves. The return current, when it is perpendicular to the shore, is called an *undertow.* When the water strikes the shore at an acute angle, a component of the return current is roughly parallel to the shore, and it is then called a *shore current.* These two currents carry away the material eroded by the action of the waves. The large fragments are moved back and forth until they are ground to a sufficient degree of fineness to be moved seaward and deposited in deeper water. In this manner, shore currents carry fine material and drop it at the entrance of bays where the water is deeper, forming ridges of deposited land called *spits.* The spit generally tends to close the bay, forming a *bar,* and thus simplifies the shoreline. Bars in certain places tie islands to the mainland; such bars are called *tombolos.* It should be noted that the effects of wave motion decrease rapidly with increasing depth, so that the sea floors of exposed coasts are seldom affected beyond a depth of 300 feet.

The force exerted by large waves may be enormous, so that erosion occurs very rapidly. The south shore of Nantucket Island, which is exposed to the waves of the Atlantic, has been known to retreat as much as six feet a year. Cliffs near Dover on the English Channel are receding at the rate of fifteen feet per year. The pressure exerted by the dashing waves against a vertical wall may rise to over 10,000 pounds per square foot during the first fraction of a second of the impact. The sand, pebbles, and rock fragments carried by the water and hurled against the cliffs or shores exert a grinding effect and hasten the undercutting, thus producing sea cliffs with steep walls. The process is repeated, and the sea cliff is undermined and finally reduced to fragments at the base. In this manner the cliff recedes,

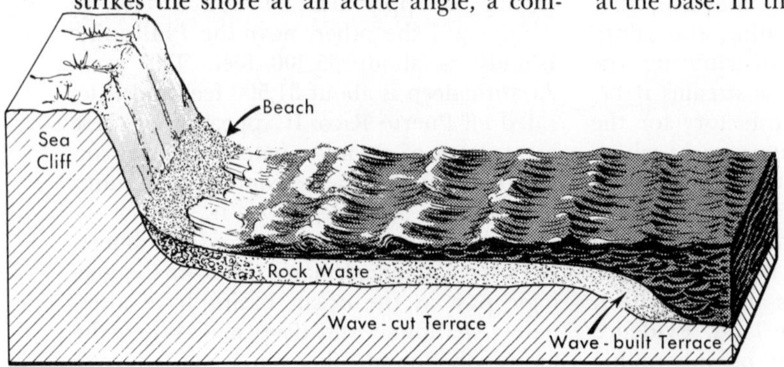

Fig. 7–24 *Diagram of the erosional work of waves.*

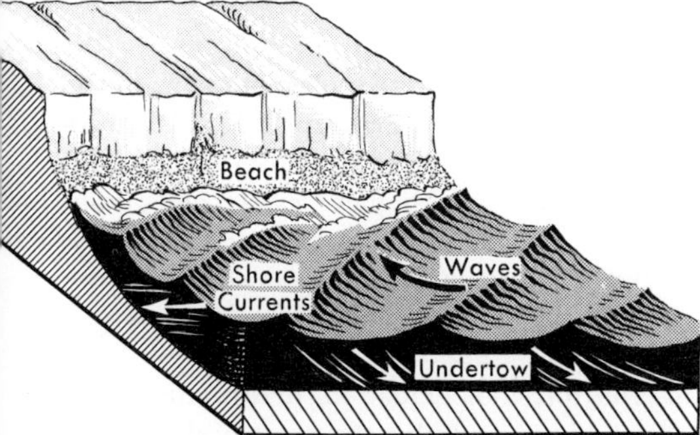

Fig. 7–25 *Diagram of waves and currents.*

and the accumulated debris from the eroded coastal land is carried seaward by the undertow, forming a *wave-built terrace.* The portion of land over which the sea has advanced by cutting back the cliffs is called the *wave-cut terrace.*

TYPES OF SHORELINES

The topographic features of shorelines are closely related to the elevation or lowering of the continental shelf. There are two general types recognized as indicating whether there has been elevation or subsidence. The first type, which consists of bold embayed coasts like that of the northeastern United States, is the shoreline of *submergence.* It is highly irregular, with many bays and promontories; it occurs along coasts where the sea has encroached deep upon the land and has drowned the lower parts of the stream valleys, forming deep bays and long headlands. There is a depressed, or drowned, valley extending about a hundred and fifty miles beyond the present mouth of the Hudson River. In such shorelines the waves tend to cut back the headlands, and the shore currents to close the bays, so as ultimately to produce a straight shoreline. The other, the low plain type like the South Atlantic and Gulf coasts, is considered as the shoreline of *emergence.* It occurs in areas where part of the continental shelf has been raised slightly above the water. This type is a flat coastal plain with numerous shallow lagoons between offshore bars and the mainland and without any cliffs. In a shoreline of this type the action of waves and shore currents has built additional bars and filled in the lagoons, thus again simplifying the shoreline. In both cases, after the shoreline has been simplified, the erosional process of cutting cliffs and building beaches and terraces continues as the cycle repeats itself.

DEPOSITION IN THE SEA

All materials eroded from the land, the muds, sands, and gravels, ultimately are deposited as sediments. A part of this disintegrated rock material is deposited on the flood plains of the valleys or in the bottom of lakes, and the rest is carried to the sea. Ultimately most of the eroded material, even if it is temporarily deposited in the continents, reaches the sea. Thus, the sea is primarily a basin of deposition. The material discharged into the sea by the streams and to a smaller degree detached from the land through the action of waves is of two kinds: material in solution and material in suspension.

The material in solution consists mostly of sodium, magnesium, and calcium compounds. Sodium chloride, or common table salt, makes up three-fourths of the dissolved matter, and the salty taste of sea water is due mainly to this compound. The bitterness is due chiefly to the magnesium compounds. The amount of dissolved matter is 3.1 to 3.7 per cent by weight. If sufficient sea water were evaporated to obtain 100 grams of solid material, its approximate composition would be as given in Table 7–2. In addition sea water contains dis-

TABLE 7–2 MATERIAL DISSOLVED IN SEA WATER

Material	Per cent
Sodium chloride (salt)	77%
Magnesium compounds	16%
Calcium compounds (lime)	3%
Potassium compounds	2%
Traces of other substances — including gold and silver in minute traces	2%
	100%

solved gases such as oxygen and carbon dioxide. From the dissolved material that is continuously brought to the sea, a part is precipitated by chemical reactions, and a large part of the calcium compounds is abstracted by shell-forming marine animals. As these organisms die, their shells may be deposited to form lime muds which later form limestone. The lime-mud deposition takes place in shallow waters, where the lime-secreting organisms abound.

The material which is in suspension is dropped on the sea floor in the order of size of the particles. As the velocity of the water decreases, the particles are sorted, gravel being dropped first, then sand, and then mud; the fine muds may be carried not only as far as the edge of the continental shelf but even to distances from land as great as two hundred miles. This indicates that on the shallow continental shelf limestones, shales, and sandstone are being deposited to form sedimentary rocks. In this manner, it is believed, most of the great deposits of sedimentary rocks found deep in the continents are formed. The sea is not stationary. Many times in the geologic past, parts of the continent were inundated by shallow seas into which streams emptied their loads, and organic life built up huge deposits of limestone. The deep-sea deposits that have been brought up by scoops and dredges show little evidence of material brought by the streams. They have a slimy consistency and are known as *oozes*. Examinations indicate that these deep-sea slimy deposits consist of volcanic ash, shells of simple types of plants and animals, and colloidal mud.

SUMMARY

1. The agents of erosion include weathering, movement of the mantle under the force of gravity (creep and landslides), running water, wind, subsurface water, snow and ice, and the sea; but of all these, running water plays the most important role. Their actions, included under the term *gradation,* tend to sculpture the face of the land in detail and then to reduce it to sea level.
2. Opposed to the forces of gradation are the internal forces of diastrophism and volcanism. The forces of diastrophism elevate land from lower to higher levels, and build mountains. The forces of volcanism cause the movements of molten rock which rise up to build high volcanic peaks and plateaus.
3. The forces of gradation, diastrophism, and volcanism underlie the geological cycle of the earth: a long period of erosion and sedimentation followed by periods of crustal adjustments resulting in uplifts, mountain building, and intrusion and extrusion of molten rock, and then a repetition of the cycle.
4. Wind erosion is predominant in arid and semiarid regions. Wind transports particles of sand and dust and forms dunes and loess deposits.
5. Ground water circulates very slowly and emerges to the surfaces to form springs, wells, and geysers.
6. Ground water by its solvent action on rocks and by deposition of dissolved mineral matter is instrumental in forming caves, sinkholes, geodes, stalactites, stalagmites, mineral veins, concretions, and petrified remains of plants and animals.
7. Running water is the greatest agent of erosion. Its erosional and depositional work results in gullies, ravines, canyons, valleys, rapids, falls, bars, fans, flood plains, levees, deltas, and marine sediments.
8. Stream erosion is accomplished by hydraulic action, solvent action, abrasion, and the transport power of water.
9. Both stream valleys and regions in moist climates have a general cycle of youth, maturity, and old age with characteristic features for each stage.
10. Long-continued accumulation of snow gives rise to glacial ice.
11. Glacial ice by its erosional and depositional action gives rise to these topographical features: moraines, glacial drift, eskers, glaciated valleys, hanging valleys, cirques, and fiords.
12. Erosional action of the waves and deposition by currents produce these topographic features along the shores: cliffs, wave-cut

terraces, wave-built terraces, spits, and bars. The general tendency of shore agents is to simplify the shoreline.

13. The sea margins form a basin of deposition. The shallow portions of the sea, or continental shelves, are inundated margins of the continents and extend for several miles into the sea. Most of the large masses of sedimentary rocks found today on the continents were deposited in such shallow seas which in the past inundated the continents.

STUDY EXERCISES

1. Cite observable evidence for the following statements:
   a. Running water is the greatest agent of erosion.
   b. A stream cuts its banks more rapidly by hydraulic action than by abrasion.
   c. A great weight of ice has plastic properties and it flows or moves slowly.
   d. Many inland places have been glaciated in the past.
   e. Though silica (quartz) is relatively insoluble in water, minute amounts may dissolve in subsurface water and be redeposited.
   f. Sedimentary rocks were formed in shallow seas, then elevated to form most of our continent.
2. State the geological cycle operative over long intervals of time on the earth and give evidence upon which this concept is based.
3. Construct a table on the agents of gradation along the following format:

Gradational Agent	Erosional features	Depositional features
EXAMPLE: ground water	caves, sinkholes	stalactites, stalagmites, concretions, geodes, etc.

4. Draw diagrams of the following: (*a*) an artesian well; (*b*) a young stream valley; (*c*) a mature region; (*d*) an old region; (*e*) a cirque.
5. Draw a rough diagram illustrating each of the following. Label all parts and give a brief statement below the diagram explaining the causes of changes depicted.
   a. The formation of a waterfall by water running over a bed of shale on top of which there is a thin cap (very thin layer) of limestone.
   b. The formation of a gully on a hillside unwisely cultivated.
   c. A glaciated young valley in which the glacier advanced down to the middle of the valley and then receded.
6. Give conditions for the following features of erosion or deposition:

a. levee	*h.* hanging valley
b. alluvial fan	*i.* fiord
c. delta	*j.* esker
d. lateral moraine	*k.* wave-cut terrace
e. terminal moraine	*l.* bar
f. outwash plain	*m.* spit
g. valley glaciation	*n.* lagoon

7. Mark *1* if produced by weathering or wind; *2,* if produced by running water; *3,* if produced by ground water; *4,* if produced by glaciers; or *5,* if produced by shore agents.

.... hanging valleys	.... bar
.... peneplain	.... flood plain
.... falls	.... salt deposit
.... alluvial fan	.... geode
.... geysers	.... unsorted deposit
.... tombolos	.... cirque
.... spit	.... loess
.... cliff	.... talus
.... polished rock	.... moraine
.... stalactite	.... petrified wood
.... levee	.... sorted deposit
.... canyon	.... lime deposit
.... sink holes	.... lagoon
.... exfoliation	.... metallic deposit
.... soil	.... delta
.... dunes	.... fiord
.... eskers	.... beach
.... striated stones	.... rapids

8. On what type of evidence is our concept of the topography of the sea floor based?
9. Give the characteristics of the two general types of shorelines and the general trend of shoreline changes.

10. From the list below give the numbers identifying the characteristics of stream valleys and regions at each of the three stages indicated:

	Stream Valley	Region
Young	....	....
Mature	....	....
Old	....	....

(1) distinctly U-shaped
(2) very gentle
(3) downcutting
(4) very wide flood plain
(5) levees
(6) falls and rapids
(7) steep-sided canyons
(8) sidecutting
(9) ox-bows
(10) V-shaped
(11) many well-developed tributaries
(12) beginning to form a flood plain
(13) steep gradient
(14) meandering
(15) carries fairly large rocks
(16) few short tributaries

11. In the following list write *W* if the change has been produced by wind; *S* if by subsurface water; *R* if by running water; *A* if the change represents deposition; and *E* if it represents erosional change.

.... loess
.... dunes
.... deltas
.... levees
.... sinkholes
.... concretions
.... geodes
.... alluvium
.... stalactites
.... pinnacles
.... alluvial fan
.... peneplain
.... flood plain
.... valleys
.... springs
.... caves

FOR FURTHER READING

1. GILLULY, J., A. C. WATERS, and A. O. WOODFORD, *Principles of Geology*. San Francisco, W. H. Freeman and Co., 1954.

   A detailed discussion of the erosion cycle will be found in Chapters 12, 13, and 14.

2. GARRELS, R. M., *A Textbook of Geology*. New York: Harper and Brothers, 1951.

   For a detailed discussion of the erosion cycle, see Chapters 4–8.

3. LONGWELL, C. R., A. KNOPF, and R. F. FLINT, *Physical Geology*. New York: John Wiley and Sons, 1948.

   Running and subsurface water is discussed in Chapters 5, 6, and 7; glaciers, in Chapter 9; wind erosion and deposition, in Chapter 10; shore agents, in Chapter 11.

4. MATHER, K. F., and S. L. MASON, *Source Book in Geology*. New York: McGraw-Hill Book Co., 1939.

   The following original papers are recommended in connection with this chapter: Agassiz, "Evidence of a Glacial Epoch," *p. 329; Humphreys and Abbot,* "The Amount of Sediment Carried by the Mississippi," *p. 367; Oldham,* "Stream Erosion and Transportation," *p. 371; Posepny,* "Ground Water and the Deposition of Ore Bodies," *p. 537; Davis,* "The Erosion Cycle in the Life of a River," *p. 649.*

5. Paperback: EDITORS OF SCIENTIFIC AMERICAN, *The Planet Earth*. Simon and Schuster, $1.45.

6. Paperback: CARSON, R. L., *The Sea Around Us*. Mentor, 35¢.

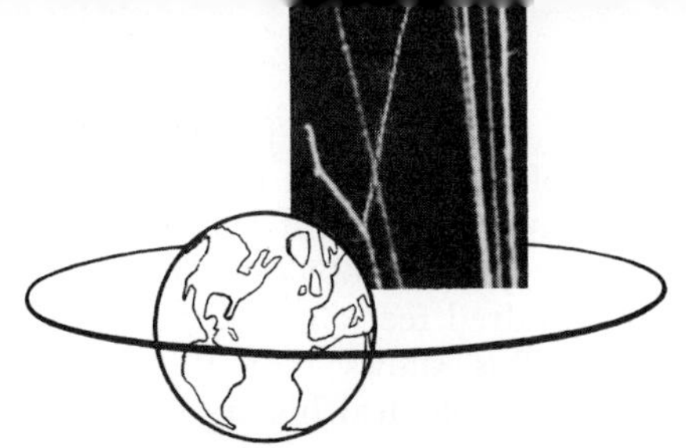

8

DIASTROPHISM AND VOLCANISM

AS THE LAST CHAPTER SUGGESTED, the logical end result of the agents of gradation would be continents with no mountains, plateaus, or hills, and eventual reduction of all continental masses to sea level. Opposing the gradational processes, however, are forces within the earth which tend to build up land. *Diastrophism,* one of these forces, comprises all movements of the outer shell of the earth; *volcanism,* the other internal force, includes all movements of molten rock within or on the earth and the phenomena that are associated with these movements. The most familiar manifestation of these forces are earthquakes and the eruption of volcanoes; but besides these spectacular demonstrations of crustal movements and the outpouring of rocks, cinders, molten lava, and gases from craters and fissures, there are extensive movements which are perceptible only after considerable time has elapsed.

The record written in the rocks of the earth indicates gigantic crustal movements which repeatedly deformed the crust of the earth, folding and bending sedimentary strata several thousand feet in thickness to form huge mountain systems; similarly the rock records show that molten rock on a gigantic scale has been discharged at intervals since the beginning of geologic time from deep fissures in the earth's crust to form enormous plateaus several thousand feet in thickness. The basalt plateau of the Columbia river valley is 200,000 square miles in extent and, as shown by the deep canyons of the Columbia and Snake rivers, the black basaltic lava is in places nearly 4000 feet thick. The purpose of this chapter is to study the evidence for the crustal and molten rock movements, their relation to the internal structure of the earth, and their effect on the development of the present outer structure of our planet.

EVIDENCE OF DIASTROPHIC MOVEMENTS

For purposes of discussion, the evidence for diastrophic movements may be considered under two headings. The first will include the type of evidence which is not difficult to discern; the second will deal with evidence requiring prolonged examination

Fig. 8–1 *Evidence of diastrophism.*

of the structure of rocks, the study of which often calls for considerable preparation and training.

Everyone can see earthquakes and recent changes of sea level. Though supposed by most people to be rare, earthquakes are very common. A major earthquake is always front-page news, for it is destructive to the life and the works of man. In the great earthquake of 1923 in Japan, 142,000 people were killed and an equal number injured. Aside from the earthquakes that are reported in the newspapers, many thousands of minor shocks are recorded yearly by seismographs. These periodic tremors are evidence that the "solid" earth is not stable but is continuously undergoing crustal adjustments. During many earthquakes there are often readily discernible horizontal displacements on the surface of the ground. For example, in the destructive San Francisco earthquake of 1906 there was abrupt offsetting of roads and fences along a huge fracture about 270 miles long which developed as a result of the crustal movement.

Evidence of recent changes of sea level is also not very difficult to find. There are many old beaches, wave-built terraces, and wave-cut cliffs found inland far above the present level of the water. In the northeast part of the Great Lakes district there are many places where the obvious shorelines are several hundred feet above the present water level. This shows that the Great Lakes in recent geological history began to tilt in a southwesterly direction. The tilting is assumed to have begun at the end of the last glaciation. Accurate measurements indicate that the area north of the Great Lakes is rising and that the Chicago area has tilted nine inches in the past one hundred years. Other evidence of subsidence of land is furnished by valleys encroached upon by the sea, such as that of the Hudson River. But the most conclusive evidence for changes of level, needing no expert interpreter, consists of shells of marine animals or ripple marks on hills found far inland. For example, Figure 8–1 presents a photograph taken several miles from Baraboo, Wisconsin. The natives called this rock formation "washboard factory," since the sedimentary rock has the appearance of corrugated washboards. The corrugations, now standing vertically, are unmistakable ripple marks; shells of marine animals are found embedded in the rock. It is obvious that this region was once the bottom of a shallow sea which was slowly elevated. After elevation, these strata were tilted by a later disturbance to an angle of about 90°.

EVIDENCE FROM STUDY OF ROCK STRUCTURES

The evidence of disturbance in the structure of the rocks beneath the surface requires studies by geologists. Such studies deal mostly with the structural features which are acquired by rocks as a result of crustal movements: (*a*) folds, (*b*) faults, (*c*) unconformities, and (*d*) metamorphism.

The structure of rocks, particularly those of sedimentary origin, reveals in some places at the surface evidence of past crustal movements. Sedimentary beds which were originally laid with parallel strata are

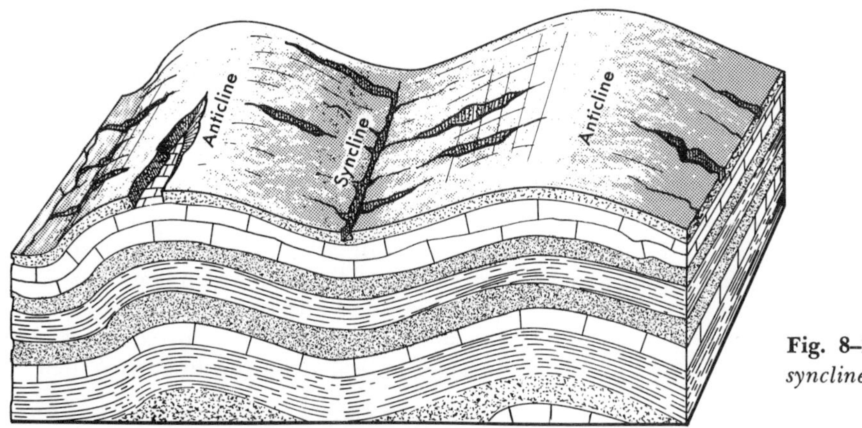

Fig. 8–2 *Diagram of a syncline and anticline.*

found buckled into *folds.* Where the beds are arched up, as in an upfold, they are called *anticlines.* Corresponding to these crests are downfolds in the form of troughs called *synclines.* In some places the arches and troughs of the rocks are only a few feet across and are therefore easily discernible, but in most regions the folds are of very large dimensions and so complex that only a geologist can decipher the structure. The bending of brittle rocks may at first sight appear as abnormal behavior. It should be realized, however, that the bending did not take place in a few hours, but slowly over long periods of time at depths where the pressure of the overlying strata prevented the folds from breaking.

The small folds shown in Figures 8–3 and 8–4 are not typical or very common. Erosion and subsequent movement make the study of the structure of a particular region especially difficult. Although originally synclines formed valleys and anticlines ridges, erosion eventually reduces both to a peneplain. Yet the folded structure of the syncline and anticline persists to a considerable depth below this nearly level surface. Erosion commonly reverses the original structure, producing a valley by cutting into anticlinal beds. The methods used in the study of rock structures are beyond the scope of this text.

Although the dimension of folds may vary from a few feet to a few miles, there are huge warps in the continents which extend for hundreds of miles. The great continental downwarps, or *geosynclines,* as they are called, serve as the basins of deposition for eroded material and later may become the seat of crustal movements. A study of great mountain chains extending for hundreds of miles shows folded sedimentary strata of sandstones, conglomerates, shales, and limestones, indicating that these have been laid down in great troughs of deposition. As the sediments are eroded from the high portions of the continent, the transported material is deposited in shallow sea basins covering the geosynclines. As the material accumulates, the basin sinks with

Fig. 8–3 *Sedimentary beds forming an anticline. Maryland. (U.S. Geological Survey)*

Fig. 8–4 *Sedimentary beds forming a syncline. Tennessee. (U.S. Geological Survey)*

slow downwarping. The sediments may be only a few hundred feet deep, but the bottom of the geosyncline sinks, not chiefly because of the weight of the sediments, but because the basin is already an area of weakness. During crustal movements of the strata the geosyncline may be folded into mountains. This topic is discussed in greater detail in another section of this chapter.

FAULTS

Besides folding, there is another type of rock structure that indicates crustal movements. The surface of rocks is not continuous but is interrupted in many directions by fractures or by breaks called *joints.* These fractures are caused chiefly during broad upwarps and downwarps by the unequal hardness and elasticity of the rocks. When the rock on one side of the fracture moves with respect to the other, the fracture is known as a *fault.* The fracture may be very narrow, so that later it may close; or it may widen and rock debris may fall into it, thus obscuring the relation of the two rock masses. The surface of the fracture along which the movement has taken place is called the *fault plane;* this may be vertical, horizontal, or inclined in any intermediate position. In an inclined fault, the side that overhangs is the *hanging wall* and the side beneath is the *foot wall.* Faults are classified according to the relative displacement of the two sides. In the *normal fault* (Figure 8–6), the hanging wall has gone down with relation to the foot wall, and an elongation of surface results. This is shown in the diagram by line *ac.* Faults of this type result from tension. If in a fault the hanging wall appears to have gone up over the foot wall, it is called a *thrust* (or *reverse*) *fault.* As is shown in Figure 8–7, a thrust fault results from compression, and the movement produces shortening of the surface, indicated by the line *bc.* When a

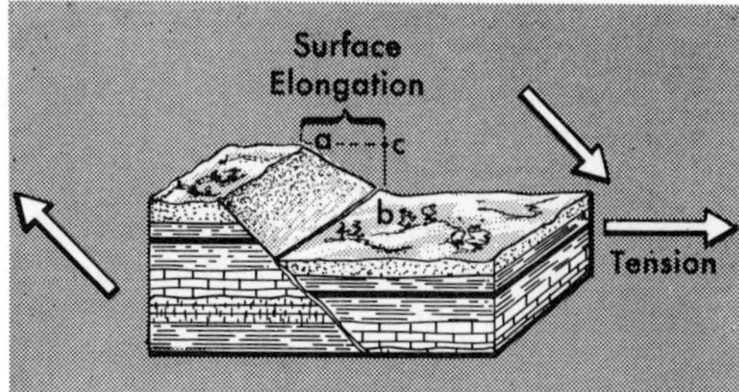

Fig. 8–6 *Diagram of a normal or tension fault.*

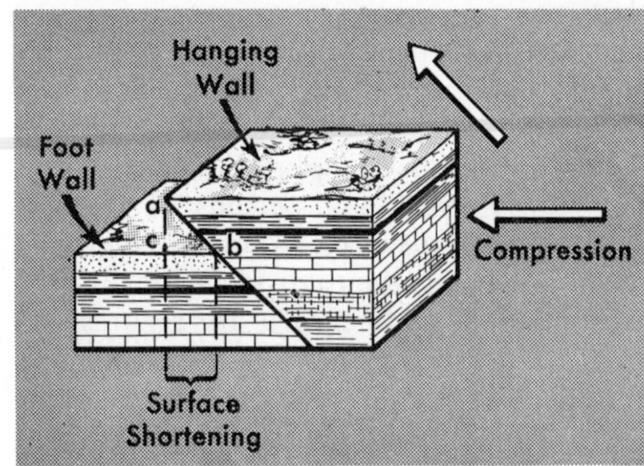

Fig. 8–7 *Diagram of a thrust fault.*

Fig. 8–5 *Small fault in sandstone.* (*U.S. Geological Survey*)

Fig. 8–8 *Eastern slope of the Sierra Nevada, California, an example of a relatively recent fault scarp.* (*Josef Muench*)

fault elevates one side of a rock with relation to the other so that a cliff is formed; this cliff is called a *fault scarp*. Many of our mountain systems have been built up through complex folding and faulting.

Many examples of fault scarps can be traced in the western United States where large crustal movements have occurred in recent geological history. The difficulties are, of course, that as soon as a fault scarp begins to form it is subjected to erosion and becomes altered and may even be entirely peneplained and disappear. The east slope of the Sierra Nevada and the west slopes of the Wasatch Mountains, however, are examples of relatively recent fault scarps.

UNCONFORMITIES

Let us suppose that in a shallow sea where there was an abundance of lime-secreting organisms, limestone was deposited. The region slowly rose as streams brought in eroded debris, and the sediment became mostly mud, which ultimately changed to shale. The sea became more shallow, the sediment changed to sand, and sandstones were formed. Deposition ceased as the area rose above sea level. The sandstone, shale, and limestone beds are *conformable;* that is, they have been deposited continuously with no break in the orderly sequence of deposition. Then came further uplift, erosion took place, and most of the sandstone was removed. Now if the region were again submerged, and other sedimentary beds were deposited, the latter series of rocks would be *unconformable* with the first. There would be a break in the sequence of deposition, a break represented by the eroded sandstone formation. The plane of contact between the two series of

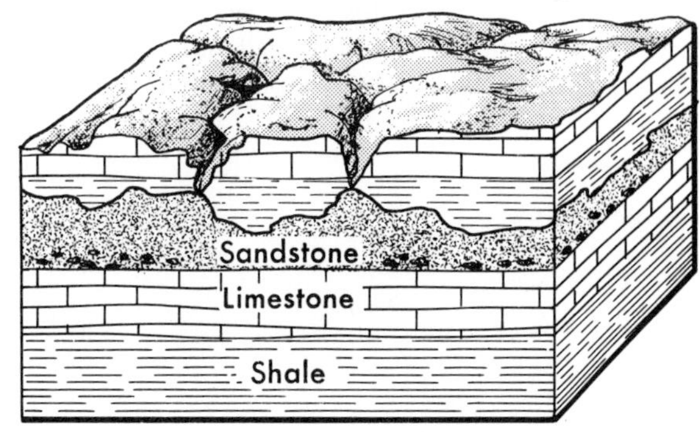

Fig. 8–9 *Diagram of erosional unconformity.*

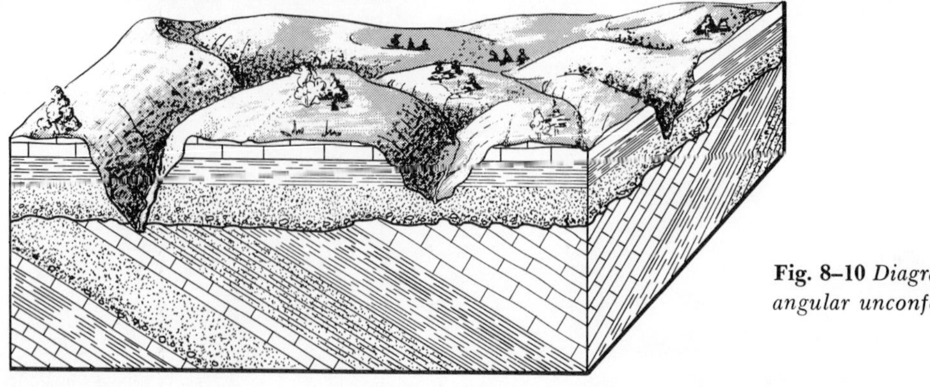

Fig. 8–10 *Diagram of an angular unconformity.*

beds would be a *plane of unconformity.* Such a "break" in the strata, recording an ancient period of erosion, is important in geological history. If there is no folding below the "break," that is, if the beds above and below the plane of unconformity have the same inclination, it is called a *disconformity.* If the beds in the lower series were folded or tilted and then deeply eroded or peneplained before the other series were deposited, it is called an *angular unconformity.*

Unconformities are important records in attempting to reconstruct the probable past history of a particular region. For example, the angular unconformity represented in the diagram of Figure 8–10 indicates large crustal disturbances and a long period of erosion. The lower beds of limestones, sandstones, and shales form an angle with the younger upper horizontal beds. This indicates that the lower beds were first deposited as a horizontal series. Then they were uplifted and tilted. The mountains which were formed from these tilted beds were afterwards exposed to a long period of erosion until the folds were worn down to a low relief, then submerged, and new sedimentary beds were deposited. After this sedimentation the region was lifted above the sea level and erosion has set in anew, carving the present valleys.

EVIDENCE FROM METAMORPHISM OF ROCKS

The formation of metamorphic rocks (page 71) from both igneous and sedimentary furnishes an extensive record of past crustal movements. The formation of slates and schists from shales, of quartzites from sandstones, and of gneisses from igneous rocks shows that great pressures and temperatures were involved in such extensive metamorphosis of the rock strata. In many places the crystals are rotated so that the long axis is in the direction of the least pressure; the general direction of the crustal movement is at right angles to the long axes of these minerals.

The general trend underlying all metamorphic changes is adjustment to the environment; that is, metamorphic changes produce those rocks that are most stable under the pressure and temperatures developed by crustal movements. It should be noted here that radioactive changes in the

Fig. 8–11 *Unconformity in rock strata. Northeast of Socorro, New Mexico. (U.S. Geological Survey)*

Fig. 8–12 *Metamorphic rock showing effect of pressure, folded and contorted limestone. Mineral Ridge, north of Silver Peak, Nevada.* *(U.S. Geological Survey)*

rocks are partly responsible for the high temperatures existing in deeply buried rock strata. During metamorphic changes rearrangement of crystals occurs and new minerals may be produced by chemical reactions. The rearrangement of minerals will be toward denser materials, enabling them to occupy less volume; crystals are rotated so that the long axis is in the direction of the least pressure. In the metamorphism of a shale to slates or schists, abundant mica flakes are commonly formed, all oriented in the same direction, causing these rocks to split readily along planes parallel to the arrangement of the mica flakes. Bonded arrangements of coarse crystals produce schists and gneisses.

EARTHQUAKES

The relation of earthquakes to diastrophism was given at the beginning of this chapter, where it was stated that earthquakes are one of the effects of diastrophic movements. The term *earthquake* is applied to all movements that produce shaking or trembling of the ground. The terror and destruction that earthquakes have brought to man have resulted in careful study of the regions most affected by earth tremors and in the development of methods for detecting and predicting them. This scientific study of earthquakes is called *seismology*.

Most earthquakes occur along belts where there has been recent mountain building or where the work of gradation makes adjustment necessary. The sudden yielding to stress in the earth's crust by the abrupt displacement along the walls of existing faults or by the formation of new fractures furnishes the impulse. Hard rocks are to a certain extent compressible and elastic, and the force of the movement of the fault is transmitted as vibrations or waves into the surrounding parts of the earth. In California a great fault zone (known as the San Andreas fault and responsible for most of the earthquakes in that region) can be traced for several hundred miles from north to south.

In areas where there are volcanic eruptions earthquakes may be caused by the shifting of molten matter deep within the earth. Then, too, the collapse of the roof of a cave or an extensive landslide may produce minor tremors. Most earthquakes, however, are not caused by such events.

Earthquakes are exceedingly common. Some thirty thousand occur each year, but most of the shocks are very slight. Earthquakes that cause considerable loss of life and property occur not more than once or twice a year. The loss of life is often due to sudden high sea waves caused by sudden movement along the fault. In the earthquake which destroyed Lisbon on November 1, 1755, sixty thousand people were killed. The greatest part of this destruction was due to waves sixty feet high that rushed in an hour after the quake. Huge waves accompanied the earthquake of 1923 in Japan. The disastrous effect of earthquakes is due chiefly to the suddenness of the vibrations, rather than to the amplitude of the vibrations. A sudden shock with an amplitude of one-eighth of an inch will shatter a chimney. At the *epicenter,* which is the location on the surface above the subterranean place of origin of the disturbance, bodies are projected upwards.

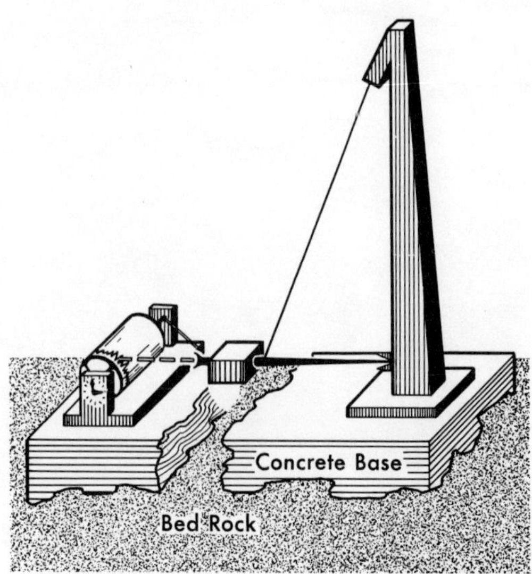

Fig. 8–13 *Diagrammatic sketch of a seismograph.*

STUDY OF EARTHQUAKES

When a quake occurs, elastic waves in the surrounding rocks radiate in all directions. When they reach the surface of the earth, they set up additional vibrations which, locally, are often quite destructive. The elastic waves are sorted out according to their speed, as determined by an instrument called a *seismograph.* This is essentially a pendulum with a long period. A heavy mass of metal is suspended like a horizontal pendulum. The base of the instrument is mounted on solid rock. The suspended mass of the pendulum remains essentially stationary when the ground oscillates. The vibrations are magnified by means of a lever, and are recorded on the paper strip of a revolving drum, which is driven by clockwork. Such a record is known as a *seismogram.* In general, three sets of waves are recorded by the instrument, for as the waves travel out from the center of disturbance they become separated into three more or less distinct sets. Each set proceeds at varying speed, depending upon the density and elasticity of the rocks, as follows:

1. *Primary Waves:* These are longitudinal (compression-expansion) waves, and travel at an average speed of about six miles per second. The speed varies with the depth; for example, at a depth of 1800 miles the speed rises to 8.5 miles per second, and in rocks near the surface the speed falls to about three miles per second. Primary waves arise from compressions of the rock at the center of disturbance, and are similar to sound waves. They travel through solids or liquids.

2. *Secondary Waves:* These are transverse waves, and travel at an average speed of about four miles per second; hence they lag behind the primary waves. The secondary waves do not travel through liquids. Both the primary and the secondary waves travel along the chords of arcs beneath the surface of the earth, and are called *body waves.*

3. *Surface Waves:* These waves travel slowest of all – about two miles a second – and move along near the surface of the earth. They are largely transverse, and are set up when the body waves reach the surface of the earth.

Between the successive waves there is a

time lag which varies with the distance between the earthquake center and the seismograph observatory. By means of curves called *time-distance graphs* it is possible to tell how far away the earthquake originated. Three observatories acting together are able to locate the center very accurately. As the earthquake waves are recorded at various stations, the distance to the center of the disturbance can be calculated. The distance from each station is laid out as a radius, and a circle is drawn to scale on a map. The three circles thus drawn intersect at the point of disturbance. When earthquakes occur in remote areas, the observatories are often able to publish the location before word arrives from the stricken area.

The propagation of earthquake waves through the earth affords considerable information as to the composition of the earth's interior. This topic is treated at the end of this chapter.

VOLCANISM

The term *volcano* designates an opening or fissure from which gases, molten rock, and solid rock fragments are ejected. The term is usually associated with a steep cone having an opening at the top called a *crater,* but a number of volcanoes are known without the cone structure. The term *volcanism,* however, includes all movements of molten rock and the phenomena that are associated with these movements. Studies of the igneous rocks of the crust, both at the surface and at some depth, indicate that molten rock, called *magma,* rises along fissures from depths of thirty to forty miles toward the surface. There are two phases in the movements of magma. In one, it fails to reach the surface and solidifies underground, forming igneous rocks which when later exposed by erosion are called *intrusions.* In the other phase, the mobile magma rises along fissures, flows over the surface, and solidifies, forming igneous rocks called *extrusions* (lava flows). All rocks of volcanic origin are called *igneous.*

ERUPTIONS

The nature of volcanic activity, or eruptions, depends on the nature of the ejected materials. The eruption of a volcano may lead to a quiet flow of molten rock called *lava,* or may be explosive, giving off large quantities of gases, ash, and cinders, with little or no flow of liquid rock; still other eruptions include the ejection of rock material and of gases, ash, and cinders also. The fluidity of the magma and the amount of gases in it determine the type of eruption.

The lava coming up to the surface may flow from fissures and cover large areas without building the characteristic cone of volcanoes. In the fissure type of eruption, it may flow from one or more long, deep cracks. In Iceland, one fissure is nineteen miles long and in many places four hundred to six hundred feet deep. As noted on page 103, huge basaltic flows cover parts of Idaho, Washington, and Oregon – a total area of about 200,000 square miles. Similar basaltic flows of great thickness covering large areas are found in Brazil, Argentina, and India. The outpouring of lava through fissures proceeds quietly. As the flow con-

Fig. 8–14. *A seismograph with a seismogram. (Fordham University Seismic Observatory)*

tinues, the lava slowly solidifies on the sides of the fissure, and in time the passage to the surface closes.

TYPES OF VOLCANIC ACTIVITY

The eruption of some volcanoes is often preceded and accompanied by earthquakes and rumblings of the ground; these rumblings and the explosive eruptions are due to the gases held under pressure in the rising magma. In the eruption on the island of Tamboro Sumbawa in the Dutch East Indies in 1815, the rumblings were heard over an area of about a thousand miles. In the explosion, the surface of the vent is blown up as dust and ashes, leaving a pit which marks the site of the wrecked cone. In the explosion of Tamboro, which is the greatest recorded in history, about thirty-five cubic miles of material were blown into the air and fell on an area of a million square miles. The pit formed by this explosion is nearly four miles in diameter. In other volcanic eruptions the outpouring of lava proceeds after initial explosions which release the gases under pressure, accompanied by smaller periodic explosions which send fragmental materials upward. The solid fragments vary in size from fine dust to large masses of rock; part of these are derived from the solid walls of the volcanic channel, others from the liquid rock which is thrown upward in great bulks by the escaping gases and solidifies in its flight through the air. Between the two types of eruptions – the quiet type, which emits fluid lava, and the violent explosive type, which ejects mostly ashes and great amounts of gases – there are intermediate phases of volcanic activity.

The volcanoes of Hawaii illustrate the first type of activity. The island has been built by basaltic flows from the bottom of the ocean three miles below sea level. Hence these islands are the largest volcanoes on the face of the earth. Mauna Loa rises 13,700 feet and Kilauea 4000 feet above sea level. The crater of Kilauea, called Halemaumau (Everlasting House of Fire), was 1300 feet in diameter prior to 1924 and contained a lake of basaltic lava, kept constantly boiling by the escaping hot gases. The temperature of the lava ranges from 1000° to 1200° C. In 1924 the column of lava dropped about seven hundred feet in the pit, and this fall was followed by explosions which sent vast clouds of gases and rock debris more than 8000 feet into the sky. The pit was enlarged to 3000 feet across. No explosive eruptions had occurred for 134 years up to 1924, and it is thought that sudden penetration of water into the hot rocks generated the superheated steam which caused the explosions.

Violent explosive activity is illustrated by the eruption of Tamboro mentioned above and the explosion of Mont Pelee on Martinique, an island of the West Indies. The most catastrophic eruption of Mont Pelee occurred on May 8, 1902, when after a week of little activity it blew out a great cloud of superheated steam, laden with hot dust, which rolled down from the mountain toward the sea, killing the 28,000 inhabitants of the city of Saint Pierre, which was situated six miles from the volcano. No lava was ejected in this eruption.

The intermediate phases of volcanic activity are illustrated by the volcanoes of the Mediterranean region. On Lipari Island near Sicily, the lava of the volcano is viscous, and crusts solidify in the vent until gas pressure accumulates sufficiently to explode. Lipari erupts mostly fragmental material. Not far away the volcano of the island of Stromboli erupts with successive mild explosions. Active from antiquity, its visibility at night has given it the name of "the lighthouse of the Mediterranean." Its eruptions consist in the upward ejection of molten lava, which falls mainly back into the crater, and the expulsion of clouds of glowing gases. Vesuvius, the best-known volcano in history, is situated above Naples. Prior to A.D. 79,[1] there had been no record

[1] Strictly speaking, it was not Vesuvius that exploded in A.D. 79 but a greater volcano, Monte Somma. Its top was blown off and a new volcano, Vesuvius, was built inside the remnants of Monte Somma.

of any eruption, although the Romans had recognized the site as a volcanic region. In A.D. 79 a violent eruption blew off the upper part of the cone, sending out vast quantities of cinders and ashes which buried the cities of Herculaneum, Pompeii, and Stabiae. There was no lava flow. The eruption is graphically described by Pliny the Younger in a letter to Tacitus. Minor eruptions occurred between A.D. 79 and 1538; in the latter year a hill of 440 feet arose across the bay during a week's activity. Eighteen thousand persons were killed in an eruption in 1631. The last great eruption was in 1906, during which lava and tremendous amounts of gases and ash were emitted. Since that time its only activity has consisted in sending up clouds of steam.

In the United States there are many sites of recently active volcanoes. The flow of lava from a volcano near Grants, New Mexico, is still to be seen, in the form of black frozen rivers along the road leading to Albuquerque. The only active volcano in the United States, Mount Lassen in northern California, had a small eruption in 1914. Its present activity is confined to mud geysers. This illustrates the life cycle of a volcano. At first there is considerable activity; a cone is built and intermittently changed. Finally the volcanic activity diminishes, the vent closes, and the solidified material below slowly cools. During this last phase, water percolating below becomes heated and gives rise to hot springs, geysers, and *fumaroles* (vents from which gases escape). Mounts Rainier, Hood, Baker, and Shasta, and Crater Lake form a chain of recently active volcanoes in the same general area.

By successive eruptions volcanoes build structures which usually have a conical shape. If the ejected material consists mostly of cinders, the cone is steep; if a considerable amount of lava is emitted, as from the volcanoes of Hawaii, a plateau structure with gentle slopes is built up. A succession of lava flows and cinders produces composite cones with symmetrical walls. Mayon volcano in the Philippine Islands is considered one of the best examples of a composite cone.

Fig. 8–15 *Eruption of Mt. Vesuvius.* (*Official U.S. Navy Photograph*)

PRODUCTS OF ERUPTIONS

The chief products of volcanic eruptions are gases, fragmental material, and lava. The composition of gases varies with various volcanoes and probably with various stages of eruption. The greater part is steam. Sulfur gases are abundant in the Mediterranean volcanoes, while those of Alaska contain hydrochloric and hydrofluoric acids; ammonia, carbon dioxide, carbon monoxide, and other gases have been found to be emitted from volcanic vents. It will be noted that a number of these gases are poisonous.

Fragmental material thrown up from volcanoes originates either from the sides of the vent or from ejected lava. As the magma nears the surface, the pressure is released, and the expanding gas carries with it lumps of viscous molten rock which so-

Fig. 8–16 *Scoria. Grants, New Mexico.*

lidify rapidly as they sail upward through the air. If the mass is large, it falls back either in the crater or on the sides of the cone; depending on its size, it is called a *bomb, ashes,* or *cinders.* If the size of the particle is very small, the result is *volcanic dust* or *ash,* which is carried to great heights and to great distances. Ash from some explosions has circled the earth. Deposits of volcanic dust of several hundred feet in thickness and covering many square miles are known.

Lava has a variable composition. A preponderance of ferromagnesian minerals gives black *basaltic* lavas. An excess of silica gives light *felsite* lavas which on cooling may result in either rhyolite or andesite rocks, depending on the amount of quartz present. Most oceanic volcanoes emit basaltic lavas. All the great fissure eruptions are of basaltic lava. The fluidity depends on many factors, especially composition and temperature. Lava within the crater has a temperature between 1200° and 1500° C., and as it issues from the crater it is still red-hot. As it flows it begins to cool. The crystallization and texture depend on the rate of cooling, the composition, and the amount of gases that it contains. Many solidified lavas have numerous pores formerly occupied by the gases. If the pores are so abundant that the rock has a spongy structure it is called volcanic *scoria.* The upper part of some lavas, particularly those which contain large amounts of silica and are viscous, may form a froth-like rock owing to the escaping gases. Such rock is called *pumice,* and it will float in water for some time.

PRODUCTS OF VOLCANIC INTRUSIONS

When magma solidifies without reaching the surface of the earth it gives rise to igneous rocks which are named according to their shape and their relation to the surrounding rocks. These intrusions may later be exposed at the surface of the earth as a result of removal of the overlying rocks by erosion. Intrusions of huge dimensions enlarging downward to unknown depths are called *batholiths* (deep rocks). The cores of many mountain ranges are made up of

Fig. 8–17 *Diagram of volcanic intrusions.*

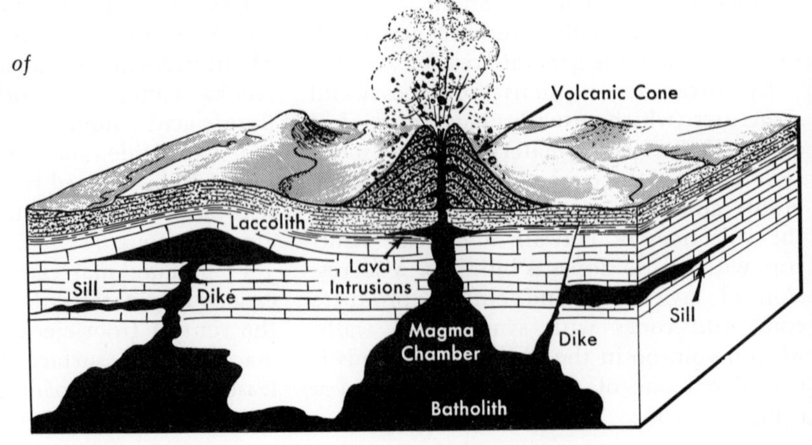

immense batholiths, indicating that these gigantic intrusions occurred during or shortly after large crustal movements. A conception of the dimensions of batholiths may be obtained from the exposed surface of the batholith in central Idaho which covers an area of 16,000 square miles. The rocks of most batholiths are coarse-grained granites.

Magma may work its way between cracks and fissures of pre-existing rocks, usually sedimentary. If the crack cuts across the vertical layers, the solidified intrusion is called a *dike;* if the fissure is parallel to the layers of the sedimentary rock, the solidified intrusion is called a *sill.* Lava may produce an arch by pushing upwards the overlying strata; then the intrusive mass is called a *laccolith* or cistern rock. Figure 8–17 shows diagrammatically the various types of intrusions.

Dikes and sills are common. The best-known sill in America is the Palisade sill on the west side of the Hudson River in New Jersey. Networks of dikes are found in many places (particularly in folded strata), varying in thickness from layers of thousands of feet to seams of a fraction of an inch. Both sills and dikes show baked zones in the layers of rocks which they intrude. Many metallic compounds are deposited in these contact zones. Ninety per cent of the world's nickel comes from a sill in Sudbury, Ontario; gold and silver are mined from such intrusions in Cobalt, Ontario. Similarly, gold is found in many districts of Colorado in dikes.

As mentioned in the section dealing with the deposition effected by ground water (page 84), many mineral vein deposits are thought to have been formed by magmatic waters associated with igneous intrusions.

INTRUSIVE AND EXTRUSIVE ROCKS

The mode of formation of igneous rocks was briefly discussed in Chapter 6. It was stated that the color and texture of a rock depend on its chemical composition and on the geologic environment in which the rock was formed. Rocks formed as a result of a volcanic eruption differ markedly in appearance from the rocks formed by solidification of magma at great depths. The chief differences are in the size, shape, and

Fig. 8–18 *A dike in a coal mine, Pope County, Illinois.* *(Illinois State Geological Survey)*

Fig. 8–19 *Igneous rocks. (top) Felsite, Hyde Park, Massachusetts. (center) Syenite (hornblende), Cuttingsville, Vermont. (bottom) Rhyolite, Deadwood, South Dakota.*

arrangement of the individual crystals of the minerals which make up the rock; these characteristics, which are summed up by the term *texture*, are to a large extent determined by the rate of cooling of the liquid rock. It is evident that the solidification of lavas at or near the surface of the earth will take place at a much faster rate than the solidification of magma at great depths, where it is insulated by the large amount of surrounding rock.

Granite and rhyolite rocks do not differ greatly in chemical composition. Both contain about the same amounts of quartz, feldspars, and ferromagnesians; although individual samples may differ widely, it is possible to find a specimen of granite and a specimen of rhyolite with little chemical difference. But physical examination of two such rock specimens will disclose some important differences. In the granite, even by a superficial examination, it is possible to distinguish large individual crystals of black mica (biotite), but these are not apparent in the rhyolite specimen. Examination of a thin section of granite through a microscope shows that its black mica and its feldspars have well-defined crystal faces, but its quartz crystals have few or no crystal faces well developed, and these seem to be crowded in between the crystals of black mica and feldspar. From these observations we can infer that, in the formation of granite, quartz was the last mineral to crystallize out, and that mica crystallized out first, followed by feldspar. Since the crystals in granite are large as compared with those in rhyolite, we can infer that the cooling was very slow and that the individual crystals had sufficient time to grow to large size. On the other hand, the cooling of lava that resulted in rhyolite rocks was relatively rapid; a large number of crystals began to form simultaneously, and only few crystals had sufficient time to grow; and hence most of the crystals grew to small size, forming a fine-grained rock.

By the use of the reasoning illustrated in the preceding paragraph it is possible to reconstruct the probable mode of formation of the various types of igneous rocks.

RECONSTRUCTING THE FORMATION OF IGNEOUS ROCKS

First, of course, we divide the rocks on the basis of their appearance into coarse-grained, fine-grained, and glassy; the latter do not have discernible crystals, but appear as homogeneous solids similar to glass. A number of rocks with large conspicuous crystals imbedded in a mass of very small crystals, called *porphyries* (see Figure 6–8, page 69), can be considered intermediate between the coarse and the fine-grained.

A large mass of magma which moves toward the surface along fissures and cracks heats and ultimately melts part of the solid rocks with which it comes in contact; these rocks may be sedimentary, metamorphic, or igneous in origin. Thus, in its upward movement, the chemical composition of the magma is changing, with new chemical reactions taking place and new minerals being formed. If the upward movement of the magma becomes slow as a result of loss of heat and consequent loss of fluidity, a point may be reached where crystallization begins long before the magma has found its way to the surface. The resulting intrusions may be batholiths, dikes, sills, or laccoliths. The type of intrusive rocks formed depends largely on the chemical composition of the magma, and to some extent on the pressure. If the amount of metallic oxides present in the magma combine with silicon dioxide to form ferromagnesian minerals and feldspars and there remains an excess of silicon dioxide, the rock will be a granite. As outlined in the preceding paragraph the ferromagnesian minerals, biotite or hornblende, separate out first, followed by the feldspar; lastly the excess or uncombined silicon dioxide crystallizes out as quartz; filling the spaces which are left by the crystals of the other minerals. If the chemical composition of the magma is such that there is no excess of silicon dioxide but an abundance of feldspar and less ferromagnesian, the resulting rock is *diorite.* And finally if the ferromagnesians predominate over the feldspars, the resulting rock is a coarse-grained dark rock called *gabbro.*

When the magma rises to the surface and pours out from a volcano as a lava flow, the extrusive rocks are mainly either fine-grained or glassy. If the composition of the magma is highly silicic, as is true of granites, the extrusive rock is *rhyolite;* if the composition is intermediate, as in the case of diorite, the rock is *andesite;* and if the ferromagnesian minerals predominate, the dark rock is called *basalt.* In a lava flow the conditions of crystallization are not uniform.

In the beginning, while the mass is very hot and fluid, some individual crystals of minerals may develop to a size that can be detected by the eyes, until the cooling is very rapid and the whole mass crystallizes out into minute crystals. Therefore some rhyolites may contain well-defined crystals of biotite, feldspar, and quartz set in a mass of fine crystals, whereas another specimen may consist entirely of such minute crystals that they cannot be distinguished by the unaided eye. When this is so, it is very difficult to tell a rhyolite from an andesite, and such rocks are usually called *felsites.*

In magmas that reach the surface the crystallization of minerals may begin at depth. A rock thus formed will show in its texture the changed conditions of crystallization. In an environment which permits slow cooling, large crystals will be formed, in contrast to the minute crystals formed at the surface. These are porphyritic rocks. A granite porphyry consists of well-defined crystals of biotite, feldspar, and quartz set in a mass of very fine crystals similar to those found in rhyolites. When the rate of cooling of a lava flow is very rapid and there is an absence of gases within the liquid rock, solidification in a glasslike homogeneous mass results. If the volcanic glass is brilliant, it is called *obsidian;* and if dull, *pitchstone.* Finally, among the rocks formed by igneous activity are classed those which are formed by compression and cementation of the fragmental material ejected in volcanic eruptions. Rocks from coarse fragmental materials are known as *volcanic breccia,* and those from finer materials are known as *tuff.*

VOLCANIC ZONES

From the foregoing discussion, we may conclude that volcanism has existed ever since the earth took shape, and that the rise of magma has occurred many times in different parts of the earth. The present active volcanoes, which number about four hundred, are mostly of recent origin; a very large number of volcanic cones are extinct. The distribution of the active volcanoes follows remarkably the earthquake zones and the zone of the most recent rugged mountains. One zone is along the margins of the Pacific Ocean basin, forming the famous "belt of fire," from the tip of South America to Alaska, from Alaska to Japan, from Japan to the Philippines. The other zone (the Mediterranean) extends east and west from Central America through the West Indies to the Azores, the Canary Islands, and the Mediterranean; and from the Mediterranean through Asia Minor and Persia to the East Indies, where it crosses the Pacific belt which includes the Hawaiian volcanoes. The distribution of volcanoes and young mountains along the same zone points to some relation between the two. The inference is drawn that since mountains, as discussed in the following section, are produced by extensive folding and faulting (fracturing), the folded zones develop fissures clear through the solid crust of the earth. Through these fissures the magma rises, causing the volcanic eruption and producing intrusions or extrusions. The question, however, remains as to the source and upward movement of the magma. An answer involves an elementary discussion of the composition of the crust and of the interior of the earth.

THE PROBLEM OF THE EARTH'S COMPOSITION

We have spoken repeatedly about the composition of the outer part of the earth. The composition of the outer ten miles of the lithosphere is considered to be fairly well known from the boring of wells which have gone to a depth of more than four miles and from the work of erosion which has laid bare rocks that were once buried five to ten miles or even more. The approximate composition is given in Table 8–1.

TABLE 8–1 COMPOSITION OF OUTER TEN MILES OF LITHOSPHERE

Igneous rocks	95.0%
Shales	4.0%
Sandstones	0.75%
Limestones	0.24%
All other deposits nearly	0.01%

This table shows that the igneous rocks are by far the most abundant and that man's most prized materials – soil, salt, coal, and others – are quantitatively insignificant.

The composition of the interior, however, is not known by accumulation of observable facts since we have no means of observing the nature and structure of the inner parts of the lithosphere. If we consider that the earth's radius is about four thousand miles and that man has penetrated scarcely more than two miles under the surface, we realize that we know directly less than one-thousandth of one per cent of the volume of the lithosphere. The problem becomes difficult when we consider that there is evidence indicating that the interior is different from the outer rocks. For example, the average density of the rocks that come under our observation is about 2.79, whereas the density of the earth as a whole is 5.52; obviously we should assume that the material of the deep interior must be of much greater density than that of the outer part, much greater than 5.52, in fact.

In order to explain available facts it is the accepted mode of procedure in science to propose an hypothesis; in some cases, like the present, the hypothesis cannot be tested experimentally or by direct observations. Any hypothesis concerning the interior of the earth will always be a speculative one. But the scientific method demands that even a speculative hypothesis should account in a satisfactory manner for all the available facts. This, then, becomes the criterion in choosing among several speculative hypotheses advanced to explain a particular set of facts. In the present problem, the easiest explanation fails to satisfy this criterion; this is to assume that the earth was once a molten mass, and that by cooling it formed slowly an outer solid crust; and since it is liquid in the interior and loses heat by radiation, we could reasonably assume further that the crust shrinks and develops cracks through which the hot liquid rock of the interior is squeezed to the surface, furnishing spectacular evidence of the molten condition of the earth in the past. Though this assumption seems at first sight to fit with the known facts about volcanoes, it fails to account for a number of other facts. Before giving the hypothesis as to the composition of the earth that is at present considered most acceptable, it will be useful to enumerate the facts that any such hypothesis should be able to explain. This list need not be memorized; it is presented merely for reference and to throw light on our subsequent discussion.

1. *Density.* The average density of the rocks found in the outer ten miles is 2.8 to 3.3 g/ml, but the average density of the earth as a whole is 5.52, definitely indicating a heavier core within.

2. *Temperatures in the Interior of the Earth.* Hot lavas are constantly ejected from volcanoes. The magma comes up from below, from a depth of about 40 miles. The average temperature of lava is 1000° to 1200° C. Most of the lavas are basaltic.

Deep holes bored in various parts of the world show an increase of temperature with depth. The deepest are about 4 miles or 6.5 kilometers in depth. The average increase in temperature is 1° C. for every thirty meters (1° F. for every sixty feet). The temperature in a California well 16,000 feet deep was recorded as 400° F. Hence, at a depth of a hundred kilometers (sixty miles) the temperature will be over 3000° C., assuming the above rate of change of temperature with depth. This temperature is far above the melting point of the rocks. The presence of radioactive elements in rocks, particularly in granites, has been mentioned. Radioactive disintegration (page 351) liberates heat; it has been estimated that about half of the heat observed to reach the earth's surface is derived from this source.

3. *Pressure of the Overlying Rocks.* The overlying rocks exert pressure upon the rocks on which they rest. This pressure becomes tremendous with increasing depth. It has been calculated that, at a depth of one mile, each square foot of rock bears a weight of 450 tons; at a depth of a hundred kilometers or 62 miles, the pressure is about 27,000 atmospheres, or 400,000 pounds per square inch. Near the center of the earth pressures amount to nearly four million atmospheres. But even at the depth of 40 to 50 miles the pressures are such that the compressed rock acquires a plastic flow.

4. *Propagation of Seismic Waves.* Evidence from the propagation of earthquake waves through the earth indicates that the composition of the earth changes with increasing depth. The long surface earthquake waves, which travel around the earth beneath the surface rocks at two miles per second, proceed faster in ocean floors. As previously mentioned, the velocities of the primary and secondary seismic waves are determined by the density, compressibility, and rigidity of the rock material through which they pass. The propagation of seismic waves through the outer eighteen hundred miles of the earth is at a speed which increases with depth. This indicates that this part is not fluid, since transverse waves (secondary seismic waves) do not travel through liquids. Further, the increased speed indicates greater rigidity due to the terrific pressure from above. At eighteen hundred miles the secondary waves disappear and there is a sharp bending of the primary waves, indicating a radical change in the composition.

It should be noted that at a depth of about fifty miles below the earth's surface

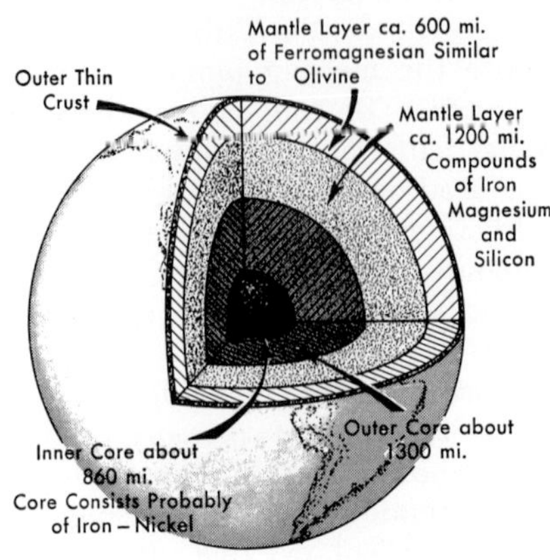

Fig. 8–20 *Diagram showing composition of the earth's interior.*

the velocities of these waves fall off noticeably for about one hundred miles, then the velocity increases again. This is of importance in the discussion of the origin of magma. In other words, it can be assumed that rocks near the melting temperature behave differently as media of propagation for the seismic waves.

5. *Composition of Meteorites.* The composition of the earth must be related to the other matter that exists in the solar system. Although this statement at first sight may seem purely dogmatic, there is evidence that supports it. In the first place, as is shown in Chapter 17, the elements found in the sun are not different from those found on earth. In the second place, the earth is constantly pelted from outer space by small bodies of matter existing in the solar system and related, it is reasonable to assume, to its members. When they enter the earth's atmosphere, these small bodies become heated by friction and become incandescent. They are commonly called shooting stars, and are known scientifically as *meteorites.* Although some meteorites are of stony composition, a large number are composed entirely of nickel and iron, metals which are not common on the earth's surface. The density of the nickel-iron meteorites is comparable to that calculated for the earth's core.

HYPOTHESIS AS TO THE EARTH'S COMPOSITION

Consideration of the facts enumerated in the preceding section shows that a number of them cannot be well accounted for by the molten-interior hypothesis. For example, the transmission of secondary seismic waves through the outer eighteen hundred miles of the sphere is difficult to account for if the interior is fluid, because transverse waves do not travel through liquids. Further, if we assume a fluid interior and then consider the pressure of the overlying rocks, we shall arrive at the conclusion that the pressure will turn the fluid into a solid. For example, lead melts at 327° C., but if a pressure of two thousand atmospheres is applied, lead can be heated to 340° C. and still be solid. The modern conception of the composition of the earth regards it as essentially rigid to the core, with the heaviest material at the center and the lightest near the surface; it quite probably may once have passed through a molten condition. From the evidence of meteorites and the calculated density of the core of the earth, it is inferred that the central part is composed of iron and nickel. This core is assumed to have a radius of nearly two thousand miles. Since the propagation of earthquake waves indicates a change in composition at six hundred and at eighteen hundred miles from the surface, it is reasonable to assume that when the earth was in its molten condition the heavier metallic core settled toward the center and the other materials underwent a similar progressive rearrangement according to density, with the lighter material at the surface. The outer veneer is composed of sedimentary rocks to a depth of one to two miles and in some places five to six miles or more. In many places the sedimentary rocks have been eroded and granitic masses are exposed. The shell from two miles down to about twenty-five miles is essentially granitic. It should be noted that the granitic upper part of this outer shell is missing beneath the ocean basins. Below twenty-five miles (forty to fifty kilometers) the rigidity increases rapidly as the rate of earthquake waves increases up to six hundred miles, and then it changes somewhat until it reaches the core. Therefore it is assumed that the composition changes to basic dense rocks similar to the ferromagnesian olivine. The next twelve hundred miles (from six hundred to eighteen hundred) down to the core within is assumed to be composed of a mixture of iron and magnesium silicates. The core, having a radius of nearly two thousand miles, is assumed to have an outer layer of about thirteen hundred miles and an inner layer of nine hundred miles. The inner layer is assumed to consist of iron and nickel, like most meteorites. This hypothetical composition is shown diagrammatically in Figure 8–20. In the most recent speculation there is a trend to assume that part of the outer layer of the core is essentially fluid because the speed of the secondary seismic waves drops to practically zero at a depth of eighteen hundred miles.

ORIGIN AND MOVEMENT OF MAGMA

From the preceding discussion it follows that diastrophic and volcanic activity are closely related. The temperature increases with depth, partly because of pressure and partly because of the heat liberated by the changes of radioactive minerals. These minerals contain such elements as uranium, radium, and thorium, which undergo spontaneous transformation to other elements and give off heat; these changes are discussed in some detail in Chapter 22. Therefore, the rocks at depth of thirty or forty miles are heated above their melting point, but remain in a solid condition because of pressure from above. It follows that if the pressure is diminished, the rock will often change into magma. The crustal adjustments which result in extensive folds and fractures initiate the formation and rise of magma. Let us assume that as a result of folding and fracturing (faulting) a fissure develops, extending to a depth of thirty to forty miles. The pressure along the fracture naturally diminishes, and consequently the basaltic substratum, which is far above its melting point and kept in the solid state only through the great pressure from above, liquefies. Now, the change of solid rock to fluid magma is accompanied by a slight drop in density. In other words, the liquid magma occupies a greater space, and hence it is lighter than the adjoining rock; therefore it begins to flow upward.

In this manner the magma may work its way up along the fissures and other zones of weakness to form dikes, sills, laccoliths, or batholiths, or it may reach the surface and cause an eruption. Gases accumulate from the chemical changes in the magma, and also when sedimentary rocks along the fissures change on being fluxed (liquefied). For example, limestone, when it becomes fluxed in this manner, breaks up into lime and carbon dioxide, and the latter is held in solution by the magma because of the pressure, in much the same way that a "pop" bottle under pressure holds carbon dioxide in solution. The water vapor which is the chief constituent of the magmatic gases is assumed to originate partly from chemical reactions in the formation of magma and partly from entrapped water. Sometimes the magmatic water vapor may be derived from ground water with which the magma comes in contact near the surface. Depending on the pressure developed by the magmatic gases, the eruption may be quiet or explosive.

THE ROCK CYCLE

The movement of magma performs another function in that it completes the rock cycle. Thus far we have seen that by the various erosion agents all rocks are weathered and that they are transported eventually to a shallow sea and deposited as *sedimentary rocks.* Weathering, erosion, and deposition tend to change all rock to the sedimentary type. But during crustal movements, either igneous or sedimentary rocks which are in the outer veneer of the earth's crust are caught within the folds and are

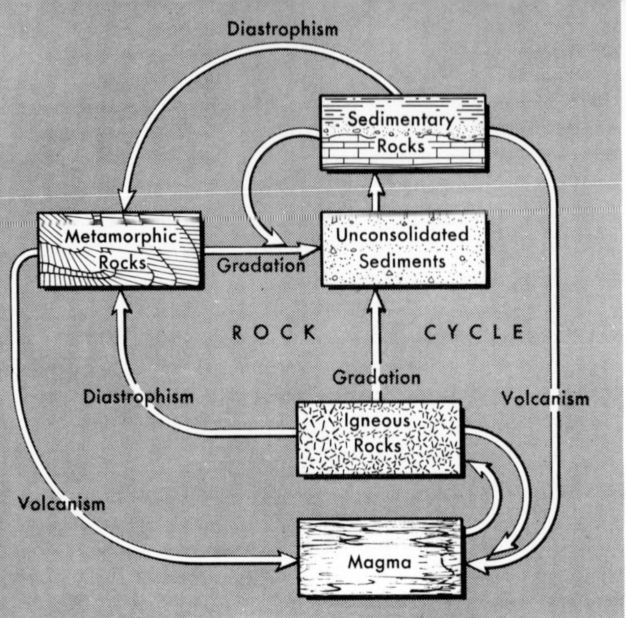

Fig. 8–21 *The rock cycle.*

distorted and squeezed, transforming them in extreme cases into *metamorphic rocks.* Finally, as the magma rises to the surface it forms large chambers and fluxes the adjoining rocks. The sedimentary, igneous, or metamorphic rocks which adjoin the large magma chambers become fluxed and thus revert to the original material from which they were formed, namely *magma.* This cycle is shown diagrammatically in Figure 8–21. Through the forces of gradation, all three types of rocks, as indicated by arrows, give rise to unconsolidated sediments which, on deposition, give sedimentary rocks — shales, limestones, and sandstones. Both igneous and sedimentary rocks when acted on by the forces of diastrophism give rise to metamorphic rocks — gneisses, schists, quartzites and others. All three types of rocks when acted on by the forces of volcanism become fluxed and form magma, which rises upward and upon solidification forms igneous rocks — granites, rhyolites, andesites, gabbros and other extrusive and intrusive rocks — which if they reach the surface will be eroded and deposited as sedimentary rocks. Thus the cycle is completed, only to start anew.

In recent years there has been a trend toward a newer concept of the changes of the sedimentary beds of geosynclines to the granitic cores found in the complex mountain systems. Instead of considering these granitic cores as huge intrusions of molten magma which rose and crystallized slowly with the folding of the sedimentary strata, the newer concept assumes that the heat generated by the disruption of the crust and the accompanying faulting and folding produces hot gases and solutions carrying silica which rise toward the earth's surface from the lower parts of the crust. These chemical vapors and solutions change basalt to rocks richer in silica and convert shales and sandstones into schists and gneisses and ultimately into granites. This *granitization* of the sedimentary rocks would account for the occurrence of granitic cores 500 to 1000 miles long and 100 or more miles thick in many of our complex mountain systems.

MOUNTAINS AND THEIR ORIGIN

Land masses which rise *high above low surroundings and which have a limited width at the top* are described as *mountains.* The term *plateau* is applied to *high land masses which have considerable flat area at the top.* Most of the great mountains occur in groups. A series of related ridges, such as the Sierra Nevada, is often called a *mountain range* and a group of ranges which have related structure and form is called a *mountain system.* Thus the Rocky Mountain system is a group of ranges which rose at about the same time; extending from the Mexican border to Canada it forms, so to speak, the spine of the United States. Mountains may be classified in accordance with the hypothetical causes of their origin: (*a*) differential erosion; (*b*) volcanic action; (*c*) crustal movements of the earth.

DIFFERENTIAL EROSION

Mountains may be produced by differential erosion of rocks. The rate of erosion depends in part on the hardness of the rocks; as was shown previously, deep canyons have been eroded by streams. As a high plateau is dissected by running water, the more resistant parts remain as high hills between stream divides. These ultimately may be carved to such heights as to be called mountains. The Catskill Mountains in New York were formed in such a manner. The rock strata are not folded or crumpled like those of the Appalachians but in many places are nearly horizontal. Such mountains of erosion are being slowly carved at the present time in many parts of the western United States.

VOLCANIC ACTION

The volcanic mountains are unusual in that they are mountains of accumulation with no diastrophism involved in their formation. This type may occur singly, or in groups in the form of cones. They are built by the piling up of lava, cinders, and the other products of volcanic activity discussed earlier in the chapter. The Hawaiian Islands, which rise high above the sea level, are great volcanic piles more than thirty thousand feet in height, built from the sea floor by volcanoes in that region. Other volcanic mountains appear as cones, either singly or in rows, in regions which are relatively flat and which do not show crumpled and deformed rock strata.

CRUSTAL MOVEMENTS

Most of the great chains of high mountains are assumed to be the results of crustal movements on a gigantic scale. The present huge mountain chains are the result of *folding,* or *faulting,* or more often a complex combination of folding and faulting complicated by igneous intrusions and later erosion.

Examination of the arched rock structure of many high mountain systems reveals thick layers of conglomerates, sandstones, shales, and limestones, all of sedimentary origin. Though the original sedimentary rocks have been deformed, the stratification and the presence of marine shells and fossils clearly indicate that these folded strata were once the flat bottom of shallow seas in areas of deposition. The folded strata of these mountains also indicate that the sedimentary beds were pushed upward in the form of arches or folds by intense compressional forces acting horizontally from both sides. To visualize roughly the formation of folds, take a dozen different colored pieces of cardboard about eight inches square, arrange them flat on top of each other, and hold with the edges resting against the palms of the hands. Push the palms toward each other, so that the layers of the cardboard crumple and arch upward. It will be noted that as the fold of the cardboard "strata" arches upward, there is a shortening of the original flat distance from edge to edge. To state the same thing in another way, if after folding the cardboard strata, the folds are leveled by pulling the palms outward, there will be an increase in the width of the cardboard "region. In the same manner, if the mountain folds of the Appalachians and the Rockies were leveled out again by pushing downward from above, these regions would become fifty to a hundred miles wider; hence the North American continent was shortened by fifty to a hundred miles across when each mountain chain was made. The present mountain heights do not indicate the original height of the fold, because erosion has been actively at work since their formation. Many mountains, for example the Appalachians, represent only the stumps of the once high peaks which were peneplained and then uplifted again.

Besides the fold mountains just discussed, whose structure consists of large synclines and anticlines, there are mountains which have been produced by *faulting* on a gigantic scale. Assume that the North American continent from the Atlantic to the Pacific is divided into hypothetical segments or blocks five hundred miles in length north and south and a hundred miles in width, east and west. These blocks of rock are mostly granitic and rest at lower depths on top of heavier or denser basaltic rock. By movement of these blocks it is possible to explain the formation of mountains due to faulting. For example, one block may slip down several thousand feet, leaving the adjacent block in its original position as a steep mountain on one side. Several adjacent blocks may move, one being elevated to mountain height, and the other depressed. Or one side of a block may rise, the other sinking at the same time, forming a tilted block. In general, the movement is of the fault type and such mountains are called *block* or *fault mountains.* An example of this type is the Sierra Nevada range in California. This range is a single tilted block about four hundred miles in length and eighty to one hundred miles in width. The eastern edge has been uplifted more than two miles. Thus, the approach from the east is precipitous and abrupt, while the approach from the Pacific side is a long, gentle slope. Many smaller ranges of similar origin occupy the region between the Sierras and the Rockies. This region is still the seat of active faulting as is attested by the large number of earthquakes occurring throughout the area.

The great mountain systems are very complex in their structure. The Rockies in America, the Alps in Europe, the Himalayas and other chains of Eurasia show evidence of complex folds, normal faults, thrust faults, igneous intrusions, stream dissection, and the effects of other forces; their detailed treatment is beyond the scope of this text. For our present discussion it is sufficient to note a few general features about them. Many of these mountain systems, like the Andes, the Japanese mountains, and the Philippines, are fronted by troughs of deep oceanic depressions which may be regarded as water-filled downwarps. There seems to be a general trend in mountain-building along continental margins. Many of the mountain belts like the American Cordilleras and the Appalachians are parallel with the continental margins and straight in plan, while others like the Alps and the Himalayas bend in the form of a bow. Some of the huge folds found in these complex mountains are composed of sedimentary strata, five thousand to twenty thousand feet or more in thickness, thus indicating a tremendously long period of deposition preceding the mountain-building movement. The relation between the folded sedimentary strata of the mountain, and the geosyncline in which they were once horizontally deposited, is a fundamental one in orogenesis.

Based on this brief discussion, an hypothetical outline of the origin of these complex mountains may be given. Refer to Figure 8–22. Alongside a continental mass which is rising, an elongated shallow basin or geosyncline forms on which the eroded material is carried by the streams and deposited to form sedimentary beds (*ABC*). The rise of the continental mass and the downbending of the crust to form the geosyncline are manifestations of the same horizontal compressional forces within the earth's crust. As the load of sediments accumulates in thickness, it increases the sinking of the basin. Lines *AD, BE,* and *CF* represent columns of rock at three places. The weakest point in the region is that where the geosynclinal sediments are thickest — the column of rock represented by line *BE.* Hence, with the increase in compressional forces (indicated by arrow), the weakest rock column which is being pushed from either side by horizontal pressure begins to buckle and to be arched upward in the form of a

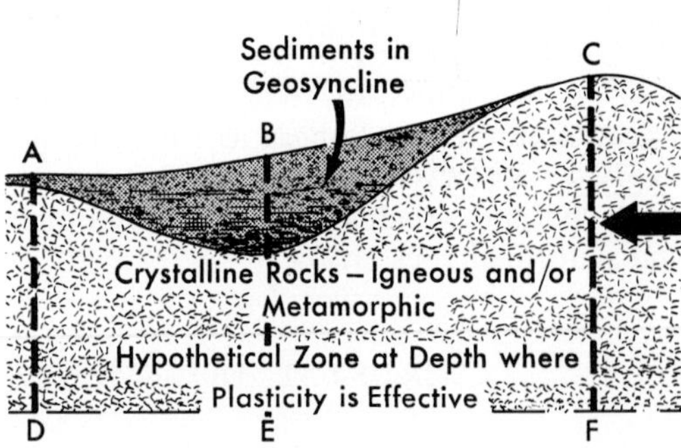

Fig. 8–22 *Geosyncline into which sediments of eroded material accumulate.*

Fig. 8–23 *Orogenic folding.*

Fig. 8–24 *The compression fold passes into a thrust fault.*

fold as shown diagrammatically in Figure 8–23. Further down, in the lower parts of the thickened folds where the pressure is greatest, the temperature rises and fluxing of the rocks of magma formation occurs. This eventually leads to the formation of batholiths, dikes, or extrusion of volcanic material, or all of these manifestations of a movement of fluid rock. As the uplift increases, the highlands are attacked by erosion and carved into rugged land forms. The formation of steep folds may, however, develop further with increased compression into a thrust fault, as shown in Figure 8–24. As the soft sediments of the geosynclinal strata are arched into steep folds, the crest breaks, and rock strata may be driven over the underlying mass for several miles. In the Alps great masses of the older rocks were pushed over the younger rocks beneath for more than fifty miles, and in the Northern Rockies the older stratum was driven eastward for more than five miles. The younger rocks which are overridden suffer extreme deformation. Though most of the older thrust rocks have been removed by erosion, some remain as isolated peaks standing over younger strata; Chief Mountain in Montana is an example.

THE FORCES THAT PRODUCE CRUSTAL MOVEMENTS

Some of the crustal movements, like faulting, can be explained by the adjustments in equilibrium of the hypothetical block which forms the continents as outlined on page 124. The big crustal movements, however, which formed the great mountain chains of the earth, involve forces that stagger the imagination. No existing hypothesis adequately accounts for the forces of these gigantic orogenic movements, and only a brief delineation of various speculative hypotheses which have been proposed will be given here.

The early hypotheses on mountain building were associated with speculations about the birth of our planet. It was assumed that the young earth was liquid for at least a part of its history. During this period some of the heavier minerals and elements sank toward the center, while the lighter layers began to rise, cool, and form the crust. The formation of the crust reduced the rate of cooling tremendously, but did not entirely arrest it. Accordingly, there was, and still is, a constant loss of heat by thermal conduction through the crust. Ultimately the outer shell had to readjust itself

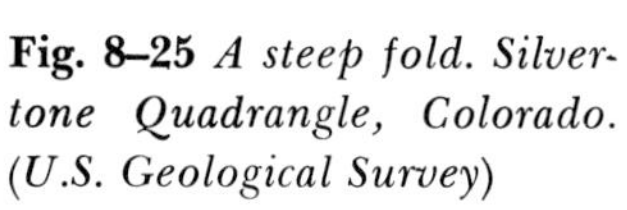

Fig. 8–25 *A steep fold. Silvertone Quadrangle, Colorado. (U.S. Geological Survey)*

to the shrinkage of the inner shell and was horizontally compressed, thus initiating all the complex crustal movements.

When this hypothesis of an essentially liquid earth with a comparatively thin crust was abandoned, the "contraction" idea was modified to fit an earth which has essentially a solid core. Under the enormous temperatures and pressures (discussed on page 119) existing in the inner layers of the earth, the various minerals are rearranged into denser compounds which settle toward the interior. Since the inner core contracts, the outermost solid layer follows, and is horizontally compressed. This necessitates profound movements in the crust, which we see as faults, thrusts, folding, mountain building, and other adjustments.

Arguments against the contraction hypothesis are calculations by some geochemists which indicate that the disintegration of radioactive materials within the crust furnishes far more heat than is lost by thermal conduction at the surface. It is highly probable, therefore, that more heat is generated inside the earth than escapes. Some geochemists have even proposed that the excess heat ultimately accumulates and gives rise to subcrustal currents which cause mountain building and volcanic activity. Accordingly, a part of the accumulated heat is transformed into kinetic energy to produce mountains while much of the rest escapes through the rise of hot lavas.

Still another hypothesis proposes the drifting of continental blocks as a result of subcrustal currents. According to this view, the mountain chains of the globe were formed by the horizontal crushing of geosynclines which lay in front of slowly migrating continents. In the formation of the Alps, Africa is assumed to have moved northward, crushing the old Mediterranean geosyncline. Similarly, the Rockies were formed when the North American continent slipped to the west away from Europe. The westward migration of the American continental block involved such force that the strata of the Rocky Mountain geosyncline were thrust into mountain folds and thrusts. The problem appears to be a complicated one, and at present there does not exist an hypothesis that can account for the ultimate causes of the crustal movements involved in the formation of the great mountain chains of the earth.

SUMMARY

1. *Diastrophism* designates all the crustal movements of the earth, and volcanism all the movements of molten rock; together these two forces build up land and tend to offset the work of gradational agents.
2. Earthquakes, recent elevation and subsidence, and folds and faults in the rock structure are evidence for diastrophic movements.
3. Synclines are downfolded rock structures, and anticlines are upfolded crests. Geosynclines are continental downwarps of very large dimensions. Faults are movements of one rock mass with respect to another along a fracture. Tensional forces produce a normal fault, and compressional forces produce a thrust fault. Most mountain systems have been built by complex folding and faulting of rock strata which have been deposited in ancient geosynclines.
4. An unconformity between two rock masses indicates that there was a period during which the lower mass was eroded, followed by a period of submergence during which new sedimentary strata were deposited on the eroded surface.
5. Earthquakes are movements which produce trembling of the ground, and occur along definite belts of recent mountain building caused by faults.
6. Through the seismograph earthquake waves are differentiated into three types, each traveling at a different speed. The long waves which travel two miles per second and move along the surface of the earth are destructive of the works of man.
7. A volcano is an opening through which gases, molten rock, and solid rock fragments are ejected. The ejection of hot materials from a volcano may be of the quiet type, emitting lava; it may be of the violent ex-

plosive type, ejecting mostly ashes and gases; or it may be of an intermediate type between the two.

8. The products of volcanic ejections are gases, fragmental material, and lava. Volcanic gases consist mostly of water vapor; gases of sulfur and other poisonous gases, however, are often present. The fragmental material varies in size from large blocks of rock to a fine dust. Most lavas are of basaltic composition — that is, they contain a preponderance of ferromagnesian minerals.
9. Magma which solidifies without reaching the surface forms batholiths, dikes, sills, and laccoliths; the names of these intrusive bodies are related to their shape.
10. The intrusive igneous rocks have a coarse texture; the extrusive igneous rocks have a fine texture; a glassy rock forms when crystallization is rapid if the amount of silica is high.
11. The chief types of igneous rocks are: granites, rhyolites, diorites, andesites, gabbros, basalts, obsidians, and volcanic breccias and tuffs.
12. The distribution of active volcanoes follows closely the earthquake zones and the most recent rugged mountain systems.
13. The interior of the earth is inferred from a large number of facts. It has an iron-nickel core with the denser rocks toward the inner core and the lighter rocks toward the surface.
14. The origin and movement of magma is believed to be related to (*a*) internal heat of the earth from radioactive changes, (*b*) pressure of the overlying rocks, (*c*) release of pressure along fractures or folds caused by diastrophic movements.
15. Most mountain systems have been built by complex folding and faulting and igneous intrusion.

STUDY EXERCISES

1. Enumerate all the available evidence that indicates movements of the earth's crust. Arrange the evidence in two sections: the first to include evidence which is easily discerned; and the second, evidence which requires considerable training.
2. Make rough drawings of a syncline, an anticline, a normal fault, a thrust fault, and an erosional unconformity.
3. Draw up a table of earthquake waves giving the following information about each type of wave (Primary, Secondary, and Surface waves): speed in miles per second; type of wave motion; probable origin.
4. Make a rough diagram showing the following intrusions and extrusions:

dike	sill	volcanic neck
laccolith	lava flow	cinder cone
batholith	magma chamber	composite cone

   Indicate the type of rocks which are likely to be encountered in each.

5. Make a rough diagram of the composition of the earth. Then, after each of the items listed below, place first the factual information requested. Then place the letter *L* if the fact is in accord with an earth having a liquid core; the letter *S* if in accord with an earth having a solid core; the letters *LS* if in accord with both.
   a. Average density of the outer shell ......
   b. Average density of the earth as a whole ....
   c. Average density of the inner core.......
   d. Calculated pressure at a depth of 60 miles within the earth's crust................
   e. Calculated pressure near the center of the earth................................
   f. Observable temperature at a depth of three miles..........................
   g. Calculated temperature at a depth of 60 miles................................
   h. Propagation of primary and secondary waves up to 1800 miles deep...........
   i. Propagation of primary and secondary waves after 1800 miles depth...........
   j. Composition of meteorites.............
6. Write *D* if the following are caused by diastrophic changes; *V* if by volcanic changes; *G* if by gradational changes. More than one cause may be involved.

.... shale	.... ripple marks in rocks on top of a hill
.... marble	.... gneiss
.... slate	.... limestone beds
.... pumice stone	.... schistose structure
.... mica	.... quartzite beds
.... obsidian	

7. Make a diagram of the rock cycle as on page 122 of the text but greatly enlarged to include the following: (*a*) all the various types of metamorphic, sedimentary, and igneous rocks that we have studied (list these under each section); (*b*) the kind of unconsolidated sediments. Briefly explain the rock cycle, the formation of magma, the rise of magma, the composition of the outer and inner shells of the earth, the degradation of rocks and transportation of sediments and their consolidation into sedimentary rocks, and finally the crustal movements which gave rise to metamorphic rocks.
8. Indicate how you would recognize each of the following: (*a*) a mountain produced by volcanism; (*b*) a mountain produced by erosional dissection; (*c*) a mountain range produced by block faulting; (*d*) a mountain range produced by folding and thrust faulting, then altered by stream dissection.
9. By referring to the diagram below, select the given alternative that correctly completes each of these statements:

   The symbol *II* stands for (*a*) layers of igneous rock; (*b*) layers of sedimentary rock; (*c*) an anticline; (*d*) a syncline; (*e*) a batholith........................

   The strata represented by *II* were originally (*a*) the result of volcanic activity; (*b*) the result of diastrophism; (*c*) deposited below sea level; (*d*) an unconformity; (*e*) result of glacial action..................

   The strata represented by *II* were elevated because of (*a*) erosion; (*b*) sedimentation; (*c*) weathering; (*d*) diastrophism; (*e*) faulting ....

   After elevation the erosion of the strata represented by *II* resulted in the formation of (1), now known as (*a*) a thrust fault; (*b*) a tension fault; (*c*) a syncline; (*d*) an anticline; (*e*) an unconformity...........

   The erosion resulting in (1) was followed most immediately by (*a*) subsidence and inundation; (*b*) volcanic activity; (*c*) penetration of igneous material; (*d*) sedimentation; (*e*) faulting......................

   The next stage was (*a*) faulting; (*b*) sedimentation; (*c*) erosion; (*d*) intrusion of igneous material; (*e*) glaciation..........

   The next stage was (*a*) faulting; (*b*) sedimentation; (*c*) erosion; (*d*) an uplifting of the region; (*e*) subsidence and inundation; (*f*) glaciation......................

   The next stage was (*a*) faulting; (*b*) intrusion of igneous material; (*c*) glaciation; (*d*) sedimentation; (*e*) subsidence.........

   The next stage was (*a*) faulting; (*b*) intrusion of igneous material; (*c*) glaciation; (*d*) sedimentation; (*e*) metamorphosis.

   The symbol (2) represents a (*a*) batholith; (*b*) laccolith; (*c*) sill; (*d*) dike; (*e*) fault..............................

   The symbol (3) represents a (*a*) laccolith; (*b*) batholith; (*c*) sill; (*d*) strike; (*e*) dip................................

   The symbol (4) represents (*a*) a tension fault; (*b*) a thrust fault; (*c*) a strike; (*d*) an unconformity; (*e*) a batholith......

   The symbol (5) stands for (*a*) an unconformity; (*b*) a dip; (*c*) a strike; (*d*) a scarp; (*e*) an anticline..................

   Water is likely to be found in the rocks labeled (1), (2), (3), (4), (5).

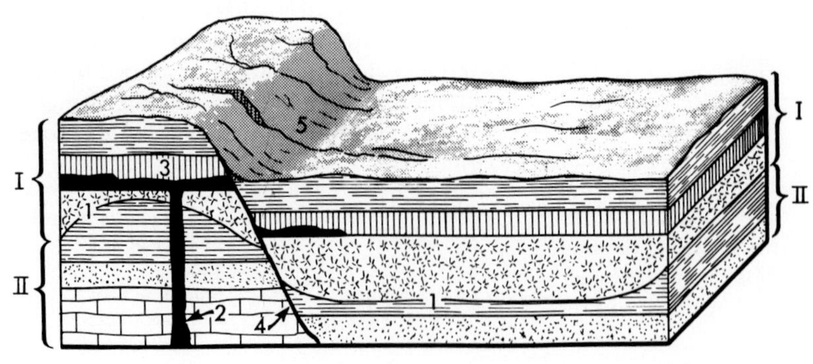

FOR FURTHER READING

1. GILLULY, J., A. C. WATERS, and A. O. WOODFORD, *Principles of Geology*. San Francisco: W. H. Freeman and Co., 1954.

   Evidence of movements of the earth's crust is discussed in Chapters 9, 10, and 11; earthquakes and the earth's interior, in Chapter 18; mountains, in Chapter 19; and igneous activity, in Chapter 17.

2. GARRELS, R. M., *A Textbook of Geology*. New York: Harper and Brothers, 1951.

   For a discussion of the movements of the earth's crust and associated phenomena, see Chapters 13 and 18.

3. LONGWELL, C. R., A. KNOPF, and R. F. FLINT, *Physical Geology*. New York: John Wiley and Sons, 1948.

   Chapter 15 gives a thorough discussion of diastrophism; and Chapter 16, of earthquakes. For volcanoes and volcanism, see Chapter 14; for the earth's interior and the structure and history of mountains, Chapters 18 and 19.

4. MATHER, K. F., and S. L. MASON, *Source Book in Geology*. New York: McGraw-Hill Book Co., 1939.

   The following original papers are recommended in connection with this chapter: Leonardo da Vinci, "The Earth and the Sea," *p. 1; Boyle,* "Conditions at the Bottom of the Sea," *p. 27; Von Humboldt,* "Volcanic Activity in America," *p. 179; Cuvier,* "Revolution and Catastrophes in the History of the Earth," *p. 188; de Beaumont,* "The Origin and Cause of Mountain Building," *p. 288; Dana,* "On the Origin of Continents and Mountain Ranges," *p. 419; Favre,* "Experimental Reproduction of Mountain Structures by Lateral Compression," *p. 448; Chamberlin,* "On the Interior Structure, Surface Temperature and Age of the Earth," *p. 612; Bertrand,* "Overthrusting in the Alps," *p. 631.*

5. Paperback: EDITORS OF SCIENTIFIC AMERICAN, *The Planet Earth*. Simon and Schuster, $1.45.

   The following sections are of especial interest in connection with this chapter: "The Lithosphere: Core and Mantle," *pp. 19–39;* "The Crust of the Earth," *pp. 58–80.*

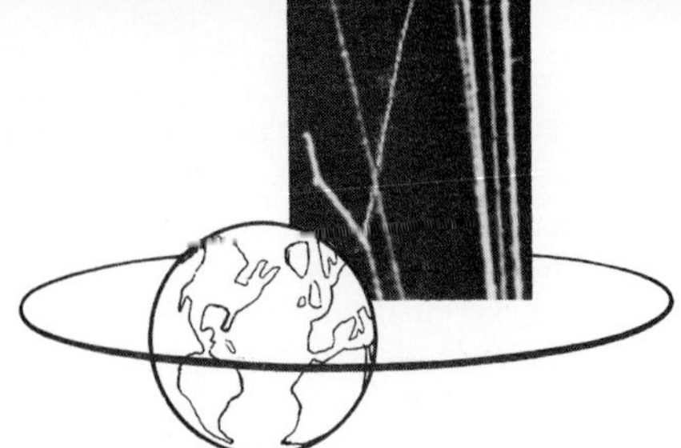

9

APPROACH TO THE EARTH'S HISTORY

THE PRECEDING CHAPTER frequently referred to ancient seaways, ancient crustal movements, and ancient geosynclines whose strata were later folded, fractured, and mashed to give rise to mountain ranges which, in turn, were subsequently peneplained. In attempting to describe the present changes of the earth's surface, past changes were referred to, and we assumed that the forces which are now in operation work in the same way as in the past, and that "the events of the past history of the earth are adequately explained by processes now in operation." This last statement, often called the law of uniform change, is a fundamental principle in earth science. It was established, after considerable controversy, only about a hundred years ago. The object of this chapter is to describe the methods used in deciphering from the records written in the rocks the major events which took place in the past of our planet.

The interpretation of historical data of past cosmic events is at best an extremely complicated and difficult matter, even today. Obviously the principle of uniform change as it applies to human events must have been recognized as early as the fifth century B.C. when Thucydides wrote in the introduction to his history of the Peloponnesian War, "The present in the course of human events must resemble if it does not entirely reflect the past." But such a principle could not have been applied to tracing the origin of the hills and valleys and mountains until there was an organized earth science.

If we today find it somewhat surprising that it took so long for man to recognize that the record of the earth's history was always present and written in the stones and rocks, we should first realize that we see more only because we are standing on the shoulders of past observers. The human race had lived on this planet for several hundred thousand years before it abandoned the idea that earthquakes, volcanic eruptions, floods, rain, and sunshine were controlled by capricious gods and spirits. Then it took another two thousand years before even scientists began to make a systematic approach to these and other natural phenomena.

DEVELOPMENT OF THE SYSTEMATIC APPROACH

Just as in all progress there are sporadic, isolated, unconnected attempts toward a new approach, so in the development of science new ideas often lie dormant for long periods of time until strong and imaginative personalities give them the propulsion that brings them to the arena of scientific controversy out of which a new approach is developed. Numerous isolated attempts to explain the changes on the earth had been made over the centuries. For example, the great artist Leonardo da Vinci (Italy, about A.D. 1500) interpreted fossils correctly as the living imprints of the dead and argued that they were the shells of animals once living in the places where they were found. This brilliant and imaginative interpretation, however, could not be accepted in the charged social atmosphere of the Renaissance. After a controversy lasting over a century, during which the adherents of this biological interpretation were often subjected to persecution, fossils were said to be "devices of the devil" or freaks of nature placed in the rocks to delude mankind. As more and more fossils were found, they were accepted by the majority (which is always resistant to change of ideas) as the remains of the animals that perished in the biblical Flood. Not until about the year 1800 were fossils universally recognized as records of life in the geologic past. By this time James Hutton (Scotland, 1726–1797) had propelled his *Theory of the Earth* into the arena of controversy, and out of this arena in the course of about fifty years emerged the systematic approach. Hutton recognized the endless cycle of erosion and elevation of the shallow sea basins to continents. He concludes his book by saying, "In the phenomena of Earth, I see no vestige of a beginning, no prospect of an end."

Hutton's ideas that the processes of change on the earth today furnish the key to the past were opposed to the ideas of Werner and his adherents. Werner was a brilliant mineralogist who fell into the blunder of generalizing from insufficient evidence. Near Freiberg, where he taught, Werner found a series of rock strata in which granite was at the bottom, then metamorphosed rocks, then flat sedimentary beds on top. From this observation he generalized that all the rocks of the earth were precipitated sediments. He postulated a primeval ocean out of which the granites were precipitated first and the flat upper beds last, followed by the disappearance of most of the water. Eventually, after considerable controversy between the adherents of the two schools and with the collection of new facts to bolster the arguments of each side, the principle that former changes of the earth's surface can be explained by forces now in operation was established by Sir Charles Lyell (England, 1797–1875).

Lyell revitalized Hutton's concept that geologic time extends back for millions of years and that the processes which produce imperceptible changes on the surface of the earth in the span of a human life can, given enough time, produce vast changes. To the many baffling riddles of the present face of the earth, Lyell sought the answers in the deposition of deltas, of alluvial fans, of receding and submerging shores, in the outpourings of ashes and lavas from volcanic cones, in the distorted beds exposed on canyon walls, and in the correlation of the fossils found in marine strata with species still alive. The theory of organic evolution (Darwin, 1859) helped to establish the systematic approach in deciphering the past history of the earth.

The present form of the systematic approach has been modified as new facts have been discovered and correlated. The principle of uniform change is accepted as a broad, guiding generalization; geologists, however, also agree that the way present processes operate has varied in the geologic past. There have been vast fluctuations in the amount of heat reaching the earth from the sun, vast variations of climate, widespread advances and recessions of huge glacial ice sheets on the continents, submergence of large areas of the land by the sea, widespread orogenic movements and outpourings of lava.

The methods employed by geologists in the reconstruction of the history of the earth, then, are based upon the broad principle that the processes which operate now to change the face of the earth operated also in the past with varied intensity. In the preceding two chapters, we have studied most of these processes. It is now necessary to outline how, out of present observations on the operations of these processes, we can develop guiding principles which will permit us to read in the records of the rocks past geologic events. The most important of these principles are (*a*) uniform mode of change, (*b*) repeated inundation of the land by the sea, (*c*) superposition of rock strata and unconformities, (*d*) law of igneous intrusion; and (*e*) index fossils and organic correlation.

PRINCIPLE OF UNIFORM CHANGE

This principle was discussed in the preceding section. A number of examples will illustrate its application. Figure 9–1 shows a vertical slab of rock in Utah marked with ripples and imbedded with the shells of marine animals. Since these marks and shells are associated today with marine mud flats, the conclusion is drawn that the rocks were formed in shallow seas, then elevated and tilted. By the same process of reasoning, the presence of similar sedimentary rocks in the heights of Mount Everest implies that even these high-altitude strata were formed by marine deposits in shallow seas, as they are formed today. Again, glaciers today as they move down their mountain valleys, scratch and polish the rock surfaces; hence the presence of glacial scratches and polish on exposed surface rocks anywhere in the northern part of our country proves that this region was once buried beneath an ancient ice sheet.

Fig. 9–1 *Ancient ripple marks. Consolidation of a ripple-marked stratum of sand or silt into sandstone or limestone may preserve the ripple as shown.* (*U.S. Geological Survey*)

INUNDATION OF LAND BY SEA

If the land surfaces of the continental areas were swept free of mantle to expose the bedrocks, about 75 per cent of these bedrocks would be sedimentary. Since these rocks are formed in shallow seas by the deposit of sediments, they are a record that the larger part of the land surface was at one time covered by shallow seas. The sequence of events in the deposition of a series of conformable beds of limestone (oldest), shale, and sandstone (youngest), indicates that the region in which these beds were formed was first inundated by a shallow sea, and that the waters later retreated. The presence of the limestone at the bottom indicates that the region in which these beds were formed was first a sea of moderate depth in which limestone sediments formed from lime-secreting organisms. The presence of the shale beds on top of the limestone beds indicates that the sea became more shallow and that mud sediments were deposited which, when compacted later, gave rise to the shales. Then the sea withdrew still more so that sands accumulated on its shores just as they accumulate on the seashores today, and eventually the sands gave rise to the beds of sandstones on top of the shales. Similarly, if on top of these sandstone beds we find another bed of shales and another bed of limestone, we can conclude that the re-

Fig. 9–2 *Fossil mud cracks, Hubbard Springs, Virginia. Evaporation and compaction of water-filled mud flats produces a system of shrinking cracks. If these remain open and are later filled with sediment from above, they provide means for determining the relative ages of the layers of sedimentary rock that results.* (*U.S. Geological Survey*)

treat of the sea (regressive sequence) was followed by another advance (transgressive sequence). The interior of much of the North American continent has been alternately above and below sea level many times. In the lower part of the United States a depression of the land levels of only 250 feet would again bring the Gulf of Mexico as far north as St. Louis. During the many periods of inundation the present sedimentary rocks found in every state of the United States were deposited.

SUPERPOSITION OF ROCK STRATA AND UNCONFORMITIES

As noted above, sedimentary rocks are laid down as sediments layer upon layer on sea floors. Such beds may be elevated without appreciable folding or tilting. Suppose now a stream cuts a canyon deep into these strata. On the canyon wall we would see gradual change from one type of sediment to the other, limestone, for example, grading into shale. In such *conformable* strata, the oldest bed is at the bottom and the youngest at the top. However, if crustal movement causes elevation of the region and parts of the sedimentary beds are eroded and the region is resubmerged and a new series of beds are deposited, these new beds are *unconformable* to the older beds. (See pages 107–108.) The erosional unconformity represents a missing interval of time in the rock record. As discussed on page 108, angular unconformities are frequent in the rocks of mountain ranges which were eroded, tilted, resubmerged, and, after more sediment accumulated, were elevated again. The unconformities, often difficult to recognize, become guideposts in tracing the relationship between crustal movements, erosion, and sedimentation in a particular region.

LAW OF IGNEOUS INTRUSION

As developed in the preceding section, a sedimentary bed at the bottom of a conformable stratum is older than one above it. An igneous sill, however, in the bottom of such a bed is younger (page 115), since the sedimentary bed had to be present so that igneous magma could penetrate between its fractures and joints.

INDEX FOSSILS AND ORGANIC CORRELATION

The term *fossil* is applied to any remains or evidences of prehistoric life. Fossils may be actual remains, altered or unaltered; they may also be casts or molds, such as imprints of leaves, of bony structures, and tracks of animals and birds. Usually fossils are found in sedimentary rocks, and usually they have been buried so long that none of the original plant or animal survives except as a cast or mold, or as altered remains. The conditions favorable to fossil formation are the presence of hard parts and quick and deep burial by fine-grained material. This means that the organic re-

A

Fig. 9–3 *Examples of index fossils. A. Cryptozoon algae — Ordovician from the great Appalachian trough. (U.S. Geological Survey). B. Trilobites — Middle Devonian. (American Museum of Natural History). C. Ferns — Carboniferous (American Museum of Natural History). D. Dinosaur tracks, Mesozoic; the larger print was made by Brontosaurus, and the smaller print by the three-toed Allosaurus. (Brooklyn College, Department of Geology). E. Fish — Eocene. (American Museum of Natural History).*

B

D

C

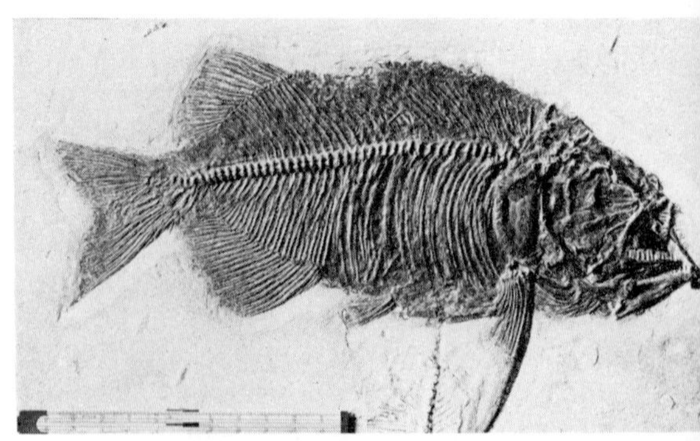

E

Fig. 9–4 *Skeleton of a dinosaur from the Mesozoic Era (Tyrannosaurus rex), another example of an index fossil.* (*American Museum of Natural History*)

mains are protected from the action of air under conditions which favor preservation. Then the hard parts of organisms are slowly replaced by calcium carbonate (calcification) or silicon dioxide (silification) from the materials dissolved in the ground water, a process called *petrification*. Occasionally the organic matter in buried plant and animal life decays in such a way as to leave only carbon (carbonization).

Most sedimentary rocks contain fossil remains of the animals and plants that lived while the sediments were accumulating. The aggregate of animal species which lived in a given region in a given geological period is called the *fauna*, and the aggregate of plant species, the *flora*. It was first found by William Smith (England, 1769–1839) that each sedimentary rock formation has a fauna that differs in some degree from those above it or below it. The characteristic faunas of rock formations deposited in widely separate areas are essentially the same if they were deposited at the same time and if the environmental conditions such as depth of water or temperature of water were similar. The *characteristic* fossils in this formation serve as a *guide* or *index* to the recognition of rock formations deposited at the same time under similar conditions. Thus geologists use index fossils to identify rocks of the same age in widely separated regions or continents. For example, since the limestones at Niagara Falls contain the same index fossils as the limestones of the Chicago area it is inferred that the rocks in both regions were formed at the same time in the geological calendar.

The principle of organic evolution explains the reasons for *the definite succession of faunas and floras found in undisturbed strata.* As life evolved continuously from the protozoa to the mammals, different kinds of animals have succeeded one another in time, and hence rocks formed at the same geological age could have the same faunas. To be useful as index fossils they should possess certain characteristics: (*a*) they should have wide geographical distribution in order to permit correlation of

TABLE 9–1 GEOLOGICAL TIME CHART

ERAS	PART OF GEOLOGICAL TIME	PERIODS	DURATION IN YEARS	YEARS FROM PRESENT	DOMINANT LIFE	CLOSED WITH
Cenozoic	0.03%	Recent[1] Pleistocene[1] Pliocene[2] Miocene[2] Oligocene[2] Eocene[2]	10,000 2,000,000 10,000,000 18,000,000 10,000,000 20,000,000	60,000,000	Man Mammals	Cascadian Revolution
Mesozoic	0.07%	Cretaceous Jurassic Triassic	70,000,000 38,000,000 32,000,000	200,000,000	Flowering plants, grasses Reptiles	Laramide Rocky Mountain Revolution
Paleozoic	0.17%	Permian Carboniferous[3] Devonian Silurian Ordovician Cambrian	35,000,000 80,000,000 35,000,000 25,000,000 70,000,000 105,000,000	550,000,000	Amphibians First plant life Fishes Invertebrates	Appalachian Revolution
Proterozoic	0.33%	Upper Pre-Cambrian	650,000,000	1,200,000,000	Primitive multicellular forms	Killarney Grand Canyon Revolution
Archeozoic	0.40%	Lower Pre-Cambrian	800,000,000	2,000,000,000	Unicellular forms possible	Laurentian Revolution
Azoic	Interval from birth of sun to formation of earliest sedimentary rocks.		1,000,000,000 to 3,000,000,000 (?)		No Life	

[1] Also called the Quaternary Period.
[2] Also called the Tertiary Period.
[3] Often divided into Pennsylvanian and Mississippian Periods.

rock strata over entire continents or from continent to continent; (*b*) they should be very abundant and easy to identify; (*c*) they should be distributed over a narrow time-interval; that is, a form of life that persisted over too great a time-interval cannot be used to place a particular stratum of rock in its proper niche in the geological timetable.

GEOLOGIC TIME

Geologists, geochemists, and astronomers now set the beginning of geologic time at about 2,300,000,000 years ago (see Chapter 39). This figure is not based on speculative hypotheses as to the origin of the earth but on actual measurements of the radioactive content of rocks found on the earth's crust. Uranium, as will be shown in detail in Chapter 39, is the heaviest of the naturally-occurring elements and undergoes spontaneous disintegration into helium and lead. The rate of disintegration is very slow and is unaffected by changes of temperature, pressure, or the presence of other materials. Accurate measurements show that 1 gram of uranium yields 1/7,600,000,000 grams of lead in one year. Hence, if we analyze a uranium-bearing rock for uranium and lead we can find the age of the rock in years = $Pb/U \times 7{,}600{,}000{,}000$. A rock from an igneous dike in South Dakota, gives an age by the Pb/U ratio of 1,420,000,000 years, and a rock found in Winnepeg River, Manitoba, Canada, gives an age of 2,300,000,000 years. Though the dating of other rocks may push back the beginning of geologic time to nearly three billion years we shall take the round number of two billion years for our present discussion of the age of the earth.

DIVISIONS OF GEOLOGIC TIME

Table 9–1 represents a modern version of the geologic time chart. It will be noted that the time is divided into eras, and each era into several *periods*. Eras are based upon the state of advancement (evolution) of plants and animals: **Archeozoic** (primitive life), Proterozoic (early life), Paleozoic (ancient life), Mesozoic (medieval life), Cenozoic (recent life). These divisions result from the correlations of rocks from the entire continent by studies in composition, manner of occurrence, and kinds of fossils present. The importance of Table 9–1 lies in the fact that it gives in very broad outlines the major events in the development of the North American continent – as the result of diastrophism or mountain building, and in the development of life during geologic time. The five great divisions of time are based upon the events recorded in the last two columns.

It is natural to inquire about the basis for the division of geologic time into five eras, and the subdivision of the eras into periods. The answer is that these correspond to natural breaks in the story of the earth's history caused by diastrophic disturbances resulting from widespread adjustments in the earth's crust. These adjustments, as we have seen, resulted in alternate elevation and resubmergence of large areas of all the continents and the formation of large mountain systems. For example, various parts of the North American continent have been flooded by the seas at least twenty times. These widespread submergences, either because of a general rise of sea level or because of downwarping of the continent, often brought about profound changes in climate which caused many land forms of life either to disappear or to evolve into other forms which could survive in the new environmental conditions. Such widespread continental disturbances are called *geological revolutions.*

From the time of the Greek philosophers to about 1800, scientists have been puzzled by the widespread continental distribution of many different forms of marine shells, often at an elevation of thousands of feet above any present seas. The answer to the puzzle was simple, but it did not come until the clear recognition of the basic truths of geological history stated above on page 132. We now know, for example, that the eastern coast of the United States has

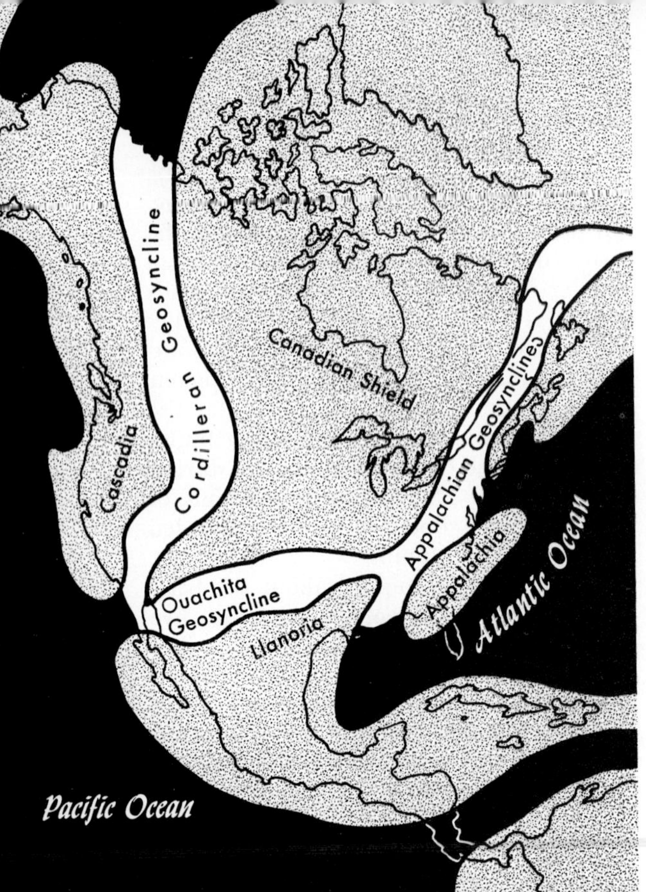

Fig. 9–5 *Appearance of North America in the early part of the Paleozoic Era, Cambrian Period.* (*Adapted by permission from* Outlines of Historical Geology, *by C. Schuchert and C. O. Dunbar, copyright 1950, published by John Wiley and Sons, Inc.*)

recently settled, geologically speaking, allowing the Atlantic Ocean to flood the low coast lands. This accounts for the drowned valleys such as the Chesapeake Bay, which is the drowned portion of the Susquehanna Valley. The annual rate of rising or falling of a portion of continent may be difficult to detect, but geologic time must be reckoned not only in millions of years, but in tens and hundreds of millions of years. A change in elevation of one centimeter a year would be difficult to detect, but during a normal lifetime it would equal about two feet. This rate, if continued for a million years, would form mountains higher than the present Himalayas.

THE CYCLE ILLUSTRATED IN THE PALEOZOIC ERA

The cycle of submergence, emergence, and mountain building characteristic of a geological era can be illustrated by what happened in our own continent during the Paleozoic Era. In the early part of the era, the North American continent began to be submerged. There is evidence to indicate that the degree of submergence increased with time until a very large part of the continent was under water, as indicated in Figure 9–5. There were three distinct regions of uplands: Appalachia, Cascadia, and the Canadian Shield. The Canadian Shield represented the remnants of the Laurentian Mountains, which had been largely eroded away during the Proterozoic Era. During a part of this early period, the Killarney Mountains of Wisconsin, which had been built at the close of the Proterozoic Era, were still conspicuous in the interior of the continent.

Thanks to the abundance of water and a mild climate, the forces of gradation operated rapidly, and the eroded materials from the highlands were deposited into three great troughs called *geosynclines:* the Appalachian, the Cordilleran, and the Ouachita. A cross-section through the present central United States would appear as shown in Figure 9–6. These geosynclines caught all the debris eroded from the adjacent highlands, until in some places the deposits of the resulting sedimentary rocks were as thick as fifty thousand feet.

During the latter part of the Paleozoic Era, diastrophic disturbances on a wide scale shortened the earth's surface in the eastern part of the present United States about a hundred miles. Those forces pushed the remnants of the old Appalachian Highlands westward, crushing and folding the sedimentary rocks in the Appalachian geosyncline into a mountain chain that extended from the present Nova Scotia to Alabama – the new Appalachian Mountains. The Blue Ridge faults in these mountains extend over 700 miles from Alabama into Pennsylvania. Contemporane-

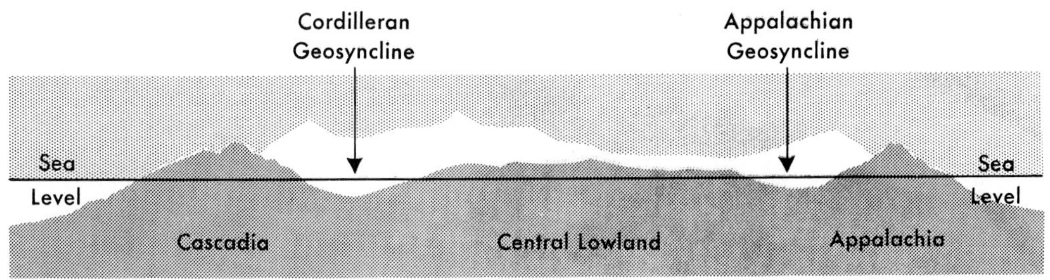

Fig. 9–6 *A cross-section through the present United States during the Early Paleozoic Era.*

ous with this uplift there was a minor disturbance that produced uplands in southern Arkansas and southeastern Oklahoma now called the Ouachita Mountains. (Refer to Figure 9–8.)

NORTH AMERICA IN THE MESOZOIC ERA

This same cycle or sequence is admirably illustrated also by the Mesozoic Era, during which the eastern half of our continent was emergent with forces of erosion in operation. Gradually a huge geosyncline in the general region of the former Cordilleran trough came into existence, and it continued to increase until it reached its climax during the Cretaceous period. Into this trough was poured the debris that later was to form the present Rocky Mountains. The North American continent was divided into two distinct land masses by the seas in the Rocky Mountain geosyncline. In various parts of Wyoming, Colorado, and Utah – which during the Mesozoic Era formed the western shore of the sea in the Rocky Mountain geosyncline – we have a rich source of fossil remains of dinosaurs, one of the most characteristic forms of life in the Mesozoic Era. After an existence long enough to accumulate sediments many thousands of feet thick, compressional forces coming from the west eventually elevated the deposits in the geosyncline to create the first generation Rocky Mountains. This is designated as the *Laramide Revolution*. Again a great mountain-making cycle had been repeated: (1) The era begins with the close of the Appalachian elevation; (2) then follows a long period of erosion and sedimentation in a new geosyncline and transgression of the sea; (3) the era closes with a new mountain-building upheaval (Figures 9–9 and 9–10).

To sum up, then, a geological era is a major division of geologic time marked off by extensive emergence of parts of continents submerged during the early part of the era. These widespread movements of land masses which result in the raising and lowering of large areas are called epeirogenic movements. The eroded materials are carried to huge troughs called geosynclines. As discussed on page 105, the downbending of the crust to form geosynclines and the use of the adjoining continental masses are manifestations of the forces resulting from crustal adjustments. These forces may eventually lead to folding and faulting, which, when they become sufficiently great, result in a geological revolution, the latter being always marked by orogenic movements, or mountain building, a final process which closes a geological era. New characteristic forms of life often followed geological revolutions as a result of rapid evolutionary changes due to changed environmental conditions.

GEOLOGICAL PERIODS

During every geological era there were regions where submergence and emergence occurred on a much smaller scale which nevertheless resulted in definite transforma-

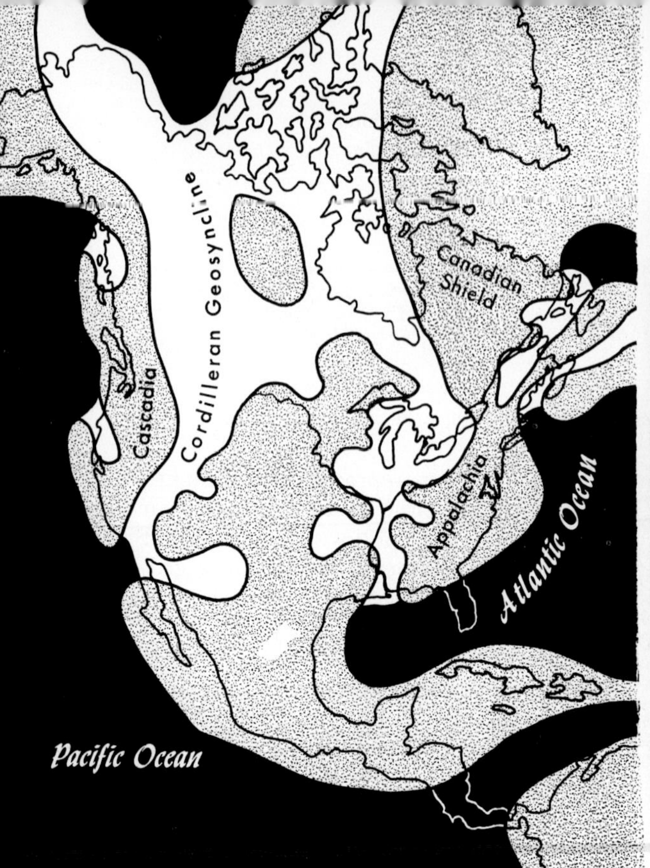

Fig. 9–7 *North America in the Middle Paleozoic Era (Middle Silurian Period)*.[1]

Fig. 9–8 *North America in the Late Paleozoic Era (Pennsylvanian and Mississippian Periods)*.

tions in the appearance of the continent. The time interval between significant changes, confined to regions within a continent, are called geological periods. For example, in the Middle Paleozoic Era (Figure 9–7) a region in the east central part of the United States was submerged, and during this period the Niagara limestone, exposed at Niagara Falls and in many places in Ohio, Indiana, Illinois, Wisconsin, and Michigan, was laid down. The Middle Paleozoic time, divided into Silurian and Devonian periods, was terminated with the formation of the Acadian Mountains in New England and eastern Canada. Again, during the latter part of the Paleozoic Era, a region stretching from Pennsylvania to Texas fluctuated above and below sea level many times. This alternately formed a vast shallow sea and swampy lowlands (see Figure 9–8). The climate at this time was very humid and mild and supported extremely dense vegetation. This formed deposits of organic matter in the swamps which, when later buried and subjected to the forces of compaction, formed our great coal deposits. This period of time has been labeled the *Carboniferous* period, and it is divided into the Mississippian and Pennsylvanian. The most important coal-producing regions are distributed in rocks of the Pennsylvanian period along an arc running from Texas, through Oklahoma, Kansas, Missouri, Iowa, Illinois, Kentucky, Indiana, Ohio, West Virginia, and Pennsylvania. These coal regions are the result of changes occurring during a geological period.

[1] Figures adapted by permission from C. Schuchert and C. O. Dunbar, *Outlines of Historical Geology*, copyright 1950, John Wiley and Sons, Inc.

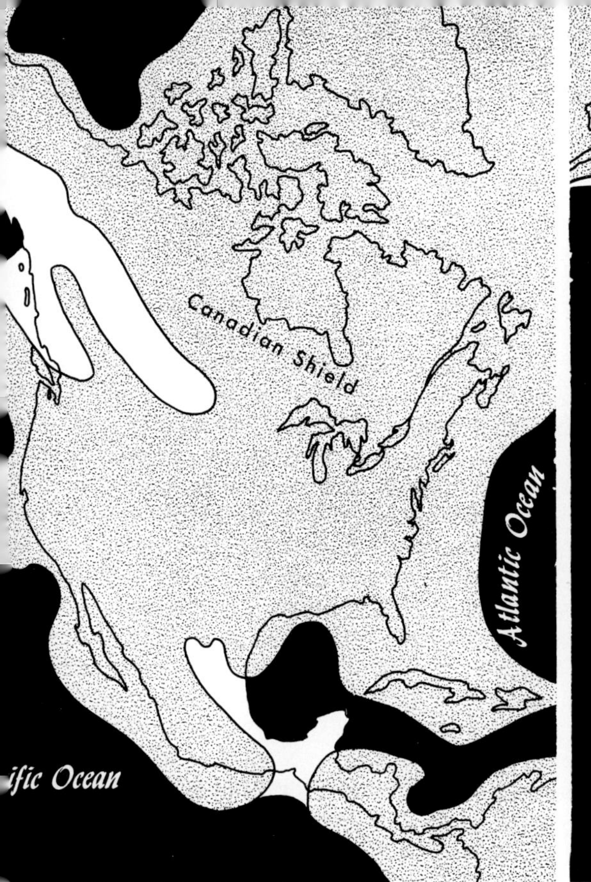

Fig. 9–9 *North America in the Middle Mesozoic Era (Middle Jurassic Period).*

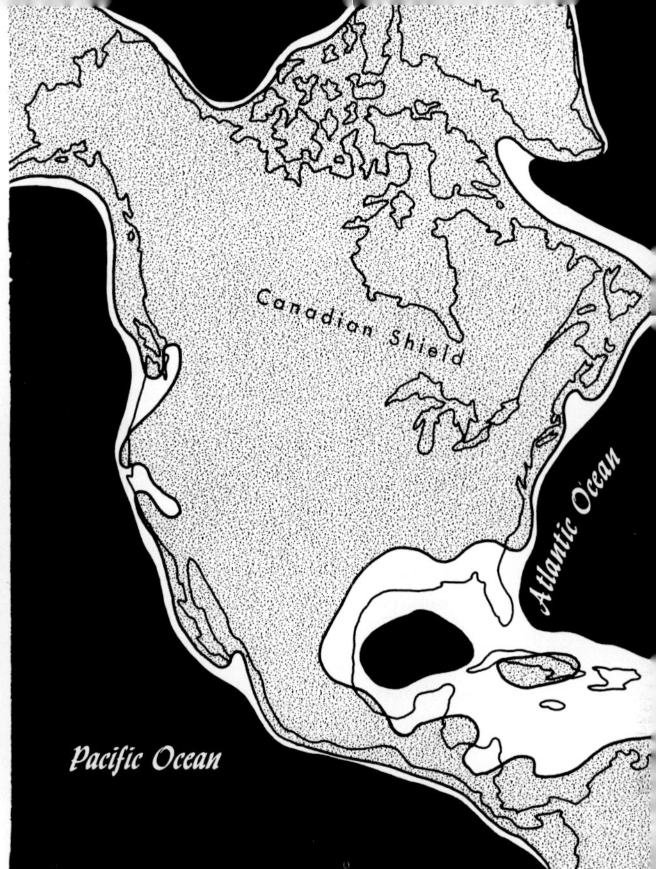

Fig. 9–10 *North America in the Early Cenozoic Era.*

SUMMARY

1. It is possible to reconstruct the past history of the earth from the records revealed by the rocks on the assumption that the events of the past are adequately explained by processes now in operation.
2. The basic principles used by geologists to interpret the changes on the earth during geologic time as revealed by studies of the rocks are as follows:
   a. Large portions of the present continents have been alternately above and below sea level.
   b. The geological processes which operate now to change the face of the earth operated also in the past though with varied intensity (principle of uniform change).
   c. In conformable series of sedimentary rocks, the youngest rocks are on top and the oldest rocks on the bottom (principle of superposition of rock strata).
   d. The presence of an unconformity indicates a break in the rock record, since the lower layer of rocks was deposited, uplifted, and eroded away before the upper series were deposited (principle of unconformity of rock strata).
   e. Igneous rocks are younger than the sedimentary rocks which they have penetrated (principle of igneous intrusion).
   f. Rocks which contain the same index fossils are of similar age (principle of index fossils and organic correlation).
3. Fossils which evolved and disappeared during a relatively short period of time and which can be used to correlate the rocks of one region with those of another are called index fossils. Index fossils should have the following characteristics:

a. They should be very abundant and easy to identify.
b. They should have existed over a narrow time interval.
c. They should have wide geographical distribution.

4. The age of the oldest rocks found on the earth's crust is 2,300,000,000 years. This figure is obtained by measuring the Lead/Uranium ratio in the rocks and using the rate of spontaneous disintegration of radioactive uranium into helium and lead to calculate how long the uranium has been disintegrating. The beginning of geologic time is usually placed at the round number of two billion years, though it is considered likely that rocks may be found which will place this figure closer to three billion years.
5. The span of two billion years since the beginning of geologic time is divided into five great eras, each subdivided into periods. The names, length in terms of years, and principal biological events for each interval are summarized in Table 9–1.
6. Each geological era is characterized, first, by widespread crustal movements (epeirogeny) which elevate and also submerge large parts of the continents; second, the formation of great geosynclines; third, a long period of erosion of the exposed portions of the continents which produced thick sediments in the geosynclines; fourth, the evolution of characteristic forms of life; and fifth, an accumulation of great strains within the earth's crust which are eventually relieved by mountain building (orogeny) in the regions of the great geosynclines.
7. The extensive orogenic movements which mark the close of each era are called geological revolutions.
8. Minor changes over a smaller area of the continents, similar to those characteristic of a geological era and completed in relatively short intervals of time, divide the eras into periods.

STUDY EXERCISES

1. Outline the development of the systematic approach to the reconstruction of the earth's history, giving the chief contributions of Hutton, Lyell, and Darwin.
2. Give evidence for the statement, which is regarded as a principle, that "fossil faunas and floras succeed one another in a definite and determinable order."
3. Give evidence to support each of the following statements: (*a*) In the past there was repeated inundation of large areas of the North American continent by the sea. (*b*) In some regions, especially in complex mountain ranges, older sedimentary strata may be found on top of younger rock formations. (*c*) A series of conformable rock strata of limestone, shale, coal, shale, limestone indicates submergence of the region, then elevation above sea level for a considerable period of time, followed by another submergence below sea level.
4. In the space before each statement below write the letter –

A if the statement applies to the principle of intrusion.
B if the statement applies to the principle of uniform change.
C if the statement applies to the principle of organic correlation.
D if the statement applies to the principle of superposition.
E if the statement applies to the law of unconformity.

.... Certain kinds of fossil plants and animals are characteristic of a formation of a given geologic age. Widely separated formations containing the same kind of fossils are therefore of the same geologic age.
.... A lost interval is indicated when it is evident that a series of rocks was deposited, uplifted, eroded, and then submerged and covered by the deposition of a new series.
.... In a series of rock formations, the younger rocks are at the top and the older ones at the bottom, unless the former have been transposed by some violent disturbance.
.... Intrusive rock is younger than that which is intruded.
.... The processes of gradation, volcanism, and diastrophism, with which we are

familiar today, have been in operation throughout geological history in essentially the same form; and from the evident results of these processes we can interpret the history of the earth.

5. Check those characteristics listed below which are true of index fossils:
   .... are very abundant.
   .... persisted without appreciable change through several geological eras.
   .... have a wide geographical distribution.
   .... have a restricted geographical distribution.
   .... have a limited geological distribution.
   .... are easily identified.

6. The following exercises refer to the diagram below. In each exercise underline the *one* alternative in parentheses that correctly completes the statement:
   a. There is evidence of (*A,* no; *B,* one; *C,* two; *D,* three; *E,* four) main period (s) of sedimentation.
   b. There is evidence of (*A,* no; *B,* one; *C,* two; *D,* three; *E,* four) period (s) of diastrophism.
   c. There is evidence of (*A,* no; *B,* one; *C,* two; *D,* three; *E,* four) period (s) of volcanism.
   d. There is evidence of (*A,* no; *B,* one; *C,* two; *D,* three; *E,* four) main period(s) of erosion.
   e. There is a thrust fault at (*A,* 1-1; *B,* 2-2 and 7-7; *C,* 3-3 and 5-5; *D,* 4-4; *E,* no location).
   f. There is a tension fault at (*A,* 1-1; *B,* 2-2 and 7-7; *C,* 3-3; *D,* 4-4; *E,* no location).
   g. There is an unconformity at (*A,* 1-1; *B,* 2-2 and 7-7; *C,* 4-4; *D,* 6-6; *E,* no location).
   h. There are dikes at (*A,* 1-1 and 7-7; *B,* 2-2 and 7-7; *C,* 3-3 and 4-4; *D,* 5-5 and 6-6; *E,* no location).
   i. There is a sill at (*A,* 1-1; *B,* 2-2 and 7-7; *C,* 4-4; *D,* 5-5; *E,* no location).
   j. There is a batholith at (*A,* 1-1; *B,* 2-2 and 7-7; *C,* 3-3 and 5-5; *D,* 4-4; *E,* no location).
   k. There is a laccolith at (*A,* 1-1; *B,* 2-2 and 7-7; *C,* 3-3 and 4-4; *D,* 5-5; *E,* no location).
   l. There is evidence of a long period of erosion at (*A,* 1-1; *B,* 2-2 and 7-7; *C,* 4-4; *D,* 6-6; *E,* no location).
   m. There is evidence of a relatively short period of erosion at (*A,* 1-1; *B,* 2-2 and 7-7; *C,* 4-4; *D,* 6-6; *E,* no location).
   n. There is evidence of a period of mountain building at (*A,* I; *B,* III; *C,* 1-1; *D,* 4-4; *E,* no location).
   o. The rocks at III are most likely to be (*A,* granite; *B,* basalt; *C,* marble; *D,* schist-like; *E,* sandstone).
   p. The rocks at I are most likely to be (*A,* granite; *B,* basalt; *C,* limestone; *D,* schist-like; *E,* sandstone).
   q. The rocks in 3-3 are most likely to be (*A,* granite; *B,* gneiss; *C,* limestone; *D,* schist; *E,* shale).
   r. Recognizable fossils are most likely to be found in (*A,* I; *B,* III; *C,* 3-3; *D,* 4-4; *E,* no location).
   s. The earliest event among the following is the formation of (*A,* 1-1; *B,* 2-2; *C,* 3-3; *D,* 4-4; *E,* 6-6).

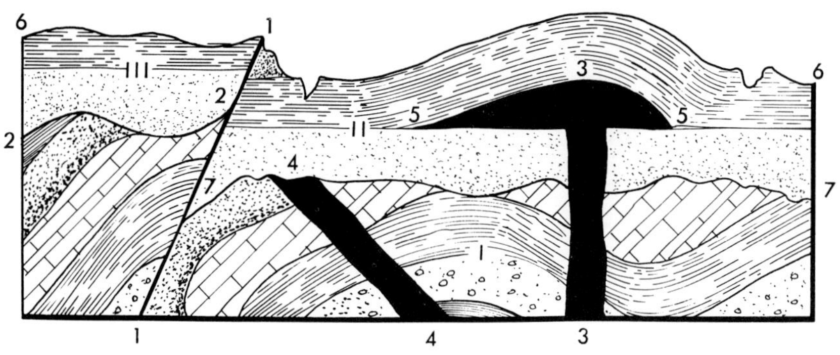

t. The structure 7-7 was formed after the formation of (*A,* 1-1; *B,* 3-3; *C,* 4-4; *D,* 5-5; *E,* 6-6).

FOR FURTHER READING

1. Garrels, R. M., *A Textbook of Geology.* New York: Harper and Brothers, 1951.
   The problems involved in reconstructing the past history of the earth are treated in Chapters 3, 14, and 15.
2. Dunbar, C. O., *Historical Geology.* New York: John Wiley and Sons, 1949.
   An excellent text in historical geology. The first four chapters deal with the principles used in deciphering the record written in the rocks of the earth.
3. Mather, K. F., and S. L. Mason, *Source Book in Geology.* New York: McGraw-Hill Book Co., 1939.
   The following original papers are recommended in connection with this chapter: Leonardo da Vinci, "Origin and Meaning of Fossils," *p. 3; Hutton,* "Theory of the Earth," *p. 92; Smith,* "The Strata of England," *p. 201; Darwin,* "The Imperfections of the Geologic Record of Life Development," *p. 363; Lyell,* "Uniformitarianism," *p. 263.*
4. Paperback: Verrill, A. H., *The Strange Story of Our Earth.* Premier, 35¢.

10

RECONSTRUCTION OF EARTH HISTORY

THE HYPOTHESES as to the mode of the formation of the earth are discussed in connection with the origin of the solar system (Chapter 39). No matter which hypothesis we accept, it appears definite that the earth came into being at the same time as the other members of the solar system; this event, according to present speculation, is assumed to have taken place about five billion years ago. Further, it appears certain that the earth passed through a molten stage. Hence a long interval of time in hundreds of millions of years must be allowed for cooling, formation of crust, formation of an atmosphere, condensation of waters, and the beginnings of erosion and sedimentation. We have no record in the rocks for this interval of time; nowhere do we find rocks that represent original parts of the earth's crust. The events of this long era of crust formation can only be surmised through imagination based on our observations of the lava in the craters of Hawaiian and other volcanoes. As the crust formed there would be periodic eruptions of liquid which would engulf the solid fragments; then new crusts would form. Eventually a solid crust formed over the major part of the planet, and cooling and igneous activity on a gigantic scale continued for millions of years, until the waters condensed to fill the depressed ocean basins and the familiar water cycle began and the sequence of erosion, sedimentation, and crustal and molten rock movements started on a large scale. As shown in Table 9–1, page 136, the interval of time from the birth of the solar system to the formation of the earliest sedimentary rocks is called the Azoic (lifeless) Era, and its duration is placed hypothetically at one to three billion years.

PRE–CAMBRIAN INTERVAL

The rocks from the beginning of sedimentation to the beginning of the Paleozoic Era are without fossils to date them and, for the most part, are extensively gnarled and metamorphosed. The beginning of life must have started in the early part of this interval which covers nearly three-fourths of geologic time or $\frac{3}{4}$ of 2 billion = 1,500,000,000 years (minimum). This interval is called Pre-Cambrian because in the first period of the Paleozoic Era, the Cambrian, the fossil record is abundant. However, in order that there should be an abundance of relatively complex invertebrates at the beginning of the Cambrian a long interval of time is required for the evolution of unicellular forms of life to highly developed invertebrates. The absence of hard parts in the lower plants and animals and the deformations of the Pre-Cambrian rocks account for the absence of fossils. The only evidences of animal life in Pre-Cambrian rocks are a few deposits of calcareous algae and the trails and burrows of wormlike creatures.

The ancient Pre-Cambrian rocks are extensively deformed and metamorphosed. In North America they are found in the gorge of the Grand Canyon (see page 156ff.) and in the Canadian Shield described in the next section. It should be noted that the major part of the mineral wealth of North America (iron, copper, nickel, and other metals) is found in the Pre-Cambrian rocks. As shown in Table 9–1, the Pre-Cambrian interval is divided into two eras: the lower Pre-Cambrian or Archeozoic and the upper Pre-Cambrian or Proterozoic. Both of them are marked by extensive orogenic movements and huge granitic intrusions.

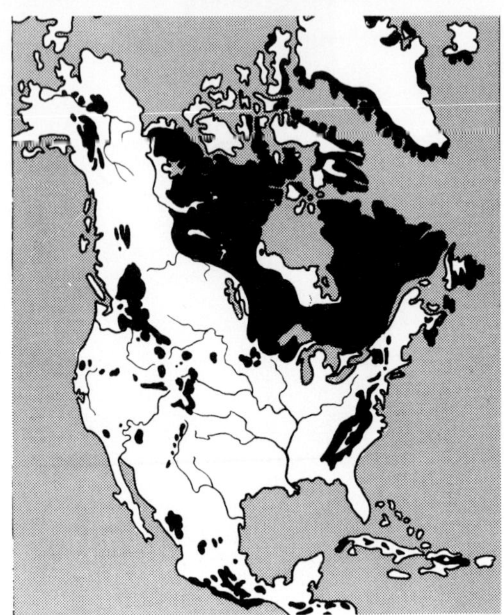

Fig. 10–1 *Areas in North America where Pre-Cambrian rocks are at the surface. (U.S. Geological Survey)*

ARCHEOZOIC ERA: THE CANADIAN SHIELD

The rocks of the Archeozoic Era are also conspicuously exposed throughout large parts of northeastern Canada. (Refer to Figure 10–1.) Throughout this whole region, referred to as the Canadian Shield, can be seen ancient granites, all that remains of former mountain ranges called the Laurentians formed during the close of the Archeozoic Era. It is, of course, impossible even to surmise the height of this great mountain range when it was reared out of the depths of the earth. In Labrador some peaks still have an elevation of four thousand feet, and the Adirondacks, a conspicuous extension of these mountains into New York State, have an elevation of five thousand feet. Both of these mountainous areas have been re-elevated since their formation. The rugged character of certain parts of Wisconsin and Minnesota around the western and northern shores of Lake Superior is due to the resistance to erosion of these ancient outcropping Archeozoic granites and diorites. Since they have been subjected in places to processes of erosion during the last four geological eras, it is easy to believe that these mountains when first formed must have been a mighty range.

The Canadian Shield comprises about two million square miles of granitic gneiss which must have been intruded as molten magma into older rocks which have been removed by erosion. It represents a region of great crustal stability. During most of geologic time, while the seas were advancing and then retreating and while great geosynclines were being formed and filled with materials which later formed the great mountain systems of the North American continent, the Canadian Shield was relatively stationary, a large island of resistant igneous rocks in a changing continent.

PROTEROZOIC ERA

On the edges of the island-like Canadian Shield with its core of Archeozoic rocks can be found Proterozoic rocks. These rocks are prominently exposed through large parts of Ontario in the vicinity of the Great Lakes and in northern Michigan. Lake Superior occupies a great trough where the edge of Proterozoic rocks lies upon the older Archeozoic rocks. From an economic point of view these rocks are of very great significance. The great iron-ore bodies of the Mesabi Range in northern Minnesota, the native copper-bearing formations of the Keweenaw Peninsula in upper Michigan, the rich deposits of nickel, silver, and gold found in Ontario, and many other important ore bodies are found in the Proterozoic rocks on the edge of the Canadian Shield. Similarly, many important mineral deposits in other parts of the world occur in Proterozoic rocks. These deposits are the result of extensive flows of magma which produced a great mountain system, the Killarnies, running in an easterly-by-north direction from northern Wisconsin into Canada. They have since been largely eroded away, though the remains of the granitic batholiths are still conspicuous in northern Wisconsin.

Just when forms of life appeared, of course, is uncertain. Although evidence of life in the Proterozoic rocks is relatively meager, it is known that life existed in the form of marine algae, sponges, and simple forms of life having no hard parts which would favor preservation.

Reference has already been made to the evidence of extensive crustal movements in the region of the Grand Canyon. Thus, the Hakatai Shale (*H*) and the Bass Limestone (*B*) shown in Figure 10–7 are Proterozoic.

Pre-Cambrian Rocks in the United States. There are a number of interesting regions in the United States where Pre-Cambrian rocks are found. The present Appalachians were formed in a great geosyncline which filled with debris from the erosion of former mountains farther east, the so-called Older Appalachian Mountains. The picturesque Highlands of the Hudson, the Blue Ridge Mountains of Virginia, and the Great Smokies of North Carolina are the remnants of a former Pre-Cambrian mountain system. The monotony of the great plain east of the Rocky Mountains is broken by the Black Hills of South Dakota. Here are found the highest mountains east of the Rockies. The Black Hills were formed by sharp upwarping of the earth's crust in this region. The area was first domed by a great vertical uplift; then erosion removed the younger rocks (Paleozoic and Mesozoic) from the central part of the dome, exposing a core of Pre-Cambrian rocks beneath. The Black Hills not only are of interest scenically, but also are one of the important mineral-producing regions of this country. The largest

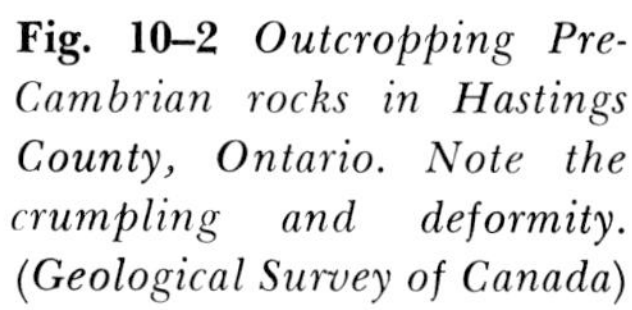

Fig. 10–2 *Outcropping Pre-Cambrian rocks in Hastings County, Ontario. Note the crumpling and deformity. (Geological Survey of Canada)*

gold mine in the United States is the Homestake Mine in South Dakota.

PALEOZOIC ERA

With the beginning of this era the seas inundated more than 30 per cent of the present continent; life appeared in great abundance in these seas. Evolutionary processes resulted in many forms of life. The two earliest periods are often called the Age of Marine Invertebrates because the trilobites, brachiopods, and shell-bearing mollusks were the highest forms of life during these periods. During Middle Paleozoic time – the Silurian and Devonian periods – the freshwater vertebrates became more common, and gradually some of these adapted themselves to life on land. These were the first amphibians. During the Devonian period another very significant form of life appeared. Land plants became common. During the Carboniferous period, the land became covered with a great variety of plants, some of which have persisted down to the present time. Thus, the rocks formed from sediments of this whole era contain numerous index fossils which make the task of correlating them relatively simple. This is one reason why the rock record for this era, which constitutes one-sixth of geological time, is so much more complete than the record of Pre-Cambrian time. The era has been divided into six geological periods: Cambrian, Ordovician, Silurian, Devonian, Carboniferous, and Permian – named in order of time from earliest to latest, on the basis of definite orogenic movements in localized regions throughout the world. The Ordovician period, for example, was closed by the Taconian disturbance which produced highlands running in a northeasterly direction from eastern Pennsylvania, across New York, to include the present Green Mountains in Vermont.

Many significant events occurred during the Paleozoic Era which later were to affect the economic development of our country. For example, during Silurian time a large part of the interior of the North American continent was beneath the seas. (Refer to Figure 9–7.) Most of the states of Michigan, Ohio, Indiana, Illinois, Iowa, and large parts of Wisconsin and Oklahoma were then submerged. In these seas were deposited the extensive sediments which have become the limestones now of such great economic importance. These are the Niagaran limestones, which are exposed at Niagara Falls and in many places in Michigan, Ohio, Illinois, and Wisconsin. The Silurian rocks along the length of the Appalachian Mountains also contain extensive deposits of iron ore, especially important near Birmingham, Alabama.

The fluctuations of level of the interior of the North American continent continued during the latter part of the Paleozoic Era, at times being uplifted, at other times depressed, thus repeatedly forming vast lowland swamps. The climate was very mild and supported a luxuriant vegetation, such as is found in the tropics today. In time, the swamps became filled with a thick accumulation of vegetable matter, which, when later submerged and subjected to pressure from above, formed our present coal deposits. (Refer to Figure 9–8.) In some regions this fluctuation of the earth's surface occurred so many times that six to eight or even more different seams of coal can be found separated by shale, limestone, and sandstone. Two-thirds of the world's known reserves are found in the United States and Canada. Scientists have not yet come to complete agreement as to the mode of formation of petroleum and natural gas, but geologists agree that many of the great oil-producing rocks are Paleozoic in age, especially those of the Carboniferous and Ordovician periods.

The Permian period, at the end of the Paleozoic Era, was marked by many striking changes. The interior of our continent gradually emerged and the climate became arid, resulting in the evaporation of certain arms of the former seas. The dissolved salts, principally sodium chloride and calcium sulfate, then were deposited to form the extensive layers of salt and gypsum now found in Kansas, Oklahoma, Texas, and New Mexico. The great deposits of salt in Michigan and New York resulted from the evaporation of Silurian seas. The southwestern deposits have taken on greater economic significance during recent years because of the discovery of potash in New Mexico. These represent the first extensive deposits of potash — an essential in fertilizers — found in the United States.

The Paleozoic Era was closed by a very significant event: the elevation of the Newer Appalachian Mountains. Reference has already been made to the Older Appalachian Mountains, Pre-Cambrian in age, extending from the Hudson Highlands in New York through Pennsylvania and including the Blue Ridge Mountains and the Great Smokies. These are a striking remnant of a once much more conspicuous mountain system in this part of the continent. During most of Paleozoic time, there existed a huge geosyncline just to the west of this mountain system. (Refer to Figure 9–5.) Whether the crustal forces that elevated the great depth of sediments in this trough into the present Newer Appalachian Mountains came from the southeast or from the northwest is impossible to say; but these forces were great enough to form peaks which may have been five miles in height. The folding throughout the length of this mountain system was intense. There is reason to believe that the crustal shortening in this region may have been as much as one hundred miles. The Appalachian Mountains are now much reduced in altitude as a result of gradational forces. They have been peneplained at least three times and re-elevated as many times.

MESOZOIC ERA

The rock records of events in this era, which represents one-fourteenth of geological time, are found principally in the western part of our continent. The era opened with a sea creeping down from the north along the present location of the Rocky Mountains. Eventually this sea reached from the Arctic to the present Gulf of Mexico. (Refer to Figure 9–9 and page 139.) Farther to the west, along the edge of the present continent, there were located smaller geosynclines. One of these became the region which eventually gave rise to the present Sierra Nevada. The strata of that geosyncline during the middle Mesozoic were folded strongly and intruded by huge batholiths. During the late Mesozoic, these complex mountains were worn away by erosion, and in the early Cenozoic there began large-scale faulting which eventually produced the present Sierras. The highest peak in the United States, Mount Whitney, 14,501 feet in elevation, is in the Sierra Nevada. The Yosemite National Park, famous for its superb mountain scenery, glacier-cut valleys, and high waterfalls, is in the Sierra Nevada. These igneous rocks have been a rich source of gold. The placer deposits of gold which were responsible for the gold rush to California in 1849 were formed by water washing gold from disintegrated rock into the stream channels.

The Mesozoic Era was closed in a characteristic fashion by (1) general orogenic movements, (2) extensive intrusive and volcanic activity. During the era the Appalachian Mountains, which had been reared at the end of the Paleozoic Era, were almost planed to base level. At the end of Mesozoic time, they were re-elevated perhaps as much as half a mile, and the cycle of erosion started anew. This accounts for the many entrenched meanders and rejuvenated stream systems in the Appalachians. Mountain building occurred on a grand scale to form the present Rocky Mountains — the so-called Laramide Revolution. Mountains were upthrust from Mexico to Alaska through the overlying Paleozoic and Mesozoic sediments. With the passage of time, however, the Paleozoic and Mesozoic rocks have been removed by erosion from the core but not from the flanks, thus exposing the present granitic core of the Rockies which is Pre-Cambrian in age. One of the features of this orogeny was the formation of great thrusts faults (see page 124) which follow in general the central backbone of the system. As previously noted, there are places where the older Paleozoic rocks have slid eastward several miles over younger Mesozoic rocks. Such an overthrust, the Lewis, can be seen in Glacier National Park. The Rockies were peneplained and were re-elevated during the Cenozoic Era.

The Mesozoic Era is the age of reptiles. One kind of amphibian that had appeared during late Paleozoic time gradually evolved into reptiles, which flourished during the Mesozoic Era on the land, in the seas, and in the air. In the latter part of this era there were many forms of seed flora, and these forms of life have continued to develop to the present day. Birds appeared during this era. But the most spectacular forms of life were the dinosaurs. These animals increased in such numbers and sizes that they were the rulers of their age and were the most unusual animals the world has ever seen. Some dinosaurs measured from sixty to eighty feet in length and had a body weight as great as forty tons. Not all dinosaurs, however, were huge. Some were carnivorous and lived on the land; some lived a sluggish existence in swamps and were vegetarians; some were alert and rapid in gait; some had a protective armor. They throve over a period of time twice as long as that of the mammals which are dominant today. The dinosaurs had characteristics in common: they reproduced from eggs, were true reptiles, had an unusually low brain capacity, and required a comparatively mild climate for existence. One of the unsolved problems of science is the reason for their sudden disappearance. It is believed that the evolution of the fleeter, more intelligent mammals, together with cooler climates, the changing vegetation which was their food, and the disappearance of the

Fig. 10–3 *Hypothetical reconstruction of a landscape of the Mesozoic Era, Jurassic period. (From Wolfgang F. Pauli,* The World of Life, *published by Houghton Mifflin Company)*

Fig. 10–4 *North America during the Pleistocene Ice Age.* (*U.S. Geological Survey*)

swamps in which the huge dinosaurs lived are the main causes of their relatively rapid extinction. As the huge dinosaurs began to disappear, the descendants of a small, short-legged, long-faced species, not unlike the modern hedgehog, which had appeared during the Middle Mesozoic, began to evolve rapidly and gave rise to the dominant form of animal life during the next era — the mammals.

CENOZOIC ERA

During the Cenozoic Era, and in no other era, the North American continent remained emergent, except for coastal regions, and changes up to the present in the appearance of the continent have in general been due to four geological forces: (1) long-continued erosion, (2) volcanism, (3) crustal movements (epeirogeny), and (4) extensive glaciation. Thus, during the early part of the Cenozoic Era, there occurred great fissure eruptions in Washington and Oregon that covered an area of 300,000 square miles with basalt flows in places as thick as five thousand feet. The most significant event, however, of the Cenozoic Era, geologically speaking, was the long period of glaciation that covered most of the northern part of the North American continent. This occurred during the last period of the Cenozoic Era — the Pleistocene (most recent time) — which began about a million years ago.

The surface features of much of the northern half of the North American continent are, in large part, due to the work of the vast ice sheets which extended from Long Island westward through southern Ohio, Indiana, Illinois, Kansas, North Dakota, and Montana to the Pacific Ocean. An area as large as four million square miles was covered with ice, which undoubtedly approached in thickness that of the ice sheet covering Greenland today, which in places is known to be about 9700 feet thick. The mass of accumulated ice flowed out principally from a region east of Hudson Bay, the Labrador Cap, and from a center west of Hudson Bay, the Keewatin Cap, though there were other minor centers of origin. It slowly moved in a southerly direction, and at the time of its greatest advance came as far south as the present Missouri and Ohio rivers. There is evidence indicating that during pre-glacial times the Missouri River flowed into Hudson Bay. But the advance of the ice forced the Missouri to move south, and the present course is approximately where the ice had its farthest advance. Similarly, in the vicinity of Cincinnati, the advance of the ice helped to establish the present course of the Ohio River. During the million years of Pleistocene time, there have been at least four main advances and retreats of the ice sheet. (Refer to Table 10–1.)

TABLE 10–1 CALENDAR OF PLEISTOCENE TIME

PERIOD	NAME	YEARS FROM PRESENT ESTIMATED
Fourth interglacial	Present	25,000
Fourth glacial	Wisconsin	125,000
Third interglacial	Sangamon	250,000
Third glacial	Illinoisan	350,000
Second interglacial	Yarmouth	650,000
Second glacial	Kansan	750,000
First interglacial	Aftonian	950,000
First glacial	Nebraskan	1,000,000

The ice of the first advance, the Nebraskan, came as far south as Kansas City, Missouri. The Kansan came almost as far. The Illinoisan ice originated in Labrador and did not go very far beyond the triangle formed by the Ohio and Mississippi rivers. The glacial ice of the most recent ice age, the Wisconsin, advanced and retreated more than once, but never went beyond the center of the present states of Indiana, Illinois, and Iowa.

The mantle soil all through the glaciated region, of course, is glacial till. As it moved southward, the great mass of ice ground and crushed the surface rocks. It thus acted as a huge transporting agent, transferring and depositing the glacial drift which composes the earth's surface throughout the whole glaciated area. The transported materials are of all dimensions, from fine glacial flour to huge boulders weighing as much as six thousand tons. The landscapes of the northern states and those of Canada show the many characteristics of a glaciated region – a soil composed of glacial till entirely different in composition from the bedrock, numerous moraines, eskers, thousands of glacial lakes, outwash plains, and alluvial fans, poor surface drainage, glacial striae in the surface of the bedrock where it had been exposed to moving ice – all the phenomena discussed in Chapter 7.

There is no accepted explanation for the temperature and snow condition which caused the advance and retreat of these continental ice sheets. It is known that the interglacial periods were warm enough to cause the retreat of the ice and long enough to allow plant life to re-establish itself on the new glacial deposits and to permit extensive disintegration of mantle soil by weathering and the formation by growing plants of a fine soil known as *gumbo till.* In many places the successive sheets of glacial drift are separated by a layer of gumbo till including a layer of buried wood and other vegetation. The mantle from the last Wisconsin advance of the ice is not covered with a layer of fine gumbo till like that of the earlier ice sheets. This is evidence that the retreat of the Wisconsin ice is so recent that not enough time has elapsed to form gumbo till. By dating [1] through studies of remnants of a forest in Wisconsin pushed over and buried by an advancing glacier, the length of time back to the last ice sheet is found to be less than 12,000 years.

With the final disappearance of the enormous ice load on the northern part of the continent, the accumulated strains of a million years within the earth's crust were able to exert themselves, and the northern part of the continent itself began to rise. This elevation of the land es-

[1] By means of radioactive carbon present in fossil wood (see Chapter 39, page 647).

tablished the present drainage of the Great Lakes from Lake Erie by way of the Niagara River into Lake Ontario and the St. Lawrence.

Mountain Building. All during Cenozoic time, the seas never encroached upon the present North American continent. In many regions the continent was being elevated, especially in the west. The cutting of the Grand Canyon in Arizona occurred during Cenozoic time as that whole region was gradually uplifted. Re-elevation of the Rocky Mountains after a long process of erosion also occurred during this era. This caused every river system which originated in the Rocky Mountains to cut a channel through some mountain range. The channel of the Arkansas River through the Royal Gorge in Colorado was established before the mountains in that vicinity were uplifted. The stream did not cut its present canyon outlet until the whole region began to rise. A few years ago there were a series of several earthquake shocks in the vicinity of Helena, Montana, caused by crustal adjustments along faults in that region. The Cascade Mountains, which run parallel to our western coast, were formed during the latter part of the Cenozoic Era. While these mountains were being elevated, volcanism was active throughout this whole region. The geysers and hot springs of Yellowstone National Park are the dying ashes of this episode of volcanic activity. Mount Shasta (14,161 feet) in northern California and Mount Rainier (14,363 feet) in the Cascades in Washington are extinct volcanoes originally formed during this period. The latest volcanic activity in the region was a minor eruption from Mount Lassen in northern California in 1914.

Changes in Life. There were many significant changes in the forms of plant and animal life during the Cenozoic Era. Mammals which appeared during the latter part of the Mesozoic Era became as dominant as the reptiles had been in the preceding era. The mammals were much more agile and intelligent than the ponderous dinosaurs, and adapted themselves to changing environments more readily. The important changes in life forms were (1) the modernization of plants and animals and (2) the development of the present mammalian strains such as the horse, camel, elephant, and the primates, which had their culmination in man. The word Cenozoic means *recent life.* Most present-day forms of life evolved during this era, which is the shortest of the geological eras, representing only about one-thirtieth of geologic time. Trees of modern types – oaks, maples, beeches, palms, pines – appeared. Fishes were likewise modernized. Amphibians were represented by salamanders, toads, and frogs; reptiles included crocodiles and turtles; birds no longer were reptilian in character, but belonged to modern types. Mammals differed from former types of animals in that they were warm-blooded and had milk glands to nourish their young. They penetrated farther into the colder climates of the earth because of an outer covering of fur. In brain capacity mammals greatly exceeded previous forms of animal life.

THE RISE OF MAN

Man's gradual emergence and rise to dominance took place in the Pleistocene period of the Cenozoic Era. There is general agreement that man evolved from lower forms of primates and that he has been in existence for more than 500,000 years. Our knowledge of his development is fragmentary compared to our knowledge of the dinosaur or of the horse. Because of his greater intelligence, as compared with other animals, he was able to avoid sudden death under circumstances favorable to deep burial, which is necessary for the preservation of fossil remains; and it is very probable that at an early date he began the practice of burying his dead. Interment in a shallow grave or above ground, where the processes of weathering are in full operation, does not favor the preservation of fossil remains. These facts account for the comparative rarity of authentic fossil remains of early man. They have also added to the difficulty of tracing, in detail, the story of his rise. The discoveries that are largely responsible for our present knowledge concerning early man can be briefly discussed.

1. *Java Ape-Man.* His are considered to be among the oldest of human remains—*Pithecanthropus erectus* (the ape-man who walked erect). They were discovered in Java in 1891 in a gravel bed by Eugene Dubois, a Dutch army surgeon. Many extinct mammals occurred in the same bed and indicate early or mid-Pleistocene age. This man stood about five feet six inches in height and had a brain volume of about 985 milliliters, as compared with about 600 milliliters in the largest apes and 1240 milliliters in the Australian bush savage, the lowest type of living race.

2. *Peking Man.* In 1928, in a cave near Peking, China, were discovered many examples of *Sinanthropus pekingensis.* The brain cavity was a little larger than that of the Java man. Three of the best-preserved skulls have a brain volume of about 1000 milliliters. Charred animal remains and many crude stone instruments were also found, a fact which indicates that *Sinanthropus,* though he may have been a species of *Pithecanthropus,* was close to man since he was already exercising intelligent use of tools to alter the conditions imposed by the environment. For example, he knew the use of fire and fashioned simple weapons and tools. An abundance of extinct mammals in the same deposits date the remains as early or mid-Pleistocene.

3. *Australopithecus africanus.* On the plateau plains of South Africa there have recently (1936–48) been found many skeletal remains which may prove to have been earliest man, *Australopithecus africanus.* From the evidence that has been uncovered, anthropologists, geologists, and paleontologists seem to believe (1958) that *Australopithecus* was a progressive ape and was closer to man than to the anthropoids, that he had a brain capacity between that of the highest living apes and the smallest-brained human beings, and that he was living about a million years ago during the Pliocene or very early Pleistocene period. If later discoveries substantiate this judgment, it will prove that this early man used fire and hunted even before *Pithecanthropus erectus* flourished.

4. *Neanderthal Man.* In 1856, interesting human remains were found in the valley of Neander, near Düsseldorf, Germany. Since then similar skeletons of men, women, and children have been found in caves in Belgium, France, Gibraltar, and Croatia. This race apparently also occupied parts of Asia and Africa and is the best known of all extinct species of man. The Neanderthals were short and stocky, about five feet four inches tall, with legs slightly curved at the thighs to compensate for the fact that the spine lacked the cervical curvature, and with very large heads set forward on the shoulders. The face was probably huge and brutal, yet the brain was about equal in size to that of modern man (1400 to 1600 milliliters). The Neanderthals made fairly good stone and bone implements and ornamental objects, and dressed in furs. They appeared during the third interglacial stage of the Pleistocene age, about 250,000 years ago. They disappeared suddenly about the middle of the last glacial age and were replaced by the modern species of *Homo sapiens,* the *Cro-Magnon Man.* It is possible that some of the lowest type of living human beings (the bushmen of Australia) may have a mixture of Neanderthaloid strains.

5. *Cro-Magnon Man.* We have said that the entire story of the development of man took place in the Pleistocene Period, a span of probably a million years. (See the geological timetable on page 136.) If all the events of geological time were crowded into a span of seventy years, then primitive man appeared on the earth eight hours ago, and the first modern man appeared less than a second ago.

Cro-Magnon man, who was modern in appearance, came to western Europe during the last ice age. He walked erect, had a cranial capacity fully equal to that of modern man, and had a high forehead. Many of his ancient cave homes have been found in southern Europe adorned with drawings of animals and scenes of his times. His people were the ancestors of certain living southern Europeans. As a race they were distinct from *Homo primigenius* and have been called *Homo sapiens,* or discerning man. Their weapons were much improved over those of preceding man. The bow and arrow were common. They developed the art of self-adornment with shell beads, bracelets, and improved clothing. All living human beings are apparently varieties of this single species, *Homo sapiens.*

The rise of man is usually described in terms of his culture as revealed by his weapons and tools, as follows: Paleolithic (Old Stone) Age; Neolithic (New Stone) Age; Bronze Age; Iron Age. The Cro-Magnon people represent the last of the Paleolithic cultures. What we now call civilization began with Neolithic peoples, the descendants of the Cro-Magnons. They appeared in large numbers just after the passing of the last ice age about 12,000 years ago. They developed unusual techniques for shaping and polishing articles of stone. They learned to make pottery, weave baskets, spin thread, and make cloth; they constructed homes, domesticated animals, cultivated grains, established villages, and started community life.

There is much evidence of the presence of man in Pleistocene time in North America. In 1925, for example, there were discov-

Fig. 10–5 *Hypothetical reconstruction of the evolution and relationships of man and of the anthropoid apes. Key: 1, Primitive primate. 2, Prototypal anthropoid. 3, Primitive anthropoid. 4, Pithecanthropus erectus. 5, Sinanthropus pekingensis. 6, Australopithecus africanus. 7, Neanderthal man. 8, Cro-Magnon man. 9, American (Caucasian). 10, Australian black-fellow. 11, Chinese (Mongolian). 12, Hottentot (Negro). a, Anthropoid apes.* (*American Museum of Natural History*)

ered near Folsom, New Mexico, crude stone implements and many arrowheads along with the bones of an extinct species of bison. The arrowheads have a distinctive appearance, and similar ones have been found in many other places in North America. The culture revealed by these stone instruments has come to be referred to as the *Folsom Culture* and was widely distributed over this country as early as about ten thousand years ago. But when the first Europeans reached this country, the culture of the aborigines was still that of the Stone Age.

The neolithic cultures of Asia Minor, Persia, and Egypt were supplanted by the historical cultures of the Bronze Age, which can be traced in Egypt back to about 5000 B.C. and in Chaldea, in the valley of the Tigris and Euphrates, to about 4500 B.C. Copper and bronze could be fabricated into tools and weapons far superior to those made of stone – at the cost of much less labor – and could be used for many articles, such as nails and wire, for which stone is not adaptable at all. Iron came into use in Egypt in about 3000 B.C. With the steady accumulation thenceforth of material means, man became more and more free to devote himself to exploring the resources of his mind and develop the instruments and collect the data that led to the growth of the sciences.

HISTORY OF THE GRAND CANYON

The Grand Canyon of the Colorado River in Arizona comprises one of the most beautiful exposures of rocks on the entire earth. This brief reconstruction of the history of the region is given because here the rocks that formed during the long interval of more than a billion years from the Archeozoic Era to the Mesozoic Era, inclusively, can be studied in relation to each other in a single locality. Thus this description will serve to summarize the principles studied in this and the preceding chapters.

The canyon is a young V-shaped valley, and the process of downcutting is still going on rapidly. In places the canyon is about six thousand feet deep, and it varies in width from five to fifteen miles. Most of the rock walls are sedimentary rocks, but at the bottom the river has cut a channel one thousand feet deep into metamorphosed rocks of the Archeozoic Era. These rocks are of great interest, because they are among the oldest readily accessible on the

Fig. 10–6 *The rocks in the Grand Canyon.* (*After L. F. Nobel*)

ERA	PERIOD and EPOCH	GROUP AND FORMATION	KIND OF ROCK	THICKNESS IN FEET
PALEOZOIC	CARBONIFEROUS – PERMIAN	UNCONFORMITY Kaibab limestone	Limestone and sandstone	525
		Coconino sandstone	Sandstone	350
		Hermit shale	Sandy shale	225
		Supai formation	Sandstone and shale with some limestone	825
	CARBONIFEROUS – MISS.	UNCONFORMITY Redwall limestone	Limestone	450 to 500
	DEVONIAN	Temple Butte ls.	Limestone and sandstone	0-36
	CAMBRIAN	GREAT UNCONFORMITY Tonto group: Muav limestone	Sandy shale and limestone	100
		Tonto group: Bright Angel shale	Sandy shale	450 to 650
		Tonto group: Tapeats sandstone	Sandstone	225
PROTEROZOIC	ALGONKIAN	GREAT UNCONFORMITY Pu Unkar and Chuar groups of Grand Canyon series	Sandstone and shale with some limestone; contains sheets and dikes of lava	0 to 12000
	ARCHEAN	GREAT UNCONFORMITY Au Vishnu schist	Schist, granite, and gneiss	Not known

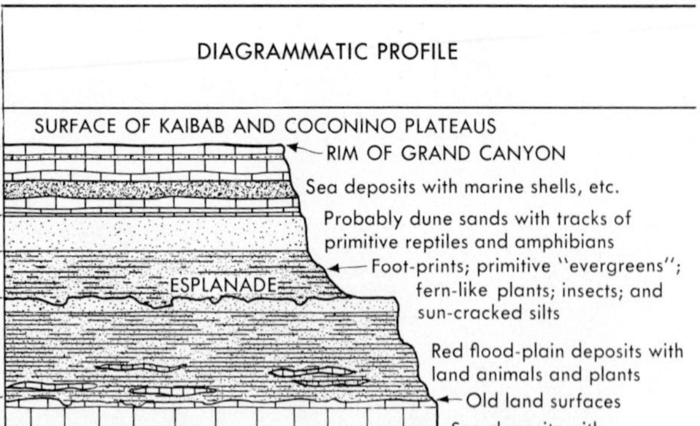

Fig. 10–7 *The Grand Canyon of the Colorado River, north wall.* *(N. W. Carkhuff, U.S. Geological Survey)*

face of the earth. There is no doubt that these rocks were originally deposited as fine mud beneath an ancient sea, but after consolidation into shale they were subjected to enormous pressures and heat to form a schist — the Vishnu schist. (Refer to Figures 10–6 and 10–8.) The enormous pressures were due to mountain-building forces which folded the shales in an extremely complex manner and metamorphosed them to schists. This conclusion is supported by the fact that there are granitic intrusions into the Vishnu schist. Recall that in Chapters 6 and 8 it was pointed out that coarse-grained igneous rocks are formed either by slow cooling at considerable depth below the earth's surface, or as a result of granitization of other rocks under the stresses generated in mountain-building upheavals.

The evidence of a great erosional period in this region is indicated by the very distinct unconformity which marks the upper boundary of the Vishnu schist. This unconformity is indicated in Figures 10–6 and 10–7 by the symbol *Au*. The Vishnu schist (*V*) is immediately below this unconformity. The rocks immediately above the *Au* surface in Figure 10–7 are sedimentary rocks, though now inclined at an angle, such as the Bass limestone *B*, and the Hakatai shale *H*. It is here that there are to be found the first evidences of life. These rocks were deposited during a period of submergence when this whole region, undoubtedly, was an extension of the present Pacific Ocean. Interestingly enough, the rocks belonging to the second geological era are exposed only in the north wall of the canyon. Not a trace of them can be seen along the south wall. In fact, the unconformity at the bottom of the canyon in the south wall marks a lost time gap of many millions of years, since the superincumbent rocks are Paleozoic in age. These Proterozoic rocks when deposited were horizontal. But at the close of the era this region had a second emergence and was uplifted many

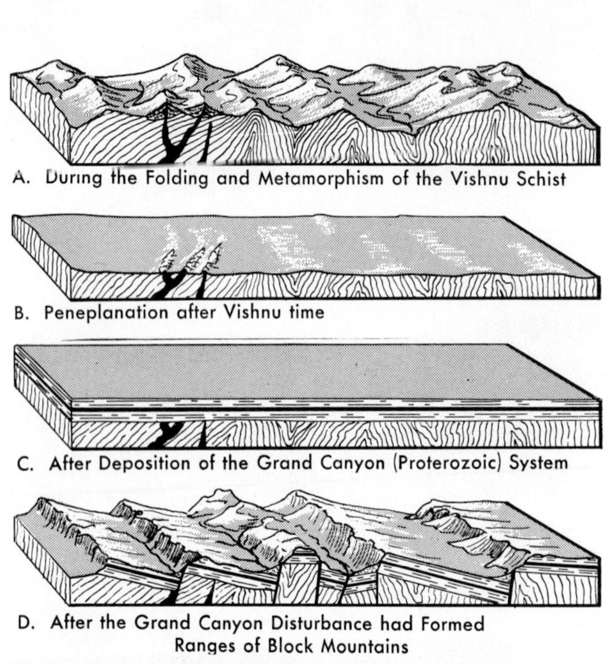

A. During the Folding and Metamorphism of the Vishnu Schist
B. Peneplanation after Vishnu time
C. After Deposition of the Grand Canyon (Proterozoic) System
D. After the Grand Canyon Disturbance had Formed Ranges of Block Mountains

E. Near Peneplanation at the Close of Proterozoic Time

Fig. 10–8 *Six stages in the Pre-Cambrian history of the Grand Canyon region. (Adapted by permission from* Outlines of Historical Geology, *by C. Schuchert and C. O. Dunbar, copyright 1950, published by John Wiley and Sons, Inc.)*

thousands of feet above the sea. The uplift was accompanied by extensive tilting and faulting as evidenced by the many faults that have been discovered in the Proterozoic rocks. (Refer to Figures 10–7 and 10–8.) In some places, the displacement of rock along the faults amounts to hundreds of feet. But with the passage of time, degradational forces again leveled this whole region to a second prominent erosional surface, forming an unconformity marked *Pu* in Figures 10–6 and 10–7.

Just above the *Pu* unconformity are many thousands of feet of Paleozoic rocks. These were deposited after the peneplained region at the end of Proterozoic time had been again submerged. (Refer to Figure 10–8.) However, there is not a continuous record of deposition of sedimentary material, because rock correlations definitely indicate the presence of three unconformities. In these rocks are many fossil remains of plants and animals, and the complexity of the forms of life increases with the elevation of the rocks.

The diastrophic movements in this whole region during Paleozoic and Mesozoic time were not extensive, as indicated by the horizontal position of these rocks. That the movements were slow is indicated by an entire absence of faults and folds in these younger rocks. Another long period of submergence for this region is indicated by the great thickness of rocks of the Mesozoic Era. However, these are not present in the immediate region of the canyon, but can be seen a slight distance south and east of the Grand Canyon, where an elevation known as Cedar Mountain consists of Mesozoic rocks.

A person with a pair of binoculars can stand on the south wall of the canyon and study events which have left their impression on the canyon's north wall: evidence of volcanic activity, the submergence and emergence of this region at least five times, and violent periods of diastrophism which probably accompanied mountain building on a large scale. As stated before, the Grand Canyon is still a young valley, cut during Cenozoic time. In the distant future, millions of years from now, this impressive plateau with its awe-inspiring canyon will disappear and be carved by erosion, first into a network of ridges, then into huge flat-topped rock masses, remnants of their former grandeur.

TRENDS IN GEOLOGICAL CHANGE

Our consideration of the reconstruction of the past history of the earth completes the study of the gross changes which have occurred and are occurring now over the face of the earth: the changes of atmospheric pressure and of temperature; the blowing of the winds; the changes brought about by water on surface and subsurface; the mighty changes which build mountains and give rise to rivers of molten lava; and finally, the changes of elements to form compounds. During this study, a number of principles were introduced in a qualitative manner: for example, the expansion of gases and liquids when heated, the increase of the rigidity of solids with increase of pressure, and the combination of elements in definite ratios by weight. Finally, as a summary, a very general principle may be derived from the study made thus far, namely, that *the tendency of the changes studied is toward a system of greater stability*. The waters of the earth tend to reach sea level, whence they cannot fall to a lower level. Rocks caught in folds or faults rearrange their atoms toward denser materials in order to occupy a smaller volume, and their crystals arrange themselves in such manner as to offer the least resistance to pressure. Minerals when crystallized from magma achieve characteristic internal atomic structures which are the most stable in their particular environment. Similarly, in the few chemical changes that were studied it was found that these changes tend to proceed in the direction that can produce the most stable system of substances. Other observations indicate that this is a general trend in many changes occurring in nature — a *trend to pass from the least stable to the most stable condition.*

The study of principles thus far has been made in a qualitative manner. Quantitative data and mathematical calculations were mostly avoided, in order to give the student an opportunity to obtain a bird's-eye view of a large number of changes before attempting to isolate certain important changes and to study them in detail. The first of these, discussed in Chapter 12, is the concept of motion and force, the *agent of change*. However, in order to undertake a simple mathematical treatment it will be profitable first to review certain elementary concepts in Chapter 11.

SUMMARY

1. There is no record of the rocks which originally formed the crust of the earth. The interval of time from the birth of the earth and solar system to the formation of the earliest sedimentary rocks is placed hypothetically at one to three billion years and is called the Azoic Era.
2. The interval from the formation of the first sedimentary rocks to the beginning of the Paleozoic Era is called Pre-Cambrian and covers nearly three-fourths of recorded geologic time or 1,500,000,000 years. It is usually divided into the Archeozoic and Proterozoic eras.
3. The Pre-Cambrian rocks are without fossils to date them and most are extensively gnarled and metamorphosed. Only scant evidence of algae and trails of wormlike creatures found in Pre-Cambrian rocks indicate the appearance of low forms of life.
4. Pre-Cambrian rocks are found in North America in the Gorge of the Grand Canyon and in the Canadian Shield. The latter comprises about two million square miles of granitic gneiss rocks in Northeastern Canada and represents a region of great stability; it has been relatively stable since the end of the Proterozoic Era.
5. There are a number of conspicuous outcrops of Pre-Cambrian rocks in the United States, such as the Adirondacks, the Older Appalachian Mountains, including the Blue Ridge Mountains and the Great Smokies, the Black Hills of South Dakota, and the core of the Rocky Mountains. Most of the metallic mineral wealth (iron, copper, nickel, and so on) of North America is found in Pre-Cambrian rocks.
6. During the Paleozoic Era, the interior of the North American continent fluctuated above and below sea level many times, and thus formed the extensive deposits of salt, gypsum, and limestone of the Silurian and Devonian age, and the coal deposits of the Carboniferous period.
7. The Paleozoic period closed with the uplift of the sediments in a great geosyncline which had existed throughout the period to form the Newer Appalachian Mountains.

8. During the Paleozoic Era, forms of life gradually changed from marine invertebrates, to marine vertebrates, amphibians, and reptiles. Plants also evolved and began to cover the land.
9. The North American continent was largely emergent during Mesozoic time except for a trough running from Alaska to the Gulf of Mexico. The sediments in this trough were uplifted at the close of the era to form the first Rocky Mountains. The region of the Sierra Nevada mountains was extensively folded, intruded, and eroded during the late Mesozoic and faulted during the Cenozoic Era.
10. The Cenozoic Era was marked by (1) vast basalt flows in Oregon and Washington, (2) re-elevation of the Rocky Mountains after the first Rockies had been extensively reduced in elevation by erosion, (3) re-elevation of the plateau in Arizona which made the Grand Canyon possible, and (4) four extensive periods of glaciation.
11. Much of the geography of the upper part of the United States east of the Rockies is the result of the work of ice during four different stages of glaciation – the Nebraskan, Kansan, Illinoisan, and Wisconsin. These ice sheets were responsible for the typical glacial topography in this part of the country, the establishment in their present courses of the Mississippi, Missouri, and Ohio river systems, and the formation of the Great Lakes with the probable exception of Lake Superior.
12. The youngest mountains in North America, the Cascades, were uplifted during the Cenozoic Era. Their uplift was accompanied by considerable volcanism, which has only recently subsided.
13. The rise of man took place during the entire glacial period of Cenozoic time. *Pithecanthropus erectus* (Java man), Peking man, *Australopithecus africanus,* and Neanderthal man represent various stages of *Homo primigenius.* The culture of *Homo sapiens* started with Cro-Magnon man about 12,000 years ago.
14. The Grand Canyon in Arizona and the plateau in which it is incised contain certain rocks deposited in proper sequence from the first four geological eras. The last elevation of this region, which made the canyon possible, occurred during Cenozoic time. Thus, events associated with all five geological eras can be studied in this single locality.

STUDY EXERCISES

1. Of the following recordings, which are expected to be fair and which poor and which absent in Pre-Cambrian rocks: (*a*) index fossils; (*b*) unconformities; (*c*) intrusions?
2. What regions in the United States have outcroppings of Pre-Cambrian rocks; why are these outcroppings economically important?
3. Which fossils found in the Paleozoic Era are extinct in the later eras? Can these be used as index fossils?
4. Reconstruct the probable formation of a coal seam found today in Pennsylvania.
5. What were the important changes that occurred in plant and animal life during the Cenozoic Era?
6. Outline briefly the story of the rise of man. What is meant by the "Folsom Culture"?
7. In the column at the left are listed localities that represent recognized physiographic regions or places of unusual scenic interest in North America. Identify each by number with the geological era or period in which it originated.

.... Adirondack Mountains	1. Archeozoic
.... Niagara limestone	2. Proterozoic
.... Salt and gypsum deposits in Michigan and New York	3. Pre-Cambrian
.... Mineral deposits (ores of iron, copper, nickel, and gold) in Minnesota, Michigan, and Ontario	4. Paleozoic
.... Sierra Nevada	5. Paleozoic – Silurian
.... Cascade Mountains	6. Paleozoic – Carboniferous
.... Black Hills	7. Mesozoic
.... Canadian Shield	8. Cenozoic
.... Cutting of the Grand Canyon	9. Cenozoic – Pleistocene
.... Rocks found in the gorge of Grand Canyon	
.... Initial elevation of Rocky Mountains	
.... Great Smokies	
.... Formation of Great Lakes	

.... Elevation of Newer Appalachian Mountains
.... Formation of coal deposits in an arc from Pennsylvania to Kansas
.... Glaciation of northern United States
.... Evidence of man on North American continent
.... Re-elevation of Appalachian Mountains after a long period of erosion

8. In a canyon the following strata are encountered. Reconstruct the probable history of the region.

Soil
mantle containing pebbles
clay
sandstone
shale
coal
shale
limestone
shale
coal
shale

9. Underline the best answer to the following statements:
   a. The Pennsylvanian period is best noted for (*A,* a warm climate with abundant plant life; *B,* the folding and faulting of strata; *C,* saline deposits; *D,* the rise of the dinosaurs).
   b. The era in which fossil forms are unknown is the (*A,* Archeozoic; *B,* Proterozoic; *C,* Paleozoic; *D,* Mesozoic; *E,* Cenozoic).
   c. The importance of dinosaurs is due to the fact that (*A,* they had an unlimited geological distribution; *B,* they were found in the last three eras of geologic time; *C,* they are useful as index fossils; *D,* they could withstand changes in climate; *E,* they were rulers of the earth since the earliest times).
   d. The presence of a trilobite in a layer of limestone means that (*A,* plants were able to live in water; *B,* a subsidence occurred, followed by an inundation of the land; *C,* mammals must have been present; *D,* the climate was very hot; *E,* the time of deposition was during the Early Paleozoic Era).
   e. The close of each geologic era has (*A,* developed less complex species; *B,* brought about a culmination of all forms of life; *C,* seen the formation of mountains; *D,* been accompanied by a period of submergence; *E,* been marked by extensive glaciation).
   f. The remains of early man (*A,* have never been discovered; *B,* are always associated with the remains of dinosaurs; *C,* may be classified in the late Mesozoic Era; *D,* indicate a period in the latter part of the Cenozoic Era; *E,* belong to the Paleozoic Era).
   g. The Laurentian Revolution (*A,* produced the oldest mountains; *B,* occurred after the dominance of trilobites; *C,* started the Archeozoic Era; *D,* terminated the Paleozoic Era; *E,* destroyed the fossils of vertebrate forms).

10. In the column at the right, the geologic eras are numbered and the periods are lettered. On the *first* line preceding each item at the left place the *number* which designates the *era.* On the *second* line (if a second line is given), place the *letter* which designates the *period.*

.... Glaciation in Northern Hemisphere
.... Coal deposits formed
.... First horses
.... Neanderthal man
.... Oldest sedimentary rocks
.... Laramide Revolution
.... Age of marine invertebrates
.... Deposits of iron in Minnesota and of copper in Michigan
.... First amphibians and land plants
.... Spread of placental mammals
.... Extinction of dinosaurs

1. Archeozoic
2. Proterozoic
3. Paleozoic
   A. Cambrian
   B. Ordovician
   C. Silurian
   D. Devonian
   E. Carboniferous
   F. Permian
4. Mesozoic
   A. Triassic
   B. Jurassic
   C. Cretaceous
5. Cenozoic
   A. Eocene
   B. Oligocene
   C. Miocene
   D. Pliocene
   E. Pleistocene

.... Appalachian Revolution

.... Dominance of mammals and land floras

.... Shortest era listed

.... Formation of Niagara limestone

.... Earliest rocks studied in geology of Canadian Shield

.... }Longest eras listed
....

FOR FURTHER READING

1. Dunbar, C. O., *Historical Geology*. New York: John Wiley and Sons, 1949.

   Chapter 6, dealing with the Pre-Cambrian history of the earth, and Chapters 19 and 20, dealing with the age of mammals and the coming of man, are recommended.

2. Richards, H. G., *The Geological History of Eastern North America*. New York: Ronald Press, 1953.

   A detailed account of the history recorded in the rocks of eastern North America. The first two chapters give a good introduction to the organization of the geologic records.

3. Atwood, W. W., *The Physiographic Provinces of North America*. Boston: Ginn and Co., 1940.

   Presents the principal features of the main physiographic regions of North America. The work of the Ice Age, including a history of the Great Lakes and Niagara Falls, is given on pp. 196–224.

4. Mather, K. F., and S. L. Mason, *Source Book in Geology*. New York: McGraw-Hill Book Co., 1939.

   The following original papers are recommended in connection with this chapter: Murchison, "The Silurian and Permian Systems," *p. 244; Logan,* "Divisions of the Azoic Rocks," *p. 295; Rogers,* "An Inquiry into the Origin of the Appalachian Coal Strata," *p. 346; Hall,* "Correlation of Paleozoic Rocks of New York with Those of Europe," *p. 406.*

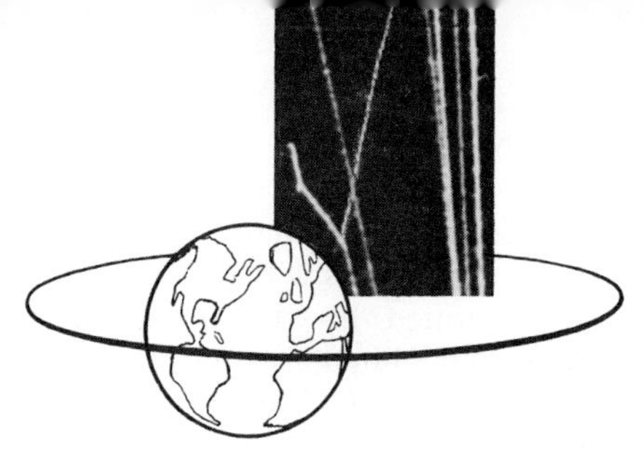

11

THE RELATION OF MATHEMATICS TO SCIENCE

THE SYMBOLS and language of mathematics are basic to scientific thinking. Science without mathematics is impossible, and our modern social and economic life would be impossible without mathematics.

The man of the machine age is a calculating animal. We live in a welter of figures: cookery recipes, railway time-tables, unemployment aggregates, fines, taxes, war debts, overtime schedules, speed limits, bowling averages, betting odds, billiard scores, calories, babies' weights, clinical temperatures, rainfall, hours of sunshine, motoring records, power indices, gas-meter readings, bank rates, freight rates, death rates, discount, interest, lotteries, wave lengths, and tire pressures.[1]

In science, just as in life, the process of making comparisons cannot be avoided. Quantitative measurements are of the essence of science, but that should not be a matter of concern for the person unfamiliar with many of the special techniques of the mathematician. The only mathematics needed for the introductory material in this book is the mathematics of ordinary living.

[1] Lancelot Hogben, *Mathematics for the Million*, rev. ed. (New York: W. W. Norton Company, 1943), Chapter 1.

MATHEMATICS IS A LANGUAGE

Historically, mathematics has always been intimately associated with practical, everyday affairs. Numbers came into being to help answer the ordinary problems of making a life and making a living. Mathematics is very definitely a language perfected in response to certain social and scientific needs. An inability to understand this language means an inability to understand our modern economic and industrial age and many phenomena of nature that concern us all. If we are to understand either the way Newton derived the law of universal gravitation or the mechanics of this machine age, we cannot avoid learning to speak, read, and write in a quantity language, a size language, a position language, and a time language. As early as 1100 B.C., Phoenician navigators sailed through the Pillars of Hercules, out into the Atlantic, and north to the tin mines of Cornwall, England. They successfully solved the problem of navigating this long voyage. The maps used by these ancient navigators to depict the then known world were surprisingly accurate, even when judged by mod-

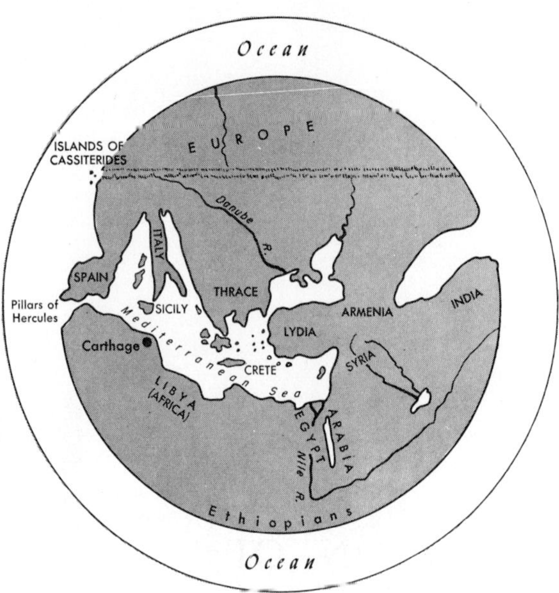

Fig. 11–1 *Map of the World by Hecataeus, 517* B.C. *(Adapted from Breasted,* Ancient Times, *courtesy of Ginn and Company)*

ern standards (see, for example, Figure 11–1).

The Phoenician navigators were also traders. They early learned that to sell their wares in terms of volume was often very difficult or impossible. The purchaser of a load of tin from England, for example, wanted to know the amount of matter in his shipment – a problem of weight or mass. In life situations today, we must continually talk in terms of a size language dealing with lengths, areas, volumes and weights. We carry out these measurements by comparisons with certain standards which constitute a system of weights and measures. Our modern system of weights and measures differs only in ease and precision of application, not in principle, from the one used by the ancient Phoenicians or Babylonians. The Babylonian units of length, for example, were the finger, about two-thirds of an inch, the cubit or thirty fingers, the surveyor's cord or 120 cubits, and the league, which was 180 cords (or about 6.65 miles). The talent was their unit of weight, about $67\frac{1}{2}$ pounds.

Before he became a merchant or agriculturist, primitive man was a herdsman. His wealth was reckoned by the number of sheep he possessed. There is objective evidence that early man used a great variety of methods to keep track of the amount of his wealth, such as tallying in pebbles, or with small sticks, or making notches on a stick. Many clay tablets found on the site of ancient Babylon show the gradual evolution of that people's number system. Thus, the possessor of eleven sheep would record that fact in cuneiform characters as follows, with a stylus in soft clay:

Eventually, the familiar grouping of ten seen in the fingers of both hands led to a simplification: . Here the horizontal impression was the symbol for the quantity ten. The number sixty was very prominent in the Babylonian number system, and was indicated by a wedge-shaped impression similar to that for the number one except that it was considerably larger. Large numbers were represented then by some simple combination of three cuneiform characters. Thus, the number eighty-one was considered as one sixty, plus two tens, plus unity, and was represented:

The Egyptians devised a number system based upon the number ten, which was indicated by the symbol: 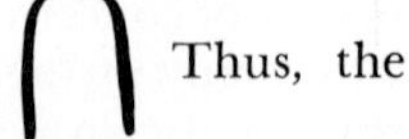 Thus, the number 81 was considered as eight tens, plus unity, and was represented:

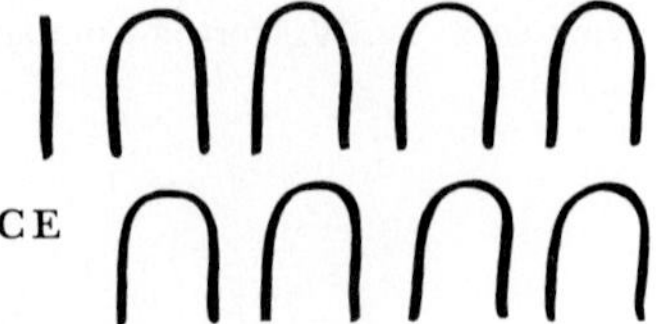

A number system based upon the number ten is called a *decimal* system. Various peoples have developed number systems on a base of twenty, a *vigesimal* system, and on the base number twelve, a *duodecimal* system. We still have evidences of these former number systems, as in the vigesimal expressions, "three score years and ten" as found in the King James version of the Bible, and the phrase "fourscore and seven years ago," used by Lincoln in his Gettysburg Address. The division of the circle into three hundred and sixty degrees, the degree into sixty minutes, and the minute into sixty seconds, we owe to the *sexagesimal* system of the Babylonians, using the base number sixty. The prominence of the number twelve, the dozen, the gross, the yard of thirty-six inches, the foot of twelve inches, the clock numerals, and many other examples that can be given show the convenience of the twelve-base duodecimal system.

The number system that prevailed longer than that of any other (not excluding our present one) was that of the Romans. The Roman system could systematically represent very large numbers, but it was difficult or impossible to use for all mathematical operations of addition, subtraction, multiplication, and division. Because of its convenience in these respects, especially, the so-called Arabic system of numerals has superseded all former number systems.

The Arabic system introduced two new concepts, the zero and the principle of position. The zero indicates absence of number. The principle of position indicates various multiples of the base number 10. These two devices make it possible to indicate concisely any number by employing the nine digits, 1, 2, 3, 4, 5, 6, 7, 8, 9, and the zero (0) with the base number 10. For example, what is the meaning of the number 3027 in the Arabic system?

$$\begin{aligned} 3027 = 3 \times 1000(10^3) &= 3000 \\ 0 \times 100(10^2) &= 000 \\ 2 \times 10(10^1) &= 20 \\ 7 \times 1(10^0) &= \underline{7} \\ & 3027 \end{aligned}$$

or $3027 = 3(10^3) + 0(10^2) + 2(10^1) + 7(10^0)$

The value assigned to any digit depends, then, upon its position in the number. Another example should make this clear. The number 50207 is a short notation for the operations indicated here:

$$\begin{aligned} 50207 &= 5(10^4) + 0(10^3) + 2(10^2) + 0(10^1) + 7(10^0) \\ &= 50000 + 0000 + 200 + 00 + 7 \end{aligned}$$

Without the concept of the zero, implying lack of number in a particular column or position, it would be impossible to represent large numbers conveniently.

The Arabic system is a decimal system. The significance of this will be appreciated when it is understood that if used with another base number the present Arabic notation would represent entirely different quantities. In the duodecimal system, the notation 127 would represent 175 objects, since,

$$\begin{aligned} 127 &= (1 \times 12^2) + 2(12^1) + 7(12^0) \\ &= \quad 144 \quad + \quad 24 \quad + \quad 7 \\ &= \quad 175 \text{ objects.} \end{aligned}$$

The Arabic system readily lends itself to the most difficult computations. This system actually originated among the Hindus, and the Arabs should be credited only with its introduction into Europe by way of Spain.

Fig. 11–2 *The Roman number system. The equivalent number in the Arabic notation is given for comparison.*

I	II	III	IV	V	VI	VII	VIII	IX
1	2	3	4	5	6	7	8	9
X	XX	XL	L	LX	LXXX	XC	C	
10	20	40	50	60	80	90	100	
CC	CD	D	DC	DCCC	CM	M, etc.		
200	400	500	600	800	900	1000		

Units of Measurement. The physical sciences have been built upon a mass of objective quantitative fact-material. It is necessary, therefore, that the student have a working conception of the system of units now in scientific use. Every student has some familiarity with the English system of weights and measures. The basic system of weights and measures, however, in the scientific world is the *metric system*. The English system lacks a complete rational basis, with the result that the relationships between the various units are difficult to remember and involve awkward arithmetical relationships. The metric system, on the other hand, is deliberately designed to be simple arithmetically and capable of indefinite expansion as it becomes necessary to invent new units.

The scientist recognizes two types of units, fundamental and derived. The fundamental units are three in number: the *meter* to measure lengths, the *kilogram* to measure mass and weight, and the *second* to measure time. From these three units nearly all other units can be derived. A unit of area such as the square meter, or a unit of volume such as the cubic meter, is a derived unit. Similarly, multiples or submultiples of the various fundamental units are derived units. The standard fundamental units for length, mass, and time are:

THE METER. This is the distance between two marks on a platinum-iridium bar kept at the Bureau of Standards in Washington, D.C., at the temperature of melting ice, 0° C. The bar [1] is a faithful copy of the original which is kept at the International Bureau of Weights and Measures in Sèvres, near Paris, France. The meter is slightly longer than the yard, being 39.37 inches.

THE KILOGRAM. The U.S. standard is a reference mass of platinum-iridium kept in Washington, D.C.[2] The original (at Sèvres) was intended to be the same as the mass of one thousand cubic centimeters of water at its maximum density, 4° C. Owing to an error, however, the space occupied by this kilogram of water is actually 1000.028 cubic centimeters. This volume is defined as the liter. From some points of view it can be considered the fundamental unit of capacity. The milliliter is a common submultiple of the liter which is very nearly the same as the cubic centimeter.

THE SECOND. The second is one-sixtieth of one-sixtieth of one-twenty-fourth of one mean solar day. Another time unit is the tropical year – the time required for the passage of the sun from vernal equinox to

[1] The primary standard for all measurements of length in this country is the United States Prototype Meter, No. 27.

[2] The primary standard of mass for both the metric and customary systems in this country is the United States Prototype Kilogram No. 20.

Fig. 11–3 *The national standard kilogram and meter bar maintained by the National Bureau of Standards. They are made of a very stable alloy of 90 per cent platinum and 10 per cent iridium. These standards are periodically checked against the international standards; no significant change has taken place in them. (National Bureau of Standards)*

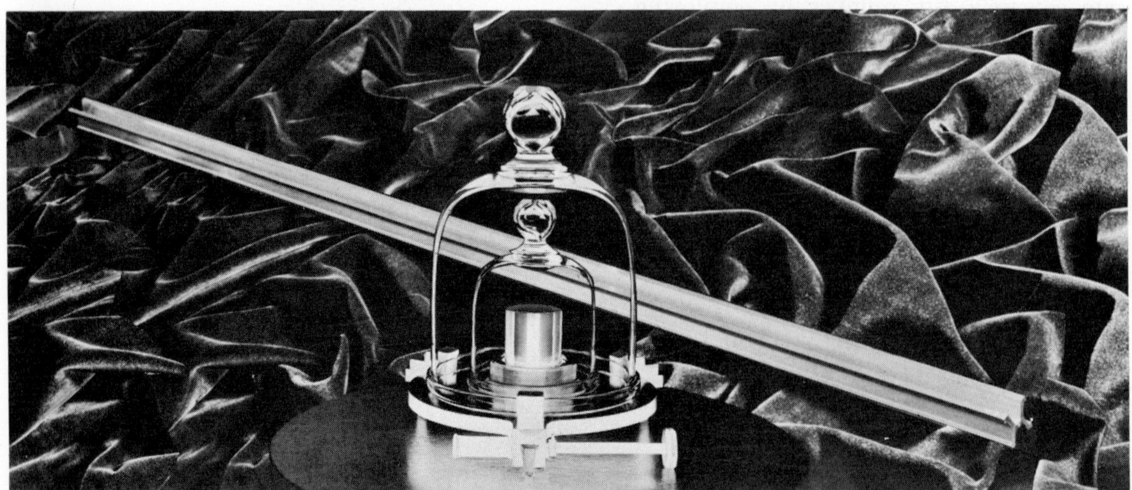

TABLE 11–1

SOME RELATED UNITS OF MEASUREMENT

SUBMULTIPLES	UNIT	MULTIPLES
Decimeter: 0.100 Centimeter: 0.010 Millimeter: 0.001	Meter	Kilometer: 1000
Milligram: 0.001	Gram	Kilogram: 1000
Milliliter: 0.001	Liter	Kiloliter: 1000

vernal equinox. (If necessary the reader may review the time units based upon the motions of the earth; refer to Chapter 4.)

The metric system is simpler than other systems because the multiples and submultiples of the fundamental units are related by the factor ten or a multiple of ten. Thus, one-tenth of a meter is called a decimeter; one-hundredth of a meter is a centimeter; and one-thousandth of a meter is a millimeter. Similarly a unit a thousand times larger than the meter is a kilometer. The process of dividing the fundamental unit of length is sometimes carried even farther. Thus, the diameter of a red blood corpuscle is usually expressed in terms of the micron (μ), which is one-millionth of a meter. The millimicron ($m\mu$) is a thousand times smaller than the micron.

As has been mentioned before, units of area are derived units. A square one centimeter on a side is a square centimeter, designated cm^2. Similarly a cubic centimeter is designated cm^3, a cubic meter, m^3, and so on. A common symbol for the cubic centimeter is cc.

The metric system may seem a little strange, but it is not difficult. Our coinage system, which we use so familiarly every day, is a "metric system" in which the fundamental unit of value is the dollar, with the multiples and submultiples related by factors of ten. Consider Table 11–2; the decidollar, of course, is the common dime, the centidollar is our cent. The millidollar is usually referred to as the mill. We have no trouble in handling our units of coinage; the other units of the metric system are no more difficult.

We have had our metric system of coinage since 1792, but when it was adopted the force of tradition was so strong that some of the English system of measures was retained. By action of Congress, however, the basic system of weights and measures has been since 1893 the metric system. The legal definition of a yard, for example, is "a unit of length equal to 3600/3937 of a meter"; the pound avoirdupois is "a unit of mass equal to 0.453592427 kilogram."

It is unfortunate that our thinking must be in two systems of weights and measures. Only in the British Commonwealth and the United States do we find systems other than the metric in extensive use. In practically all the rest of the world, students are spared the task of becoming familiar with two systems of weights and measures. As long as this situation prevails in the United States, students will find it necessary to familiarize themselves with certain relationships between the two systems:

1 inch = 2.54 cm	1 kg = 2.2 lb
1 m = 39.37 in.	1 l = 1.057 liq qt
1 km = 0.62 mile	1 lb = 453.6 g

That the metric system is slowly gaining ascendancy in the commercial world is indicated by the fact that sizes of motion-picture films, weights on food labels, quantities in physicians' prescriptions, tire sizes, caliber of guns, and so on, are now often

TABLE 11–2

METRIC MONETARY UNITS

SUBMULTIPLES	FUNDAMENTAL UNIT	MULTIPLES
Decidollar: $0.100 Centidollar: $0.010 Millidollar: $0.001	Dollar	Kilodollar: $1,000 Megadollar: $1,000,000

expressed in metric units. The metric system has also come into popular speech in another way. The sizes of bombs are given in megatons or kilotons, that is, equivalent to millions of thousands of tons of TNT. Similarly, bomb casualties are spoken of in megadeaths.

THE LANGUAGE OF POSITION

We are continually confronted with the elementary task of locating an object or an observer. Only one who has been lost in a great forest or at sea can truly appreciate the feeling of helplessness that comes over one when he has absolutely no frame of reference by which to locate himself. A frame of reference is a pictorial representation of some surface, often with suitable lines of reference known as coordinates. A familiar frame of reference is the neighborhood of one's own home. In many cities, the streets are laid out at right angles to each other to form a pattern of rectangular blocks. Often two streets at right angles to each other are designated as the reference streets, and then any place in the city can be located in relation to them. A map of such a city, then, is a simple frame of reference with *rectangular coordinates*. When we go on a trip by automobile, we transfer our frame of reference to a road map.

One of the momentous discoveries of the ancients was that we have no *permanent* frame of reference on the earth. The fortunes of war will change boundaries of countries; rivers change their courses; seas disappear; shorelines are augmented; mountain ranges slowly disintegrate or appear where none were found before. To get a permanent frame of reference, it is necessary to go to the heavens above us. This is one reason why astronomy was among the first of the sciences to develop; it made possible a language of space.

The grand assemblage of stars and constellations, whose positions with respect to each other remain fixed over long intervals of time, is known as the *celestial sphere*. As we have already seen in Chapter 4, positions on the surface of the earth are located with reference to the celestial sphere by giving their latitude and longitude. *Latitude* means angular distance north or south from an east-west reference line, the earth's equator. *Longitude* means angular distance east or west of the north-south reference line through Greenwich, England, which is called the *prime meridian*. Thus, in Figure 11–4 the city of Washington is uniquely located by giving its latitude and longitude. Its latitude, 39° north, is the distance in degrees along an arc of a circle perpendicular to the earth's equator, which also passes through the north pole of the earth. Its longitude, 77° west, is the distance in degrees along the arc of a circle which is perpendicular to the prime meridian through Greenwich, England, and parallel to the earth's equator.

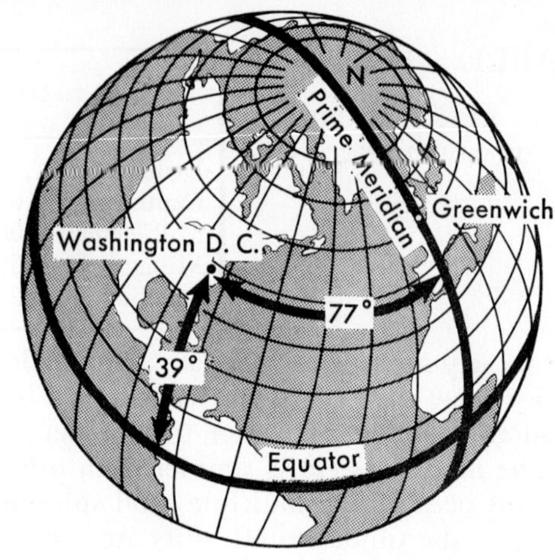

Fig. 11–4 *The coordinate system of the earth.*

QUANTITATIVE BASIS OF THE PHYSICAL WORLD

Physics, chemistry, astronomy, and the other physical sciences differ from the social sciences in that the fact-material is more quantitative in nature. We can describe an object in *qualitative* or in *quantitative* terms. Quantitative information means knowledge expressed in objective terms of measurement; qualitative information must by its nature be colored with subjective thought and is, therefore, often unreliable. For example, one can say, "Miss Jones is heavy," or "Miss Jones has keen eyesight." These are qualitative statements of fact. The interpretation of these statements by different individuals will vary because of their differing conceptions as to the meaning of "heavy" and "keen eyesight." On the other hand, if one says, "Miss Jones is five feet tall and weighs one hundred and fifteen pounds," or "Miss Jones can read characters one-sixteenth of an inch high at a distance of two feet," quantitative statements are being made. The interpretation of these two statements by different readers should be substantially the same. It should be remembered, however, that even quantitative measurements vary in precision. Every physical measurement is subject to a certain amount of error from the imperfections of instruments and the variability of human performance. The magnitude of these errors may be progressively reduced, but can never be entirely eliminated. The smaller the permissible error, the greater the precision of measurement.

Lord Kelvin, one of the greatest scientists of the nineteenth century, expressed the importance of quantitative information thus:

> When you can measure what you are speaking about and express it in numbers, you know something about it; when you cannot express it in numbers, your knowledge is of a meager and unsatisfactory kind; it may be the beginning of knowledge, but you have scarcely in your thoughts advanced to the state of science.

DECIMAL NOTATION

Many of the measurements made in science must be expressed in very large or very small numbers. Thus, the diameter of a molecule is about one-hundredth of one-millionth of a centimeter, or 0.00000001 cm. The number of molecules in a cubic centimeter of air is about twenty-five million million million, or 25,000,000,000,000,000,000. The decimal character of the metric system has greatly simplified the writing of quantities of this nature and mathematical operations with them. Any number, whether very large or very small, can be concisely written as a small number multiplied by ten raised to a certain power. Raising a number to a certain power simply means multiplying it by itself that many times: thus raising 10 to the third power means multiplying 10 times 10 times 10, which gives 1000. Raising a number to a minus power means dividing it into one that many times: thus 10 to the minus third power means one divided by 10 divided by 10 divided by 10, which gives 0.001. Thus,

$$0.0000065 = 6.5 \times 10^{-6}$$
$$870{,}000{,}000 = 8.7 \times 10^{8}$$

Understanding decimal notation requires a review of the mathematical use of exponents.

ALGEBRAIC OPERATIONS WITH EXPONENTS

Multiplication: In the notation of algebra,

$$a^m \times a^n \times a^{-o} = a^{(m+n-o)}$$

This means that the product of the same quantity raised to various powers is the quantity raised to a power which is the sum of the exponents.

EXAMPLE: $4^2 \times 4^3 \times 4^{-1} = 4^{2+3-1} = 4^4$

PROOF:

$$\frac{(\not{4} \times 4)(4 \times 4 \times 4)}{\not{4}} = 4 \times 4 \times 4 \times 4 = 4^4$$

Division: $a^m \div a^n = \dfrac{a^m}{a^n} = a^{m-n}$

EXAMPLE: $5^5 \div 5^3 = 5^{5-3} = 5^2$

PROOF:

$$\frac{5 \times 5 \times \not{5} \times \not{5} \times \not{5}}{\not{5} \times \not{5} \times \not{5}} = 5 \times 5 = 5^2$$

Addition and subtraction: To find the sum of five bushels of potatoes and two gallons of gasoline is meaningless because the terms are unlike. In like manner, algebraically only like terms can be added. Thus,

$$20a^m + 5a^m - 8a^m = 17a^m,$$

and

$$6a^m + 20a^m + 5b^m = 26a^m + 5b^m$$
$$30a^{\frac{1}{3}} + 6a^{\frac{1}{3}} - 30a^2 = 36a^{\frac{1}{3}} - 30a^2.$$

Mathematical simplification often results in rewriting a fraction by bringing the numerator into the denominator, or vice versa. This is a proper procedure, provided the signs of the exponents of the terms which are moved are changed. Examples:

$$\frac{a^m}{a^n} = a^{m-n} = \frac{1}{a^{-m}a^n} = \frac{1}{a^{n-m}}$$

$$b^x \cdot c^{-y} = \frac{b^x}{c^y} = \frac{1}{b^{-x}c^y}$$

$$\frac{4^8}{4^3} = 4^{8-3} = 4^5$$

HANDLING VERY LARGE OR VERY SMALL NUMBERS

The decimal notation for very large or very small numbers is illustrated below:

$$1.0 = 1 \times 10^0$$
$$10.0 = 1 \times 10^1$$
$$1000.0 = 1 \times 10^3$$
$$1{,}000{,}000 = 1 \times 10^6$$
$$870{,}000{,}000 = 8.7 \times 10^8$$

$$0.10 = \tfrac{1}{10} = 1 \times 10^{-1}$$
$$0.01 = \frac{1}{100} = \frac{1}{10^2} = 1 \times 10^{-2}$$
$$.000001 = \frac{1}{1{,}000{,}000} = \frac{1}{10^6} = 1 \times 10^{-6}$$
$$.0000065 = \frac{6.5}{1{,}000{,}000} = \frac{6.5}{10^6} = 6.5 \times 10^{-6}$$

To handle very large or very small numbers mathematically by the usual methods of arithmetic is ordinarily a very laborious task. The same operations may easily be carried out in the decimal notation by keeping in mind the laws concerning exponents given previously. Some examples:

$$6000 \times 210 = 6 \times 10^3 \times 2.1 \times 10^2 = 12.6 \times 10^5$$
$$0.00012 \times 0.000036 = 1.2 \times 10^{-4} \times 3.6 \times 10^{-5} = 4.32 \times 10^{-9}$$
$$0.00012 \div 0.000036 = \frac{1.2 \times 10^{-4}}{3.6 \times 10^{-5}} = 0.333 \times 10 = 3.33$$

General Procedure. (1) Rewrite all quantities so that the first number is between 1 and 10, followed by 10 raised to the appropriate power; (2) perform all the indicated operations of multiplication or division, putting the decimal in the proper place; (3) determine the proper exponent for the multiplier, 10^x. The problems following are examples of the application of the decimal system:

1. Compare sizes of a red blood corpuscle with a diameter of 7.5 microns and a white blood corpuscle with a diameter of 0.0015 centimeter.

$1 \text{ micron} = 10^{-6}$ m

$$\text{Ratio: } \frac{\text{Diameter white corpuscle}}{\text{Diameter red corpuscle}} = \frac{.0015 \text{ cm}}{7.5\mu \times \frac{10^{-6}\text{ m}}{\mu} \times \frac{10^2 \text{ cm}}{\text{m}}} = \frac{1.5 \cdot 10^{-3}}{7.5 \cdot 10^{-4}} = 0.2 \cdot 10 = 2$$

Hence, the diameter of a white corpuscle is twice that of a red corpuscle. Note that all units cancel, leaving a pure number.

2. A molecule has a diameter of about 0.00000001 centimeter and there are 25 million million million molecules in one cubic centimeter. If it were possible to lay these molecules side by side, how many times around the earth would they reach? (Earth's circumference at the equator is 25,000 miles.)

Diameter of 1 molecule $= 1 \times 10^{-8}$ cm
25 million million million $= 25 \times (10^6)^3 = 25 \times 10^{18}$

Therefore, distance

$$= (1 \times 10^{-8}\text{ cm})(25 \times 10^{18}) = 25 \times 10^{10}\text{ cm}$$
$$= 25 \cdot 10^{10}\ \cancel{\text{cm}} \times \frac{1\ \cancel{\text{in.}}}{2.5\ \cancel{\text{cm}}} \times \frac{1\ \cancel{\text{ft}}}{12\ \cancel{\text{in.}}} \times \frac{1 \text{ mile}}{5280\ \cancel{\text{ft}}}$$
$$= \frac{25 \cdot 10^{10}}{2.5 \times 12 \times 5280}\text{ miles} = 1.58 \times 10^6 \text{ miles}$$
$$= 1.58 \times 10^6 \text{ miles} \times \frac{1 \text{ time around earth}}{25000 \text{ miles}}$$
$$= 63 \text{ times around the earth.}$$

3. The actual mass of an atom of hydrogen is known to be 1.66×10^{-24} gram. How many atoms of hydrogen are present in one gram of hydrogen?

$$\text{Number} = 1\text{ g} \times \frac{1\text{ atom}}{1.66 \cdot 10^{-24}\text{ g}}$$
$$= 0.602 \times 10^{24}\text{ atoms}$$
$$= 0.602 \times (10^6)^4$$
$$= 0.602\text{ million million million million atoms.}$$

MEANING OF ZERO; POSITIVE AND NEGATIVE QUANTITIES

The problem of locating a point always requires a designation of direction within the frame of reference. This is done in terms of plus and minus quantities. As an example, consider an elevator in a tall building with several sub-basements. Obviously the location of the floor of the elevator could be determined by measuring its elevation from the bottom of the shaft, as shown in Figure 11–5. The usual starting place, however, for actually using the elevator would be the ground floor. Hence, the location of the elevator *with respect to the ground floor* can better be indicated by using a system of plus and minus quantities in which the *reference* starting point is designated as the zero floor. It is obvious that either method is an arbitrary procedure, adopted for convenience.

The concept of zero is another example of our debt to the past. It is a concept that has not always been held by man. The mathematicians of early Greece and Rome, for example, were handicapped because they did not have a zero. The zero originated in India among Hindu thinkers, but it has always been a prominent part of the Arabic system of numerals. Careless thinkers frequently say that the character 0 means "nothing." This is far from the truth. It is used to indicate a reference point or line in making measurements and thus the absence of quantity either positive or negative. Thus a person on the equator is at 0 degrees latitude. Water freezes at 0 degrees on the Centigrade heat scale. The heights of mountains and the depths of the ocean are usually measured from the level of the ocean itself. Elevations above sea level are considered plus, and elevations below sea level are considered minus. Similarly, directions north or east of any given reference point are considered plus; directions south or west are taken as minus. In circular travel, motion in the direction of the hands of a clock is considered plus, and counterclockwise motion is minus.

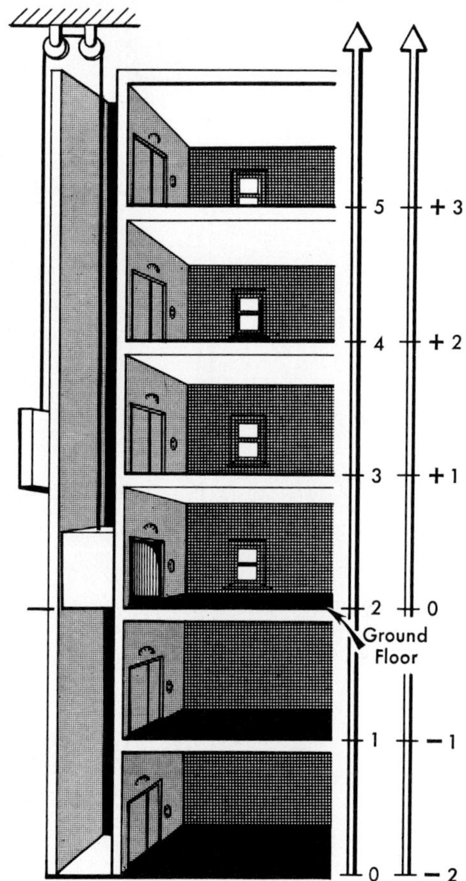

Fig. 11–5 *The use of zero as a reference point in floor numbering.*

GRAPHICAL REPRESENTATION

After accumulating experimental data it becomes necessary to find the various relationships within the body of the experimental data. The relation between two quantities, for example, can be represented in the form of a table, in a diagram, or in a graph. Frequently, various relationships can be quickly observed in a graph that are difficult or impossible to see in unorganized

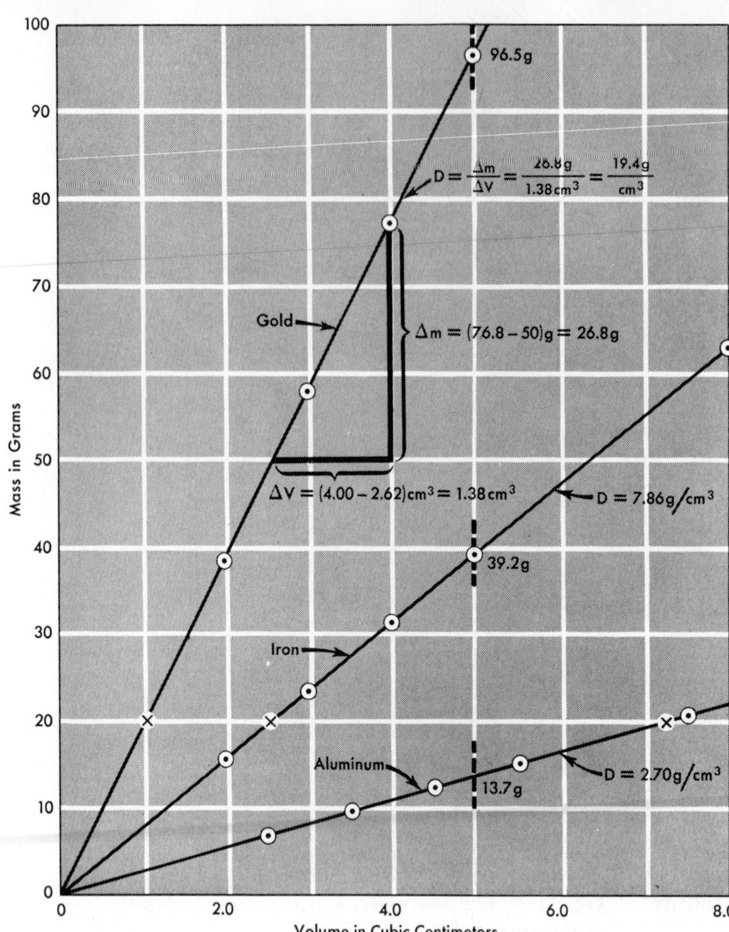

Fig. 11–6 *Mass-volume graph for gold, iron, and aluminum.*

data. Figure 11–6, for example, shows the relation between the mass and volume for various samples of three different metals, gold, iron, and aluminum. The data upon which these three graphs are based are shown in Table 11–3. The volumes are given as abscissas on a rectangular coordinate system with the corresponding masses as ordinates. The graph reveals much more than the tabulated data. The mass, for example, of 5 cubic centimeters of each metal can be read directly from the graph for each metal; 96.5 grams of gold, 39.2 grams of iron, and 13.7 grams of aluminum.

Each graph can be expressed in an equation with the form

$$y = k \times x.$$

It is customary to use y for values along the vertical axis and x for values along the horizontal axis. Using the symbols employed in the graph, the

$$\begin{aligned} m(\text{ass}) &= k \text{ (a constant)} \times V(\text{olume}) \\ &= D(\text{ensity}) \times V(\text{olume}). \end{aligned}$$

(Equation 11–1)

The constant in this case is called the density — the mass in grams of one cubic centimeter. This number is a characteristic number for any pure substance.

The density for gold, for example, can be determined directly from the graph. From Equation 11–1,

$$D(\text{ensity}) = \frac{m(\text{ass})}{V(\text{olume})} = \frac{m}{V} = \frac{\text{change in } m}{\text{change in } V}.$$

The symbol Δm is used to designate any change in m along the y-axis, and ΔV is any change in V along the x-axis. In the

TABLE 11–3

MASS-VOLUME RELATION FOR GOLD, IRON, AND ALUMINUM

Gold:					
Mass in grams (g)	38.6	57.9	76.8	96.5	
Volume in cubic centimeters (cm^3)	2	3	4	5	
Iron:					
Mass in g	15.7	23.6	31.4	39.2	62.8
Volume in cm^3	2	3	4	5	8
Aluminum:					
Mass in g	6.75	9.45	12.2	14.9	20.30
Volume in cm^3	2.5	3.5	4.5	5.5	7.5

example given in the mass-volume graph for gold,

$$D = \frac{\Delta m}{\Delta V} = \frac{(76.8 - 50)\ g}{(4.00 - 2.62)\ cm^3}$$
$$= \frac{26.8\ g}{1.38\ cm^3} = 19.4\ \frac{g}{cm^3}.$$

What deductions can be read from the graphs in Figure 11–6? Some of these will be enumerated.

1. The density of all samples of each pure substance, as indicated by the constant slope of each curve, is constant.

2. The masses of each metal for a given volume, as 5 cubic centimeters, are directly proportional to the densities, or

$$m_{gold} : m_{iron} : m_{aluminum}$$
$$= 96.5\ g : 39.2\ g : 13.7\ g$$
$$= 7.04 : 2.86 : 1.00, \quad \text{and}$$
$$D_{gold} : D_{iron} : D_{aluminum}$$
$$= 19.4 : 7.86 : 2.70$$
$$= 7.19 : 2.91 : 1.00.$$

3. The volumes of each metal for a given mass as 20 grams vary inversely as the densities, or

$$V_{gold} : V_{iron} : V_{aluminum}$$
$$= 1.08\ cm^3 : 2.56\ cm^3 : 7.28\ cm^3$$
$$= 1 : 2.37 : 6.74, \quad \text{and}$$
$$= \frac{1}{19.4\ g/cm^3} : \frac{1}{7.86\ cm^3} : \frac{1}{2.70\ cm^3}$$
$$= 1 : 2.47 : 7.19.$$

NOTE: The discrepancies in the ratios are due to inaccuracies. These could be further reduced by improving the graph.

THE CONCEPT OF FUNCTION

One of the most useful mathematical concepts is that of function. Where one quantity changes in value as another quantity changes, the first quantity is said to be a *function* of the other. A concise statement in the symbolism of mathematics is often employed to express the functional relationship between the two variable quantities. This statement is a mathematical equation. For example, y is said to be a function of x if the value of y is determined when the value of x is known. The relation is written $y = f(x)$. The function is represented by a "formula" or a "mathematical definition," which permits the calculation of one quantity if all the other terms that enter into the expression are known. Consider, for example, the relationships involved in the determination of the perimeters and areas of squares and circles, and of the areas and volumes of cubes and spheres. (Refer to Table 11–4.) Note that the perimeter of a square or circle is a function of a basic dimension l or r. This can be stated in the concise expression, $P = f(x)$, which can be read, "the perimeter is a function of x," or "the perimeter is directly proportional to x." [1] The generalized functional expression for the areas, however, involves the square of the basic dimension; that is, $A = kx^2$. Similarly, the functional expression for the volume involves the cube of the basic dimension; that is, $V = kx^3$. In all cases, the

[1] When the value of f is known, it becomes k (constant).

TABLE 11–4 SOME COMMON FUNCTIONAL STATEMENTS

GENERALIZED FUNCTIONAL STATEMENT	SQUARE	CIRCLE	CUBE	SPHERE
(*P*)erimeter				
$P = kx$	$P = 4l$ $k = 4$	$P = c = \pi d$ $k = \pi$	.....	.....
(*A*)rea				
$A = kx^2$	$A = l^2$	$A = \frac{\pi}{4} d^2$	$A = 6l^2$	$A = \pi d^2$
	$k = 1$	$k = \frac{\pi}{4}$	$k = 6$	$k = \pi$
(*V*)olume				
$V = kx^3$	.....	.....	$V = l^3$	$V = \frac{\pi}{6} d^3$
			$k = 1$	$k = \frac{\pi}{6}$

first quantity in each equation can be calculated if both the value of k and the variable basic dimension x are known. The value of k is determined by the type of surface or solid involved. (Refer to Table 11–4.)

GRAPHICAL REPRESENTATION OF FUNCTIONS

The simplest function is a constant, $y = b$. For example, a body of water can be losing heat to its surroundings at the same rate as it is gaining heat from the sun. Its temperature, therefore, would remain constant. (Refer to Figure 11–7.) This situation can be represented in a graph. (Refer to Figure 11–8.)

The next simplest function has the form $y = m'(x)$, where m' is a constant which indicates how y changes if x changes. The constant m' is also called the slope, since $m' = \frac{y}{x} = \frac{\Delta y}{\Delta x}$. (Refer to Figure 11–9.) Thus the surface area of a cube or sphere is a function of its $(\text{length})^2$ or $(\text{diameter})^2$. This can be represented, $A = kl^2$ or $A = kd^2$. The calculated areas for a number of cubes

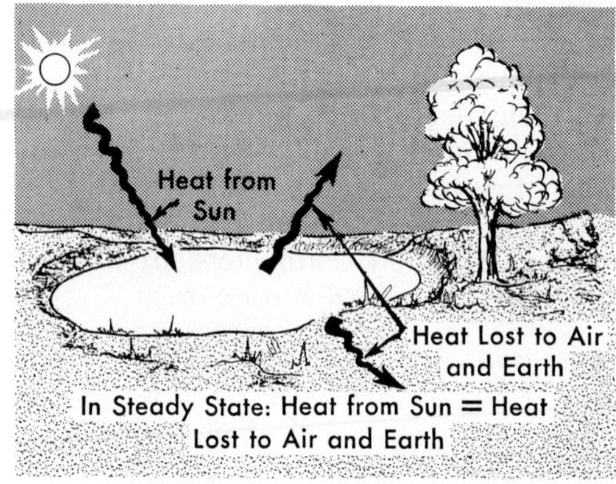

Fig. 11–7 *Example of heat and temperature remaining constant.*

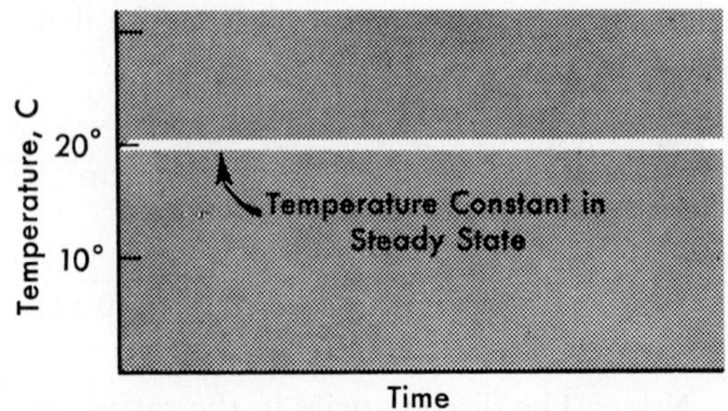

Fig. 11–8 *Temperature-time graph for situation in Figure 11–7.*

and spheres are plotted against the squares of the lengths or diameters. Each graph is a straight line and thus each has the form $y = m'f(x)$. This is read, "y equals a constant times some function of x." The constant of proportionality in the equation $A = kl^2$ for a cube is readily determined from the appropriate graph.

Thus,

$$k = \text{slope} = \frac{\Delta A}{\Delta l^2} = \frac{(150 - 100)\ \text{cm}^2}{(25 - 16.5)\ \text{cm}^2} = \frac{50}{8.5} = 5.9 \doteq 6,$$

and the surface area of a cube $= A = 6 \cdot l^2$.

In the graph for a sphere, $A = k \cdot d^2 = \text{slope} \cdot d^2$, and

$$\text{slope} = \frac{\Delta A}{\Delta l^2} = \frac{(95 - 40)\ \text{cm}^2}{(30 - 12.8)\ \text{cm}^2} = \frac{55}{17.2} = 3.20 \doteq 3.1416.$$

Hence, $$A = \pi d^2.$$

These two examples show how the constant of proportionality can be determined directly from a linear plot of experimental data. This procedure is frequently used in the physical sciences. The symbol $\doteq$ is read "approaches." Thus 5.9 approaches 6 in value. The departure from agreement represents inaccuracies in preparing and reading the figures on the graph.

Figure 11–9 also reveals that for a given dimension the surface area of a cube is always greater than that of a sphere. Thus the areas for a dimension of 25 cm² are 150 cm² to 79 cm² or 1.90 : 1.

From the equations

$$\frac{A_{\text{cube}}}{A_{\text{sphere}}} = \frac{6l^2}{\pi d^2} = \frac{6}{\pi} = \frac{1.91}{1}$$

Expressing functional relationships in the precise symbolism of mathematics enables us to think about them more quickly. Consider the following examples:

1. How does the area of a sphere four inches in diameter compare with that of a four-inch cube? This can, of course, be solved by actually calculating the area of both the sphere and cube and making a comparison of the computed areas. A more direct solution is the following:

$$\frac{\text{Surface cube}}{\text{Surface sphere}} = \frac{6l^2}{\pi d^2} = \frac{6}{\pi} = \frac{1.91}{1}$$

Hence, the surface of the cube is 1.91 times larger than that of the sphere.

2. How does the volume of a sphere four inches in diameter compare with one of two-inch diameter? The simple direct solution is:

$$\frac{V_1}{V_2} = \frac{d_1^3}{d_2^3} = \frac{4^3}{2^3} = 8.$$

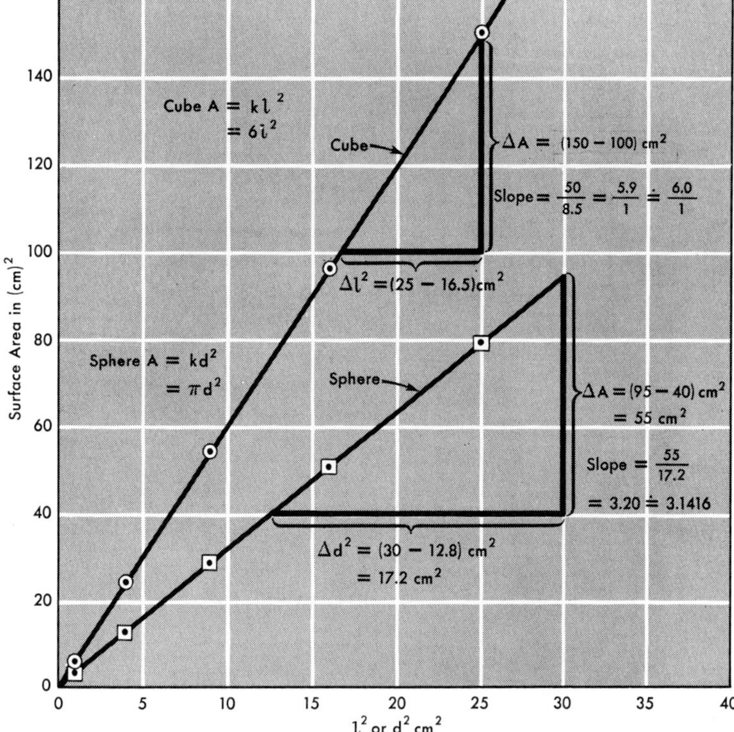

Fig. 11–9 *Plot of surface area of a cube and sphere against the basic dimension squared.*

Hence, doubling the diameter increases the volume 8 times.

PROPORTIONS AND PROPORTIONALITY CONSTANTS

The equations used in Figure 11–9 represent generalizations long known from the study of geometry. In tackling unsolved problems involving two or more variables, the functional relationship between the variables must be determined by a careful analysis of experimental data. This often results in equations with proportionality constants. For example, that there is a mathematical relationship between the mileage covered by a car and the amount of gasoline put into the tank is common knowledge. This is an example of what is called a *direct ratio* or *direct proportion.* It can be expressed mathematically as follows:

d(istance) varies as (is proportional to) *g*(allons) of gasoline, or

$$d \propto g.$$

We then transform this expression into an equality,

$$d = kg.$$

The term *k* in this equality is called a *constant of proportionality.* This expression is capable of a precise mathematical solution if the value of *k* is known. The constant *k* in this problem is obviously the average mileage per gallon for the car in question. Suppose that, by experiment, it was found that ten gallons of gasoline were consumed for one hundred and fifty miles of average driving. How far could the car be expected to travel on one hundred and fifty gallons of gasoline?

SOLUTION:

$$k = \frac{d}{g} = \frac{150 \text{ mi}}{10 \text{ gal}} = \frac{15 \text{ mi}}{\text{gal}}.$$

Then,

$$d = kg = \frac{15 \text{ mi}}{\text{gal}} \times 150 \text{ gal} = 2250 \text{ miles.}$$

Essentially this same method of procedure is followed in deriving the equation for more complicated functional relationships. For example, Galileo discovered by experimentation that the distance covered by a freely falling object varied as the square of the time. It is also known that an object starting from rest falls sixteen feet the first second. How far, then, should a stone dropped from a tower fall in five seconds?

SOLUTION:

$$d \propto t^2, \quad \text{or} \quad d = kt^2$$

In this case,

$$k = \frac{d}{t^2} = \frac{16 \text{ ft}}{(1 \text{ sec})^2} = 16 \frac{\text{ft}}{\text{sec}^2},$$

then,

$$d = 16 \frac{\text{ft}}{\text{sec}^2} \times (5 \text{ sec})^2 = 400 \text{ ft.}$$

Inverse Proportions. There are many situations where a certain quantity *decreases* in value as another quantity *increases.* These are described as *inverse ratios* or *proportions.* Thus, on page 173, it was shown that volumes of different substances required for a certain mass vary *inversely* as their densities. Likewise, the time required to travel a given distance becomes less as the speed of travel increases. Consider the time necessary to travel one thousand miles by airplane at different speeds.

Speed	*Time required*
100 mi/hr	10 hrs.
200 "	5 "
250 "	4 "
300 "	3.3 "
350 "	2.8 "
400 "	2.5 "

Symbolically, the relationship between speed and time is expressed,

$$t \propto \frac{1}{S}, \quad \text{or} \quad t = \frac{k}{S}.$$

These relationships indicate that the time is halved if the speed is doubled. This is an inverse proportion.

MEASURING THE DISTANCE TO INACCESSIBLE OBJECTS

Many situations arise in which it is necessary to measure the distance to an object where it is impossible to use an ordinary measuring rod or a surveyor's chain. When we want to get the height of a tall building, the distance to a ship at sea or to the moon, direct measurement is either difficult or impossible. These distances, however, may be calculated by the methods of trigonometry, which may be considered as a combination of the algebraic concept of function with geometry. The foundations of trigonometry were laid by the Greek scientist Hipparchus (*ca.* 130 B.C.). With this new mathematical tool, Hipparchus successfully determined the distance to the moon as sixty times the radius of the earth, a relatively accurate result.

The right triangles ABC, $AB'C'$, and $AB''C''$ in Figure 11–10 with corresponding sides a, a', a'', and b, b', b'', and c, c', c'' are similar. They all have the common angle x, and the angles y, y', and y'' which are equal. Now note that certain ratios involving the three sides of all three triangles are equal and these ratios can be given arbitrary names.

$$\frac{a}{b} = \frac{a'}{b'} = \frac{a''}{b''} = f(x) = \text{sine } x$$
$$\frac{c}{b} = \frac{c'}{b'} = \frac{c''}{b''} = f(x) = \text{cosine } x$$
$$\frac{a}{c} = \frac{a'}{c'} = \frac{a''}{c''} = f(x) = \text{tangent } x$$

These ratios are called *functions* of x, since they vary in a definite manner as x varies in value from 0 degrees to 90 degrees.

A simple method for the determination of the trigonometrical ratios is shown in Figure 11–11. AOD is one quadrant of a circle with a radius ten units in length. The resulting angle of 90° is divided into six equal divisions of 15°. There then can be constructed a series of five right triangles in which the base angle varies from 15° to 75°. With an ordinary ruler, it is then possible to measure the lengths of the two legs of each right triangle. Thus, $BC = 5$ units, $OB = 8.7$ units, $B'C' = 9.6$ units, $OB' = 2.6$ units. The hypotenuse of each triangle is ten units in length. Then,

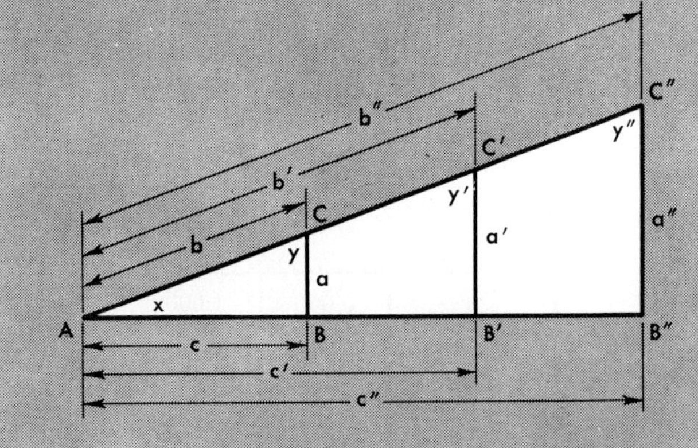

Fig. 11–10 *Similar triangles. Corresponding sides are proportional.*

$$\sin 30^\circ = \sin BOC = \frac{BC}{OC} = \frac{5}{10} = 0.50,$$
$$\cos 30^\circ = \cos BOC = \frac{OB}{OC} = \frac{8.7}{10} = 0.87,$$
$$\tan 30^\circ = \tan BOC = \frac{BC}{OB} = \frac{5}{8.7} = 0.58,$$

and

$$\sin 75^\circ = \sin B'OC' = \frac{B'C'}{OC'} = \frac{9.6}{10} = 0.96,$$
$$\cos 75^\circ = \cos B'OC' = \frac{OB'}{OC'} = \frac{2.6}{10} = 0.26,$$
$$\tan 75^\circ = \tan B'OC' = \frac{B'C'}{OB'} = \frac{9.6}{2.6} = 3.70.$$

Fig. 11–11 *Determination of the functions of angles.*

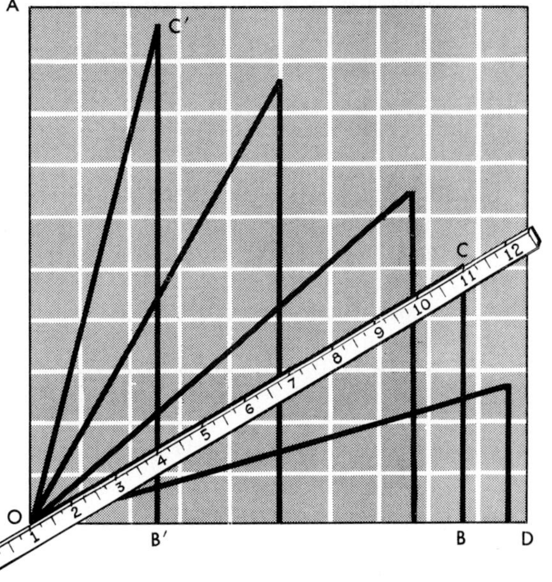

TABLE 11–5 PARTIAL TABLE OF TRIGONOMETRICAL RATIOS

ANGLE A	SIN A	COS A	TAN A
0	0.000	1.000	0.00
$7\frac{1}{2}$	0.131	0.991	0.13
15	0.259	0.966	0.27
$22\frac{1}{2}$	0.383	0.924	0.41
30	0.500	0.866	0.58
$37\frac{1}{2}$	0.609	0.793	0.77
45	0.707	0.707	1.00
$52\frac{1}{2}$	0.793	0.609	1.30
60	0.866	0.500	1.73
$67\frac{1}{2}$	0.924	0.383	2.41
75	0.966	0.259	3.73
$82\frac{1}{2}$	0.991	0.131	7.56
90	1.000	0.000	∞

In a similar manner, the trigonometrical ratios for angles of 15°, 45°, 60°, or of any other angle can be calculated. By methods of greater precision, the more accurate values of these quantities as given in Table 11–5 have been determined. The definitions for these various functions are as follows, referred to the diagram below:

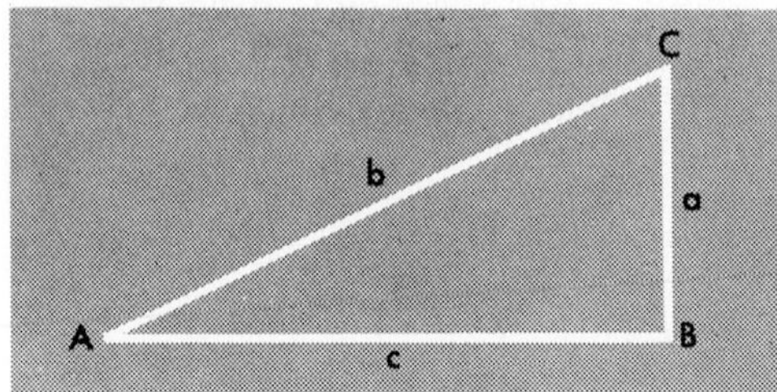

$$\text{sine } A = \frac{\text{side opposite the angle}}{\text{hypotenuse}} = \frac{a}{b}$$

$$\text{cosine } A = \frac{\text{side adjacent the angle}}{\text{hypotenuse}} = \frac{c}{b}$$

$$\text{tangent } A = \frac{\text{side opposite the angle}}{\text{side adjacent the angle}} = \frac{a}{c}$$

The numerical values of these functions for any angle have been carefully computed and recorded in tables of the trigonometrical functions (ratios). (Table 11–5.)

The usefulness of trigonometry for the determination of distances to inaccessible objects will be illustrated by two examples.

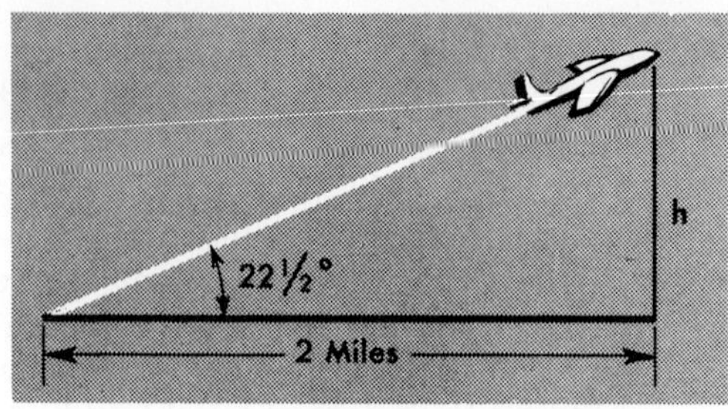

Fig. 11–12

EXAMPLE 1. An airplane climbs steadily at an angle of $22\frac{1}{2}$ degrees. After it has gone two miles, measured along the ground from the starting point, what is its elevation?

SOLUTION: The elevation is the vertical height in Figure 11–12. By the definition of a tangent,

$$\tan 22\tfrac{1}{2}° = \frac{h}{2 \text{ mi}} = 0.41.$$

The numerical value of the tangent is obtained from Table 11–5. Then,

$$\begin{aligned} h &= (2 \text{ mi})(.41) = .82 \text{ mile} \\ &= (.82)(5280) = 4330 \text{ feet.} \end{aligned}$$

EXAMPLE 2. A somewhat more difficult problem is involved in the determination of the height of the top of the lighthouse above the beach, shown in Figure 11–13. A represents the top of a lighthouse above the beach BCD below. At C, the angle to A was $37\frac{1}{2}°$, while at location B, the angle was 30°. The distance between B and C was found to be one hundred and fifty feet. Now recall the definition for the tangent of an angle: the ratio of the side opposite the angle to the side adjacent to the angle. From this,

Fig. 11–13

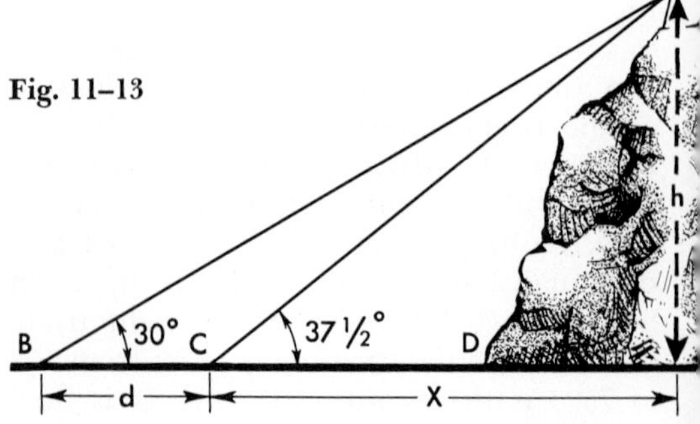

$$\tan 30^\circ = \frac{h}{d+x} = \frac{h}{150+x} = 0.58, \quad (1)$$

$$\tan 37\tfrac{1}{2}^\circ = \frac{h}{x} = 0.77. \quad (2)$$

From equation (1),

$$h = 0.58(150 + x)$$
$$= 87 + .58x.$$

Substituting this value of h in equation (2), we have:

$$\frac{87 + .58x}{x} = 0.77,$$

or $\quad 87 + 0.58x = 0.77x,$

and $\quad 0.77x - 0.58x = 87, \quad$ or $\quad 0.19x = 87,$

and $\quad x = \frac{87}{0.19} = 457.9$ feet.

Then, substituting this value of x in equation (1), we have:

$$h = (150 + 457.9)(.58) = 607.9(.58)$$
$$= 352.6 \text{ feet.}$$

The general process of finding the distance to inaccessible objects using the methods of trigonometry is called *triangulation*. The appropriateness of the term is brought out in the use of locator stations to detect distant aircraft. (Refer to Figure 11–14.) The locator stations can "spot" a distant airplane either visually or by relying upon sound or radio waves or radar impulses which are detected by a suitable "pick-up" and amplifying system. "Spotting" means in this case measuring the angle made by a line from the airplane to the locator station and the base line between the two locator stations. The length of this base line is known accurately. The data from at least two locator stations, after being telephoned to a plotting station, are all that is needed to locate the airplane. In the plotting station, a triangle is constructed from the length of the base line and the angles a and b. The various needed dimensions of this triangle and the location of the airplane, can then be calculated by the use of trigonometry or by drawing a triangle to scale, using a suitable scale for the length of the base line.

NOTATIONS FOR POWER AND ROOT

It is often necessary to multiply a quantity by itself. The exponential notation is the briefest way to indicate this operation. For example:

$$2 \times 2 \times 2 \times 2 \times 2 = 2^5 = 32$$
$$10 \times 10 \times 10 \times 10 \times 10 \times 10 = 10^6 = 1{,}000{,}000$$
$$\frac{1}{10^4} = 1 \times 10^{-4} = 0.00010$$

The reverse operation is called extraction of the indicated root of a number. The sixth root of 64, written $\sqrt[6]{64}$, is that number which when multiplied by itself six times will give the number 64. In this case, $\sqrt[6]{64} = \sqrt[6]{2^6} = 2$. Students are often puzzled as to the best way to proceed in problems of this sort. Those who have not had advanced courses in mathematics should realize that there is one method which can always be used – the method of inspection and successive approximations. Suppose it were necessary to get the cube root of 18, or $\sqrt[3]{18}$ = what value? The starting point is to realize that the $\sqrt[3]{8} = 2$ and $\sqrt[3]{27} = 3$; hence, we can assume that the desired value will be closer to 3 than to 2, say 2.7. Then, by actual trial,

$$2.7 \times 2.7 \times 2.7 = 19.7.$$

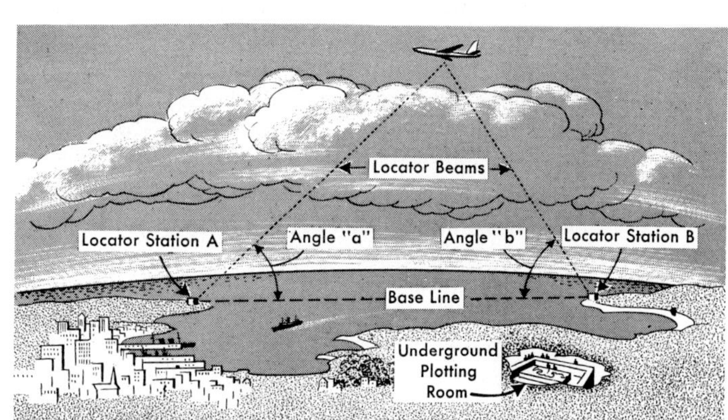

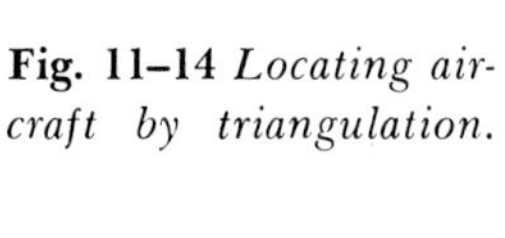

Fig. 11–14 *Locating aircraft by triangulation.*

Hence, 2.7 is a little too large. Suppose we try 2.5:

$$2.5 \times 2.5 \times 2.5 = 15.6,$$

which is a little too small. We then can "pinch off" a better value by intelligent and persistent application. We can systematize our efforts by tabulating our results:

$2.6^3 = 17.6$	Too small
$2.65^3 = 18.6$	Too large
$2.62^3 = 17.98$	A little too small
$2.63^3 = 18.19$	A little too large

By this method of approximation, we can now know that $\sqrt[3]{18}$ is a little larger than 2.62 and a little smaller than 2.63. If it is necessary to have a more accurate value, the method of approximation can be carried even farther.

SUMMARY

1. Mathematics is a language which originated out of the needs of daily living. In order to understand our environment, we need a quantity language, a size language, a position language, and a time language.
2. Our language of quantity, using the Hindu-Arabic numerals, employs:
   a. the digits, 1, 2, 3, 4, 5, 6, 7, 8, and 9;
   b. the base number 10;
   c. the principle of position; and
   d. the concept of the zero,
   to represent any quantity, large or small.
3. Object measurements require a system of units made up of a few fundamental standard units and many derived ones. The fundamental standard units of the metric system are the *meter* for the measurement of length, the *kilogram* for mass, and the mean solar *second* for time.
4. In the metric system various additional units are submultiples or multiples of the fundamental standard units and are obtained in a uniform, rational manner. Thus, the fundamental unit can be divided into ten, one hundred, one thousand, or one million equal parts, the parts being indicated by the prefixes *deci-*, *centi-*, *milli-*, and *micro-*. A unit a thousand times larger than the fundamental is indicated by the prefix *kilo-*, and a million times larger by *mega-*.
5. The basic system of weights and measures in this country, including our money system, is the metric system and is under the supervision of the Federal Bureau of Standards. The following conversion factors are very useful when it is necessary to work with both the metric and English systems:

1 in.	= 2.54 cm
1 m	= 39.37 in.
1 km	= 0.62 mile
1 kg	= 2.2 lb
1 l	= 1.057 liq qt
1 lb	= 453.6 g

6. The location of an object or point on a surface or in space requires the use of a suitable frame of reference. A frame of reference may be a plane surface, or a curved surface, such as the face of the earth or the celestial sphere. Objects may be located on the frame of reference by means of two coordinates which are perpendicular to each other.
7. Elevations above a suitable reference surface are considered plus, and elevations below this are considered minus. Directions north or east of any given reference point are considered plus; directions south or west are taken as minus. In circular travel, motion in the direction of the hands of a clock is considered plus.
8. The decimal notation is used in science for writing very large or very small numbers.
9. An expression in symbols which indicates how one quantity changes in value as another quantity changes is known as a function. Functional quantities which contain proportionality constants are very common.
10. Equations to express scientific principles are important, because (*a*) they represent the end-product of scientific investigation, and (*b*) they summarize in concise form general scientific principles.
11. The branch of mathematics which combines algebra and geometry is trigonometry. By means of trigonometry it is possible to measure the distance to physically inaccessible points.
12. The sine, cosine, and tangent of an angle refer to certain fixed ratios of the sides of a right triangle containing that angle.

STUDY EXERCISES

1. Many students of numbers believe that a duodecimal system would have decided advantages over our present decimal system. From what standpoints would this be true? What are some of the reasons that such a change probably will not be made?
2. Classify the following as fundamental (*f*) or derived (*d*) units.

.... decimeter	.... square centimeter
.... meter	.... cubic centimeter
.... kilogram	.... inch
.... milligram	.... gallon
.... gram	.... microgram
.... pound	.... dollar

3. Find the sum of:

a. 4 dollars = ...
7 dimes = ...
18 nickels = ...
36 pennies = ...
4000 mills = ... Sum = ...

b. 3 meters = ...
2 decimeters = ...
22 centimeters = ...
108 millimeters = ... Sum = ...

4. With the digits, the principle of position, and the zero as in the decimal system, 2012 would be a notation for what quantities in the quinary, duodecimal, and sexagesimal systems?

2012 = ... in the quinary system
= ...... in the duodecimal system
= ...... in the sexagesimal system

5. Our money system is a metric system and the basic system of weights and measures in the United States is the meter-kilogram system. How can you account for the widespread use of the awkward English system of weights and measures in this country?
6. What arguments can be advanced for abolishing the English system in this country? What arguments can be advanced in favor of retaining this system?
7. *a.* Express a body weight of 150 pounds in kilograms, in grams, and in milligrams.
   b. How many millimeters in a kilometer?
8. Express the following quantities in the decimal notation:

(*a*) 2,200,000 =

(*b*) $\frac{425000}{1800}$ =

(*c*) 7,829,000,000 =

(*d*) $\frac{.00012}{.0000040}$ =

9. A certain photographic film measures 6.5 cm × 9 cm. What is size in inches?........
10. The blood of a normal person contains about 5,000,000 red blood corpuscles per cubic millimeter. How many red blood corpuscles would there be in 500 cm^3 of blood (about a pint)?..................
11. During a gas-consumption test, a certain car was found to travel 270 miles on 15 gallons of gasoline. How many gallons would be needed at this rate of consumption to travel 1500 miles?..........................
12. At a large banquet the dessert was to be slices of ice cream cut from "bricks." The caterer planned to serve each person a portion *q*. The size of *q* (in terms of fractions of a single brick) will depend upon two variable quantities, the number (*n*) of bricks available and the number of persons (*p*) to be served. Which of the following is the correct expression for the size of each portion?

(*a*) $p \propto \frac{n}{q}$ (*c*) $q \propto \frac{p}{n}$

(*b*) $q \propto \frac{n}{p}$ (*d*) $q \propto np$

13. Refer to Figure 11–11. Estimate the length of the "side opposite" and the "side adjacent" for angles of 15°, 45°, and 60°. Calculate numerical values for the sine, cosine, and tangent for each of these angles. Record your data in the following table.

	15°	45°	60°
Side adjacent			
Side opposite			
Sine			
Cosine			
Tangent			

How do your values compare with those given in Table 11–5? How can you account for differences?

14. From the mass-volume graphs for iron and aluminum in Figure 11–6, deduce values for the densities of iron, of aluminum, and of gold from the slope of each plot.

15. *a.* From Figure 11–6 determine the volume of iron which has a mass of 45 grams.
b. Using the density of iron obtained in Exercise 14 above, calculate the volume of iron whose mass is 45 grams. How do your answers compare?

FOR FURTHER READING

1. The articles on "Numerals" and "Numeral Systems" in the *Encyclopaedia Britannica* show the great variety of number systems that have actually been used and how intimately related they are to different cultures.

2. WILDER, R. L., *Introduction to the Foundations of Mathematics.* New York: John Wiley and Sons, 1952.

   Chapter 12 points out that mathematics is not a branch of thought that "just had to be." Mathematics evolves out of culture and it will change as our culture changes.

3. HOGBEN, LANCELOT, *Mathematics for the Million.* New York: W. W. Norton and Company, Inc., 1943.

   This volume has helped many to gain a real appreciation of the social and scientific significance of mathematics. The following chapters are recommended reading: Chapter II on the early history of mathematics; Chapter VI on the uses of trigonometry; Chapter IX on graphs; and Chapter XII on arithmetic and human welfare.

4. WHITEHEAD, ALFRED NORTH, "An Introduction to Mathematics," in *Readings in the Physical Sciences* by H. Shapley, H. Wright, and S. Rapport, page 244. New York: Appleton-Century-Crofts, Inc., 1948.

   A discussion of the history, significance, and uses of mathematics by one of the greatest of modern mathematicians. Very readable.

5. Paperback: DANTZIG, T., *Number, the Language of Science.* Anchor, 95¢.

6. Paperback: STRUIK, DIRK J., *A Concise History of Mathematics.* Dover, $1.60.

12

MOTION AND FORCE

THE TREMENDOUS CHANGES and processes described in preceding chapters suggest that nothing is static or permanent. The relentless forces of the atmosphere, the winds, and the waters are slowly eroding the hills and mountains and transporting their fragments to lower areas and to the sea. Against these forces, other gigantic forces within the earth lift or crumple or fold the rock strata to build plateaus and mountains. Except for the work of catastrophic storms, earthquakes and volcanic eruptions, geological changes are too gradual for direct observation. There are, however, many other changes which, like geological processes, are recurrent, but which complete their cycles in much shorter periods. The movements of the planets and the moon, the seasons, night and day, the birth, growth, and death of living things, and many other phenomena are visible and thus indicated the prevalence of change long before the science of geology was developed. Five hundred years before the Christian era the Greek philosopher Heraclitus wrote, "All is flux, nothing is stationary."

If we are to understand and explain even some of the simpler aspects of the physical world we must now extend our study far beyond the mere qualitative description of things and events. We shall examine more closely a number of less involved physical phenomena, make quantitative measurements, and show how certain mathematical relations or laws have been formulated. In this chapter we shall develop the basic concept of *motion* and of that which causes change in motion — *force*. In the next two chapters the present picture of the solar system is established, and the law of universal gravitation is formulated. These and related developments extending over the sixteenth and seventeenth centuries mark the beginnings of modern science.

MOTION

A body in motion is constantly changing its position relative to some other object serving as a point of reference. Motion is therefore definable only with reference to something else and is always *relative*. It would not be possible, for example, to determine whether or not a lone body isolated in space is moving. The motion of a distant star can be detected only as it slowly changes its position with reference to its neighbors. A car parked on the street is at rest relative to the trees, the houses, and all objects fixed on this planet, but in motion with respect to the sun and other astronomical bodies.

All natural events and human activities are characterized by motion. It plays an essential part in all changes, mechanical, physical, chemical and nuclear. It is the very essence of the many forms of energy, including heat, light, sound, and electricity. All things large and small, from stars to electrons, are in motion. The first motions studied were those of objects visible to the unaided eye — celestial bodies, things dropped from heights, and the stone thrown into the air.

UNIFORM MOTION

The actual motions ordinarily observed, like those of an automobile or of a rifle bullet, are very complex. It is therefore best to start with the very simplest case. Imagine an automobile driven very carefully and steadily along a smooth and straight road so that in each small fraction of time (for example, a second) it moves the same distance as in each preceding fraction of time. Such motion, although seldom observed in nature, is *uniform*. The distance covered in a given direction in one unit of time is known as *velocity*. In uniform motion the velocity is therefore unchanging, or constant. Distance traveled is directly proportional to time, and the velocity is the constant of proportionality.

If the steady automobile driver travels on the straight road a distance of two hundred and twenty feet in five seconds, the velocity for the trip is forty-four feet per second or thirty miles per hour. This simple problem, and all others like it, may be represented by a general mathematical expression. Since velocity is the time *rate* of change of distance from a fixed point, it may be found by dividing that distance by the time required to cover the distance.

$$v(\text{elocity}) = \frac{d(\text{istance})}{t(\text{ime})} \quad \text{or} \quad v = \frac{d}{t}$$

(*Equation 12–1*)

The time rate of change of any quantity is always the amount of change divided by the time required to make the change. An expression of this kind may be used to calculate any one of the quantities if the other two are known. Thus:

$$d(\text{istance}) = v(\text{elocity}) \times t(\text{ime}),$$

$$t(\text{ime}) = \frac{d(\text{istance})}{v(\text{elocity})}.$$

There is no special name given to the unit of velocity. It is measured in the dimensions $\frac{\text{length}}{\text{time}}$ and is therefore expressed in terms of two other units (page 166) as: meters per second, miles per hour, feet per minute, or the like, depending on the system of measurement being used.

The relationship between the two variables, time and distance (the velocity is a constant), may be shown by a simple graph, Figure 12–2, in which the distance is plotted along the vertical axis and the time along the horizontal axis.

While the terms velocity and speed are commonly used interchangeably, each has an exact meaning for the scientist. Speed implies only the distance covered in one unit of time, and since it expresses only magnitude, it is known as a *scalar* quantity. The population of the United States and the price of wheat are also scalar quantities. Velocity is the distance covered per

Fig. 12–1 *Illustrating uniform motion. The velocity remains unchanged (constant velocity), equal distances being traversed in equal intervals of time.*

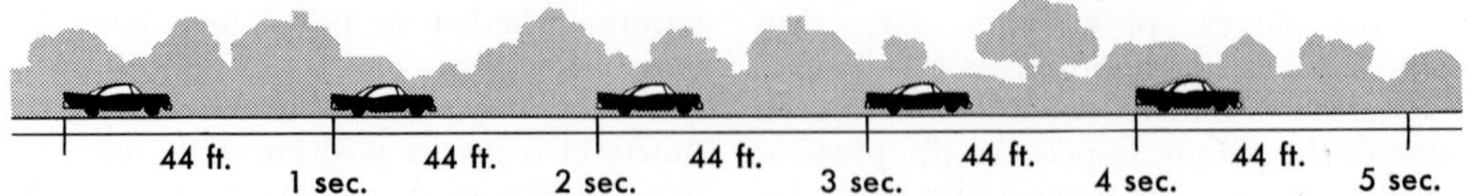

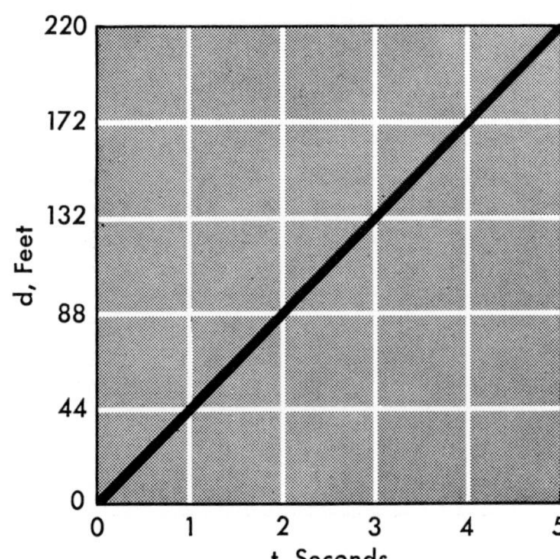

Fig. 12–2 *Time-distance relationship (constant velocity)*.

unit of time in a given direction and therefore implies not only magnitude but also direction. Such a quantity is known as a *vector* and is represented by an arrow whose length indicates to scale the magnitude and whose tip points the direction. Two cars, each moving at the rate of fifty miles per hour, meet and pass on a boulevard. They have the same speed but not the same velocity, for they are moving in different directions. The velocities may be represented as shown in Figure 12–3. It is important to remember that every mathematical expression which includes velocity (v) represents a vector quantity.

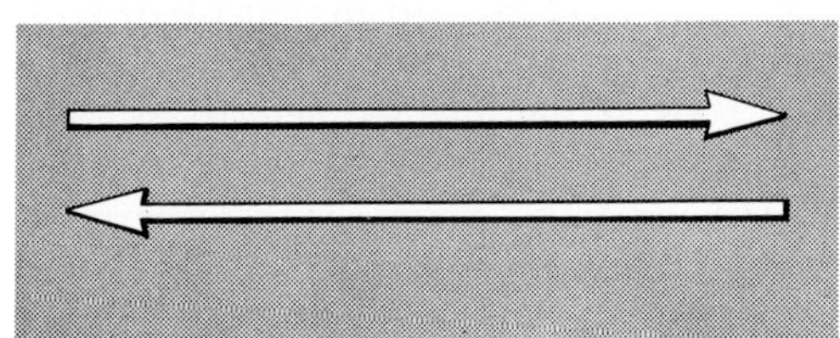

Fig. 12–3 *Vectors representing the same speed, but different velocities.*

ACCELERATED MOTION

Most moving bodies constantly undergo changes in velocity. When one presses the accelerator of a moving automobile the velocity increases; when the pedal is released the velocity decreases. Motions of this kind are said to be *accelerated* and the change in velocity per unit of time is called the *acceleration*. We shall consider only those cases in which the acceleration is constant, that is, *uniformly accelerated motion*. An experimental study of this type of motion may be made with a freely falling body or with a ball rolling down a smooth inclined plane. The distances the body falls in equal successive time intervals may be measured by electrical devices or by photography.

The equations for uniformly accelerated motion were originally formulated by Galileo Galilei (Italy, 1564–1642) from experimental data. This work represents only a small fraction of the total contribution of his great creative genius. Galileo was interested in the motions of freely falling bodies but found that they moved too rapidly to permit accurate time measurements with the apparatus he had at his disposal. To retard the motion he used an inclined grooved wooden beam down which a ball rolled. He could not measure the velocity of the ball but he could measure the time and the distance. From these data he was able to calculate the velocity at the end of each interval. Let us now consider some hypothetical data similar to those which Galileo might have obtained. (Refer to Table 12–1.) The figures at the left represent experimental data and those at the right have been calculated. From these data we may conclude:

1. Column 5. The change in velocity per unit of time is constant, that is, the motion is uniformly accelerated.
2. Columns 1 and 4. The velocity is directly proportional to the time.
3. Columns 2 and 3. The distance is directly proportional to the second power of the time.

The relationships between the various quantities, time (t), distance (d), velocity (v), and acceleration (a), may be reduced to simple mathematical equations. Since acceleration is the *rate* of change of

TABLE 12–1 HYPOTHETICAL DATA ON AN ACCELERATED BODY

OBSERVED		CALCULATED		
(1) t(ime) in sec	(2) d(istance) in cm	(3) [t(ime) in sec]^2	(4) v(elocity) cm/sec $= \frac{2d}{t}$	(5) Change in velocity cm/sec
0	0	0	0	0
1	20	1	40	40
2	80	4	80	40
3	180	9	120	40
4	320	16	160	40
5	500	25	200	40

velocity, it is the change divided by the time required:

$$a = \frac{v_{\text{final}} - v_{\text{initial}}}{t}$$

Since we shall consider those cases in which a body is initially at rest, v_{initial} is zero and the v_{final} is itself the change in velocity. Hence

$$a = \frac{\Delta v}{t}$$

and the final velocity,

$$v_{\text{final}} = \Delta v = at. \qquad \textit{(Equation 12–2)}$$

The acceleration of an automobile which started from rest and reached a velocity of 88 feet per second in eleven seconds may be calculated by use of the above equation,

$$a = \frac{v}{t} = \frac{\text{88 feet per second}}{\text{11 seconds}}$$
$$= \text{8 feet per second per second, or 8 ft/sec}^2$$
(change in velocity, in this time unit).

The unit of acceleration therefore has the dimensions $\frac{\text{length}}{\text{time/time}}$. Although it is customary to use the same unit of time, appearing twice in the above expression, the meaning of acceleration is better understood if two different time units are used. For example, since 88 feet per second is 60 miles per hour,

$$a = \frac{\text{60 miles per hour}}{\text{11 seconds}}$$
$$= 5\tfrac{5}{11} \text{ miles per hour per second,}$$

which means that the change in velocity taking place every second is $5\frac{5}{11}$ miles per hour. In the examples just studied the velocity increases with time and the acceleration is therefore *positive*. If the driver applies the brakes in such a way that exactly the reverse process takes place, the acceleration is *negative*.

CALCULATION OF DISTANCE FOR ACCELERATED MOTION

The equation for uniform motion (Equation 12–1) may be used for calculating the distance traveled by a uniformly accelerated body if the *average velocity* is used. For example, an automobile starts from zero velocity and, moving with uniform acceleration, attains a velocity of seventy-two feet per second in eight seconds. Then

$$v\ (\text{average}) = \frac{v_{\text{final}} + v_{\text{initial}}}{2}$$
$$= \frac{\text{72 ft/sec} + \text{0 ft/sec}}{2}$$
$$= \text{36 feet per second.}$$

And by Equation 12–1,

$$d = v_{\text{average}} \times t = \text{36 ft/sec} \times \text{8 sec} = \text{288 ft.}$$

Though the acceleration was not used in this calculation, it may be incorporated in the equation for distance by a simple substitution. From Equation 12–2,

$$v_{\text{final}} = at$$

Therefore, $v_{\text{average}} = \frac{v_{\text{final}}}{2} = \frac{at}{2}$

and substituting $\frac{at}{2}$ for v_{average} in the equation for distance,

$$d = \frac{at}{2}t = \tfrac{1}{2}at^2 \qquad \textit{(Equation 12–3)}$$

Now, we test the equation by making the same calculation as above. The acceleration of the automobile is calculated from one version of Equation 12–2.

$$a = \frac{v}{t} = \frac{72 \text{ ft/sec}}{8 \text{ sec}} = 9 \text{ ft per sec per sec.}$$

Substituting in Equation 12–3:

$$d = \tfrac{1}{2}at^2 = \tfrac{1}{2} \times 9 \text{ ft per sec per sec} \times (8 \text{ sec})^2$$

$$= 288 \frac{\text{feet} \times \text{seconds}^2}{\text{seconds}^2} = 288 \text{ feet,}$$

which is identical with the answer obtained above. *It should be noted that when all the units are carried along in the calculation they may be combined or canceled to give the correct unit dimensions of the answer.*

Equation 12–3 confirms the conclusion drawn from the experimental data (page 186) that the distance a uniformly accelerated body moves varies with the square of the time, that is, $d \propto t^2$, since, for a given case, $\frac{1}{2}a$ is constant. This principle is of value to automobile drivers. With perfectly uniform acceleration, it takes twice as long to attain a velocity of sixty miles per hour as it does to attain a velocity of thirty miles per hour, and the car therefore moves four times as far in reaching the higher velocity. Of greater significance to our safety is the reverse process, the distance required to stop a moving car (that is, the distance traveled by the car between the time the brakes are applied and the time the car stops). Referring to Figure 12–4, let us assume that the brakes are capable of giving the automobile a uniform deceleration or negative acceleration of twenty-two feet per second per second. When it is moving at a velocity of sixty miles per hour (eighty-eight feet per second), it can be brought to a stop in four seconds after the brakes are applied: at thirty miles per hour (forty-four feet per second), only two seconds are required to bring it to a stop. In interpreting Figure 12–4, the distances traveled may be calculated:

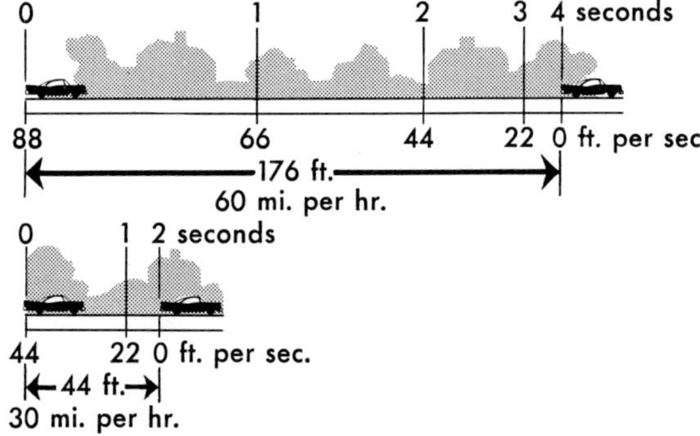

Fig. 12–4 *Uniform deceleration (under ideal conditions). The distance required to stop a moving car, after the brakes are applied, varies as the square of the velocity. The velocity at the end of each second is shown and the distance traversed during each second is indicated to scale.*

$$d = \frac{1}{2} \times \frac{22 \text{ feet}}{\text{second}^2} \times (4 \text{ seconds})^2 = 176 \text{ feet}$$

$$d = \frac{1}{2} \times \frac{22 \text{ feet}}{\text{second}^2} \times (2 \text{ seconds})^2 = 44 \text{ feet}$$

Four times the distance is therefore required to stop the car moving with twice the velocity. In general, the distance required to bring a moving body to rest varies with the square of the velocity. But this is true only if there is a uniform and constant decrease in the velocity.

FORCE

The study of motion evokes a number of questions. First, how may a body at rest be put in motion? How may its velocity be changed? We know from the preceding paragraphs that any change in the state of motion or the state of rest of a body means that an acceleration is imparted to it. We know from experience that such a change requires a continuous action or effort, which from now on will be designated as *force*. A force, therefore, is that which produces a change of motion or, better, imparts an acceleration to a body.

Second, what is the natural state of motion for a body; that is, what does an object do when the net external force acting upon it is zero?

Of all the intellectual problems which have confronted the human mind, this is among the very crucial. The unsatisfactory theory of motion developed by Aristotle (Greece, 384–322 B.C.) was the complete antithesis of the modern ideas which were fully developed by the close of the seventeenth century. According to Aristotelian doctrine, rest was the natural state and all heavy bodies came to rest on the earth. "Violent" motion, that is, motion in any direction other than toward the center of the earth, required a mover (force). If the mover ceased to function the body fell to the earth. Moreover, Aristotle maintained that the application of a continuous and constant force caused uniform motion — not uniform acceleration. A thrown stone or some other projectile continued to move in the air after leaving the hand or the bow because the air, which it compressed in front, streamed round to the rear to destroy the vacuum which "not even God could create." Hence, the primary problem of the Aristotelian theory was to explain motion, not rest — why the stone continues at all after it leaves the hand.[1]

[1] In fairness to Aristotle, it should be said that he included in his concept of "motion" things we include in the term "process." He tried to formulate laws that would apply to erosion, for example, or plant growth, as well as to falling bodies.

Galileo's view of the problem was just the reverse. He assumed that all bodies have what he called the property of *inertia,* the resistance to change of motion. The problem, therefore, was not why the thrown stone continues to move, but why it ever stops. His conclusion, that once a velocity is imparted to a body it will continue to move in a straight line with uniform velocity as long as no external forces act upon it, was stated in more precise language by Descartes in 1644. The answer, then, to our original question is that a body which is acted upon by a net force of zero continues to do precisely what it was doing.

The solution of the problem of motion discredited the Aristotelian theory, which had been a formidable barrier against new concepts and ideas for nearly two thousand years, and opened the way for a great wave of scientific discovery and a complete change in intellectual outlook (pages 200–208).

THE FIRST LAW OF MOTION

The First Law of Motion, also called the Law of Inertia, may be stated as follows: *Every body continues in its state of rest or uniform motion in a straight line, unless it is compelled to change that state by a force.*

How may one experimentally prove or verify this law? Proof for the first part of the law is quite apparent to any observer. A body at rest (not in motion relative to its surroundings), remains at rest as long as the net force acting upon it is zero.

Proof of the second part of the law is a more difficult problem. A stone, when thrown, continues to move, but its motion is neither uniform nor in a straight line and it soon comes to rest. The main influence which arrests the flight of the stone is the force of attraction of the earth (see next section). To free the body from this force requires its complete isolation in space — something which we obviously cannot bring about.

The only experimental course open, then, is to keep this force constant and to limit its effect as much as possible. Accordingly, the spherical body whose motion we are studying is rolled along a smooth horizontal plane. After a push the ball rolls some distance before stopping. It cannot curve toward the earth because of the surface on which it rests, but it does not deviate to the right or left from a straight path. The attraction of the earth still brings it to rest, by pulling it against the surface and thereby creating friction. If both the ball and the surface are made smoother by polishing, the same amount of push makes the sphere roll longer and farther and with a less rapid decrease in velocity. If the polishing and smoothing of the objects is continued with each succeeding trial, the sphere rolls farther and farther as the friction is diminished. As we know, friction cannot be entirely eliminated, but the experiment shows that bodies continue to move uniformly in a straight line.

On the other hand, if just enough force to counterbalance the friction is applied in the direction of the motion of the ball, it continues to move uniformly. Here balanced forces are in operation. Their combined effect is zero, and the ball rolls on. One experiences the same phenomenon in pushing a small cart (Figure 12–5). To start the cart – that is, to give it an acceleration – requires force. But once it is in motion, only a small fraction of the original force is required to balance the effects of friction and air resistance and to keep it moving uniformly and in a straight line.

Fig. 12–5 *Balanced forces. If just enough force, F, is applied to the moving cart to equal the retarding force, F′, due to friction and air resistance, the cart moves on uniformly (First Law of Motion).*

Fig. 12–6 *The analytical balance is used to determine the mass of a body or sample of material which is balanced against known masses or weights.* (*Wilkens-Anderson Company*)

INERTIA AND MASS

The First Law of Motion describes a fundamental property of matter, namely, inertia. Inertia is the resistance offered by a body to any change of motion. The amount of such resistance or inertia depends upon the quantity of matter in the body, or its *mass.* The mass of the body, which is the measure of its inertia, is an invariable quantity; it remains constant regardless of the body's position and regardless of the circumstances under which it is measured. The mass is usually determined by balancing it against another object whose mass is already known. The analytical balance (Figure 12–6) which one commonly sees in a physics or chemistry laboratory is so used. The known masses are called "weights" and have been carefully calibrated by comparison with the standard kilogram and its fractions which are preserved in the Bureau of Standards.

MEASUREMENT OF FORCE

A mathematical expression, if understood, shows clearly and effectively how a force is measured and how it may be calculated. Since a force in itself is not a tangible thing and manifests itself only by its action on a body, a measure of that action, that is, of the acceleration imparted to a given mass, gives both the amount of the force and its dimensions. For example, a force applied to a body of mass m gives the body an acceleration a as long as the force is applied. The quantity of force F depends upon the two factors m and a. That fact may be expressed mathematically: F(orce) $\propto$ m(ass) $\times$ a(cceleration).

$$F \propto ma$$

In order to change a proportionality of this kind into an equality it is customary to insert a constant. If, however, the proper units are devised, this constant becomes unity and then the equation for force is

$$F = ma. \qquad \textit{(Equation 12–4)}$$

THE SECOND LAW OF MOTION

The relationship expressed in the equation, $F = ma$, was formulated by Newton as the Second Law of Motion. This law may be stated thus: *The acceleration imparted to a body is proportional to the force acting and takes place in the same direction as the force applied.*

The concept of force may be more clearly established and the relationships among the three quantities better understood if we apply the equation to some practical cases. As the law is stated above, we would apply different forces to the same mass or to identical masses to show that the accelerations imparted to the mass are in direct proportion to the respective forces. For example, the driver who successively has his automobile move with accelerations of three, six, and nine feet per second per second really causes the engine to exert successive forces which are in the ratio of 1:2:3. This relationship is shown in Figure 12–7, where force and acceleration are represented by vectors.

On the other hand, if identical forces are applied to two different masses, the greater acceleration will be given to the smaller mass. The law could, of course, be restated to the effect that the accelerations imparted to two different bodies by identical forces vary inversely as the masses. If the masses are represented by M and m and the corresponding accelerations by A and a, then: $F = MA = ma$ and $\frac{A}{a} = \frac{m}{M}$.

For example, a man exerting his full force may give to a stalled car an acceleration of 0.5 feet per second per second. Applying the same force to a heavier type of car which has twice the mass of the lighter one, he is able to impart only one-half as much acceleration, or 0.25 feet per second per second. It is this principle that is utilized in the determination of mass by the inertia balance. Identical forces are used, accelerations are measured, and the mass or inertia of one of the bodies is calculated relative to the other, which is a standard mass.

UNITS OF FORCE

The units of force are defined in terms of the fundamental units. The absolute or invariable unit employed throughout this

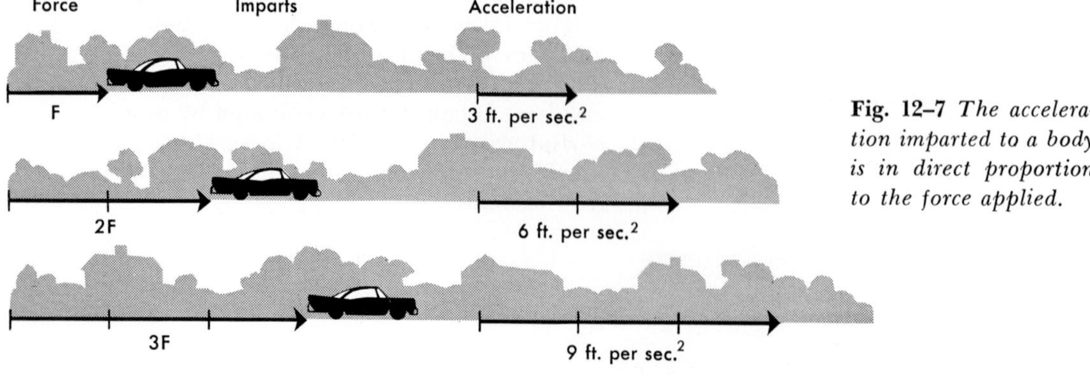

Fig. 12–7 *The acceleration imparted to a body is in direct proportion to the force applied.*

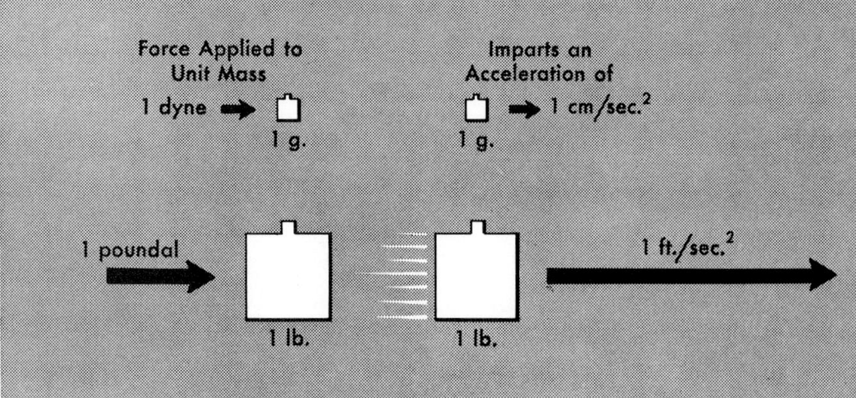

Fig. 12–8 *A comparison of the dyne and the poundal. Unit forces involve unit masses (represented as solid cubes) and unit accelerations (represented as vectors).*

text may be described as that force which gives to one unit of mass an acceleration of one unit of length per second per second. The dimensions of the absolute unit of force are, therefore,

$$\frac{\text{mass} \times \text{length}}{\text{time}^2}.$$

Specifically, two different units are in use:

The metric unit is that force which gives to a mass of one gram an acceleration of one centimeter per second per second; in terms of these units it is

$$\frac{\text{gram} \times \text{centimeter}}{\text{second}^2}$$

and, as this is a rather long title, it is given the shorter name *dyne*.

The British unit is similarly that force which imparts to a pound mass an acceleration of one foot per second per second, or

$$\frac{\text{pound} \times \text{foot}}{\text{second}^2}$$

and it is given the name *poundal*. See Figure 12–8 for a comparison of the dyne and the poundal.

CALCULATION OF FORCE

Force, mass, and acceleration may each be calculated, provided the other two quantities are known, by use of Equation 12–4 on page 190. Let us assume that a certain automobile that was given an acceleration of $2\frac{8}{11}$ miles per hour per second has a mass of three thousand pounds. What force is exerted by the engine? To solve, it is first necessary to change $2\frac{8}{11}$ miles per hour to feet per second, since the unit of force is in terms of feet per second per second.

$$\frac{2\frac{8}{11}\ \text{mi/hr} \times 5280\ \text{ft/mi}}{3600\ \text{sec/hr}} = 4\ \text{ft/sec change in velocity every second.}$$

The acceleration is therefore 4 ft per sec per sec.

$$F(\text{orce}) = m(\text{ass}) \times a(\text{cceleration}),$$

and substituting,

$$F = 3000\ \text{lbs} \times 4\ \text{ft/sec}^2 = 12{,}000\ \text{lb ft/sec}^2$$
$$= 12{,}000\ \text{poundals, the force required.}$$

A force of three hundred thousand dynes is applied to a small hand truck whose mass is fifty kilograms. What acceleration is given to the truck?

Since $$F = ma, \quad a = \frac{F}{m}$$

and since

$$50\ \text{kilograms} = 50{,}000\ \text{grams},$$

$$a = \frac{300{,}000\ \text{g cm/sec}^2}{50{,}000\ \text{g}}$$
$$= 6\ \text{cm/sec}^2\text{, the acceleration imparted.}$$

a

b

Fig. 12–9 (*a*) *In* A.D. *100, Hero of Alexandria demonstrated jet power. Water in the ball was converted to steam with the heat from a Roman Lamp. Steam issuing from the nozzles made the ball spin.* (*b*) *A simple demonstration of action-reaction producing motion.*

THE THIRD LAW OF MOTION

The first two Laws of Motion were based upon the experimental work of Galileo, and the First Law had, prior to Newton, been clarified by Descartes. The Third Law, however, was first formulated by Newton: *To every action there is always opposed an equal reaction; or, the mutual actions of two bodies on each other are always equal and opposite.*

The words "action" and "reaction" mean opposing forces; for forces always occur in pairs. If a man pushes against a table, the table resists with an opposite and equal force. This is true even where the force is great enough to cause the table to move, but then the man pushing the table must have more traction against the floor than the table has. He pushes backward on the floor with his feet, and the floor pushes with an equal force — and the man and the table move forward. All self-propelled objects exert a force backward and are moved forward by the reaction; the pedestrian and the horse move through the force of their feet against the earth; the automobile and locomotive, through drive wheels against the road and track; the steamship, through its propeller against the water; and the airplane, through its propeller against the air.

The rotating lawn sprinkler, the first steam engine of Hero (Figure 12–9), the jet-propelled rocket or plane — all owe their motions to the reaction or recoil due to escaping matter. When a gun is fired, the bullet leaves the muzzle with a high velocity; the gun and the man holding the gun are propelled or "kicked" backward with the same force, but, because of their greater mass, with less velocity than the bullet. This recoil shock is absorbed by the earth, and, in theory, the earth is also moved. The center of gravity (center of mass) of the whole system — bullet, gun, and man (assuming the man absorbs all of the recoil) — does not change. (This recoil force is utilized in the operation of machine guns. The gun barrel recoils against a spring which is distorted and by recovery operates the loading and firing mechanism.)

Two simple experiments may further serve to illustrate the Third Law of Motion. In a small becalmed sailboat, a large electric fan (Figure 12–10) is placed so as to

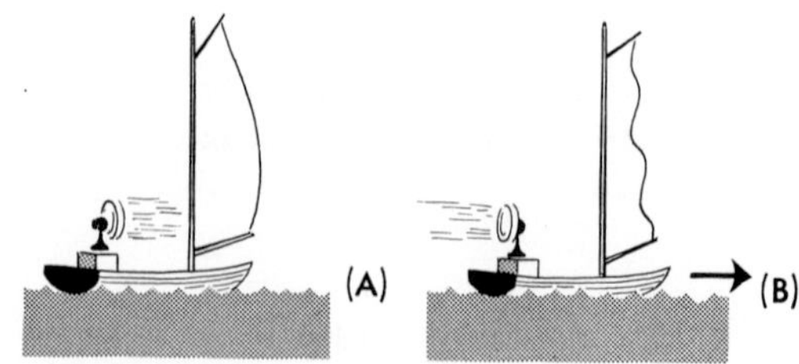

Fig. 12–10 *The boat will move when conditions are as shown in* (*B*), *but not when conditions are as shown in* (*A*). *Why?*

blow against the sail. There is no motion of the boat. The action by the fan, which is on the boat, is against the sail, which is also a part of the boat. This is of no more effect than is the push of one of the passengers against the mast or sail. If the fan is then turned around so as to blow to the rear of the boat, where there is no sail, the boat moves, for there is a reaction against something external to the boat — the air.

A second experiment concerns two boys of different weight on ice skates, roller skates, or anything that moves with little friction on a uniform surface. The two boys stand facing each other several feet apart and each holds to the end of a rope held taut between them (Figure 12–11). Boy A pulls sharply on the rope while Boy B holds it firmly. The boys approach each other and meet at a point C, which is carefully marked. They resume their former positions and repeat the experiment, but this time B pulls the rope. They meet at the same point as before. In the next trial both pull simultaneously on the rope and with the same results.

Finally, it will be shown in Chapter 14 that the attraction between the earth and the sun or between any two celestial bodies is mutual. The earth attracts the sun, and the sun attracts the earth with an equal, but opposite, force. Thus there can be no push or pull on one body unless there is a corresponding pull or push on another body.

MOMENTUM

A rifle bullet, moving with a velocity of only a few feet per second, would not injure anyone it happened to strike, whereas the same bullet fired with a high velocity from a rifle could be fatal. On the other hand, a hundred-pound mass moving at even a slow rate of speed would probably knock one over and cause injury. This combination of mass and velocity, sometimes called quantity of motion, depending upon both of these quantities for its value, is known as momentum and is represented by the formula:

$$M(\text{omentum}) = m(\text{ass}) \times v(\text{elocity})$$

$$M = mv. \qquad (\textit{Equation 12–5})$$

Since velocity, a vector quantity, appears in this formula, momentum is a directed, or vector, quantity.

FREELY FALLING BODIES

Apples fall to the earth and objects roll or slide down hills or inclines because of the force of gravitational attraction exerted by the earth. This force is continuously in operation and is constant at any one place although it varies slightly with the geographic position. For example, an athlete can throw a javelin about 6 inches farther in Australia than he could in Finland.

Since this force of attraction acts constantly, it must impart a uniform acceleration to freely falling bodies. According to the Aristotelian theory, a heavy body fell at a faster and faster rate because of the increasing amount of air above it and the diminishing amount below it, and in some instances because it hastened as it approached its natural place or home. Probably misled by observing leaves and feathers floating slowly to the ground the Aristotelians maintained that a heavier object fell faster than a lighter one — that a ten-pound sphere of metal fell ten times as rapidly as a one-pound sphere. Galileo questioned these conclusions, and by 1590 had

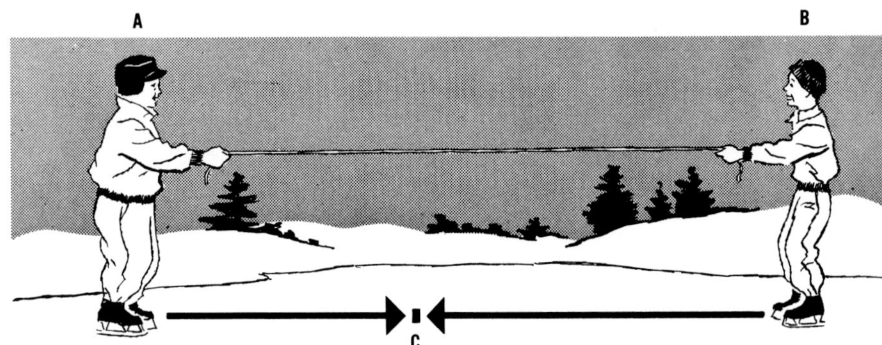

Fig. 12–11 *Action and reaction are equal and equal momenta are imparted to the two boys.*

completed significant experimental studies, some of which have already been described. He found that when metal balls of different masses were dropped simultaneously they struck the ground at the same time.

We may now invoke the Second Law of Motion in order to interpret the experiment of Galileo in precise terms. The two bodies of masses M and m each fall freely with acceleration a, due to the forces F and f.

$$F = Ma \quad \text{and} \quad f = ma.$$

Since a is common to the two equations,

$$a = \frac{F}{M} = \frac{f}{m}.$$

Rearranging, $$\frac{F}{f} = \frac{M}{m},$$

which means that the forces of attraction exerted on bodies by the earth at any given place are proportional to the masses of the bodies.

This force acting on a body is commonly called the *weight*. Since the earth is slightly flattened at the poles, the weight is greater there than on the equator. At the center of gravity of the earth, the weight would be zero, and out in space a few thousand miles the weight would be considerably less than at the surface of the earth. In contrast to weight, the mass of a given body is constant regardless of the place at which it is measured.

The equations for uniformly accelerated motion, $v = at$ and $d = \frac{1}{2}at^2$, may be used for calculating the velocities attained and the distances the bodies fall. For this application we substitute for a the value of the acceleration due to gravity. This value, g, is approximately 32 feet per second per second, or 980 centimeters per second per second. These values have been accurately measured at various points on the earth; at Washington, D.C., g is 980.095 centimeters per second per second, or 32.155 feet per second per second. With these values established, calculations for falling bodies may be readily made.

EXAMPLE: A brick falls from the top of a high building and reaches the ground in five seconds.

1. With what velocity does it strike the ground? The equation $v = at$ is used, and since we have a special value for acceleration, which is g, the equation becomes $v = gt = 32 \text{ ft/sec}^2 \times 5 \text{ sec} = 160$ feet per second, which is the final velocity.

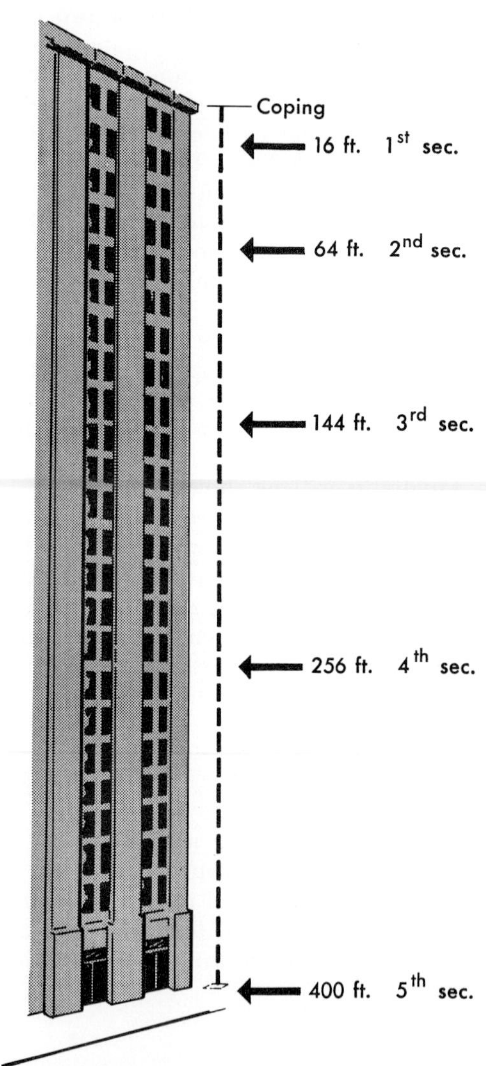

Fig. 12–12 *The distance through which a body falls is proportional to the square of the time. The above diagram represents the fall of a brick from the top of a skyscraper.*

2. How high is the building? In other words, how far does the brick fall in five seconds? Here the formula for distance may be used. $d = \frac{1}{2}at^2 = \frac{1}{2}gt^2 = \frac{1}{2}$ 32 ft/sec^2 × (5 sec)^2 = 400 feet, which is the height of the building. Another solution may be used: A falling body always falls sixteen feet during the first second (since the average velocity for the time interval is sixteen feet per second). According to the above equation, the distance varies with the square of the time. Hence the ratio holds that d(istance) : 16 ft = (5 sec)^2 : (1 sec)^2 and

$$d = \frac{16 \text{ ft} \times (5 \text{ sec})^2}{(1 \text{ sec})^2} = 400 \text{ feet.}$$

3. How far has the brick fallen at the end of each of the five seconds? Since for all cases,

$$d = \frac{1}{2}\ 32 \text{ ft/sec}^2 \times t^2 = \frac{16 \text{ ft} \times t^2}{\text{sec}^2}$$

At end of first sec: $d = 16 \times 1^2 = 16$ ft.
At end of second sec: $d = 16 \times 2^2 = 64$ ft.
At end of third sec: $d = 16 \times 3^2 = 144$ ft.
At end of fourth sec: $d = 16 \times 4^2 = 256$ ft.
At end of fifth sec: $d = 16 \times 5^2 = 400$ ft.

Thus, falling bodies under the influence of only one force, that of gravity, move vertically with uniform acceleration. Let us now consider cases where two forces act simultaneously on a body.

PROJECTILES

We shall consider first bodies which are given an initial horizontal velocity and which, according to the Law of Inertia, tend to continue their uniform straight-line motion. As soon as such an object, which may be a thrown stone, leaves the hand it becomes also a freely falling body subject to the accelerating influence of the force of gravity. The actual resultant motion of the body is a curved path, determined by *both* of the component motions.

In Figure 12–13 two stones are represented. The first is dropped from point *A*. At the same time the second is thrown horizontally from point *A*, which is 16 feet above the ground. The first stone has no horizontal velocity and falls directly downward with an acceleration g. The thrown stone, although moving in a curved path, has two component motions — a horizontal uniform motion and a vertical uniformly accelerated motion, both taking place simultaneously. By the time it moves through the horizontal distance *AB* it also moves through the vertical distance *BE*. In equal time intervals, it moves successively over equal distances *BC* and *CD* and simultaneously through vertical distances which are not equal, to points *F* and *G*, respectively. The horizontal distance from *A* at any moment may be calculated by the equation for uniform motion, $d = vt$, while the vertical distance from *A* at the same moment may be calculated by use of the equation for falling bodies, $d = \frac{1}{2}gt^2$. Both stones reach the ground at the same time, and at any moment during their flight they are both vertically equidistant from *A* or from the ground as indicated by the line *MN*. Thus, when a body is under the influence of two or more motions, the particular final effect of each motion is realized independently of the others.

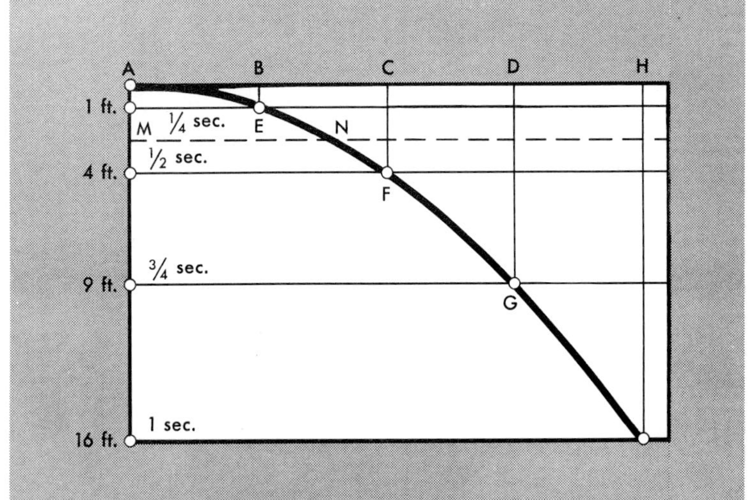

Fig. 12–13 *Influence of gravity on trajectories. A dropped object and an object projected horizontally, released at the same time, strike the ground simultaneously.*

ACCELERATION IN UNIFORM CIRCULAR MOTION

In straight-line motion, we have seen the term *acceleration* refers to a change in velocity. In uniform motion in a circle, which is very common, the term *acceleration* has a different connotation. Consider a body of mass m grams which is revolving in a circle of radius r centimeters with a constant motion of v cm/sec. The mass m will not move in a circular path unless there is a side force always operating and directed toward the center of rotation. The reader is urged to try whirling a weight on the end of a string. Just as soon as the inward force is released, the whirling mass flies off in a straight line on a tangent. The force necessary to keep the object in a circular path is measured by $F = ma$ (Equation 12–4). (Refer also to Figure 12–14.) When the force directed toward the center ceases to operate, the object will move in any time t along AB with uniform motion, v. If the force F is operating, the mass moves along the arc AE. It thus has moved a distance AC toward the center. This is the acceleration. Hence the acceleration in uniform circular motion is always directed toward the center of rotation and perpendicular to the direction of travel. Thus in circular motion there is always a continuous change in the direction of travel.

The acceleration can be evaluated as follows: The acceleration $= AC$ is $\frac{1}{2}at^2$ (Equation 12–3). If t is a small quantity, the arc AE can be taken as the diagonal of the rectangle $ABEC$. Note that the two triangles ACE and AED are similiar right triangles, and, therefore,

$$\frac{AC}{AE} = \frac{AE}{AD}, \quad \text{or} \quad AC = \frac{(AE)^2}{AD}.$$

(*Equation 12–6*)

But AE is distance of uniform motion or vt (Equation 12–1), $AD = 2r$, and $AC = \frac{1}{2}at^2$. Hence,

$$\tfrac{1}{2}at^2 = \frac{(vt)^2}{2r}, \quad \text{or} \quad a = v^2/r.$$

(*Equation 12–7*)

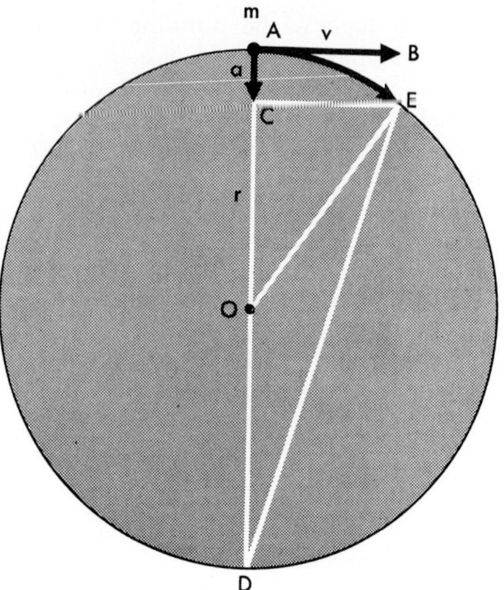

Fig. 12–14 *Uniform motion in a circle.*

Thus in *uniform circular motion,* the acceleration is given by the *square of the circular velocity divided by the radius of rotation.*

In résumé, then, a body in straight-line motion undergoes acceleration if the velocity is changed. A body traveling with uniform motion in a circle must continuously undergo a change in direction of travel and this also is called acceleration. The force required to produce these two kinds of accelerations are both measured by $F = ma$, which in the case of circular motion becomes $F = mv^2/r$.

ILLUSTRATIVE EXAMPLE: A mass of 50 grams is whirled on a string of one meter with a uniform motion of 40 cm/sec. What is the force acting on the string and weight?

SOLUTION: From Equation 12–7,

$$a = v^2/r = \frac{(40 \text{ cm/sec})^2}{100 \text{ cm}} = 16 \text{ cm/sec/sec.}$$

$$\text{Then} \quad F = ma = 50 \text{ g} \cdot 16 \text{ cm/sec}^2 = 800 \text{ g cm/sec}^2 = 800 \text{ dynes.}$$

This inward force is called a *centripetal force.* The reaction force called for by Newton's third law is directed outward and is called a *centrifugal force.*

SUMMARY

1. Motion (change of position of a body relative to some other body) is of two kinds:
   a. Uniform, in which the same distance is covered in equal successive units of time ($d = vt$). Distance varies with the time. Velocity, or rate of change of position, is a vector quantity. Speed is a scalar quantity.
   b. Accelerated, in which the velocity changes. Uniform acceleration, a special kind, is that in which the change in velocity is constant: $a = v/t$ for cases in which the initial velocity is zero. Distance varies with the square of the time: $d = \frac{1}{2}at^2$. The distance required to stop an object which is decelerated uniformly, varies as the square of the velocity.
2. A vector quantity is one which has both magnitude and direction. It is represented by a graphical arrow drawn in the appropriate direction and with a length proportional to the magnitude.
3. Force causes change of motion, or acceleration: $F = ma$. The absolute units of force are the dyne (g cm/sec^2) and the poundal (lb ft/sec^2).
4. Mass, the quantity of matter in a body, is invariable and is a measure of a body's inertia (or resistance to change of motion).
5. The Laws of Motion, formulated by Newton, are:
   a. Bodies at rest remain at rest; bodies in motion continue to move uniformly in a straight line unless acted upon by some force.
   b. The acceleration imparted to a body is proportional to the force producing it and takes place in the direction in which the force acts.
   c. To every force there is an equal counter force.
6. Momentum is the product of *mass* $\times$ *velocity*.
7. The force of the earth's attraction, which is known as gravity, imparts to freely falling bodies an acceleration (called *g*) of approximately 32 ft/sec^2 or 980 cm/sec^2. Weight is the force with which the earth attracts a body.
8. The force exerted by gravity upon different bodies is in direct proportion to their respective masses.
9. Freely falling bodies move in accordance with the equations for uniformly accelerated motion.
10. A moving body influenced by two or more directional forces responds to each independently.
11. A body traveling with uniform motion in a circular path undergoes a continuous change in direction of travel. This change is directed toward the center of rotation and this is also called acceleration. The acceleration is given by the equation $a = v^2/r$.

STUDY EXERCISES

1. For each term, compose a concise word definition or statement, and supply a mathematical expression or formula.
   a. Velocity.
   b. Acceleration.
   c. Distance covered under uniform velocity.
   d. Distance covered under uniform acceleration.
   e. Force.
   f. Momentum.
   g. Mass.
   h. Weight.
2. In the table are given four examples of motion, A, B, C, and D, with the velocities attained at the end of each second. All except C start from rest. Select for each the phrase (or phrases) below that classifies it.

Sec	Velocity at end of given second (ft/sec)			
	A	B	C	D
1	2	8	5	4
2	6	16	5	10
3	9	24	5	8
4	15	32	5	6
5	18	40	5	2

   a. Uniform motion.....................
   b. Accelerated motion....................
   c. Non-uniformly accelerated motion.......
   d. Uniformly accelerated motion..........
   e. Motion resulting from a continually varying force............................

f. Motion resulting from a constant force continuously applied....................

g. Motion resulting from the application of balanced opposing forces after the initial motion is given......................

3. An automobile travels north three hundred and twenty miles in eight hours.
   a. Calculate the average velocity (show units).
   b. Express this velocity in feet per second.
   c. How many feet does it move, at this rate, in one minute?
   d. How long would it take to travel from Chicago to Cincinnati (three hundred miles) at this average velocity?
4. A pursuit plane flies at a velocity of six hundred miles per hour.
   a. How many feet per second is this?
   b. How many miles does it travel in one and a half hours assuming uniform velocity?
   c. In what time would it overtake another plane forty miles away flying in the same direction with a velocity of four hundred miles per hour?
5. An explosion is heard ten seconds after the flash of it is seen. Sound travels at a velocity of 1150 feet per second under the existing conditions. Assuming that the light from the flash travels instantaneously, calculate the distance of the observer from the explosion.
6. How long does it take light, with a velocity of 186,000 miles per second to travel from the sun to the earth 93,000,000 miles away?
7. A plane before take-off attains a velocity of one hundred and eighty feet per second in ten seconds. Assuming a uniform increase in velocity, calculate:
   a. the acceleration;
   b. the distance required for the take-off.
8. A car starts from rest and under uniform acceleration travels two hundred feet in ten seconds.
   a. What is its acceleration?
   b. What velocity does it attain by the end of the ten seconds?
   c. How far would it travel in five seconds under the same acceleration?
9. An automobile with a mass of three thousand pounds is brought to rest from a velocity of sixty miles per hour in eight seconds.
   a. What is the negative acceleration?
   b. What is the braking or retarding force required?
   c. What distance does it move as it is being brought to a stop?
   d. What distance would it move while being braked to a stop from a velocity of thirty miles per hour?
10. An automobile weighing thirty-six hundred pounds is given a velocity of twenty feet per second in four seconds. Calculate the force exerted by the motor.
11. A force of thirty-five thousand dynes is applied to a small cart having a mass of twenty kilograms. What acceleration is imparted to the cart?
12. For each of the situations or phenomena described below, determine which one of the laws of motion is illustrated.
    a. Bodies near the moon fall to it with less acceleration than those which fall to the earth.
    b. The engine of an automobile moving with uniform velocity exerts just enough force to balance the retarding forces of friction and air resistance.
    c. If the valve on a high-pressure gas cylinder is broken off, the cylinder is propelled at high speed by the escaping gas.
    d. A steel ball bounces.
13. Construct and fill out a chart on the following model, in which uniform motion and accelerated motion are contrasted.

	Uniform Motion	Accelerated Motion
Formula for velocity		
Formula for distance		
Velocity is constant (check)		
Velocity varies with time		
Distance varies with time squared		
Distance varies with time		
Requires only balanced forces to continue		
Requires continuous force		

14. Starting with the two equations for uniformly accelerated motion, derive an equation for velocity in terms of distance and time.
15. Plot a curve to show each of the following

relationships for uniformly accelerated motion.

a. Velocity against time.

b. Distance against time.

c. Distance against the square of the time.

16. Bodies *A* and *B*, having masses of one pound and ten pounds, respectively, are dropped simultaneously from the top of a high building. Compare the two with respect to the points enumerated below, and, where there is a difference, indicate which is greater and, if possible, by how much.

.... Accelerations imparted.

.... Velocities attained at the end of *t* seconds.

.... Momenta at time of striking ground.

.... Weight of *A* on ground compared with that of *B*.

.... Weight of *A* on top of building compared with that of *A* on the ground.

.... Force which gravity exerts.

17. From the equation $F = ma$ show that the force of attraction which the earth exerts on a body at a given place is proportional to the mass of that body.

18. In the table below are experimental data obtained by observation of a ball rolling down an inclined plane. First, from the distance the ball moved during the first second, determine its acceleration and answer questions *a*, *b*, and *c*; then fill in all the blank spaces in the table, including those in the column for distance.

Time (t), seconds	Total distance, feet	t^2	Velocity at end of each second	Change in velocity each second
0	0			
1	2			
2	8			
3	18			
4				
5				

a. What is the acceleration?

b. How may it be increased?

c. What is the limit of the acceleration which the ball on the inclined plane can attain?

19. What velocity is attained by a body falling for eight seconds in a vacuum? What distance does it fall in that time?

20. An airplane is headed directly eastward at a velocity of two hundred miles per hour. A cross wind is blowing to the south at a velocity of sixty miles per hour. Make a scale drawing to show the actual path of the plane and calculate its velocity along that path.

21. A bullet with a speed of two thousand feet per second is fired in a horizontal direction four feet from the ground. What is its range? (Neglect air friction.)

FOR FURTHER READING

1. LEMON, H. B., *From Galileo to the Nuclear Age*. Chicago: University of Chicago Press, 1946.

The first six chapters give a clear and entertaining discussion of motion.

2. WHITE, HARVEY E., *Classical and Modern Physics*. New York: D. Van Nostrand Company, Inc., 1940.

Chapters 4 and 5 will help the beginner understand uniform and accelerated motion, and Newton's three laws of motion.

3. Paperback: HALL, A. R., *The Scientific Revolution*. Beacon, $1.75.

The first four chapters give an excellent background to the attacks on traditional dogmas during the sixteenth and seventeenth centuries.

13 ASTRONOMY AND COSMOLOGY

THE LAWS OF MOTION originated in observations and experiments on bodies at or very near the surface of the earth. The crucial assumption is that these laws, which describe the motions of falling bodies, thrown stones, moving vehicles, and other terrestrial objects, apply also to the motions of astronomical bodies such as the moon and the planets. The validity and importance of this particular assumption will become evident as we follow the development of our present conception of the solar system. The broader implication that other physical laws, derived by scientists in their terrestrial laboratories, apply universally is the foundation upon which modern science rests. This broad assumption is essential to the life and growth of science; it permits us to link the new or unknown with the known; it permits us to test a scientific law or theory by forecasting new observations or predicting the results of new experiments. For example, the astronomer may determine that certain chemical elements are present in the outer layer of the sun by a comparison of the sun's radiation (light) with that emitted by known elements in his laboratory. He may predict the position of a certain planet at a future date or forecast the appearance of a comet. He can do these things only because he assumes that terrestrial laws apply throughout the cosmos.

In this and several of the following chapters, we shall study cosmology, that is, the general features of the physical universe and some of the laws which govern it, starting with the solar system. A preview of the universe, or cosmos, was presented in Chapter 3. The sun is the central body of the solar system, with the earth and other planets rotating on their axes and revolving in their orbits around this massive body. Beyond the solar system in all directions are innumerable stars, thousands of which are visible to the unaided eye. These stars are distributed and grouped unevenly in diverse patterns which have undergone little or no change since they were first recorded. They serve as a background against which the motions or apparent motions of the moon, the planets, and the sun may be observed.

Cosmology has a long, wavering, and at times tempestuous history. The first scientific model of the universe was constructed by the Greeks and was accepted for approximately two thousand years. An imperfect version of the modern scheme was developed in the sixteenth century, but did not gain general acceptance for nearly one hundred and fifty years. Between the time of the Greeks and the introduction of the modern system by Nicholas Copernicus (Poland, 1473–1543), little if anything had been added to observational astronomy; there were no changes in the laws and concepts of physics which were still Aristotelian.

ANCIENT ASTRONOMY

Long before the beginning of recorded history, that is, before the invention of writing, primitive people must have acquired some familiarity with astronomy. The apparent motion of the sun, the apparent rotation of the sky, the phases of the moon, and an occasional eclipse or comet must have caught their attention and stimulated their curiosity. Confronted by the problem of survival and having little or no control over their environment, they had to adjust their habits and work to the cycle of day and night and regulate their agriculture by the rhythm of the seasons. As they traveled over land and water, only the stars could guide them. Although we have no direct evidence that prehistoric man learned to measure time and to determine direction this way, there is archeological evidence that he invented tools and implements, that he developed decorative arts and medicine, and that he learned to count and to measure distances. Not all groups of people made such advances, for there are primitive tribes living today in isolated parts of the world who have not acquired these skills. They are skills, however, that a society must develop to become organized. And since societies were in fact organized, we infer that the men of which they were composed did develop these skills. Indeed, we know that the most highly organized early societies in the valley of the Nile (Egypt), in the area around and between the Euphrates and Tigris rivers (Mesopotamia [1]) and in the Orient, made quite remarkable progress in observational astronomy.

THE BABYLONIANS AND THE EGYPTIANS

Written records dating from approximately 3000 B.C. or earlier show that these peoples had developed observational astronomy and mathematics, especially geometry. These skills were later combined into the beginnings of scientific astronomy. The eclipses of the moon and sun, the appearances of comets, and the movements of the planets were recorded over long periods of time. The length of the year was determined with surprising accuracy. The year of the Egyptians was 365 days, but they added an extra day every four years. The calendar of the Babylonians was based primarily on the moon, and for mathematical convenience they adopted a 360-day year; they also determined the periods of revolution of Venus and Mercury relative to the earth. The Babylonians' contributions were not all inspired by scientific zeal, for they held the superstition that human destiny was somehow linked with the movements of the stars. The astrology which was generally practiced throughout the Middle Ages and which even today retains some adherents was a product of the late Babylonian period. The Babylonians did not formulate any scientific conception of the universe. They believed the earth to be a disc-shaped island surrounded by a sea beyond which was a circular ring of mountains supporting the sky or firmament. As stated in the first chapter of Genesis, "God made the firmament and divided the waters which were under the firmament from the waters which were above the firmanent; and it was so."

[1] The successive cultures of Mesopotamia — Sumerian, Babylonian, Assyrian (seventh century B.C.), and Chaldean (post-Hellenic) — are for convenience all referred to as "Babylonian."

THE GREEKS

It is fortunate that the astronomy and mathematics of the Babylonians and Egyptians were handed on to the Greeks. These vigorous and intellectually daring people were relatively free from superstition and were thus able to engage in speculative thought and inquiry. They traveled and communicated with the rest of the known world and were well informed on the work and ideas of other peoples. Those who had colonized Ionia (in Asia Minor) were acquainted with the civilizations to the east of them in Babylonia, Persia, and possibly India. It was in Ionia that Greek science was born, and during the period which began with Thales of Miletus (624–*ca.* 548 B.C.) and ended with Claudius Ptolemy of Alexandria (A.D. 100–170) their astronomy and cosmology were developed. The Greeks believed that the universe was orderly and that its workings could be reduced to general laws in harmony with the great body of facts. They therefore attempted to account for the motions of the celestial bodies and for the first time to formulate a scientific picture of the universe.

Thales made some contributions to geometry and to magnetism, successfully explained the phases of the moon, determined the solstices and the equinoxes, and measured the apparent diameter of the sun. To him and to his contemporaries, the earth was a disc floating in a sea of water.

Pythagoras (572–492 B.C.) was probably the first to maintain that the earth is a sphere, at rest in the center of a rotating universe. The apparent erratic wandering of the planets he believed, if analyzed, would be reduced to uniform circular motions, an idea which greatly influenced Greek astronomy.

Eudoxus of Cnidos (407–355 B.C.) proposed a mathematical scheme for representing the motions of the stars, sun, moon and the five known planets. He assumed that these bodies were carried by a system of concentric spheres centered at the earth, each rotating uniformly. The stars were carried by the outermost sphere which made a complete rotation daily. The more complex motions of a planet required that it be carried simultaneously by several spheres, all rotating uniformly, but at different speeds and around different axes or diameters of the earth. The position of the planet at a given future time could thus be calculated and checked against observation. If the two did not coincide, the theory could be modified by an adjustment of the speeds or axes of the spheres or by the addition of new spheres. Eudoxus' system finally required a total of twenty-seven spheres.

Aristotle (384–322 B.C.) used this system as the basis for his cosmology which pictured a universe of finite size enclosed in a great sphere. In the vicinity of the earth, heavy bodies moved naturally in straight lines toward the earth, lighter matter moved away from the earth, and matter was constantly changing. Beyond this region everything, planets, sun, and spheres, were made of an unchanging material, which was called the *incorruptible aether* and which naturally moved in circular paths. In his efforts to perfect the mechanical system of Eudoxus, Aristotle added twenty-eight spheres making a total of fifty-five.

Heracleides. Not all of the cosmologies of the Greeks placed the earth at the center of the universe. (Such systems are called *geocentric* as opposed to *heliocentric* systems which put the sun at the center.) Heracleides of Pontos (*ca.* 388–310 B.C.) devised a system which was a combination of the geocentric and the heliocentric. He theorized that the sun, moon, and superior (outer) planets revolve around the earth which rotates daily. The inferior (inner) planets, Mercury and Venus, revolve about the sun.

Aristarchus of Samos (310–230 B.C.) proposed a heliocentric system with the earth and other planets rotating and revolving around the sun which was the center of the universe. He also measured the relative distances of the moon and the sun from the earth. The heliocentric theory was taught a century later in Babylonia, but did not gain wide acceptance.

Hipparchus (160–125 B.C.), who was perhaps the greatest of ancient astronomers, made a prolonged and systematic series of observations. He prepared a catalogue of about one thousand stars which, with little alteration, remained in use for sixteen hundred years. He also discovered the precession of the equinoxes. Unfortunately, he chose a geocentric system, emphasizing a scheme of uniform circular motions to account for the movements of the moon and the sun. Three hundred years later, Ptolemy, the last of the classical Greek astronomers, prepared a compendium of the then known astronomical science. In this work, which he called the *Mathematical System of Astronomy,* and which was later known from the Arabic translation as the *Almagest,* he supported and expanded the geocentric theory of Hipparchus.

THE PTOLEMAIC SYSTEM

In the scheme described by Ptolemy, the earth was the central body of the universe; it was spherical in form and at rest. The fixed stars of the heavens were studded in a great outer sphere which rotated westward around the earth daily carrying with it the other celestial bodies. The sun, moon, and planets revolved in an eastward direction around the earth, the sun requiring one year for its complete revolution.

This classical conception was accepted and survived for fourteen hundred or more years after Ptolemy. We may well ask today why such a system was ever formulated, why it was accepted in preference to the alternate heliocentric system, and why it remained the dominant cosmology for so many centuries. These questions cannot be completely answered; to find even partial answers one must have some acquaintance with the state of the physical sciences and the scientific mentality of these earlier times. Actually, at the time of Ptolemy, it was touch-and-go between the two systems, for there were no known facts nor crucial scientific reasons which favored one or the other. It is sometimes implied that the inaccuracies of the observed data may somehow have favored the Ptolemaic system, but it is a matter of record that Copernicus based his heliocentric system largely on Ptolemy's data.

Since both systems fitted the observed data, we may look for answers to the above questions in the mental processes, beliefs, and attitudes of the scientists. First, the most obvious and natural explanation for the apparent daily motions of the sun and stars was to conclude that they revolve around the earth. One has no feeling or awareness that the earth is in motion; if the earth moves, these early thinkers reasoned, would not birds in flight and objects thrown in the air be left behind? Second, the concept of a geocentric universe had some emotional appeal to human vanity and pride. It was also the view of some of the Greek philosophers that immobility was more noble than motion. Third, the Ptolemaic cosmology represented the summation of classical Greek astronomy. It was based upon the Aristotelian mechanics which dominated the physical sciences during the Middle Ages and through most of the Renaissance. Although differing from the Aristotelian cosmology in the interpretations of planetary motions, the Ptolemaic scheme was nevertheless geocentric and was therefore supported by the great prestige of Aristotle.

Planetary Motions. The most troublesome problem was to account for the irregular motions of the planets. Viewed from the earth, Mars, for example, moves directly eastward, then it slows down, and for a shorter time moves westward with retrograde motion; then it resumes its eastward motion as shown in Figure 13–1. The planets also change their speeds and distances from the earth. We have seen how Eudoxus and Aristotle, following the doctrine of Pythagoras and Plato, used the device of homocentric spheres. Ptolemy employed a number of other geometrical devices and, in doing so, departed somewhat from the doctrine of uniform circular motion.

The first of these devices, the *eccentric,* is

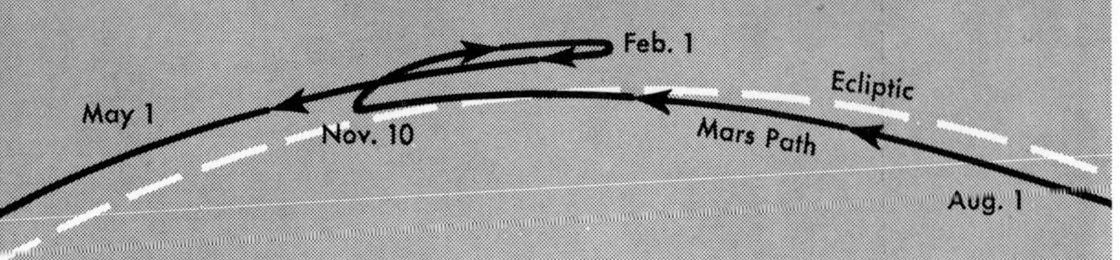

Fig. 13–1 *The retrograde motion of Mars as observed from the earth.*

shown in Figure 13-2. The planet *P* revolves uniformly in a circle about the center *C,* which is some distance from the earth. The path of the planet is eccentric with respect to the earth and is nearest to the earth at *A* and furthest from it at *B.* This device adequately represents the apparent annual motion of the sun.

The second device is the *epicycle,* a combination of two uniform circular motions. The planet *P,* Figure 13–3, describes a small circle (epicycle) about the point *A* which revolves in a larger circular orbit or *deferent* about the earth *E.* The speeds of the two circles are independent of each other, and both the speeds and diameters of the circles may be adjusted to represent the motions of a planet.

These devices were used separately or in various combinations. It is obvious that the many necessary adjustments of speed, displacement, and radii of wheels upon wheels make the system one of great complexity. The enormous amount of mathematical computation and the skill with which it was used in accounting for the motions and the positions of the planets command the respect of scientists even today. The system in a somewhat simplified form is represented in Figure 13–4. The sun was between Venus and Mars, while Venus and Mercury were between the earth and the sun with the centers of their epicycles always aligned with the earth and the sun.

Between Ptolemy and Copernicus there was little change in astronomy; more observational data had caused an increase in the number of circles involved in the planetary motions, but the general scheme remained the same. Only a limited portion of Greek learning was directly inherited by the people of western Europe; the great

Fig. 13–2 *The hypothesis of eccentrics. The orbits of planets, the moon, and the sun were assumed to be circular with the center eccentric to a stationary earth (distance from C exaggerated here). The motion of a planet would be fastest at position A, slowest at B.*

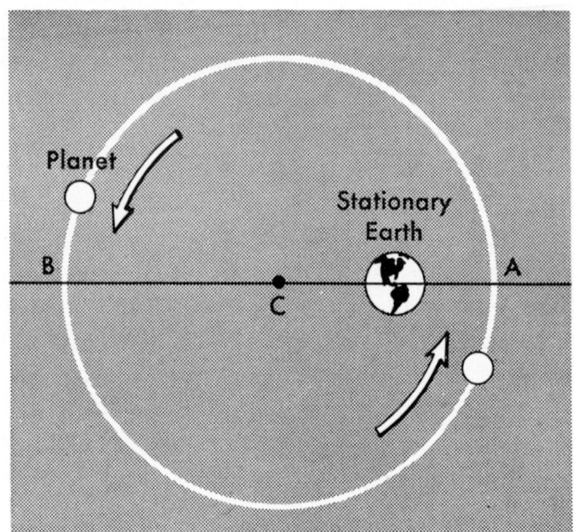

Fig. 13–3 *The epicycle of ancient astronomers. The planet P describes a circular orbit about a point A which in turn moves in a circular path about the fixed earth E. The planet in moving from m to n will be in forward motion; from n to m, in retrograde motion.*

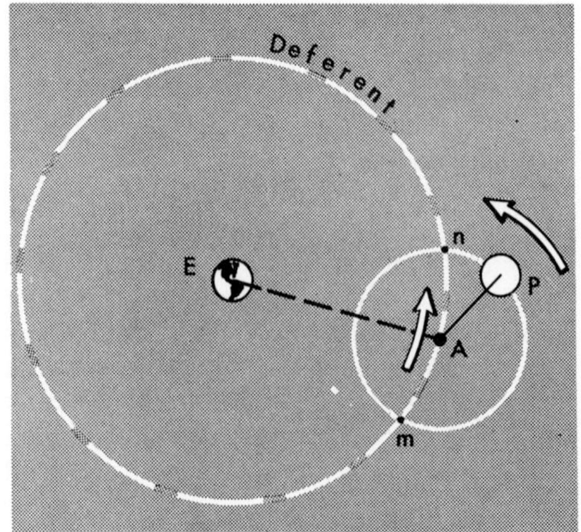

bulk of it was transmitted principally through two channels. In the Christian Byzantine Empire (A.D. 300–1453) Greek culture and science were preserved, but no notable advances were made. Farther east the Hindus and the Arabs had maintained some threads of authentic Greek culture dating from the time of the conquests of Alexander the Great. In the seventh century the Arabs, under the inspiration of their new Islamic faith, started a wave of conquest which extended through the Middle East, Egypt, and into Spain. During the three or four hundred years following the invasion, they made important contributions to science, to the arts, and to medicine. They assimilated and preserved some of the ancient learning of Greece, India, and Persia, translating many of the manuscripts into Arabic. The *Almagest* was thus brought into Italy and translated from the Arabic into Latin in 1175. The Crusades also greatly helped to spread Greek culture into western Europe. Later, many manuscripts in the original Greek were brought from the East by migrating Greek scholars and teachers, particularly after Constantinople fell to the Turks in 1453. The philosophy of Aristotle, including his cosmology, was incorporated into Christian theology by Thomas Aquinas (1225–74), and the cosmology of Ptolemy was at least tolerated by the Scholastics as representing the detailed planetary motions. The identification of these geocentric systems with theological doctrine strengthened them, and they stood unshaken for the next three hundred years.

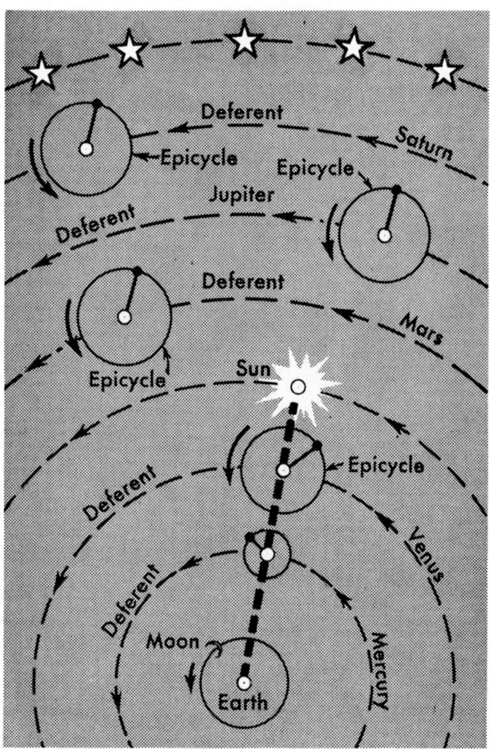

Fig. 13–4 *The solar system according to the Ptolemaic hypothesis.*

THE COPERNICAN SYSTEM

Nicholas Copernicus (1473–1543), a Polish astronomer and physician, who later became a canon of Frauenburg Cathedral, lived during an exciting and turbulent period. By 1500 the Italian Renaissance had reached its peak; there were brilliant achievements in art and literature; notable inventions (printing, mariner's compass, gunpowder, and paper); exploration (America, South Africa, India); and great political and economic changes. It was an age of ferment, of wars, and of religious conflicts. In the sciences an old era was coming to a close, but the new one was not to come until the next century. The men of the Renaissance still looked toward ancient Athens and Alexandria.

Copernicus spent several years in Italy studying law, medicine, and mathematics and there acquired an interest in the heliocentric theories of Aristarchus and others of the Pythagorean school. He was also impressed by the differences of opinion he found among the astronomers and mathematicians. When he made a thorough mathematical analysis of Ptolemy's scheme he found that it did not accurately describe planetary motions. The system, he decided, was also too complex; the number of circles necessary to approximate the paths of the planets had by this time been increased to eighty.

Fig. 13–5 *Nicholas Copernicus. (Scripta Mathematica, Yeshiva University)*

Copernicus then worked out the first mathematical heliocentric system comparable in completeness of detail to the system of Ptolemy. Indeed, there was considerable similarity between the two systems, but the Copernican model differed in three important details:

1. The sun was assigned to the central position of the universe.
2. The earth was relegated to a secondary role, but was *in motion,* rotating and revolving around the sun along with the other planets.
3. The movements of the planets were reduced to combinations of uniform circular motion. The motion was uniform with respect to the center of the circle, but there was a different center for each planetary orbit and the sun was not quite at the center of any of them.

The new model was geometrically less complex than the geocentric scheme and the number of circles was reduced from eighty to thirty-four.

The daily rising and setting of the sun, moon, planets, and stars were explained by the rotation of the earth. The assumption of daily westward rotation of the whole celestial sphere, propelled by a mysterious prime mover (Primum Mobile), was discarded. The apparent daily movement of the sun against the background of stars and the apparent retrograde motions of the outer planets were accounted for by the orbital motion of the earth. Hence no epicycles were required for these apparent planetary motions. The nearer a planet is to the sun, the shorter is its period of revolution, so that the earth overtakes and passes the superior planets. Observed from the earth against the background of fixed stars, Mars, for example, moves forward (1, 2, Figure 13–6), and when the earth overtakes (3) appears to stand still and then to move backward for a time after the earth passes. The same effect is perceived when an observer on a fast train passes a slower one, provided the observer can ignore the landscape and concentrate only on the slower train.

There were yet two crucial points of evidence to be found. One was the parallactic displacement of the nearer stars with re-

Fig. 13–6 *Apparent retrograde motion of the planet Mars.*

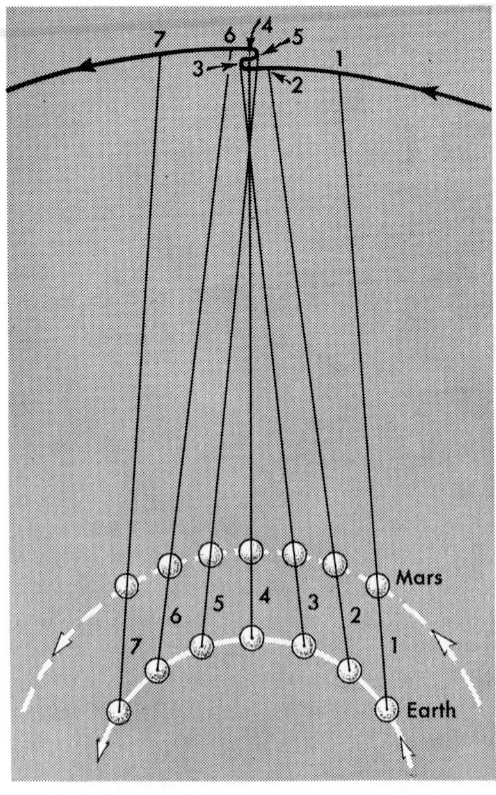

spect to those at greater distances, caused by the orbital motion of the earth (page 27), and this displacement was not observed until 1830. Copernicus explained this lack of evidence by placing the stars so far away that the earth's orbit is only a point in comparison to their great distances. The other missing piece of evidence had to do with the phases of the inferior planets, Mercury and Venus. In the Ptolemaic system, the centers of the epicycles of these two planets were permanently aligned between the earth and the sun to explain their back-and-forth motions relative to the sun. Hence only a small edge of each of these planets, illuminated by the sun, could be visible to observers (Figure 13–7). On the other hand, according to the Copernican scheme, these planets revolve in orbits between the sun and the earth's orbit. They should therefore show different phases, just as the moon does, for at times they may be on the opposite side of the sun from the earth and at other times between the sun and the earth. (Figure 13–8). Copernicus predicted such phases, although he had no way of observing them. Sixty-seven years later, Galileo, using his telescope, observed the phases of Venus.

Copernicus' data indicated that the actual orbits of the planets were not circular

Fig. 13–7 *According to the Ptolemaic hypothesis, only a small edge of Mercury or Venus is ever visible to the observer on the earth.*

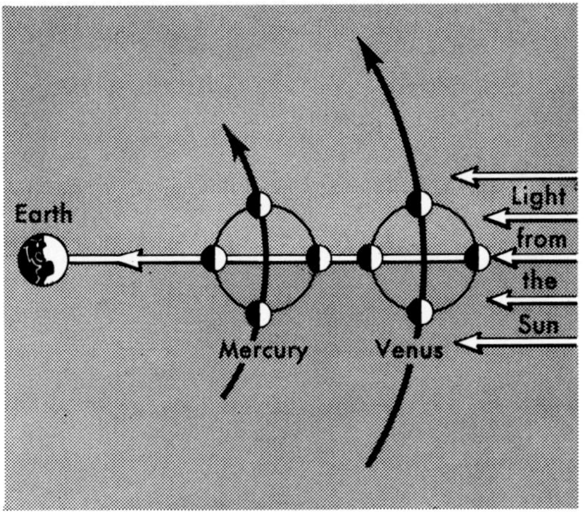

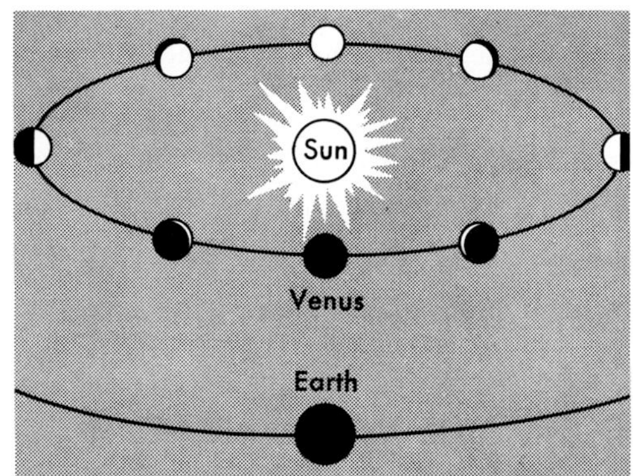

Fig. 13–8 *According to the Copernican scheme, Venus (and Mercury) undergoes phase changes as viewed from the earth.*

nor were their motions uniform. He therefore had to use eccentrics, as indicated in the preceding section, and a number of small epicycles.

SIGNIFICANCE OF COPERNICUS' WORK

The publication of Copernicus' great work, *De Revolutionibus Orbium Coelestium Libri VI* (Six Books Concerning the Revolutions of the Heavenly Spheres), was delayed until shortly before his death in 1543. The immediate effect of this work was far from sensational; the opposition it provoked among the churchmen of the various faiths did not develop into a general controversy until near the end of the century. The conflict which centered primarily on the position and movement of the earth was not to be resolved until more accurate observational data were gathered and the Aristotelian concepts of mechanics, supported by Christian doctrine, were replaced. The modern historian, Herbert Butterfield, poses the problem thus:

> In this whole picture of the universe there is more of Aristotle than of Christianity. It was the authority of Aristotle and his successors which was responsible even for those features of this teaching which might seem to us to carry something of an ecclesiastical flavour — the hierarchy of heavens, the revolving spheres, the

Intelligences which moved the planets, the grading of the elements in the order of their nobility and the view that the celestial bodies were composed of an incorruptible fifth essence. Indeed, we may say it was Aristotle rather than Ptolemy who had to be overthrown in the sixteenth century, and it was Aristotle who provided the great obstruction to the Copernican theory.[1]

In attempting to evaluate the contribution of Copernicus we must remember that he remained somewhat of an Aristotelian. He held, for example, to the Aristotelian doctrine of uniform circular motion, yet when he removed the earth from its central position and put it in motion, continuous motion without a mover, he abandoned the whole Aristotelian system with its rotating celestial spheres and its mechanics of motion and gravity (see Chapter 12). He was unable to interpret satisfactorily his system on the basis of the old concepts, and he did not develop any new ones; he did seem to anticipate gravitation in stating that other celestial bodies besides the earth may attract objects. His greatness lies in the bold formulation of his new theory, without the support of new evidence and principles, and the stimulus it gave to further research in the physical sciences. Copernicus helped to close an old era rather than to open a new one.

THE MODERN HELIOCENTRIC SYSTEM

The modern era of science starts in the seventeenth century, although its roots extend far down into the past. The towering figure of the versatile Galileo Galilei, the greatest of all naked-eye astronomical observers Tycho Brahe (Denmark, 1546–1601), and the great mathematician and astronomer Johann Kepler (Germany, 1571–1630), all made notable contributions toward perfecting modern cosmology.

Galileo became a warm supporter of the Copernican system and, hearing of the invention in 1608 of a telescope or "spyglass" by the Dutch optician, Hans Lippershey, at once saw its great possibilities for astronomical observation. A year later he completed his own telescope, which consisted of lenses placed at either end of an organ pipe and had a magnifying power of about three diameters.[2] Galileo became the leading actor in one of the great dramas of science. Turning his telescope toward the heavens, he saw things that were astonishing but indubitable. In due time he observed that Venus passes through phases just as the moon does, as predicted by Copernicus. His successive observations of sun spots convinced him of the rotation of that body. He observed many stars for the first time, nebulae, the craters on the moon, the small oscillations (librations) of that body, the rings of Saturn, and four satellites revolving around Jupiter.[3]

In further support of the Copernican view, Galileo also cited events on the earth, such as tides and trade winds, which he explained as due to the rotation of the earth. His principles of motion, particularly the First Law, explained why objects that are thrown into the air and birds in flight are not left behind, but move along with the rotating earth. Galileo presented the entire matter in discussion form in his famous work, *Dialogue on the Great World Systems* (the Ptolemaic and the Copernican), which as a piece of scientific literature ranks with Copernicus' *Revolutions* and Newton's *Principles.* In this book, Galileo set forth anti-Aristotelian arguments in astronomy and mechanics which were revolutionary and devastating. Although he had received some support from highly placed churchmen, the opposition of his Aristotelian colleagues and of some of the church officials became very bitter. The Copernican *Revolutions* was placed on the Index in 1616; and after the publication of the

[1] Herbert Butterfield, *The Origins of Modern Science* (New York: The Macmillan Company, 1951), pp. 18–19.

[2] Galileo later constructed a telescope which had a magnifying power of thirty diameters.

[3] Eight additional satellites of Jupiter were discovered after the construction of more powerful telescopes.

Dialogue, Galileo was tried by the Inquisition. He was found guilty, forced to recant, and placed under a mild house-arrest for the rest of his life.

NEW OBSERVATIONS

Tycho Brahe, a Danish nobleman using a grant from the King of Denmark, constructed the great observatory of Uraniborg (the Tower of Heaven) on the island of Hveen. There he made a series of observations over a period of twenty-one years.

He developed instruments of a size and accuracy never before known. Beginning with such crude instruments as the astrolabe (Figure 13–9), then used by navigators for observing the position of celestial bodies, he soon saw the necessity for improvement. He accordingly had constructed a huge quadrant having a radius of about nineteen feet and a finely divided scale. He also had built a large theodolite with both vertical and horizontal scales. These instruments, however, were designed for naked-eye astronomy (for the telescope had not yet been introduced) and had to be carefully sighted by the alignment of small openings or pointed in somewhat the same way as a gun is aimed. (Refer to Figure 13–10.)

Fig. 13–9 *An astrolabe. (American Museum of Natural History)*

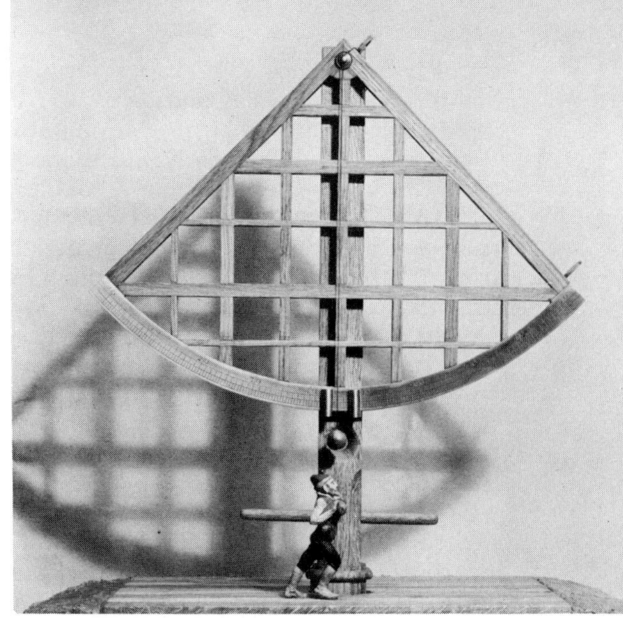

Fig. 13–10 *Tycho Brahe's quadrant. (American-Scandinavian Foundation)*

Brahe searched in vain for some parallactic displacement of the stars and, unaware that the great stellar distances made it impossible for him to see these tiny displacements with his instruments, rejected the Copernican system and developed one of his own, which resembled the cosmology of Heracleides. In the Tychonic system, as it was called, the stationary earth was at the center; the sun, moon, and superior planets revolved around the earth; Mercury and Venus revolved around the sun. This system won few adherents, and Brahe is known primarily for his accurate and extensive observations of the positions of the planets.

LAWS OF PLANETARY MOTION

While a student, Johann Kepler was converted to the Copernican doctrine. He became convinced that the universe and, specifically, the planetary motions were governed in accordance with exact principles, and he spent the greater portion of his life in research on the problem. The publication of some of his early speculations brought him to the attention of Galileo, with whom he later carried on a correspondence, and also brought him an invitation from Tycho Brahe to continue his researches with Brahe at Prague. Here he was able to test some of his hypotheses against the accurate data which Brahe had accumulated. He was so impressed with the accuracy of Brahe's instruments and observations that he discarded his own and other hypotheses which were not in agreement with them. Upon Brahe's death, Kepler inherited this vast store of accumulated observations. In accordance with a previous agreement with Brahe, Kepler completed a series of observations which were published as the *Rudolphine Tables* (after King Rudolph of Bohemia, their patron).

Despite ill health and poverty, which at times forced Kepler to teach and even to practice astrology, he kept persistently at work for more than twenty years on the problem of planetary motions. The data of Brahe showed that the planets did not follow the paths prescribed by either the Ptolemaic or the Copernican system. Each planet was shown to move at a variable

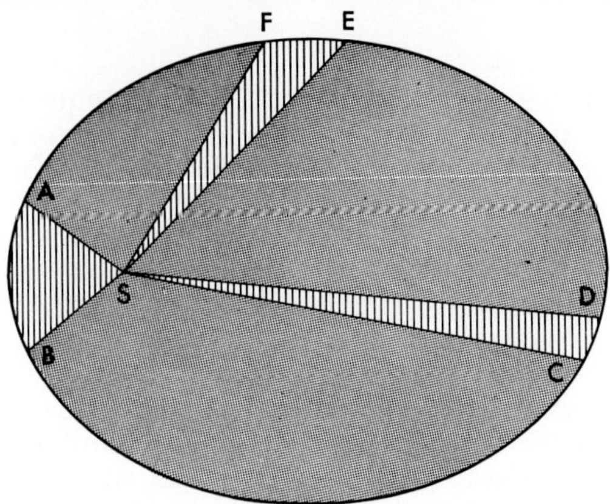

Fig. 13–12 *The orbital speed of a planet varies in accordance with the law of areas.*

speed, which increases as the planet moves closer to the sun and decreases as the planet recedes from the sun. To account for this motion Kepler tried many different curves, each hypothesis involving an enormous amount of calculation. Finally, the ellipse (page 28) occurred to him as a possibility – and it worked. He found that if the sun were placed at one of the foci, then there was a close agreement between theory and Brahe's observations.

As a result of his long analysis Kepler was able to sum up planetary motions into three very important laws, the first two of which were announced in 1609, and the third in 1619.

1. Each planet moves in an *elliptical orbit* about the sun, with the sun at one focus of the ellipse.
2. A line joining the center of each planet to the center of the sun sweeps over *equal areas* in *equal intervals of time* (Law of Areas).
3. The squares of the periods of revolution of any two planets are proportional to the cubes of their mean distances from the sun (Harmonic Law).

Fig. 13–11 *The eccentricity of the earth's orbit.*

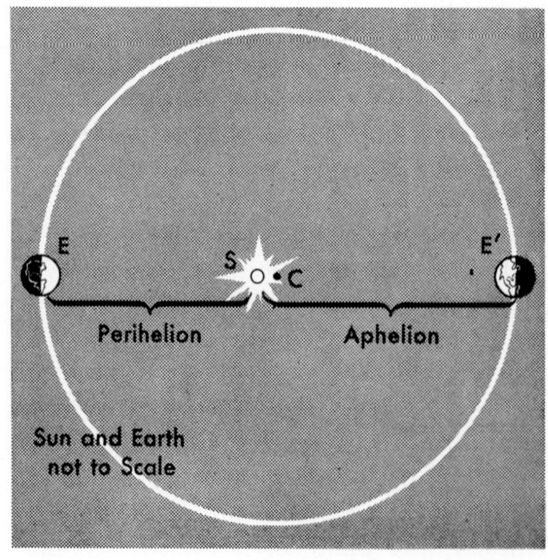

The path of the earth and, in fact, the paths of all the planets except Mercury and Pluto are ellipses of low but different eccentricities. That is, they are almost circular. Thus the orbit of the earth appears much as in Figure 13–11. When the earth is nearest to the sun, or at perihelion, on January 3 or 4, it is some 3 per cent (about three million miles) nearer than when it is far-

TABLE 13–1 PERIODS AND MEAN DISTANCES OF SOME PLANETS FROM THE SUN

PLANET	T (PERIOD) in earth years	D (MEAN DISTANCE) in miles	in astronomical units	T^2	D^3
Mercury	0.241	36×10^6	0.39	.058	.059
Venus	0.615	67×10^6	0.72	.378	.373
Earth	1.000	93×10^6	1.00	1.000	1.000
Mars	1.881	142×10^6	1.53	3.538	3.560
Jupiter	11.862	483×10^6	5.20	140.660	140.610

thest away, at aphelion, on July 3 or 4. That is, the distance from the sun to the center of the ellipse is approximately 1.5 million miles, while the distance from the center to aphelion or perihelion is roughly ninety-three million miles. Hence, the eccentricity of the earth's orbit = 1.5/93 = 0.016.

The Law of Areas expresses clearly, without the need of mathematical equations, the relationship between proximity to the sun and the orbital speed of the planet. At perihelion, for example, the earth is moving with its greatest speed and at aphelion with its least. In Figure 13–12 the eccentricity of the orbit is exaggerated. The planet moves from A to B in the same time as that required for it to move from E to F or from C to D. Hence, area BAS = area CDS = area EFS.

The Harmonic Law (Kepler's Third Law) is expressed by the equation

$$\frac{[T(\text{ime})]^2}{[t(\text{ime})]^2} = \frac{[D(\text{istance})]^3}{[d(\text{istance})]^3},$$

or

$$\frac{T^2}{t^2} = \frac{D^3}{d^3},$$

where T and t are the periods (time) required for each revolution and D and d are the mean distances, respectively, of any two planets. If we list the periods and mean distances from the sun for a few of the planets (Table 13–1) and express the former in years and the latter in astronomical units, the relationship is simpler. For the earth, t is one year and d is one astronomical unit. If we substitute these values in the equation, then,

$$\frac{(T \text{ years})^2}{(1 \text{ year})^2} = \frac{(D \text{ astronomical units})^3}{(1 \text{ astronomical unit})^3}$$

and $$T^2 = D^3$$

for any planet, provided the period is expressed in years and the distance in astronomical units. This numerical relationship may be used to calculate one of these values for a given planet if the other is known. For example, the period of revolution for Saturn is 29.46 years. What is its mean distance from the sun in miles? (One astronomical unit = 92,870,000 miles.)

$$D^3 = (29.46)^2$$
$$D^3 = 867.8916$$

and, $$D = \sqrt[3]{867.8916} = 9.537,$$

the distance from the sun to Saturn in astronomical units; thus,

$$9.537 \times 92{,}870{,}000 = 885{,}600{,}000 \text{ miles}.$$

The Laws of Kepler apply not only to the motions of the planets, but also to those of their satellites. These laws, together with the principles of dynamics developed by Galileo and more completely by Newton, tell how bodies move, but it remained for Newton to answer the question why, by combining them all into the one great universal principle of gravitation.

SUMMARY

1. Astronomy, the oldest of sciences, advanced concurrently with civilization.
   a. Primitive man probably developed a sense of *time* and *direction* by observation of *astronomical bodies and events,* but he associated them with his superstitions.

- *b.* The Babylonians and early Egyptians developed *observational astronomy* and made *accurate computations and predictions.*
- *c.* The Greeks with better instruments and more mathematics applied a more developed *scientific method* to astronomy and developed cosmologies.

2. The Ptolemaic or *geocentric* system placed the earth at the center of the universe with the planets and sun revolving around it. To explain motions of the planets, epicycles and eccentrics were introduced.

3. The Ptolemaic hypothesis was finally rejected because it did not harmonize accurately with the observations of Galileo and Tycho Brahe.

4. The Copernican or *heliocentric* system placed the sun at the center of the solar system with the planets revolving about the sun in circular orbits. A few epicycles were assumed to explain irregularities in planetary motions.

5. Circular orbits with few or many epicycles were not in accord with the extensive and accurate observations of Tycho Brahe.

6. Kepler solved the dilemma by a revision of the Copernican system in which he introduced elliptical orbits and other changes, all of which are embodied in his three laws of planetary motion:
   - *a.* Each planet moves in an elliptical orbit about the sun, with the sun at one focus of the ellipse.
   - *b.* A line joining the center of a given planet with the center of the sun sweeps over equal areas in equal intervals of time.
   - *c.* The squares of the periods of revolution of any two planets are directly proportional to the cubes of their mean distances from the sun.

7. The development of a cosmology, like that of any other great theory, followed a cycle of observation, organization, and the formulation of an hypothesis. The cycle was then repeated with better observations by improved techniques, reorganization, the rejection or revision of the old hypothesis, and the formulation of a new or modified one.

STUDY EXERCISES

1. Explain why astronomy is the oldest of the sciences. What reasons lead us to infer that primitive people developed some kind of astronomy?
2. Show that although the Babylonians and early Egyptians linked their astronomy with their superstitions they were scientific to a considerable extent. Do science and superstition wholly exclude each other? What *is* superstition?
3. Among the ancient Greek astronomers were Thales, Pythagoras, Eudoxus, Aristarchus, Heracleides, and Hipparchus. Mention briefly the contributions which each made toward the development of a cosmology, after first explaining the meaning of this term.
4. Describe briefly the Aristotelian cosmology. How does it differ from the Ptolemaic?
5. If the telescope had never been invented, is it likely that the Copernican system would have won universal acceptance?
6. Designate the system or systems for which each of the following statements is true, by writing *G* for the geocentric or Ptolemaic system, *H* for the heliocentric system as set forth by Copernicus, and *M* for the modified, or modern, heliocentric system which followed Kepler's work.
   - *a.* Sun approximately at the center of circular orbits..........................
   - *b.* Sun at one focus of elliptical orbits. ....
   - *c.* Earth at the center of the system.......
   - *d.* Epicycles required to explain retrogression; was accepted for the longest period of time..............................
   - *e.* Few epicycles needed and only for irregular planetary motions................
   - *f.* Made use of eccentrics................
   - *g.* Two planets have orbits between earth and sun............................
   - *h.* Two planets have the center of their epicycles aligned with earth and sun. ....
   - *i.* Requires that Venus and Mercury show phase changes........................
   - *j.* Requires a parallactic displacement of nearer stars relative to the more distant ones...............................

k. Planets move around the sun with uniform speeds..........................

l. Planets move around sun with variable speeds...............................

7. On the first line mark *T*, if true, or *F*, if false. On the second line indicate by 1, 2, or 3 which of Kepler's laws tells us whether or not the statement is true.

...., ... *a.* Jupiter is nearer to the sun than is Uranus and therefore has a greater orbital speed.

...., ... *b.* A line joining the center of the earth with the center of the sun sweeps over equal areas during the months of June and July.

...., ... *c.* The earth is nearest to the sun on or about January 1.

...., ... *d.* A planet which is three times as far from the sun as the earth makes one revolution around the sun in 5.20 years.

...., ... *e.* The distance from a given planet to the sun varies during its year.

...., ... *f.* A planet has its greatest orbital speed at perihelion.

8. Was the heliocentric system revived by Copernicus because he discovered new facts or because he considered it to be a better way to explain the known facts?

9. Show that the discovery of the phase changes of Venus and the observation of a parallactic displacement of nearer stars relative to the more distant stars are crucial points of evidence against the Ptolemaic system and for the heliocentric system.

10. Mark *A*, if the fact is explained by the geocentric system; *B* if it is explained by the heliocentric system; and *C* if it is explained by *both* systems.

a. Day and night.......................

b. The retrograde motion of an outer planet. ....

c. The phases of Venus and Mercury. ....

d. The parallactic displacement of the stars. ....

e. The apparent change in size of Venus and Mercury........................

f. The phases of the moon...............

g. The apparent eastward motion of the sun among the stars..................

11. *a.* If a new planet with a period of revolution of eight years were found, what would be its mean distance from the sun in astronomical units? In miles?

b. If a new planet were found at a mean distance of 0.3 astronomical units from the sun, what would be its period of rotation in earth years?

12. State specifically what each of these scientists contributed to our present-day cosmology: (*a*) Ptolemy; (*b*) Copernicus; (*c*) Galileo; (*d*) Brahe; (*e*) Kepler.

FOR FURTHER READING

1. Payne-Gaposchkin, C., *Introduction to Astronomy.* New York: Prentice-Hall, 1954.

   A well-illustrated book written in understandable language and containing numerous quotations from literature and history. Chapter VII deals with the history of our conception of the solar system.

2. Sarton, G., *A History of Science: Ancient Science Through the Golden Age of Greece.* Cambridge: Harvard University Press, 1952.

   A comprehensive and authoritative work by an outstanding historian of science, for those who wish more complete information concerning a particular era or person. The section dealing with the astronomy of Aristotle (pp. 506–513) is recommended.

3. de Santillana, G., *The Crime of Galileo.* Chicago: University of Chicago Press, 1955.

   The complete story of Galileo's encounter with the Inquisition. In the preface the author draws a parallel to a recent American cause célèbre.

4. Galilei, Galileo, *Dialogue on the Great World Systems,* in the Salusbury translation; revised, annotated, and with an introduction by Giorgio de Santillana. Chicago: University of Chicago Press, 1953.

   Galileo's great philosophical work for which he was imprisoned by the Inquisition. The Historical Introduction is recommended to those who do not wish to read the Dialogue *itself.*

5. Paperback: Armitage, A., *The World of Copernicus.* Mentor, 50¢.

14

UNIVERSAL GRAVITATION

WE NOW COME to a most significant period in the history of western civilization, a period of extraordinary productivity and intellectual advance, a period of unification and clarification. In the two previous chapters we have seen how some old concepts were thrown aside or transformed and how the new studies of motion, first of bodies on the earth and later, of the celestial bodies, prepared the way for the grand synthesis achieved by Newton. In this chapter we shall discuss the formulation of the Newtonian system in which astronomy and mechanics were blended and in which all motions, those of relatively small objects on the earth and those of astronomical bodies, were brought under one set of laws.

However, the advances made during this period were not confined to the above fields. In England, Francis Bacon (1560–1626) wrote on the inductive method and won great popular support for science; William Gilbert (1544–1603) published his treatise on magnetism, *De Magnete* (1600); William Harvey (1578–1657) discovered the circulation of the blood; and Robert Boyle (1627–91) made fundamental contributions to chemistry with the publication of his classical book, *The Sceptical Chymist.* In Holland, René Descartes (1596–1650), a native of France, invented analytic geometry, and Christian Huygens (1629–95) formulated the wave theory of light.

The seventeenth century has been appropriately described as the Century of Genius. The historian, Preserved Smith, has stated:

> The genius of seventeenth-century Europe brought forth many imperishable masterpieces in literature and art, . . . and gave birth to liberty and popular government . . . But the supreme glory of the seventeenth century – or, more accurately, of the hundred and fifty years beginning with Copernicus, . . . and ending with Newton and Huygens – and the chief importance of that period in history, lies in its scientific achievements. Among all the brilliant discoveries of that age, none was more dazzling or ultimately more momentous than that of science itself.[1]

The outstanding genius of this period and one of the most eminent scientists of all time, Isaac Newton (England, 1642–1727) was born within a year after the death of Galileo. We have already discussed his laws of motion (Chapter 12) and shall encounter more of his work in this study, for his contributions were extensive and numerous. Newton studied at Trinity College of

[1] Preserved Smith, *History of Modern Culture* (New York: Henry Holt and Company, 1930), p. 114.

Fig. 14–1 *Sir Isaac Newton. (Scripta Mathematica, Yeshiva University)*

Cambridge University and there, under the influence of a gifted and discerning professor, Isaac Barrow, displayed extraordinary mathematical and scientific ability. Barrow recognized Newton's genius and later relinquished his own professorship to his former student. During the plague of 1655–56, Newton spent eighteen months at his home in the country. In this short time he made practically all of his great discoveries; never was so much original and creative work done in so little time. He discovered the binomial theorem, laid the foundations of what is now differential and integral calculus, performed experiments on light and color, formulated the Laws of Motion and started the chain of thought and investigation which led to the formulation of the *Law of Universal Gravitation.* This great principle was shown by Newton to be the consequence of his laws of motion and Kepler's laws of planetary motion; it therefore represented the synthesis of the total knowledge in the fields of dynamics and astronomy up to that time. But its meaning and application are not restricted to events in our solar system; it is a universal principle. This subject is treated in the third "book" of Newton's renowned work, *Philosophiae Naturalis Principia Mathematica,* known as the *Principia,* which was published in 1687. We shall now see how this great law was formulated, tested and applied.

FORMULATION OF THE LAW

Prior to Galileo the problem of dynamics was to discover why thrown balls, projectiles, and even planets, continue to move. Rest was supposed to be the natural state of a body, and therefore moving bodies required some kind of impelling force. Upon Galileo's discovery of the important principle of inertia, later set forth in Newton's First Law of Motion, the problem changed completely. Since bodies in motion continue to move uniformly in a straight line, the problem for the scientist was to find out, not why they continue to move, but why they depart from uniform straight-line motion. For terrestrial events this departure was satisfactorily explained (Chapter 12). When Newton gave his attention to the motions of celestial bodies, he had already formulated his laws of motion; he knew that the earth attracts bodies on or near it, and he knew that the planets move in accordance with Kepler's laws. The great problem for him was, therefore, to find why the planets and other celestial bodies depart from the straight-line motion and move in Keplerian orbits. In other words, why does the planet at point A in its path (Figure 14–2) move in the curved path toward C instead of continuing in a

Fig. 14–2 *Curvilinear and rectilinear motion compared. Planets move in curved paths.*

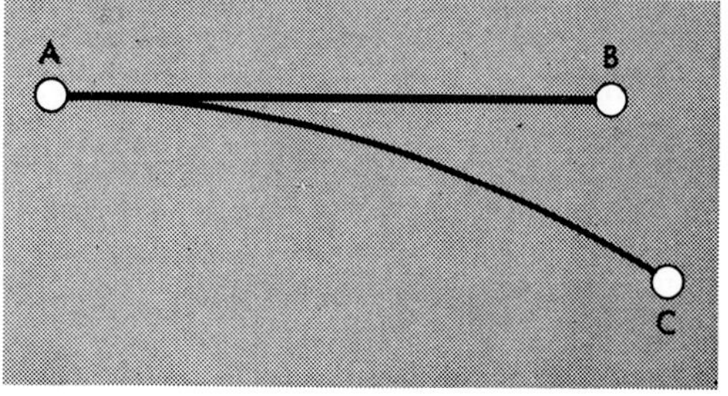

straight line toward B? The First Law of Motion and the known behavior of earthly projectiles gave the general answer: each planet is acted on by an external force. But what is this force? In what direction does it act? Upon what does its magnitude depend?

It took the genius of Newton to conceive the idea that the same force which acts on a falling apple, or which causes a projectile to deviate from a straight path, holds the moon in its orbit. It will be shown in a later paragraph how he tested and verified this hypothesis. He further extended this hypothesis beyond the earth to the motions of the planets with reference to the sun. On the basis of his own laws of motion, and with great mathematical skill, he arrived at a number of inferences from Kepler's laws:

1. *Each planet is acted upon by a force which is directed toward the sun.* He demonstrated mathematically that a body moving under the influence of a force directed always toward a fixed center obeys the Law of Areas (Kepler's Second Law). Conversely, therefore, the planets which obey this law must each be constantly subject to a force directed toward this center (the sun).

2. *The force of attraction between the sun and a given planet varies inversely as the square of the distance between the two bodies.* Newton proved that for a body moving under the inverse-square law the orbit may be an ellipse with the attracting body at one of the foci. Conversely, an elliptical orbit (Kepler's First Law) implies the inverse-square law for the force.

3. *The force of attraction is directly proportional to the mass of the planet* and is not in any way dependent upon the size, shape, composition, or temperature. This inference was made from Kepler's Third Law and is in harmony with the Second Law of Motion.

4. *The force of attraction is a mutual one* (Third Law of Motion).

The mathematical proof for inferences (2) and (3) is somewhat beyond the scope of this text, but may be readily shown if we assume circular orbits. As shown in Equation 12–1 (Chapter 12), the velocity of a body moving with *uniform linear speed* in a circular path is:

$$v = \frac{2\pi r}{t}, \qquad \textit{(Equation 14–1)}$$

where r is the radius of the circle (planet's orbit) and t the time required for one revolution. A body traveling uniformly in a circular path must continuously change its direction of travel toward the center. Otherwise it would fly off tangentially in a straight line. A continuous change in direction is also called acceleration (refer to page 185). The equation for the acceleration in this case is given by Equation 12–7:

$$a = \frac{v^2}{r}, \qquad \textit{(Equation 14–2)}$$

If we substitute the value for v in Equation 14–1 for v in Equation 14–2, we get

$$a = \frac{4\pi^2 r}{t^2}. \qquad \textit{(Equation 14–3)}$$

And since force, $f = ma$ (Second Law of Motion), the force due to the sun,

$$f = \frac{4\pi^2 mr}{t^2} \qquad \textit{(Equation 14–4)}$$

For a second planet with mass M, moving in a circle at distance R from the sun and with a period of revolution T, the force due to the sun,

$$F = \frac{4\pi^2 MR}{T^2} \qquad \textit{(Equation 14–5)}$$

Dividing 14–4 by 14–5 we get

$$\frac{f}{F} = \frac{mrT^2}{MRt^2} \qquad \textit{(Equation 14–6)}$$

According to Kepler's Third Law,

$$\frac{T^2}{t^2} = \frac{R^3}{r^3};$$

substituting in Equation 14–6 we have:

$$\frac{f}{F} = \frac{mR^2}{Mr^2}$$

which for the limited case of circular motion implies that the forces exerted by the sun on two different planets are inversely proportional to the squares of their respective distances from the sun and directly proportional to their respective masses.

Newton finally consolidated all his inferences into one general principle which applies not merely to the solar system but to the entire physical universe — the law of universal gravitation:

Every particle of matter in the universe attracts every other particle with a force which is proportional to the product of their masses, and inversely proportional to the square of the distance between them. The law is expressed by the proportionality:

$$F(\text{orce, gravitational}) \propto \frac{M(\text{ass}) \cdot m(\text{ass})}{d(\text{istance})^2} \qquad (\textit{Equation 14–7})$$

In order to change this proportionality into an equality, the *constant of gravitation G* (to be evaluated later) is inserted and the equation reads:

$$F = G\frac{Mm}{d^2} \qquad (\textit{Equation 14–8})$$

TESTING THE THEORY

In order to test a principle of this kind, it is necessary to compare results obtained by calculations based on the principle with those found experimentally. If the results check, the "theory" is substantiated. Twenty years before publication of his great principle, Newton tested his idea by a comparison of the force exerted by the earth on a falling body with that exerted by the earth on the moon. He tentatively assumed that the attractive force exerted by a body like the earth was directed toward its center, as if the entire mass of the body were concentrated at that point. It follows that a falling body on the earth's surface is approximately four thousand miles from the center of attraction of the earth and that the moon is sixty times as far away, since the distance from the earth to the moon is about 240,000 miles.

We may recall that according to the Second Law of Motion ($F = Ma$), the force of attraction exerted by the earth on a body is in direct proportion to the mass of that body. If an apple and the moon were at equal distances from the earth, they would fall with equal accelerations. But with the moon at a distance from the center of the earth sixty times that of the apple, Newton reasoned, it should fall with only $1/(60)^2$ of the acceleration with which the apple falls. The experimental method of measuring acceleration is to obtain the distance covered in a given time. During the first second the apple falls 16.08 feet (one-half of its acceleration). Hence, if the inverse-square part of the law of gravitation is true, the moon should be drawn toward the earth

$$1/(60)^2 \times 16.08 \text{ ft} = \frac{16.08 \text{ ft}}{3600} = 0.00447 \text{ ft}$$
$$= 0.0536 \text{ inch in one second.}$$

The actual deviation from a straight path or "fall" of the moon toward the earth may be calculated from observational data. In $27\frac{1}{3}$ days the moon moves in its orbit around the earth (E) (Figure 14–3) at a distance of approximately 240,000 miles

Fig. 14–3 *Gravity keeps the moon from flying off at a tangent. The moon "falls" toward the earth the distance BC while moving from A to C in its orbit.*

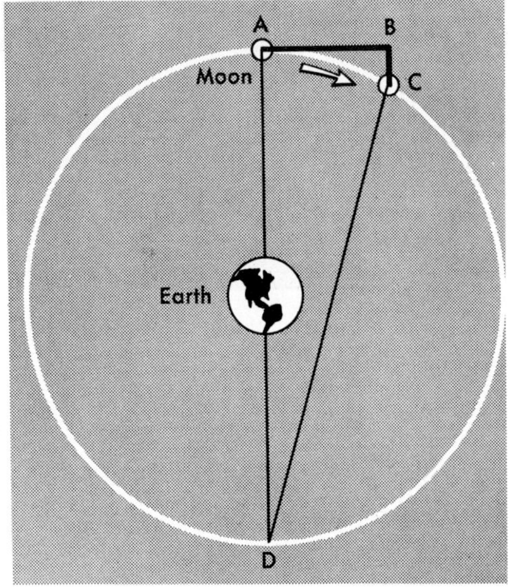

from E. For practical purposes we may assume a circular orbit. While moving from A to C in one second (the drawing is not to scale) it also "falls," or deviates from a straight line, the distance BC. For the relatively short distance it moves in one second, the arc AC may be regarded as a straight line. Since the right triangles ABC and ACD are similar,

$$\frac{BC}{AC} = \frac{AC}{AD} \quad \text{and} \quad BC = \frac{(AC)^2}{AD}.$$

Now AC, the distance the moon travels in one second, is

$$\frac{2\pi(AE)}{\text{seconds in } 27\frac{1}{3} \text{ days}}$$

$$= \frac{2 \times 3.1416 \times 240{,}000 \text{ mi} \times 5280 \text{ ft/mi}}{27\frac{1}{3} \times 24 \times 3600 \text{ sec}}$$

$$= 3372 \text{ feet per second.}$$

$$\text{And} \quad BC = \frac{(AC)^2}{AD} = \frac{(3372 \text{ ft})^2}{2 \times 240{,}000 \times 5280 \text{ ft}} = 0.00449 \text{ foot} = 0.0539 \text{ inch.}$$

The same result may be obtained by using the equation $a = \frac{v^2}{r}$, a being the "sidewise" acceleration of the moon toward the earth. The distance the moon moves toward the earth in the first second is

$$d = \tfrac{1}{2}a = \frac{v^2}{2r},$$

and substituting

$$d = \frac{(3372 \text{ ft})^2}{2 \times 240{,}000 \times 5280 \text{ ft}} = 0.00449 \text{ foot} = 0.0539 \text{ inch.}$$

The agreement between theory and observation is especially good in view of the approximations assumed in the calculations.

Even after such excellent verification, Newton, uncertain as to the validity of his tentative assumption, withheld announcement of his discovery. Only after he was able to prove that a sphere attracts external bodies as if all its mass were concentrated at its own center could he elaborate his new principle and incorporate it into his renowned *Principia*.

Fig. 14–4 *Jolly's method for determining the value of the constant of universal gravitation.*

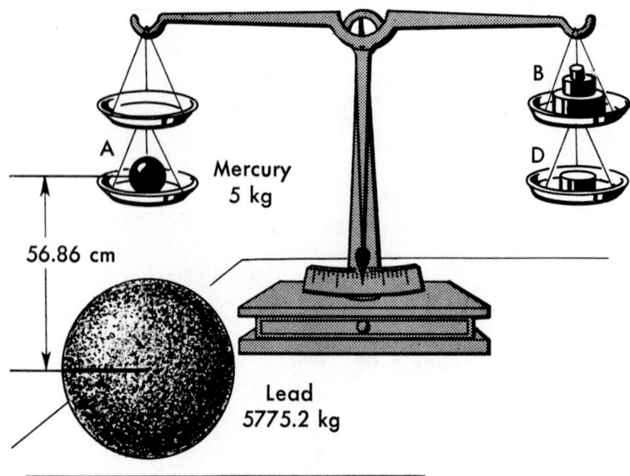

CONSTANT OF GRAVITATION

From the expression for the Law of Gravitation, $F = G\frac{Mm}{d^2}$, it can be seen that any of the quantities may be calculated if the values for the others are known. The constant G may thus be evaluated. If M and m are each one gram and d is one centimeter, then $F = G$. That is, G is the force of attraction between unit masses at unit distance apart, but the great difficulty attending such a determination is that the force of attraction between such small masses is so very slight that it cannot be detected. Hence, larger masses must be used. An ingenius method was employed by Jolly, who used a double-pan balance (Figure 14–4). He placed five kilograms of mercury in the spherical flask A and accurately counterbalanced it by weights in pan B. He then placed a sphere of lead C, weighing 5775.2 kilograms, below the mercury at a distance of 56.86 centimeters (from center to center). A definite attraction was observed and was balanced by 0.589 milligram on the pan D. With these data G may be calculated. The force F is expressed in dynes, and since one gram of force (weight) equals 980.3 dynes,

$$F = 0.000589 \text{ g} \times 980.8 \frac{\text{cm}}{\text{sec}^2}$$

$$= \frac{G \times 5000 \text{ g} \times 5{,}775{,}200 \text{ g}}{(56.86 \text{ cm})^2}$$

Hence, $$G = 6.465 \times 10^{-8} \frac{\text{cm}^3}{\text{g sec}^2}$$

The value for G has been corrected by modern scientists to:

$$G = 6.670 \times 10^{-8} \frac{\text{cm}^3}{\text{g sec}^2}.$$

Two one-gram masses placed one centimeter apart therefore attract each other with a force of 6.670×10^{-8} dynes. This is one of the important constants of science.

MASS OF THE EARTH

Now we are ready to determine the mass of the earth. Any body whose mass or weight we know or can determine may be used. For convenience, a kilogram is selected. Its weight is the force with which the earth attracts it — in other words, the force necessary to support a thousand-gram mass (see Chapter 12) — and it has therefore a thousand grams of weight and represents a force of 1000×980 dynes. It is at a distance from the center of the earth equal to the earth's radius, or 6,370 kilometers. Since the gravitation constant is expressed in c.g.s. units, it is necessary to express all quantities in those units.

$$F = 980{,}000 \text{ dynes}$$

$$G = 6.670 \times 10^{-8} \frac{\text{cm}^3}{\text{g sec}^2}$$

$$m = 1000 \text{ grams}$$

$$d = 6.370 \times 10^8 \text{ cm}$$

$$M = \text{mass of earth in grams}$$

Substituting in the equation

$$F = G \frac{Mm}{d^2},$$

which may be rearranged to solve for M:

$$M = \frac{Fd^2}{mG}$$

$$= \frac{9.8 \times 10^5 \text{ g cm/sec}^2 \times (6.370 \times 10^8 \text{ cm})^2}{1000 \text{ g} \times 6.670 \times 10^{-8} \text{ cm}^3/\text{g sec}^2}$$

$$= 5.96 \times 10^{27} \text{ grams},$$

or 1.314×10^{25} pounds, or 6.57×10^{21} tons, the mass of the earth.

The masses of the sun, of the other planets, and of some of the stars have also been determined on the basis of the laws of gravitation and Kepler's laws. If the "fall" of the earth toward the sun is determined just as we determine that of the moon toward the earth, this value may be used to calculate the mass of the sun in terms of that of the earth. Similarly, the combined masses of planets with moons, or of two stars revolving about one another, or of any system in which one body revolves around another under its gravitational force, may be determined.

SOME LOCAL APPLICATIONS

Looking about us on this planet, we see many examples of gravitational attraction, always between the earth and some other body of relatively smaller mass. Bodies fall, remain on the earth, and have weight because the earth attracts them. But they also attract the earth. As this force of attraction between two bodies is a mutual one, it behaves, in effect, as a stretched rubber band or spring between two carts. The same force is exerted on the two bodies and gives the greater acceleration to the body of smaller mass. If an airplane with a mass of twenty tons is falling to the earth, whose mass is 6.57×10^{21} tons, the earth will be given $20/6.57 \times 10^{21}$ or 1/328,000,000,000,000,000,000 of the acceleration given the plane, and will move a proportionate distance. Hence the earth will be moved only imperceptibly by the falling body.

That the earth has a rugged surface with mountains and valleys does not change appreciably the direction of its force of attraction for bodies external to it. Locally, however, a mountain does draw aside slightly a plumb line, and this phenomenon was once used to estimate the mass of the earth. As the scientist who made this determination had to estimate first the mass of the mountain, his results were not highly satisfactory.

The fact that the earth is flattened at the poles and has an equatorial bulge (Chapter 3) has a number of consequences. The acceleration of gravity and the weight of a given object vary over the earth's surface in accordance with the law of gravitation. A mass weighing exactly one pound at the equator will weigh more at one of the poles. We now have the means of computing how much more. The earth's equatorial radius is 3963.34 miles, and its polar radius is 3949.99 miles. Hence, the weight of the object, increasing inversely as the square of the distance from the center of the earth, becomes

$$1 \text{ lb} \times \frac{(3963.34)^2}{(3949.99)^2} = 1.0067 \text{ lbs}$$

if no other factors modify it. The centrifugal force due to the earth's rotation is greatest in the equatorial regions and effects a slight additional decrease in the weight there, but is zero at the poles.

ESCAPE VELOCITY

All gases tend to expand. If a bottle of ammonia, for example, is left in a room unstoppered, it will not be long before the odor is apparent throughout the room. Obviously the particles (molecules) that compose ammonia have motions of their own. Why then does the sun exist since it is composed of hot gases? Why does our atmosphere not expand into outer space? If the moon ever had an atmosphere, why doesn't it have one now? The answer to all these questions is found in the law of universal gravitation and the concept of *escape velocity*.

A planet holds a moving molecule of gas for the same reason that it holds any body, the pull of gravity. To escape from the earth, an object must have an outward velocity sufficient to overcome the pull of gravity. That is, if the pull of gravity on an object moving away from the earth is not great enough to de-accelerate it to bring it to rest, the object will continue moving away from the earth. It is then said to have a velocity greater than the escape velocity. The escape velocity for any celestial body increases with the mass but decreases with an increase in radius. Theoretical considerations show that the critical velocity for the earth is given by $v = \sqrt{2gR}$, where g is the value for the acceleration of gravity at the earth's surface and R is the radius of the earth. The escape velocity for any body moving away from the surface of the earth – molecule or jet space ship – is about 7 miles per second. The escape velocities of some celestial bodies are given in Table 14–1. The moon and Mercury are barren of atmosphere simply because their gravitational pulls are not great enough to overcome the speed of gas molecules that may have been present on these bodies at one time. On the other hand, the speed of gas molecules does not exceed the escape velocity on the sun, Mars, and the earth, so these retain their gaseous envelopes.

TABLE 14–1 SOME IMPORTANT ESCAPE VELOCITIES

BODY	ESCAPE VELOCITY miles/second
Earth	7.
Moon	1.5
Sun	386.
Mercury	2.7
Mars	3.2

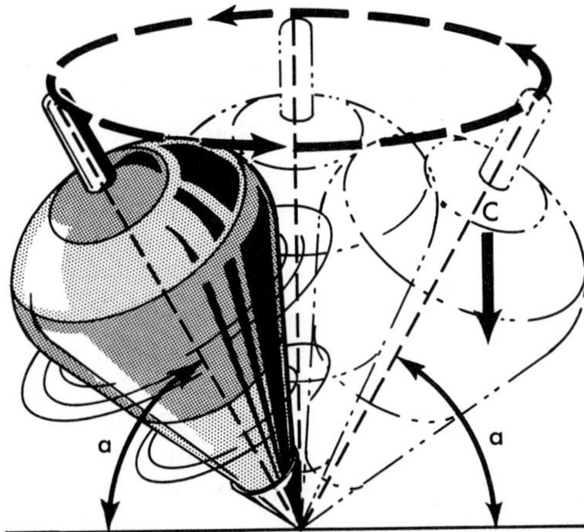

Fig. 14–5 *A spinning top keeps the same angle with the floor while precessing in a circle. Point on which top balances corresponds to earth's center of gravity.*

WEIGHT ON THE MOON

If a body is transported to the moon, its weight due to the attraction of the earth alone becomes only 1/3600 of its former value. But the moon now attracts it much more than the earth does, for it is right on the moon's surface, within 1080 miles of the moon's center of gravity. In our calculations of the moon's surface gravity, or the "moon weight," we shall therefore ignore the earth's attraction. As the moon's radius is approximately one-fourth that of the earth, the weight of the body would be sixteen times as much on the moon if the moon and earth had equal masses. The mass of the earth, however, is 81.5 times that of the moon. Hence we have a factor tending to reduce the weight of the body on the moon to 1/81.5 of that on the earth. Combining the two and using more exact figures for the radii —

$$\frac{1}{81.5} = \frac{(3960\text{ mi})^2 \text{ radius of earth}}{(1080\text{ mi})^2 \text{ radius of moon}}$$
$$= 0.165, \text{ or about one-sixth.}$$

That is, the surface gravity on the moon is one-sixth of that on the earth. Our body would weigh only one-sixth of its earth weight on the moon. Projectiles on the moon would attain six times the height they reach on the earth, athletes could soar to new jumping records, and strong men who on the earth lift five hundred pounds could handle six times that mass.

PRECESSION OF THE EQUINOXES

The play of gravitational forces on the spinning and revolving earth causes it to undergo a slow movement known as *precession.* This movement of the earth, somewhat like that of a tilted spinning top, is one of slow gyration. (Refer to Figure 14–5.) The axis of rotation of the earth swings around, always inclined at approximately the same angle to the earth's orbit, and makes a complete circuit in 25,800 years. The axis extended describes a vertical cone (Figure 14–6). The earth, unlike the top, does *not* precess in the same direction as its spin (ro-

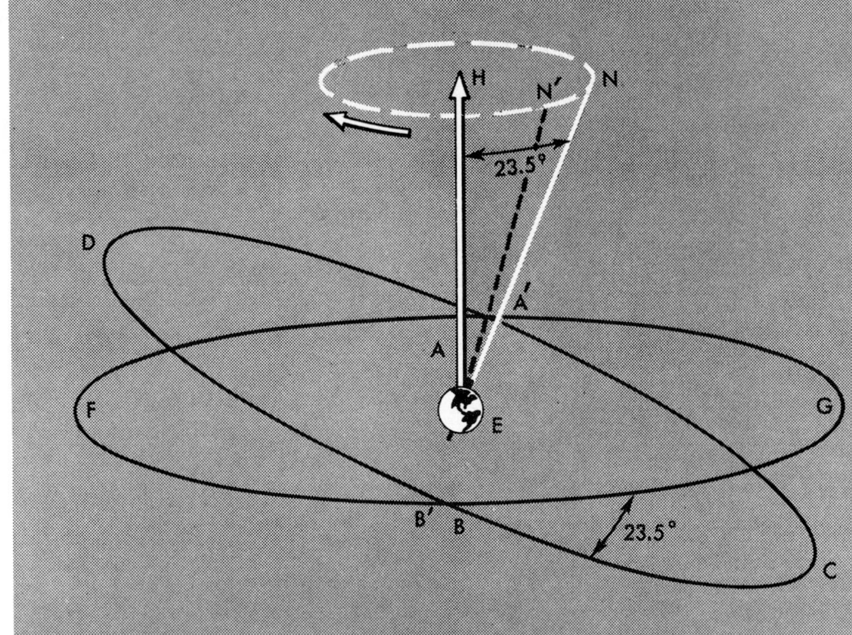

Fig. 14–6 *The precession of the equinoxes. Note the simultaneous gyration of the earth's axis. (Compare with Fig. 14–5).*

tation); its rotation is eastward but the precession *westward.*

Since the plane of the celestial equator (earth's equator extended) moves with the earth, the points of its intersection with the plane of the earth's orbit (ecliptic) must also shift as the earth precesses. These points of intersection, the vernal and autumnal equinoxes (see Chapter 4, Figure 4–3), shift westward 50.2 seconds of angle per year, the same angle through which the earth precesses. The vernal equinox may be located as the position of the center of the sun when it crosses the celestial equator moving from south to north and marks the beginning of spring. When Hipparchus discovered (*ca.* 140 B.C.) this westward shift of the equinoxes, i.e., the precession of the equinoxes, the sun was in the constellation Aries at the time of the vernal equinox; at present it is in the constellation Pisces. Similarly the earth's axis extended shifts its direction and the celestial pole toward which it is pointing is slowly but continuously changing. Polaris, "the north star," is not quite at the celestial pole and will not be until about 28,000 A.D.

The cause of the precession of the equinoxes was not known until Newton in his *Principia* gave an explanation. The gravitational pulls of the moon and the sun on the equatorial bulge of the tilted earth tend to right it so as to bring the plane of the earth's equator into coincidence with the ecliptic. The effect of this force on the spinning earth is to produce a turning force at right angles to the earth's axis. If the earth were perfectly spherical there would be no precession; if it did not rotate it would not have retained its inclination.

THE TIDES OF THE OCEAN

Along the shores of the ocean, waters rush in toward the beaches and inlets and out again at definite intervals. This periodic rise and fall of the water level (not waves), some two to three feet in deep waters and hence not so apparent there as along the coasts, are known as *tides.* The tides follow a time schedule which, although more complex, is approximately that of the moon and, to a lesser degree, that of the sun. If there is a high tide at a given place on the earth today, there will be another at the same place tomorrow, but about fifty-one minutes later. On the next day it will be still later by an additional fifty-one minutes. This interval (see page 239) is the same as the daily lag in the rising and setting of the moon. But between these high tides at intervals of twenty-four hours and fifty-one minutes, there is another high tide and two low tides. For example, high tide at 6 P.M. is followed by low tide at 12:13 A.M., high tide at 6:25 A.M., low tide at 12:38 P.M., and high tide again at 6:51 P.M. There is actually considerable variation in the tide intervals over the earth because of the moon's behavior and differing local conditions.

Causes of Tides. It is evident that the moon's gravitational pull is the important factor. In order to understand how it can cause the tides, we must recall that the force of gravitation varies inversely as the square of the distance between the two bodies involved and that a rigid body responds to gravitational attraction as if all of its mass were concentrated in its center of gravity. The solid portion of the earth is rigid, but not rigid enough to prevent slight earth tides; the water is mobile and each particle of it may respond to gravitational pull. If we assume that the earth is completely covered with water, the tides will be high in regions *C* and *D* and low in regions *A* and *B* (Figure 14–7). The water

Fig. 14–7 *How the moon causes tides.*

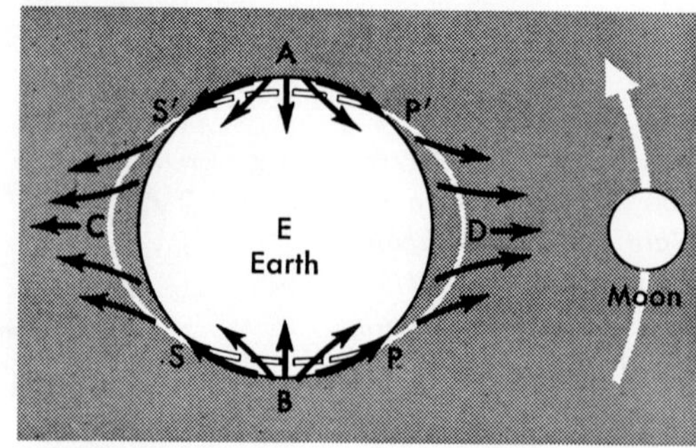

at D is nearer to the moon than is the center of gravity of the earth E, which in turn is nearer than the water at C. The gravitational force exerted by the moon is, therefore, greater at D than at E and greater at E than at C. Since the water is not lifted away from the earth (the earth's gravitational force is also constantly in operation), the force exerted by the moon is effective in directions parallel to the earth's surface and toward the moon at P and P'. At S and S' the resultant of the earth's gravitational pull and of the moon's pull is parallel to the earth's surface but away from the moon. The total effect is to heap up water on the sides of the earth at C and D, toward and away from the moon, and to draw it downward from A and B, leaving a belt of low tide round the earth between the regions of high tide. The water does not travel these great distances; the tides are cumulative effects of smaller movements.

As the earth rotates more rapidly than the moon revolves, the tides are dragged forward a little with the rotating earth (Figure 14–8). The high tide B is east of the moon instead of directly under it. The water is not held in check by the moon, however, but only the tidal bulge or wave. At any given point A on the earth, therefore, the high tide appears at some time after the transit of the moon. This lag in tides is not constant over the earth. The varying depths of the ocean, shoals, and shorelines all contribute to make the tides a very complex phenomenon. In most places they are predictable only on the basis of long observation.

The Sun as a Factor. The sun also acts independently of the moon to cause tides, and these are at all times superposed on those caused by the moon. When the earth, sun, and moon are in alignment either at new moon (conjunction) or at full moon (opposition), the sun's high and low tides coincide respectively with those of the moon. The results are very high and very low tides. These are called the *spring tides.* At the two quarters, when the moon and sun are ninety degrees apart as viewed from the earth, the sun's high tide coincides at a given place with the moon's low tide and vice versa. These tides, representing the difference between the effects of moon and sun, and having a much smaller range, are known as *neap tides.*

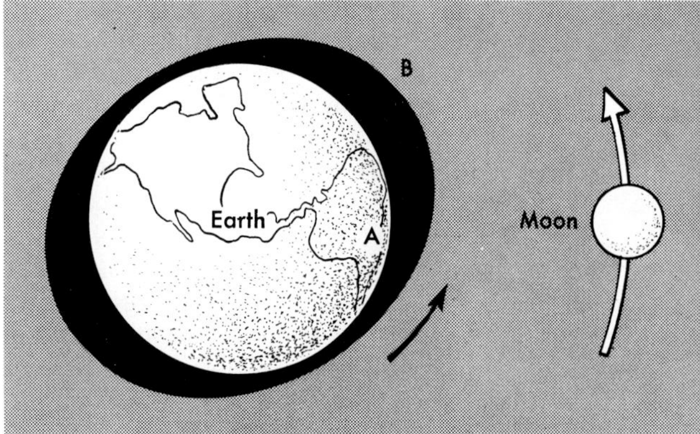

Fig. 14–8 *The lag of the tides behind the moon.*

The mass of the sun is 27,600,000 times that of the moon, but it is approximately four hundred times as far away. If we apply the principle of gravitation we conclude that the gravitational effect of the sun on the earth is about 175 times that of the moon. Yet the sun's tidal effect is only about 45 per cent of that of the moon. The reason for this is that, since the moon is much nearer to the earth, the *difference* between its pull on the water and on the earth is greater.

THE DISCOVERY OF NEPTUNE

According to the Law of Gravitation, every particle of matter in the universe attracts every other particle. The planets are each attracted by the sun, which they in turn attract, but each planet also exerts a mutual attraction on all the other planets. The moon, which we are inclined to regard as under the total dominance of the earth, is attracted by the sun to the extent that if the earth were to stand still, the sun would pull the moon away from it. Since the planets change positions relatively to each other and to the sun, as do also the earth, moon, and sun, the mutual attractions vary. The variations, though slight, cause small but definite irregularities in the motions of these bodies. These departures from the orbits prescribed by Kepler's laws are known as *perturbations,* and their prediction and observation are further confirmation of the Law of Universal Gravitation.

The discovery of the planet Neptune, perhaps the greatest triumph of mathematical astronomy, came as a direct result of the study of perturbations in the orbit of the planet Uranus. After the discovery of Uranus, its orbit was determined and its motions carefully followed. After taking into account the perturbations due to the then known planets, there was still a lack of agreement between the observed positions and those calculated – discrepancies of as much as two minutes of arc. It was suggested that the departures from the calculated motion might be due to the presence of a more remote and unknown planet. Two young men independently undertook to solve the problem – J. C. Adams of Cambridge, England, and U. J. Leverrier of Paris, France. After about two years of work, Adams, who had begun before Leverrier, completed his calculations, but, before complete observations had been made in England, the planet was discovered. Leverrier, who in the meantime had completed his calculations, had immediately sent his results to J. G. Galle in Germany. On the very night after he received the letter, February 23, 1846, Galle turned his telescope to the sky and in less than an hour found the planet within half a degree of the position calculated by Leverrier. Since the calculations of Adams and Leverrier were in close agreement, both received equal credit.

ARTIFICIAL SATELLITES

A striking example of the power of Newtonian science was the launching of the first man-made satellite by Russian scientists on October 4, 1957. Perhaps no other scientific event has so immediately and so completely caught the imagination of so many people – from the man in the street to persons in positions of responsibility in government, scholarship, and industry. The launching of Sputnik (Russian for *satellite*) is already recognized as one of the two or three most unusual developments of the twentieth century.

What is the scientific significance of Sputnik? It demonstrated how the science of the study of the laws of motion and force (the science of mechanics), a principal contribution of Sir Isaac Newton, has contributed to man's ability to control and add to his environment. The launching was possible because of predictions based on Newton's three laws of motion and his Law of Universal Gravitation. Sputnik, until its lifetime ended, became a true heavenly body. Sputnik and the earth became a typical Newtonian two-body system with the satellite revolving around the earth in an elliptical path, just as the moon does.

On being launched into its orbit, Sputnik, a sphere 22 inches in diameter, weighing 184 pounds, circled the earth about every 96 minutes, at an elevation of nearly 600 miles at its highest point, traveling with a speed of 18,000 miles per hour. Its perigee (lowest point) was in the northern hemisphere and its apogee (highest point) in the southern hemisphere. It was easily visible from the earth at twilight and morning hours if it passed overhead. Under these circumstances it shone by reflected light from the sun.

Two of the principal problems of getting any artificial satellite into its orbit are (1) the procedure to follow to get the satellite through the earth's atmosphere into outer space against the attraction of the earth, and (2) the procedure to follow to give the satellite a sidewise motion sufficiently great to put it into an elliptical orbit.

Two different rockets were used to shoot the satellite ensemble about 500 miles into outer space. A rocket carries its own fuel and oxygen. The upward motion of the ensemble was due to the reaction of the rocket (Newton's third law) against the hot exit gases produced by the very rapid burning of the fuel within the rocket. If the upward thrust required to start Sputnik's rocket was approximately six million poundals, the power expended was equal to that of the world's largest hydroelectric station. This force was utilized to accelerate the rocket upward through the lower atmosphere and against the pull of gravity to give the whole ensemble sufficient momentum to carry it to the point where the second rocket took over. The second rocket probably had considerably less power than the first but carried the satellite to its highest altitude of about 600 miles. The calculations which set the requirements for getting Sputnik to an altitude of 600 miles are based on the fundamental equations $F = ma$ (Equation 12–4, page 190) and $M = mv$ (Equation 12–5).

A third rocket imparted a sidewise motion of 18,000 miles per hour to put the satellite in an elliptical orbit around the earth. The velocity requirements were predicted by the use of the equation for acceleration in a circular path, $a = v^2/r$ (Equation 12–7). Without the third rocket the satellite would soon return to the earth.

The first successful launching of a satellite was not the result of special and unusual knowledge. Rockets have been in use for centuries. The theory of the reaction effect has been known a long time. Experimental work with rockets has been in progress for many years. The V–2's dropped on London in World War II were true long-distance rockets fired from Holland. In the United States, scientists had succeeded by 1956 in sending rockets 680 miles into outer space, though the first satellite (called "Explorer") was not put into orbit until January 31, 1958. The launching of artificial satellites was an inevitable result of the march of science aided by an economy capable of furnishing the funds necessary to build and fuel the very costly rocket-driven machinery.

Through the instruments they carry the satellites transmit information about cosmic rays, micrometeorites (high-velocity dust particles in space), and temperature conditions within the satellites themselves. In short, they are but auguries for future advances in technology, including space ships and travel to the moon.

SIGNIFICANCE OF THE SCIENTIFIC REVOLUTION

As we follow the threads of fact and theory down the centuries, we become aware that the scientists of one era build upon the knowledge and ideas of the preceding ones. The Greeks inherited from the Babylonians and Egyptians; Ptolemy constructed his system upon the work of the earlier Greeks; Copernicus borrowed heavily from Ptolemy and Aristotle; and much of the science of our time originated in the ideas developed during the seventeenth century. It is also apparent that the growth and progress of science is not always limited to the acquisition of new facts, the revision of existing principles, or the development of new concepts within the inherited framework. There are very rare occasions of drastic change, of repudiation, or transformation, in which the old framework is shattered and a new one emerges. The most extreme and the most comprehensive of such occasions, up to the present century,[1] was the so-called scientific revolution which started in the sixteenth century and extended through the seventeenth. This period stands out as one of great significance for several reasons. First, the well entrenched and complex dogma of Aristotelian mechanics and cosmology had to be repudiated. Second, the scientists who led this movement had to create entirely new fundamental principles and concepts out of their own thoughts and activities. It is because they were dealing with the basic elements of modern science, the very beginnings, that their achievement is so tremendous. Herbert Butterfield gives an interesting evaluation:

> Since that revolution overturned the authority in science not only of the middle ages but of the ancient world — since it ended not only in the eclipse of scholastic philosophy but in the destruction of Aristotelian physics — it outshines everything since the rise of Christian-

[1] The close of the nineteenth century marks the beginning of a series of fundamental discoveries which have altered some of the classical concepts and extended the scope of the physical sciences (see Chapters 21 and 22).

ity. . . . [It] changed the character of men's habitual mental operations even in the conduct of the non-material sciences, while transforming the whole diagram of the physical universe and the very texture of human life itself. . . .[1]

10. The Law of Universal Gravitation, the most important scientific principle ever formulated, had revolutionary and lasting effect upon human thought.

SUMMARY

1. Isaac Newton formulated the Law of Universal Gravitation: Every particle of matter in the universe attracts every other particle with a force which is proportional to the product of their masses and inversely proportional to the square of the distance between them. This is expressed by the equation

$$F = G\frac{Mm}{d^2}.$$

2. The principle of gravitation was verified by a calculation of the moon's actual "fall" toward the earth and comparing a predicted value based on the principle.
3. The gravitation constant was evaluated by Jolly and others. The latest figure is: $G = 6.670 \times 10^{-8}$ cm³/g sec².
4. The mass of the earth may be calculated by the use of the gravitation constant and the law of gravitation.
5. The gravitational attraction between even very massive man-made objects, like ships or airplanes, is very small.
6. The gravitational force or "weight" on the moon is one-sixth of that on the earth.
7. The tides of the ocean are caused by gravitational pull, primarily that of the moon, but also, to a smaller degree, that of the sun.
8. The precession of the equinoxes is in reality the precession of the earth due to the gravitational pull of the moon on the earth's equatorial bulge. If the earth were not spinning or if it had no bulge, there would be no precession.
9. Calculations based on the Law of Gravitation with respect to the perturbations of the planet Uranus led to the discovery of the planet Neptune.

[1] Herbert Butterfield, *The Origins of Modern Science* (New York: The Macmillan Company, 1951), Introduction, p. viii.

STUDY EXERCISES

1. Check each item which is a direct consequence of the force of gravitation.
   a. Weight ....
   b. Mass ....
   c. Atmosphere ....
   d. Elliptical orbits of planets ....
   e. Kick of a gun ....
   f. Effectiveness of armor-piercing bomb ...
   g. Inertia ....
   h. Satellites (moons) ....
   i. Friction ....
   j. Tides ....
   k. Precession of the equinoxes..........
   l. Effectiveness of a bullet ....
2. The gravitational force of attraction between two bodies at a given distance from each other has a certain value. Below are listed a number of possible changes. Mark *A,* if the change *increases* the force of attraction; *B,* if the change *decreases* the force of attraction; *C,* if it *does neither.*
   a. Distance between the two bodies is increased..........................
   b. Shape of one is altered without changing the distance of its center of gravity from the other..........................
   c. One becomes fluid without altering the position of its center of gravity........
   d. The size of one of the bodies is increased without altering its total mass or the position of its center of gravity. ....
   e. The mass of one of the bodies is decreased..........................
   f. They are put in motion, one around the other, without any other change........
3. Mark *M* if the statement is true for the motion of the moon relative to the earth; *P* if true for the motion of a projectile; *B* if true for both.
   a. Has an initial uniform motion in a straight line. ....

b. Is pulled from straight-line path by force of gravitation........................
c. Path is an ellipse.....................
d. Path is a parabola.....................
e. Moves in accordance with the principle of independence of motion. ....
f. Follows Kepler's laws. ....

4. Explain the meaning of the gravitation constant G.
5. An apple at the surface of the earth falls from rest a distance of sixteen feet in one second. How far would it fall in the first second if it were 18,000 miles from the earth's surface? How far would it fall in the second if it were 240,000 miles from the earth's center? (Use 4000 miles as the earth's radius.)
6. Refer to Figure 14–3, page 217.
   a. Calculate the fall of the moon toward the earth in one second if the moon were twice as far away as at present.
   b. Why may BC be regarded as the fall of the moon toward the earth?
   c. In the geometrical proof, what two approximations are made?
7. a. Given the gravitation constant G (page 219), calculate the force of attraction between two spheres of lead weighing ten kilograms each and placed forty centimeters from center to center.
   b. If the mass of one of the spheres is doubled, what is the force of attraction?
   c. If the masses of both spheres are tripled, what is the force of attraction?
   d. If the distance between the two spheres is tripled, what is the force of attraction?
   e. If the distance between the two spheres is reduced to twenty centimeters, what is the force of attraction?
8. If you were building a house at the foot of a large, steep mountain, would you use a plumb line to make the walls vertical? What do you mean by "vertical"?
9. What would a man weigh at the equator if his weight is one hundred and fifty pounds at the north pole?
10. The mass of the planet Neptune is approximately seventeen times that of the earth, and its radius is approximately four times that of the earth.
    a. If mass alone determined the surface gravity of a planet, what would a body which weighs one hundred pounds on the earth weigh on the surface of Neptune?
    b. The body on the surface of Neptune is how many times as far from the center of gravity of the attracting planet as one on the earth? This would have what effect on its weight if it were transported from the surface of the earth to the surface of Neptune?
    c. Combine (a) and (b) to calculate the weight of the one hundred pounds (earth weight) on the surface of Neptune.
    d. If g is 32 feet per second per second on the earth, what would it be on Neptune?
11. The sun exerts 175 times as much gravitational pull on the earth as the moon does. Explain why the tidal effect of the moon is greater than that of the sun.
12. a. Briefly explain what is meant by *precession* and what causes it, using the spinning top as an example.
    b. By analogy explain how and why the earth undergoes a similar motion.
    c. Would there be any precession of the earth if it were perfectly spherical? If its axis were not inclined to the ecliptic?
13. What are perturbations? Show how observation of them leads to the discovery of new planets.
14. Write a paper of several hundred words on the life and achievements of Newton, pointing out particularly the importance and significance of his Law of Universal Gravitation.

FOR FURTHER READING

1. SKILLING, W. T., and R. S. RICHARDSON, *A Brief Text in Astronomy*. New York: Henry Holt and Company, 1954.
   Part of Chapter 2 is recommended for a study of precession.
2. PAYNE-GAPOSCHKIN, C., *Introduction to Astronomy*. New York: Prentice-Hall, 1954.
   Parts of Chapters II, VI, and VII deal respectively with precession, tides, and gravitation.

3. BUTTERFIELD, H., *The Origins of Modern Science*. New York: The Macmillan Company, 1951.

Chapter 8 gives an excellent discussion of the significance of the Law of Gravitation.

4. SHAPLEY, H., H. WRIGHT, and S. RAPPORT, *Readings in the Physical Sciences*. New York: Appleton-Century-Crofts, 1948.

Contains original reports by many outstanding scientists. Part Two contains a report by Copernicus which is recommended, "A Theory That the Earth Moves Around the Sun."

5. HOLTON, GERALD, *Introduction to Concepts and Theories in Physical Science*. Cambridge, Mass.: Addison-Wesley Press, 1952.

Chapter 11 has a very full presentation for the general student on the origin and significance of the Law of Universal Gravitation.

6. Paperback: REICHENBACH, H., *From Copernicus to Einstein*. Wisdom Library, 95¢.
7. Paperback: HALL, A. R., *The Scientific Revolution*. Beacon, $1.75.
8. Paperback: EDITORS OF SCIENTIFIC AMERICAN, *Lives in Science*. Simon and Schuster, $1.45.
9. Magazine Article: COHEN, I. BERNARD, "Isaac Newton," *Scientific American*, 193:6 (December, 1955), pp. 73–80.

An interesting biographical sketch.

15

THE SOLAR SYSTEM

IN TRACING the historical development of our present conception of the universe, we have directed our attention primarily to the members of the solar system and to other celestial bodies visible to pre-telescope observers. We shall now make a more detailed study of modern astronomy, looking first at the solar family and, in the following chapters, at the sun, the stars, and the methods of making some of the simpler astronomical measurements.

The solar system consists of the sun, nine planets, thirty-one satellites, thousands of asteroids (small planets), hundreds of comets, and innumerable meteors. The sun is the central and dominant body; it contains nearly 99.9 per cent of the total mass of the system and thus holds the planets and other bodies in their orbits by its gravitational force. However important the sun may be to the members of the solar system, it is, in the universe as a whole, only one relatively small and cool star among hundreds of billions of others.

THE PLANETS

Five of the planets, Mercury, Venus, Mars, Jupiter, and Saturn are visible to the unaided eye and were thus known to the ancient astronomers. They and the three more remote planets shine by reflected light; they superficially resemble stars and some of them are frequently called "evening stars" and "morning stars." Planets are distinguished from the fixed stars by their wanderings among the constellations and by their steadfast light in contrast to the twinkling light of the stars. Observed through a telescope the nearer planets appear disc-like whereas the stars appear as smaller points of light.

The planets are conveniently classified in two groups. The *terrestrial planets,* Mercury, Venus, Earth, Mars, and Pluto, are somewhat like the earth in the order of size and in having relatively high densities. Of these only the earth and Venus appear to have appreciable atmospheres. The *major planets,* Jupiter, Saturn, Uranus, and Neptune, are much larger than the terrestrial planets, are of low density, and have atmospheres. Some of the physical characteristics of the planets are shown in Table 15–1.

The members of the solar system, with few exceptions, move about the sun in orbits which are nearly in the same plane. They can therefore be represented by a drawing on a flat surface or by a model

TABLE 15–1

SOME PHYSICAL CHARACTERISTICS OF THE PLANETS

PLANET	MEAN DIAMETER (miles)	MASS (Earth = 1)	DENSITY (g per cc)	MEAN DISTANCE FROM SUN (million of miles)	PERIOD OF ROTATION
Mercury	3,100	0.045	4.1	36	88 days
Venus	7,700	0.82	4.9	67.3	30 days?
Earth	7,918	1.000	5.52	93	23 hr. 56 min
Mars	4,266	0.11	3.96	141.7	24 hr. 37 min
Jupiter	86,844	318.4	1.33	483.9	9 hr. 55 min
Saturn	71,520	95.3	0.72	887.1	10 hr. 38 min
Uranus	31,690	14.6	1.26	1784	10 hr. 42 min
Neptune	31,069	17.3	1.60	2795	15 hr. 48 min
Pluto	3,630	1.0?	?	3675	?

* In mean solar days and tropical years.

which would take the form of a thin, almost circular disc. Because of the great distances of the outermost planets from the sun, however, such a model or chart, unless of tremendous size, cannot show both their sizes and distances based on the same scale. Their relative sizes, but not distances, are as in Figure 3–1 (page 20). If we adopt as a scale of length 1/32 inch (the diameter of a pin head) = 8000 miles (the approximate diameter of the earth), our own planet must be placed on the chart thirty feet from the sun, whose diameter would be nearly three and one half inches. Pluto would be twelve hundred feet from the sun on the same scale.

If we extended our scale chart to include the nearest star, it would be at a distance of nearly sixteen hundred miles; thus the solar system, although a member of a galaxy of possibly one hundred billion stars, is relatively isolated from its neighbors.

Fig. 15–1 *Orbits of the planets Mercury, Venus, Earth and Mars, sometimes designated the "inner planets." Note the eccentricity of Mercury's orbit. Distances to scale. (For relative sizes but not distances, refer to Figure 3–1, page 20.)*

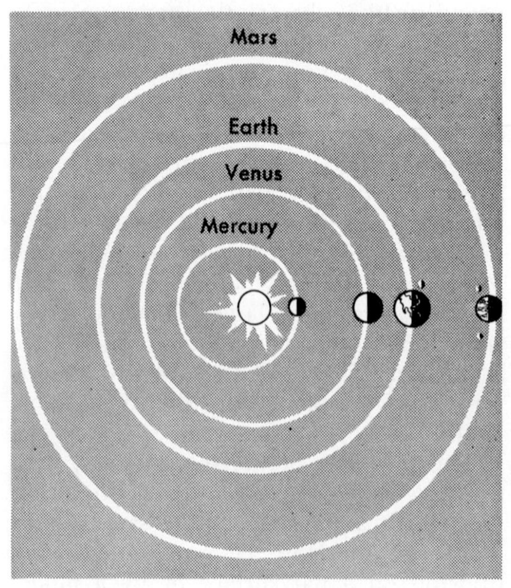

MOTIONS OF THE PLANETS

The planets revolve in elliptical orbits which in general are of low eccentricity; that is, they are nearly circular. Mercury, Mars, and Pluto move in more eccentric orbits (see Table 15–1). None of the orbits are inclined to the plane of the ecliptic more than 3° 24′ except those of Mercury (7°) and Pluto (17° 09′). The planets move in an eastward direction, which is counterclockwise when viewed from above by an imaginary observer in the northern celestial hemisphere. All of them rotate from west to east except Uranus. The orbits are shown in Figures 15–1 and 15–2.

It must be kept in mind, however, that actual observations are made from the earth which is in motion. In accordance with Kepler's Third Law of Motion, the nearer a planet is to the sun, the faster is its orbital motion. The *inferior* planets,

ERIOD OF VOLUTION * (sidereal)	ECCENTRICITY OF ORBIT	INCLINATION OF ORBIT TO ECLIPTIC	NUMBER OF SATELLITES
7.97 days	0.206	7° 00′	0
4.7 days	0.007	3° 24′	0
5.256 days	0.017	0° 00′	1
6.98 days	0.093	1° 51′	2
1.86 years	0.048	1° 18′	12
9.46 years	0.056	2° 29′	9
4.0 years	0.047	0° 46′	5
4.8 years	0.009	1° 46′	2
8.4 years	0.249	17° 09′	0

Mercury and Venus, therefore, have shorter periods of revolution than the earth and appear to swing slowly from one side of the sun to the other. Each may occupy two positions of *conjunction,* that is, may be in the same direction from the earth as the sun. If the planet is between the earth and the sun (position *V*, Figure 15–3) it is said to be in *inferior conjunction* and where it is on the opposite side of the sun from the earth (*V′*) it is in *superior conjunction.*

The planets whose orbits lie outside the orbit of the earth (*superior* planets) have longer periods of revolution than the earth which overtakes and passes them at intervals determined by their periods of revolution. The apparent motion of Mars, for example, against the background of fixed stars was discussed in Chapter 13. With respect to the sun these planets appear to be continuously moving westward, although at an irregular rate. A superior planet may be in *superior conjunction* (*M,* Figure 15–4), but never in inferior conjunction;

Fig. 15–2 *Orbits of the outer planets. That of Pluto is inclined 17.1° to the ecliptic and is so eccentric that at perihelion it is nearer the sun than is Neptune. Scale is one-twentieth of that used for Figure 15–1.*

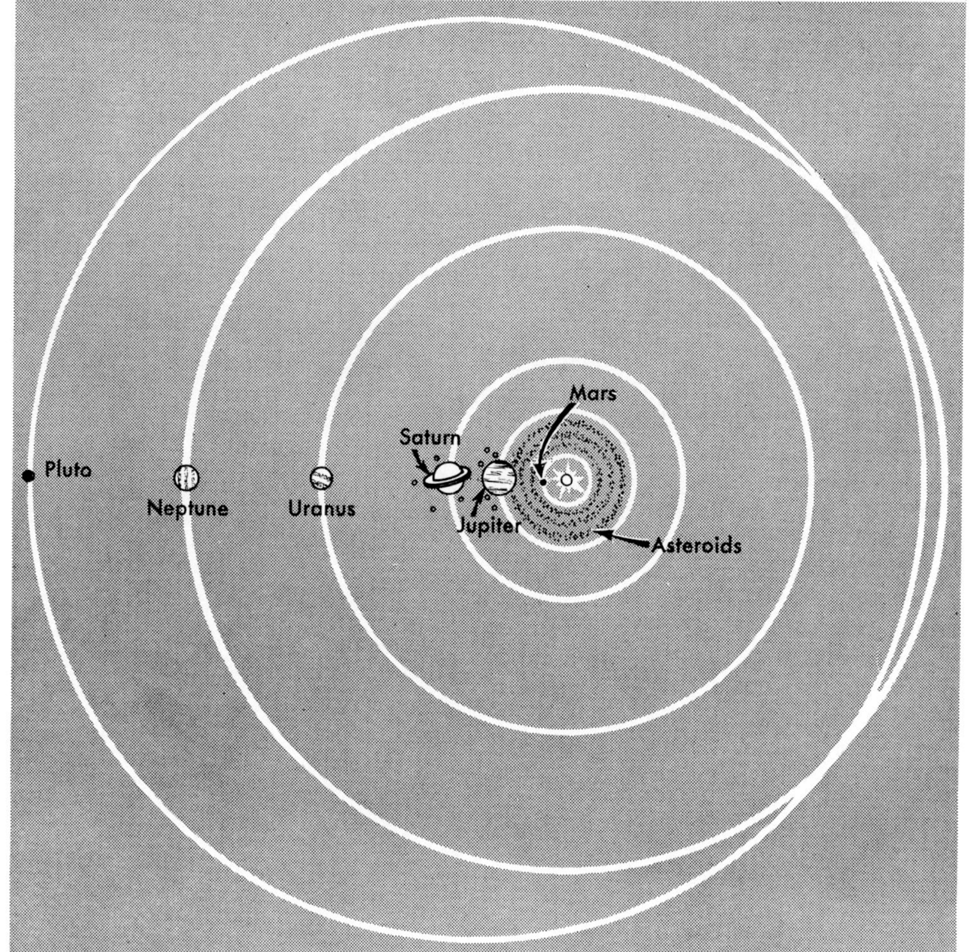

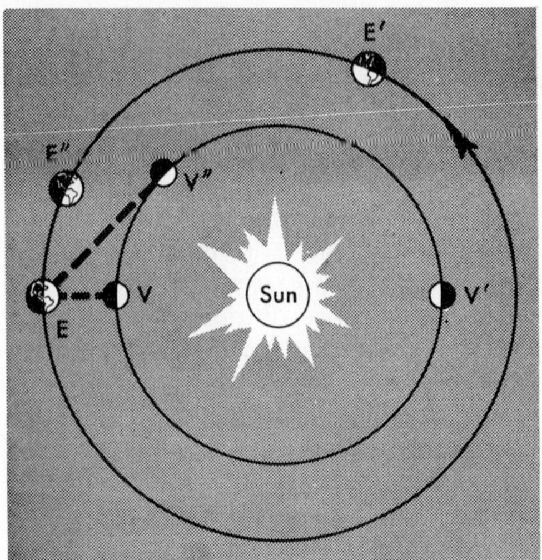

Fig. 15–3 *Inferior planets with respect to earth and sun: inferior conjunction (V), superior conjunction (V').*

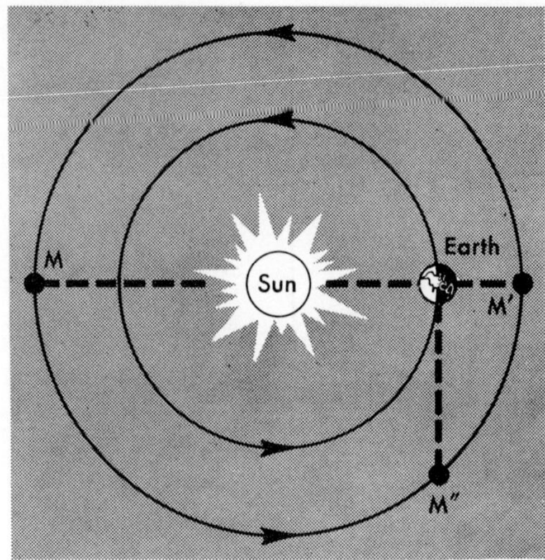

Fig. 15–4 *A superior planet may be in conjunction or in opposition or have an elongation of 90°.*

when it is just opposite in direction to the sun as observed from the earth (*M'*), it is said to be in *opposition.*

Since each planet has its own orbit and period of revolution, it is usual for a number of them to be visible at the same time along the ecliptic (Figure 15–5). When a planet is visible above the horizon at sunset it is called an *evening star;* when it is above the horizon at sunrise, it is called a *morning star.*

MERCURY

Among the nine planets Mercury, the nearest to the sun, is unusual. It is the hottest, the coldest, the smallest (in size and in mass), and the fastest moving. With the exception of Pluto it has the most eccentric orbit; at perihelion it is 28,600,000 miles from the sun and moves with an orbital velocity of thirty-five miles per second; at aphelion it is 43,400,000 miles from the sun and has an orbital velocity of twenty-three miles per second. Mercury always presents the same face to the sun, that is, the period of rotation is the same as the period of revolution, eighty-eight days. Because of its proximity to the sun, Mercury receives seven times as much sunlight per unit area as the earth. The constant exposure of one face to the intense rays of the sun and the absence of any protective atmosphere give Mercury a surface temperature as high as 415° C. when it is nearest to the sun. The other side is perpetually

Fig. 15–5 *Rarely are as many as six planets visible at the same time, as shown here at the latitude of New York or Chicago (February, 1940).*

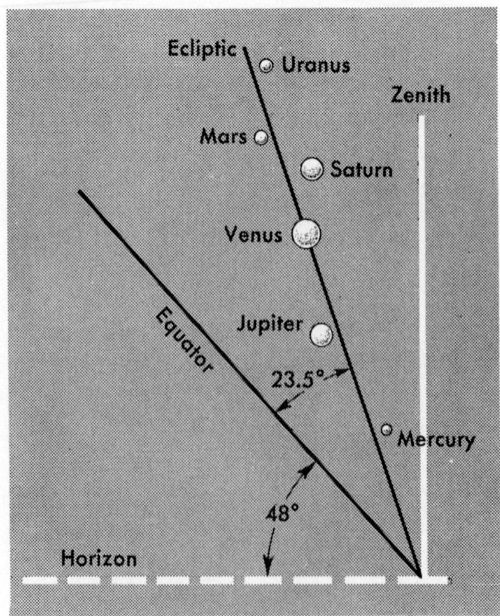

dark and its temperature is estimated to be within 25° C. of absolute zero (−273° C.).

Owing to the inclination of its orbit to the ecliptic, Mercury does not pass directly between the sun and the earth at every inferior conjunction. It crosses or transits the face of the sun only about thirteen times in a hundred years. The last transit of Mercury was on November 14, 1953. Observed through a telescope during transit, Mercury appears as a small clear-cut black dot (Figure 15–6). Mercury is always near the sun; it rises in the morning shortly before or after sunrise and sets soon after or before sunset. It is most readily observed when it is at its greatest angular distance from the sun just after sunset or just before sunrise, near the horizon.

Because of its high orbital velocity, Mercury provides us with an interesting application of the theory of relativity of Einstein. The Newtonian laws are generally applicable to the motions of the celestial bodies if their velocities are relatively small as compared with the velocity of light. The velocity of Mercury, however, is large enough to cause an observable relativity effect. The line of the major axis of Mercury's orbit rotates slowly, advancing the perihelion (point nearest the sun) by about 9′ of angle per century. The actual rate of advance is somewhat in excess of that predicted by gravitational theory, but the observed excess is in very close agreement with that predicted by the theory of relativity.

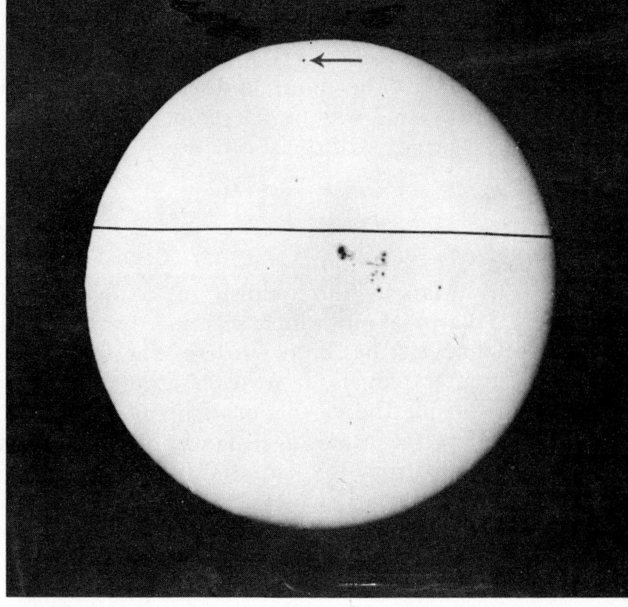

Fig. 15–6 *Transit of Mercury over sun's disc, November 4, 1907. (Yerkes Observatory photograph)*

VENUS

Venus is the brightest and most conspicuous object in the sky, with the exception of the moon and the sun. It is bright because of its relative nearness to the sun and to the observer, and because its surface reflects about 71 per cent of the light which strikes it. It is frequently visible during daylight, and at night Venus is bright enough to cast shadows. After superior conjunction (*V′*, Figure 15–3), it moves eastward from the sun and may be seen as an evening star above the horizon in the west at sunset, setting after the sun. It continues as an evening star until it approaches inferior conjunction (*V*, Figure 15–3). After passing westward from the sun, it appears in the morning sky as the morning star, rising in the east before the sun and completing the cycle at superior conjunction. Since the planet completes its revolution in 224.7 days, the earth must lag behind it, and Venus completes the cycle described above by gaining one lap on the earth. The average time required for this is 584 days.

Venus resembles the earth in size, in density, in mass (see Table 15–1), and in its surface gravity which is 86 per cent of that of the earth. It is evidently covered by a layer of white clouds which reflect sunlight without changing the color of the light. There is further evidence for an atmosphere: its ends extend during the crescent phase and a ring of light appears around its disc just before it moves in front of the sun during transit. The principal constituent of the atmosphere is carbon dioxide; there is little, if any, free oxygen or water. The period of rotation has not been accurately determined, but is estimated to be about 30 days. The last transit of Venus was on December 6, 1882; the next one will occur on June 8, 2004.

MARS

Mars is the reddish or orange-colored planet about which so much controversial material has been written. The first of the outer planets, it revolves around the sun, outside the earth's orbit, in 686.98 of our days, at a mean distance of 141,700,000 miles from the sun. Its distance from the earth varies widely. At conjunction the average distance from the earth is over 234 million miles; at opposition it is close to 49 million miles. Since the planet's orbit has a fairly high eccentricity, it comes even closer to the earth when opposition occurs near the planet's perihelion. On September 7, 1956, it came within 35,120,000 miles of the earth, its closest approach since 1924. In some respects Mars resembles the earth, although smaller and less dense (see Table 15–1). Permanent markings observed as early as the seventeenth century have permitted accurate measurement of its period of rotation, which is 24 hours, 37 minutes, 22.58 seconds. The equator of Mars is inclined to its orbit by 25° 12′. It is flattened at the poles more than the earth.

Finer details, some of which appear to change, were first observed by Schiaparelli in 1877–79. These were long and narrow dark lines, called *canali,* literally, "channels." Unfortunately this term was mistranslated as "canals," and since "canals" suggest engineering feats, all sorts of notions about highly intelligent "Martians" grew up. Let us consider the facts. There are seasonal changes on Mars, for the planet is tilted, and there are climatic zones. The seasons are twice as long as the earth's seasons, and the Martian temperature is lower (30° C. to considerably below zero) than that of the earth. Mars' reflection of sunlight, the presence of some kind of material, possibly ice crystals, which forms the polar caps, and the appearance of faint clouds establish the existence of an atmosphere. The atmosphere is very thin, though; the water vapor content is not more than 5 per cent of that of the earth's atmosphere, and the oxygen not more than a trace. The polar caps also undergo seasonal changes. During the long Martian summer, in its southern hemisphere, the polar cap becomes very small and on occasion has entirely disappeared; during the winter in the same hemisphere, the ice cap becomes very large – larger than the winter cap of the northern hemisphere. The southern hemisphere, therefore, which is the upper one on the inverted image of the photograph (Figure 15–7), has the greater extremes of climate. The dark markings, which appear grayish or greenish, become darker and greener during the Martian summer and become brownish or fade out during the winter. The general light and reddish surface of the planet does not change. These variations of color have been studied in great detail with the aid of various filters to utilize infrared, ultraviolet, and some of the visible radiation. The green areas are probably covered by some sort of living material, possibly lichens which are able to live under unfavorable conditions.

The two satellites of Mars, Deimos and Phobos, were discovered in 1877. They are both very small; the outer one, Deimos, is

Fig. 15–7 *Mars, region of Syrtis Major. (Yerkes Observatory photograph)*

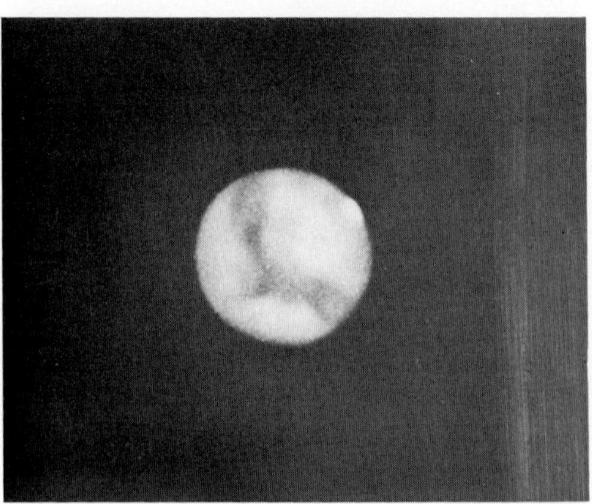

about one-half the size of Phobos, and the diameter of Phobos is estimated to be only about ten miles. These satellites are the smallest celestial bodies visible to us and are useful in the determination of the mass of Mars. Phobos is unique in that its period of revolution is less than one-third of Mars' period of rotation. This satellite, as observed from Mars, therefore rises in the west, moves eastward across the sky, and sets in the east, going around Mars more than three times while the planet is making one rotation.

JUPITER AND ITS MOONS

Jupiter is the largest of all the planets and also the brightest, except for Venus and, at times, Mars. Its diameter is approximately eleven times that of the earth, and its volume, therefore, is thirteen hundred times the earth's. Its mass, which is roughly only one-thousandth of the sun's, is nevertheless greater than the masses of all the other planets combined. In shape it is very oblate, with a polar diameter about one-fifteenth less than the equatorial diameter. This is not surprising, in view of its extremely high speed of rotation, the period of which is less than ten hours. The equatorial region appears to complete its rotation in a little less time than the regions of higher latitude. There is no entirely satisfactory explanation for the faster rotation of Jupiter near its equator as compared with the rotation at higher latitudes. It can be pointed out that this phenomenon occurs on other large rotating bodies which are largely gaseous and of low density, such as the sun and Saturn. This peculiar motion may be related to the method of formation of the original rotating body. In some manner, matter near the equator was given greater angular momentum, which has been retained. Refer to Chapter 39.

Parallel to the equatorial region of Jupiter are dark belts of reddish-brown color and others of different tints which become less conspicuous at higher altitudes. (Refer to Figure 15–8.) These belts vary in number and width from year to year and even change from day to day; they are obviously clouds. Dark bands in the spectra of Jupiter have been identified as the molecular spectra of ammonia and methane. The spectra indicate an amount of ammonia equivalent to a thirty-foot layer of the gas at one atmosphere of pressure and a half-mile layer of methane. At the low surface temperature of Jupiter (about −100° C.) any water present would be frozen and most of the ammonia would be in the solid state. The low density of the planet (1.33) suggests that hydrogen and helium, the most abundant elements of the universe, must be present in very large amounts. This was confirmed in 1952 by a study of the light transmitted through Jupiter's atmosphere from a star.

Fig. 15–8 *Jupiter.* *(Yerkes Observatory photograph)*

The satellites of Jupiter have played important roles in the history of astronomy. When Galileo used his telescope for the first time in 1610 (Chapter 13), he discovered the four largest — Io, Europa, Ganymede, and Callisto. There are eight more satellites, the last having been discovered in 1951. The first five satellites move in almost circular orbits, nearly in the plane of the planet's equator and orbit. The eighth, ninth, eleventh, and twelfth satellites revolve in the *retrograde* direction from east to west. Two of the satellites are larger than the planet Mercury. Observations of the four largest satellites by Roemer in 1675 gave the first proof that light travels with very great but measurable velocity.

SATURN AND ITS RINGS

To the naked eye, Saturn, the most remote planet known to the ancients, appears as a yellowish star. Through a telescope, it is one of the most beautiful and interesting of all celestial bodies. A system of three concentric rings, encircling the planet in the plane of its equator and with the outer limit 86,300 miles from its center, makes it unique and beautiful. (Refer to Figure 15–9.) Galileo was the first to see these rings, but he thought they were two other planets on either side of Saturn. These rings are neither solid nor fluid, but probably consist of solid particles which move independently. It has been suggested that these particles may be the residue of some other body, perhaps a satellite, which came too close to Saturn and was disrupted.

Saturn is almost as large as Jupiter and has surface features very much like those of Jupiter. Its period of rotation is 10 hours, 38 minutes; like Jupiter, it has a slightly longer period at higher latitudes. Like Jupiter, too, it appears to have a very deep atmosphere, with a low surface temperature of about −150° C. Its equator is inclined to the ecliptic nearly 27°.

Fig. 15–9 *Saturn and its rings.*

Saturn has nine satellites, all of which revolve outside of its rings and most of which revolve in orbits that lie almost in the plane of the rings. The smallest satellite, Phoebe, which is less than two hundred miles in diameter, revolves in a retrograde direction from east to west.

URANUS, NEPTUNE, AND PLUTO

Uranus was discovered in 1781 by Sir William Herschel, who thought he had found a comet. Later, after close observation of its motion, an attempt to calculate its orbit as a comet proved it to be a planet. Through the telescope it appears as a bluish-green disc, and although not as large as Jupiter and Saturn it resembles them in structure, with a solid core, a layer of ice, and an atmosphere which is mostly hydrogen. The equator of Uranus is inclined to the plane of its orbit 98°; its rotation around its axis is therefore *retrograde* but the orbital motion is direct (eastward). Uranus has five satellites which revolve in the same direction as the planet rotates and they all move precisely in the plane of the planet's equator.

The dramatic discovery of the planet Neptune was discussed in Chapter 14. Although Neptune is extremely remote, its diameter has been estimated to be a little less than that of Uranus, its twin planet. Like Uranus, it appears as a bluish-green disc and is probably covered by a similar atmosphere. Two satellites of Neptune are known, one revolving in a *retrograde* orbit which is inclined 40° to the planet's orbit.

A careful study of the motions of Uranus and Neptune indicated to Percival Lowell the possibility of an ultra-Neptunian planet. The planet was sought, not by telescopic observation, but by a thorough search of photographs of that part of the sky. In 1930, C. W. Tombough found the image of the new planet. As photographs dating back to 1919 recorded the position of the planet, calculations of its path, its

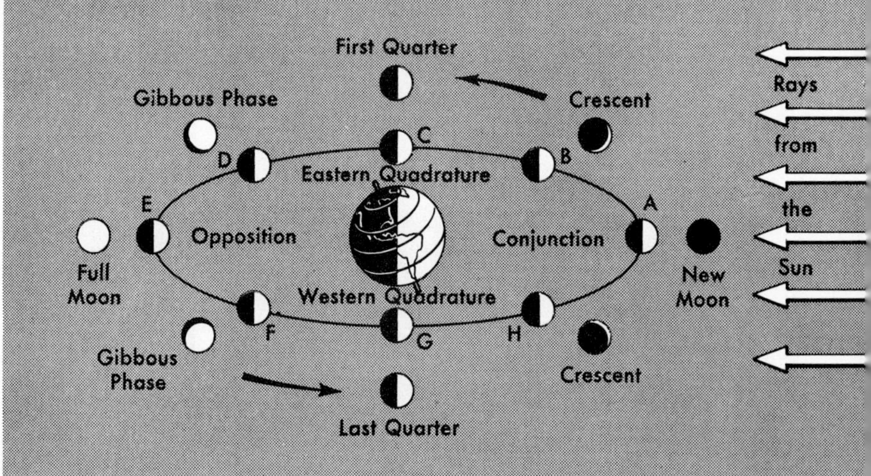

Fig. 15–10 *Phases of the moon and the corresponding positions in its orbit.*

distance from the sun, and its period of rotation were made. Pluto, as the new planet was named, is smaller than the earth. Its high inclination and eccentricity have been noted. In the vicinity of its perihelion, Pluto is nearer to the sun than Neptune. It has been suggested that Pluto may actually be an escaped moon of Neptune.

THE MOON

The moon, the most conspicuous object in the night sky; has always been a source of wonder and speculation for man. Because it is the closest of all heavenly bodies, it appears to an observer on the earth to be almost as large as the much more distant sun. To the astronomer the moon is important because it is near enough to permit close study of its surface, its complex motions, and its gravitational reaction to both earth and sun.

The Phases of the Moon. The moon is the earth's only satellite. As it revolves in its orbit about the earth each month we see varying fractions of its illuminated face, ranging from a thin crescent to the full disc. The moon is illuminated by the sun, and the cycle of *phases* is caused by the changes in the relative positions of moon, earth, and sun. The waxing and waning of the moon has, in all ages, excited man's imagination and has provided the poet with an inspiring subject for song. Thus Shakespeare's Juliet addresses Romeo:

> O! swear not by the moon, the inconstant moon,
> That monthly changes in her circled orb,
> Lest that thy love prove likewise variable.
>
> *Romeo and Juliet,* II, ii, 109–111.

When the moon is in *conjunction* with the sun, that is, when the two have the same longitude, the moon is "new." At this position, *A* in the diagram (Figure 15–10), the dark portion of the moon is turned toward the earth. The new moon rises and sets with the sun, and at noon the moon is on the meridian, as is also the sun, but the moon is not visible. After a day or two a thin crescent becomes visible at *B*. When the moon is at or near the new phase, its disc may be faintly illuminated by "earthshine"; this light travels from the sun to the earth to the moon and is again reflected back to the earth. A week later the moon is at the eastern quadrature, *C,* for its longitude with reference to the sun is 90° east and the phase is the first quarter. We now see a half-moon which rises about noon, crosses the meridian, and sets six hours after the sun.

After passing through the more enlarged, or "gibbous," phase, *D,* practically the full face of the moon is visible within a week after the first quarter. Here the moon is in opposition with the sun, its longitude being 180°, so the full moon is twelve hours behind (or ahead of) the sun. As the sun sets, the full moon rises. After this the phases wane and successively pass through the gibbous, the last quarter or western quadrature, and the crescent, to the dark, or

Fig. 15–11 *Moon at 3.85 days (inverted). (Yerkes Observatory photograph)*

Fig. 15–12 *Moon at 22½ days (inverted). (Yerkes Observatory photograph)*

new, phase. The horns, or cusps, of the crescent moons always point away from the sun.

Physical Data. The moon is fifth in size among the thirty-one satellites, but relative to the size of its mother planet, the earth, it is the largest. The numerical data are as follows:

Mean diameter	2,160 miles
Mean distance from earth	239,000 miles
Density	3.36 g per cc
Period of revolution (sidereal month)	27.3217 days
Mass (Earth = 1.00)	0.0123
Inclination of orbit to ecliptic (average)	5° 8′
Inclination of axis to orbit	6° 5′
Eccentricity of orbit	0.055
Gravitational attraction (Earth = 1.00)	0.16
Velocity of escape	1.5 miles per sec

Motions of the Moon. To the observer on the moving earth, the moon appears to move around the celestial sphere in the course of a month in an orbit which is inclined to the ecliptic. The moon rises and sets daily, always later each succeeding day, and, with the earth, it travels about the sun. The inclination of its orbit to the ecliptic varies, and the orbit slowly turns, shifting its points of intersection with the ecliptic (nodes). The moon wobbles on its axis and its motion undergoes many other perturbations. Indeed, the motions of the moon are extremely complex, for they result from the interplay of the mutual gravitational attractions of three bodies, earth, moon, and sun, whose relative positions are constantly changing. We must therefore limit ourselves to a discussion of several over-all or average motions.

Revolution. The moon revolves around the earth, or, more precisely, the two bodies move around their common center of gravity in elliptical orbits. Since the mass of the moon is 0.0123 that of the earth, and the mean distance from the center of the earth to the center of the moon is 239,000 miles, the center of gravity of the earth-moon system is $\frac{0.0123}{1.0123} \times 239{,}000$ miles = 2900 miles from the center of the earth. The center of gravity therefore lies within the earth about 1000 miles from the surface facing the moon. If supported at this point, the two would balance each other.

The moon travels completely around the earth relative to the fixed stars in a period of 27.3217 mean solar days or at the rate of $360°/27.3217 = 13.2°$ per day. This period of revolution of the moon with respect to the stars is the *sidereal month.*

The earth, around which the moon is revolving, moves eastward in its orbit at the rate of approximately one degree per day. To the observer on the earth, the sun appears to move eastward against its background of stars at the same rate, one degree per day. Hence, if we measure the period of revolution of the moon with respect to the sun, we get a longer month. While the moon is making its revolution around the earth, our reference point, the sun moves ahead about thirty degrees and it takes the moon two more days to catch up with it. In Figure 15–13 the earth moves in its orbit from E to E' while the moon makes a complete revolution from M to M' in one sidereal month. In the meantime the sun has apparently moved ahead (owing to the earth's revolution) relative to the stars. In order to bring the moon, earth, and sun into the same alignment as before, the moon must continue on to M''. This longer time interval is known as the *synodic month* and over a very long period of time averages a little more than 29.5 days.

Apparent Daily Motion of the Moon. As the earth rotates, the moon appears to rise in the east, move westward across the sky, cross (transit) the meridian, and set in the west. During a complete rotation of the earth, beginning with the moon, M, on the meridian of the observer at A (Figure 15–14) and ending when the observer is back at the same position A with respect to the sun, the moon advances $\frac{360°}{29.5} = 12.2°$ to M' relative to the sun. The earth must

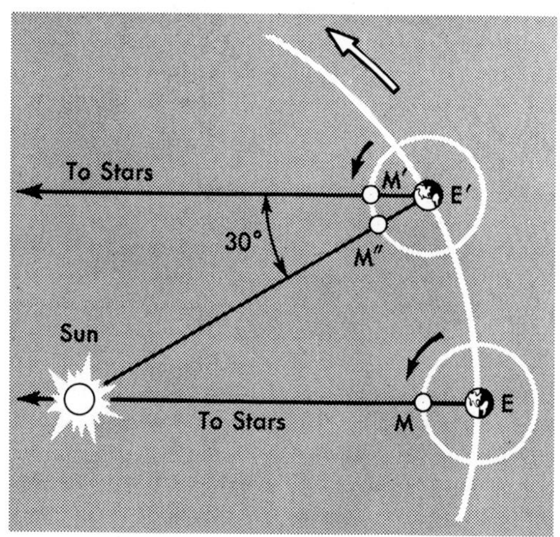

Fig. 15–13 *The synodic month is longer than the sidereal month by the time required for the moon to move from M′ to M″.*

therefore rotate through an additional angle of a little more than 12.2° to overtake the moon. The time required for this additional rotation is, on the average, about fifty-one minutes; the moon rises, crosses the meridian, and sets (on the average) fifty-one minutes later each day.

Motion of Moon and Earth Relative to the Sun. Could we observe the motions of the moon and earth about the sun from a point in space, it would appear quite different from what we might expect. The moon and earth are approximately four hundred times as far from the sun as they are from each other. The path of the moon, therefore, nearly coincides with the orbit of the earth, and, like that of the earth, is always circumsolar. In Figure 15–15 the

Fig. 15–14 *Moonrise lag diagrammatically explained: moon advances in its orbit from M to M′ while earth completes one rotation plus arc through which moon advances.*

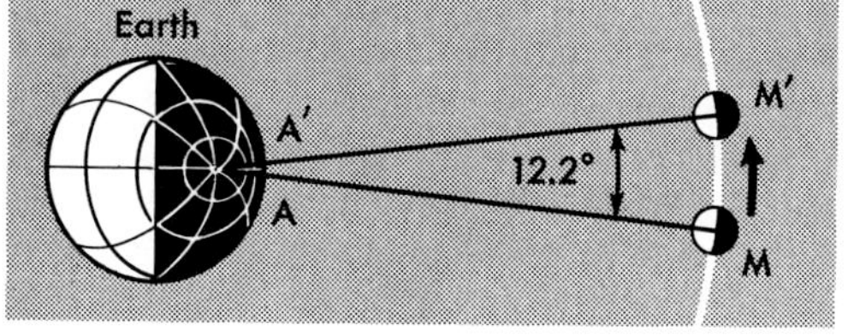

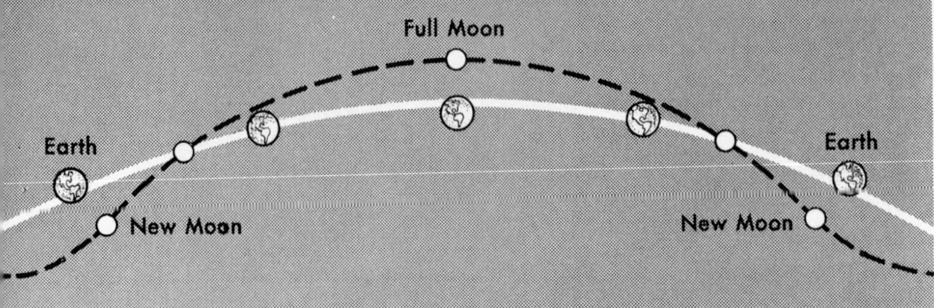

Fig. 15–15 *The moon pursues a sinuous path around the sun as it revolves around the earth. Its path is always curved toward the sun.*

path of the center of gravity of the earth-moon system is represented by the solid line and that of the moon by the dotted line, though the deviation of the paths is exaggerated. The moon must at some times overtake and pass the earth, and at others be overtaken and passed by the earth. As a result the moon's orbit is irregular and its speed likewise variable, but its path is always curved toward the sun.

Rotation. The same side of the moon is constantly turned toward the earth. It therefore makes one complete rotation with respect to the sun and all bodies other than the earth, in one sidereal month which is also its period of revolution. (Refer to Figure 15–16.) It rotates on its axis at a uniform rate, but revolves at a variable rate in accordance with Kepler's Law of Areas. Hence, there is some rocking back and forth on its axis relative to the earth. This motion permits us to see further around the edge of the moon first on one side and two weeks later on the other. The axis of the moon is inclined to its orbit by 6° 5′ and always points in the same direction, thus permitting us to see alternately beyond its two poles. These rockings, known as *librations,* together with observations from various positions on the earth's surface make it possible for us to see at various times a total of 59 per cent of the moon's surface.

Surface Features. Careful examination of the moon fails to show any evidence of atmosphere or water. There are no clouds, storms, no evidence of erosion, no twilight, refraction of light, or evidence of light scattering as in a haze. Shadows are absolutely black. During an eclipse of the sun the edge of the moon's disc appears sharp and dark, with no partly illuminated atmospheric ring. When the moon occults a star — that is, passes in front of the star — there is no gradual disappearance. The star suddenly vanishes behind the moon and a little later just as suddenly reappears on the other side. We do not know if the moon ever had an atmosphere, for it does not have sufficient gravitational force to hold water vapor or gases which are known to be in the atmospheres of some of the planets. The velocity of escape for the moon is only 1.5 miles per second (for the earth it is 7 miles per second); that is, a projectile or gas molecule must have that much initial velocity in order to leave the moon against its gravitational pull. While this velocity is greater than the average velocities of the molecules of water vapor, nitrogen, oxygen, and all gases except hydrogen, a certain fraction of the molecules of any of the gases may exceed this value so that there is a gradual escape. The high surface temperature of the moon (100° C.) reached dur-

Fig. 15–16 *During each revolution around the earth the moon rotates on its axis only once, keeping the same face (A) always toward the earth.*

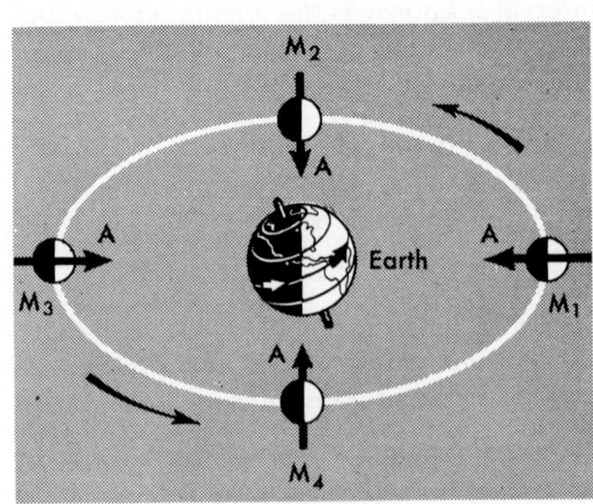

ing the two-week daylight period would have aided this escape by increasing the molecular speeds. Since no atmosphere blankets the moon, the surface temperature changes quickly and during the two-week lunar night it drops to −130° C. or lower.

The moon's surface is rocky and bleak with mountain ranges, isolated peaks, craters, rays, rills, and relatively smooth plains; all of it appears to be covered by finely pulverized dust. Most of the *mountain ranges* are short, narrow, and steep by terrestrial standards; some of the peaks extend as high as 26,000 feet above the plains. The heights of the mountains and the rims of the craters are calculated from the lengths of their sharp, dark shadows and the known position of the sun. Other large areas appear darker in contrast to the mountains and craters and were called *maria* (seas) by earlier observers, including Galileo. They have relatively smooth surfaces and are possibly solidified lava beds. *Rills* are long narrow crevices or wrinkles which extend over the maria. *Rays* are light-colored streaks which radiate out from some of the craters.

The *craters,* of which more than 30,000 have been mapped, are the most remarkable of the moon's features. The smaller ones resemble somewhat the volcanic craters on the earth, but the larger ones are great plains with diameters of almost 150 miles ringed by mountains as high as 20,000 feet. The diameter of the crater Copernicus is 56 miles; that of Clavius, one of the largest, is 140 miles. (Refer to Figure 15–17.) The origin of these craters is not known, but two possibilities have been considered. The first is that they were produced by volcanic activity. Their great size, the absence of great amounts of material which may have been ejected, and the total absence today of any indication of volcanic activity on the moon are plausible objections to this hypothesis. The other possibility is that the craters were produced by the impacts of large meteors, with such force that the surface rocks and at least part of the meteor would have been vaporized. The lunar craters show a significant resemblance to those made by explosive bombs.

ECLIPSES

The earth and the moon cast conical shadows which point into space directly away from the sun (Figure 15–18). The average length of the earth's shadow is 859,000 miles; that of the moon's shadow is 232,100 miles, somewhat less than the average distance from the moon to the earth. If the moon revolved around the earth in the plane of the ecliptic, it would pass through the earth's shadow at full moon and we would have a total eclipse of the moon each month. About two weeks later when the moon was new it would pass between the earth and the sun causing a total eclipse of the sun *provided the moon's shadow extended to the earth.* This condition is fulfilled when the sun is at a greater distance from the moon, thereby giving a longer shadow, or when the earth-moon distance is smaller. The moon's orbit, however, is inclined to the ecliptic by 5° 8′ and therefore

Fig. 15–17 *Lunar crater Copernicus. (Cf. Figure 15–12.) At lower left is the crater Eratosthenes. Note the streams of lava surrounding Copernicus. (Yerkes Observatory photograph)*

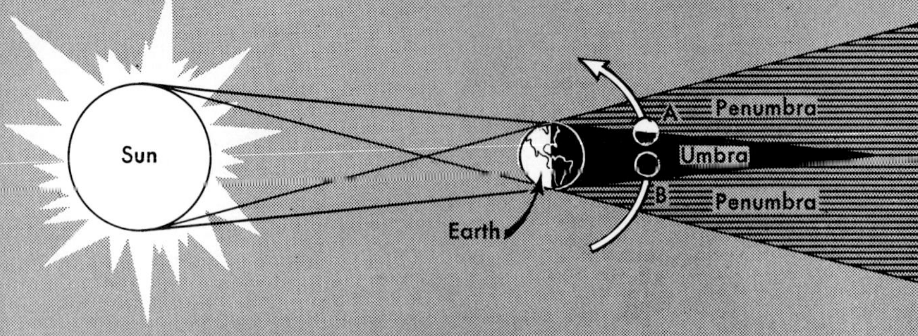

Fig. 15–18 *How the earth eclipses the moon.*

the moon must also be near the ecliptic, that is, at or near one of its nodes, if a lunar eclipse is to occur at full moon or a total solar eclipse at new moon.

Lunar Eclipses. The relative positions of the sun, earth, and moon are shown at the time of an eclipse of the moon in Figure 15–18. If the moon (*B*) is completely inside the earth's conical shadow (umbra) the eclipse is total; if it is partly inside (*A*), so that its disc is not entirely obscured, the eclipse is partial. An eclipse of the moon may be observed from any point on the dark side of the earth, and the total eclipse may last for more than an hour. Generally the moon and sun will not be both in opposition and near the nodes (within 10°) more than twice a year, and in some years not at all.

Solar Eclipses. When the moon's conical shadow reaches the earth (Figure 15–19), a total eclipse of the sun occurs for the observer within the umbra. If the observer is within the diverging shadow (penumbra), he will see a partial eclipse. When, owing to the eccentric orbits of earth and moon, the moon's shadow cone does not reach the earth even though the moon is in the plane of the ecliptic, the observer in the extended cone will see the moon on the sun's disc, smaller than the sun and with a ring of light around it, an *annular* eclipse. (Refer to Figure 15–20.) The duration of a solar eclipse is short, less than eight minutes. Not more than five solar eclipses occur in one year.

From the diagram it is apparent that the umbra sweeps across relatively narrow portions of the earth. Astronomers frequently travel great distances to photograph a solar eclipse, for it is of much greater scientific importance than an eclipse of the moon.

ASTEROIDS

Moving about the sun, generally in the same direction as the planets, are thousands of small bodies known as *asteroids.* These dwarf planets, sometimes called

Fig. 15–19 (*Above*) *Conditions for a total eclipse of the sun.* (*Below*) *Conditions for an annular eclipse. Not to scale.* (*After Cecilia Payne-Gaposchkin,* Introduction to Astronomy. *Copyright 1954, by Prentice-Hall, Inc.*)

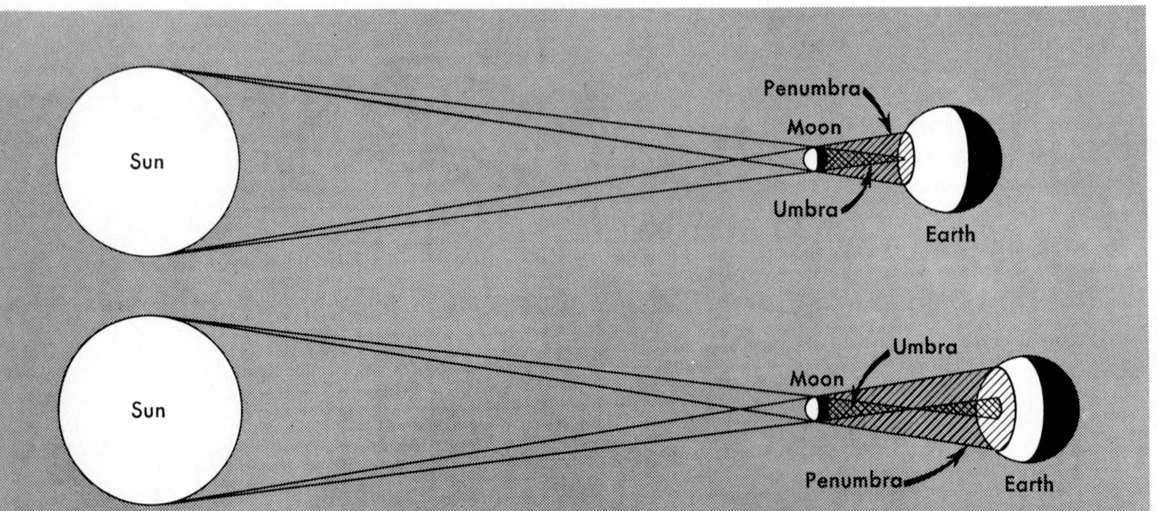

planetoids, move in orbits which vary widely from near circles to ellipses of eccentricities as high as 0.65. The orbits of some are inclined to the ecliptic more than 40°. Most of them travel in the vast space between the orbits of Mars and Jupiter, but those with relatively small and highly eccentric orbits swing around the sun at perihelion within the orbits of the earth or Venus. The asteroid Icarus passes within the orbit of Mercury and comes closer to the sun (17 million miles) than any other known astronomical body. In 1937 another asteroid, Hermes, passed within a half-million miles of the earth.

The first asteroid was discovered in 1801 by the Sicilian astronomer, Guiseppe Piazzi; he named it Ceres. Within a few years three more, Pallas, Juno, and Vesta, were found; the last named is the only asteroid at times visible to the naked eye. Many more asteroids have been discovered by the use of photography; long exposures, by means of a telescope driven to follow the stars across the sky in the region of the ecliptic, record the asteroids as streaks or trails and the stars as points. The orbits of about two thousand asteroids have been determined. The diameter of the largest known asteroid, Ceres, is 480 miles; about five hundred have estimated diameters of more than 30 miles and the others range down to a few inches.

A cloud of very small particles seems to extend outward from the sun, approximately in the plane of the ecliptic, beyond the earth's orbit. This cloud, which consists of particles probably ranging from several inches down to one-half inch or less in diameter, apparently reflects sunlight to give what are known as the *Zodiacal light* and the *counterglow*. The Zodiacal light, a band or zone of faint light which lies along the ecliptic, is best observed after sunset or before sunrise on a moonless night. After dusk it extends above the western horizon, a long tapering band wider at the base. Before sunrise it is brightest in the east, always in the direction of the sun. In either instance, a faint counterglow may be observed on the opposite side of the ecliptic.

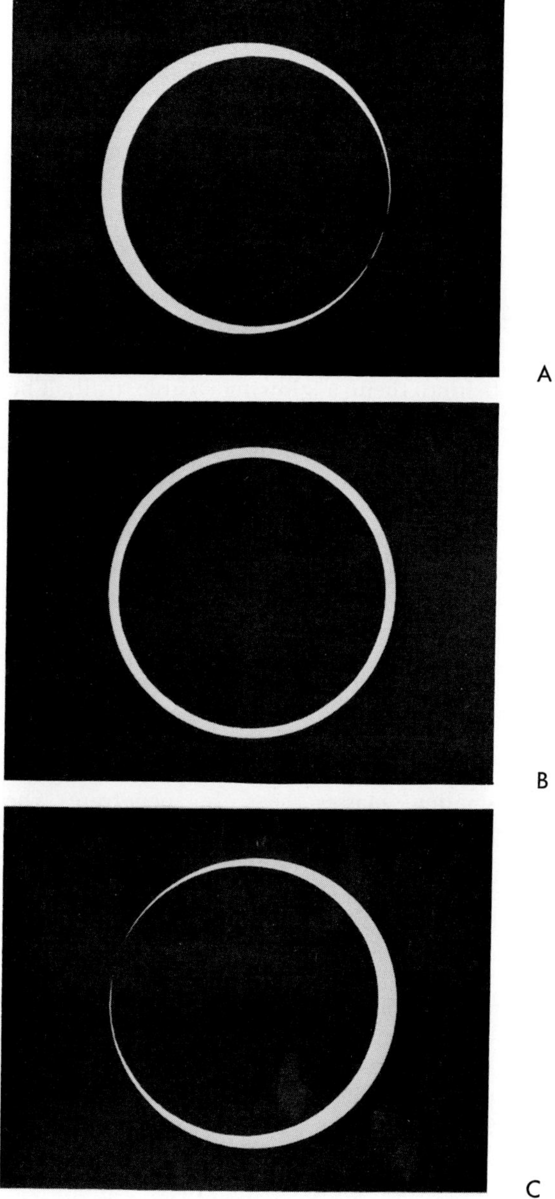

Fig. 15–20 *Annular eclipse of the sun. (From photographs taken in Conroe, Texas, on April 7, 1940, by Dr. N. Wyman Storer of the University of Kansas.) A. Contact at 2 h 49 m 45 s p.m., C.S.T. B. Central eclipse, 3 h 53 m 00 s p.m., C.S.T. The ring of light (annulus) represents the difference between the apparent sizes of sun and moon. C. Contact at 3 h 56 m 01 s p.m., C.S.T.*

METEORS AND METEORITES

On a clear night one may see meteors (shooting stars) which suddenly appear, streak across the sky, and vanish. They are small, solid bodies which move from interplanetary space into the earth's atmosphere with an average speed of 35 miles per second. At a height of 70 to 80 miles above the surface of the earth the air becomes dense enough to offer effective resistance. The bodies therefore are heated by friction with the air and vaporize leaving behind them a glowing visible trail. The typical meteor is no larger than a few grains of sand, but there are some which weigh many tons. It is estimated that more than ten million visible meteors and possibly a total of several billion enter the earth's atmosphere each day.

Occasionally larger meteors generate unusually brilliant light; these are called *fireballs;* others may explode with loud reports. Those which survive the passage through the lower atmosphere to reach the earth are known as *meteorites.* Their speeds are so reduced by the air that those of smaller masses scarcely penetrate the ground; the more massive ones do not suffer such a reduction in speed and bury themselves in the earth. The meteorites we usually see in museums are metallic, consisting of an alloy of iron and nickel with traces of other elements. Others are composed of an iron-nickel sponge with silicate minerals filling the cavities. A third group, known as stony meteorites, contain a large percentage of magnesium and silicon oxides with other terrestrial elements and a little iron and nickel. All contain gases. The largest single meteorite on exhibit was brought back from Greenland by Admiral Peary and is at the American Museum of Natural History in New York City. It is a thirty-six-ton mass of iron-nickel alloy. A huge mass, possibly 125 × 300 × 300 feet, is reported to have been found buried in the sands of the Sahara Desert. Meteor Crater (Figure 15–21), near Winslow, Arizona, is a great cavity six hundred feet in depth and nearly a mile in diameter. Thousands of fragments of meteoric iron have been found in the vicinity. Attempts are being made to locate the huge meteorite which some think is buried beneath the southern wall of the crater.

At times an unusual number of meteors are observed in a single night; the greatest meteoric shower of recent times occurred on October 9, 1946. Other great showers were observed in 1799 and in 1833, and recurrence was predicted for every thirty-three years, but while those of 1866, 1900, and 1933 were large, they were not as large as the earlier showers. Some of the showers seem to be associated with comets; clouds of meteoric material are often scattered along the orbit of a comet, and when the earth crosses it, showers of meteors fall. A number of such clouds are known to be moving along the orbits of extinct comets.

COMETS

The spectacular and often unexpected appearance of comets, so unlike the other objects in the sky, has always aroused great interest and often fear. They appear in the sky moving in no particular plane, sweep around the sun, and recede. Their visits have been regarded as portents, and even

Fig. 15–21 *Aerial view of Meteor Crater near Winslow, Arizona. (Yerkes Observatory photograph)*

Fig. 15–22 *Halley's Comet, June 6, 1910. Shows a discarded portion of the tail drifting away from the comet. The diameter of the head at this time was 320,000 miles, and its distance from the sun 110,000,000 miles. When first seen in September, 1909, the head was only 140,000 miles in diameter, its distance from the sun 200,000,000 miles. In April, 1911, the diameter had dwindled to 30,000 miles at a distance of 400,000,000 miles from the sun.* (*Yerkes Observatory photograph*)

the cause of such human disasters as wars, plagues, and famines. Most comets move in extremely elongated elliptical orbits in accordance with Kepler's laws; some move in parabolic or hyperbolic orbits. The larger ones consist of a starlike nucleus surrounded by a cloudlike, nebulous mass called the *coma* (Gr., *hair*), which often extends as a long, filmy, streaming tail that may be more than a hundred million miles in length. Only the nucleus of the comet, which seems to consist of solid particles, appears dense enough to obstruct light. Stars may be seen through the tail, which has an extremely low density, far below that of the highest vacuum we are able to achieve in the laboratory. The tail is usually turned away from the sun and is probably formed as a result of electrical repulsion or radiation pressure exerted by the sun. Part of the light given off from the comet is reflected sunlight; the coma and tail appear as a glowing gas which sometimes erupts, throwing out luminous material. This may be due to the explosion of instable substances which decompose when heated slightly by the sun.

About one thousand comets are known, and more are discovered each year, some by amateur astronomers. They are named for their discoverers. One of the great comets is named for Halley, an associate of Newton. Applying Newton's principle of gravitation to the motion of this comet, which appeared in 1682, Halley showed that it had an elliptical orbit. On the basis of records of its visits as far back as 240 B.C., he predicted its return in 1759. The comet appears every 75.5 years, and its next return is predicted for 1985 (Figure 15–22). Just before its last appearance in 1910, the many newspaper stories about its close approach to the earth and a possible collision caused some apprehension. The earth at that time passed through the tail of the comet, but the only effect observed was a slight iridescence of the sky. It is likely that a head-on collision of the earth with a comet would do no more than shower us with myriads of shooting stars which would disintegrate in the earth's upper atmosphere.

SUMMARY

1. The solar system consists of nine planets, thirty-one satellites, and many asteroids, meteors, and comets, all moving about the sun.
2. The inferior planets, Mercury and Venus, may each occupy positions of inferior and superior conjunction with respect to the earth and sun. Both appear as morning and evening stars and show phase changes.
3. The superior planets may occupy positions of superior conjunction and opposition.
4. Mercury, the planet nearest the sun, and Pluto, the most remote, have orbits which are more eccentric and more inclined to the ecliptic than those of the other planets.
5. Physical data of the planets are given in Table 15–1. Other matters of interest are:
   a. The possibility of life on Mars.
   b. The two satellites of Mars, Deimos and Phobos, the latter revolving faster than Mars rotates.
   c. Jupiter, the largest planet, its twelve satellites, three of which revolve in a retrograde direction; its atmosphere.
   d. Saturn's rings; its nine satellites.
   e. Uranus inclined to its orbit 98°
6. The phase changes of the moon as observed from the earth undergo a complete cycle each month. At *conjunction* with the sun the moon is *new* and rises and sets with the sun; at opposition the moon is *full* and rises when the sun sets.
7. The motions of the moon are numerous and complex:
   a. It revolves around the earth with reference to the stars in *one sidereal month of* $27\frac{1}{3}$ *mean solar days;* with respect to the sun its period of revolution around the earth is *one synodic month of* $29\frac{1}{2}$ *mean solar days.* The difference is due to the orbital motion of the earth which gives the sun an apparent eastward motion of one degree per day.
   b. The daily rising and setting of the moon occurs on the average 51 minutes later each day. This lag is due to the orbital motion of the moon which moves eastward around the earth 12.2 degrees per day.

c. The moon's period of rotation is equal to its period of revolution; one face is always turned toward the earth, but due to its librations we can observe a total of more than one-half of its surface.

8. Solar eclipses occur at new moon (conjunction) when the sun is in the direction of the node; lunar eclipses at full moon (opposition) when the sun and moon are on or near opposite nodes.
9. Asteroids, small planet-like bodies, are found mostly in the space between the orbits of Mars and Jupiter.
10. Meteors are small solid bodies which enter the earth's atmosphere where, heated by friction, they appear as shooting stars. Those which survive to fall to the earth are known as meteorites.
11. Comets consist of a starlike nucleus and a tenuous tail.

STUDY EXERCISES

1. What two points of difference enable an observer to distinguish between planets and stars?
2. List the planets as indicated below:
   - *a*. The smallest..........................
   - *b*. The largest..........................
   - *c*. The nearest to the sun...............
   - *d*. The most remote......................
   - *e*. The one having the most eccentric orbit..............................
   - *f*. The one whose orbit is most inclined to the ecliptic..........................
   - *g*. Those which transit the sun...........
   - *h*. The one having the greatest orbital speed..............................
   - *i*. The one which crosses its neighbor's orbit..............................
3. Consult a current monthly sky map and prepare a drawing showing the location of the visible planets. Locate these in the sky and note their relative change in position after a week and after a month.
4. Write *T* if the statement is wholly true, and *F* if any part of the statement is false.
   - *a*. If the orbit of Mercury were in the plane of the ecliptic, it would transit the sun every eighty-eight days................
   - *b*. To an observer on Venus the earth would at times appear to move backwards. ....
   - *c*. The rings of Saturn mark approximately the plane of its equator................
   - *d*. As Mars is inclined to its orbit at about the same angle as the earth to its orbit, the seasons on Mars should be of the same length as those on the earth.......
   - *e*. One of the planetoids has approached nearer to the earth than any other body. ....
5. List and discuss the factors which are important in considering the possibility of life on another planet.
6. The mass of Jupiter is 318.4 times that of the earth, and its diameter is eleven times that of the earth. Calculate the acceleration of a falling body near its surface.
7. In the diagram below, the moon is shown in four different positions, *A, B, C,* and *D,* relative to the earth, *E,* and the sun.

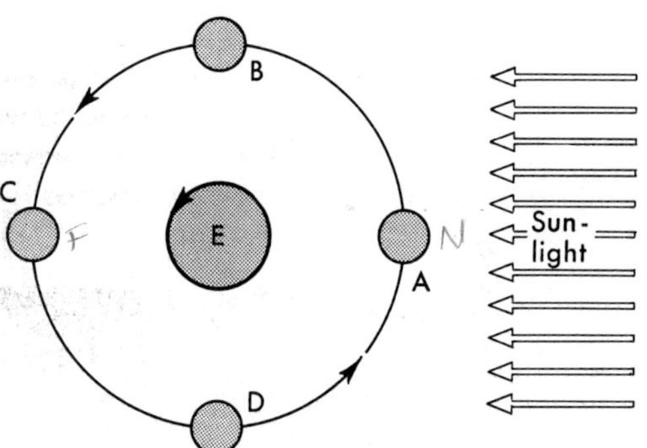

   - *a*. Indicate the position of the moon at each phase by letters *A, B, C,* or *D* and give its age:
     Moon is new at ______ and is ______ days old.
     Moon is full at ______ and is ______ days old.
     Moon is in third quarter at ______ and is ______ days old.
     Moon is in first quarter at ______ and is ______ days old.
   - *b*. Indicate by letters *A, B, C,* or *D* the phase of the moon at which, for the observer on the earth, the moon:

Rises and sets with the sun............

Rises and sets 6 hours ahead of the sun.
....

Rises and sets 6 hours behind the sun.
....

Rises when the sun sets and sets when the sun rises.........................

8. Which of these phenomena do not take place on the moon? Erosion in general; rain; exfoliation; lithosphere tides; ocean tides; day and night; shooting stars.
9. Explain why we do not have a lunar eclipse and a solar eclipse at every revolution of the moon around the earth.
10. Refer to Figure 15–13 in answering the following questions:
    a. What is meant by eastward direction among the stars — clockwise or counterclockwise when observed from the earth?
    b. Does the sun actually move 1° per day with reference to the stars? Explain.
    c. How long does it take for the moon to travel completely around the earth relative to our fixed guidepost, the stars? What is this time-interval called? How many degrees, then, does the moon move eastward per day relative to the stars?
    d. Explain why a longer interval is required for the moon to move around the earth with respect to the sun, that is, from new moon to new moon. What is such a time-interval called? How many degrees does the moon advance each day with respect to the sun?
11. Explain why the moon rises, crosses the meridian, and sets approximately fifty-one minutes later each day.
12. The period of rotation of the moon is equal to the period of revolution. From a knowledge of Kepler's laws, which of these motions is irregular and variable? Explain other reasons why our view of the moon is not always restricted to 50 per cent of its surface. Can we see more than 50 per cent of its surface at any one time?
13. Write *C* if the statement is true of comets, *M* if true of meteors, and *P* if true of planetoids. (A statement may apply to more than one body.)
    a. At times shine by their own light. ......
    b. Shine by reflected light. ....
    c. At times come in contact with the earth. ....
    d. Move in accordance with law of gravitation. ....
    e. Part is repelled away from the sun. ......
    f. Move mostly in region between Mars and Jupiter. ....
    g. Add to mass of Earth. ....
    h. May be observed at times without telescope. ....

FOR FURTHER READING

1. BAKER, R. H., *Astronomy.* New York: D. Van Nostrand Company, 1957.
   Chapters 5, 6, 8, and 9 discuss in detail the moon, eclipses, planets, and meteorites.
2. PAYNE-GAPOSCHKIN, C., *Introduction to Astronomy.* New York: Prentice-Hall, 1954.
   Chapters V, VIII, and IX are recommended.
3. SKILLING, W. T., and R. S. RICHARDSON, *A Brief Text in Astronomy.* New York: Henry Holt and Company, 1954.
   Chapters 3, 11, 12, 13, and 14 contain understandable material on the members of the solar family.
4. Paperback: BERNHARD, H. J., D. A. BENNETT, and H. S. RICE, *New Handbook of the Heavens.* Mentor, 50¢.
   Well-written and readable with information for the observer. Chapters 6–11 deal with the solar system.

16

ASTRONOMICAL MEASUREMENTS

BECAUSE OF THE FORCES of gravitation and certain technical difficulties, which so far have been overcome only in science fiction, man is chained to the earth. This may appear to place the astronomer at a disadvantage, for he cannot travel about the universe on "field trips" as does the geologist in his domain. He cannot as yet obtain a rock specimen from the moon or a sample of the atmosphere of Jupiter for laboratory examination and study; nor can he experiment with stars and other celestial bodies. He must obtain his astronomical information from the earth, itself an astronomical body, and from whatever comes to the earth from outer space. The most important and richest source of information is light, both visible and invisible, which is radiated by the sun and other stars. There are also very short radio waves from the sun and from outside the solar system, high-speed particles (cosmic rays), and from within the solar system, meteorites.

In spite of the inaccessibility of the heavenly bodies, a vast amount of knowledge, much of it quantitative, has been derived from the rather meager sources listed above. To obtain data from the available radiation, the astronomer uses the instruments of modern science. For example, a telescope gathers in light from a star whose brightness may be measured by a photoelectric eye. A spectroscope analyzes the light and a camera makes a permanent photographic record of the observations. From data of this kind the astronomer may learn something about a given star, its chemical composition, temperature, relative motion, and its distance from the earth. He is aided in his study and interpretation not only by astronomical theory but also by the related subjects, physics, chemistry, nuclear science, and the most basic of all the sciences, mathematics. With these and similar tools, many of them relatively new, the science of astronomy, which for more than two thousand years was primarily concerned with the solar system, has been extended to include the whole universe – stars, groups of stars or galaxies, and interstellar matter. These achievements testify to the creativeness and productivity of modern science.

In this chapter, we shall center our discussion on some of the methods used to

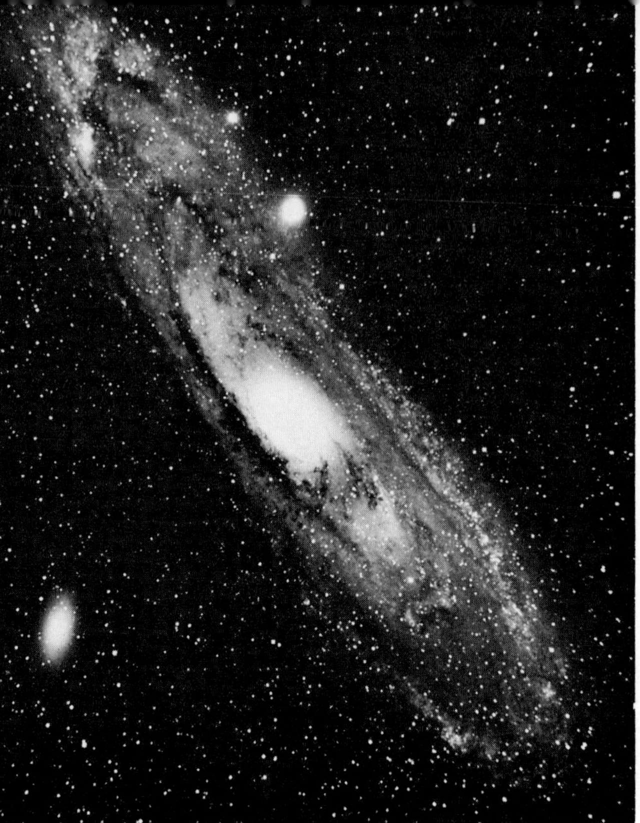

Fig. 16–1 *The great Spiral Nebula in the constellation of Andromeda. (Yerkes Observatory photograph)*

obtain numerical data about the solar system and stars. Of first importance are the measurements of astronomical distances and sizes. Most of the methods are quite simple in theory but more complex in actual operation. The measurements are difficult primarily because the distances of the bodies beyond the solar system, stars and star groups, are so huge. For example, one of the nearer spiral galaxies, Messier 31[1] (M31) located in the constellation Andromeda, is at a distance of 1,500,000 light years from the earth. This means that light, traveling at a speed of 186,000 miles per second, reaches the earth 1,500,000 years after leaving the galaxy. When we look out into space at M31 or photograph it (Figure 16–1) we are also looking back in time; we see the galaxy as it was when the light reaching us left it one and one half million years ago!

MEASUREMENT OF DISTANCE: GENERAL METHOD

The oldest and most important method of measuring astronomical distances is the same in principle as that employed by the surveyors. It is a simple trigonometric method based upon the relationship between the sides and angles of a triangle. If two angles and one side can be measured, the third angle is obtained by subtracting the sum of the other two from 180° and the other two sides calculated by the use of trigonometry (see Chapter 11). To illustrate, let *C*, Figure 16–2, be the object whose distance is to be determined, *AB* the

[1] Listed as No. M31 in the Catalogue of "Odd Objects" prepared by the French astronomer, Charles Messier (1730–1817).

Fig. 16–2 *Use of trigonometry to determine the distance to inaccessible objects. The base line AB is of known length. The angle CAB is measured. Then the angle* $ACD = 180° - (90° + a°)$, *and* $\frac{AB/2}{AC} = \sin\,[180° - (90° + a°)]$ *or*

$$AC = \frac{AB}{(2)\sin\,[180° - (90° + a°)]}.$$

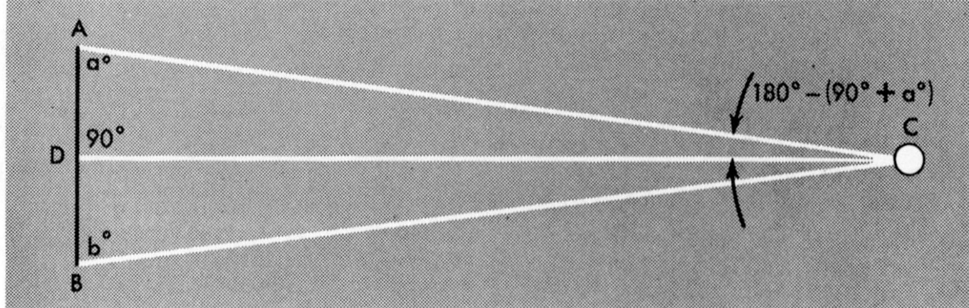

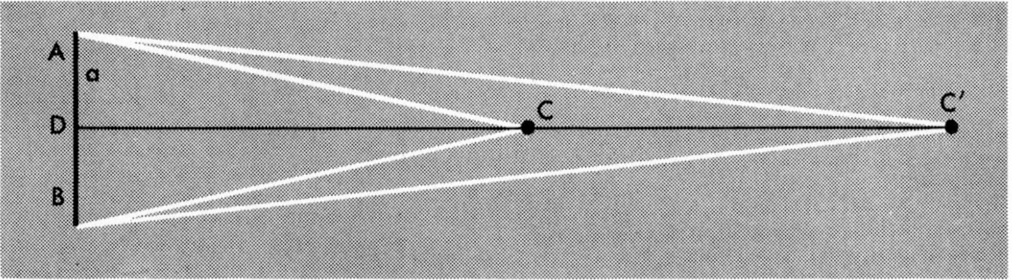

Fig. 16–3 *Trigonometric methods fail when the distance to celestial objects is very large. At great distances the angle a becomes 90° and the angle at the object is essentially zero.*

base line whose length is known. The observer sights to *C* from *A* and from *B* measuring the angles *CAB* and *CBA*. The distance from *A* or from *B* to *C* can thus be calculated. For astronomical distances it is apparent that the base line must be as large as possible and, even so, the distances to be measured are so great that the triangle must be stretched out or elongated as shown in Figure 16–3. As the distances undertaken become greater the angle at *C* becomes smaller and smaller until it cannot be measured accurately; that is, the directions of *C* from the observers at *A* and *B* are indistinguishable. This direct method is therefore limited and can actually be used only for the bodies within the solar system and the nearer stars. It gives us, however, an accurate yardstick of astronomical distances and is the ultimate basis for other methods employed for the more distant stars.

The first problem in the operation of the above method is to secure a base line, the ends of which must be accessible. Two widely separated points on the earth's surface may define one suitable for measuring distances within the solar system. (A much longer base line provided by the earth's orbit will be discussed in a later section.) The second problem is the accurate measurement of very small angles that mark the slight shift in the direction of a distant body as observed from the two ends of the base line. Such fine measurements were not possible until after powerful telescopes had been developed.

DISTANCE TO THE MOON

The determination of the distance from the earth to the moon illustrates the general method outlined in the preceding section. This distance was first measured by the Alexandrian scientist, Hipparchus, inventor of trigonometry. His results, expressed in terms of the earth's radius were fairly accurate, indeed, quite good for pretelescopic measurements. The two observatories, *A* and *B*, Figure 16–4, are assumed to be on the same meridian. The angles Z_1AM and Z_2BM, each known as the moon's zenith distance, are measured simultaneously at the respective observatories. By solving a series of triangles the distance *CM* from the center of the earth to the center of the moon can be calculated:

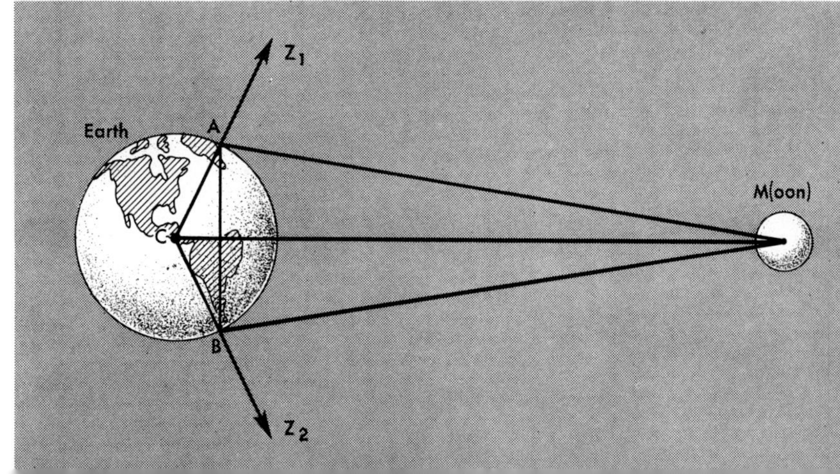

Fig. 16–4 *Determination of the distance from earth to moon (center to center) by trigonometry.*

1. In the triangle ABC the known quantities are:
   The angle ACB = numerical sum of latitudes of A and B.
   Sides AC and BC are radii of earth (see Chapter 3 for the determination of the size of the earth).
   From this angle and the two sides, side AB and angles CAB and CBA may be calculated. AB, the distance between the observers, is the base line.
2. In the triangle ABM the known quantities are now:
   The side AB.
   The angles BAM and AMB, obtained by subtraction, that is, angle $BAM = 180° -$ (angle Z_1AM + angle CAB).
   From the side and two angles, the sides AM and BM, the respective distances of the moon from the observers, may be calculated.
3. In the triangle ACM the known quantities are:
   Sides AC and AM.
   Angle $CAM = 180° -$ angle Z_1AM.
   From the two sides and the angle, the side CM, the distance sought can be calculated.

The problem may be more directly formulated if we consider the four-sided figure $ACBM$ all of whose angles and two of whose sides (AC and BC) are known. The diagonal CM can be calculated by trigonometric methods, but since we confine our calculations in this text to the solution of right-angle triangles, no illustrative problems are given for the more direct formulation.

The mean distance of the moon from the earth is 238,857 miles varying from 221,000 miles at perigee to 253,000 miles at apogee.

SIZE OF THE MOON

The apparent size of an object depends not only upon its actual size, but also upon its distance from the observer. A small coin held at arm's length, for example, more than covers the disc of the moon, and the moon has about the same apparent size as the sun (see page 242). This is not surprising if we consider that, although the sun's diameter is about 400 times that of the moon, it is about 400 times farther from the earth. The average angular diameter of the sun, that is, the angle its disc intercepts when viewed from the earth, is 31 minutes, 59.30 seconds of angle (31′ 59.30″), while that of the moon ranges from 29′ 21″ at apogee to 33′ 30″ at perigee. (Refer to Figure 16–5.)

Knowing the distance to the moon, we need only measure its angular diameter to find its actual diameter in miles or kilometers. The mathematical relationship between distance, angular diameter, and diameter is shown in Figure 16–6. A body, which may be the moon, revolves around the earth in an orbit which, for convenience, is assumed to be circular with the symbol d representing the mean distance. The angle CAB is the angular diameter and BC the linear diameter of the body. For very small angles the arc BC may be regarded as equal to the chord (straight line) BC. The circumference of the circle or mean path of the body is $2\pi d$. For an angular diameter of:

$$1° \text{ (1 degree)}, BC = \frac{2\pi d}{360} = \frac{d}{57.30},$$

$$1' \text{ (1 minute)}, BC = \frac{2\pi d}{360 \times 60'} = \frac{d}{3438},$$

$$1'' \text{ (1 second)}, BC = \frac{2\pi d}{360 \times 60' \times 60''},$$

$$= \frac{d}{206,265}.$$

If the angular diameter of a body is 1′, its linear diameter is 1/3438 of its distance

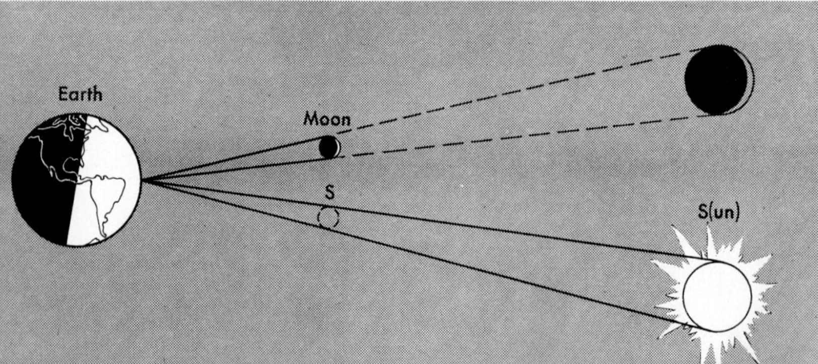

Fig. 16–5 *The moon and sun have nearly the same angular size. Drawing not to scale.*

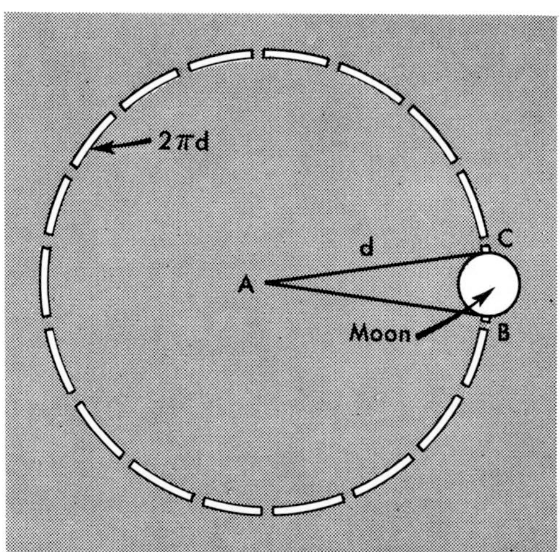

Fig. 16–6 *Approximate relation between angular diameter and distance.*

from the observer; if the angular diameter is 1″, the linear diameter is 1/206,265 of the distance from the observer. The average angular diameter of the moon is 31′ 7″ or 1867″. Its linear diameter is therefore:

$$\frac{1867''}{206{,}265''} \times 238{,}857 \text{ miles (mean distance of moon)} = 2162 \text{ miles.}$$

The above relationship is useful in measuring astronomical distances as we shall see in a later section. It is essentially based upon simple trigonometric functions. In the triangle *CAB* the angle *A* is so small that both the angles, *ACB* and *ABC*, are practically 90°. The tangent (or sine) of $A = \frac{CB}{AB}$. If $C = 1'$,

$$\tan C = 0.0002909 = \frac{1}{3438}.$$

MASS OF THE MOON

The mass of an astronomical body is found by the gravitational effect it has upon the motion of some other body. The monthly revolution of the earth and moon around their center of gravity, described in the preceding chapter, indicates the influence of the moon upon the rotation of the earth. The problem is to locate the point around which the two bodies move. The motion of the earth around this point is somewhat like that of a wheel turning about an axle located some distance from the center. Bodies viewed from the earth seem to shift alternately eastward and westward from their average positions at two-week intervals. The sun's apparent displacement is about 12″, which indicates a corresponding shift by the earth of about 2900 miles. This is the radius of the monthly orbit of the earth's center. The mean distance of the moon from the common center of gravity is: 238,857 − 2900 = 235,957 miles, and since the system is balanced as a lever:

$$\text{Mass (moon)} \times 235{,}957 = \text{Mass (earth)} \times 2900$$

$$\text{Mass (moon)} = \frac{6.57 \times 10^{21} \times 2900}{235{,}957}$$

$$= 8.06 \times 10^{19} \text{ tons}$$

The mass of the moon may also be determined by other methods, its effect on the motion of Eros, for example.

RELATIVE DISTANCES

Before any of the distances of the planets and their satellites were accurately measured, their relative distances had been determined by triangulation. The method is illustrated in Figure 16–7 by a very simple case. *P* represents an inferior planet, *E* the

Fig. 16–7 *Relative distances of planets from the sun by trigonometry.*

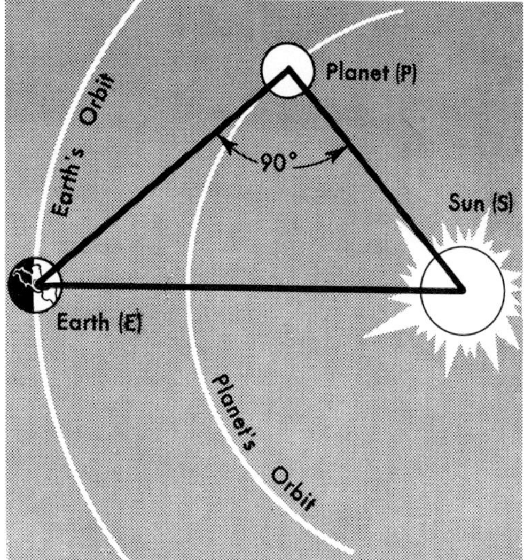

earth and S the sun. An observer on the earth measures the angle SEP when the planet P is at its greatest angular distance from the sun. If we assume the orbits of the planets are circles, the angle EPS is 90° when the angle SEP reaches its maximum value. Then,

$$\text{sine } SEP = \frac{SP \text{ (distance of } P \text{ from sun)}}{SE \text{ (distance of earth from sun)}},$$

or

$$SP \text{ (distance of } P \text{ from sun)} = SE \text{ (distance of earth from sun)} \times \text{sine } SEP.$$

For the planet Venus $SEP = 48°$. And sine $48° = 0.74$. The distance of Venus from the sun is approximately 0.74 of the distance of the earth from the sun. However, the orbits of the planets are ellipses; their distances from the sun and relative positions change as they revolve. To obtain an accurate ratio of their *mean* distances requires much more observational data; orbits of the planets have to be carefully mapped out and their periods of revolution determined. As with all scale maps or blueprints, it is necessary to know accurately at least one distance before the others can be computed. Distances are now determined and even defined by the use of a quantity known as *parallax*.

GEOCENTRIC PARALLAX

Parallax is the difference in the apparent position or direction of an object as viewed from two different points. For example, a finger held vertically at arm's length before the eyes appears to shift position relative to the wall or other objects in the background when observed first with one eye closed and then the other closed (Figure 16–8). A similar shift of a nearer star against a background of more distant stars, when observed from opposite sides of the earth's orbit, was described in Chapter 3 and offered as evidence for the earth's orbital motion. In the one case the base line is the distance between the eyes; in the other the base line is the diameter of the earth's orbit. The difference in the direction, represented by the angle at the object sighted, is called the *parallax*.

For a given base line, the parallax (angle) defines the distance of a body. The standard base line used for the measurement of distances within the solar system is the radius of the earth. For example the moon's *mean equatorial horizontal parallax* is 57′ 2.7″. It is so named because it defines the *mean* distance of the moon from the earth; the base line is the *equatorial* radius, and the parallax p is the difference in direction of the moon if observed on the *horizon* at point a and then from point b (Figure 16–9). The parallax of the moon may also be defined as one-half of the angular diameter of the earth as viewed from the moon. Since it is based upon the *earth's* radius it is a *geocentric* parallax.

To measure the geocentric parallax of a body, observations may be made simultaneously from two or more points on the earth or successively from the same observatory at intervals of six hours.

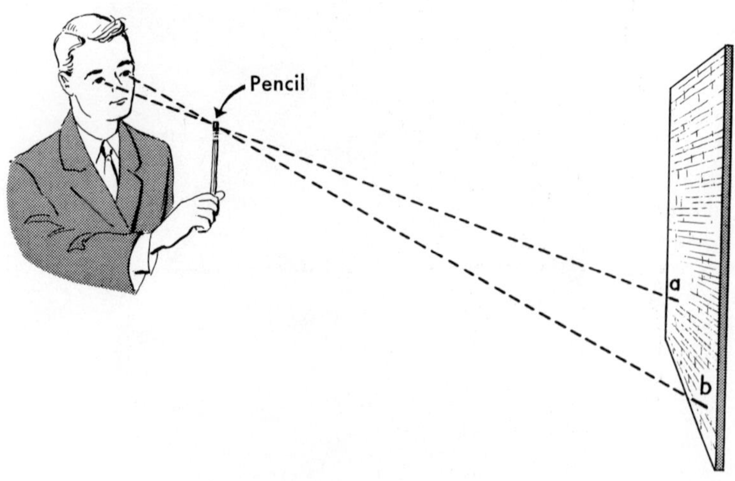

Fig. 16–8 *Illustration of parallax. a = position when observed with left eye. b = position when observed with the right eye.*

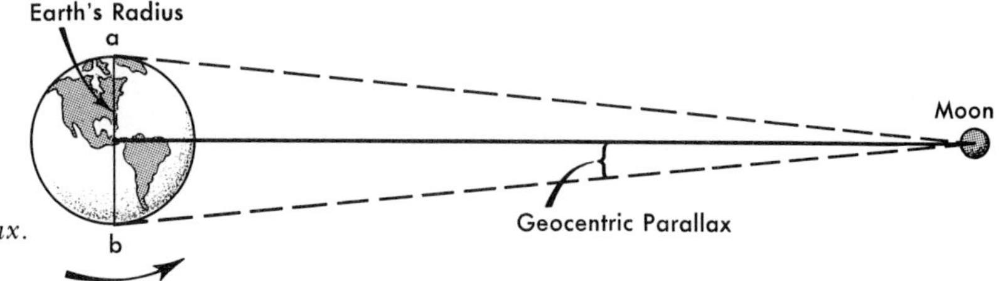

Fig. 16–9 *Geocentric parallax.*

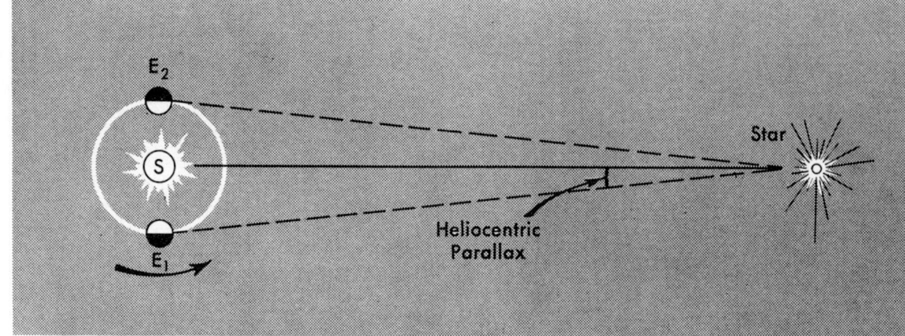

Fig. 16–10 *Heliocentric parallax.*

Because the distances of the planets are often expressed in terms of the *mean* distance of the earth from the sun it is of utmost importance to determine this quantity with a high degree of accuracy. It is the average of the greatest and least distance of the sun from the earth, which is equal to one-half of the major axis of the earth's orbit (semi-major axis). It is an important astronomical unit of distance – in fact, it is called *the astronomical unit* – and is the base line for the determination of stellar parallaxes.

DISTANCE TO THE SUN

The direct measurement of the solar parallax is difficult because of the great distance and the consequent smaller angle (less than 9″) which must be accurately measured. Also the large disc of the sun, like that of the moon, does not offer to the observer a point or landmark precisely at its center. A better method is to measure the parallax of a nearer planet or asteroid whose distance *relative* to that of the sun has been accurately determined. The parallax of Mars, the nearest planet to the earth, gave fairly good results but its disc, although smaller than that of the sun, offered similar difficulties. The planetoid Eros, approximately fifteen miles in diameter, has a small point image almost like a star. At times it comes nearer to the earth than any other major body except the moon. At one close approach its parallax was found to be 59.07″ and from this its distance from the earth was found to be 13,840,000 miles. On the scale map of the solar system it was found that the distance of Eros at this point in its orbit is 0.149 of the mean distance of the earth from the sun. It has already been noted that the *greater* the distance of a body from the base line the smaller is the angle of parallax. Since the parallaxes are very small angles, it may be assumed with fairly high accuracy, that they vary inversely as the distances from the base line. In Figure 16–11, E represents the earth with its equatorial radius r which is the base line (3963.34 miles), p the parallax of Eros, and s the parallax of the sun. The relative distance of Eros is 0.149; that of the earth 1.00, and

$$\frac{s}{p} = \frac{0.149}{1.000}$$

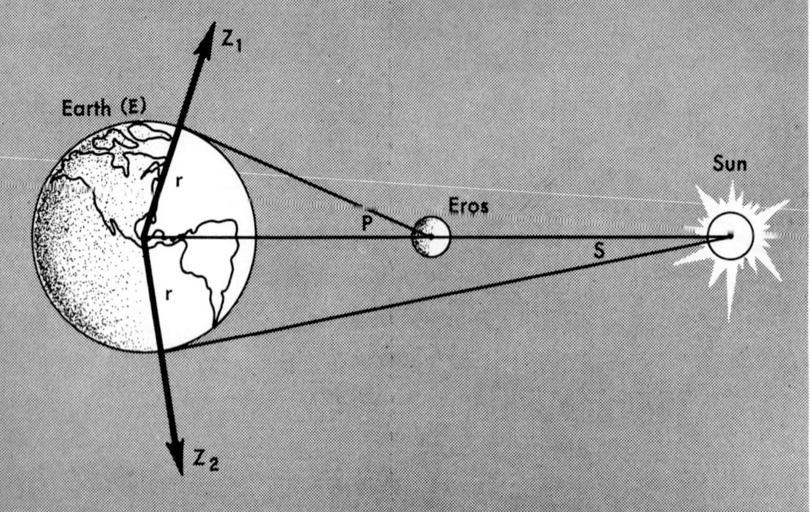

Fig. 16–11 *Indirect determination of the parallax of the sun. The drawing is not to scale. Only the parallax of Eros can be measured directly with relative ease.*

and since the parallax of Eros = 59.07″,

$$\frac{s}{59.07''} = \frac{0.149}{1.000},$$

s (parallax of sun) $= 0.149 \times 59.07'' = 8.80''$.

The final value was not determined by calculations as simple as those in the above illustration. Nor were the data obtained by a single or even a few observations; the measurement of the parallax of Eros was begun in 1901, shortly after the planetoid was discovered.

The mean value of the sun's equatorial horizontal parallax obtained by this method is 8.803″. From this and the radius of the earth given above, the mean distance of the earth from the sun – the astronomical unit – was found to be 92,870,000 miles.

SIZE AND MASS OF THE SUN

The mean diameter of the sun may be calculated from its average angular diameter (31′59.30″ or 1919.30″) and its mean distance from the earth:

$$\frac{1919.30''}{206{,}265''} \times 92{,}870{,}000 \text{ miles} = 864{,}100 \text{ miles}$$

This is about 109 times the mean diameter of the earth; the volume of the sun is therefore 109^3 or about 1,300,000 times that of the earth.

The mass of the sun is determined by its gravitational effect on the earth. If the orbital motion of the earth should stop, it would fall toward the sun with an acceleration of 0.234 inches per second per second. From this figure, the mass of the sun can be calculated by the law of universal gravitation; it is 333,400 times that of the earth or 2×10^{27} tons.

DISTANCE OF THE PLANETS

The mean distances of the various planets from the sun, that is, the lengths of their semi-major axes, were determined by methods similar to those outlined above. But to describe precisely the orbit of a planet, planetoid, or satellite, we must know a number of other quantities as well: some of these are the period of revolution, the eccentricity of the orbit, and the inclination of the orbit to the ecliptic; they are given in Table 15–1, page 230. It is also necessary to know the location of the planet's perihelion, the exact time it is at perihelion, and the location of the points of intersection of the orbit with the ecliptic. From these, the exact position of the planet can be calculated for any past or future time. On the other hand the above quantities, known as the *orbital elements,* can now be calculated from just four accurate observations of a planet's position, taken at intervals of several weeks.

TABLE 16–1 MEAN DISTANCES OF PLANETS FROM THE SUN IN ASTRONOMICAL UNITS

	MERCURY	VENUS	EARTH	MARS	ASTEROIDS	JUPITER	SATURN	URANUS	NEPTUNE	PLUTO
Series	0	3	6	12	24	48	96	192	. . . . .	384
	4	4	4	4	4	4	4	4		4
Sum	4	7	10	16	28	52	100	196		388
Sum/10	0.4	0.7	1.0	1.6	2.8	5.2	10.0	19.6		38.8
Distance A.U.	0.39	0.72	1.00	1.52	2.70?	5.20	9.54	19.19	30.07	39.52

An interesting approximate relationship between planetary distances was noted by J. H. Bode in 1772. This relationship, known as Bode's law may be shown by listing the series of numbers: 0, 3, 6, 12 . . . , each number after the second being twice the preceding one. We then add the number 4 to each member of the series. Each sum divided by 10 gives the mean distance of a planet from the sun in astronomical units, as shown in Table 16–1. The ninth term of the Sum/10 series is closer to the mean distance of Pluto rather than that of Neptune, while the fifth term gives the average distance of the asteroids. The agreement between the "Bode numbers" and the actual distances is quite close for the planets known in Bode's day. It is not known whether or not this mathematical regularity of the distances is due merely to chance.

STELLAR DISTANCES

As we extend our measurements beyond the solar system to the stars, we find that the geocentric base line, the earth's equatorial radius, is far too small. The nearest star is approximately 270,000 astronomical units from the earth; its geocentric parallax is too small (0.000033″) to be measured. Hence we must adopt a much longer base line from whose ends we can make observations. The orbit of the earth provides a distance more than 23,000 times the earth's radius. Six months from now we will be approximately 186 million miles from where we are at present. Observations can be made at intervals of six months; the earth carries us along back and forth from one extreme of our base line to the other.

HELIOCENTRIC PARALLAX

Since the length of the base line used in measuring the parallax is a distance across the earth's elliptical orbit, it varies somewhat depending on the position of the earth at the start of the six-month interval of observation. That is, the first observation might be made when the earth is at or near aphelion and at the end of six months it would be at or near the other end of the longer axis; or it might be made so that the earth traverses from one end of the minor axis to the other, or somewhere in between. By common agreement – the standard base line for calculating the *heliocentric parallax* from observational data is the mean distance of the earth from the sun – the semi-major axis of the earth's orbit (92,870,000 miles or one astronomical unit). The heliocentric parallax is therefore the difference in the direction of a star as observed from the sun and the earth.

But even with the long base line the parallax of the nearest star, Alpha Centauri, is only 0.762 seconds. The distance of this star is 4.3 light-years, which is approximately 25,000 billion miles (2.5×10^{13} miles). The smallest parallax that can be measured with accuracy is about 0.01 second. Of the billions of stars only five or six thousand are near enough for direct measurement of their parallaxes, and of these about 600 are less than 65 light-years away.

The heliocentric parallax is used to define a unit of stellar distance, the *parsec;* it is the distance corresponding to a *paral*lax of one *sec*ond. At a distance of one parsec the semi-major axis of the earth's orbit subtends an angle of one second (Figure 16–10). The distance in parsecs is the reciprocal of the parallax in seconds:

$$\text{Distance (parsecs)} = \frac{1}{\text{parallax (seconds)}}$$

For Alpha Centauri:

$$\text{Distance} = \frac{1}{0.762} = 1.3 \text{ parsecs}$$

Since one second of angle corresponds to a linear diameter which is 1/206,265 of the distance, the parsec = 206,265 astronomical units. The astronomical units may now be summed up.

1 astronomical unit = 92,870,000 miles
1 light-year = 5.88×10^{12} miles
= 63,300 astronomical units
1 parsec = 1.915×10^{13} miles
= 206,265 astronomical units
= 3.258 light-years

MEASUREMENT OF STELLAR PARALLAX

As the earth moves around the sun, *S,* (Figure 16–12) going from position E_1 to E_2 in about six months, a parallax star (nearer star) *P* appears to describe an orbit against the background of distant stars. The angle of displacement *a* is measured and from it the parallax is calculated. In this and other types of astronomical measurements, photography rather than direct visual observation is used. Photographs, usually about twenty, are taken at appropriate time-intervals; the slight apparent shift of the nearer star is measured on the photographs. The background stars are at such great distances that their images remain in the same positions relative to each other on a series of photographs; their parallactic shift is negligible. However, some other corrections are necessary. For example, the parallax star may have moved relative to the sun during the interval between photographs. This motion could be detected by comparing two photographs taken twelve months apart. The earth would be in exactly the same position in its orbit both times and any shift in the relative position of the parallactic star must be because of its own motion. The shift shown for a six-month interval could thus be corrected to give the true parallactic displacement.

MORE DISTANT STARS

The measurement of the distances of stars and star groups too far away to show any appreciable heliocentric parallax has been achieved by several ingenious methods. We shall describe two of them. The first is merely an extension of triangulation, *but with a longer base line.* The second is the determination of distance from the brightness and some of the properties of the stars' radiation.

The Longer Base Line. We have already exploited fully the greatest distance through which an observer moves with re-

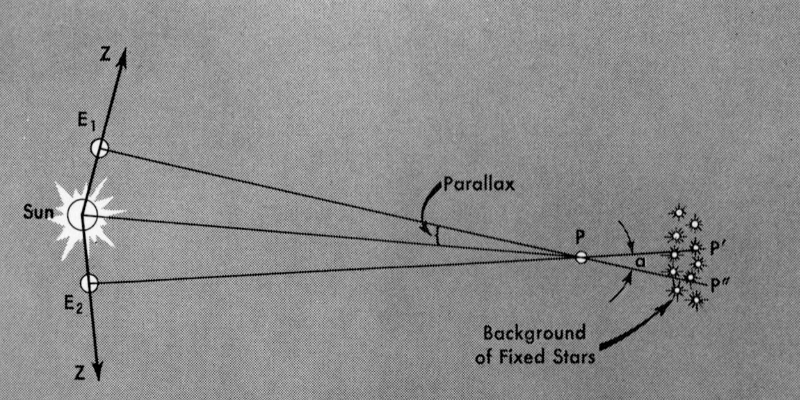

Fig. 16–12 *Determination of parallaxes photographically.*

TABLE 16–2 STAR MAGNITUDES AND RELATIVE BRIGHTNESS

Magnitudes	+5	+4	+3	+2	+1	0	−1	−2	−3	−4	−5	−10	−20
Relative brightness	1	2.51	6.31	15.85	39.81	100	251	631	1585	3981	10,000	10^6	10^{10}

spect to the sun — the diameter of the earth's orbit. There is another motion, however, which can provide a base line of ever-increasing length. The sun, carrying the solar system along with it, moves in the general direction of the constellation Hercules at a velocity of 12.2 miles per second. This motion which is relative to the nearby stars (also in motion) amounts to about four astronomical units per year — forty in ten years. As the solar system moves along, the stars appear to back up, those nearer undergoing a greater shift. This parallactic shift of groups of stars and the base line traversed during the shift, can be measured. Only the mean distance of the group, however, not of individual stars, can be calculated.

Star Brightness. When Hipparchus prepared his catalogue of stars (120 B.C.), he classified them according to apparent brightness, the most striking way wherein stars seem to differ from one another. The apparent brightness of a star is the amount of light that comes from it to the observer on the earth. It is measured by a photometric device, usually a photoelectric cell. The apparent brightness alone does not tell us a great deal about the star unless we know in addition one of the two quantities upon which it depends: (1) real or intrinsic brightness, and (2) distance of the star from the observer. The brightness of a star varies inversely as the square of the distance from the observer; at twice the distance it would appear only one-fourth as bright, and at one-third of the distance it would appear nine times as bright. Hence, if we know the distance at which the apparent brightness is observed we can calculate the brightness at some arbitrarily defined distance — that is, the intrinsic brightness. On the other hand, if we know the intrinsic brightness, *we can calculate the distance* at which the apparent brightness was observed. Our particular problem, therefore, is to find some way to determine the intrinsic brightnesses of stars. But first we must show how brightness is expressed on a quantitative scale of star magnitudes.

STAR MAGNITUDES

This seemingly awkward scale starts with magnitude *one* as the average brightness of a number of the brightest stars. For stars of decreasing brightness the magnitude increases: 2, 3, 4, 5, . . . to 22.5, which is about the faintest star which has been photographed by the 200-inch Hale telescope. In the other direction, the magnitudes decrease: 0, −1, −2, −3, −4, . . . to −26.72 which is the apparent magnitude of the brightest object, the sun. The scale is not linear; the ratio of brightness indicated by a difference of 1 magnitude is 2.512. A star with magnitude 4 is 2.512 times as bright as one with magnitude 5. A difference of 5 magnitudes, as between stars of magnitudes −1 and +4 means that the former is $(2.512)^5$ or 100 times as bright as the latter. Or if we wished to use exponents with 10 as the basic number (logarithms),

$$(2.512)^5 = 10^2 \quad \text{and} \quad 2.512 = 10^{0.4}.$$

A portion of the scale is shown in Table 16–2. The magnitudes given range from +5 (fairly faint to the unaided eye) to −20, and for convenience, a relative brightness of 1 is assigned to the +5 magnitude. The value given above for the sun (−26.72) is the apparent magnitude; that for the full moon is −12.5; and for the brightest star, Sirius, it is −1.52. The difference between the apparent magnitudes of the sun and

Sirius is approximately 25. Hence the apparent brightness of the sun is 10^{10} or 10 billion times that of Sirius. Yet if the sun were as far away as Sirius, its brightness would be only 1/26 of that of the star. Obviously if we are to compare the stars with each other in terms of real brightness, we must first determine their magnitudes for a standard distance which by common agreement is 10 parsecs or 32.58 light-years. The magnitudes at this standard distance are called *absolute magnitudes.* If we know the distance of the star and the apparent magnitude, the absolute magnitude may be calculated by the equation:

$$M = m + 5 - 5 \log d \qquad (\textit{Equation 16–1})$$

where M is the absolute magnitude, m the apparent magnitude, and d the distance expressed in parsecs. For example, one of the brighter stars, Procyon A, has an apparent magnitude of +0.53 and a measured parallax of 0.291″. Its distance is therefore 1/0.291 or 3.44 parsecs, and substituted in Equation 16–1 gives a magnitude

$$\begin{aligned} M &= +0.53 + 5 - 5(0.537) \\ &= +2.85, \text{ absolute magnitude.} \end{aligned}$$

This equation is also used to calculate *distance* from the apparent magnitude (observed) and the absolute magnitude. We now return to our main problem, the key to the measurement of vast stellar distances: how can absolute magnitudes be determined?

DETERMINATION OF ABSOLUTE MAGNITUDES

The absolute magnitudes of a great many stars can be deduced from their spectra and those of certain classes of variable stars from their behavior.

Spectra. When a beam of light from the sun or another star passes through a glass prism it is spread out into a band of colors which is called a *spectrum.* The spectrum of a star also contains many dark lines; from the intensities of the various colors and lines, the temperature and chemical composition of the star's atmosphere and the motions of the star away from the earth may be derived. A more detailed treatment of spectra is given in Chapter 37; for the present, we need only to know that a quantitative relationship exists between certain features of the spectra and the absolute magnitudes of the stars. These relationships were derived by studies of the spectra of stars whose distances were determined by other methods and whose absolute magnitudes were therefore known. They can be used to determine with fair accuracy the distances of hundreds of thousands of more distant stars.

Variable Stars. While most stars, including the sun, shine steadily with an unchanging brightness, there are thousands whose light changes with time. Some pulsate irregularly; others change from a minimum brightness to maximum and back to minimum in definite and regular *periods* of time. It is the latter class, the regularly pulsating stars, that make possible the measurement of distances beyond the parallax range, thus pointing to the immensity of cosmic distances.

Of the two types of variables which we consider, the *RR Lyrae stars,* have the shortest periods, ranging from 88 minutes to 29 hours. These stars, named after the first member of the type to be studied were formerly called "cluster-type variables" because they were discovered in some of the star clusters (globular clusters). They travel more rapidly than any other class of stars, show unusual spectra, and are widely scattered over the sky. These stars serve as distance indicators for *they all have the same absolute magnitude,* zero (0.0), or an intrinsic brightness nearly one hundred times that of the sun. Let us suppose an observer finds an RR Lyrae star in a stellar group. He recognizes it by its short period, high velocity, and spectrum. He measures its apparent magnitude and, knowing its absolute magnitude, he can calculate the distance of the group. RR Lyrae stars have thus been most helpful in surveying our own galaxy, the Milky Way, and in determining the distances of a few of the not-too-distant extragalactic systems. They cannot, however, be used as indicators for distances much beyond 200,000 parsecs.

Then there is the second and more important class of variable stars, up to 300 times as bright as the RR Lyrae stars, and suitable as distance indicators up to about 4 million parsecs. These are the *Cepheids,* named for Delta Cephei, one of the brightest of the class. The periods of the Cepheid variables range from 1.5 to 40 days. Unlike the RR Lyrae stars, the brightnesses of the Cepheids are definitely related to their periods – the longer the period the greater the brightness. This relationship, known as the period-luminosity law, was first shown by Miss H. S. Leavitt (1868–1921) of Harvard University. The Cepheids investigated were in the Magellanic clouds, two stellar systems outside our galaxy which to the unaided eye appear as luminous clouds about 20° from the south pole. The periods plotted against the apparent magnitudes gave a fairly smooth curve. But before the relationship could be used to determine absolute magnitudes and hence distance, it was necessary to know accurately the absolute magnitude corresponding to Cepheids of a given period. The Cepheids in our galaxy are too far away for direct parallax determinations. The problem was solved by Harlow Shapley (United States, 1885–   ) while at Mount Wilson Observatory (later Director of the Harvard Observatory). Shapley determined the absolute magnitudes for eleven Cepheids in our galaxy by a study of their motions, thus establishing the *period-absolute magnitude relationship* on the curve. Thereafter one need but measure the pulse period of a Cepheid, wherever found, in order to obtain its absolute magnitude; the absolute magnitude combined with the apparent magnitude gives the distance. Cepheids were discovered in Andromeda and the distance was estimated to be 750,000 light-years.

An interesting, significant, and large-scale revision of all distances based on the Cepheids was made in 1952. The incident is more indicative of progress than of error. The theory underlying the method outlined above is perfectly correct; the inaccuracy lay in the calibration of the period-absolute magnitude curve and therefore the resulting scale of cosmic distance. It was found that there are really two types of Cepheids, and studies made with the 200-inch Mount Palomar telescope showed that one type was brighter than the other by 1.5 magnitudes. Yet the brighter type which was used to determine the distance to Andromeda and other stars and groups had been assigned the same absolute magnitude as the less bright Cepheids. Now since our yardstick stars have an intrinsic brightness *four* times as great (1.5 magnitude) as they were formerly thought to have they must be *twice* as far away. It was therefore necessary to *double all astronomical distances* beyond the solar system. The distance to Andromeda is now estimated to be 1,500,000 light years. There is one exception; the dimensions of our own galaxy were measured by the RR Lyrae stars and therefore are not included in the change. The distances of the brighter type of Cepheids within our galaxy, however, were doubled.

The more distant galaxies cannot be resolved into individual stars. We can assume, however, that they have about the same absolute magnitudes as the nearer galaxies whose values have been determined by the above methods.

Thus our conception of the universe has grown from the small world of the ancients to one of tremendous dimensions. A cluster more than one billion light-years away was recently photographed by the 200-inch telescope. With special devices it is expected to reach objects two billion light-years from the earth.

SUMMARY

1. Our knowledge of astronomical bodies is derived from the radiation which they emit or reflect.
2. Distances of bodies within the solar system and of the nearer stars are determined by

the method of the terrestrial surveyor, i.e., *triangulation*. This method requires: (*a*) a base line of suitable length whose ends are accessible to the observer, and (*b*) instruments for the accurate measurement of small angles.

3. The distance to the moon, determined by triangulation, permits the calculation of its linear diameter from the angular diameter. The moon's mass is determined by its gravitational effect on the earth's motion.
4. The difference in the direction of a body as observed from the two extremes of a base line is its *parallax*. The parallax is expressed in degrees, minutes, and seconds of angle and for a given base line it defines the distance of a body.
5. The geocentric parallax has for its base line the earth's equatorial radius. It is used to determine the distance to the nearer planets, the moon, and the planetoids. The accurate measurement of one distance in the solar system, earth to Eros, for example, enables us to determine the parallax of the sun (8.80″) and the mean distance from the earth to the sun.
6. The base line of the heliocentric parallax, used to determine distances of stars up to 100 parsecs, is the mean distance of earth to sun – one astronomical unit.
7. The diameter of the sun is computed from its angular diameter and the mass of the sun from its gravitational pull on the earth.
8. Commonly used astronomical units are:
   a. The semi-major axis of the earth's orbit, known as the *astronomical unit*. It is 92,870,000 miles.
   b. The *light-year* = 5.88×10^{12} miles = 63,300 astronomical units.
   c. The *parsec* = 206,265 astronomical units = 3.258 light-years.
9. The distance of a star in parsecs is the reciprocal of the parallax in seconds.
10. The brightness of a star is expressed on a scale of star magnitudes; an increase of one magnitude corresponds to a division of the brightness by 2.512 ($10^{0.4}$). An increase in brightness is indicated by a decrease in magnitude.
11. The apparent magnitude expresses the brightness of a star as observed from the earth; the absolute magnitude expresses the brightness as it would be observed at a distance of ten parsecs; it may be computed from the apparent magnitude and the distance of the star.
12. Distances greater than 100 parsecs may be determined:
    a. For star groups, by parallax derived from the longer base line of the sun's linear motion.
    b. By the RR Lyrae stars (variable) as distance indicators. They all have the same absolute magnitude and may be recognized by short periods, high speed, and distinctive spectra.
    c. By the Cepheid variable stars, whose absolute magnitudes vary with periods.

STUDY EXERCISES

1. Explain why the accuracy of the measurement of the distance to the moon, the sun, or any other astronomical body must depend on the precision possible in the determination of the radius of the earth. (Refer to Figure 16–2.) With what precision is the radius of the earth known?
2. Mars approaches the earth at times as close as 35,000,000 miles. If its angular diameter at the time is twenty-five seconds, what is its diameter in miles?
3. If x_1 and x_2 represent the parallaxes of two stars at distances d_1 and d_2, respectively, which of the following expressions correctly indicates the relation that exists between the parallax and the distance?

   (*a*) $\frac{d_1}{d_2} = \frac{x_1}{x_2}$

   (*b*) $\frac{d_1}{d_2} = \frac{x_2}{x_1}$

   (*c*) $d_1x_1 = d_2x_2$

   (*d*) $d_2 = \frac{d_1x_1}{x_2}$

   (*e*) $d_2 = \frac{d_1x_2}{x_1}$
4. The parallax of the star Proxima Centauri is 0.78 second, and its distance from the earth is 4.2 light-years. How far from the earth is the

star Cordoba which has a parallax of 0.26 second?

5. The parallax of Sirius is 0.37 second. What is its distance in miles and light-years? In making this calculation use the parallax and distance data for Proxima Centauri given in the preceding problem. Sirius is the brightest star in the southeastern sky.
6. Are the parallaxes of the nearer stars heliocentric or geocentric? Explain.
7. If the heliocentric parallax of a star is so small that it cannot be reliably measured, will there be any observable annual apparent motion (parallactic displacement) of that star with respect to stars behind it? Explain.
8. *a.* About 30° beyond the end of the handle of the Great Dipper, Ursa Major, is a very conspicuous star, Arcturus. Its parallax is 0.088 second. Its star magnitude is 0. What is its distance in (1) parsecs, (2) light-years, and (3) astronomical units?

   b. How many times brighter is Arcturus than Polaris, whose star magnitude is 2?

FOR FURTHER READING

1. WHIPPLE, F. L., *Earth, Moon, and Planets.* Philadelphia: The Blakiston Company, 1941.
   The author, an outstanding astronomer, is very successful in bringing the subject in a meaningful manner to the general reader. This little volume is concerned with the solar system. The significance of star parallax and of Eros is discussed on pages 45–50.

17

SUN AND STARS

Observe how system into system runs,
What other planets circle other suns.
— ALEXANDER POPE

TO THE EARTH-BOUND OBSERVER, the sun, nearest of all the stars, is the most magnificent and dazzling of the heavenly bodies. It is a massive and, by earth standards, gigantic globe of incandescent gases, exerting a tremendous gravitational force. The importance of the sun as the dominant body of the solar system, around which the planets, their satellites, and lesser bodies move, was noted in the preceding chapters. Moving rapidly through space, the sun carries along its brood, each member performing its own precise movements relative to the controlling body. The sun is important to the astronomer because it is so near. It is the only star close enough to permit a detailed examination of its surface; much of our knowledge of stars in general has therefore been obtained from studies of the sun's disc.

The sun and its radiation account for practically all of the energy of the solar system. The sun gives us light and heat, and is the ultimate source of power for almost every kind of activity on the surfaces of the planets and the other bodies of the system. Other sources of earth energy are radiation from the stars, radioactive changes within the earth, and the forces of compression in the interior of the earth, but they are insignificant by comparison. Finally, the sun's radiation is absolutely essential to all life on this planet and whatever life may exist on any of the other planets.

THE SUN AS A STAR

As a star the sun is not particularly distinctive; it is of average size and of somewhat greater than average brightness. It is only one of possibly one hundred billion stars in our own galaxy, and it is estimated that there are about ten billion observable galaxies. Our galaxy, however, is one of the largest, the average galaxy having a star population of approximately one billion. The sun has an absolute magnitude of +4.86 while Alpha Centauri, a member of our nearest double star, has a magnitude of +4.7. The sun and Alpha Centauri are similar in other respects and when we look at the latter we see what the sun would look like at the same distance. We, however, can only see the sun from "close-up."

THE SURFACE OF THE SUN

If one looks at the sun through dark glasses or some other light filter which adequately protects the eyes,[1] it appears to be a bright uniform disc with a sharply defined edge or limb (Figure 17–1). The disc seems brightest at the center and somewhat darker toward the edge. If a telescope is used to give us a closer view, it is found that the surface is not uniform but covered with bright patches and granulations which continually change their shapes, appear and disappear. Visible at times are more prominent groups of darker patches or *sunspots*. Some of these are quite large; Galileo saw them with his small telescope and occasionally they are large enough to be seen with the naked eye. Associated with the sunspots are bright areas or flares. Indeed, the sun's visible surface is a turbulent mass of gases with violent storms and vast disturbances.

[1] Serious damage, even permanent blindness, may result if one looks directly at the sun with the eyes unprotected. If a telescope is used, the sun's image should be photographed or projected on a screen.

The bright surface of the sun which is described above is called the *photosphere* or light sphere. It is opaque and is the surface from which nearly all of the sun's radiation is emitted. The photosphere is a

Fig. 17–1 *Rotation of the sun shown by sunspots.* (*Yerkes Observatory photograph*)

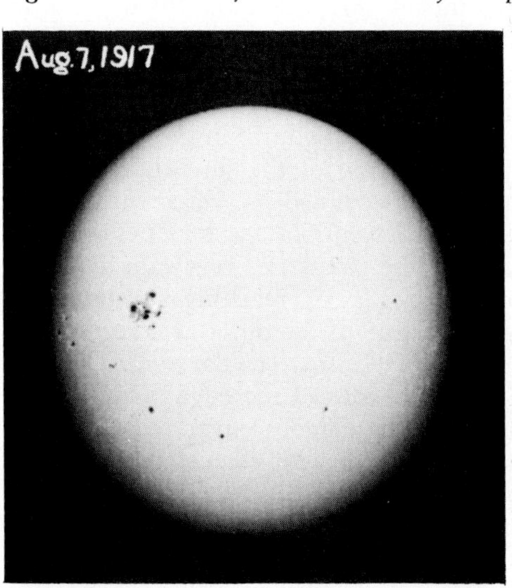

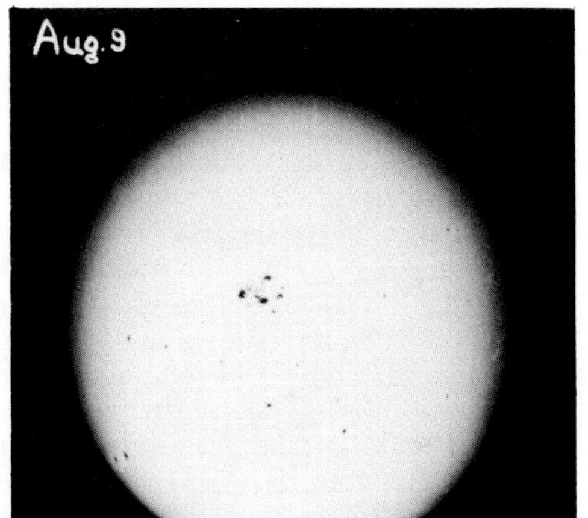

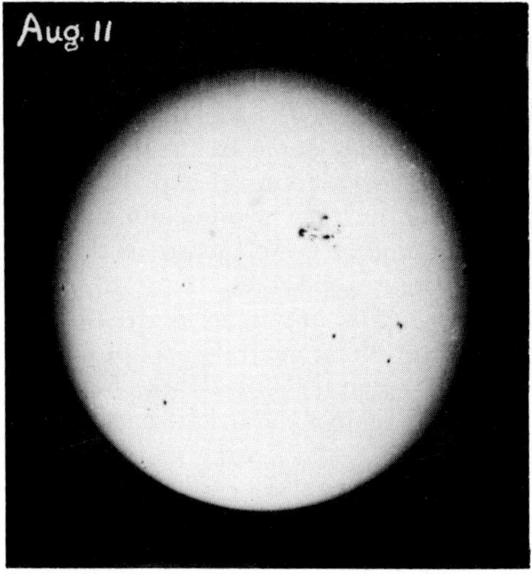

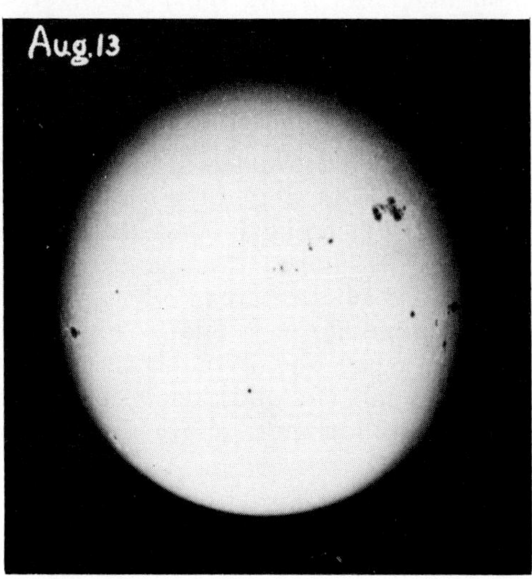

Fig. 17–2 *Eclipse of sun showing chromosphere and corona.* (*Mt. Wilson and Palomar Observatories*)

gaseous layer about 200 miles thick. In its inner region the pressure is about one-fifth of that of the earth's atmosphere and the temperature, 6000° C., is above the boiling points of all known substances.

Above the photosphere is a bulging envelope of fairly transparent gases, the solar atmosphere. The lower few hundred miles of the atmosphere next to the photosphere is called the *reversing layer*. It contains the vapors of many of the chemical elements and its temperature is slightly lower than that of the photosphere. The dark lines in the spectrum of the sun which show its chemical composition are formed in this layer. The next portion of the sun's atmosphere up to a height of more than five thousand miles above the reversing layer consists mostly of the lighter gases, hydrogen and helium. It has a pinkish tint and is for that reason called the *chromosphere* (color sphere). During a total eclipse of the sun when the photosphere is hidden by the moon, the bright ring of the chromosphere is visible. Extending beyond the chromosphere is the outer and larger envelope of the sun called the *corona* which also becomes visible during a total eclipse. It appears as a vast and irregular pearly halo extending in some directions to heights of about a million miles above the chromosphere (Figure 17–2). Formerly its feeble light, hidden by the glare of scattered sunlight, could be seen and studied only during the few minutes of total eclipse of the sun. Now daily studies and a continuous record on film can be made by the use of an instrument, the *coronagraph,* which, in effect, produces artificial eclipses. The color of the coronal light and its spectrum are most unusual. Unlike the light from other parts of the sun, certain bright lines in the spectrum of the corona have never been duplicated in any laboratory, and it was once suggested that they came from a new and unknown substance called "coronium." However, it has been shown that the spectrum comes from the known elements, iron, nickel, and calcium, which are present in the very thin gas of the corona. They are in an extraordinary state which could be brought about only at temperatures of approximately one million degrees!

Thus the disc of the sun which appears to be sharply defined is covered with a great thickness of tenuous gases. The temperature of these gases rises very rapidly above the reversing layer, reaching an almost incredible value in the outermost region, the corona. The apparent darkening of the photosphere toward the edge of the disc is caused by the gaseous envelope. The light coming to us from the edge of the disc must travel through a greater depth of the sun's atmosphere than that coming from the center of the disc.

PROMINENCES

Direct photographs of the sun show the disc in "all colors," that is, in the almost white sunlight which is a blend of the colors in a rainbow. Some of the surface details can be seen more clearly in photographs taken in light of one color which is emitted by one of the elements in the sun. A telescope can be fitted with a device which transmits only the desired light, blocking out the remainder. Photographs taken in this manner show "dark" filaments or eruptions against the bright background of the chromosphere. When the bright face of the sun is artificially eclipsed by use of the coronagraph, these appear over the sun's edge as great flamelike sheets or clouds of glowing gases called *prominences* (Figure 17–3). They assume various shapes but most of them are relatively thin; the average one has a height of 30,000 miles, a length of 125,000 miles, and a thickness of 6000 miles. They move with velocities as great as 450 miles per second and the greatest height observed is approximately one million miles. Some of the prominences appear to swirl upward out of the chromosphere but actually there is more downward motion toward the sun. It has been suggested that some of the prominences result from condensations of material in the corona.

SUNSPOTS

Sunspots are of various sizes, ranging from less than 500 miles in diameter to 80,000 miles. They are not really dark but appear so because they are 1000° C. or more cooler than the surrounding photosphere. Most of them disappear after a few days, but some, especially the larger spots, may exist for 100 days or more. Sunspots occur in pairs and also in large groups or clusters; they occur within 45° of the sun's equator, seldom at the equator and never within 45° of the poles.

The number of sunspots varies periodically from a minimum to a maximum, then to a minimum and so on, the average time to complete a cycle being 11.1 years. In 1923, 1933, 1944, and 1954 there were relatively few sunspots, whereas in 1928, 1937, and 1947 there was a great deal of sunspot activity. At minimum the few sunspots of the old cycle lie near the sun's equator and new ones appear at higher latitudes. As the number increases to a maximum the drift is toward the equator until at maximum most of them appear at latitudes to 10° north and south. The cause and significance of the sunspot cycle and the latitude shifts are not known.

The sunspots are often accompanied by great solar flares and an increase in the number of prominences, although there are many prominences which cannot be associated with spot activity. Also, the shape of the corona changes with the sunspot cycle. At maximum sunspot activity the corona is nearly circular; at minimum it bulges at the equator and contracts into short streamers at the poles. There may possibly be some relationship between the change in the form of the corona and the

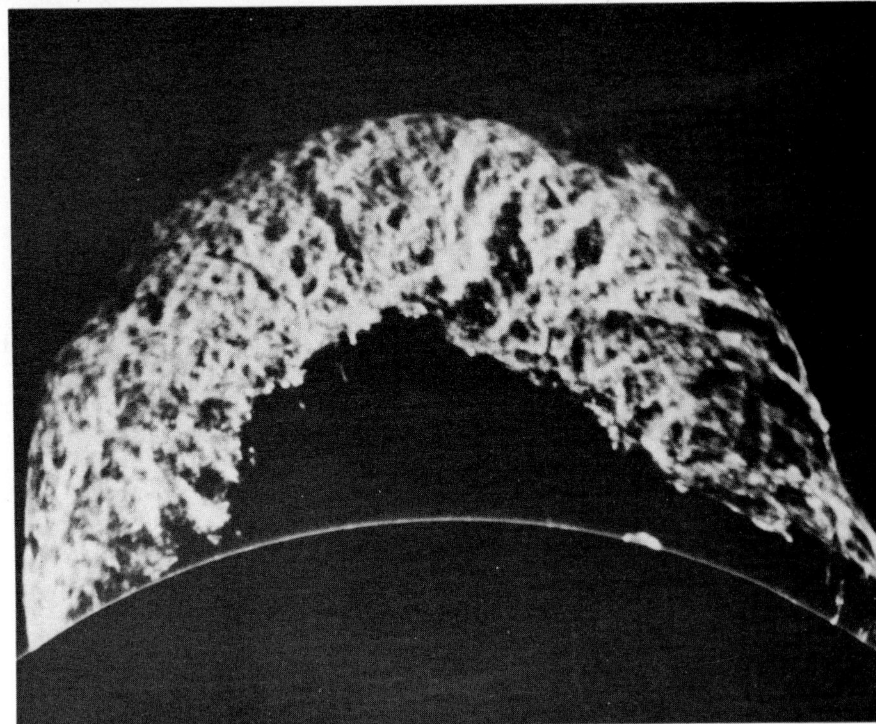

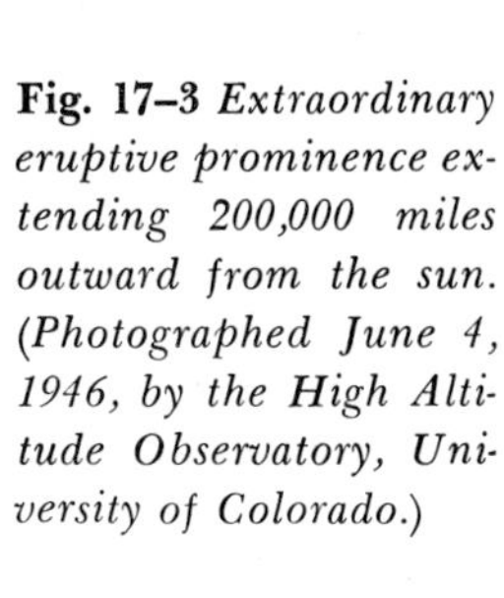

Fig. 17–3 *Extraordinary eruptive prominence extending 200,000 miles outward from the sun. (Photographed June 4, 1946, by the High Altitude Observatory, University of Colorado.)*

strong magnetic field which is at the center of the sunspot.

There is evidence that sunspots or the great flares which often occur in or near them are the cause of magnetic and electrical disturbances on the earth. Apparently high-speed, electrically charged particles are ejected from the sun and reach the earth's upper atmosphere one day later. They move inward toward the earth's magnetic poles producing auroral displays; they often interrupt telegraph and telephone operations, and interfere with radio and television reception. There is also an effect which does not lag behind the solar flare-ups. There is a fade-out of short-wave radio transmission the instant a solar flare can be observed. This implies that whatever causes the short-wave blackout travels from the sun to the earth with the same speed as visible light; that is, it must be some other form of radiation, possibly an intense blast of ultraviolet light.

When Galileo observed the apparent movement of sunspots across the disc of the sun, he correctly concluded that the sun rotates. The rotation is in the same direction as the planets move in their orbits, west to east, and is about an axis inclined at an angle of 82°49.5′ to the plane of the earth's orbit. The rotation is not that of a rigid body; parts of the sun's surface turn faster than others. The belt near the equator rotates in 24.65 days while the areas nearer the poles move more slowly. At 30° the period is 25.85 days; at 60° it is 30.93 days; and in the polar regions, 34 days.

INSIDE THE SUN

We cannot see through the photosphere, the relatively thin blanket of luminous gases from which most of the sun's radiation is emitted. Yet the astronomers and other specialists have been able to derive a great deal of information concerning the interior of the sun from their observations of the sun as a whole and from its radiation. A series of nuclear reactions was proposed to show the possible origin of the sun's energy; a similar series of reactions involving the same net changes can now be produced in the so-called hydrogen bomb (see Chapter 38).

From the photosphere inward toward the center of the sun, the density rises from about one per cent of that of the earth's atmosphere (the pressure in the photosphere is about one-fifth of an atmosphere, but it is at a temperature of 6000° C.) to about 80 times that of water or nearly four times that of the most dense chemical element, osmium. The pressure rises from about 3 pounds per square inch to possibly 2000 billion pounds per square inch. Were the sun relatively cool, the pressure due to the gravitational pull on its great mass toward the center would still be tremendous. The pressure at the center of the earth, for example, is estimated to be 50 million pounds per square inch. In the sun the pressure is far greater, even though the temperature of the sun steadily rises to about 20 million degrees centigrade near the center.

Under these extraordinary conditions, the sun constitutes a giant nuclear furnace in which four million tons of matter are converted into energy every second. These thermonuclear reactions involve the conversion of hydrogen into helium as in an exploding hydrogen bomb. But the sun does not explode. It is held together by great gravitational forces; the weight of matter pressing toward the center counterbalances the pressures exerted by the highly compressed hot gases. If the internal pressure were to drop, the sun would collapse, and in doing so it would generate more heat and a new pressure balance that might not be stable.

THE SUN'S RADIATION

In the preceding paragraphs we have used the term *energy* without defining or explaining it. Energy, the last of the important concepts of mechanics to be developed, will be fully and precisely treated in the next chapter. It is intangible — we cannot examine it as we do a piece of matter — but it is usually associated with matter. Energy originates in matter and we can detect and measure it only by its effect on matter. There are several forms of energy — they are all familiar: thermal (heat), electrical, chemical, mechanical, nuclear, and radiant energy. We can see that energy does our work, brings about change, and that our machines convert one form of energy into another. A battery, for example, converts chemical energy into electrical energy; an automobile engine converts the heat of burning gasoline into mechanical energy.

On this planet our prime source of energy, as indicated in an earlier section, is the sun. In the sun's interior, matter is heavily charged with energy which moves outward toward the cooler photosphere. At first the energy travels by radiation, then for part of the distance it is carried by the churning and turbulent matter, just as heat is carried to the radiators in a building by circulating hot water or steam. Near the photosphere radiation takes over again, and the energy passes through the photosphere but not without some absorption and re-emission.

From the photosphere, the radiation passes through the thin atmosphere of the sun into space in all directions, reaching the earth in about eight minutes. In addition to visible light, the sun sends to us radiation of much greater energy, such as ultraviolet. Most of this radiation is absorbed by the earth's atmosphere. The less energetic radiation, infrared, is absorbed in part by water vapor in the air. The total radiation of the sun is at the rate of 5×10^{23} horsepower and only about one-half a billionth of it is intercepted by the earth. However, each square mile of the earth's surface receives more than 4.5 million horsepower — enough to operate about 50,000 automobiles. The direct utilization of the sun's energy to operate solar engines and batteries will be treated in Chapter 40.

The amount of energy that the sun radiates is equal to the amount produced by the nuclear processes taking place in its interior. Should it radiate less, the surface temperature would become hotter; if it reached several million degrees the earth would quickly vaporize. The outer layers of the sun would probably be lost by a great explosion, a cosmic catastrophe which some of the stars have suffered. The sun, however, has undergone very little change in the past 4 billion years and it has sufficient fuel (hydrogen) to continue for possibly 30 billion more years. It is extraordinary that the sun gives off just the right amount of energy from a surface which is relatively cool, and that the earth is at just the proper distance to receive the amount of energy necessary for life processes.

Utilizing the energy of sunlight, plants manufacture foods from carbon dioxide, water, and a few other chemicals by the process of *photosynthesis.* Our two principal fuels, coal and oil, are both modifications of things that once grew. The movements of the atmosphere, the evaporation of water which later falls as rain or snow, the processes which bring about geological changes on the surface of the earth, the turning of the wheels of industry — all are possible because of the sun's rays. Only controlled nuclear energy, now being used and further developed, appears to be unrelated to the sun; but that would be useless on a dead world.

CHEMICAL COMPOSITION AND OTHER DATA

Of the 92 chemical elements which occur in the outer crust of the earth, 66 have been identified in the sun's atmosphere. It is also thought that the remaining 26 elements may be present in the solar atmosphere, but they have not yet been detected. It is likely that most of the elements, except hydrogen and helium, occur in about the same relative amounts in the sun as in the earth. The sun as a whole, however, consists mostly (possibly 95 per cent) of these two gases. Because of the high surface gravity of the sun and the consequent high escape velocity (see Chapter 14), it is able to retain these very light gases.

Important data pertaining to the sun are summarized below:

Mean distance from earth	92,870,000 miles
Diameter	864,100 miles
Mass	2.2×10^{27} tons
	1.99×10^{33} grams
Mean density	1.41 g/cm^3
Surface gravity	28.0 (earth = 1)
Velocity of escape	384 mi/sec
Period of rotation	24.65 to 34.00 days
Surface temperature (photosphere)	6,000° C.
Temperature of interior	2×10^7 ° C.

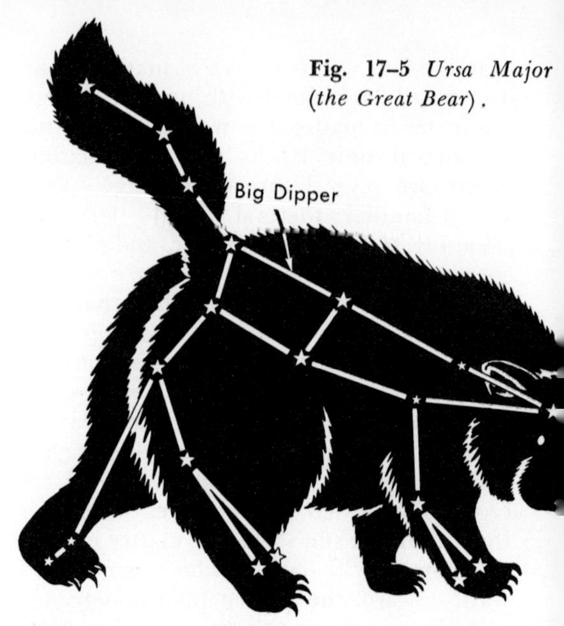

Fig. 17–5 *Ursa Major (the Great Bear).*

STARS

On a clear, moonless night the stars can be seen as twinkling points of light against the dark dome-like background of the sky, unevenly distributed in various and apparently unchanging patterns. As the earth rotates, the whole scene appears to move across the sky. To an observer at the equator the visible stars all rise and set; to one at either pole they appear to swing around the corresponding celestial pole. (Refer to Figure 3–6, page 25.) For those anywhere between the equator and the poles, for example at latitudes of about 40°, as at Philadelphia or in the southern hemisphere near Wellington, New Zealand, the stars near the pole star circle around it while those near the equator rise and set.

Fig. 17–4 *The changing dipper. (Redrawn from J. C. Duncan,* Astronomy, *published by Harper and Bros.)*

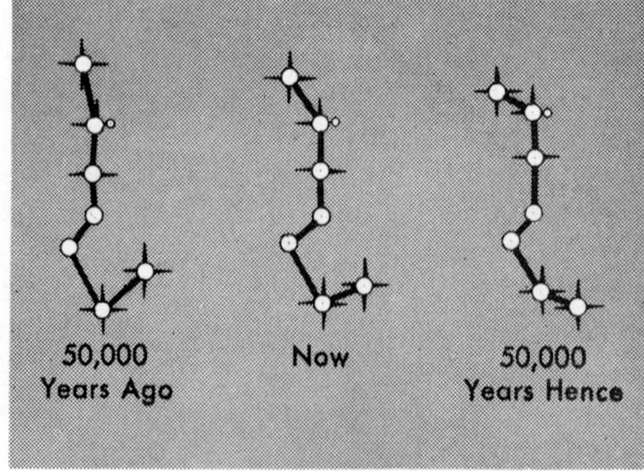

About 2000 stars are visible to the eye at any one time, and during the course of a year a total of more than 6000 may be seen. With a small telescope the number is increased by several hundred thousand and with a large telescope, such as those used in the observatories, the number of visible stars runs into hundreds of millions.

As we watch the stars night after night, they seem to be fixed in their positions relative to each other. Nevertheless the stars do move (recall the motion of the sun, Chapter 16) with velocities that range from about 10 miles per second to several hundred miles per second. They are so far away, however, that the changes in their relative positions during a lifetime are not perceptible to the unaided eye. More than two hundred years ago the eminent English astronomer, Edmund Halley, reported that several stars, among them, Sirius and Arcturus, had moved slightly from their positions as indicated in the star catalogue of Ptolemy (second century A.D.). The familiar pattern of stars known as the Big Dipper consists of seven stars, five of which are moving in the same general direction, almost the opposite of that of the other two. In 100,000 years the pattern will have quite appreciably changed (Figure 17–4).

CONSTELLATIONS

The patterns or apparent groupings of some of the visible stars are called constellations. Many of the constellations were known to the ancient astronomers who gave them mythical names based on an imagined resemblance to some object or living thing. The Big Dipper, also called Ursa Major or the Great Bear, is unusual in that it does resemble the outline of a dipper, but its resemblance to a bear would require the utmost in imagination or poetic fancy; it would also have to include some of the nearby stars (Figure 17–5). The constellations are useful as guideposts in the location of stars; for example, the North Star, Polaris, around which the stars in the northern hemisphere appear to swing, is located by the two stars (pointers) opposite the handle of the Big Dipper. Polaris is the end star on the handle of the Little Dipper (Ursa Minor). The constellations which appear to circle around the pole star (Polaris) when the observer is at about 40° north latitude are shown in Figure 17–6. For convenience the celestial sphere is divided into 88 regions each containing a constellation. The belt around the ecliptic (apparent path of the sun) is marked by twelve constellations, the signs of the Zodiac, which are useful in locating the equinoxes and

Fig. 17–6 *The constellations near the celestial north pole are easily seen in northern latitudes. (Redrawn from J. C. Duncan,* Astronomy, *Harper and Bros.)*

★ = Magnitude 0 ⯐ = Magnitude 1 to 2 o = Magnitude 3 or greater

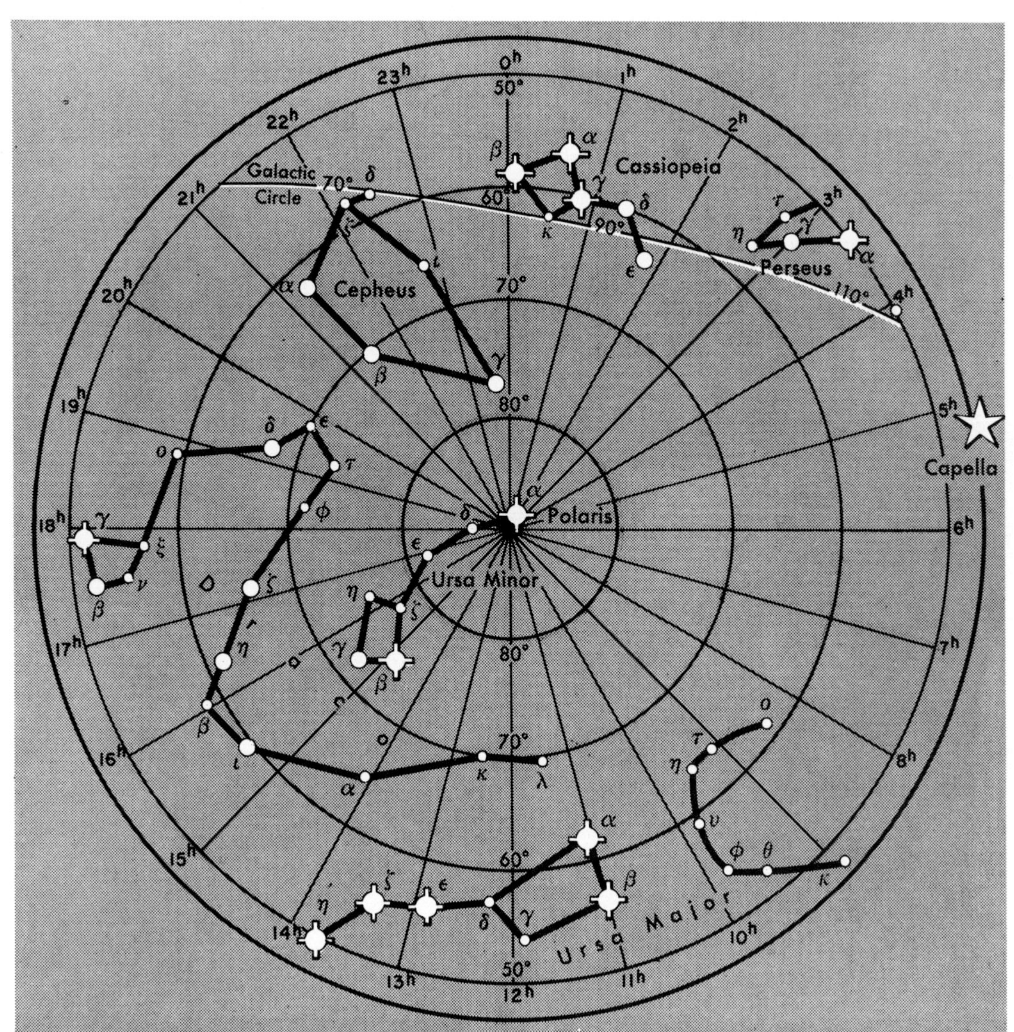

Fig. 17–7 *The twelve constellations along the celestial equator — the signs of the Zodiac.*

certain stars and are also the working tools of the astrologers (Figure 17–7).

The stars in a constellation may appear to be near each other because they are in approximately the same direction from the earth. Actually they are separated from each other by great distances.

GENERAL CHARACTERISTICS OF STARS

Stars, like the sun, are self-luminous gaseous bodies, each held together by gravitation and moving through space with different velocities. The cross movement of the stars, that is, the motion across our line of sight, may be detected and measured with modern instruments; the motion toward or away from the earth may be determined by the star's spectrum. All stars are enveloped by atmospheres which contain the familiar terrestrial elements; many show flares, prominences, and coronas like the sun's. All are thought to derive their energy from nuclear processes similar to those taking place in the sun. Yet stars differ widely in many other respects: in size, density, surface temperature, and brightness.

Fig. 17–8 *The dimension of the great star Antares. Relative dimensions of Arcturus and Aldebaran are also shown.*

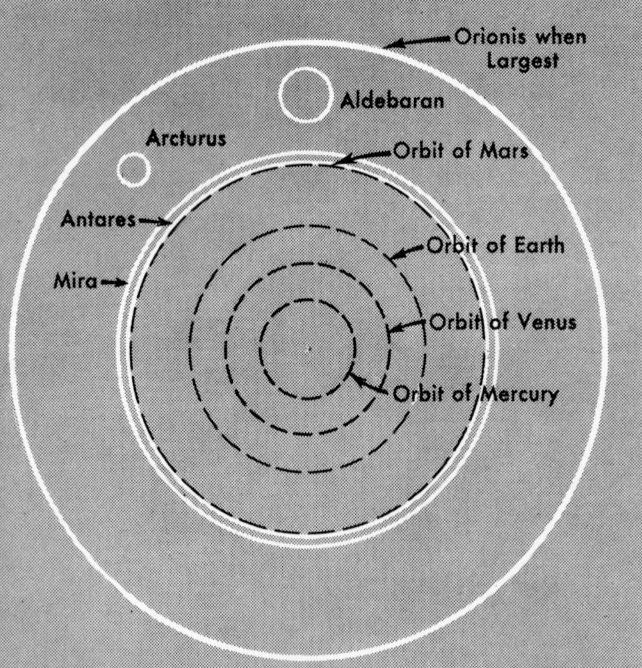

A very small star, one of the smallest known (Ross 627), has a diameter less than 1/250 of that of the sun – about the same size as the smallest planet, Mercury. The giant star Antares, in contrast, has a diameter about 428 times that of the sun; if its center were at the sun it would occupy the solar system almost to the orbit of Mars (Figure 17–8). The stars' masses, however, vary over a much smaller range, from less than one-tenth of that of the sun to about one hundred times the sun's mass. It follows that the mean densities of the stars must extend over a very wide range, from one-millionth of that of the sun (supergiant stars) to several hundred thousand times the density of the sun (dwarf stars). For example, the smaller companion of Sirius, the Dog star, known as Sirius B and sometimes called the Pup, has a mass almost as great (0.96) as that of the sun. Its diameter is only 0.034 and its volume 1/25,500 of that of the sun; hence it is 26,500 times as dense as the sun (1.41 g/ml) and more than 37,000 times the density of water. A thimbleful of this material would weigh nearly 100 pounds. Surface temperatures of the stars range from less than 2000° C. to greater than 500,000° C.

As indicated in the preceding chapter, the intrinsic brightnesses of the stars vary by a tremendous factor – possibly a thousand billion. The stars which appear the brightest to the eye are listed in Table 17–1 in descending order of their apparent magnitudes. The absolute magnitude, parallax, and distance of each star are included.

TABLE 17–1 STARS WHICH APPEAR BRIGHTEST TO THE EYE (IN DESCENDING ORDER OF APPARENT MAGNITUDE)

NAME	CONSTELLATION	APPARENT MAGNITUDE	ABSOLUTE MAGNITUDE	PARALLAX	DISTANCE IN LIGHT YEARS
Sirius	Canis Major (Great Dog)	−1.52	+1.36	0.377″	8.6
Canopus	Carina (Keel)	−0.86	−5.0	0.015?	220. (?)
α Centauri	Centaurus (Centaur)	+0.33	+4.7	0.750	4.3
Vega	Lyra (Lyre)	0.14	+0.6	0.124	26.
Capella	Auriga (Charioteer)	0.21	−0.5	0.073	45.
Arcturus	Boötes (Herdsman)	0.24	+0.2	0.098	33.
Rigel	Orion (Orion)	0.34	−5.8	0.006	550.
Procyon	Canis Minor (Little Dog)	0.53	+2.8	0.291	11.
Achernar	Eridanus	0.60	−2.6	0.023	140.
β Centauri	Centaurus	0.86	−3.0	0.017	192.
Altair	Aquila (Eagle)	0.89	+2.5	0.21	15.5
Betelgeuse	Orion (Orion)	0.92	−5.6	0.005	650.
α Crucis	Southern Cross	1.05	−2.7	0.018	180.
Aldebaran	Taurus (Bull)	1.06	−0.1	0.059	55.
Pollux	Gemini (Twins)	1.21	+1.0	0.091	36.
Spica	Virgo (Virgin)	1.21	−2.6	0.017	188.
Antares	Scorpio (Scorpion)	1.22	−4.0	0.014	228.
Fomalhaut	Southern Fish	1.29	+2.1	0.145	23.
Deneb	Cygnus (Swan)	1.33	−4.8	0.0055	590.
Regulus	Leo (Lion)	1.34	−0.7	0.039	84.

Stars can thus be grouped or arranged by any of the above characteristics. There are also two interesting types of stars: variable, two classes of which were discussed in the previous chapter, and double stars.

DOUBLE STARS

If we could move out into our galaxy and observe the motion of the sun from a distance of several parsecs, over a period of fifty or more years, we should find that it is traveling in a straight line. The sun's motion is not appreciably influenced by any other bodies; the effect of the combined masses of the planets and other members of the solar system is negligible and the nearest star is 1.3 parsecs away. Since the sun is a single, isolated star, we may infer that other stars which move in straight lines are also single stars. On the other hand, a great many stars — Sirius, for example — follow a wavy or sinuous path, which implies orbital motion around a second nearby body of mass sufficient to exert an effective gravitational pull, that is, another star. The second body, the companion of Sirius, was first observed in 1862, and like Sirius travels across the sky in a sinuous path. Thus we have a double or binary system; the two stars revolve around their common center of gravity and around each other in elliptical orbits. At the same time the whole system moves forward, its center of gravity describing a straight path (see earth-moon system, page 239).

The brighter member, Sirius A, has a mass 2.4 times that of the sun, while the mass of the rather dim companion is approximately equal to that of the sun. The average distance between this pair of stars is 20.4 astronomical units; the period of revolution around each other is about 50 years. In accordance with gravitational theory the star of greater mass, being nearer to the common center of gravity than the other, moves in a smaller orbit. For the motions of two such bodies around their common center of gravity, see Figure 17–9.

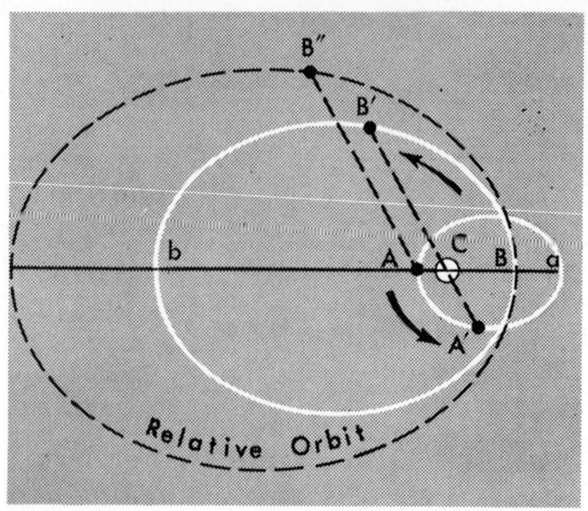

Fig. 17–9 *The orbits of Sirius (A) and its companion (B). C is the common center for both elliptical orbits. Absolute orbits are shown by solid lines; the orbit of B relative to A, by the dotted ellipse.* *(Redrawn from J. C. Duncan,* Astronomy, *Harper and Bros.)*

Nearly 40 per cent of the known stars have been identified as members of binary or multiple systems. Of the six stars nearest the earth, one is a triple, four are doubles, and the remaining one has not yet been resolved, but is probably a member of a multiple system.

Binaries are classified according to the method by which they are detected. If the two companion stars can be observed as separate bodies, the system is a *visual binary*. Several visual binaries can be seen with the naked eye; many more with a telescope. Among the well-known visual binaries are Sirius, Capella, Procyon, Alpha Centauri, and Kruger 60. Alpha Centauri is actually a triple star, but the two brighter components form a visual binary and the third member, Proxima Centauri, is a faint dwarf star. Alpha Centauri also happens to be the nearest of all the stars to the earth (except, of course, for the sun).

If the components of a double star are relatively close to each other or at a great distance from the earth, they may be visually indistinguishable. They can, however, be detected by the use of a spectroscope and for that reason are known as *spectroscopic binaries.* If the orbital plane of a double star lies edgewise to our line of sight, one of the stars will periodically pass between the other and the observer, causing an eclipse (Figure 17–10). Beta Persi, also called Algol, was known to the ancients as a changing star, going through its bright-dim cycle in a little less than three days. Nearly two hundred years ago it was interpreted correctly as an *eclipsing binary,* whereas the real variable stars were at one time incorrectly given the same interpretation.

A number of binaries can be detected by more than one of the above methods. Procyon and Capella, for example, are both visual and spectroscopic binaries. Castor in the constellation Gemini is visually a triple star, and two of the components are spectroscopic binaries, while the third is an eclipsing star. Polaris is a binary star and also a Cepheid variable. Eclipsing double stars that are also spectroscopic binaries are sources of valuable observational data. From these data we can derive detailed information about the member stars, such as their masses, temperatures, sizes, densities, and atmospheric conditions.

STAR GROUPS AND SYSTEMS

In the preceding sections we have discussed the characteristics of individual stars. We have also considered the simplest groups of stars: the binary and multiple systems, the latter containing as many as six stars. We now continue with the larger aggregations in increasing order of size and complexity: star clusters, galaxies, and clusters of galaxies.

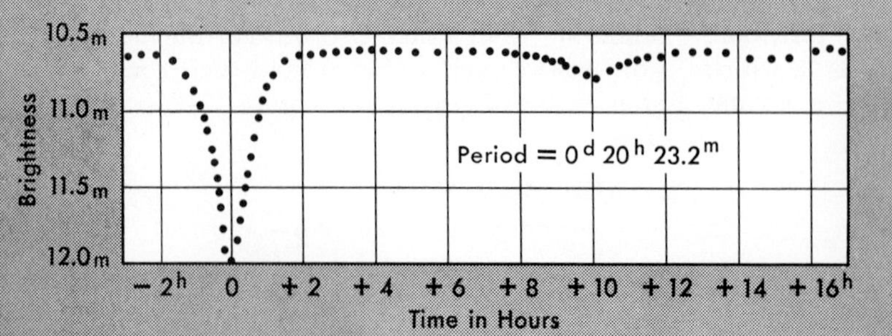

Fig. 17–10 *Change in light-brightness curve for an eclipsing binary. (Adapted from* Astronomy, *Vol. II, by Russell, Dugan and Stewart, by permission of Ginn and Co.)*

Fig. 17–11 *The Pleiades star cluster against a background of nebulosity. About seven stars are visible to the naked eye.* (*Mt. Wilson and Palomar Observatories*)

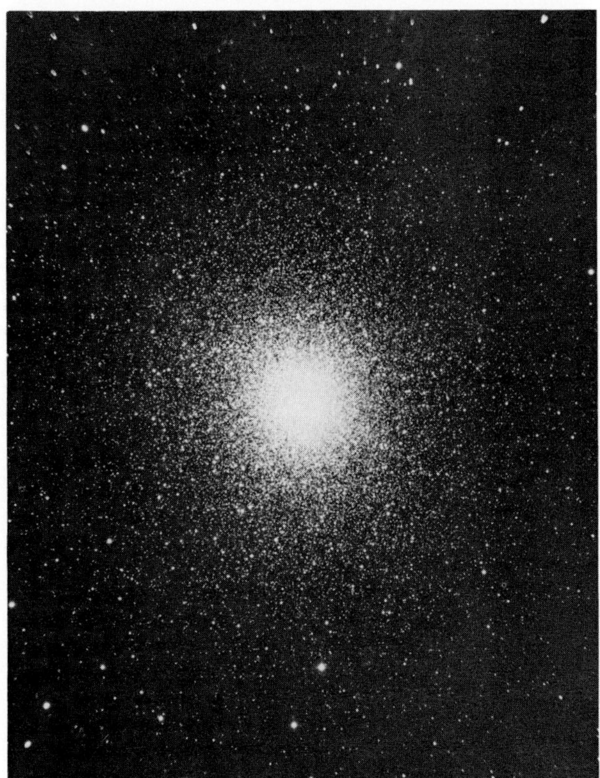

Fig. 17–12 *Globular star cluster in Hercules Messier 13. Taken with 200-inch Mount Palomar telescope.* (*Mt. Wilson and Palomar Observatories*)

Star Clusters. A star cluster is an association of stars that move together at the same rate and in the same direction. There are two quite different kinds, open or galactic clusters and globular clusters. *Galactic clusters* are groups of several hundred stars that lie in or near the plane of the Milky Way. About 300 have been observed, some being visible to the naked eye. The stars in a galactic cluster are relatively far apart and can be identified by their common motion when passing through a region occupied by other stars. Two well-known galactic clusters are the Pleiades, a cluster of about 500 stars, and the Ursa Major cluster which contains, among others, five stars of the Big Dipper and Sirius which is widely separated from the group. The Pleiades (Figure 17–11) are in a gas cloud or nebula which the bright stars illuminate. Galactic clusters are also seen in some of the neighboring galaxies.

Globular clusters, however, consist of hundreds of thousands of stars — possibly millions, in some instances — symmetrically grouped and apparently free from dust and gas clouds (Figure 17–12). They appear to be distributed around the central portion of our galaxy and revolve *en masse* about that region very rapidly and in highly eccentric orbits. Within a cluster the stars evidently revolve about the center. More than 100 globular clusters have been located in our galaxy and about 200 in the M31 galaxy of Andromeda. RR Lyrae stars are found in many of the clusters, thus enabling us to measure their distances.

Galaxies. Galaxies are complex systems consisting of individual stars, star clusters, interstellar dust, and gas. It is estimated that there are about ten billion galaxies within the range of the large modern telescopes; as many as 1000 galaxies may show on a single photograph. Those near the present observational limit of the 200-inch Hale telescope appear as faint smudges of light; they are possibly one billion parsecs away. At a distance of about 400 million parsecs, galaxies consisting of billions of stars appear as fuzzy dots, less bright than some of the single stars in our own galaxy. There are, however, galaxies near enough for their structural details and shapes to be observed and used as criteria for a general classification. There are three main types:

1. Irregular galaxies are relatively rare (2 to 3 per cent of those known). They are without symmetry and contain many stars including Cepheid variables which in the nearby systems can be studied individually. Gas clouds (nebulae) and dust pervade the irregular galaxies. The two Magellanic clouds, our nearest galaxies, are examples of this type (Figure 17–13).

Fig. 17–13 *Our nearest galaxies, the Magellanic clouds. These are the two irregular shaped masses toward the bottom. The smaller one is at a distance of 95,000 light-years. A prominent globular cluster (Tucanae) is also in the field of view. (Yerkes Observatory photograph)*

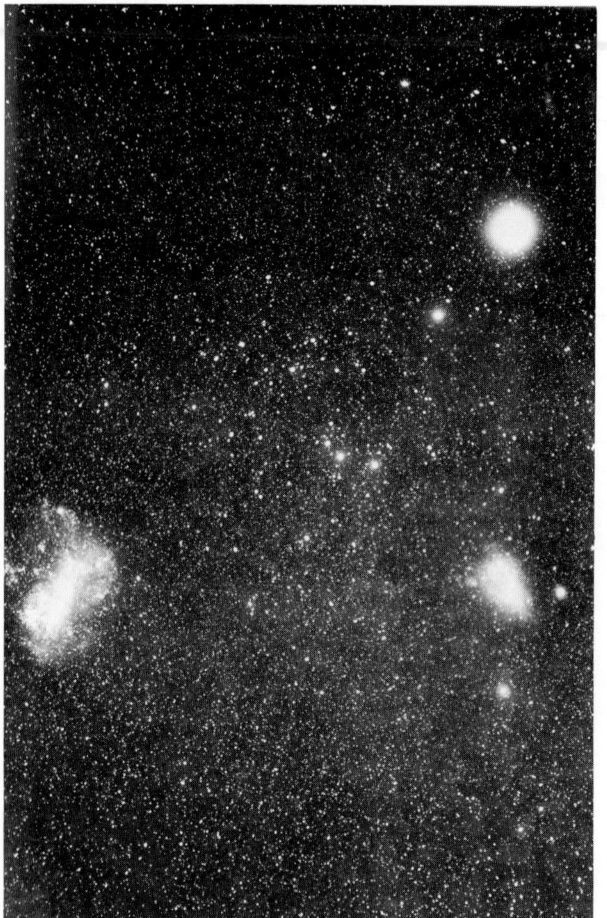

2. Spiral galaxies, viewed face on, resemble pinwheels. Each consists of a bright nucleus with spiral arms more or less tightly wound; nebulae and dust clouds obscure parts of the latter. About 80 per cent of the known galaxies are of this type (Figure 17–14).

3. Elliptical galaxies are symmetrical, free of dust and gas clouds, and in form range from spheres to flattened discs (Figure 17–14). In some instances the elliptical galaxies resemble the nuclei of spiral systems.

Clusters of Galaxies. Our own galaxy, known as the Milky Way System or simply the Galaxy, is surrounded by a vast number of other galaxies. On a grand scale, that is, within an observable radius of possibly one billion parsecs, the distribution of galaxies in space appears to be uniform. There *is* a patch in the sky where no galaxies can be observed because they are hidden by the clouds of the Milky Way; even so, there are holes in the clouds through which some galaxies can be seen. We can therefore expect to observe about the same number of systems in all directions provided our observations extend to distances comparable to that mentioned above. Over smaller distances and limited portions of space the distribution is not uniform, for the galaxies, like the stars, form groups or *clusters.* Clusters of galaxies, the largest aggregations of matter known, may contain up to hundreds of galaxies. The associated galaxies in any cluster other than our own are at approximately the same distance from an observer.

The Milky Way System is a member of a cluster of nineteen, possibly more, galaxies including the two Magellanic clouds, M 31 in Andromeda and M 33 in Triangulum, the only galaxies visible to the naked eye. This cluster, known as the local group,

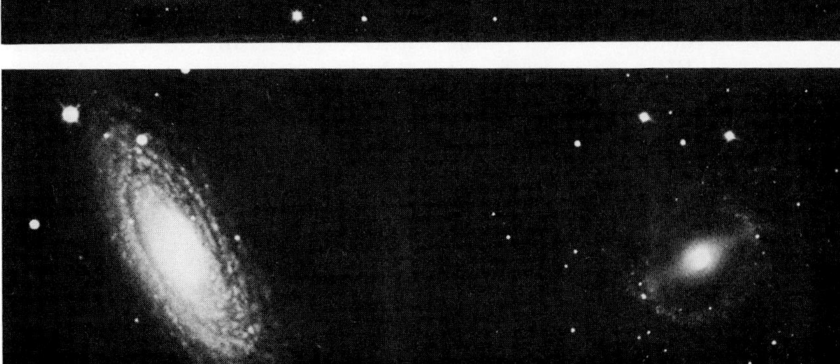

Fig. 17–14 *Types of galaxies: spiral and elliptical. (Mt. Wilson and Palomar Observatories)*

contains galaxies of all three forms. Other clusters have a greater population of galaxies: Coma, that is, the cluster in the constellation of that name, is at a distance of 28 million parsecs and consists of about 800 galaxies; Hydra is 112 million parsecs away and contains over 200 galaxies.

And now, having considered briefly the various aggregations of stars and stellar groups including the local cluster of galaxies, we can examine more closely our own galaxy.

THE MILKY WAY SYSTEM

The irregular belt of light extending across the sky from horizon to horizon and tilted at an angle of 62° to the celestial equator has long been known as the Milky Way. It is the visible portion of our galaxy, one of the largest, with a diameter of approximately 25,000 parsecs and, as indicated previously, a star population of about 100 billion. Most of the individual stars that we can see are in the Milky Way System. The sun is about 8000 parsecs from the center of the Galaxy and 4000 parsecs from the edge.

Although we are enabled to make a close and detailed study of our solar system, we know less about our own galaxy than we do about some of the others. We are on the inside near the fringe of the system, and between us and many of the stars and star groups is a haze of interstellar dust. With modern equipment we can view and photograph the *whole* of an external galaxy such as Messier 31 in Andromeda (Figure 16–1). We can note its general structure, spiral arms, and shape; determine its size, distance, and motion; and observe individual stars and estimate its star population. How can similar information about our own galaxy be obtained? We cannot see the Galaxy as a whole, because we must make our observations from within the structure. We must piece together whatever information can be derived from the visible parts: star groups, nebulae, and individual stars. Moreover, as we learn more about the Galaxy, we find there are certain fortunate and interesting resemblances to Messier 31. We see in Messier 31, sometimes referred to as our twin galaxy, the probable image of the Milky Way System. Certain aspects of Messier 31 – for example, its spiral arms – have suggested to astronomers fruitful lines of investigation for our galaxy.

We can tell the shape of the Galaxy and the location of the sun in it by a survey of the stars over all parts of the sky. It should be kept in mind that stars are generally far from each other – the nearest one to the sun is 1.3 parsecs – and that the fainter stars are usually the more distant ones. Stars can be seen over all parts of the sky, but they are more concentrated, particularly those at greater distances, along the band of the Milky Way. In both directions perpendicular to the Milky Way they are thinly scattered. These facts suggest that the Galaxy is a flattened lens-like disc and that we are located in or near its plane. As we look at any part of the Milky Way, our line of sight is along the central plane and toward an edge; some sections of the band are brighter than others, indicating a greater concentration or depth of stars.

The region occupied by the constellation Sagittarius is the brightest of all, although in part obscured by clouds (Figure 17–17). In this densely populated and bulging section is a variety of stars and stellar groups; one-third of the known globular clusters of the Milky Way are visible in a relatively small area. Numerous RR Lyrae stars dot the clusters and the bright mass of stars around which the clusters are grouped. These distance indicators occur most frequently at a distance of slightly more than

Fig. 17–15 *The great spiral nebula in the constellation of Andromeda. From this isolated universe, light must travel 900,000 years before reaching earth.* (*Mt. Wilson and Palomar Observatories*)

Fig. 17–16 *The spiral nebula in the constellation of Andromeda, on edge. Photographed thus, the nebula is shown as a disc-like assemblage of suns.* (*Mt. Wilson and Palomar Observatories*)

8000 parsecs from the sun and mark what is thought to be the center of the Galaxy.

In the opposite direction the region of the constellation Taurus (which can be most favorably observed in the winter) is relatively dim. The most remote measurable star in this region is only a little more than 4000 parsecs from the sun. This evidence supports the earlier statement that the center of the Galaxy is in the direction of Sagittarius and that the solar system is closer to the rim than to its center. The probable shape of the system, seen edgewise, is shown in Figure 17–18.

There are two additional noteworthy facts concerning the Galaxy. First, the whole system is rotating about its center at an estimated rate of one rotation in 200 million years. The speed of the sun and solar system is about 140 miles per second. Second, the Galaxy has a spiral shape; three spiral arms have been located and it appears that the sun is near the inner edge of one.

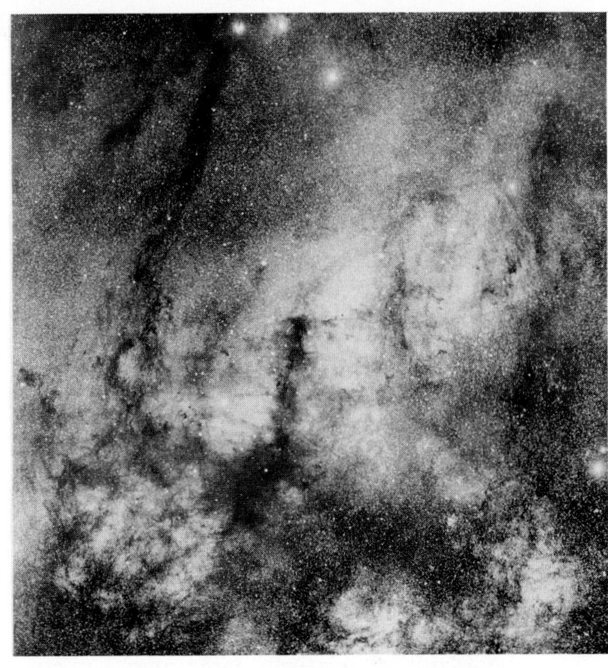

Fig. 17–17 *Milky Way in the region occupied by the constellation Sagittarius.* (*Yerkes Observatory photograph*)

Fig. 17–18 *Probable shape of our galaxy if it could be viewed from outside; a diagrammatic edgewise view. Our sun and solar system are off center with respect to the entire galaxy.*

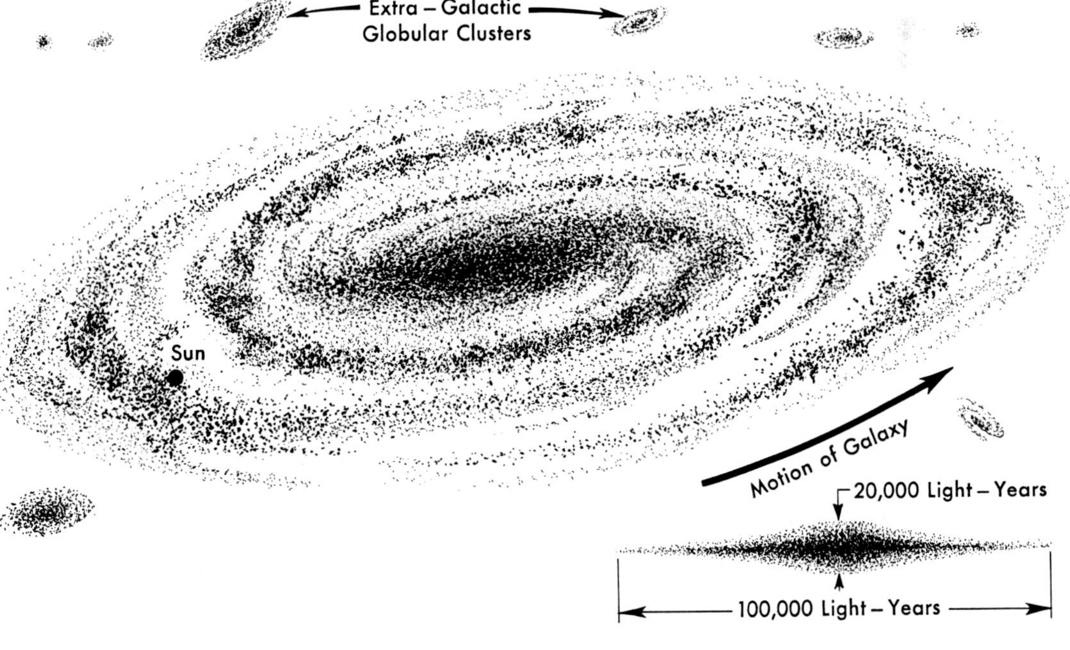

OTHER SOLAR SYSTEMS?

The lines of Alexander Pope, quoted at the beginning of the chapter, pose a very old problem which is inevitably linked with a study of our planetary system and the stars. Are there other solar systems, that is, do "other planets circle other suns"? The planets of our solar system, stars, and many other astronomical bodies were discovered by direct observation. Unfortunately, the nearest stars are at such great distances that a planet as large as or even much larger than Jupiter moving around one of them could not be seen. Being nonluminous and shining only by reflection, it would be lost in the brilliant light of its star. There is, however, a more promising, but limited, means of detection — the effect of gravitational attraction (see page 217). A planet of relatively large mass — greater than that of Jupiter — would cause a perturbation (shift in position) of its primary star which might be observed. This method (as well as direct observation) has been used to discover the "unseen" companions of some of the double stars, but their relative masses are much greater than those of the possible planets.

If, for want of visual evidence, we assume that the stars do not have planetary systems, we must conclude that the sun is unique and the solar system was formed by a series of cosmic accidents. Present-day theory does not support this point of view; on the contrary, it is believed that all the stars were formed by the same processes as the solar system. In that case most of the stars would have developed planetary systems and in the Milky Way System there would be millions of planets not unlike the earth. This hypothesis has, of course, proved a great boon to science-fiction writers.

We now leave our study of astronomy and follow the developments of some of the important physical and chemical concepts — atomic structure, the chemical elements, electricity, radiation, and spectra. We shall then (Chapter 39) consider the broader aspects of the universe, the classifications of stars on the basis of their radiation, and the theories dealing with their origin and evolution.

SUMMARY

1. The sun, important because of its proximity, is a star of average size and greater-than-average brightness.
2. The visible surface of the sun, the *photosphere,* is enveloped by a transparent, *tenuous* atmosphere consisting of the *reversing layer,* the *chromosphere,* and the *corona.*
3. *Prominences* are striking features of the sun's surface; they may be due to material moving *into* the sun, *sunspots* which recur in cycles, and *flares* which cause electrical and magnetic disturbances on the earth.
4. *Solar energy* is due to thermonuclear changes taking place in the interior, a region of extremely high temperature and pressure.
5. *Solar radiation,* visible and invisible, emitted from the photosphere is the source of practically all of our energy.
6. The stars, like the sun, are self-luminous bodies; they vary widely in size, surface temperature, density, distance, and brightness.
7. A number of stars in approximately the same direction which appear to be grouped in an unchanging pattern is a *constellation.* Constellations are useful as guideposts of the sky.
8. The various groups or aggregations of stars are: double or multiple systems (up to six or seven members), star clusters (galactic clusters and globular clusters), galaxies (irregular, spiral, and elliptical), and clusters of galaxies.
9. Our own galaxy, the Milky Way System, is a spiral galaxy, and a member of a relatively small cluster of about nineteen galaxies.
10. Present theory points to the existence of other solar systems, but there is no visual evidence.

STUDY EXERCISES

1. How can the astronomer be sure that the sun actually rotates? What is its period of rotation? What is unusual about this rotation?
2. Describe the series of changes that would occur on the earth if, by some catastrophic event, the sun should suddenly cease to shine.
3. How long does it take for light to reach the earth from the sun?
4. One half of the earth is always illuminated, and the earth turns on its axis in a uniform manner. Why, then, do the days vary in length and why do we have seasons?
5. In what way would conditions on the earth change if the earth's axis should suddenly shift until it was perpendicular to the ecliptic? Explain.
6. In what way would conditions on the earth change if the axis of the earth should suddenly shift until it was parallel to the ecliptic? Explain.
7. As an astronomical body, how should the sun be classified? How does it compare with other members of its class?
8. The following terms are often used in discussing the sun; associate them by number with the definitions given below: (1) Corona; (2) Total eclipse of the sun; (3) True local noon; (4) Aphelion; (5) Perihelion; (6) Inferior conjunction; (7) Astronomical unit; (8) Chromosphere; (9) Escape velocity; (10) Ecliptic.
   a. Mean distance of sun from earth........
   b. Position of earth at maximum distance from sun..............................
   c. A planet has the following relative position: sun–planet–earth.................
   d. Passage of moon across sun's disc. ....
   e. Apparent path of sun's center among the stars..................................
   f. Actual path of earth's center among the stars..................................
   g. Time when sun is on the meridian. ......
   h. Minimum velocity for gaseous molecules to escape gravitational attraction........
   i. Halo of light extending many miles beyond the surface of the sun but visible only at times of total eclipse. ....
   j. The reddish outer layer of the sun. ......
9. The stars in the vicinity of Polaris, the North Star, appear to travel in a circular path around Polaris. The stars above the equator appear to sweep by the earth in straight lines. What is this evidence of? Explain.

FOR FURTHER READING

1. GAMOW, GEORGE, *The Birth and Death of the Sun*. New York: The Viking Press, 1940.
   The entire volume deals in simple language with the story of our sun and of stars.
2. PAYNE-GAPOSCHKIN, CECILIA, *Stars in the Making*. Cambridge, Mass.: Harvard University Press, 1952.
   Very readable account of the evolution of stars and galaxies. The volume contains many fine photographs.
3. Paperback: HOYLE, F., *The Nature of the Universe*. Mentor, 50¢.
   Discusses the universe in non-technical language.

18

THE CONCEPT OF ENERGY

IN PREVIOUS CHAPTERS we have been largely concerned with the first great synthesis of modern science, in which the ideas of velocity, mass, force, momentum, and inertia were clarified. This first great synthesis culminated in the laws of motion and of universal gravitation. The great stature of scientists like Galileo and Newton stems from their contributions to this first great achievement of modern science. The second great synthesizing principle of modern science eventually followed, though over two hundred years were required before it came to be generally accepted. Our modern technological age would be impossible without our present understanding of *energy* and *machines*. In the unraveling of the mysteries of energy, we will learn of the contributions of great scientists like Huyghens, Rumford, Carnot, Joule, and finally Albert Einstein. Their work culminated in a broad synthesizing principle that we call the *law of conservation of mass and energy*.

The story of the development of machines is the story of the liberation of man from the drudgery of prolonged and hard physical labor. All early civilizations were based to a large extent upon the institution of slavery. The Pyramids, for example, represent the work of literally hundreds of thousands of slaves. Slavery as an institution, except perhaps in time of war, is a thing of the past, not so much because it was immoral or cruel, but because modern machines are more efficient, need fuel only when actually working, are tireless, and, most important, are cheaper to operate than slave power. Many electric light companies have been boosting the sale of electricity with the slogan, "You can do it better and cheaper with electricity." This slogan has a real scientific basis. For example, a farmer finds it necessary to pump water for irrigation purposes during a period of drought. A pump is installed and is operated by a laborer to whom the farm operator agrees to pay five dollars per eight-hour day. It is estimated that an average man can do work at the rate of about one-seventh of a horsepower. If a one-seventh horsepower motor were substituted for the laborer, the cost of continuous operation during an eight-hour day would not exceed ten cents. Furthermore, the laborer working for five dollars a day will find it impossible to work as steadily as the untiring electric motor.

Both the workman and the motor require energy to perform work. By *energy* we mean simply *the capacity for doing work.* The complexities of our modern machine age grow directly from our present understanding of the nature of energy which enabled us to develop many different types of machines to utilize many different forms of energy. Much of the rest of this book will be devoted to discussing energy in its various forms: gravitational (potential and kinetic), thermal, electrical, and radiant energy, such as visible light and gamma or X rays. It is still true that basically we do not know what energy really *is.* We are dependent for our knowledge of the physical world upon our five senses — sight, taste, smell, touch, and hearing. As electrical energy surges through a power line, our five senses are of very little help in detecting it, for the electrical energy cannot be seen, heard, tasted, or smelled. Our notions of energy, therefore, rest largely on indirect perceptions. We infer that electrical energy is present if we can accomplish any one of a variety of effects, such as to convert the energy into heat, for example, in a toaster, or into light, or into motion in a motor. These effects we can observe and measure, though the real nature of energy still eludes us. We continuously measure energy by measuring the effects of the consumption of energy, because it is energy that is responsible for changes *of any kind.* In this chapter we shall learn how energy is measured in terms of the amount of change which is produced.

WHAT IS ENERGY?

Energy cannot be utilized or studied except in relation to man or some device made by man. Man (in this sense) and these man-made devices are called *machines.* Thus an inclined plane, an electric light bulb, an automobile, a pulley, a shovel, or a person (from the point of view of energy) are all machines. They are used to perform work through the effective application of force. They all operate on energy. Hence *energy* and *work* are related.

What then is energy? It is that "something" which apparently disappears in any machine when work is performed. The amount of energy consumed is measured by the amount of work performed. It is to be noted that the term *work* does not mean mere physical personal effort. A man who stands in one place holding a hundred-pound weight may be utterly exhausted in a matter of minutes, but he has not done any work. For work to be accomplished there must be an *effective* application of force which results in a *change in motion or position.*

HOW ENERGY IS MEASURED

Work means useful accomplishment: work is performed if we move an object from one place to another, stop an object that is in motion, or make it move faster. It is evident, then, that the amount of work accomplished depends upon the *magnitude* of the force that is applied, and the *time* of application of the force which produces a *change in motion or position* of a body or the *distance* through which the force is applied. Thus there is an *intensity* factor — the force — and a *quantity* factor — the distance. Since it is usually easier to measure distance experimentally than to measure time, work is measured in terms of the force applied and the distance through which it acts.

That is, $W(\text{ork}) \propto F(\text{orce})$, and $D(\text{istance})$.

This means, then, that, $W \propto FD$,
or, $W = kFD$.

By inventing suitable work units, the numerical value of the proportionality constant (k) can be made unity. Thus, if F is one poundal and D is one foot, the work unit is called the *foot-poundal.* If F is one dyne and D is one centimeter, the work

Fig. 18–1 *Examples of machines. In each there is consumption and a conversion of energy.*

unit is called the *dyne-centimeter* or *erg.* This term was coined by using a part of the word "en-*erg*-y." The erg is a very small unit; therefore, a much larger unit, the *joule,* is also in general use. It is equal to 10^7 or ten million ergs. The small size of the erg can be indicated by this example: A mosquito has a weight of about one dyne; to lift a mosquito one centimeter means the expenditure of about one erg of energy.

The defining relationship for the measurement of work and energy consumption in objective terms, then, becomes —

$$W = F \times D \text{ in foot-poundals or ergs.}$$

(*Equation 18–1*)

It is to be noted that the applied force must be in *poundals* or *ergs,* and the distance in *feet* or *centimeters,* respectively. The force included in this definition is only the force which is exerted in the *same direction* as the motion which results.

For example, the amount of work performed in rolling a barrel six feet up the incline in Figure 18–2 is exactly half that required to roll it up the entire length of the incline, a distance of twelve feet, If, therefore, the force F needed was sixteen hundred poundals, the work in rolling the barrel from a to b would be,

$$W_b = F \times D_b = 1600 \text{ poundals} \times 6 \text{ ft} = 9600 \text{ foot-poundals.}$$

But to roll the barrel the entire length of the incline (a *to* c), the work required would be,

$$W_c = F \times D_c = 1600 \text{ poundals} \times 12 \text{ ft}$$
$$= 19{,}200 \text{ foot-poundals.}$$

Similarly, if the barrel weighed twice as much, the force necessary would be thirty-two hundred poundals, and the work required to roll it on to the truck platform would also be increased by a factor of two; that is,

$$W = 3200 \text{ poundals} \times 12 \text{ ft}$$
$$= 38{,}400 \text{ foot-poundals.}$$

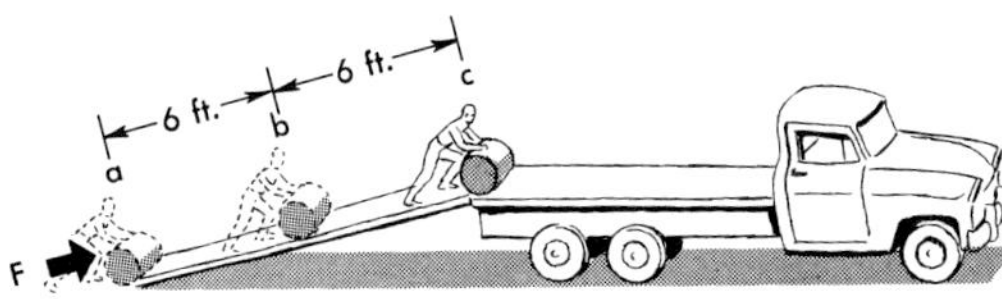

Fig. 18–2 *Inclined plane applied in loading.*

SOME COMMON EXAMPLES OF WORK

Work is necessary to overcome friction. Consider the motorist who runs out of gasoline near a filling station. Turning the steering wheel over to his wife, he gets out and pushes. After much effort he gets the car in motion. He then, by a judicious application of force, can keep the car moving

Fig. 18–3 *Uniform motion of a car.*

at a *uniform speed.* The force he is applying is just sufficient to overcome all the opposing forces of friction. Just as soon as the applied force is removed, the opposing forces of friction soon decelerate the car to rest. In a specific example, the motorist had to apply a force of 400 poundals,

$$12.5 \text{ lbs} \times g \frac{\text{ft}}{\text{sec}^2} = 12.5 \text{ lbs} \times \frac{32 \text{ ft}}{\text{sec}^2}$$
$$= 400 \text{ poundals,}$$

through a distance of 200 feet. Hence, the work performed and energy expended amounted to:

$$W = \frac{400 \text{ ft-lbs}}{\text{sec}^2} \times 200 \text{ ft}$$
$$= \frac{80{,}000 \text{ ft}^2\text{-lbs}}{\text{sec}^2} = 80{,}000 \text{ foot-poundals}$$

Note that the man acts as a machine, and the energy expended within the man is equal to the work accomplished. The energy within the man results from the transformation of food (chemical energy). Furthermore, the weight of the car is not involved in the solution of the problem, since we are concerned only with the *force needed to overcome friction* to keep the car moving uniformly.

Work is necessary to overcome inertia. Overcoming inertial resistance is necessary to set a body in motion, or to make it move faster or slower, or to change its direction of travel. Consider the motorist again. He must exert a force to overcome inertia to get the car in motion. During this period the car is undergoing *accelerated motion,* which is measured by $F = ma$. Refer to Equation 12–4 (page 190).

Let us assume that the motorist used a force of 800 poundals for 15 seconds through a distance of 30 feet before he had the car in uniform motion. The car weighs 3000 pounds. What is the work expended to overcome inertia?

SOLUTION: $W = F \times D = maD$ (*Equation 18–1*)

From the laws of uniformly accelerated motion, we have

$$v = at$$
$$D = \tfrac{1}{2}at^2.$$

Then, $$t^2 = \frac{v^2}{a^2}.$$

Substituting and rearranging,

$$D = \tfrac{1}{2}a \cdot \frac{v^2}{a^2} = \frac{v^2}{2a},$$

or $$\frac{v^2}{2} = aD.$$

Hence, $$W = F \times D = \frac{mv^2}{2}.$$

(*Equation 18–2*)

To apply Equation 18–2, note that the acceleration is given by

$$a = \frac{2D}{t^2} = \frac{2 \cdot 30 \text{ ft}}{(15 \text{ sec}^2)} = 0.267 \frac{\text{ft}}{\text{sec}^2}.$$

Hence, the velocity at the end of 15 seconds is

$$v = at = 0.267 \frac{\text{ft}}{\text{sec}} \times 15 \text{ sec} = 4 \frac{\text{ft}}{\text{sec}}.$$

Then,

$$\begin{aligned} W_{\text{expended}} &= \tfrac{1}{2}mv^2 \\ &= \tfrac{1}{2}\, 3000 \text{ lbs} \times \left(\frac{4 \text{ ft}}{\text{sec}}\right)^2 \\ &= 24{,}000 \frac{\text{ft}^2\text{-lbs}}{\text{sec}^2} \\ &= 24{,}000 \text{ foot-poundals.} \end{aligned}$$

Equation 18–2 also permits a calculation for the magnitude of the force applied since

$$F = \frac{1}{D} \times \frac{mv^2}{2} = \frac{3000 \text{ lbs} \times \left(\frac{4 \text{ ft}}{2}\right)^2}{30 \text{ ft} \times 2}$$

$$= 800 \frac{\text{ft-lbs}}{\text{sec}^2} = 800 \text{ poundals.}$$

Work must be performed to change the level of a body. It takes work to climb a ladder. Consider a person who weighs 150 pounds, who climbs 30 feet up a vertical ladder. What amount of work is expended?

Solution:

$$\begin{aligned} W &= F \times D = ma \times D \\ &= mg \times D \qquad (\textit{Equation 18–3}) \\ &= 150 \text{ lbs} \times 32 \frac{\text{ft}}{\text{sec}^2} \times 30 \text{ ft} \\ &= 144{,}000 \frac{\text{ft}^2\text{-lbs}}{\text{sec}^2} = 144{,}000 \text{ foot-poundals.} \end{aligned}$$

Equation 18–1, then, represents a "packaging" of the concepts of work and energy — the second great synthesis in physical science. It is important to learn these fundamental notations. It will probably be necessary to study the reasoning and mathematics in the preceding three examples more than once in order to understand them.

POTENTIAL AND KINETIC ENERGY

Any body in motion possesses *kinetic energy*. The amount of energy is given by

$$W_{\substack{\text{expended or}\\\text{recovered}}} = E_{\text{kinetic}} = \tfrac{1}{2}mv^2. \quad (\textit{Equation 18–2})$$

This simple equation immediately gives the amount of kinetic energy associated with any mass m having any known velocity v. The energy is in foot-poundals if the mass is in pounds and v is in feet per second. It is in ergs if the mass is in grams and the velocity in centimeters per second.

Any body elevated with respect to the surface of the earth possesses *potential energy*. It requires an expenditure of energy to elevate the body against the attraction of the earth and this is proportional to the vertical height lifted. Or,

$$\begin{aligned} P.E. = W_{\text{expended}} &= Fh_{\text{vertical}} \\ &= mgh_{\text{vertical}} \end{aligned}$$

(*Equation 18–4*)

The sport of skiing will serve to bring out the meaning of potential and kinetic energy. (See Figure 18–4.) To trudge from the bottom a to the top d of the hill requires a personal expenditure of effort (energy). Path b is not nearly so steep as path c, and might seem easier to climb because the personal expenditure of effort in a given time will be considerably greater in certain parts of path c. The explanation commonly employed is to say that path c is steeper and hence more difficult. However, paths b and c have one characteristic in common: the change in elevation h is identical. It has been shown in Chapter 14

Fig. 18–4 *Difference in level (vertical height), and not the length of the incline, determines the amount of potential energy. The horizontal velocity at a is the same for path b or c. Why?*

that bodies fall or travel down an incline because of the attraction of gravity. Conversely, to raise a body from level a to level d, by any route whatever, requires the continuous application of force, since the force of gravity must be overcome, and this means an expenditure of work or energy. The amount of energy involved in this change can be calculated by Equation 18–4,

$$W = F \times D = mgh \text{ ergs, or foot-poundals.}$$

Notice that the amount of work is independent of the route. A person climbing to position d possesses something that he has gained. It is called *potential energy*. Potential energy is usually defined as the energy that a body possesses as a result of having some agency do work upon it. This usually results in a change in the *configuration* or *position* of the body with reference to its original condition or position. When one does work against the attraction of gravity, as when a skier climbs a hill, the body acquires potential energy. The amount of potential (latent) energy thus acquired is measured by Equation 18–4:

$$P\text{(otential) } E\text{(nergy)} = F \times D = mgh \text{ (or mass} \times g \times \text{vertical height)}$$

If the mass of the body is in pounds, g in feet per second per second, and the vertical height through which the body is raised is expressed in feet, the potential energy is expressed in foot-poundals. In c.g.s. units, m must be expressed in grams, g in centimeters per second every second, and h in centimeters, and the potential energy will be in dyne-centimeters, or ergs. Note that the foot-poundal is indicated by the symbol "lb-ft^2/sec^2" and the erg by "g-cm^2/sec^2."

What becomes of the potential energy of the skier as he glides down the hill? When the skier reaches the bottom of the hill and coasts along the level, he has lost all his potential energy. But that he still possesses energy is obvious, since it requires an application of force (expenditure of energy) to bring him to rest. His energy at the bottom of the hill is now entirely *kinetic* (pertaining to motion) or by Equation 18–2,

$$K\text{(inetic) } E\text{(nergy)} = \tfrac{1}{2}mv^2 \text{ foot-poundals or ergs.}$$

If m is expressed in pounds and v in ft/sec, the energy will be in foot-poundals. In c.g.s. units, m is expressed in grams, v in cm/sec to give the energy in dyne-centimeters or ergs.

The following problems represent typical applications of the expressions for potential and kinetic energy:

1. A person weighing 150 pounds climbs a cliff overlooking a lake until he is thirty-six feet above the surface of the water. What potential energy does he possess?

SOLUTION:

$P.E.$ = Work expended in climbing vertically 36 feet

$= mgh = 150 \text{ lb} \times 32 \text{ ft/sec}^2 \times 36 \text{ ft}$

$= 172{,}800 \text{ lb-ft}^2/\text{sec}^2$

or $= 172{,}800$ foot-poundals.

2. If the person in the above exercise dives into the lake, what is his potential and kinetic energy when he strikes the water?

SOLUTION: His potential energy becomes zero as he enters the water. His energy is then entirely kinetic and must be equivalent to the original potential energy, or 172,800 foot-poundals. However, if one calculates the velocity after falling the distance of thirty-six feet, the kinetic energy can be calculated: Since $h = \frac{1}{2}gt^2$, it follows that the time needed to fall thirty-six feet is

$$t = \sqrt{2h/g} = \sqrt{\frac{2 \times 36 \text{ ft}}{32 \text{ ft/sec}^2}}$$
$$= \sqrt{2.25 \text{ sec}^2} = 1.50 \text{ sec.}$$

Hence the velocity at the time of striking the water is expressed as, $v = gt$, or,

$$v = 32 \text{ ft/sec}^2 \times 1.50 \text{ sec} = 48.0 \text{ ft/sec},$$

and

$$K.E. = \tfrac{1}{2}mv^2$$
$$= \tfrac{1}{2} \times 150 \text{ lb} \times (48.0 \text{ ft/sec})^2$$
$$= 172{,}800 \text{ foot-poundals.}$$

3. What force is exerted by a catcher in stopping a five-ounce ball traveling 50 ft/sec?

SOLUTION: It is important to realize that the force exerted by the catcher depends upon the stopping distance. The force needed would be infinitely large if the stopping distance were made infinitely small. Every catcher has learned by experience the necessity of moving the hands backward a short distance before bringing the ball to a dead stop. Let us assume a stopping distance of six inches. The solution of this problem lies in realizing that the work performed in stopping the ball must be equal to the kinetic energy possessed by the moving ball, or

$$K.E. \text{ of ball} = \tfrac{1}{2}mv^2$$
$$= \tfrac{1}{2} \cdot \tfrac{5}{16} \text{ lb } (50 \text{ ft/sec})^2$$
$$= 391 \text{ foot-poundals.}$$

If F represents the stopping force exerted by the catcher, then the work expended in stopping the ball is

$$W = F \times D = F \times \tfrac{1}{2} \text{ ft} = 391 \text{ foot-poundals,}$$

or

$$F = 391 \times 2 = 782 \text{ poundals.}$$

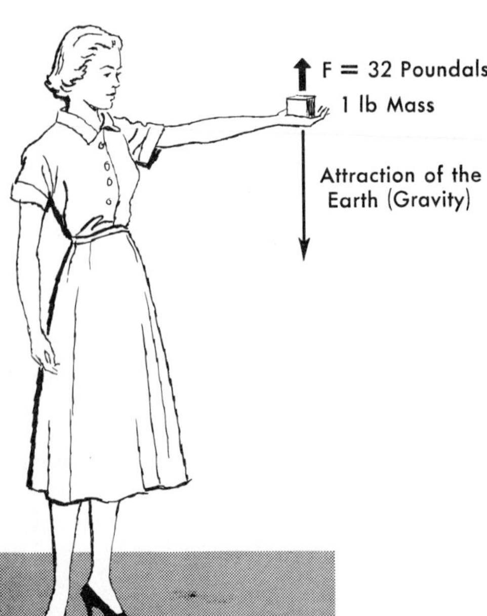

Fig. 18–5 *Relation between poundal and pound of mass. A force of 32 poundals supports a mass of one pound at sea level.*

POUND AND POUNDAL

The pound is a unit of mass, the poundal a unit of force, and the foot-poundal a unit of work or energy. Keep these distinctions always in mind when solving problems involving work. The minimum amount of force that must be applied to lift a one-pound mass is that necessary to overcome the attraction of the earth, or

$$F = mg = 1 \text{ lb} \times \frac{32 \text{ ft}}{\text{sec}^2} = \frac{32 \text{ ft-lb}}{\text{sec}^2}$$
$$= 32 \text{ poundals.}$$

Hence, a force of thirty-two poundals will support a one-pound mass. In the third example above, the force needed to stop the ball was 782 poundals, which is a force large enough to support a mass of 782/32 or 24.4 pounds.[1]

INTERCONVERSION OF POTENTIAL AND KINETIC ENERGY

A body at rest may possess potential energy. A body in motion possesses kinetic energy. That these are often readily con-

[1] If this force represents the maximum required force to stop the ball, why does the catcher always wear a relatively heavy catcher's mitt?

Fig. 18–6 *The pendulum experiment of Galileo.*

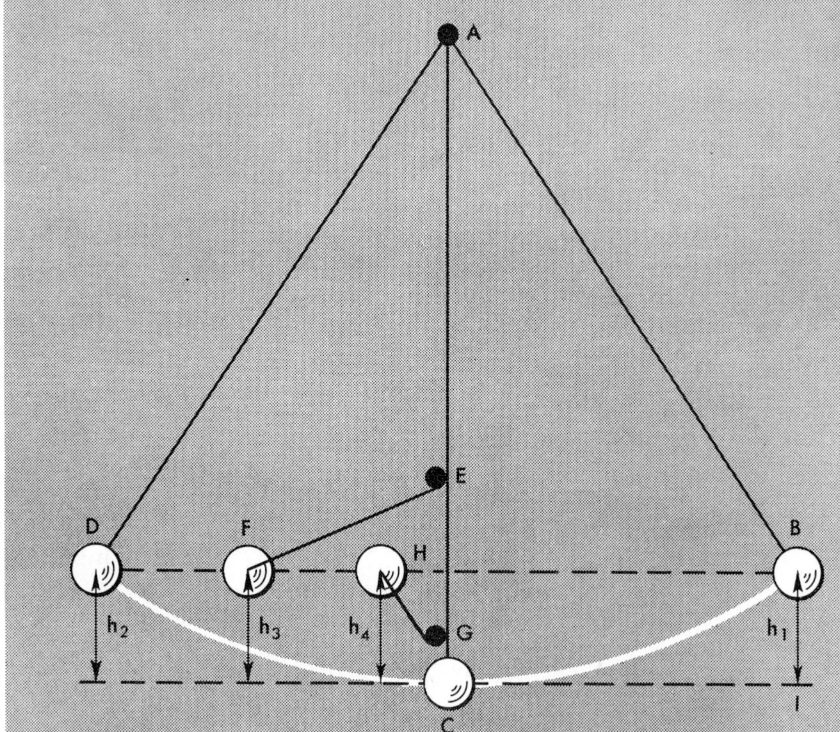

vertible into each other can be easily demonstrated by an experiment first studied by Galileo. He made a simple pendulum with a heavy ball on a long string. (See Figure 18–6.) The pendulum in being pulled to position *B* is lifted a vertical height, h_1, above the level of *C*. It possesses potential energy at *B* with respect to its position at *C*. When allowed to swing, it falls vertically as it moves sideways. At the midswing point its energy is all kinetic and it possesses no potential energy. The inertia of the pendulum carries it to *D*, where it is momentarily at rest. The energy at *D* is entirely potential. If we disregard the small effects of friction against the air — these are relatively small if the mass is large — the potential energy at *D* is the same as at *B*. Galileo inferred also that the kinetic energy at *C* had to be equal to the potential energy at *B* and *D*. Hence in a swinging pendulum there is a continuous conversion of potential into kinetic energy, and vice versa. Galileo further showed that if a pin was placed at *E* while the pendulum was swinging it reached a position *F*. If a pin was placed at *G*, the pendulum traveled to position *H*. It was easy to show that the vertical heights, h_1, h_2, h_3, and h_4 were all the *same*. In other words, the potential energy was fixed by the work originally done in raising the pendulum from *C* to *B* through the vertical height h_1. This can only mean that the potential energy depends upon the mass *m* and the vertical height *h*. Thus,

$$P.E. = mgh \text{ foot-poundals or ergs.}$$

When the pendulum returns to *C*, *h* becomes zero and the energy is entirely kinetic and equal to the original potential energy. Hence,

$$(K.E.)_C = (P.E.)_B$$

$$\text{or} \quad K.E. = \tfrac{1}{2}mv^2 = mgh \text{ foot-poundals or ergs.}$$

In any intermediate position from *B* to *D*, it follows that

$$\begin{aligned} P.E. + K.E. &= \text{a constant} \\ &= \text{original } P.E. \text{ at } B. \end{aligned}$$

The horizontal speed at *C* would be the *same* as its downward speed at *I* if it fell freely from *B*. Why must this be true?

THE LAW OF CONSERVATION OF ENERGY

The pendulum experiment of Galileo led to the conclusion that the total energy of the swinging pendulum, except for small losses due to friction, was constant. The relative amounts of potential and kinetic energy were continually changing but the sum was constant. Thus the energy at point C was entirely kinetic, but entirely potential at B, and these had to be equal. This is an application of the law of conservation of energy: energy can neither be created nor destroyed though it can be transformed from one form into other forms.

The common lever is a very efficient machine and serves to illustrate the law of conservation of energy. (Refer to Figure 18–7.) The relatively large mass M is easily lifted by a relatively small force F_1, if the ratio of l_1 to l_2 is large. The force F_1 can be called the applied effort E. This operates through a small arc S_1 downward, while the large mass M moves upward along the arc S_2. If the angle of motion is small, the arcs can be considered straight lines. Then by the law of conservation of energy the input $(E \times S_1)$ must equal the output $(M \times S_2)$, or

$$E \times S_1 = M \times S_2, \quad \text{or} \quad E = \frac{M \times S_2}{S_1}.$$

The l's and S's constitute the corresponding sides of two similar triangles, and thus,

$$\frac{S_2}{S_1} = \frac{l_2}{l_1}.$$

Finally, then,

$$E = M \frac{l_2}{l_1}.$$

Thus if l_2 and l_1 were one foot and five feet, respectively, the applied effort E will only be one-fifth the weight of mass M. The ratio of the lever arm of the effort to the lever arm of the resistance (M) is called the *mechanical advantage* of the lever.

The effectiveness of a force in producing rotation, as in the case of a lever, depends upon the magnitude of the effort (E) and the lever arm l_1. This is expressed as the *torque*. It is numerically equal to the product of the force and the lever arm, or El_1.

PRINCIPLE OF THE INCLINED PLANE

The input involved in the operation of an inclined plane usually consists of a relatively small force acting through a great distance, while the output consists of a relatively large force acting through a short distance. In effect, then, the inclined plane results in a multiplication of forces.

For example, in Figure 18–8, the highway comes to the river's edge. To eliminate the inconvenience of a ferry, a bridge with an elevation of twenty feet is constructed to carry the traffic across the river. Consider an approach six hundred feet in length. To lift a 3000-pound car directly upward from level a to level b would require a relatively large force,

$$\begin{aligned} F_2 = mg &= 3000 \text{ lbs} \times 32 \text{ ft/sec}^2 \\ &= 96{,}000 \text{ poundals.} \end{aligned}$$

The force F_1 needed to urge the car uniformly along the inclined plane, however, is very much less. If we call the energy utilized in driving the car up the incline the input, we can write,

$$\text{Input} = (F_1)(600 \text{ ft}).$$

The output represents the effective result: the lifting of the car twenty feet against the pull of gravity. Hence,

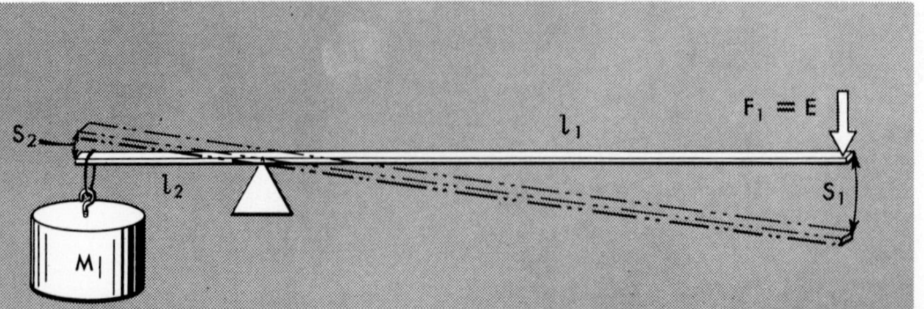

Fig. 18–7 *The common lever.*

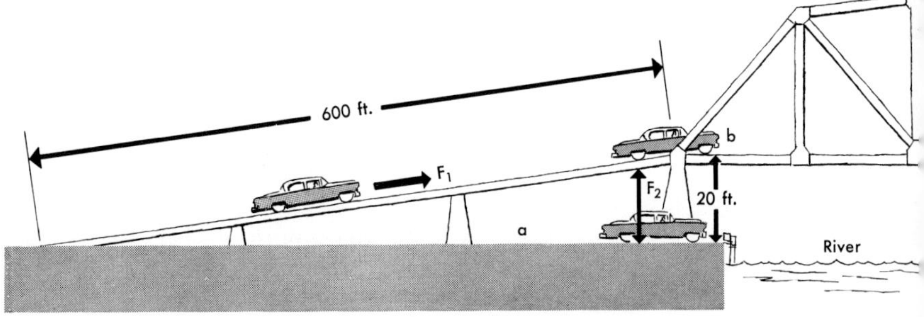

Fig. 18–8 *An application of an inclined plane.*

$$\begin{aligned}\text{Output} &= F_2 \times h = mgh \\ &= 3000 \text{ lbs} \times 32 \text{ ft/sec}^2 \times 20 \text{ ft} \\ &= 1{,}920{,}000 \text{ foot-poundals.}\end{aligned}$$

But, since no other forces have been involved, it must be theoretically true, neglecting the force needed to overcome friction, that

$$\begin{aligned}\text{Input} &= \text{Output, and} \\ (F_1)(600 \text{ ft}) &= 1{,}920{,}000 \text{ ft}^2\text{-lbs/sec}^2, \\ \text{or,} \quad F_1 &= 3200 \text{ poundals.}\end{aligned}$$

The significance of this answer is apparent when compared with the force of 96,000 poundals that would be needed to lift the car vertically. A machine then transforms input energy into output energy with different characteristics. The output, however, cannot exceed the input, unless we are to get something for nothing. This explains why the output was made equal to the input in the problem above.

TYPES OF ENERGY

Our study of energy thus far has been concerned only with gravitational potential energy and kinetic energy — the energy of a body due to its position or to its motion. The basic notions concerning energy, including its measurement, developed around these two concepts. But work can also be accomplished by *radiant energy* and *nuclear energy*. The energy which streams to us from the sun travels with the velocity of visible light and is responsible for all plant growth, the circulation of the atmosphere, the evaporation of water from the oceans, and other significant changes; it is one kind of radiant energy. This energy is not associated with ordinary matter as it travels through space. Because of its unusual character a full discussion of radiant energy is postponed to Chapter 34. Similarly, the implications of nuclear energy will be postponed to Chapter 38.

The radiant energy from the sun eventually assumes many different forms on the earth. Some of this energy is absorbed by the oceans as heat, which evaporates water into the atmosphere. The water vapor possesses *energy in the form of heat* and also another kind of energy as a result of being lifted against the pull of gravity — potential energy. Eventually some of this water cools to form snow on some inland mountain range. Here it absorbs more heat from the sun, changes to a liquid which collects in streams, and starts on its way back to the sea. Some of its energy is now *kinetic energy* — water in motion. On its way to the sea this fast-flowing water may pass through the turbines of a hydroelectric plant. Here the water loses some of its kinetic energy, which reappears as *electrical energy*. Electricity is energy that can be used to perform work such as operating trains, elevators, or vacuum cleaners.

Plants cannot grow without a continuous supply of energy from the sun, which the plant uses to produce starch or cellulose. Starch and other plant foods are an important source of energy for animals. This energy from the sun remains with the plant structure even though the latter may be converted into coal. Coal still retains the capacity for furnishing energy in the form of heat, and this capacity represents yet another form of potential energy — *chemical energy*. The storage battery of an automobile does not contain electricity as such, though it has a certain capacity (chemical energy) for furnishing electrical energy. The energy locked within the nuclei of atoms is now called *nuclear energy*. This is the kind of energy that made the atomic bomb possible.

The distinctions between different forms of energy are often subtle. The broad definition of potential energy, for example, states that it is the energy that a body possesses due to its position or configuration. Chemical energy is due to certain definite arrangements of atoms, molecules, or ions. From this point of view, chemical energy is a form of potential energy. Both heat and an electrical current can be considered to be kinetic energy since they are concerned with movement of molecules and electrons, respectively. Further study of the various forms and types of energy and the methods for their measurement will come in later chapters.

THE SIGNIFICANCE OF MACHINES

Energy *per se* cannot accomplish useful work; it requires a machine on which or through which to operate. The first machine was man himself, a device to utilize the chemical energy of food in order to carry on the tasks of life. Man is the only animal who consciously uses energy other than that from his body to do the tasks of life. Primitive man domesticated certain wild animals to serve as beasts of burden or sources of energy. For a long time during the early history of man, the only machines for performing work were men — freemen or slaves — and domesticated animals. History does not record when man discovered the usefulness of the wheel, the inclined

Fig. 18–9 *The first simple machines. (Refer also to the discussion of the lever on page 290; and of the inclined plane on page 291.)*

Name	Contains What Simple Machine	Mechanical Advantage (Neglecting Friction)	
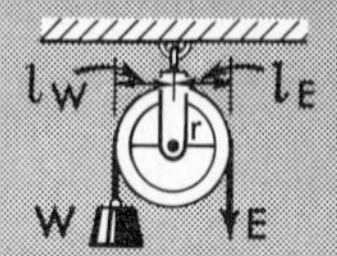 Fixed Pulley	Lever	$\frac{W}{E} = \frac{l_E}{l_W} = \frac{r}{r} = 1$	Used Principally to Effect a Change in Direction of Application of Force
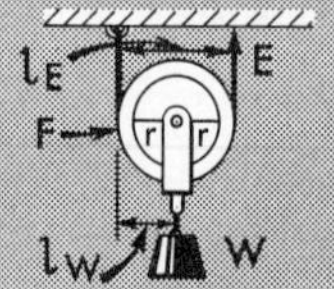 Movable Pulley	Lever	$\frac{W}{E} = \frac{l_E}{l_W} = \frac{2r}{r} = 2$	Movable Pulleys often used in Blocks of 2-4 Pulleys; Each Movable Pulley Multiplies Mechanical Advantage by 2
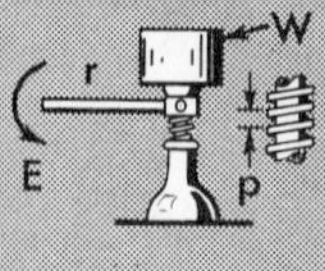 Jackscrew	Lever and Inclined Plane	$\frac{W}{E} = \frac{2\pi r}{p}$ p = Thickness of One Thread	Employed in Auto Jack, Common Meat Grinder, etc.
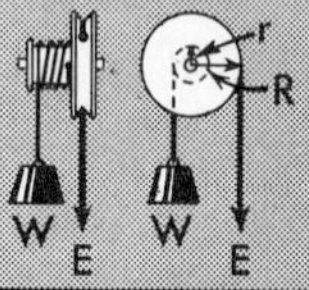 Windlass	Lever	$\frac{W}{E} = \frac{2\pi R}{2\pi r} = \frac{R}{r}$	Numerous Applications in Machinery, as Hand Brake on a Street Car
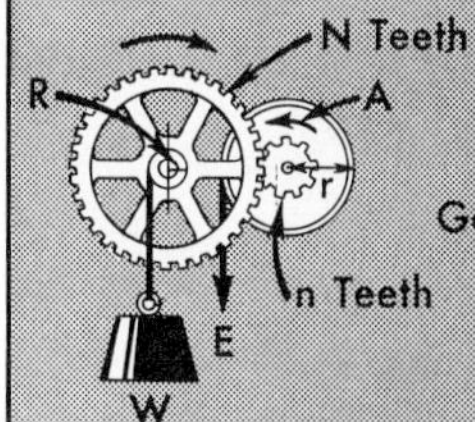 Gear	Lever	$\frac{W}{E} = \frac{r}{R} \times \frac{N}{n}$	Very Frequently Used

plane, the lever, and other simple machines, but the effects were far-reaching. With a simple inclined plane, for example, man can move a very heavy object by the expenditure of a relatively small force. The Pyramids, for example, would not have been possible if the wheel, the lever, and the inclined plane had not been invented.

Complex societies never developed until man learned to increase the effectiveness of his own efforts by utilizing singly or in various combinations six simple machines: the lever, the inclined plane, the screw, the pulley, the wheel and axle, and the gear (see Figure 18–9). The machines of modern man, whether it be a common watch or a huge complex Diesel engine, still employ these simple mechanical devices. But to them have been added the machines which serve to transform one form of energy into some other form. Thus, we have many forms of heat engines which transform heat energy into work, and electric devices which transform electrical energy into other useful forms of energy, such as light, heat, or motion. Some examples of engines are:

HEAT ENGINES:	*Transforms —*
The human body	the energy of food into heat and energy of motion.
Steam turbine	the heat of steam into energy of motion.
Internal combustion engine	the energy of a fuel (gasoline) into energy of motion and heat.
Jet engine	the energy of a fuel into energy of motion.
ELECTRIC DEVICES:	
Electric light bulb	electrical energy into light and some heat.
Electric motor	electrical energy into energy of motion.
Electric generator	kinetic energy into electricity.
Electric toaster	electrical energy into heat.

MACHINES ARE NOT PERFECT

Throughout the discussion of machines thus far, the assumption has been made, for purposes of simplification, that the machine is perfect — that the energy output is exactly equal to the energy input. Actually, there are imperfections in the operation of real machines and the output is always *less* than the input. The ratio of the output to the input is referred to as the mechanical efficiency, and only in a perfect machine could this ratio be unity, or one hundred per cent.

$$\text{Mechanical efficiency} = \frac{\text{work performed by a machine}}{\text{energy supplied the machine}} = \frac{\text{output}}{\text{input}}$$

The energy obtained in the form of motion from the average steam locomotive as compared with the energy supplied in the form of coal is so low that the efficiency is often less than five per cent. The efficiency of a well-designed lever system, on the other hand, is almost one hundred per cent.

The failure of a machine to achieve perfect efficiency can be ascribed to useless work or *friction*. What becomes of the energy that does not appear as useful work? In all machines, wasted energy or work appears in the form of *heat*. An electric motor, if perfect, would remain at the same temperature as its surroundings. Actually, an operating motor is always warm, and the less efficient the motor, the warmer it is. A vessel of water shaken vigorously is warmed; a stiff band of metal rapidly flexed gets warm or even hot. You can perform the experiment of rapidly rubbing the palms of your hands against each other and determine for yourself that work against friction generates heat. These results are summarized in Figure 18–10.

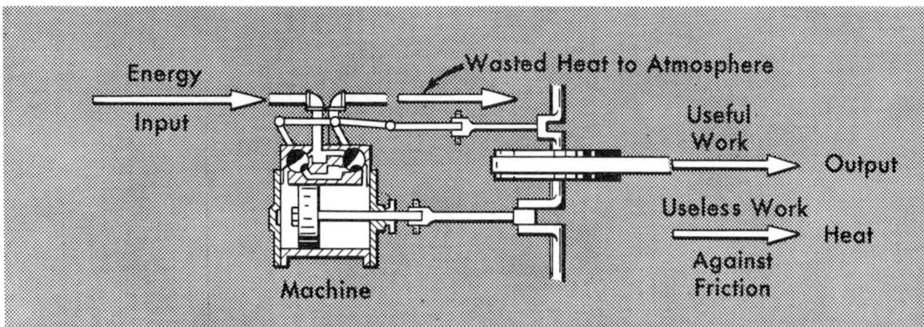

Fig. 18–10 *Relation of useful work to output in any actual machine: output equals input less wasted energy.*

The operation of any machine requires that energy in some form be continuously supplied to the machine. This is the input, which usually must be purchased. The fuel needed to operate a Diesel train must be charged against the cost of operation. Efficiency demands that the value of the ratio

$$\frac{\text{output}}{\text{cost of energy input}}$$

must be as large as possible. There are only two ways of bringing about this result. One is to use the cheaper forms of fuel; the other is to increase the mechanical efficiency of the machine itself by cutting down the fraction of the energy converted into useless work or heat. Modern technology accomplishes the latter result by using jeweled, ball, and roller bearings in ever-increasing numbers.

The common sources of energy, arranged in the approximate order of increasing cost per unit of energy, are:

Sunlight
Coal
Natural gas
Petroleum
Artificial gas
Electricity
Nuclear or atomic energy

With the exception of sunlight, the consumer must purchase these forms of energy.

This necessity has fostered one of the great will-o'-the-wisps of the mechanical age: the search for a machine so free of friction that, after it is once started in motion, it will keep going forever. This is the delusion of "perpetual motion" in a machine designed to perform work. Hundreds of applications for patents on so-called perpetual-motion machines have been submitted to the Patent Office, and all have been rejected, because "the law of the machine" rules out the possibility of such a machine. In other words, there can be no output without input. This principle applies to human beings as well as to inanimate engines.

LAW OF THE MACHINE

The truth just stated constitutes one of the fundamental principles in science. It is usually referred to as the Law of Conservation of Energy, or the Law of the Machine. Energy can neither be created nor destroyed, and when a certain amount of one kind of energy disappears in one place, an equivalent amount of some other kind of energy appears somewhere else. This principle is so broad and has so many applications that its true significance will be better appreciated after one has seen some of its myriad applications. The experimental basis for this principle will be presented in connection with the study of heat in the next chapter.

SUMMARY

1. *Energy* represents the capacity for performing work. Some common forms are heat, electrical, chemical, and nuclear (matter).
2. *Work* results whenever force is applied to any object through a measurable distance. Work, therefore, represents the effective application of force in the sense of changing the position or motion of a body. The common units of work are the *foot-poundal,* the *erg,* and the *joule.* The defining relationship for work is $W = F \times D$.
3. *Potential energy* is the energy possessed by a body as the result of having some agency do work upon it to change its configuration or position with reference to its original condition or position. The potential energy of a body which has been elevated against the attraction of the earth is given by $P.E. = mgh$ foot-poundals or ergs.
4. The energy of a body due to its motion is called *kinetic energy.* Kinetic energy in foot-poundals or ergs is given by $K.E. = \frac{1}{2} mv^2$.
5. The force needed to support a one-pound mass against the pull of gravity at sea level is approximately thirty-two poundals. Similarly, the force needed to support a one-gram mass is approximately 980 dynes.

6. Machines enable man to perform tasks that otherwise would be impossible and enable him to work with energy other than that supplied by himself.
7. Machines are of two types: (1) simple machines, lever, inclined plane, pulley, screw, wheel and axle, gear, and (2) machines which convert one form of energy into another.
8. The mechanical advantage of a simple machine is a number which indicates its effectiveness in decreasing the effort necessary to perform a given task. The mechanical advantage of any machine is given by the ratio

$$\frac{\text{Weight of object moved}}{\text{Effort applied}} = \frac{W}{E}.$$

The mechanical advantage of a frictionless inclined plane and of a lever are given by the ratios

$$\frac{\text{length of plane}}{\text{vertical height}} = \frac{l}{h},$$

and

$$\frac{\text{lever arm of effort}}{\text{lever arm of weight being moved}} = \frac{l_e}{l_w}.$$

9. The effectiveness of a force on a lever in producing rotation about a center is called *torque*. It is numerically equal to the product of the applied force $\times$ lever arm.
10. Only in perfect machines can the output equal the input. In any real machine, the output is always less than the input because of useless work against friction. The latter energy is converted into heat. The mechanical efficiency of a machine is given by the ratio $\frac{\text{output}}{\text{input}}$.
11. The principle that the output of a machine cannot exceed the input is known as the Law of Conservation of Energy. Another common statement of the law: energy can neither be created nor destroyed; when a certain amount of energy disappears in one place, an equivalent amount appears somewhere else.
12. The rise and fall of civilizations is intimately connected with the availability of low-cost energy and the kinds and efficiencies of machines in common use.

STUDY EXERCISES

1. At the right appear certain terms or scientific expressions. Associate these by number with the definitions or statements given at the left.

   a. That which represents the capacity for doing work. . . . .
   b. The expression often used as a defining relation for work. . . . .
   c. A common unit of force. . . . .
   d. The work performed when a force of one dyne operates through a distance of one centimeter. . . . .
   e. The fundamental English absolute unit of work. . . . .
   f. The unit of work in the English system that corresponds to the erg in the c.g.s. system. . . . .
   g. The kind of energy that a body possesses as a result of its position with respect to the surface of the earth. . . . .
   h. The kind of energy possessed by a moving body. . . . .
   i. The kind of energy that a body possesses as a result of doing work upon it in such a way that the energy is recoverable. . . . .
   j. The expression used to measure potential energy. . . . .
   k. The expression used to measure kinetic energy. . . . .
   l. The ratio of the resistance to the effort in in a simple machine. . . . .
   m. The ratio of the useful work obtained from a machine to the total amount of energy supplied to the machine. . . . . . .
   n. The principle which states that it is hopeless to try to construct a machine which is so free from friction that it will be possible to get "something for nothing." . . . .

   1. Conservation of energy
   2. Kinetic energy
   3. Potential energy
   4. $\frac{1}{2}mv^2$
   5. Foot-poundal
   6. Mechanical advantage
   7. $F \times D$
   8. Erg
   9. Energy
   10. Poundal
   11. mgh
   12. Efficiency

2. *a*. A 50-pound load was carried to the top of a building 64 feet high. Encircle correct answers.

(1) What was the force in poundals that had to be exerted by the carrier?

50 poundals. 1600 poundals.
3200 poundals.

(2) What work was expended by the carrier in taking it to the top of the building?

1600 poundals. 102,400 poundals.
102,400 foot-poundals.

(3) If the carrier had paused for rest at the 32-foot level and then continued to the top, would the amount of work necessary to be expended be the same, more, or less?

Same. More. Less.

b. The load was then allowed to fall.

(1) How far did the object fall in one second?

16 feet. 32 feet. 64 feet.

(2) How far would the object be from the ground after one second?

0 feet. 32 feet. 48 feet.

(3) What would be the velocity after falling one second?

16 ft/sec. 32 ft/sec. 48 ft/sec.

(4) What would be the kinetic energy of the object after falling one second?

32 foot-poundals. 76,800 foot-poundals.

25,600 foot-poundals.

(5) What would be the potential energy after falling one second?

32 foot-poundals. 76,800 foot-poundals.

25,600 foot-poundals.

(6) How does the sum of the kinetic energy and the potential energy after falling one second compare with the original potential energy?

Same. Less. More.

(7) How long a time will elapse before the object reaches the ground?

1 second. 2 seconds. 3 seconds.

(8) What will be its velocity when it reaches the ground?

32 ft/sec. 64 feet. 64 ft/sec.

(9) What will be the kinetic energy just as the object reaches the ground?

0 foot-poundals. 102,400 poundals.

102,400 foot-poundals.

(10) What will be the potential energy just as the object reaches the ground?

0 foot-poundals. 102,400 poundals.

102,400 foot-poundals.

(11) How does the kinetic energy just as the object reaches the ground compare with the original potential energy?

Less. More. Same.

(12) What transformation of energy occurs as the swiftly moving object collides with the ground?

Kinetic energy is converted into potential.

Potential energy is converted into kinetic.

Kinetic energy is converted into heat.

3. Explain how Problem 2 illustrates the Law of Conservation of Energy.
4. Examine closely a common household mechanical device, such as an eggbeater or the thermostat on a furnace. How many examples of simple machines do you find have been used in its construction?
5. A truck ramp at a freight station rises five feet for every one hundred feet along the ramp.
   a. What is the mechanical advantage?
   b. If the truck and its load weigh four tons ($4 \times 2000 \times 32$ poundals), what is the minimum force needed to hold the truck stationary on the ramp?
   c. Will the actual force needed to cause the truck to move up the ramp be the same as the calculated minimum force, or more? Explain.

6. A common way to get hot water in a home is to place a hot water heating coil in the furnace. The owners of many such coils believe that this hot water is obtained at no cost because they have to operate the furnace anyhow. Apply the Law of Conservation of Energy to this situation. Is the operator of such a coil really obtaining hot water at no cost to himself?

FOR FURTHER READING

1. LEMON, H. B., *From Galileo to the Nuclear Age*. Chicago: University of Chicago Press, 1946.
   The author in a very entertaining manner presents the fundamental notions concerning matter and energy. Chapters 9, 10, and 11 consider the meaning of work and energy, potential and kinetic energy and their measurement, and the Law of Conservation of Energy.
2. DUNNING, J. R., and H. C. PAXTON, *Matter, Energy, and Radiation*. New York: McGraw-Hill Book Company, 1941.
   Chapter VI has an excellent discussion on "Ideas about Energy."
3. FURNAS, C. C., "Conceptual Forms of Energy," *page 304 in* H. SHAPLEY, H. WRIGHT, and S. RAPPORT, *Readings in the Physical Sciences*. New York: Appleton-Century-Crofts, 1948.
   Excellent discussion of the significance of energy in its various forms.
4. Paperback: FREEMAN, I. M., *Physics Made Simple*. Made Simple, $1.00.
   The principles of physics presented with practical illustrations.

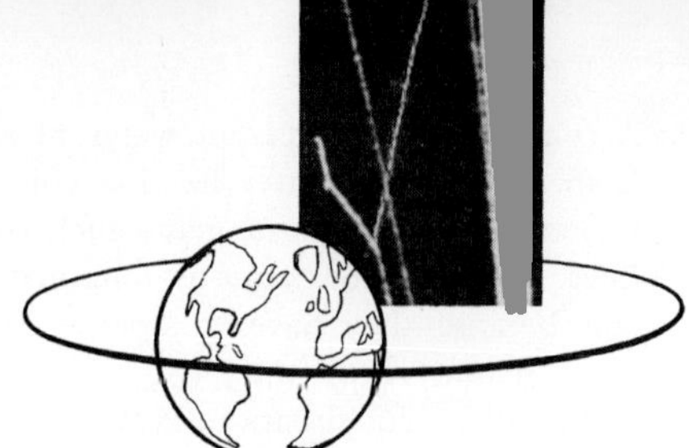

19

HEAT AND MOLECULES

HEAT IS THE FORM of energy we associate with life. Primitive man had to learn how to kindle a fire before he could migrate northward away from the tropics, for only with fire could he dispel the dampness of his cave home and provide it with warmth during the winter season. The discovery of the methods of making fire was one of the truly great discoveries of all time. The countless benefits of fire have made so many imprints on man's unconscious self during past time that universally today we take a fire crackling in the fireplaces of our homes as the center of home life, even though, in an era of central heating and air-conditioning, a fireplace is an anachronism difficult to justify except on the basis of sentiment.

Reverence for fire was an essential part of many primitive religions. The early Greeks considered all matter as manifestations of only four primordial substances, earth, water, air, and fire. The alchemist of the Middle Ages resorted to the use of fire in his search for gold, the only metal then known that would withstand the effects of intense heat. The myriad chemical changes employed by the modern chemist in making better dyes, medicines, or textiles would not be possible without the aid of heat. It was the development of the steam engine that brought about the Industrial Revolution, when mechanical power was widely substituted for the power of men and animals. The first heat engine with greater mechanical efficiency than the steam engine was the internal combustion motor. The most recent improvement in heat engines is the jet engine which has made supersonic air speeds possible. All these engines depend, ultimately, on fire.

Our understanding of the nature of heat and fire depends upon our conception of matter. Through all philosophic thought since the days of the ancient Greeks can be found the idea that all matter must consist of tiny particles. The whole of a body consists of many small parts. The smallest of these particles were called *atoms.* The word goes back to the Greek philosopher Democritus (*ca.* 460–370 B.C.), who on the basis of logic alone reasoned that matter could not endlessly be subdivided. The word "atom" means, literally, indivisible. The atoms of Democritus were visualized as tiny, invisible particles which "were uncaused, existent from eternity, and never annihilated."

The ancient Greeks were not experimentalists. They depended upon the laws of logic in their search for truth. Experimental techniques to test the ideas of Democritus were lacking. Thus the atomic hypothesis of that early day was only a very attractive abstraction. Today we know that atoms are very real, but they are not the atoms visualized by Democritus. Instead, the ultimate particle of any pure substance — sugar, water, or oxygen, for example — which can exist in the free state, is the *molecule*. In Chapter 20 it will be shown that molecules may be simple or complex, consisting of combinations of atoms of the elements.

SOLID, LIQUID, AND GASEOUS STATES

Nearly all pure substances can exist in a solid, liquid, or gaseous state. The changes are usually reversible and depend only upon the temperature. Liquid water placed in the freezing compartment of a refrigerator becomes ice. Liquid water if heated disappears as water vapor or steam. Similarly, solid mercury melts at −38.9° C., and liquid mercury boils to form mercury vapor at 356.9° C. These temperatures are called transition temperatures and they vary over a wide range for different substances. Thus, solid helium melts at −272.2° C., while iron melts at 1535° C. One reason for using tungsten for the filaments in electric light bulbs is its very high melting point of 3370° C.

THE PROPERTIES OF GASES

The unraveling of the many puzzles involved in understanding the solid, liquid, and gaseous states of matter first came through a study of gases. This may seem surprising because gases apparently are so intangible. Fortunately, however, the many properties of *different* gases are very similar. This was early recognized by scientists. The structure of gases must be simpler than that of either liquids or solids since the ultimate particles — molecules — are much fewer per unit of volume. For example, one gram of water at 100° C. occupies approximately one milliliter as liquid but 1740 milliliters as vapor. If we accept the hypothesis that equal numbers of molecules of water are involved, it is obvious that the spaces between molecules in the vapor are very significantly larger (about 12 to 1) than in the liquid state (Figure 19–1).

One of the first regularities observed among gases was that the pressure exerted by a sample of a gas is an *inverse* function of its volume, if there is no change in temperature. This simple truth was found experimentally by Robert Boyle (England, 1626–91). A crude representation of this *inverse* relationship can be observed by squeezing an inflated toy balloon between the palms of the hands. The volume of the balloon is observed to *decrease* as the pressure exerted by the hands *increases*. This is

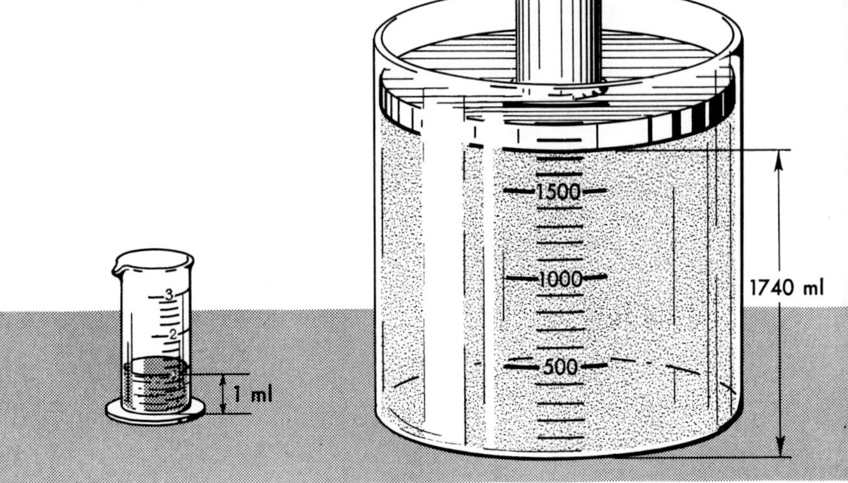

Fig. 19–1 *A vapor occupies much more space than an equal weight of a liquid.*

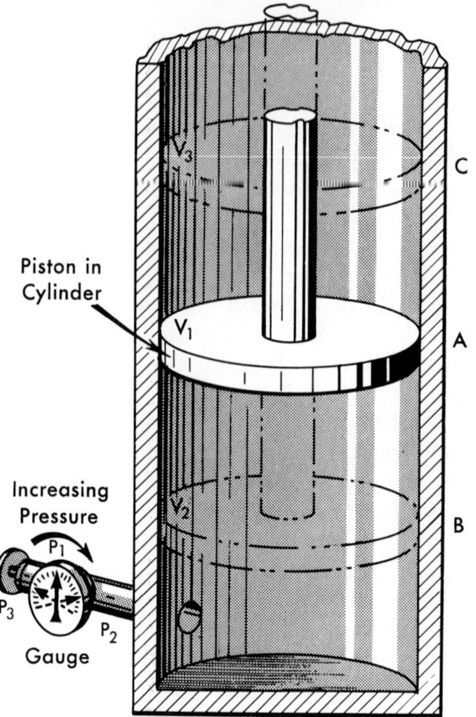

Fig. 19–2 *Apparatus showing pressure-volume relationships for a sample of air.*

a rough qualitative representation of the facts. The quantitative law derived experimentally by Boyle was based upon the interpretation of actual pressure and volume data in the language of mathematics. In the apparatus shown in Figure 19–2, the pressure P is observed to *increase* if volume V is decreased – piston moved from A to B. Moving the piston from A to C means a volume *increase* but with a pressure *decrease*.

The data accumulated in a typical experiment are recorded in Table 19–1. In Figure 19–3 each of these pressures is plotted as ordinate against the volumes as abscissae. Note that the curve graphically shows that P gets *smaller* as V gets *larger*, or vice versa.

Column (3) in Table 19–1 records the inverse $1/V$ value for each pressure. The data are plotted in Figure 19–4. This curve indicates a straight-line relationship between P and $1/V$. That is, if the pressure (P) is doubled, then the value of the inverse of the volume ($1/V$) is also doubled. Column (4) records the product PV obtained by multiplying each pressure by the corresponding volume, and these figures are plotted in Figure 19–5. The figure clearly shows that the product (PV) for changes in pressure of a given sample of a gas is *constant.*

Figures 19–3, 19–4, and 19–5 are all graphical statements of Boyle's Law. In the language of mathematics Boyle's Law can be stated in the following ways:

(1) $P \propto \frac{1}{V}$ (T constant) (Figure 19–3)

(2) $\frac{P_1}{P_2} = \frac{V_2}{V_1}$ (T constant) (Figures 19–3 and 19–4)

(3) $PV = \text{constant} = k$ (T constant) (Figure 19–5)

Another basic law of gaseous behavior is that the pressure exerted by a gas (in a fixed volume) changes if the amount (mass m) of the gas present changes. Imagine a confined sample of gas in vessel A in Figure 19–6. The initial pressure was 15 lbs/sq. in. when the weight of the gas was one pound. If the valve is opened until only half a pound of gas remains, the pressure becomes 7.5 lbs/sq. in. The relation of the pressure P to the mass of the gas present at constant volume can be summarized,

$$P \propto m \ (V \text{ constant}).$$

TABLE 19–1 PRESSURE-VOLUME RELATION FOR A GAS IN A TYPICAL EXPERIMENT

(1) V (cubic feet)	(2) P (pounds/square inch)	(3) $\frac{1}{V}$	(4) PV
10.0	15.	0.10	150
20.0	7.5	0.05	150
5.0	30.	0.20	150
2.0	75.	0.50	150
30.0	5.0	0.033	150

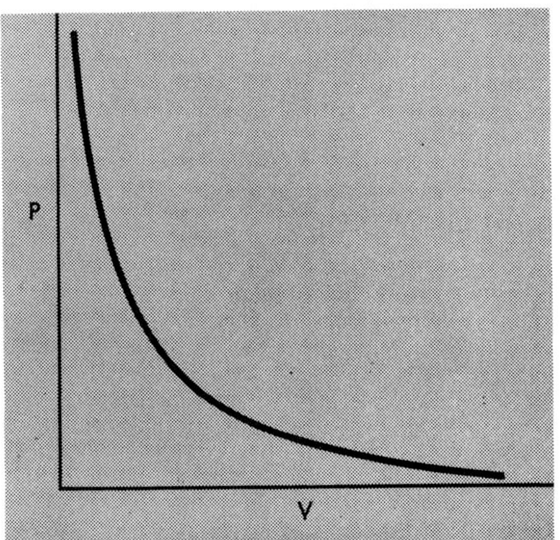

Fig. 19–3 *Relation between P and V for a gas. P gets* smaller *as V gets* larger, *or vice versa.*

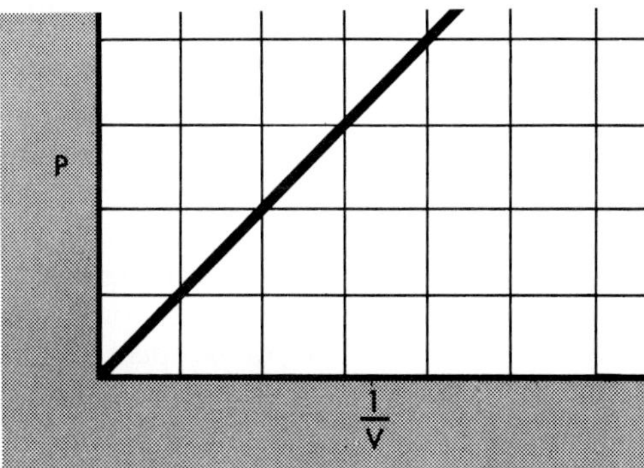

Fig. 19–4 *Relation between P and 1/V for a sample of gas.*

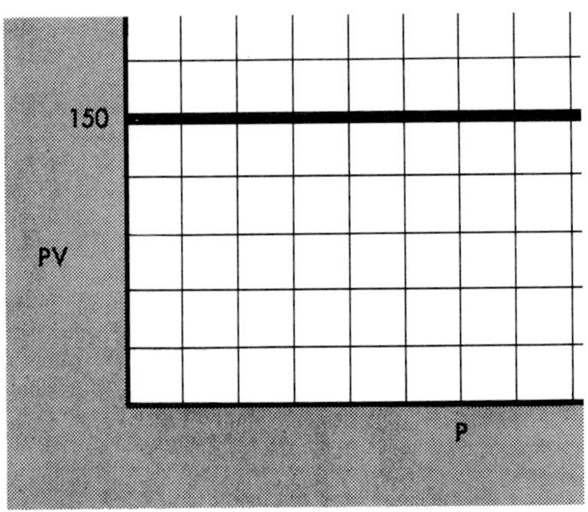

Fig. 19–5 *Relation between PV product and P for a sample of gas.*

In 1802, a French scientist, Gay-Lussac, showed experimentally that the pressure exerted by a given sample of gas changed with the temperature if the volume was constant. If the temperature is expressed in centigrade, the observation of Gay-Lussac can be summarized:

$$P = P_0 + P_0 \cdot \beta t \text{ (}V\text{ constant)} \qquad \text{(Equation 19–1)}$$

The term β is the fractional increase in the initial pressure P_0 at 0° C. for a degree centigrade change in temperature (t). Remarkably (β) was found to be 1/273 for *all* gases. Note that (t) is negative for temperatures below 0° C. Hence if any sample of gas is cooled to −273° C., its pressure should become zero since

$$\begin{aligned} P &= P_0 + P_0(\tfrac{1}{273})(-273) \\ &= P_0 + P_0(\tfrac{1}{273} \times -273) \\ &= P_0 - P_0 = 0 \end{aligned}$$

This value of −273° C. has come to be accepted as the *absolute zero of temperature,* since the pressure becomes zero. Lower temperatures are impossible.

For convenience in computations, it was found simpler to express the pressure changes in gases as influenced by temperature changes in terms of another temperature scale — absolute temperature scale (or Kelvin Scale). In essence, this merely expresses the change in pressure of a sample of gas in terms of its temperature change (in Centigrade degrees) above *absolute*

Fig. 19–6 *Pressure changes at constant volume if the mass of the gas changes.*

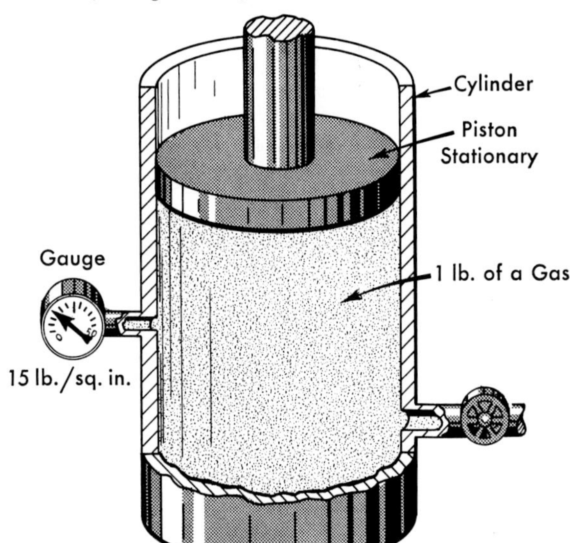

zero, and not in a change from the pressure at 0° C. The absolute temperature (T) scale is simply related to the Centigrade scale (t),

$$T(\text{Absolute or Kelvin}) = t(\text{Centigrade}) + 273°$$

Thus water freezes at 0° C. or 273° K., and boils at 100° C. or 373° K.

The invention of the absolute temperature scale greatly simplified the use of the law of Gay-Lussac, that the pressure of a given sample of any gas at constant *volume* is *directly proportional* to its *absolute* temperature, or

$$P \propto T\ (V\ \text{constant}), \text{ or } \frac{P_2}{P_1} = \frac{T_2}{T_1}\ (P\ \text{constant})$$

(*Equation 19–2*)

Furthermore, in heating a sample of gas, the pressure can be kept constant. It is then found that the volume changes with the absolute temperature. This can be stated:

$$V \propto T\ (P\ \text{constant}), \text{ or } \frac{V_2}{V_1} = \frac{T_2}{T_1}\ (P\ \text{constant})$$

(*Equation 19–3*)

This is the law of Charles.

THE GENERAL GAS LAW

One of the principal functions of science is to summarize large masses of data into concise mathematical form. We have seen that for all gases

$$P \propto \frac{1}{V} \quad \text{(Boyle's law)}$$

$$P \propto T \quad \text{(Gay-Lussac's law)}$$

$$P \propto m$$

These observations can be combined in a single statement,

$$P \propto \frac{mT}{V}, \quad \text{or} \quad PV \propto mT.$$

If the mass m of the gas does not change,

$$PV \propto T, \quad \text{or} \quad PV = kT. \qquad (\textit{Equation 19–4})$$

The generality and usefulness of this law will be appreciated only after frequent use. The physician uses it in working with problems involving respiration. The engineer uses it whenever he is concerned with quantities of industrial gases. Scientists continuously use some form of this law whenever they are concerned with volumes of gases. It is so useful because it tells so much. It deals with the three variables (P, V, and T) with which we are concerned whenever we work with gases. Mathematically, the law indicates that if the changes in any two of three variables P, V, and T are known, the change in the other variable can be calculated. For this purpose, the general gas law is often used in this form:

$$\frac{P_2V_2}{T_2} = \frac{P_1V_1}{T_1} \qquad (\textit{Equation 19–5})$$

The general gas law strictly applies only to so-called ideal gases. Actual gases — carbon dioxide, for example, or oxygen — do not obey the general gas law exactly. However, the deviations between calculated and observed values for volumes and for moderate changes in pressure or temperature are so small that they can be neglected except for precise experimental work. The deviations are usually one or two per cent.

WHAT IS HEAT?

The synthesis of great unifying principles frequently comes very slowly in science. This was true of the kinetic molecular theory which is now commonplace but necessary to account for many properties of matter as influenced by their energy content. In 1738 a Swiss scientist, Daniel Bernoulli, had shown that many properties of gases could be accounted for if a gas were imagined to consist of particles called molecules in motion in all directions. Thus the impact of the molecules on the walls of the containing vessel would explain the pressure, the pressure would increase in an inverse ratio to the change in volume, and the pressure would increase if the molecular

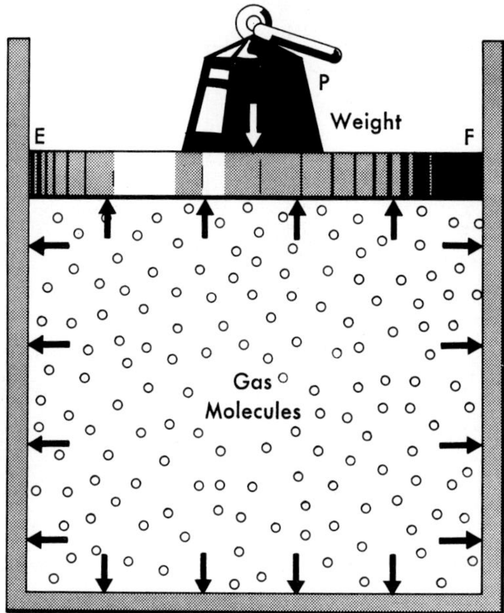

Fig. 19–7 *Bernoulli's hypothesis of gas pressure.*

motion of the molecules were increased by raising the temperature. All the facts concerning the pressure and volume relations of gases were in accordance with the hypothesis of Bernoulli. Over a hundred years were to pass before Bernoulli's ideas evolved into our present kinetic molecular theory. According to this theory, heat is merely a manifestation of molecular activity.

THE KINETIC MOLECULAR HYPOTHESIS (THEORY)

The impact of machine-gun bullets will result in a nearly continuous push (force) on a heavy steel target. The bullets of mass (m') and velocity (u') possess kinetic energy.[1] This energy is transferred to the target on collision. Similarly molecules of mass (m) and velocity (u) would likewise possess kinetic energy. That is, the kinetic energy $= E_k = \frac{1}{2}mu^2$ per molecule.

The impacts of large numbers of molecules on the walls of the containing vessel cause pressure just as in the case of machine-gun bullets. But there is a striking and remarkable difference in the two situations. The bullets, after striking the target, lose all their kinetic energy and drop to the ground. The molecules after impact rebound with *no loss* in energy. This is an essential part of the kinetic theory. Large bodies of matter, when they undergo collisions, lose a part or all of their kinetic energy. A tennis ball dropped on a table from a certain height never rebounds to the height from which it is dropped. On each bounce there is a slight loss of energy. Eventually the ball comes to rest on the table top, having lost all of its energy. The tennis ball is said not to be *perfectly elastic,* elasticity being the property of matter to return to its original shape after any kind of deformation. The molecules of a gas, however, in a closed vessel exert pressure *forever.* If they did not, they would eventually come to rest (as liquid or solid) on the bottom of the vessel. Can it be true that molecules rebound on collision with no loss of energy? Scientists had to accept this postulate as an essential part of the kinetic hypothesis. It became a unique part of the kinetic theory.

The effect of heat on a sample of gas is to increase the kinetic energy of the molecules. Since the mass (m) does not change, the velocity (u) must increase. Thus the frequency of impacts increases as well as the amount of the "push." This, then, accounts for the increase in pressure if the volume remains the same. Similarly, the other properties of gases are all accounted for by the four fundamental assumptions of the kinetic theory:

1. Gases consist of molecules at relatively great distance from each other moving in random directions at high velocities;

2. Molecules are perfectly elastic and rebound on collision from massive walls with no loss in energy;

3. There is conservation of energy (and momentum) when pairs of molecules collide;

4. The kinetic energy of the molecules $(mu^2)/2$ depends only upon the absolute temperature (T),

$$E_k = \tfrac{1}{2}mu^2 = kT. \qquad \textit{(Equation 19–6)}$$

[1] The symbol u is used for the velocity since it is customary to reserve v for volume.

TABLE 19–2

PRESSURES OF HELIUM AT LOW TEMPERATURES

(1) VOLUME	(2) TEMPERATURE CENTIGRADE = $t°$	(3) PRESSURE IN ATMOSPHERES	(4) TEMPERATURE ABSOLUTE = $T°$
1 liter	0	1	273.0
1 liter	– 136.5	0.5	136.5
1 liter	– 204.7	0.25	68.3
1 liter	– 225	0.17	48.0
1 liter	– 250	0.084	23.0

The concept of absolute zero – absence of heat and all molecular motion – led logically to the absolute temperature scale, as we have seen. All molecular activity or the kinetic energy of molecules is directly proportional to the absolute temperature. For a gas kept at constant volume the pressure is directly proportional to the kinetic energy of the molecules or the absolute temperature. Actual experiment has amply verified this relationship. Table 19–2 shows how the pressure exerted by a sample of helium decreases with the temperature. The data are plotted in Figure 19–8, where the relation between pressure and temperature is apparent from the graph. Note that the graph is a straight line and that if the temperature were sufficiently lowered the pressure would eventually become zero. (This process, extending a curve into a region where no experimental data exist, is known as *extrapolation.*) The extrapolated part of the graph in Figure 19–9 is indicated by the dotted line. Note that it intercepts the x-axis at –273° C. which is 0° Kelvin. This temperature has a tremendous significance in scientific thought. It represents the ultimate in coldness, the absolute lack of heat energy, the temperature at which the molecules of all substances are without motion. It is known as the *absolute zero.*

Absolute zero is probably an unattainable temperature, though scientists have come very close to it. There are many factors which make experimentation in the vicinity of absolute zero a matter of special techniques in heat measurement. In spite of the enormous difficulties physicists have actually reached temperatures less than one-hundredth of one degree above absolute zero.

A FORM OF THE KINETIC THEORY EQUATION

The kinetic theory is on such a sound basis that it is possible to derive theoretically the relationship between pressure (P) and volume (V) and its kinetic energy. The pressure depends only upon the number of collisions on the walls per unit time and the force exerted per collision. For n molecules the frequency of collisions in unit time will depend upon the number of molecules per unit of volume or on n/V. The frequency of collisions will also depend upon the molecular velocity u and thus it is proportional to nu/V. The force per impact will depend upon the mass m and the velocity u, and this is proportional to mu. This is the momentum per molecule. The total pressure is proportional to the product of all these effects, or is proportional to $(n/V)(u)(mu)$ or,

$$P \propto \left(\frac{n}{V}\right)(u)(mu) \propto \frac{n}{V}mu^2.$$

Introducing a constant of proportionality $(c/2)$, we have,

$$P = (c/2)\frac{nmu^2}{V},$$

or $$PV = cn\left(\frac{mu^2}{2}\right). \qquad (\textit{Equation 19–7})$$

This is one form of the kinetic theory equation. Earlier in this chapter, the (PV) product was shown on an experimental basis to be equal to (kT); that is,

$$PV = kT \text{ (the general gas law).} \qquad (\textit{Equation 19–4})$$

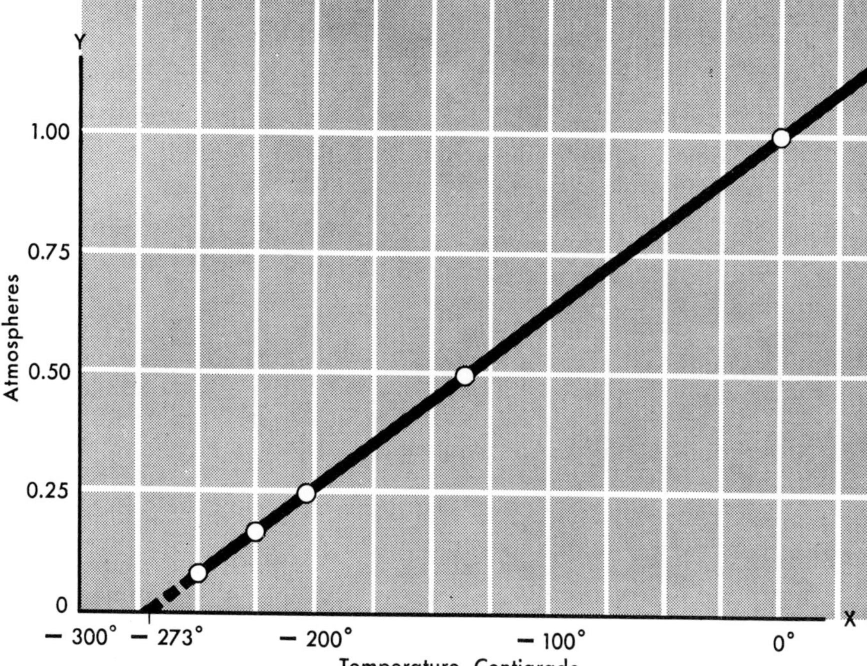

Fig. 19–8 *A decrease in temperature lowers the kinetic energy of molecules.*

Dividing Equation 19–4 by 19–7,

$$\frac{PV}{PV} = \frac{kT}{cn\left(\frac{mu^2}{2}\right)},$$

or

$$E_k = \frac{mu^2}{2} = \frac{kT}{cn} = \text{constant} \times T \qquad (Equation\ 19\text{–}8)$$

$$E_k \propto T.$$

Some important deductions from this form of the kinetic theory are as follows:

1. The kinetic energies of the molecules of *all* gases are the same for identical temperatures. This follows from Equation 19–8,

$$E_k = \text{constant} \times T.$$

2. The velocity of molecules varies inversely as their molecular masses. Indicating two different gases by the subscripts 1 and 2, we know from the kinetic theory,

$$E_k = \tfrac{1}{2}m_1u_1^2 = \tfrac{1}{2}m_2u_2^2 = kT.$$

Rearranging,

$$\left(\frac{u_2}{u_1}\right)^2 = \frac{m_1}{m_2},$$

or

$$\frac{u_2}{u_1} = \sqrt{\frac{m_1}{m_2}}. \qquad (Equation\ 19\text{–}9)$$

The movement of gas molecules due to their own molecular activity is known as *diffusion*. Thus the rates of diffusion of gases vary *inversely as the square root* of their molecular masses, or gases of low molecular weight diffuse faster than those of larger molecular weights. Hydrogen, the lightest gas, has the highest rate of diffusion of all gases, about 4000 miles per hour.

KINETIC MODEL FOR LIQUIDS

Water vapor when cooled becomes liquid water. A number of changes occur. First, there is a great decrease in volume. For example, 1740 milliliters of steam at 100° C. becomes about 1 milliliter of water at 100° C. Thus we have the picture of the molecules being very close to each other but still having motion. Second, there is a good deal of heat given off – the heat of condensation. For water this is about 540 calories per gram of vapor condensed to water. Any gas can, like water, be liquefied by increasing the external pressure and reducing the temperature. In liquids, therefore, the molecules are very close to each other and the voids between them are small compared with the voids between the molecules of a gas. However, the molecules of a liquid still undergo random motion, though lacking the freedom they have in the gaseous condition. It is this motion that accounts for the tendency of liquids to evaporate. A moving molecule possesses momentum *mu*, and there is a continual exchange of momenta between the molecules in the liquid as they collide with each other. The result is that some molecules have velocities considerably greater than that of the average. It is these faster-moving molecules that occasionally leave the liquid and pass into the space above to form a vapor. Since the slower molecules remaining in the liquid possess less energy, the temperature of the liquid falls. Hence, evaporation is a *cooling process.* A person wet with perspiration will often suffer a chill if exposed to a breeze. The air passing over the body hastens evaporation, and the heat necessary for the evaporation comes from the body itself. Rapid removal of heat from the body causes the chill.

Evaporation usually occurs at the surface of a liquid; but in boiling, evaporation also occurs within the liquid itself to form the bubbles of steam characteristic of boiling. This bubbling is called *ebullition.* The temperature at which water boils is dependent upon the pressure of the atmosphere. In boiling, steam issues from the vessel. To boil a liquid, it is necessary to supply enough energy to the molecules to enable them to push the molecules of air out of the

TABLE 19–3 PRESSURE OF WATER AT VARIOUS TEMPERATURES

TEMPERATURE CENTIGRADE	PRESSURE (mm of mercury)	PRESSURE (in atmospheres)
0°	4.60	0.0065
20°	17.50	0.023
50°	92.5	0.13
75°	289.1	0.38
100°	760.0	1.0
120.4°	1520.0	2.0
200°	11659.0	15.3
300°	64432.0	84.7

vessel. Hence, the pressure exerted by the vapor from the liquid must be equal to the pressure of the surrounding air. Furthermore, the bubbles which form at the bottom of boiling water can consist of steam alone, and they get larger as they move up through the liquid itself. A bubble just beneath the liquid surface cannot exist unless the pressure within the bubble, P_b, is equal to the pressure of the air, P_{air}, on the surface of the liquid. (Refer to Figure 19–10.) Hence, a decrease in atmospheric pressure means that bubble formation can occur at lower temperatures, and vice versa. This is shown in Table 19–3.

A boiling liquid does not necessarily mean a high temperature. Thus, water boils at 100° C. when the pressure is one atmosphere, but at 46° C. if the pressure is 0.10 atmosphere. Liquid helium boils at −268.9° C. when the pressure is one atmosphere. Mercury, on the other hand, boils at 356.9° C. A "three-minute" egg prepared on the

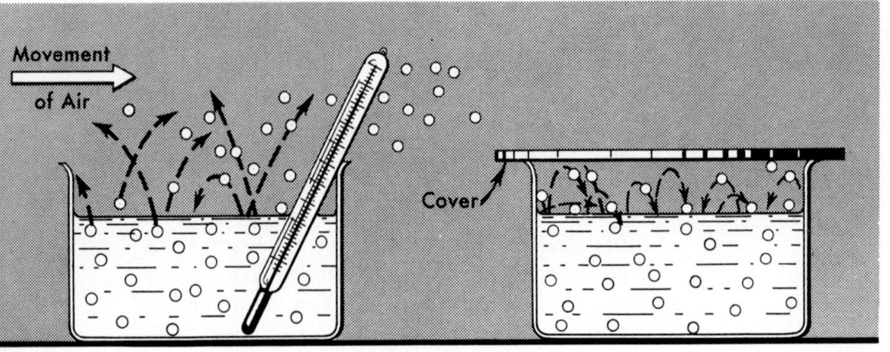

Fig. 19–9 *Liquids evaporate in an open vessel.*

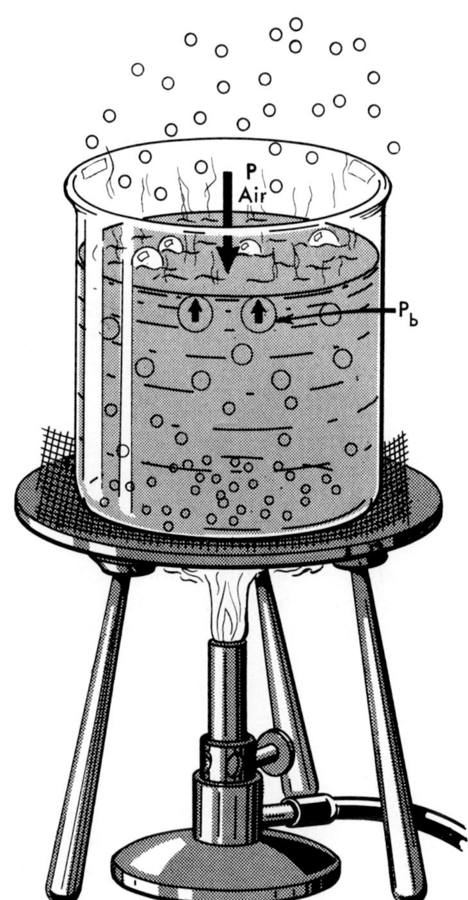

Fig. 19–10 *Conditions necessary for boiling in air. Pressure of vapor must equal pressure of atmosphere.*

top of Pike's Peak would have to be in boiling water about $8\frac{1}{2}$ minutes. At the altitude of Pike's Peak, 14,000 feet, the barometric pressure is about 455 millimeters of mercury, and the corresponding boiling point of water about 86° C. The preparation of canned food is an important industry. To save time in the cooking of the food and to insure sterilization, canned foods are usually prepared under high pressures. A household pressure cooker operated under a gauge reading of fifteen pounds per square inch (two atmospheres) will be operating at a temperature of 120° C. Food which requires an hour for preparation in an open kettle will require only a fraction of that time in a pressure cooker.

KINETIC THEORY APPLIED TO SOLIDS

The transition of a liquid to a solid also gives off heat energy. Anyone who has examined a snowflake, the frost on a window, or a crystal of salt or sugar, even under a low-power magnifying glass, will be impressed by the beautiful crystal structures. All solids are characterized by a definite orderly geometric arrangement of the units which enter into the formation of the crystal – molecules, atoms, or ions. The molecules in a crystal, however, still possess energy, so the individual molecules have a certain amount of motion, but the mean positions about which the molecules hover within the crystal do not change with respect to each other. There are various forces of attraction between the molecules within a crystal which account for its rigidity. A solid does not melt until enough heat is supplied to the individual molecules to overcome the forces of attraction. The energy needed to melt a gram of solid is called the heat of fusion. The same quantity of heat is evolved when the solid is formed from the liquid – amounting to eighty calories per gram in the case of water.

In discussing the kinetic theory, we have spoken of very small particles, called molecules, of exceedingly minute mass moving at very high velocities. Modern science has successfully answered the questions: how small, how heavy, and how fast? Information about molecules, obtained deductively by a mathematical treatment of the kinetic theory in connection with certain experimental data, is given in Table 19–4.

TABLE 19–4 CHARACTERISTICS OF THE MOLECULES IN AIR

Number in 1 ml	2.70×10^{19}
Average velocity	About $\frac{1}{3}$ mile per second
Molecular diameters	2×10^{-8} cm
Collisions per second	5×10^{9} per second
Mean free path = Average distance traveled between collisions	1×10^{-5} cm

UNITS FOR HEAT: THE CALORIE

The quantity of heat needed to raise the temperature of one gram of water one degree Centigrade (technically from 15° C. to 16° C.) is called a *calorie.* Note that this definition makes no assumption as to the nature of heat: it refers only to the quantity of heat needed to change one unit mass of water one degree Centigrade in temperature. This was the original definition of the *calorie*. The large or *kilocalorie* (1000 calories) is also frequently used.

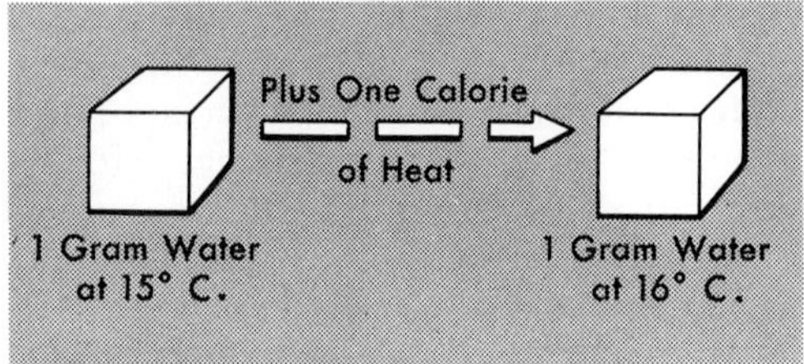

Fig. 19–11 *Concept of the calorie.*

You may wonder why water was taken to define the calorie. Water is actually a unique liquid. Its *heat capacity* (the amount of heat needed to change the temperature of unit mass of a substance one degree Centigrade) is so large that it can be used as a standard. In Table 19–5 are listed the heat capacities of a number of common substances. The large heat capacity of water is one of the reasons why water is used to transfer heat in hot water heating systems and why it is used as a cooling agent in the radiators of automobiles. It is this property of water also which accounts for the profound effect of large bodies of water on the climates of adjacent regions. Thus, Lake Michigan definitely affects the climate of the state of Michigan.

TABLE 19–5 HEAT CAPACITIES

SUBSTANCE	cals/g/deg. C. (approximate)
Liquid water	1.00
Steam	0.48 (at 110° C.)
Aluminum	0.21 (at 21° C.)
Iron	0.11 (at 20° C.)
Alcohol (ethyl)	0.58 (at 28° C.)
Glycerine	0.60 (at 58° C.)
Quartz (in soil)	0.19

A common heat unit analogous to the calorie is the British Thermal Unit, B.T.U. This is the quantity of heat needed to change the temperature of one pound of water one degree Fahrenheit. The B.T.U. is equal to 252 calories. Later (page 310) it will be shown that one calorie is 4.185×10^7 ergs or 4.185 joules.

HEAT AS MOTION

The behavior and observations of heat and matter eventually culminated in two great laws of thermodynamics. This was possible only after the clear recognition of the nature of heat — the energy of motion of molecules and atoms. Furthermore, it was possible only after the rise and demise of the first important theory of heat: the caloric theory. A brief history of the caloric theory is included for historical reasons and to show again how science must always discard even useful theories, if facts are discovered which are not in accord with the theories.

The caloric theory was originated by Joseph Black (1728–99), a famous Scottish scientist. According to this theory, heat is a "subtle, invisible, weightless fluid, passing between the particles of bodies with perfect freedom." Until recent advances in quantum theory, it was nonsensical to postulate the existence of a "weightless fluid." Nevertheless, the caloric theory had a great vogue, and it was remarkably successful in explaining many of the facts concerning heat. The theory, for example, made it possible to measure heat changes quantitatively. Thus Black devised methods of calorimetry, invented heat units, and experimentally measured heat capacities and heats of fusion and evaporation, with the guidance of the caloric theory.

But troublesome facts kept bobbing up which the caloric theory could not account for. Sir Humphry Davy in 1799 melted ice merely by rubbing two pieces together, even though the ice was below the freezing point of water. The significance of this experiment was in bringing about melting without the addition of "liquid heat" as such. About the same time, Benjamin Thompson (later Count Rumford) was impressed by the amount of heat evolved during the boring of cannon. Rumford was born in Massachusetts, but at the time of the American Revolution he left for Europe where he moved in governmental and intellectual circles both in England and on the Continent. He is remembered for his contributions to the science of heat, for adapting the advances of science to the social advancement of mankind, for founding the Royal Institution in London, and for endowing the Rumford Professorship at Harvard University.

Rumford became convinced that work against friction results in heat, but he had to combat the advocates of the caloric theory. In one experiment Rumford succeeded in bringing water to the boiling point with heat produced by boring a cannon, and the boiling continued as long as boring continued. Rumford argued that it was unreasonable that fluid caloric could come from the brass of the cannon continuously. To believe that heat inherent in matter could be extracted continuously and still leave the matter in its original condition was as unreasonable, according to Rumford, as to believe that water could be squeezed from a sponge continuously without loss of weight. In this operation, Rumford insisted, the heat came not from the brass, but from the work expended on the boring operation. According to the calorists, caloric was liberated during the boring operation. Very well, countered Rumford, the borings should differ from the original brass by having a lower heat capacity. He found no difference in the heat capacity of the metal before and after boring.

Rumford's final conclusion was definite but rather difficult to understand: *heat is motion*. In the boring experiments, the energy was furnished by horses, and the ultimate source of the heat lay in the oxidation of the fodder consumed by the horses. Rumford undoubtedly had a clear picture in his own mind of the fact that heat was energy, though his picture of heat as motion needed fifty years longer for final clarification.

THE EQUIVALENCE OF HEAT AND WORK

The epoch-making experiments of James Prescott Joule, announced in England in 1847, finally proved to a skeptical scientific world the equivalence of energy and heat. In effect, Joule sought to determine the experimental value of the proportionality constant, J, needed to transform the relationship,

$$W(\text{ork}) \propto H(\text{eat}),$$

into a mathematical equality, namely,

$$W = JH, \quad \text{or} \quad J = \frac{W}{H}. \qquad (\textit{Equation 19–10})$$

This constant is known as the *mechanical equivalent of heat*. The essential parts of the simple apparatus used by Joule to determine the value of J are indicated in Figure 19–12. The vessel A contains a known mass m of water. In this vessel the paddle wheels are rotated against the fric-

Fig. 19–12 *Joule's method for determining the mechanical equivalent of heat.*

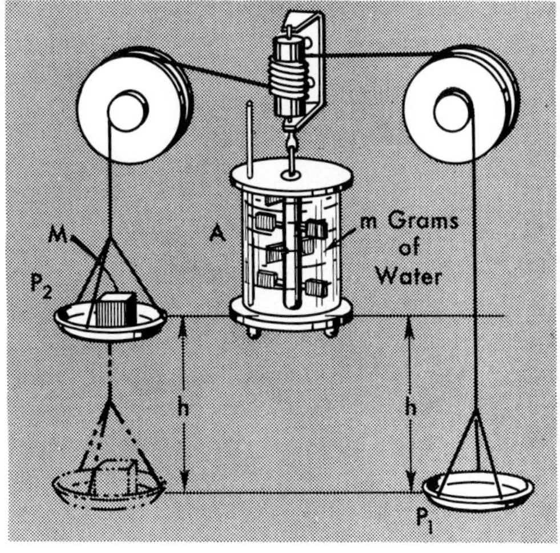

tion of the water by placing a known mass M on one of the pans, say P_2. When the mass has fallen to the floor, it is transferred to the other pan, P_1, which in the meantime has been raised a distance equal to that through which P_2 has fallen. The mass M will again fall to the floor. This operation can be repeated as many times (n) as desired. In this way a definite, measurable amount of work is performed against friction, with the result that a known amount of heat is produced:

$$\text{Work performed} = W = nMgh \text{ ergs}$$

$$\text{Heat produced} = H = m(S)(t_2 - t_1)$$

In the last expression, S = heat capacity of water = 1 calorie per gram per degree Centigrade, $(t_2 - t_1)$ = rise in temperature Centigrade of the water. Joule's many experiments showed that work may be converted into heat and that there is always a definite relationship between these two quantities; that is, a definite amount of work is equivalent to a certain amount of heat,

$J = 4.18 \times 10^7$ ergs of work to produce 1 calorie,

and

1 B.T.U. = 25030 foot-poundals of work.

This quantity is referred to as the *mechanical equivalent of heat*. Joule's equivalent of heat makes possible a much more precise definition for the calorie; the quantity of heat equivalent to 4.18×10^7 ergs of work.

THE SCIENCE OF THERMODYNAMICS

The contribution of Joule was partly responsible for the development of thermodynamics – the study of the relations between heat and mechanical energy or work, and the conversion of one into the other. Joule's contribution is variously referred to as the law of conservation of energy or the *first law of thermodynamics:* energy can be neither created nor destroyed. This means that, when a certain amount and kind of energy disappears, an exactly equivalent amount of some other form of energy appears. The formulation of this law marks one of the crowning mental achievements of the human race.

In Joule's experiments mechanical work was converted entirely into heat. What about the reverse process, the conversion of heat in any engine into work? All engines, steam, gasoline, or jet, are mechanical devices for converting heat into work. How efficient can they be? Does the first law of thermodynamics apply to them? These questions in reality were raised and answered before Joule's law had been accepted. The answers were provided by a brilliant young French army officer, Sadi Carnot (1796–1832) in 1824. He showed theoretically that 100 per cent conversion of heat into work is impossible. In every process a certain fraction of the heat becomes unavailable and lost for all practical purposes, because all heat engines operate on differences in the temperatures of the inlet and exhaust gases.

Consider a simple reciprocating steam engine: a two-cycle engine, a charging and expansion stroke, followed by an exhaustion stroke. When the piston has reached the limit of its travel to the left, steam at high temperature and pressure is admitted through the inlet valve. When the inlet valve closes, the steam expands to a lower pressure. In this process, the impact of many fast-moving steam molecules against the piston means that it acquires energy of translation (mechanical energy) which is imparted to the flywheel. At the limit of its stroke to the right, the exhaust valve opens, the inertia of the heavy flywheel now carries the piston to the left and pushes the exhaust steam at a lower temperature into the atmosphere. This completes the second cycle. Then the whole cycle repeats itself. In simplest terms, a heat engine converts a *part* of the kinetic energy of the molecules of the operating gas into mechanical energy.

On the basis of the first law, we can write,

W = Mechanical work obtained in a heat engine.

= Heat supplied (Q_1) to engine through inlet valve. − Heat lost (Q_2) to surroundings through exhaust valve.

Furthermore,

Energy heat supplied
$$(Q_1) = E_1 = nk'(\tfrac{1}{2}m_1u_1^2) = nkT_1$$
Energy exhaust steam
$$(Q_2) = E_2 = nk'(\tfrac{1}{2}m_2u_2^2) = nkT_2$$
Heat converted to work
$$W = (Q_1 - Q_2) = E_1 - E_2 = nkT_1 - nkT_2 = nk(T_1 - T_2)$$
The fraction of the heat converted to work $= W$
$$= \frac{Q_1 - Q_2}{Q_1} = \frac{E_1 - E_2}{E_1} = nk\frac{(T_1 - T_2)}{nkT_1} = \frac{T_1 - T_2}{T_1}$$

This final conclusion, which applies to any heat engine can be written,

Engine efficiency
= The fraction of the heat converted to work.
$$= \frac{T_1 - T_2}{T_1}. \qquad (Equation\ 19\text{–}11)$$

This final conclusion is often referred to as the *second law of thermodynamics.* It is this conclusion which shows that it is never possible to convert heat energy entirely into work, unless $T_2 = 0°$ K.

The reverse process, however, the conversion of a given amount of work entirely into heat, is possible. These two important conclusions can be diagrammed as follows:

The equation (Equation 19–11),
$$\frac{E_1 - E_2}{E_1} = \frac{T_1 - T_2}{T_1},$$
is a statement of the *second law of thermodynamics.* This law, with the first law, is the basis for the whole science of *energetics* — the study of energy. The whole sequence of the development of more efficient heat engines is based upon the application of these two laws.

HEAT ENGINES

It is not the purpose of this text to discuss the mechanical details of heat engines but merely to stress the principles involved in their operation and to mention their order of appearance historically. Heat engines operate on either a cyclical process, as do the steam engine and the internal combustion engine, or on a continuous process, as do the steam or gas turbine and the jet propulsion engine. In either type of engine, they operate on a gas at high temperature T_1 which flows through the engine. Some of the energy becomes useful mechanical energy (motive power), and the rest of the energy (Q_2 at temperature T_2) goes into unavoidable heat loss to the surroundings. Refer to Figure 19–13. By the ideas expressed in Equation 19–11, we know that,

$W = Q_1 - Q_2$ = Heat input minus heat lost to surroundings,
$$\text{Efficiency} = \frac{Q_1 - Q_2}{Q_1} = \frac{T_1 - T_2}{T_1}.$$

The theoretical heat efficiency of the early reciprocating steam engines was almost unbelievably low. Assume that an engine operated on steam at 200 pounds per square inch, and an exhaust temperature

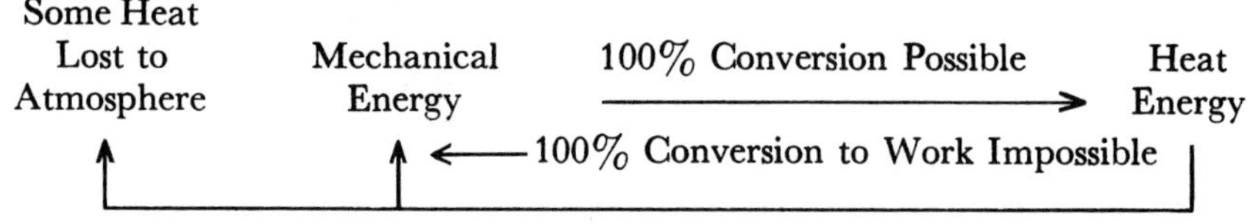

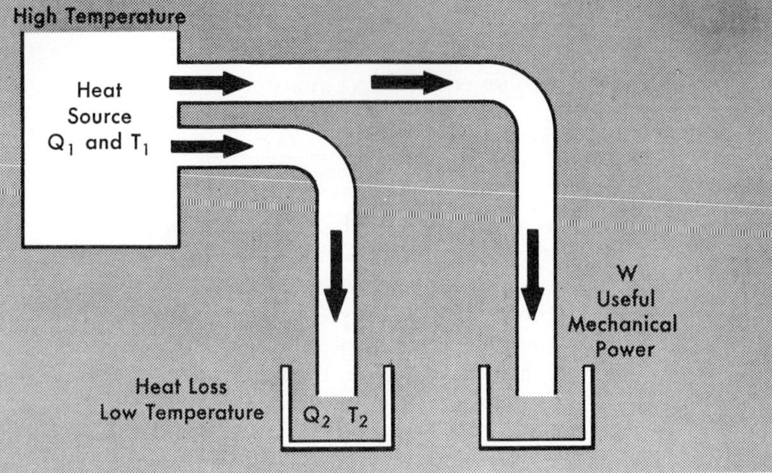

Fig. 19–13 *Heat path in a heat engine.*

(T_2) of about 50° C. The initial temperature (T_1) would be about 200° C.

Note, after changing to absolute temperatures, that

$$\text{Efficiency} = \frac{473° \text{ K.} - 323° \text{ K.}}{473° \text{ K.}} = \frac{150}{473}$$
$$= 0.32 \text{ or } 32 \text{ per cent.}$$

Actual operating efficiencies will be even less, due to frictional losses in moving parts in the engine mechanism. It should not be surprising, then, to learn that old-fashioned steam locomotives had efficiencies so low that only about five per cent of the energy of the coal was actually converted into useful mechanical work. Most of the energy was wasted as heat losses through the smokestack, from the boiler itself, and in the form of unavoidable friction.

Heat engines were steadily improved as men came to understand them better through the second law of thermodynamics. The efficiency of any heat engine can be increased by any rise in the initial temperature T_1 or by any decrease in the exhaust temperature T_2. In general, T_2 cannot be reduced much below the temperature of the atmosphere within which the engine is operating, say about 30° C. Hence, the principal means of increasing engine efficiencies is to operate on T_1, the initial temperature.

The order of appearance of increasingly efficient types of heat engines historically was as follows:

1. *The reciprocating steam engine.* This utilized steam at pressures up to about 300 pounds per square inch (214° C.). If the exhaust temperature was 30° C., the theoretical efficiency was

$$\frac{[(214°+273°)-(30°+273°)]}{(214°+273°)} = \frac{487° - 303°}{487°}$$
$$= \frac{184}{487} = .38 \text{ or } 38 \text{ per cent.}$$

2. *The steam turbine.* This engine utilizes much higher steam pressures. Pressures and temperatures are as high as 4000 pounds per square inch, and 450° C. If the inlet and exhaust temperatures were 500° C. and 30° C., respectively, the theoretical efficiency becomes

$$\frac{773° - 303°}{773°} = \frac{470}{773} = 0.61 \text{ or } 61 \text{ per cent.}$$

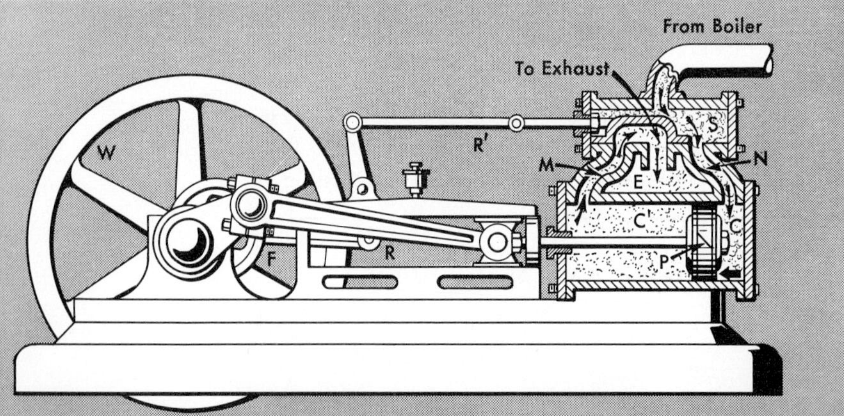

Fig. 19–14 *Sectional view of a simple reciprocating steam engine. W, flywheel; F, eccentric; R, connecting rod; R′, eccentric rod; M, opening into exhaust pipe; E, exhaust pipe; S, steam box; N, opening into cylinder; C, C′, cylinder space; P, piston.*

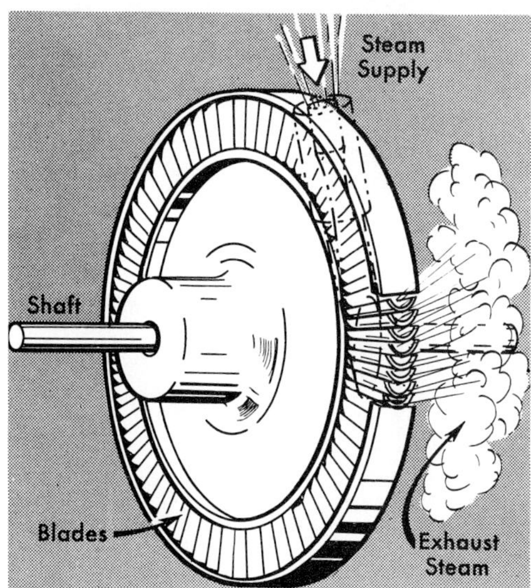

Fig. 19–15 *Principle of the steam turbine. A turbine wheel with blades and a set of nozzles. Steam from phantom nozzle may be seen impinging upon a number of blades.* (*De Laval Steam Turbine Co.*)

3. *The internal combustion engine.* In this engine a very high initial temperature is reached by burning the fuel within the cylinders. The common automobile engines and Diesel engines are of this type. The temperatures of the expanding hot gases can easily reach 550° C. Thus the theoretical efficiency becomes

$$\frac{823° - 303°}{823°} = \frac{520}{823} = 0.63 \text{ or } 63 \text{ per cent.}$$

4. *The gas turbine.* The hot gases from the burned fuel are utilized as in the steam turbine. The efficiencies are very high.

5. *The reaction engine (jet propulsion).* The basic principle of operation is to burn a fuel to form gases at high temperatures which, when ejected through a small aperture, result in very high gas velocities. Newton's third law of motion operates. The hot gases discharging in one direction produce a motion of the engine in the opposite direction. A toy balloon, when inflated and released, illustrates motion due to action and reaction. Reaction engines are considered the most efficient engines thus far developed, for they give a conversion from heat energy to work of 50 to 75 per cent.

There are two types of reaction engines. The first, called the *rocket* type, operates without air. It carries liquid or solid fuel (usually alcohol) and its own oxygen for combustion (usually in the form of 80 to 90 per cent hydrogen peroxide). Because there is no dependence on air for the oxygen supply needed in the combustion of the fuel, this type of engine can operate high above the earth's air layer. The "V–2" rocket was of this general type.

The second kind of reaction engine, called the *jet engine,* is used within the atmosphere in airplanes. The engine draws in large quantities of air which are compressed to burn the fuel, usually some low-grade oil. But whereas in a Diesel engine the gases are utilized to move pistons, in the jet they are discharged from one end of the engine with a high velocity, thus imparting motion to the engine in the opposite direction.

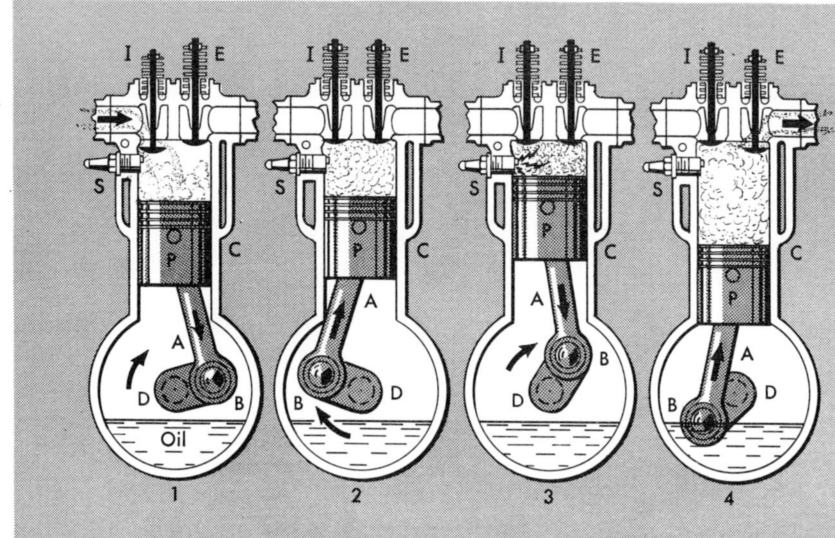

Fig. 19–16 *A simple four-cycle internal combustion engine. (1) Intake stroke. (2) Compression stroke. (3) Expansion stroke (4) Exhaust stroke.*

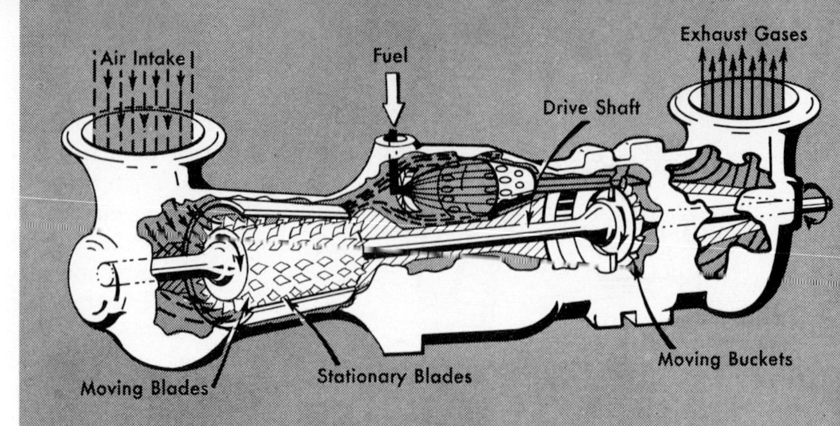

Fig. 19–17 *Principle of a gas turbine.*

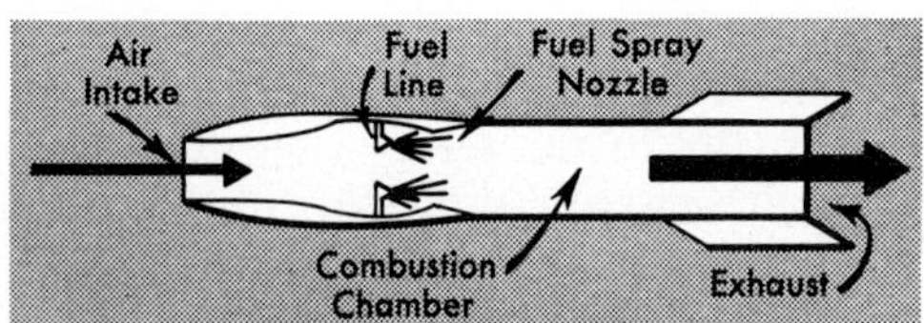

Fig. 19–18 *Principle of ram-jet propulsion.*

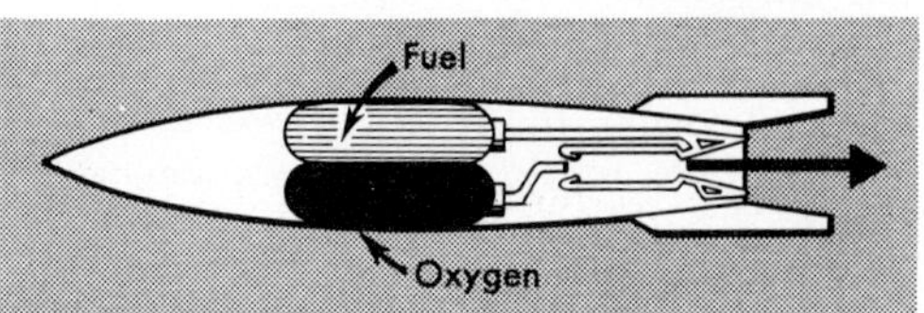

Fig. 19–19 *Principle of rocket propulsion.*

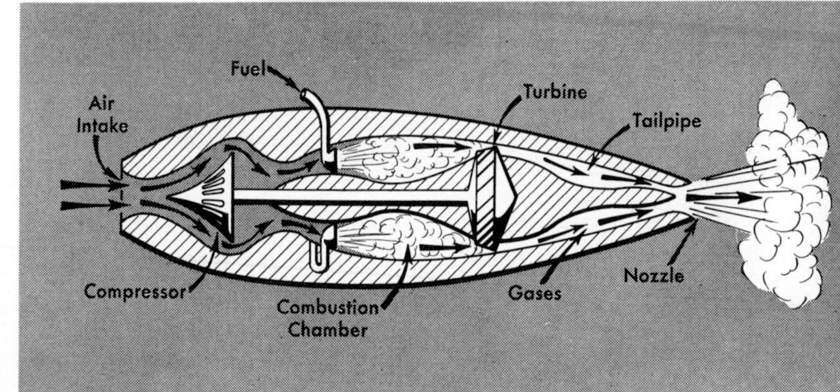

Fig. 19–20A *Principle of a turbo-jet engine.*

Fig. 19–20B *A turbo-jet engine. This type of engine contains a gas turbine to drive a propeller and also utilizes jet propulsion.* (*General Electric Company*)

REFRIGERATION

The heat engines considered thus far involve the transfer of heat from a hot to a cold region. In the steam engine, for example, water is changed by heat to steam, which is then transferred into a cylinder, where it gives up some of its heat and is condensed back to water. The latter may be returned to the boiler and recycled. The reverse of this cycle forms the basis of refrigeration. A liquid which boils at a low temperature, usually below the freezing point of water, serves as the medium to transfer heat from a cold region to a hot region. The liquid is permitted to enter a cooling (expansion) chamber, where it abstracts heat from the stored food, and then passes into the vapor state. The vapor is pumped through a compression pump into a condenser, where it is changed into a liquid in a set of condensing coils outside the food compartment. The liquid is then returned to the cooling (expansion) chamber to be recycled. Heat from the condenser escapes to the surrounding air outside of the refrigerator. Thus a kitchen with a refrigerator of this type always gets warmer as the food compartment gets cooler. A refrigerating unit is simply a heat engine with its action reversed.

The motor needed to operate the unit supplies energy through a compressor to the unit. A quantity of heat Q_1 from the cooling chamber is transferred by absorption in a suitable liquid, by means of the motor and compressor, to the condenser coils and becomes a larger quantity of heat Q_2 which escapes into the room outside the refrigerator. By the first law of thermodynamics,

$$Q_2 = Q_1 + W.$$

The cost of operation for the unit is the cost of the electrical energy input W.

The essentials of the electric household refrigerator are shown diagrammatically in Figure 19–21. The medium of heat transfer is some gas, such as sulfur dioxide, methyl chloride, or dichlorodifluoromethane (Freon). All these substances boil far

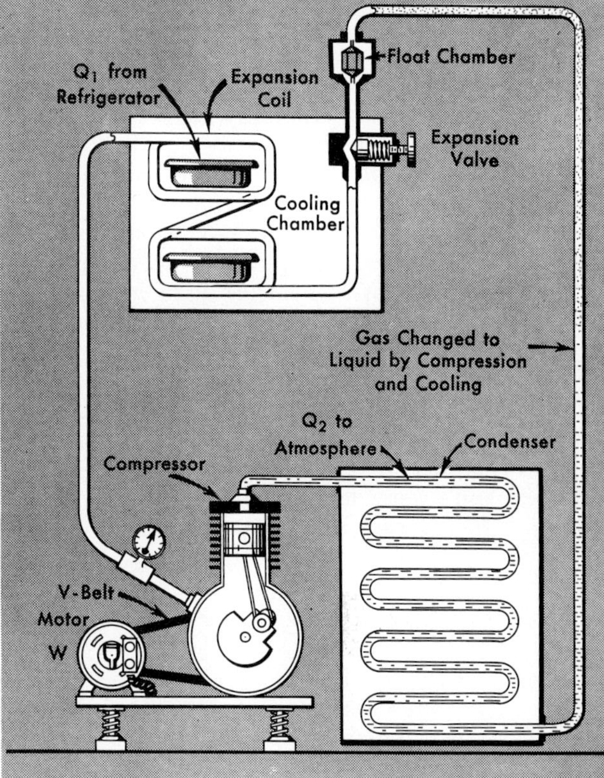

Fig. 19–21 *The essential parts of a common refrigerator.*

below the freezing point of water, and therefore require pressure to be changed into the liquid state at ordinary temperatures. The compressor, as shown in the diagram, is operated by an electric motor. It is directly connected to the cooling unit, so that the refrigerant vapor is always at low pressure. The vapor is withdrawn by the compressor and compressed to from two to three atmospheres of pressure, and then passed to the coiled condenser. The vapor, when compressed, becomes heated as the gas becomes a liquid. The heat (Q_2) from the condenser coils is lost rapidly to the atmosphere. The liquid is recycled to the cooling unit. Some type of float chamber regulates the flow of the liquid refrigerant into the cooling unit. When sufficient liquid is collected in the float chamber, the float bulb is lifted, opening a needle valve and allowing the liquid to return to the cooling unit at the top of the upper storage section of the cabinet. The liquid refrigerant in the cooling unit evaporates when the pressure on it is reduced by the partial vacuum produced within the compressor. In so evaporating, heat from the food compartment and from water contained in the ice trays is absorbed through the cooling unit. Thus refrigeration is obtained. In large refrigerators, which are used for cold-storage rooms and for manufacturing ice, ammonia is commonly used as the refrigerant medium. The process is not different in principle from that described above. In the manufacture of ice the cooling coils are immersed in large tanks of brine. Vessels of pure water left suspended in the brine are frozen solid and withdrawn as ice.

SOCIAL EFFECTS OF HEAT ENGINES

Heat engines have completely revolutionized life in economically advanced nations. The population in such countries has increased over 500 per cent. England in Shakespeare's time had a population of 5,000,000; it doubled within fifty years after the introduction of Watt's steam engine, and is 45 million today. Similarly, the population of Europe rose from 100 million to 535 million. The age of traveling peddlers, of the individual shops of smiths, shoemakers, and artisans, where work was brought to the worker, gave way by degrees to the modern scene of huge stores and factories. The age in which families raised most of their food gave way by degrees to our present social order in which a very large proportion of families are not even acquainted with the conditions under which food is raised or processed.

The modern machine age appears on the whole humane, but its early stages of development were marked by inhumanity and exploitation of both adults and children, and bore the stamp of barbarism. Huge and hideous towns sprang up overnight whose populations toiled drearily from childhood to old age under the inexorable discipline of the factory whistle. Heat engines made vast amounts of power available. Production increased and made possible the accumulation of fortunes on a scale never before dreamed of. Distances were minimized, cities became larger, and governments more powerful. Labor-saving devices and inventions multiplied rapidly, so that within a century and a half the use of leisure time became a problem in some of the more industrialized communities.

Although the heat engine has solved a great number of problems for mankind, it has at the same time confronted the average individual with a number of new problems. Life has become more complex, so that many people have wondered whether the heat engine, instead of being a deliverer, has not enslaved a large proportion of mankind, and whether it does not threaten the destruction of civilization. Machines are blamed for depriving man of work and for wholesale destruction from the air. Mankind has lost the security of a feudalistic society too rapidly and has been pushed forward at such a speed that it has been difficult to acquire new roots. Growth has been so rapid, and advance so swift, that vast new social problems have been created, many of which still await solution. It is not the machine, however, that is to be blamed, but man's inability to solve the social problems the machine created.

SUMMARY

1. Heat is the form of energy that is usually involved in chemical and physical changes and in the operation of all forms of heat engines.
2. Heat is the motion of the molecules of matter. Heat energy is the kinetic energy of atoms and molecules.
3. The amount of heat (energy) in matter is directly proportional to a temperature scale known as the absolute (Kelvin) scale.
4. The kinetic theory readily accounts for the three physical states of matter, solid, liquid, and gas or vapor.
5. Important scientific laws concerning behavior of gases are Boyle's, Gay-Lussac's, Charles's, and the ideal gas law.

6. Substances which can lose heat energy to their surroundings at a greater rate than they receive heat have a higher temperature than the surroundings.
7. The common heat units are the calorie and the B.T.U. One B.T.U. = 252 calories.
8. The number of calories needed to melt one gram of a solid without change in temperature is its *heat of fusion.* For ice this is 80 calories.
9. The number of calories needed to change one gram of a liquid to vapor without change in temperature is its *heat of vaporization.* For water at 100° C. and one atmosphere, this is 540 calories.
10. Joule established the equivalence of heat and work:

    $J = 4.18 \times 10^7$ ergs $= 4.18$ joules $= 1$ calorie.
11. The quantity of heat in calories needed to change the temperature of unit mass of substance by one degree Centigrade is its *heat capacity.*
12. The kinetic theory is largely responsible for our present understanding of the three physical states of matter. The theory readily accounts for such phenomena or facts as the following:
    a. The pressure exerted by gases and their tendency to expand is due to rapidly moving, perfectly elastic molecules.
    b. Gases are markedly reduced in volume by an increase in external pressure because of the relatively large space between the molecules.
    c. Heat as energy is the kinetic energy of rapidly moving molecules.
    d. The change in the heat energy of a substance is due to a change in the speed and thus the kinetic energy of the molecules.
    e. At the absolute zero of temperature, the molecules of a substance are stationary and the heat energy is zero.
    f. The heat content of a substance is directly proportional to its absolute temperature.
    g. A sample of liquid substance possesses definite volume, but its molecules still possess relatively great freedom of movement.
    h. A true solid consists of molecules in a crystal in positions relatively fixed with respect to each other but still having some vibratory motion about mean positions.
13. The process of evaporation requires an absorption of heat and results in cooling the surroundings. Heat is given off in condensation.
14. The process of melting requires an absorption of heat and likewise results in cooling the surroundings. Heat is given off in freezing.
15. The study of energy and the uses of energy depend upon the first and second laws of thermodynamics.
16. In heat engines part of the heat produced in the combustion of a fuel is converted into mechanical energy and performs work.
17. The steam engine and the steam turbine are external combustion engines. Steam, generated outside of the engine, is allowed to expand, thus transferring some of its kinetic energy to the moving parts of the engine.
18. The automobile, airplane, Diesel, and jet engines are internal combustion engines. The fuel is burned within the engine, and the compressed hot gases are used to perform work.
19. Mechanical energy can be wholly converted to heat, but it is impossible to convert heat wholly into work. The fraction of heat converted into work depends on the magnitude of the difference between the two temperatures at which a heat engine operates.
20. The principle of refrigeration is the reverse of the cycle of a steam engine; in refrigeration a liquid which boils at a low temperature serves as the medium to transfer heat from a cold region (the desired effect) to a hot region.

STUDY EXERCISES

1. Explain in terms of the kinetic molecular theory the transformation of the chemical energy contained in coal to the work obtained in a steam engine.
2. Assume that you have sufficient coal which, when burned, will give you one million

calories of heat. What happens to this heat energy in an efficient steam engine? Enumerate all the losses and show which ones can be eliminated.

3. In the example above, assuming that we could eliminate all the losses of heat, could we ever obtain a 100 per cent conversion?
4. Below are listed a series of changes. Place after each change a plus (+) if during the change the velocity of the molecules in the system is increased; place a minus (—) if there is a decrease in the velocity of the molecules; place a zero if there is no change in the velocity of the molecules.
   a. Passage of the refrigerant contained in a household refrigerator to the coils of the freezer chamber where ice cubes are made. . . . .
   b. Compression of the refrigerant in the above example from the freezer coils to the reservoir tank. . . . .
   c. The expansion of hot gases in an automobile engine. . . . .
   d. Passage of air from one room to another while both rooms are at the same temperature. . . . .
   e. Steam passes from the steam box to the exhaust pipe. . . . .
5. What are the essential differences between: (*a*) steam and gasoline engines; (*b*) gasoline engines and Diesel engines; (*c*) jet and piston engines; (*d*) a refrigerator and a steam engine?
6. How many calories of heat are required (theoretically) to raise a mass of one ton four hundred feet? In actual practice, if the operation is done by a crane operated by a steam engine using steam at 110° C., how many calories of fuel are (theoretically) required?
7. The operation of the automobile engine is usually resolved into a cycle of four strokes. Describe briefly the function of each stroke.
8. Discuss briefly the first and second laws of thermodynamics and show why a perpetual motion machine is impossible.
9. If the hand is placed against the back of a household refrigerator while it is in operation, heat is felt. Explain.
10. Discuss the effect of the development of steam engines on the social structure of Europe from 1850 to 1900 and on that of America during the same interval.
11. Mark true (*T*) or false (*F*):
    A heat engine:
    transforms heat into work. . . . .
    transforms work into heat. . . . .
    would have an efficiency of 100 per cent if it were not for frictional losses. . . . .
    can operate continuously in surroundings which are at constant temperature. . . .
    can operate only when heat can be supplied to it at a high temperature and be removed at a low temperature. . . . .
    has a theoretical efficiency equal to the temperature difference divided by the higher temperature. . . . .
    would have a theoretical efficiency of 100 per cent if the exhaust were at the absolute zero. . . . .
12. Below you will find certain definitions or statements pertaining to material presented in this chapter. With each, associate by number the correct response from those listed at the right.
    a. The scientist who devised the absolute temperature scale. . . . .
    b. The temperature at which a substance possesses no energy in the form of heat, i.e., there is an absence of molecular motion. . . . .
    c. The quantity of heat necessary to change the temperature of unit mass of substance one degree Centigrade. . . . .
    d. The investigator who did much to disprove the caloric theory of heat. . . . .
    e. The quantity of heat in calories needed to melt one gram of ice without change in temperature. . . . .
    f. The quantity of heat needed to change the temperature of one pound of water one degree Fahrenheit. . . . .
    g. The quantity of heat in calories needed to convert one gram of water at 100° C. into steam without change in temperature. . . . .

    1. Calorie
    2. Joule
    3. Kelvin
    4. Conduction
    5. Count Rumford
    6. Heat of fusion
    7. Heat capacity
    8. 540 cals/g
    9. B.T.U.
    10. 80 cals/g
    11. Heat of evaporation
    12. Absolute zero
    13. Helmholtz

h. The quantity of heat needed to melt one gram of a substance at its melting point without change in temperature........

i. The scientist who gave convincing experimental evidence for the equivalence of work and heat....................

13. Circle the number or numbers of the words or phrases which make the statement correct:

a. Heat engines include (1) generators; (2) steam engines; (3) gasoline engines; (4) Diesel engines; (5) transformers.

b. Most automobile engines are (1) steam; (2) Diesel; (3) gasoline; (4) hot air; (5) four-cycle internal combustion.

c. The Diesel engine differs from the gasoline engine in that (1) it has no carburetor; (2) it runs at very high compression; (3) it uses cheaper fuel; (4) no spark is necessary; (5) it is more efficient.

d. In the cylinder of a four-cycle gasoline engine the following steps take place (1) compression; (2) forcing in of explosive mixture; (3) driving out of exhaust gases; (4) mixing of gasoline and air; (5) explosion.

e. The order of these steps (item *d*) is....
....

14. Use the kinetic molecular hypothesis to explain the following phenomena:

a. If a bottle of ammonia water is left unstoppered, the odor of ammonia is soon apparent through the room.

b. A rubber balloon inflated with hydrogen soon collapses.

c. There are often alternate dark and light streaks on the plaster ceilings of heated rooms.

d. A vessel of water, if allowed to evaporate spontaneously, gets cooler.

e. A person moist with perspiration is often "chilled" if he stands in a breeze.

f. Why does dust tend to move from the warmer to the cooler part of a room?

g. If water is placed on a layer of syrup in a vessel, the two layers gradually "mix."

h. A certain vessel contained one pound of air at one atmosphere. When an additional pound of air was pumped into the same vessel, the pressure became two atmospheres.

15. Encircle correct answers:

a. What quantity of heat is needed to change the temperature of one gram of water from 15° to 16° C.?
1000 cals. 1 cal. 50 cals. 500 cals.

b. How many calories are needed to change 50 grams of water from 15° C. to 16° C.?
1000 cals. 1 cal. 50 cals. 500 cals.

c. How many calories are needed to change 50 grams of water from 15° C. to 35°C.?
1000 cals. 1 cal. 50 cals. 500 cals.

16. While playing a game of basketball you lose 400 milliliters of water by evaporation. Heat of evaporation of water is 540 cal/g.

a. How many calories of heat were lost by your body?

b. If all this heat was due to playing basketball, how many ergs of work was lost in the process as heat? (1 cal. $= 4.18 \times 10^7$ ergs)

c. A player during the course of a hard basketball game often loses from three to five pounds in body weight. Account for this loss in two ways.

FOR FURTHER READING

1. LEMON, H. B., *From Galileo to the Nuclear Age*. Chicago: University of Chicago Press, 1946.

The concepts of work, potential and kinetic energy, the relation of work to heat, and power are discussed in Chapters 9, 10, 11, 12, and 13.

2. WHITE, HARVEY E., *Classical and Modern Physics*. New York: D. Van Nostrand Company, 1940.

Excellent discussion with many simple problems of the meaning of work, energy, and power is given in Chapter 6. The principles of mechanical refrigeration are discussed on pages 163 ff.

3. CHALMERS, T. W., *Historic Researches*. London: Morgan Brothers Publishers, 1949.

A concise and interesting account of the work of Joule in establishing the principle of conservation of energy is presented in Chapter II.

4. BERRY, A. J., *From Classical to Modern Chemistry*. New York: Cambridge University Press, 1954.

Chapter II gives the historical development of our concept of heat.

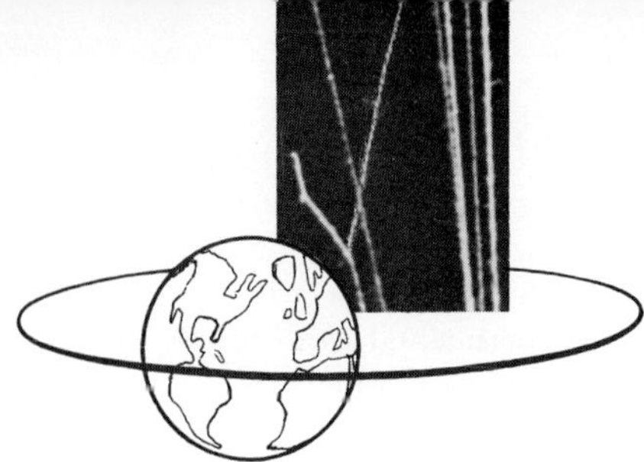

20 THE BEGINNINGS OF CHEMISTRY

THE PARTICLE of matter that we have been most concerned with thus far has been the molecule, that ultimate particle in any pure substance which determines the properties of the whole substance and which is endowed with motion or energy. It is the purpose of this chapter to show that molecules in turn consist of smaller particles called atoms. Molecules may be simple, consisting of a single atom, or complex, consisting of two or more atoms of the same or different elements.

In discussing atoms, it is necessary to deal with two entirely different scientific eras. The first era started with the contributions of Lavoisier (France, 1743–94) and John Dalton (England, 1766–1844) and lasted until about 1915. During the nineteenth century the important science of chemistry developed into one of the principal physical sciences, largely because of Dalton's atomic theory. This is a splendid example of the fruitfulness of a sound scientific theory. Definite proof for the existence of atoms was lacking, but the inferential proofs for atoms were so many and convincing that scientists had no doubt of their reality.

Our present atomic theory is a product of this century. Dalton's atomic theory had to be modified as scientists devised experimental techniques to count atoms and even to determine the composition of atoms in terms of fundamental particles smaller than atoms. We now know, for example, that atoms are real. In a later chapter we shall deal with the contributions to the present accepted atomic theory of such prominent twentieth-century scientists as Millikan, Rutherford, Bohr, Einstein, and Fermi. This chapter will be concerned with the early atomic theory of John Dalton.

LAVOISIER AND ROBERT BOYLE

Antoine Lavoisier (France, 1743–94) is considered the founder of modern chemistry but he in turn was greatly indebted to Robert Boyle (England, 1627–91) for disposing of the idea that had persisted since the time of Aristotle that everything was composed of four "elements" – air, earth, fire, and water. He called himself, "The Sceptical Chymist." He showed, for example, that even the noble metal, gold, could be alloyed with other elements or dissolved in *aqua regia* or otherwise drastically modified in form. But the gold could always be recovered as gold. Clearly, gold consisted of indestructible atoms of a form of matter properly called an *element*. Boyle went on to contribute the concept of elements which could be converted by chemical changes into many different substances. These substances we now call *compounds*.

Lavoisier continued the work of Boyle, but with an important change in procedure — the use of a chemical balance in studying chemical changes. He had no patience for experimentation without precise weight data, and his lack of patience made chemistry a quantitative science. He buried, for example, the *phlogiston theory*. This theory is another good example of the dangers of thinking in abstract terms divorced from reality. The phlogistonists explained that burning was the result of a loss of "phlogiston," which was believed to be associated with any substance capable of burning. Lavoisier reasoned that a burning substance should undergo a *decrease* in weight due to a loss of phlogiston. Lavoisier with his chemical balance proved conclusively that any burning substance undergoes an *increase* in weight, a fact incompatible with the phlogiston theory.

The beginnings of modern chemistry date from 1772 when Lavoisier clearly described the nature of the changes in ordinary burning or combustion. In that year he reported, for example, that he had discovered that "sulfur in burning, far from losing weight, rather gains it; that is to say, from a pound of sulfur may be obtained more than a pound of vitriolic acid (sulfuric acid), allowance being made for the moisture (and oxygen) of the air. It is the same in the case of phosphorus. The gain in weight comes from the prodigious quantity of air which is fixed during the combustion."

Lavoisier was not content merely to hypothesize. He was a clever inventor and experimenter and went on to pile up experimental data to support his guesses. In one of his famous experiments, which startled the scientists of his time, Lavoisier heated mercury in air in a retort. As the mercury was heated, a red powder slowly appeared in the retort. He continued the heating for twelve days, when further reaction ceased. During this time the volume of gas in the retort — originally air — decreased. The residual gas was very different from the original air. It would not support the burning of a splint, and small animals quickly died when placed in the residual gas.

Lavoisier then weighed out $45\frac{1}{2}$ grains — this was before the metric system had been invented — of the red powder mentioned above and heated this at a very high temperature in a retort. A colorless gas was formed and the red powder disappeared. The gas was collected over water. It weighed $3\frac{1}{2}$ grains. The mercury weighed $41\frac{1}{2}$ grains. Thus the weight of the products, mercury and a gas, was the *same* as that of the starting material — if we ignore an experimental error of $\frac{1}{2}$ grain. The gas caused a flame to burn more vigorously and small animals could live in it. The gas, furthermore, must have come from the air originally within the retort in the first experiment. Lavoisier named the gas oxygen and was able to show that it is present in air to the extent of one-fifth by volume.

The two changes that Lavoisier observed can be summarized as follows:

$$\text{Mercury} + \underbrace{\text{Oxygen} + \text{Nitrogen}}_{\text{Air }(\frac{5}{5}\text{ths) by volume}} \rightarrow \text{Mercury oxide} + \underset{(\frac{4}{5}\text{ths})}{\text{Nitrogen}}$$

$$\text{Mercury oxide} \rightarrow \text{Mercury} + \text{Oxygen}$$

Lavoisier called the substances mercury, oxygen, and nitrogen *elements*. The mercury oxide is a *compound*. Elements can be converted by chemical changes into compounds, and compounds can be decomposed into elements. Continued experimentation convinced Lavoisier that there was no loss nor gain in mass in these changes. For example, the weight of the mercury and oxygen in the reaction discussed above is exactly equal, except for unavoidable experimental error, to the weight of the original mercury oxide. Furthermore, all samples of mercury oxide had the same composition with respect to the amount of mercury and oxygen present in the oxide.

Similar experiments by Lavoisier on other elements led to two famous deductions that became basic principles in chemistry, namely:

1. The law of conservation of mass: in chemical changes the sum of the masses of all resultants and of all reactants is the same.
2. The law of definite proportions: all samples of every pure compound are always composed of the same elements and always in the same proportion by weight.

The new ideas of Lavoisier were widely disseminated by his great textbook published in 1789, *La Traité Elémentaire de la Chémie*. Here for the first time can be found a comprehensive listing and classification of elements, the recognition of a class of substances called acids, and a beginning in the study of organic chemistry. Lavoisier was the first person, furthermore, who studied respiration from the standpoint of energy and oxidative processes within the human body. Thus he is considered to be one of the founders of biochemistry.

CONCEPT OF CHEMICAL CHANGE

The beginnings of mathematics, astronomy, and physics go back to the works of the ancients. But the real beginnings of chemistry date only from the time of Lavoisier, the father of chemistry. Why was there such a long time-lag? It was principally due to the difficulty involved in getting a clear concept of the nature of a chemical change. This could not come until the weight relations involved in chemical changes were checked with a chemical balance. To illustrate this point further a simple chemical change will be described.

It was pointed out earlier in this chapter that two given elements combine with each other in a definite proportion by weight under specific conditions, but no experimental proof was given. Hence an experiment in which magnesium is burned to form an oxide will be discussed on a quantitative basis. Since magnesium may combine with nitrogen as well as with oxygen when burned in air, an apparatus shown diagrammatically in Figure 20–1 is arranged so that only pure oxygen flows through the tube in which the magnesium is placed. First the empty crucible is weighed, the magnesium is then placed in it and both are weighed, the difference in weight being the weight of the metal. The crucible is covered and placed in a combustion tube. Oxygen flows from the cylinder, and any moisture in the oxygen is removed by a drying substance in the U tubes, and after the air in the system has been displaced by the dry oxygen, the tube is heated. After about fifteen minutes the heating is discontinued, and the crucible is allowed to cool and is weighed again. From the data obtained the amount of oxygen which combines with one gram of magnesium is calculated:

Weight of crucible and magnesium	18.943 g
Weight of empty crucible	18.468 g
Weight of magnesium	0.475 g
Weight of crucible and contents after heating	19.252 g
Weight of crucible and magnesium before heating	18.943 g
Gain in weight due to combustion with oxygen	0.309 g

Since 0.475 g of magnesium combines with 0.309 g of oxygen, therefore 1.000 g of magnesium combines with 1.000 g/0.475 g $\times$ 0.309 g = 0.651 g of oxygen. The experiment, if repeated several times, will give results which vary slightly because of experimental error, but taken all together, they show that a given weight of magnesium always combines with the same amount of oxygen to form magnesium ox-

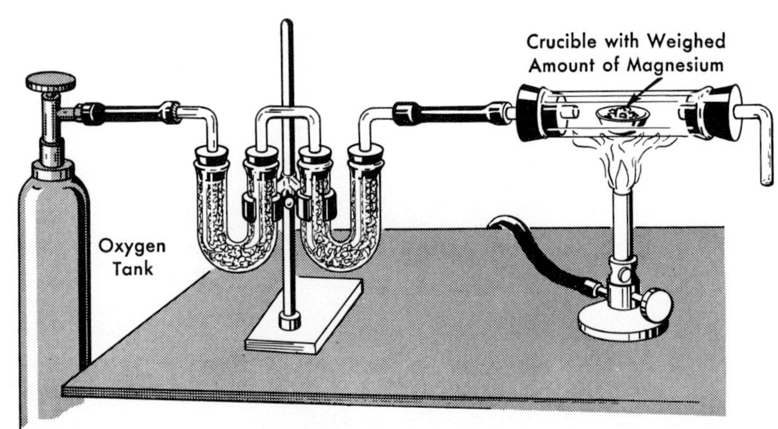

Fig. 20–1 *Apparatus for determining the weight of oxygen which combines with a definite amount of magnesium.*

ide. For example, the ratios of metal:oxygen may be 1.000 : 0.651, 1.000 : 0.658, and 1.000 : 0.660; the average of the results is 1.000 : 0.656.

If the experiment is reversed, that is, if one starts with a known amount of magnesium oxide and by appropriate chemical reactions separates the magnesium from the oxygen, the relationship is found to be the same; from 1.656 g of the oxide 1.000 g of the metal is obtained. It must therefore follow that the weight of the magnesium oxide is equal to the combined weights of the magnesium and the oxygen, and that the composition of the compound is constant regardless of its source and the method of determination.

$$\underset{1.000\text{ g}}{\text{Magnesium}} + \underset{0.656\text{ g}}{\text{Oxygen}} \rightarrow \underset{1.656\text{ g}}{\text{Magnesium oxide}}$$

and to obtain the percentage or "parts per hundred":

$$\frac{1.000}{1.656} \times 100 = 60.39\% \text{ magnesium}$$

$$\frac{0.656}{1.656} \times 100 = 39.61\% \text{ oxygen}$$

Other compounds may also be examined, for example, water, whose composition may be determined either by combining hydrogen with oxygen (synthesis) to form water, or by the decomposition (analysis) of the compound into the two elements. All methods show for *pure* water, regardless of its source, a composition of 11.19 per cent hydrogen and 88.81 per cent oxygen. This uniformity in the behavior of elements which results in the formation of compounds of constant composition is known as the *Law of Constant Composition,* or of *Definite Proportions.* It may be formally stated: *In every pure compound the relative proportions by weight of the elements present are constant and independent of the source or previous history of the compound.* For example, when element A combines with element B to form the compound AB, and the weights of the elements and the compound are represented by these letters, then

$$A + B = AB, \quad \frac{A \times 100}{AB} = \text{per cent A,}$$

$$\frac{B \times 100}{AB} = \text{per cent B.}$$

From the above experiments another principle becomes apparent, namely, that of *conservation of mass.* In all chemical changes, there is no weighable loss or gain in mass, and the sum of the masses of the reacting substances is the same as the sum of the masses of the products.

In all reactions such as the burning of wood, coal, or candles, there is an apparent loss of mass, for some of the products of combustion are gases. These may be collected and weighed, however, to show that there is no deviation from the principle. In one experiment (Figure 20–2), a candle is placed in one pan of a balance and over it a glass chimney which contains material to absorb the products of combustion. On the

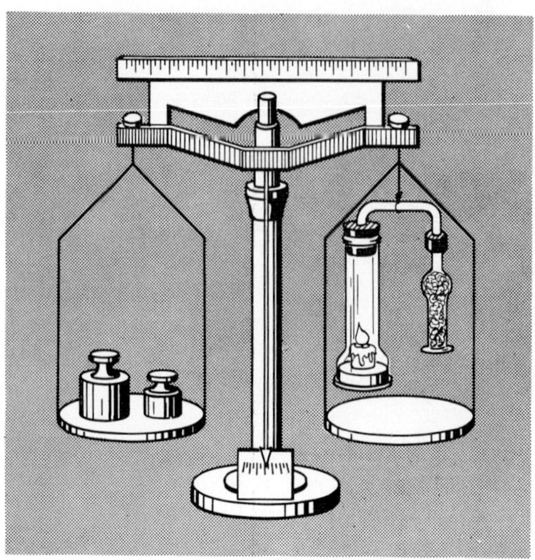

Fig. 20–2 *Apparatus to show that the products from a burning candle (carbon dioxide and water) weigh more than the original candle.*

other pan enough weights are placed to counterbalance the load, and the candle is then lighted. As the candle burns, the pan in which it is suspended slowly descends, showing a gain in weight. The gain in weight may be experimentally shown to be equal to the amount of oxygen combining with the burning candle.

THE ATOMIC THEORY

John Dalton (England, 1766–1844) was a humble schoolteacher who because of his great curiosity concerning weather and the atmosphere raised questions in his own mind that led to the atomic theory. His theory was not pure abstraction but was linked to reality by certain experimental facts. In this respect his theory was entirely different from the first atomic theory of Democritus. (Refer to page 298.) He saw that chemical changes could be explained on the basis of combinations of discrete particles of elements called atoms with definite weights characteristic of each kind of atom. He set up his postulates and then proceeded to test them. His results were in accordance with known facts and very soon his tentative hypothesis became accepted as the atomic theory. His *Now System of Chemical Philosophy,* which contained his theory, appeared in 1808, though he had published some of his conclusions as early as 1803. Dalton's theory, as in the case of nearly all scientific theories, proved to be incomplete, but it was a very fuitful one. It illustrates beautifully that one of the principal functions of any theory is to lead to new advances in knowledge.

THE ATOMIC THEORY

According to Dalton, elements consist of tiny particles called atoms with characteristic fixed atomic weights for the atoms of each element. Atoms themselves are indestructible, but atoms of different elements can combine in various relatively simple combinations to form larger particles (molecules) of compounds.

The following quotation shows the clear insight that Dalton had concerning various combinations of atoms: "If there are two bodies (elements), A and B, which are disposed to combine, the following is the order in which the combinations can take place, beginning with the most simple, namely:

1 atom of A + 1 atom of B = 1 atom [molecule] of C, binary;
1 atom of A + 2 atoms of B = 1 atom [molecule] of D, ternary;
2 atoms of A + 1 atom of B = 1 atom [molecule] of E, ternary."

It is not to the discredit of Dalton that he continually erred in confusing the ultimate particles of elements which he called atoms, and the ultimate particles of compounds which we now call molecules. Dalton was struggling with new concepts and new words and terms. He could not achieve a perfect theory in a single bound. For that reason the present designation, molecule, has been inserted in the quotation above in referring to the particles of C, D, and E.

TABLE 20–1

COMBINING WEIGHTS OF SOME COMMON ELEMENTS

SUBSTANCE	HYDROGEN	OXYGEN	CARBON	SULFUR
Water	1.0 g	8.0 g	....	.....
Hydrogen peroxide	1.0 g	16.0 g	....	.....
Carbon oxide–1	....	8.0 g	6.0 g	.....
Carbon oxide–2	....	8.0 g	3.0 g	.....
Sulfur oxide–1	....	8.0 g	....	8 g
Sulfur oxide–2	....	8.0 g	....	$5\frac{1}{3}$ g
Hydrogen sulfide	1.0 g	.....	....	16 g
Methane	1.0 g	.....	3.0 g	.....

Dalton made a start with a table of atomic weights, which he inferred from a knowledge of the composition of many compounds. The data in Table 20–1 are all experimental data obtained by the careful analysis of compounds using a chemical balance. The numbers given in the table are really combining weights. That is, 1.0 gram of hydrogen combines with 8.0 grams of oxygen in forming water. In methane, 3.0 grams of carbon combine with 1.0 gram of hydrogen.

Dalton inferred that these experimental combining weights had to have some relation to the atomic weights of elements. He knew that no experimental method existed capable of getting the atomic weight of an actual atom because atoms were invisible and in that sense unweighable. A single postage stamp cannot be weighed accurately on a postal scale. But it is easy to weigh a thousand postage stamps accurately. Dalton used a similar method to arrive at numbers which he called atomic weights, starting with experimental combining weights. Table 20–1 indicates that hydrogen was the lightest element. Dalton chose to set up his scheme of atomic weights in terms of hydrogen. For convenience alone he decided to consider combining ratios of the elements in terms of 1.0 gram of hydrogen. On this basis the combining weights of oxygen were 8.0 grams and 16.0 grams. For sulfur, they were $5\frac{1}{3}$, 8.0, and 16.0 grams. In short, the combining weight of an element as used by Dalton is merely the number of grams of the element which will combine with 1.0 gram of hydrogen, or an amount of an element equivalent to 1.0 gram of hydrogen, such as 8.0 grams of oxygen or 3.0 grams of carbon.

With the exception of hydrogen, elements often have more than one combining weight. Dalton was quick to point out that this simply meant *different proportions* of whole numbers of atoms in different compounds of the same element. Thus hydrogen peroxide, in which the H:O ratio is 1:16, have twice as many atoms of oxygen combined with a fixed weight of hydrogen as in the case of water. Similarly, carbon oxide-2 has twice as many atoms of oxygen per molecule as in the case of carbon oxide-1.

C : O in No. 2 is 3 g : 8 g or 6 g : 16 g
C : O in No. 1 is 6 g : 8 g

Thus there is twice as much oxygen (16 g) in No. 2 as compared with No. 1 (8 g), if the *same* amount of carbon is considered (6 g). This observation led to the *law of multiple proportions: In a series of compounds of the same elements, A and B, the weights of the element A which combine with a fixed weight of B, stand in the ratio of small whole numbers.* Thus there must be twice as many atoms of oxygen in each molecule of carbon oxide-2 as compared with carbon oxide-1. These relationships must be true since, according to Dalton, atoms cannot be subdivided.

Atoms are tiny and invisible. The transition from combining weights to atomic weights is not an obvious one, and Dalton could only make guesses on the basis of combining weight data which were often inadequate. His first guesses on atomic weights were often wrong. Sometimes they

TABLE 20–2

SOME EARLY ATOMIC WEIGHTS

	HYDROGEN	OXYGEN	CARBON	SULFUR
Combining weight	1.0 g	8.0 g	3.0 g	$5\frac{1}{3}$ g
Atomic weights (Dalton)	1.0	8.0	6.0	16.0
Atomic weights (modern values)	1.0	16.0	12.0	32.0

were correct even when some of his data were really in error. He assumed, for example, that water had the simplest possible structure, that is, one atom of hydrogen to one atom of oxygen. If the atomic weight of hydrogen is taken as unity, the atomic weight of oxygen must be 8.0. Assuming that the ratio by atoms of C:O in carbon oxide-1 was 1 : 1, the atomic weight of carbon was 6.0. Dalton was prone to assume that the commonest compounds of two elements were 1:1 atom combinations. On this basis, using the data for hydrogen sulfide, the atomic weight of sulfur was 16.0. The composition of the oxides of sulfur, then, should be written – since atoms cannot be divided,

	Sulfur	*Oxygen*	*Atoms Sulfur*	*Atoms Oxygen*
Sulfur oxide-1	16	16	1	2
Sulfur oxide-2	16	24	1	3

The first oxide contains molecules consisting of one atom of sulfur to two atoms of oxygen, while the second oxide contains one atom of sulfur to three atoms of oxygen per molecule. Gradually, by making numerous comparisons of the combining weights of elements in large numbers of their compounds, on the assumption that the atomic weights of hydrogen and oxygen are 1.0 and 8.0, respectively, Dalton was able to build up the first atomic weight system. Combining weights are experimental numbers involving reacting weights of elements. When the metric system is used, these weights will be expressed in grams, as shown in the first line of Table 20–2. However, ratios of equivalent weights result in pure numbers without units, that is,

$$\frac{H}{O} = \frac{1.0\,\not{g}}{8.0\,\not{g}} = \frac{1.0}{8.0}.$$

It is for this reason that the atomic weights in Table 20–2 are given without units.

Dalton's "misses" on the values of some of his atomic weights cannot be held against him. They represent, rather, the occasional missteps that had to be made in order to attain our present system of atomic weights.

Dalton represented his atoms of elements and "atoms of compounds" – we call them molecules – symbolically by drawings. (Refer to Figure 20–3.) Our present system of representing atoms and molecules with letter symbols was introduced by a contemporary of Dalton, the Swedish chemist Jöns Jacob Berzelius (1779–1848). He was the first to use letter symbols for the atoms of elements which were derived from the common or Latin names of the elements. Each symbol represents an atom and an atomic weight of an element,

Symbol	*No. Atoms*	*Atomic Wt.*
H	1	1.0
O	1	8.0
S	1	16.0
N	1	14.0

The molecule of a compound was represented by a formula, which indicated the atomic composition of the molecule. The percentage composition can be calculated from the formula by reference to a table of atomic weights. Thus the formula for sulfur dioxide according to Dalton was SO_2. This indicated that the molecule consisted of one atom of sulfur and two atoms of oxygen. The molecular weight (refer to Table 20–2) would be 16 + 2(8) = 32.0. The per cent of sulfur would be

$$\frac{\text{wt. of S}}{\text{wt. of SO}_2} \times 100 = \frac{16}{16 + 2(8)} = \frac{16}{32} = 50\%.$$

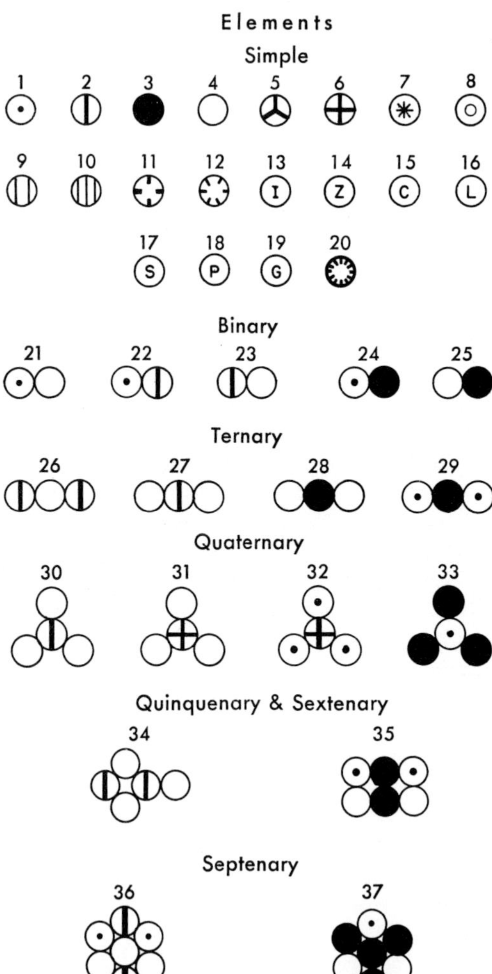

Fig. 20–3 *Dalton's symbols for "Elementary" and "Compound" atoms.* *(From G. Holton,* An Introduction to Concepts and Theories in Physical Science, *1953, Addison-Wesley Publishing Company, Inc., Reading, Mass.)*

The system invented by Berzelius for representing atoms and molecules has persisted to this day. The formulas of the compounds listed in Table 20–1 are given in Table 20–3.

Many of Dalton's formulas were correct by modern standards, but his formula for water, one of the most abundant of all compounds, was incorrect. His atomic weight for oxygen was incorrect because of his assumption of a 1 : 1 atomic ratio in water. He knew that hydrogen gas and oxygen gas combined to form water in the ratio of two volumes of hydrogen to one volume of oxygen. Dalton's explanation was that the atoms of hydrogen were twice as large as the atoms of oxygen. His unfortunate guess led to his erroneous idea of the molecule of water. Later we shall see how this error of Dalton's was corrected by Avogadro. Another source of confusion in the mind of Dalton was the failure to distinguish between atoms of elements and atoms of compounds, which we call molecules.

The work and contributions of Lavoisier represent the beginnings of the science of chemistry. Dalton's atomic theory was the great conceptual scheme which made modern chemistry possible. Chemistry rapidly became one of the most important of the physical sciences dominated by the theory of Dalton. Even though Dalton's original theory has had to be modified in certain respects, he made three very important and lasting contributions:

1. gave a logical understanding for both the law of definite proportions and the law of conservation of mass;

TABLE 20–3

SOME FORMULAS OF DALTON COMPARED WITH MODERN FORMULAS

SUBSTANCE	WEIGHT COMPOSITION	DALTON'S FORMULA	MODERN FORMULA
Water	H:O = 1.0:8.0	HO	H_2O
Hydrogen peroxide	H:O = 1.0:16.0	HO_2	H_2O_2
Carbon monoxide	C:O = 6.0:8.0	CO	CO
Carbon dioxide	C:O = 6.0:16.0	CO_2	CO_2
Sulfur dioxide	S:O = 16.0:16.0	SO_2	SO_2
Sulfur trioxide	S:O = 16.0:24.0	SO_3	SO_3
Hydrogen sulfide	H:S = 1.0:16.0	HS	H_2S
Methane	H:C = 1.0:3.0	CH_2	CH_4

2. explained the law of multiple proportions and why there are so many different compounds of the same elements; and

3. made possible the necessary start in determining the atomic weights of the elements.

THE CONTRIBUTION OF AVOGADRO

Order came to Dalton's system with the contribution which Amerigo Avogadro (Italy, 1776–1856) made in 1813, though about forty years went by before the significance of his contribution was generally appreciated. He observed that there was no reason to assume that the particles of free hydrogen and oxygen had to consist of just one atom. In fact, there were experimental observations to indicate that the molecules of ordinary hydrogen and oxygen were diatomic. Their formulas should be written H_2 and O_2, not H and O. This fact had escaped Dalton. Furthermore, Avogadro pointed out that the common gas laws, Boyle's and Charles's laws, for example, could be accounted for, if the hypothesis was made that *equal volumes of all gases under the same conditions of temperature and pressure had the same number of molecules.* The evidence for accepting this statement was so great that it came to be known as *Avogadro's theory.* It can now be called *Avogadro's law* because of developments of the twentieth century which permit the counting of molecules in spite of their very minute size. This development will be discussed in Chapter 22.

Joseph Louis Gay-Lussac pointed out that chemical reactions involving gases always involved simple numerical volume relationships. Thus in the formation of water, two volumes of hydrogen combine with one volume of oxygen to form exactly two volumes of steam. This kind of chemical arithmetic came to be known as Gay-Lussac's law of combining volumes. In the case of the formation of steam, the volume of oxygen must contain some definite number n of molecules. If Avogadro's theory is accepted, the number of molecules of hydrogen and of water is $2n$. Since oxygen atoms are indivisible according to Dalton's theory, each molecule of steam could not have less than one atom of oxygen. Hence the $2n$ molecules of steam must contain $2n$ atoms of oxygen which originated in n molecules of oxygen. Thus the oxygen molecule cannot be simpler than two atoms with the formula O_2, and not O as assumed by Dalton.

In a similar manner the study of other reactions showed that the molecules of many common gases as hydrogen, nitrogen, and chlorine could be expected to be diatomic. Their molecular formulas are written H_2, N_2, and Cl_2. Returning, then, to the reaction between hydrogen and oxygen, if hydrogen is H_2, the $2n$ molecules of hydrogen were distributed over $2n$ molecules of water. Hence the formula of water is H_2O. The reaction for the formation of water is written

$$2H_2 + O_2 \rightarrow 2H_2O.$$

This statement introduces you to the language of chemistry. This is a so-called chemical equation – a symbolic representation of a chemical reaction. It conveys the idea that two molecules of hydrogen (diatomic) react chemically with one molecule of oxygen (diatomic) to produce two molecules of water. Each molecule of water consists of a chemical union of two atoms of hydrogen with one atom of oxygen. Chemically, three molecules of reactants become two molecules of resultants.

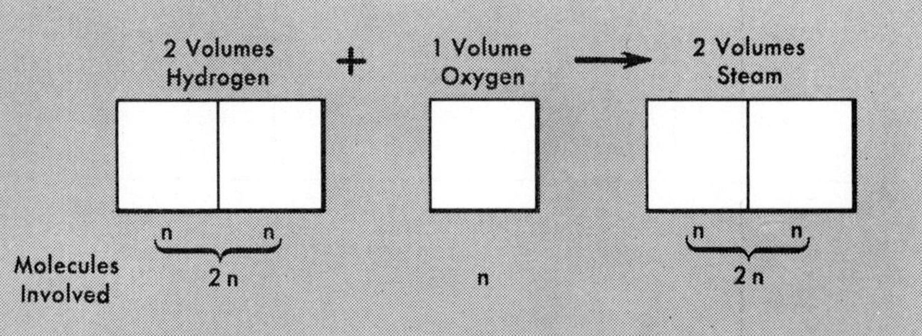

Fig. 20–4 *The reasoning of Avogadro to show that the molecules of hydrogen and oxygen must be diatomic.*

The law of conservation of mass applies when the equation is "balanced." Thus there are four atoms of hydrogen on the left and on the right of the → sign. Likewise, there are two atoms of oxygen on both sides of the sign. In balancing equations, the law of conservation of matter can be considered to be the "law of conservation of atoms." However, it is also true that the total mass of the reactants,

$$[36 = (2 \cdot 2 \cdot 1) + (2 \cdot 16)],$$

is equal to the total mass of resultants,

$$[36 = 2(2 + 16)],$$

on the basis H = 1 and O = 16.

Avogadro's solution of the problem of converting combining weights into atomic weights led to the lower line of atomic weights shown in Table 20–2. All these values are very close to the values accepted today.

MODERN ATOMIC WEIGHTS

With advances in the sensitivity of chemical balances and improvements in experimental techniques, chemists finally had to accept the fact that the atomic weights of hydrogen and oxygen were not precisely 1.0 and 16.0. There was abundant experimental proof that the combining weights of hydrogen and oxygen in water had to be written H : O = 1.000 g : 7.937 g, or H : O = 1.008 g : 8.000 g. This was a great disappointment to some chemists for it compelled making a *choice*. The choice was finally made on the basis of convenience. That is:

$$\frac{H}{O} = \frac{1.000}{7.937} \text{ or } \frac{1.008}{8.000}.$$

In terms of atomic weights, this means

$$\frac{H}{O} = \frac{1.000}{15.874} \text{ or } \frac{1.008}{16.000}.$$

Note that the atomic weight of oxygen is 16.000 if the atomic weight of hydrogen is arbitrarily set at 1.008. Eventually, it was found that many of the atomic weights were very close to being whole numbers if H = 1.008. Thus sodium, carbon, sulfur, calcium have atomic weights very close to whole numbers if H = 1.008, and O = 16.000. Other examples can be found in any atomic weight table. Refer, for example, to the inside front cover of this volume.

THE FRUITFULNESS OF DALTON'S ATOMIC THEORY

The test of any theory is its fruitfulness. The science of chemistry developed rapidly during the nineteenth century. This science as we know it could not have evolved without Dalton's theory. It made possible the intensive study of the weight relationships in all chemical changes and it led to the periodic law — the law which systematized the study of all the elements and their compounds. Dalton's atomic theory prevailed in its original form until about 1910. And yet during the entire preceding century chemists were concerning themselves about atoms when there was no objective proof of their existence.

In a later chapter, the proofs that were found during the twentieth century for the actual existence of atoms will be presented. We shall see that Dalton's theory has had to be modified, but the essentiaı aspects still prevail. It is among the most important of scientific theories.

SUMMARY

1. The experimental distinction between an element and a compound was first made by Lavoisier.
2. The experimental work of Lavoisier led to the rejection of the phlogiston theory and the acceptance of the law of conservation of matter.
3. Lavoisier discovered the law of constant composition: every pure substance is always composed of the same elements and in the same proportion by weight.

4. John Dalton discovered the law of multiple proportions: in a series of compounds of the same elements, A and B, the weights of the element A which combine with a fixed weight of B stand in the ratio of small whole numbers.
5. The attempts of Dalton to give a simple explanation for the laws of conservation of matter, the laws of constant composition, and multiple proportions led to the original atomic theory of Dalton.
6. The atomic theory of Dalton made the science of chemistry possible. Certain discoveries made during the early part of the twentieth century have made some changes in the original atomic theory, but the essential aspects remain unchanged.
7. Chemical reactions involving gases always involve simple numerical volume relationships. This is Gay-Lussac's law of combining volumes.
8. Avogadro's theory states that equal volumes of all gases under the same conditions of temperature and pressure contain the same number of molecules.
9. Avogadro was among the earliest of the scientists to make the distinction between atoms and molecules of elements.
10. The chemical basis for the determination of atomic weights rests upon the experimental determination of combining or equivalent weights: the weight of an element that will combine with or is equivalent to 1.008 grams of hydrogen or 8.000 grams of oxygen.
11. The chemical atomic weight of an element is the same as the combining weight or a simple multiple of it.
12. Modern chemical atomic weights rest upon deductions utilizing both Dalton's and Avogadro's theories.

STUDY EXERCISES

1. A compound of calcium and oxygen was synthesized, as follows: 0.7600 gram of calcium was heated in air until the weight increase became constant. The oxide was found to weigh 1.0500 grams. In a second experiment, 1.2000 grams of calcium formed 1.6820 grams of oxide. Calculate from both sets of data the per cent of calcium in this compound. What important law of chemistry is illustrated?

2. Two different oxides of carbon are known. Typical data obtained in synthesizing these compounds are given below:

	Oxide No. 1	*Oxide No. 2*
Weight carbon taken	1.000 g	1.4000 g
Weight oxide formed	3.670 g	3.2600 g
Weight oxygen	______	______

Show how these data illustrate the law of multiple proportions.

3. The percentages of carbon in a number of compounds of carbon with oxygen or hydrogen (methane and ethane) are as follows: carbon monoxide, 42.9%; carbon dioxide, 27.3%; methane, 75.0%; ethane, 80.0%. Compute the combining weight of carbon from these data. The atomic weight is a multiple of the combining weight; what is a reasonable estimate of the atomic weight of carbon from these data? Explain.

4. Dalton considered the ultimate particles of water to be HO based upon an atom of oxygen with an atomic weight of 8.000. The deductions of Avogadro led to the formula H_2O containing an oxygen atom with an atomic weight of 16.000. Discuss some of the considerations that led to the acceptance of H_2O as the formula for water.

5. The volumes of gases involved in the decomposition of ammonia into nitrogen and hydrogen are given schematically below:

2 volumes ammonia	$\rightarrow$	3 volumes hydrogen	+	1 volume nitrogen

a. Accepting the formula for hydrogen as H_2, show by an application of Avogadro's theory that the formula for nitrogen must be N_2.

b. What must be the formula for ammonia based upon information given in this exercise?

c. Complete the following equation to represent the decomposition of ammonia:

$$\_\_\_\_ \quad \_\_\_\_ \rightarrow \_\_\_\_ N_2 + \_\_\_\_ H_2$$

Show how this balanced equation illustrates the law of conservation of matter.

6. The formulas for water and hydrogen peroxide are given below; consult an atomic weight table and make the computations necessary to give the information called for:

	H_2O	H_2O_2
Molecular weight	____	____
Per cent hydrogen	____	____

FOR FURTHER READING

1. TILDEN, W. A., *Famous Chemists.* London: George Routledge and Sons, 1921.
   A very readable account of the character, work, and significance of John Dalton.
2. LEICESTER, H. M., and H. S. KLECKSTEIN, *A Source Book of Chemistry.* New York: McGraw-Hill Book Company, 1954.
   Contains a very interesting chapter on Lavoisier. Includes accounts in Lavoisier's own words of his work on oxygen, combustion, respiration, and his arguments against the phlogiston theory. A chapter on Avogadro presents his concept of molecules as contrasted with that of Dalton. A chapter on Dalton includes some of his accounts of his atomic theory.
3. Paperback: CONANT, J. B., *On Understanding Science.* Mentor, 50¢
   Very full discussion of the significance of Lavoisier's work on combustion and the overthrow of the phlogiston theory; by a famous contemporary American scientist and former president of Harvard.

21 THE NATURE OF ELECTRICITY

WITH THE CLEAR RECOGNITION of the nature of potential, kinetic, and heat energy, and the wide acceptance of the first and second laws of thermodynamics, scientists turned to the study of other forms of energy. They found that light and electricity, for example, were energy. The range of phenomena connected with light and electricity is so enormous that the solutions of the many problems which arose were possible only through the cooperative efforts of many scientists, each working on a small segment of the total problem, the usual procedure in unraveling complex problems. When the serious study of electricity and light began (between the years 1820 and 1850), scientists at first had to be content with solutions to the smaller problems. By 1925, however, understanding of light and electricity was reasonably complete, though the final synthesis of a full understanding of these two forms of energy has not yet been made. Some of the early very fundamental concepts connected with electricity will be presented in this chapter.

The study of electricity started as a pastime — it was fun to play with static or friction electricity. It has been known for a very long time that many dissimilar materials when rubbed together produce stationary electric charges. The word electricity comes from the Greek word *electron* meaning amber. This alludes to the fact that amber when rubbed with a dry cloth becomes charged with electricity. Similarly a person walking over a wool or nylon rug or when sliding off an automobile seat often becomes charged with static electricity. A good way to study these phenomena is to rub a suspended toy balloon with dry cat's fur. (Refer to Figure 21–1.) Rubbing the balloon briskly results in a state of charge on the balloon and on the cat's fur. The fur will then attract the balloon sideways, evidence of an attractive force between them. If the humidity is low, the state of charge will persist for hours. If two balloons are similarly charged, they are found to repel each other and move apart. (Refer to Figure 21–2.)

Experiments giving similar results can be made with a great variety of materials, such as paper, wood, glass, sulfur, rubber, wax, silk, wool, and nylon. It is not uncom-

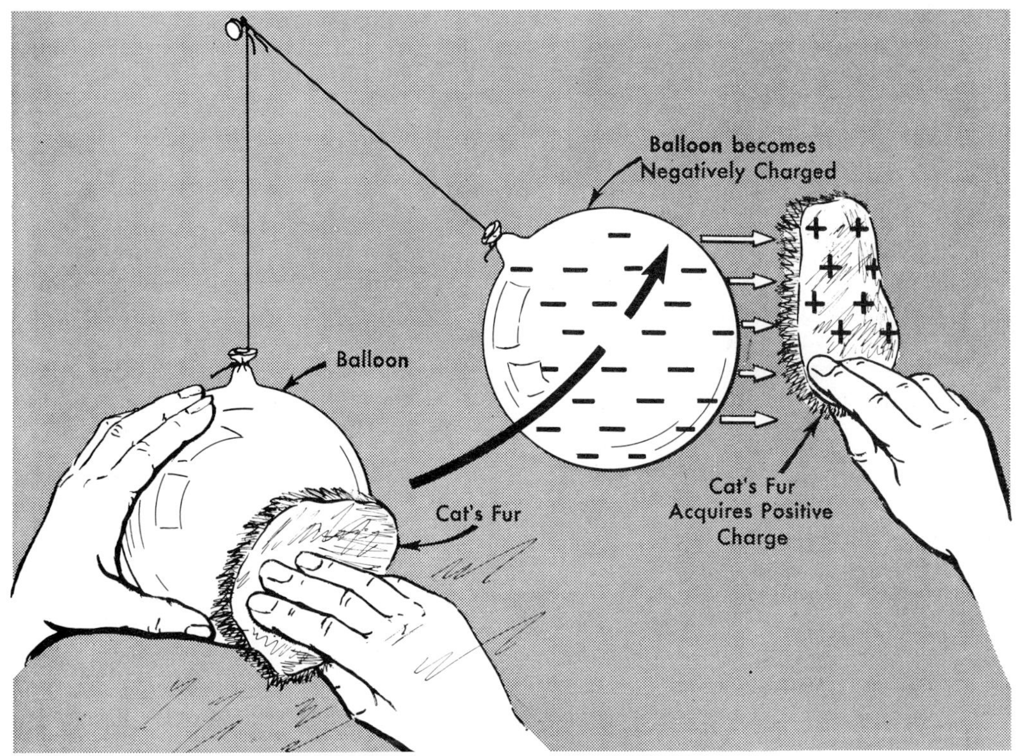

Fig. 21–1 *Producing isolated electric charges and an electric field. The charge on the balloon by agreement is called negative. The fur then is positive.*

mon for flowing water under some circumstances to generate static electricity. Similarly, the movement of gasoline within a gasoline truck can generate dangerous amounts of static electricity.

Two dissimilar materials must be used to get static electricity, and equal quantities of opposite charges always appear. The two kinds of electricity are called simply *positive* and *negative*. It has become conventional to call the charge on the balloon negative and the charge on the cat's fur positive. This is entirely an arbitrary procedure. The two charges if brought together will neutralize each other. Michael Faraday (England, 1791–1867) showed that the effects of electric charges are always the same no matter how produced.

For example, any charged body, whether positively or negatively charged, loses its charge instantly if touched with a metal wire that is grounded (connected) to the

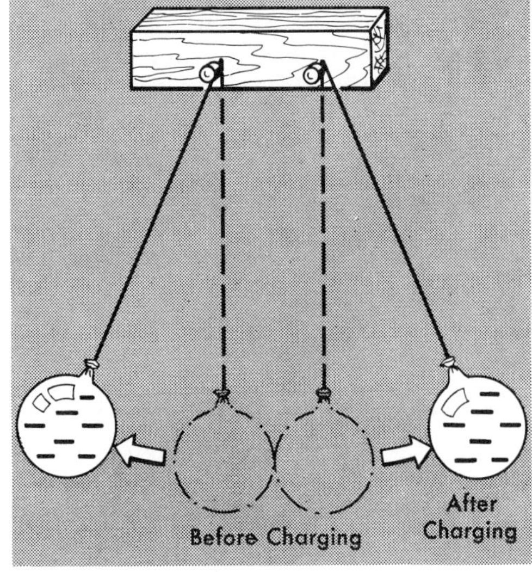

Fig. 21–2 *Two balloons with like charges repel each other.*

earth. The wire constitutes a *conductor.* All materials can be divided into two classes: *insulators* (or *dielectrics*) and *conductors.* Thus all the materials mentioned in the preceding paragraph which will produce static electricity are insulators or dielectrics. Metals, on the other hand, graphite, some minerals, and some liquids are conductors. Our usual modern sources of electricity are batteries and generators. Batteries and generators have regions (poles) of positive and negative electricity. The construction and operation of batteries and generators will be considered in Chapter 33.

COULOMB'S LAW

A French physicist, C. A. de Coulomb (1736–1806), showed that the attractive force between point charges of opposite sign or the repulsive force between charges of like sign are *directly proportional* to the product of the charges, q_1 and q_2, and *inversely proportional* to the square of the distance between them; that is,

$$F = k\,\frac{q_1 q_2}{d^2}. \qquad (\textit{Equation 21–1})$$

This *inverse-square law* for electric charges, called Coulomb's law, is entirely analogous in form to Newton's law of universal gravitation (Equation 14–8). By an appropriate invention and use of units, the constant of proportionality is made unity, and Coulomb's law takes the form

$$F = \frac{q_1 q_2}{d^2}. \qquad (\textit{Equation 21–2})$$

ELECTRICAL UNITS

The physical sciences are based upon quantitative measurements. It was necessary, therefore, to have a system of electrical units in order to build up a science of electricity. There are a large number of these units and unfortunately most of them "just grew." They were originally operational definitions that had to be devised before there was fundamental knowledge of electricity as particles. The first units of electricity were based upon certain effects which could be easily described and reproduced. There are many electrical units and the interrelationships between them are involved. Therefore, a full discussion of the units of electricity will be postponed to Chapter 33. The only units to be described and used in this preliminary study of electricity are those that measure quantities of electric charge: the *statcoulomb,* the practical *coulomb,* and the *faraday.*

The *statcoulomb.* The force of repulsion between two like charges, q_1 and q_2 (refer to Figure 21–3), placed *one centimeter apart* will depend upon the magnitude of the charges. There is a charge which will result in a repulsive force of *one dyne.* This basic charge by definition is called the *electrostatic unit* (e.s.u.) of charge or the *statcoulomb,* the unit used to measure quantities of electric charge, positive or negative.

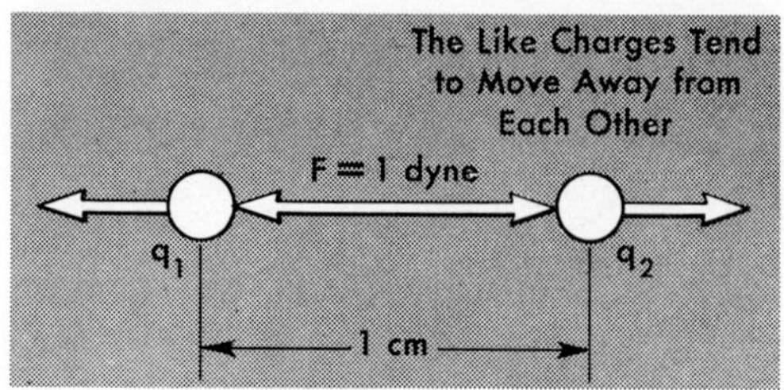

Fig. 21–3 *The statcoulomb: a basic unit of electric charge.*

The *coulomb* (practical). The statcoulomb is an inconveniently small unit. The practical unit of quantity of charge, the coulomb, is 3×10^9 larger. That is, one coulomb is 3×10^9 statcoulombs.

The *faraday* or electrical equivalent. This is 96,500 coulombs. The origin and use of this larger unit of quantity of charge will be discussed on pages 338–339.

ACTION-AT-A-DISTANCE

The earth retains the moon in its orbit at a distance of 240,000 miles. The force between them is fantastically large. How does this force operate? Actually we do not

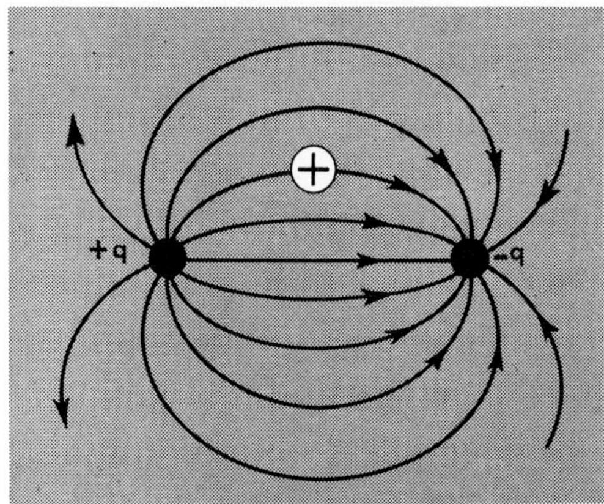

Fig. 21–4 *Electric field between two charges of opposite sign.*

know. It is one of our great mysteries. We can measure the force, but we cannot account for it. We are perforce content to talk about the force of gravitation and the gravitational field of the earth. Anything within the gravitational field of the earth tends to move toward the earth.

Another example of action-at-a-distance is illustrated in the movement of the charged balloon toward the cat's fur in Figure 21–1, or the repulsive force between the two balloons when charged similarly as shown in Figure 21–2. Obviously, there is something in the space around one of the charged balloons that causes motion in the second balloon. How does this happen? Again we do not really know, but since the days of Michael Faraday, the effects are said to be due to an *electric field* around each balloon. The character of this field can be measured in various ways and its potentialities for producing motion can also be measured.

ELECTRIC FIELDS

The unusual state in the space around any charge is described in terms of its electric field which can be detected by the force it exerts on a *test charge*. The test charge is always positive. If the charge producing the field is positive, the test charge moves away from it; if it is negative, the test charge moves toward it. The path followed by the test charge is visualized as a *line of force*. Every line of force must begin on a positive charge and end on a negative charge. The character of the field about two charges of opposite sign is shown in Figure 21–4. These lines exist only in the mind of the person trying to visualize the field, but they are real in the sense that a small positive test charge would actually move along these lines as it moves from the positive charge to the negative charge. The tendency for the charges to move toward each other can be attributed to the tendency of the lines of force to collapse. The lines of force exist because of the charges. The charges tend to move because of the lines of force. This sounds like Alice in Wonderland.

The shape of the lines of force and thus of the electric field about two like charges is shown in Figure 21–5. In this case, the effect of the similar charges and this kind of field is to cause the charges to separate.

INTENSITY OF ELECTRIC FIELDS

Just as any object placed in the gravitational field of the earth tends to undergo motion, so any charged object in an electric field tends to undergo motion. In gravitational fields the motion is always toward

Fig. 21–5 *Electric field about two like charges.*

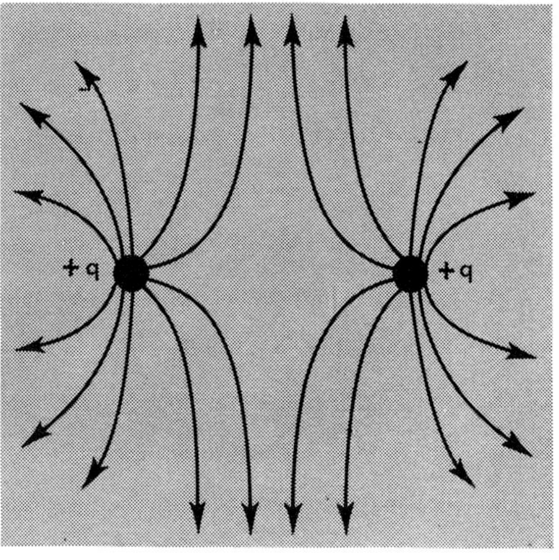

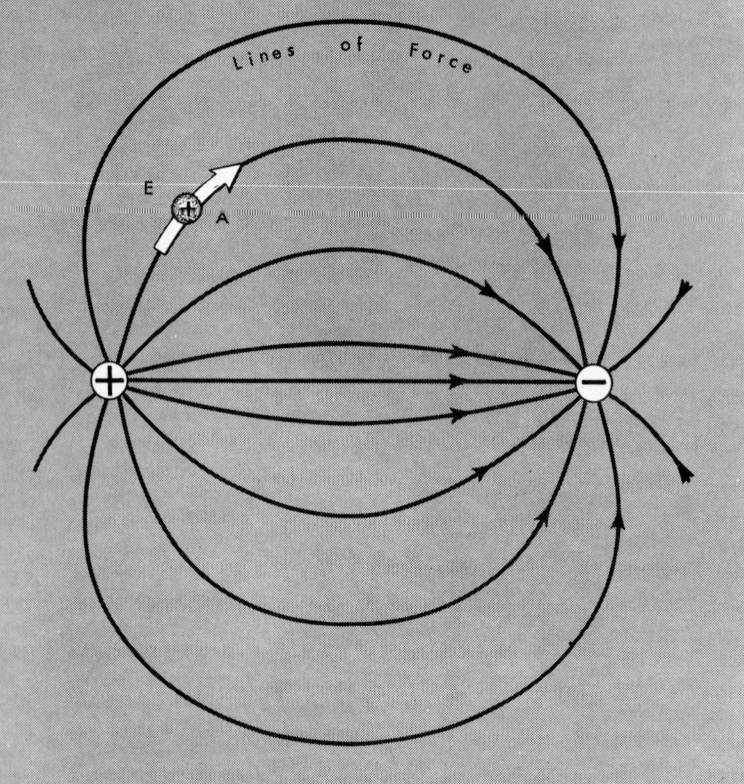

Fig. 21–6 *Concept of field intensity. Electric field is indicated by lines of force. Test charge* (A) *tends to move in the direction of the arrow along a line of force. To keep a charge of 5 statcoulombs stationary requires a force of 65 dynes. Hence the force per unit charge is 65 dynes/5 statcoulombs, or 13 dynes per statcoulomb. This is the field intensity* E.

the earth. In electric fields, however, the direction of motion depends upon the character of the two interacting electric fields. Thus charges with fields as shown in Figure 21–4 will move toward each other, but away from each other if the fields are as shown in Figure 21–5.

The tendency of a field to produce motion is expressed in terms of its *intensity*. Electric field intensity is measured in terms of the force in dynes exerted by the field on a unit positive test charge, or

$$\text{Intensity} = E = I_{\text{electrical}} = \frac{F \text{ dynes}}{q \text{ charges}} \qquad (\textit{Equation 21–3})$$

This merely means that if a charge of 5 statcoulombs is under an attractive force of 65 dynes at a certain place in the field around a positive charge, then one unit of charge would experience 65 dynes/5 units of charge, or 13 dynes of force. This is the intensity E. (Refer to Figure 21–6.)

The force acting on any charge in an electric field is readily calculated if the intensity E is known. Re-arranging Equation 21–3, it is apparent that

$$\text{Force} = F = q \times E. \qquad (\textit{Equation 21–4})$$

The force will be in dynes if q is given in statcoulombs and the intensity E is given in dynes per statcoulomb. This equation finds frequent application in problems involving electric fields.

We owe to Michael Faraday the concept of an electric field composed of lines of force. Faraday also performed the first experiments with the kind of conductors called *electrolytes*. In metallic conduction, electricity passes through a metal with no change in the condition of the metal except a slight increase in temperature. An electric current will also pass through a water solution of common salt, baking soda, sulfuric acid, or many other substances called electrolytes, but with this difference: there are always permanent chemical changes in the solution. These early experiments were the first ones to indicate that electricity consists of atoms or particles.

ELECTRICITY IS ATOMIC IN CHARACTER

Let us consider one of the crucial experiments of Faraday. (Refer to Figure 21–7.) *A* represents a copper plate which is connected to the plus (+) pole of a battery. Faraday called this plate the *anode*. *B* is also a copper plate connected to the minus (−) pole of the battery. This plate, Faraday called the *cathode*. The electric current enters or leaves the solution at these plates, which collectively are referred to as *electrodes*. The copper chloride solution is an excellent conductor of electricity. The conductivity was correctly ascribed by Faraday to *ions* in the solution. The ions were of two kinds, *positive* and *negative*. The positive ions consisted of particles (atoms) of copper carrying two positive electric charges. These positive ions migrated toward the cathode. Hence they were called *cations*. The negative ions were particles (atoms) of chlorine each carrying a negative charge. These ions migrated to the anode. Hence they were called *anions*. The picture as given by Faraday was simply a movement of ions – particles with charges – in opposite directions within the solution. In this way Faraday accounted for the conductivity of the solution.

Faraday also demonstrated that the copper plate serving as the anode *lost weight* during an experiment. The copper which disappeared passed into the solution to form *copper ions* with *plus* charges. But simultaneously the copper cathode increased in weight. At this electrode copper ions disappeared from the solution. Furthermore, the amount of copper dissolved at the anode was the same as the amount deposited at the cathode. He further found that the amount of copper dissolved or deposited depended upon the amount of electricity passed through the solution. The decomposition of any substance in water solution by the use of electrical energy is called *electrolysis*.

Fig. 21–7 *Electrolysis in a solution of copper chloride.*

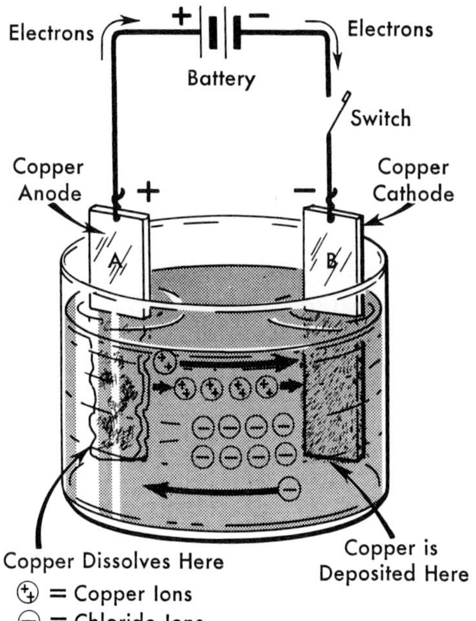

QUANTITATIVE CHANGES DURING ELECTROLYSIS

Faraday studied quantitatively the changes that occurred at the anode and at the cathode in the electrolysis of a great variety of electrolytes and thus founded the science of electrochemistry – the study of the chemical changes produced by electricity and the production of electricity by chemical changes. The terms used above, electrolysis, electrode, anode, cathode, ion, anion, cation, we owe to Faraday. By a series of masterly experiments, similar to the one we have described, Faraday reduced the many observations made in his study of electrolysis to two simple statements known as *Faraday's laws*. The first stated that *chemical changes occur at each electrode in electrolysis and that the mass of an element liberated or deposited at the electrode is proportional to the total amount of electricity passed through the solution*. The second law stated that *the amount of substance deposited or liberated by a given quantity of electricity is proportional to a quantity called the equivalent weight of the substance.* Thus if a steady current of electricity deposited 0.1000 gram of copper from a copper sulfate solution in one hour, the same current passing for two hours would deposit 0.2000 gram.

Measuring quantity of electricity. It is necessary in electrolysis experiments to measure the quantity of electricity in coulombs. This is simply done with a silver *coulometer.* (Refer to Figure 21–8.) It consists of a platinum dish — this metal is very inert chemically — which serves as a negative pole. A coil of silver wire dipping in a solution which contains silver ions (Ag^+) serves as the positive pole. When the switch K is closed, current from the battery flows through the circuit. The platinum dish (cathode) increases in weight due to deposition of silver. Each 0.001118 gram of silver deposited means the passage of one coulomb. Hence,

$$\text{coulombs passed} = \text{Weight (g) of silver} \times \frac{1 \text{ coulomb}}{0.001118 \text{ g silver}}.$$

(*Equation 21–5*)

ELECTRICITY AND ATOMIC WEIGHTS

Faraday also discovered that the weight of an element deposited by a given amount of electricity depended upon the element and that this quantity was also related to the atomic weight. Thus in Table 21–1 the weights of some elements deposited by one coulomb are tabulated. The quantity is referred to as the electrochemical equivalent of these elements.

Fig. 21–8 *A silver coulometer.*

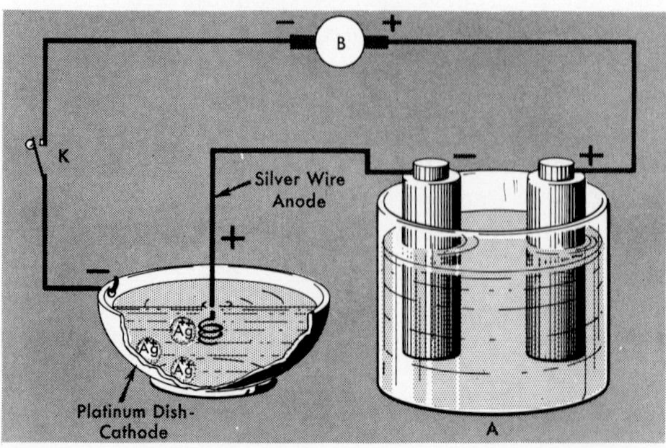

TABLE 21–1 ELECTROCHEMICAL EQUIVALENT OF SOME COMMON ELEMENTS

ELEMENT	GRAMS PER COULOMB
Silver	0.001118
Copper	0.003294
Gold	0.002044
Lead	0.001074
Hydrogen	0.00001045
Oxygen	0.0008290

The electrochemical equivalent was soon shown to be related to the equivalent (page 326) and thus to the atomic weight of an element. The equivalent weights of hydrogen and oxygen are 1.008 and 8.000 grams, respectively. With the data of Table 21–1, the number of coulombs needed to set free equivalent weights of these reference elements can be calculated. That is,

coulombs needed for 8.000 g oxygen

$$= 8.000 \text{ g} \times \frac{1 \text{ coulomb}}{0.000829 \text{ g}} = 96{,}500,$$

and coulombs needed for 1.008 g hydrogen

$$= 1.008 \times \frac{1 \text{ coulomb}}{0.00001045 \text{ g}} = 96{,}500.$$

It was soon found that the quantity 96,500 coulombs was one of the important constants of nature. It was named the *equivalent of electricity,* or *faraday.* It is in effect a large "natural package of electricity" which should be added to the units of quantity of electricity listed on page 334. The use of this concept leads to a simple statement of Faraday's law of electrolysis: an *equivalent of electricity* (96,500 coulombs) sets free or deposits an equivalent weight of an element at an electrode in the process of electrolysis.

Using the concept of the faraday, the equivalent weights of the elements listed in Table 21–1 are readily computed. These are listed in Table 21–2. The calculation

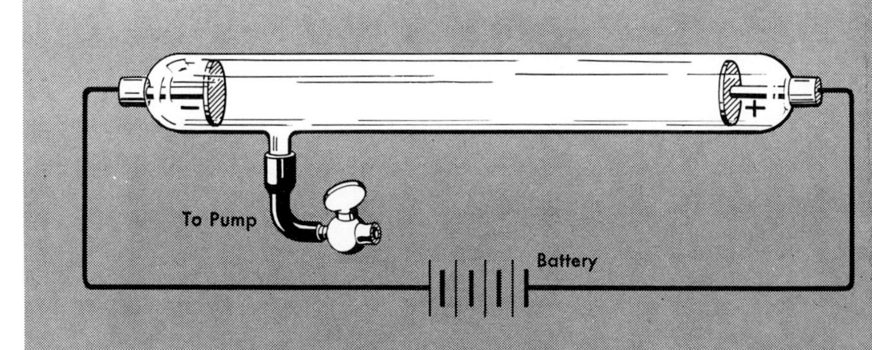

Fig. 21–9 *Electrical conduction in a cathode ray tube.*

of the equivalent weight of copper, for example, is as follows:

Equivalent weight copper

$$= 96{,}500 \text{ coulombs} \times \frac{0.003294 \text{ g}}{1 \text{ coulomb}}$$

$$= 31.78 \text{ grams.}$$

TABLE 21–2 EQUIVALENT WEIGHTS BY ELECTROLYSIS

ELEMENT	GRAMS PER 96,500 COULOMBS	ATOMIC WEIGHT
Silver	107.9	107.88
Copper	31.78	63.54
Gold	197.2	197.0
Lead	103.7	207.21
Hydrogen	1.008	1.008
Oxygen	8.000	16.000

It is to be noted that the atomic weights are the same as the equivalent weights or a simple multiple of them.

The experiments of Faraday definitely established a connection between the chemical elements and electricity. Dalton's atomic theory stated that elements consist of atoms. The changes at the electrodes in electrolysis involved atoms, and this led to the conclusion that electricity must also consist of "atoms" or discrete particles. This particle we now know is the electron, but three-fourths of a century passed before its existence was established. This lag indicates the relatively great amount of time necessary to build up some of the fundamental concepts of modern science.

ELECTRICAL CONDUCTION IN GASES AT LOW PRESSURE

Air as a gas is a relatively poor conductor of electricity. A tube filled with air as shown in Figure 21–9 does not conduct appreciable amounts of electricity. The numerous molecules of oxygen and nitrogen in the tube are obstacles to the passage of particles of electricity. The removal of enough molecules by the use of an air pump permits current to pass. The tube becomes an increasingly better conductor as more and more air is removed. (Refer to Figure 21–10.) The electrodes are connected to a source of high potential (a spark coil) and the side arm of the tube to a vacuum pump. When the pressure is reduced to about ten millimeters of mercury (1/76 atmosphere), bluish, ribbon-like streamers of light silently flash through the tube. As the pressure is further reduced, the streamers give way to a reddish glow which fills the tube. This breaks and recedes toward the positive electrode (anode), and a bluish luminous glow appears around the negative electrode (cathode) with alternate regions of light and dark spaces (Figure 21–10).

Finally, when the pressure is reduced to one-hundred-thousandth of an atmosphere, the zones of light disappear, the glass glows with a greenish light, and a faint streak of light may be discerned extending from the cathode. These rays have been the object of much study. The vacuum-discharge technique was developed by H. Geissler (1814–

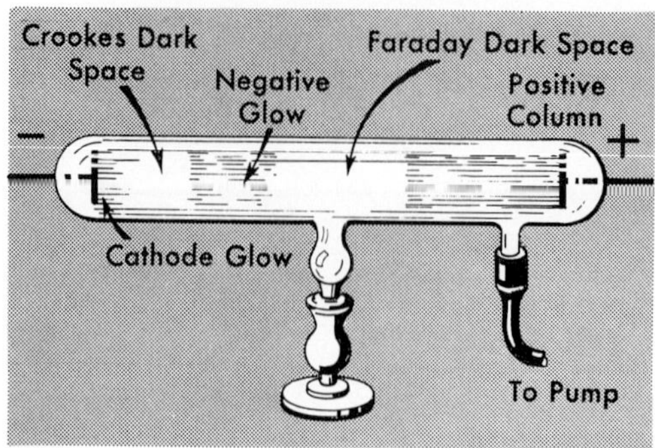

Fig. 21–10 *Conduction of electricity in partially evacuated cathode ray tube.*

79) in Germany and Sir William Crookes (1832–1919) in England. A thorough study of these *cathode rays* and related phenomena was made by Sir J. J. Thomson (1856–1940) at Cambridge University. Some of their experimental conclusions based upon observation of the cathode-ray discharge in special tubes are given below.

CATHODE RAYS

The rays which originate at the cathode are called cathode rays. These can cause an object to cast a shadow on the wall of the tube opposite the cathode (Figure 21–11). Though the rays are scarcely visible, their impact on the glass is evident from the greenish light which they cause the glass to emit. Something in the glass receives the rays or radiation and gives off visible light. This phenomenon is known as *fluorescence* and permits us to see the shadow cast by an object placed in front of the cathode. We may therefore conclude that cathode rays actually emerge from the cathode and normally travel in straight lines.

The cathode rays are deflected or bent from their straight-line path by a magnetic field and by an electric field. After some difficulty Thomson finally demonstrated the deflection of the rays by an electric field, but this was only after he had placed the field plates within the tube. (Refer to Figure 21–12.) The deflection was toward the positive and away from the negative plate. It was shown by J. Perrin (France, 1870–1942) that the rays gave a negative charge to a delicate measuring instrument upon which they were deflected. Cathode rays, therefore, consist of a stream of negative particles. These were soon named *electrons*. This name had been proposed in 1874 by G. Johnston Stoney (Britain, 1826–1911). But it required the work of J. J. Thomson to gain acceptance for the electron. He devised a special cathode ray tube, which gave an experimental value for the charge-mass ratio (e/m) of the particles originating at the cathode. The experimental value for e/m was 5.274×10^{17} e.s.u./g. Other kinds of experiments determined the charge on the electron (4.80×10^{-10} e.s.u.). Hence, the mass of the electron (m) could be calculated. That is,

$$\frac{e}{m} = 5.274 \cdot 10^{17}\,\frac{\text{e.s.u.}}{\text{g}},$$

and

$$m = \frac{e}{5.274 \cdot 10^{17}\,\frac{\text{e.s.u.}}{\text{g}}} = \frac{4.80 \cdot 10^{-10}\ \text{e.s.u.}}{5.274 \cdot 10^{17}\,\frac{\text{e.s.u.}}{\text{g}}} = 9.10 \times 10^{-28}\ \text{g}.$$

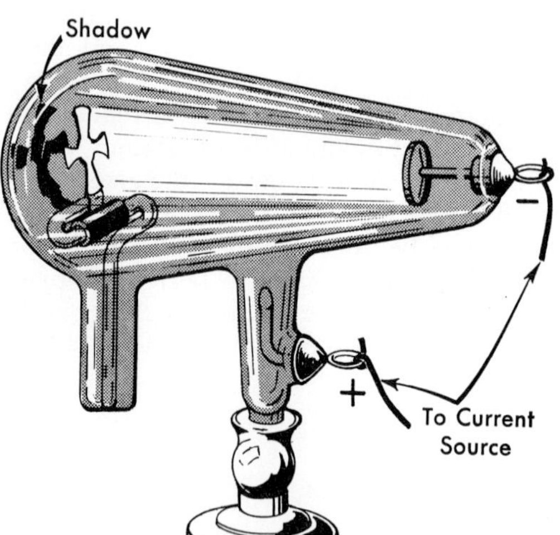

Fig. 21–11 *A shadow cast on the wall of tube opposite the cathode proves that cathode rays come from the cathode and move in straight lines.*

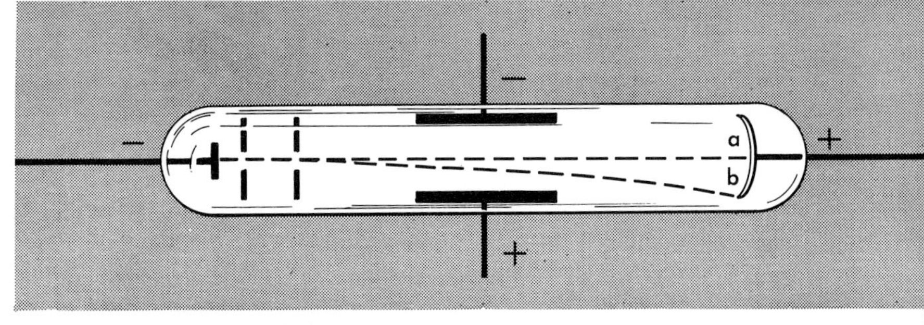

Fig. 21–12 *Cathode rays are deflected from* a *to* b *by a charge on the plates within the tube. Hence they carry a negative charge.*

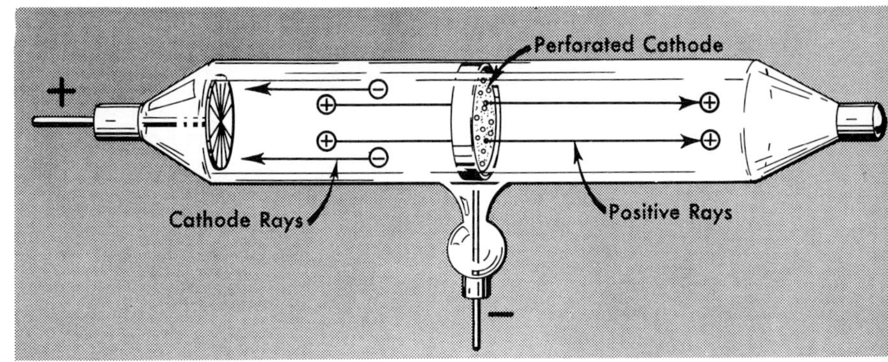

Fig. 21–13 *Positive ray tube. The inertia of the moving positive rays carries them through the holes in the cathode into the space beyond.*

The work we have outlined in a short paragraph represents that of many scientists for a decade and proved the existence of the electron. Its mass is fantastically small, but it is a real experimental number. The lightest element is hydrogen. But the electron has a mass only 1/1840 of the hydrogen atom.

Thomson carried out a series of experiments with cathode rays in which he used different materials for cathodes and a variety of gases in the tube. In all cases he obtained the same kind of negative particles (the same value for e/m), and for the first time had definite evidence that the electron is *a fundamental constituent of all atoms.*

POSITIVE RAYS AND IONS

The negative particles in the rays from the cathode of discharge tubes were shown by Thomson and others to be identical regardless of the metal in the cathode or the gas in the tube. This fact leads to a number of conclusions. First, electrons are among the fundamental constituents of all atoms. Second, it follows that all atoms which are electrically neutral except when ionized must contain positive charges equal in number to the electrons. Third, the particles with the positive charges must be very different in mass from the electrons.

The existence of positive particles was proved by the use of a modified cathode ray tube. The cathode, placed in the middle of the tube, consists of a metal disc with holes (Figure 21–13). Upon discharge, the cathode rays stream toward the anode, but on the other side of the cathode a faint luminosity is observed. This effect is due to streams of positive ions which are attracted to the cathode and which, if the field is strong enough, shoot through the holes in the cathode and pass on because of their relatively great inertia. These positive ions may be deflected by a powerful magnetic field and both their mass and charge may be determined. The charge, while positive, is always either equal to or is a small multiple of the charge on the electron. The masses of these particles vary with the nature of the gas in the tube and are almost identical to the masses of its atoms. If the tube contains hydrogen, whose atoms are the lightest and simplest of all elements, the positive ray or particle is found to have a charge equal in magnitude to the charge on the electron. Its mass, however, is eighteen hundred and fifty times that of the electron. Rutherford in 1919 suggested the name *proton* for the positive particle found in a cathode ray tube filled with hydrogen.

The early experimentation with cathode ray tubes, then, proved the existence of the important negative particle called the electron, the unit positive particle called the proton, and the existence of many kinds of positive ions, such as O_2^{++}, N_2^{+}, CO^{+}, etc. These positive ions represent the debris of molecules after the loss of one or more electrons. Thus the oxygen molecule, O_2, is electrically neutral. After the loss of two electrons, however, the positive oxygen ion O_2^{++} is formed. This process is called ionization. It may be represented

$$O_2 \rightleftharpoons O_2^{++} + 2e^-.$$

THE CHARGE OF AN ELECTRON

The determination of this minute quantity of charge — one of the fundamental constants of nature — is a remarkable achievement of both theory and experiment. As the individual electron charge is too small to be isolated and observed, it is necessary to deal with larger and measurable aggregates of matter, most of them bearing one or more of the unit charges. If a sufficient number of measurements of the total charge borne by each of a number of small bodies is made and if the charges are varied and measured each time, the highest common factor of all the different total charges should be the value of the unit charge.

This was the basis of the method used (1914–17) by the American physicist, R. A. Millikan. (Refer to Figure 21–14.) Tiny oil droplets were obtained from an ordinary atomizer. From time to time one of these would fall through a small opening into the region between two horizontal plates. Light from an intense light source *S* (a carbon arc) illuminated the drop so brightly that it could easily be seen in the field of a magnifying telescope *T*. As shown in the figure, the axis of the telescope *T* was perpendicular to the plane of the paper. In the field was a linear scale so the rate of fall or rise of the droplet could be timed by the reference marks on a scale in the field of the telescope and an ordinary stop watch. The plates were connected to the plates of a battery. The potential applied to the plates could be varied by moving the contact *D*.

Most of the droplets became charged when sprayed from the atomizer. When the plates *A* and *C* were connected to the battery, an electrostatic field *E* was established. The intensity *E* of this field was known from the applied potential from the battery. The droplets were so tiny that the rate of fall under the influence of gravity was slow enough to be easily observed in the telescope. By slowly increasing the intensity *E* of the field, the drop could be made to rise slowly if it had a negative charge. By carefully controlling the intensity of the field, the drop could be held stationary.

Fig. 21–14 *Millikan's method for the determination of the charge of an electron.*

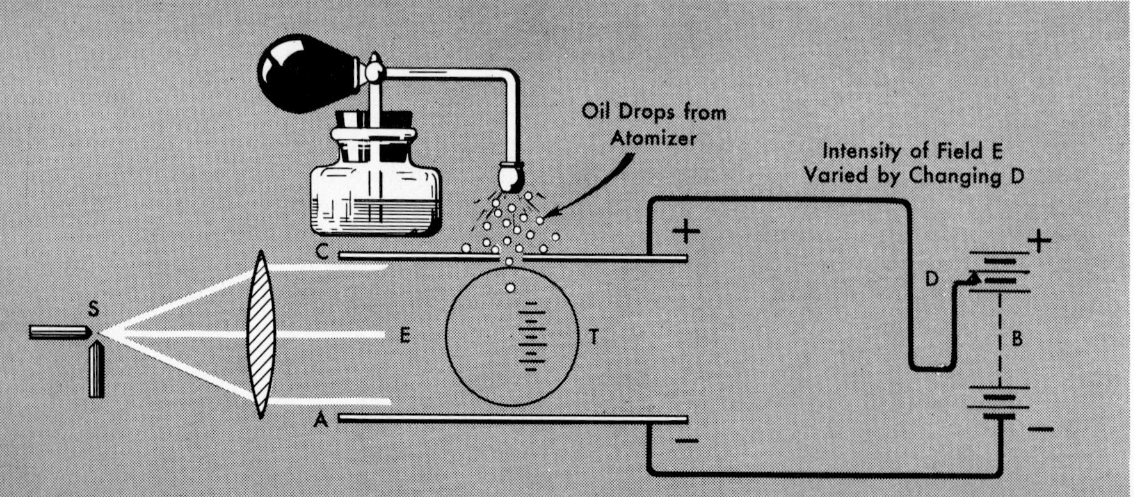

The stationary droplet was under the influence of two equal forces, a force down F_d due to the earth's gravitational field and a force upward F_u due to the electric field. The force down is merely the weight of the drop mg. The force up, using Equation 21–3 (page 336), is the product of the charge e and the intensity of the field E, or Ee. We have then, by equating these forces,

$$E \cdot e = mg = m \cdot 980 \text{ cm/sec}^2,$$

or

$$e = \frac{m \text{ grams} \cdot 980 \text{ cm/sec}^2}{E \text{ dynes/unit charge}}$$

$$= \frac{980m \text{ g cm/sec}^2}{E \text{ g cm/sec}^2\text{/unit charge}}$$

$$= \frac{980m}{E} \text{ unit charge (e.s.u.)}$$

(*Equation 21–6*)

The mass m of the drops was determined in each experiment as well as the value of the intensity of the field E.[1] Millikan carried out many hundreds of experiments on individual oil drops carrying electric charges. In every case, it was found that the charge was a certain value e, or e multiplied by some whole number depending upon the number of charges picked up by a droplet. The value for the smallest charge is 4.803×10^{-10} e.s.u. or statcoulombs. This is of course the charge on the fundamental negative particle of electricity which though tiny is one of the building blocks of all matter. It is one of the very important constants of nature. Millikan was awarded a Nobel Prize for his achievement.

SIGNIFICANCE OF THE ELECTRON

The data relative to the mass and charge of the electron had tremendous influence in all fields of science. It is of course the hypothetical particle called for by the electrolysis experiments of Faraday during the 1830's. It was recognized to be a normal constituent of all matter. But the most interesting development was that this discovery proved the existence of atoms and gave scientists for the first time experimental data for the small size of atoms and a method for counting them. Recall, for example, the electrolysis experiments with silver described on page 338. Thus, one coulomb of electricity deposits 0.001118 gram of silver. The atomic weight of silver has been shown by chemical methods to be 107.880 amu. The weight of 107.880 grams of silver, the quantity called the mole of silver, will require

$$107.880 \text{ g} \times \frac{1 \text{ coulomb}}{0.001118 \text{ g}} = 96500 \text{ coulombs}$$

for deposition. The change at the cathode was assumed to be silver ions accepting electrons to form atoms of silver, that is,

$$Ag^+ + e^- \rightarrow Ag.$$

If N is the number of atoms of silver in one mole of silver, N electrons are necessary. Hence we can write,

1 electron needed for 1 atom silver,
N electrons needed for N atoms silver, and
N electrons needed for 107.880 grams silver.

Also, N electrons = 96,500 coulombs.

Knowing, then, the relationship of the coulomb to the e.s.u., and using Millikan's value for the charge on the electron, it was possible to set up two simple equations,

$$Ne = N \times 4.803 \times 10^{-10} \frac{\text{e.s.u.}}{e} \times \frac{1 \text{ coulomb}}{3 \times 10^9 \text{ e.s.u.}} = 96{,}500 \text{ coulombs}$$

(*Equation 21–6*)

$$N \text{ atoms} \times m \frac{\text{g}}{\text{atom}} = 107.88 \text{ g.}$$

(*Equation 21–7*)

Hence, m = actual mass of silver atom $= 1.79 \times 10^{-22}$ grams,

and $N = 0.602 \times 10^{24}$ = 0.602 million million million million.

[1] Only the broad outlines of this experiment can be discussed here. A full description will be found in R. A. Millikan, *Electrons* (+ and −), *Protons, Photons, Neutrons, and Cosmic Rays*, University of Chicago Press, 1947.

The number N (0.602×10^{24}) is universally called *Avogadro's number* to honor the Italian scientist who contributed the principle (page 328) which made possible our system of atomic weights. This number, one of the important constants of nature, finds numerous uses in the physical sciences. It is the number to be associated with the quantity called the mole. Thus a faraday is N electrons, a mole of oxygen atoms (16 grams) is N atoms, and a mole of oxygen gas (32 grams) is N molecules.

Experiments involving Avogadro's number N and e make it possible to count atoms and to determine their actual masses. Atoms therefore are no longer hypothetical particles. As has been stated once before, it is impossible to weigh a postage stamp on a grocer's scale. However, it is possible to weigh 1000 stamps on a grocer's scale, then to compute the weight of one stamp. In an analogous manner, it is impossible to determine the mass of an atom, for example, of oxygen. But it is easy to weigh 16 grams (1 mole) of oxygen atoms, which is N atoms Hence,

$$0.602 \times 10^{24} \text{ atoms oxygen} = 16 \text{ grams, and}$$

$$1 \text{ atom oxygen} = \frac{16 \text{ g}}{0.602 \times 10^{24} \text{ atoms}} = 2.66 \times 10^{-23} \text{ gram.}$$

SUMMARY

1. *Metallic conduction* is due to a transfer of electrons through a metal with no permanent change in the metal.
2. *Electrolytic conduction* is due to a transfer of positive and negative ions through a solution of an electrolyte with a permanent change in the composition of the electrolyte.
3. The meaning of the following terms in electrochemistry has been discussed: electrolysis, electrode, anode, cathode, anion, and cation.
4. The mass of an element liberated or deposited at an electrode in electrolysis is directly proportional to the quantity of electricity passed and to the equivalent weight of the element. This is Faraday's law of electrolysis.
5. Studies based upon Faraday's law of electrolysis led to the conclusion that both elements and electricity must consist of particles, or are atomic in nature.
6. The discharge of electricity through gases at reduced pressures yields *cathode rays,* which show the following characteristics:
   a. they are deflected by electric and magnetic fields;
   b. they cause fluorescence and X-radiation;
   c. they move in straight lines;
   d. they exert mechanical and heating effects; that is, they possess a high energy content.
7. Experiments with cathode ray tubes resulted in the identification of the electron.
8. The electron has a definite mass and charge of negative electricity. It is one of the very important particles in all matter.
9. Cathode rays are streams of electrons which originate at the cathode in an evacuated discharge (Crookes) tube.
10. All electron streams in gases show the same properties; hence we conclude that electrons are fundamental particles of matter and constituents of all atoms.
11. Positive rays move toward the cathode in a discharge tube. They consist of the positive fragments of atoms or molecules which have lost electrons. They vary with the kind of gas in the tube.
12. The positive ion or ray from hydrogen is the lightest and smallest of all cathode rays and is called the proton. This particle, with eighteen hundred and fifty times the mass of the electron, has a positive charge equal in magnitude to that of the electron.
13. The inverse-square law of Coulomb states that the attractive force between unlike electric charges or the repulsive force between like charges is directly proportional to the product of the charges and inversely proportional to the square of the distance between them, or $F = q_1q_2/d^2$.
14. The important units of quantity of electric charge are the statcoulomb, the coulomb, and the faraday (96,500 coulombs).
15. Electric fields always appear about electric charges. They are visualized in terms of hypothetical lines of force which run from the positive to the negative charge.

16. Electric fields tend to produce motion on isolated charges of electricity. The motion of a positive charge is along a line of force toward a negative charge.
17. The intensity of an electric field is the force in dynes exerted by the field on a unit positive charge at any point in the field.
18. The charge on the electron was first precisely determined by Robert A. Millikan.
19. J. J. Thomson determined the e/m ratio for the electron. This, combined with the knowledge of the charge of e, led to the determination of the mass of the electron.
20. Millikan's value for the charge on the electron permitted a precise determination of Avogadro's number N, the number of particles in a mole of any substance or the number of electrons in a faraday.

STUDY EXERCISES

1. Write *C* if true of cathode rays, *P* if true of positive rays, or *B* if true of both:
   a. Consist of the residue of molecules which have lost one or more electrons..........
   b. Consist of streams of electrons...........
   c. Consist of the same particles irrespective of metal in anode or cathode or gas in tube..................................
   d. Vary with gas or material in tube.......
   e. Simplest of them is called proton........
   f. Move toward cathode.................
   g. Move toward anode...................
   h. Are deflected by magnetic or electrical field..................................
   i. Magnitude of charge is either equal to or a multiple of the fundamental charge on the electron..........................
   j. Have mass greater than that of the electron. ....
2. Refer to the diagram at the top of the page and compute the force of attraction *F* in dynes between the charges *A* and *B* under the following situations:
   a. What is *F* when *A* is 4 e.s.u., *B* is 5 e.s.u., and the distance *d* is 5 centimeters?......
   b. What is *F* if *A* is made 40 e.s.u.?........
   c. What is *F* if *A* is 40 e.s.u., and *d* is 100 centimeters?..........................
   d. What is *F* if *A* is 4 e.s.u., *B* is 10 e.s.u., and *d* is 1 centimeter?..................

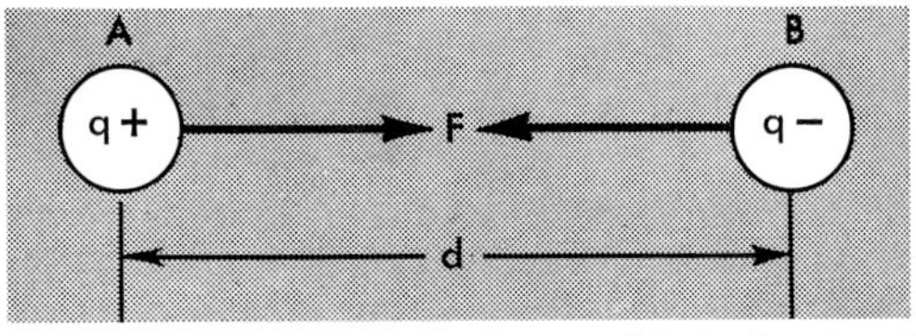

3. A test charge of 5 e.s.u. (positive) is placed at a point in an electric field where the intensity *E* is 20 dynes/e.s.u. What is the force exerted by the field on the charge?.........
4. The cathode of a silver coulometer increased in weight by 0.2000 gram during a certain electrolysis experiment. How many coulombs passed through the circuit?................
5. What is the actual weight of a hydrogen atom?..................................
6. In a certain experiment 8.000 grams of oxygen were collected. Express this quantity as:
   a. Moles of atoms.......................
   b. Moles of molecules...................
   c. Number of oxygen atoms...............
   d. Number of oxygen molecules...........
7. Explain how Faraday's experiments dealing with electrolysis of electroytes showed that atoms and electricity both must consist of tiny particles. Why did the ideas suggested by these experiments have to wait eighty years for confirmation?

FOR FURTHER READING

1. LEMON, H. B., *From Galileo to Nuclear Energy.* Chicago: University of Chicago Press, 1946.

   Very readable accounts of static electricity, electric fields, and Coulomb's law are presented in Chapters 19, 20, and 24; conduction in solutions and electrolysis in Chapter 28; conduction in gases and Millikan's oil-drop experiments in Chapter 29.
2. WHITE, HARVEY E., *Classical and Modern Physics.* New York: D. Van Nostrand Company, 1940.

   Chapter 28 discusses the early experiments concerning the electron including the studies with cathode ray tubes, the e/m experiments of J. J. Thomson, and the oil-drop experiments of Millikan.
3. Paperback: BRAGG, W., *Concerning the Nature of Things.* Dover, $1.35.
4. Paperback: DEVILLE, E., *Electricity.* Pelican, 65¢.

22

THE FUNDAMENTAL PARTICLES OF MATTER

THE PRECEDING CHAPTER told how the work of Faraday .pointed toward a conclusion that took a long time to establish, namely, that electricity must consist of *particles* which are atomic in nature, and further, that there was a definite link between the behavior of elements and electrical currents. This inference, vague at first, began to take form as facts began to accumulate from studies on the electrical discharge in evacuated tubes. Cathode rays and positive rays were discovered. The cathode rays were shown to be deflected by electric and magnetic fields, to have motion, to exert pressure when allowed to impinge upon objects, or, in other words, to consist of *material particles* of high energy content. It was further shown that the production of the cathode rays in evacuated tubes was accompanied by the production of mutilated molecules and atoms which were positively charged – in other words, positive rays. In this manner the first delineation of the electrons (in cathode rays) and protons (in positive rays) began to take shape. In the present chapter further evidence will be presented to show how the modern concept of atomic particles finally emerged.

THE DISCOVERY OF X-RAYS

The studies of electrical discharge in vacuum tubes conducted by Lenard and Crookes culminated in the work of J. J. Thomson (see Chapter 21) who proved about 1895 that, no matter what residual gas was left in the evacuated cathode ray tube, and no matter of what metal the cathode was made, the mass and the charge of the negative particles emitted from the cathode remained the same. It was obvious, therefore, that if the negatively charged particles were emitted from the cathode or from the molecules of the residual gas in the tube, they constituted one of the fundamental building blocks of which matter was made. In the next five years (1895–1900) a series of discoveries was made which ultimately revolutionized our whole concept of the material universe and ushered in the modern nuclear age. These discoveries were X-rays and radioactivity.

The production of X-rays by electrons in cathode ray tubes was discovered by Wilhelm Roentgen (1845–1923) in Germany in 1895. Earlier Crookes had observed that photographic plates stored in closed drawers of the room in which he was working with cathode rays became "fogged" or partially exposed. Roentgen found that cathode ray tubes give off rays which have different properties from the negatively charged particles within the tube. These invisible rays were not bent by either magnetic or electric fields; they passed through glass and many opaque objects. Their presence can be demonstrated by placing a dark cloth on the cathode ray tube and placing a photographic plate in back of an opaque object such as a ring of keys. The keys form a dark image against the background. Furthermore, certain minerals like zinc sulfide glow in the dark (fluoresce) when placed in the vicinity of the covered cathode ray tube. The inference is that penetrating *non-material* rays are emitted through the cathode ray tube. In the modern X-ray tube, shown in Figure 22–1, the velocity of the electrons is increased by placing a high potential between the cathode, consisting of a hot filament, and the metallic target serving as the anode. The high-speed electrons, on hitting the atoms of the metal, produce energy transformations of the electrons in the metal which result in the emission of energy of very short wave length known as X-rays.

THE DISCOVERY OF RADIOACTIVITY

It was observed by Roentgen that many minerals when exposed to X-rays show *fluorescence* and that a number also exhibit *phosphorescence,* that is, an emission of light or glow which continues for some time after the removal of the X-rays. Henri Becquerel (France, 1852–1908), in investigating the properties of materials which glow when exposed to X-rays, found accidentally that minerals containing uranium affected a covered photographic plate without being exposed to X-rays. Further, it was shown that the uranium compounds and minerals produced ions in air and could do so even when the uranium minerals were kept in the dark for days. This indicated that whatever affected the photographic plate and ionized the air was *spontaneously emitted* by the uranium compounds and could not be controlled in any way. Thus radioactivity was discovered, and in an element which was unique only because of its large atomic weight (238) – it was then the heaviest known element. By 1950, however, it was one of the best known of the elements.

Pierre Curie (France, 1859–1906), a young physicist working with Becquerel, and his assistant Marie Sklodowska (Poland and France, 1867–1934), later Madame Curie, assumed the task of further investigating substances which exhibit these phenomena. An ore from Austria called *pitchblende* produced a greater ionizing ef-

Fig. 22–1 *Modern X-ray tube.*

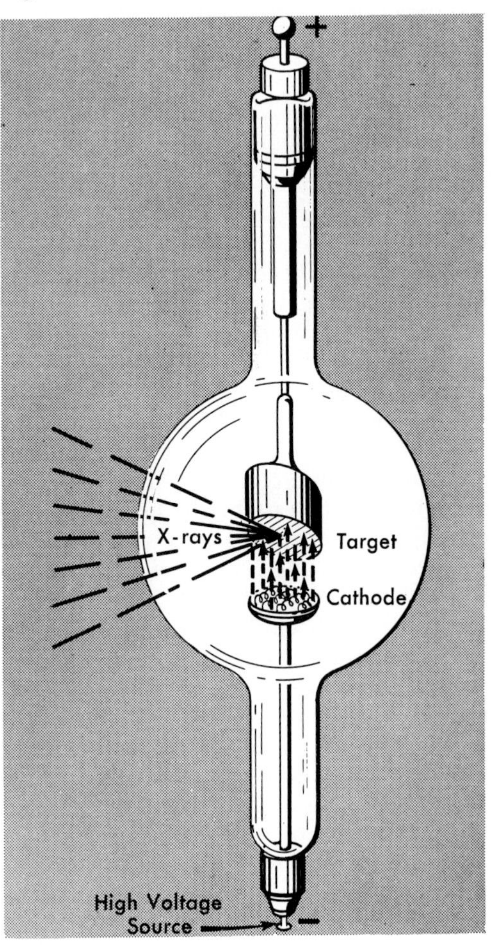

fect than uranium salts. The logical inference was that this ore contained an element which had a greater activity than uranium. After much arduous work in a primitive chemical laboratory, using methods of ordinary chemical separations, the Curies were able to isolate two new elements which had a greater activity than uranium. The first was named *polonium* after Madame Curie's native land, Poland; the second was called *radium* because of the intensity of the emission of the rays which affected photographic plates and ionized gases. Pierre and Marie Curie shared in 1903, with Becquerel, the Nobel award for the discovery of radioactivity with the isolation of the salts of the radioactive element; and in 1911 Madame Curie was honored by a second Nobel prize, the only person who has ever received this highest award twice.

INSTRUMENTS FOR THE STUDY OF CHARGED PARTICLES

The Curies and other investigators of radioactivity have used three basic instruments to study charged particles. These instruments have been the guides and pathfinders in all the discoveries which ushered in the so-called atomic or nuclear age.

The Electroscope. The simplest and the first to be developed was the electroscope shown in Figure 22–2. It consists of a piece of gold foil attached to a metal rod and enclosed in a glass case. The rod is insulated from the case by the use of a sulfur or rubber stopper. The electroscope is charged by placing a piece of hard rubber which has been previously rubbed with a piece of woolen cloth on the knob of the rod. The gold leaf flies apart from the rod, since both rod and leaf have been charged negatively and repel each other. For a positive charge the knob is touched with a glass rod previously rubbed with a silk cloth. If the position of the leaf is noted through a telescope with an eyepiece having crossbars (see Figure 22–2), the rate at which the electroscope discharges can be followed. For example, for a particular

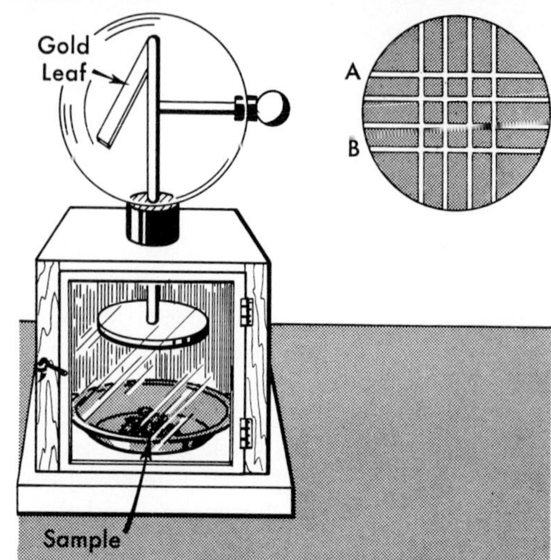

Fig. 22–2 *Simple electroscope.*

reading, let us assume that it takes 30 minutes for the gold leaf to fall from position A to B in Figure 22–2.

The electroscope has a "natural leak" due to the ions which are always present in the air because of the action of radiation, heat, and other forms of energy upon the air molecules. If, for example, an electric light is placed at a distance of ten feet from the electroscope, the time required for the leaf to fall from position A to position B is less than 30 minutes. A lighted match placed about an inch from the knob produces an instantaneous discharge of the electroscope. If a gram of copper or iron is placed on a dish inside the electroscope, the time required for the leaf to fall from position A to B is the same as if nothing were present. If one gram of uranium oxide, however, is placed inside the electroscope, the time required becomes shorter than the natural leak time, because uranium oxide is radioactive and emits particles which *ionize* the air within the electroscope and produce the rapid discharge of the gold leaf. This method has been used to measure the relative ionizing activity of various substances. If, for example 0.1 gram of substance x gives a discharge (fall of the leaf from A to B) in 20 minutes and 0.1 gram of substance y in 15 seconds, then y is $20 \div 15/60 = 20 \times 60/15 = 80$ times more active as an ionizing material than x.

The Geiger Counter. Figure 22–3 shows the Geiger–Müller type of ionization chamber often called a *counter,* which reveals the presence of ionized particles by flashing a light bulb or by a clicking sound. The ionization chamber *a* with thin aluminum window *b* contains a central electrode *p* charged positively with reference to the negative electrode formed by the case. The potential between the two electrodes is not high enough to cause ionization by cathode ray formation in the gas *d* contained within the chamber. However, the potential is high enough so that even the slightest ionization within the chamber will cause a discharge. An electron or a positive ion *c* with high speed will pass through the window and cause ionization of the gas, resulting in a discharge or sudden surge of current. This current is amplified and by appropriate devices causes a flash in a small light bulb or makes a clicking sound in a loudspeaker or activates a counting device. This is the type of apparatus most frequently used to detect radioactivity through the presence of charged ions in the atmosphere. Thus, a sample of uranium mineral brought near the counter produces rapid flashes. Safety regulations now dictate that workers with radioactive substances have a Geiger counter or similar instrument always available to detect the presence of radiation in dangerous amounts.

The Cloud Chamber. Figure 22–4 shows diagrammatically a cloud chamber. The air in the chamber above the piston is saturated with water vapor. The piston can be moved up and down so that the air can be alternately compressed and expanded. During the expansion movement the air is cooled and becomes supersaturated with water vapor. As a result of this supersaturation, the water vapor has a tendency to condense to minute droplets provided there are nuclei present. Any ions produced by radiation entering the chamber serve as nuclei upon which the moisture condenses, thus producing a fog. If a particle moves across the chamber and knocks off electrons from neutral molecules producing ions, there will be a fog track visible in the path of the particle which can be photographed through the glass window.

Cloud-track machines are usually constructed so as to be entirely automatic, and require no attention during the exposure

Fig. 22–3 *(below) Principle of the Geiger-Müller counter: (a) ionizing chamber; (b) window for rays; (c) radioactive substance; (d) ionization by alpha or beta particle, or gamma rays; (p) central electrode. (right) Portable radiological survey meter for detecting and measuring beta-gamma radiation. (Universal Atomics Division of Universal Transistor Products Corp., Westbury, New York)*

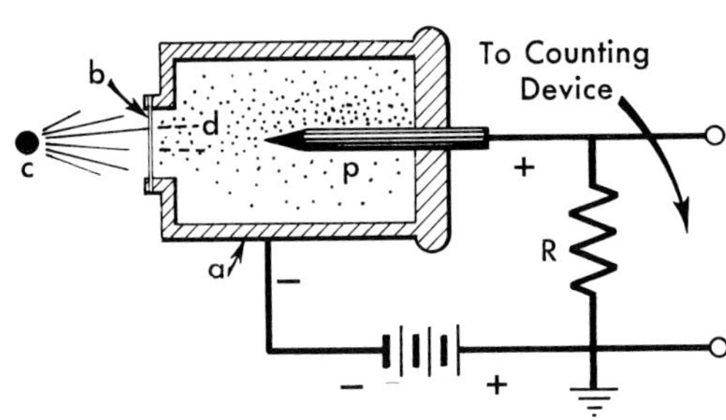

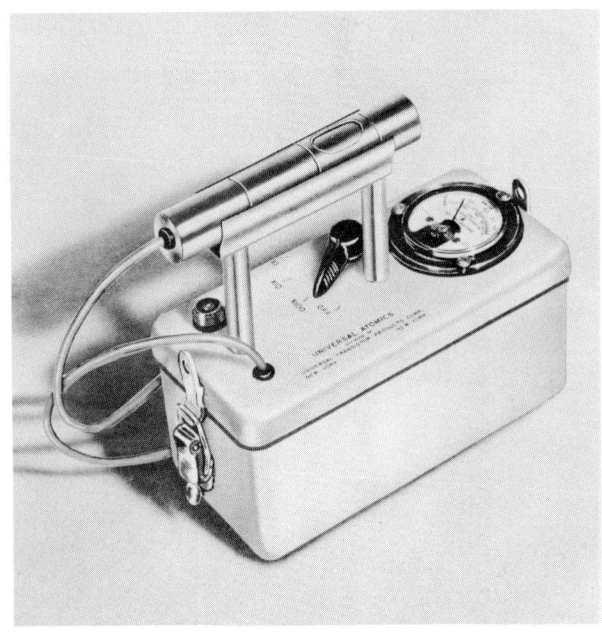

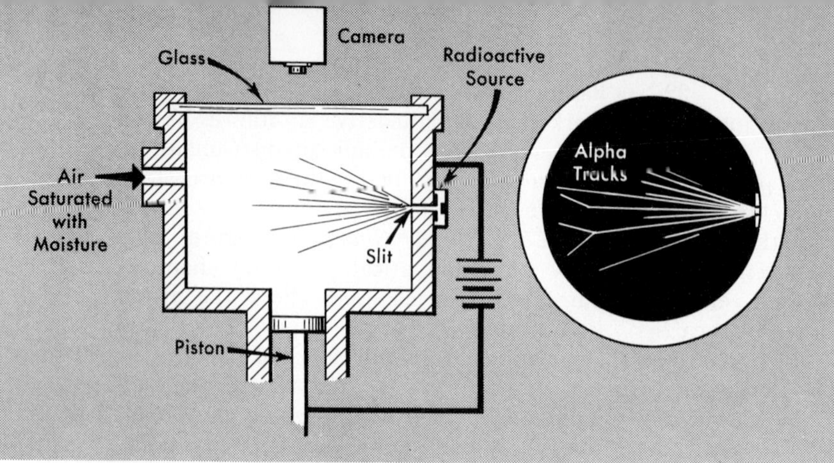

Fig. 22–4 *Cloud chamber. View looking down through glass plate to inner chamber is shown at right.*

of as much as a thousand feet of motion-picture film. After exposure the individual pictures can be thrown on a screen for examination. Most of the tracks are straight lines (Figure 22–5). Occasionally a charged particle will collide with the nucleus of an atom, and the collision will be revealed by a sudden change in direction, or by the formation of two tracks. The latter event is evidence of collision of a particle with a nucleus of an atom and will be discussed in a subsequent section.

Fig. 22–5 *Cloud chamber tracks of alpha particles. (Photograph by P. M. S. Blackett, Imperial College, London)*

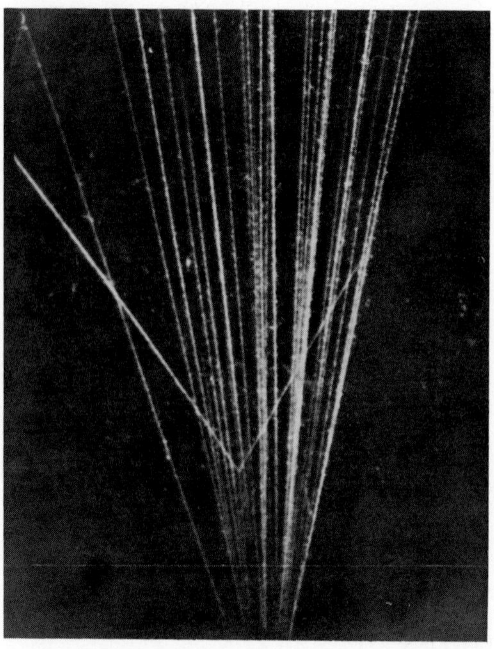

RADIOACTIVE FRAGMENTS

Following the discovery of radium and polonium by the Curies, it was soon found that each radioactive element disintegrates in a characteristic manner. The nature of radiations given off by radioactive elements was not known at first and hence these radiations were called by Greek letters: alpha rays (α-rays), beta rays (β-rays), and gamma rays (γ-rays). The rays were recognized by their behavior in a magnetic field as shown in Figure 22–6. Alpha and beta rays are deflected, while gamma rays are not affected. The deflection of the rays in a magnetic or electric field is in such a manner as to indicate a positive charge for the alpha rays and a negative for the beta rays.

From studies of the behavior of the radiations emitted from radioactive substances in electric fields and also of their penetration through various media, it was determined that the alpha rays were positively charged atomic fragments, the beta rays were identical with electrons, and the gamma rays were intense invisible light of shorter wave length and greater penetrating power than X-rays. The alpha particle has a charge of plus two and a mass of four on the basis of the hydrogen nucleus having one plus charge and a mass of one atomic unit. Since the alpha particles eventually formed helium atoms, it was inferred that the alpha particle is a helium nucleus. The velocity of the alpha particle is in the range of 10,000 miles per second. The par-

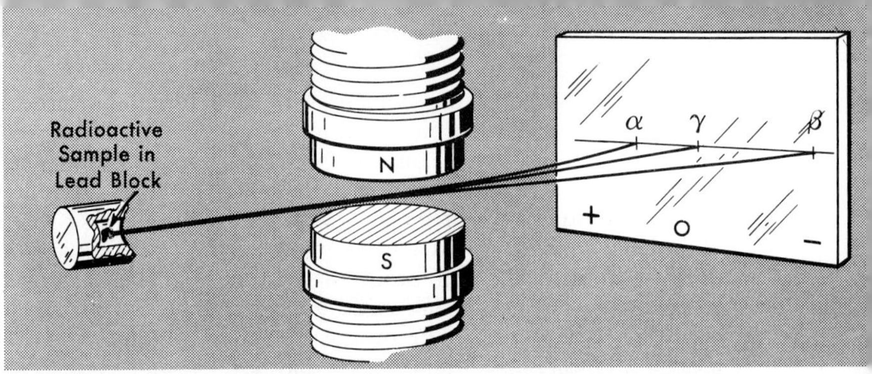

Fig. 22–6 *Behavior of radioactive rays in a magnetic field.*

ticle is stopped by a fairly thin foil of metal or a few centimeters of air. However, its mass plus its enormous speed gives the alpha particle a large amount of kinetic energy. As the particles are emitted from the disrupting nuclei they behave like projectiles, colliding with atoms and molecules in their paths and ionizing them.

The beta rays are electrons, which are propelled from the disrupting nuclei with high velocities which may reach 160,000 miles per second; they collide and ionize the molecules which they encounter. The proof of their identity is the negative charge and the value of e/m which is the same as that of electrons. They have greater penetrating power than the alpha particles due to their smaller charge and high velocity.

The gamma rays, or photons, have great penetrating power; those given off by an appreciable amount of radium (100 mg) will pass through a plate of iron many inches thick. Being an intense form of radiation (light) with no electrical charge, they are not affected either by magnetic or electric fields. They affect living tissue profoundly; the danger from radioactive substances is due mostly to gamma radiation.

RADIOACTIVE ELEMENTS

The disintegration of radioactive elements is spontaneous and proceeds at a constant rate not altered by temperature or other conditions. Man has found no way to hasten or retard this decay.[1] Heat in large quantities is evolved. Radium keeps itself above the temperature of the surrounding air and continues to disintegrate, yielding fast-moving particles and rays, all carrying enormous quantities of energy, without any drop in temperature. The expulsion of alpha particles, which easily pick up electrons to become neutral atoms of helium, is also an unparalleled phenomenon. Here, it has been observed for the first time that one element is formed from another.

At least eighteen of the chemical elements with a total of forty-seven different atomic masses (isotopes) are naturally radioactive. Over eight hundred additional radioactive isotopes have been made in the laboratory by methods which will be discussed in a later chapter. Most of the naturally occurring radioactive elements have heavy nuclei, since their atomic weights are above 206 atomic weight units. Uranium has an atomic weight of 238 and radium 226. They are unstable and disintegrate spontaneously into more stable elements. The disintegrative process proceeds stepwise, as illustrated by the nuclear changes of radium:

$^{226}_{88}$Radium (1620 y) $\xrightarrow{\alpha}$ $^{222}_{86}$Radon (3.8 d) $\xrightarrow{\alpha}$

$^{218}_{84}$Radium A (3.05 m) $\xrightarrow{\alpha}$ $^{214}_{82}$Radium B (26.8 m) $\xrightarrow{\beta}$

$^{214}_{83}$Radium C (19.7 m) $\xrightarrow{\beta}$ $^{214}_{84}$Radium C′ (1.6×10^{-4} s) $\xrightarrow{\alpha}$

$^{210}_{82}$Radium D (20 y) $\xrightarrow{\beta}$ $^{210}_{83}$Radium E (5.0 d) $\xrightarrow{\beta}$

$^{210}_{84}$Polonium (138.4 d) $\xrightarrow{\alpha}$ $^{206}_{82}$Lead (stable)

The superscript denotes the mass number (A) of the atom, for example, 226 for radium; the subscript, the atomic number (Z). The figure below the element indicates

[1] However, neutron capture by radioactive elements leads to nuclear changes.

the *half-life period* of the element. For example, if we start with one million atoms of radium, in 1620 years one-half million atoms of radium remain. Compare this relatively slow rate of disintegration with that of radon which is the first element of radium disintegration. An atom of atomic number 88 and atomic mass 226 gives off an alpha particle of atomic number 2 and mass 4. So the new atom *radon* has an atomic number of $88 - 2 = 86$ and a mass number of $226 - 4 = 222$. Radon has a half-life period of 3.8 days; if we start with one million atoms of radon, after 3.8 days one-half million have disintegrated; in other words, radon disintegrates about 147,000 times faster than radium ($1620 \text{ y} \times 365.25/3.8$). The half-life period is a determinable number, whereas the total time for all atoms to disintegrate is theoretically infinite. The concept of half-life will be further discussed on page 625.

By three stepwise changes of alpha-particle emission, radium *B* is produced which emits a beta particle or an electron to give radium *C*. The atomic mass number in this change remains the same, since the electron has a very small mass; the atomic number increases by one unit, since loss of a negative particle is equivalent to the gain of one unit positive charge by the nucleus. The over-all final products of these radioactive disintegrations are alpha particles plus electrons which form atoms of helium and atoms of lead, which are stable elements.

THE PLANETARY ATOM

The accumulating observations and facts from the studies of electrical discharge in vacuum tubes and of radioactive transformations pointed out during the first decade of this century the rough outlines of the structure of the atom. The nature of cathode rays indicated that all molecules and atoms had an outer cloud or shell of negative electrons, some of which could be readily "pulled off." The production of positive rays in vacuum tubes and the alpha particles from radioactive disintegrations definitely indicated that somewhere within the atoms there were positively charged particles. Since normal atoms are neutral, the obvious inference is that in any given atom the number of negative and positive particles are equal in number. But how are these particles arranged in the atom? Obviously there was a need for a synthesis of the accumulated facts. This was furnished by a young New Zealander, Ernest Rutherford (1871–1937), who had gone to Cambridge to study under J. J. Thomson. After the Curies discovered radium and polonium and the types of radiation emitted by radioactive elements, it was Rutherford who explained these phenomena. Working with radioactive fragments, he was able to prove that alpha particles capture electrons and become helium atoms. Using the alpha particles as projectiles, he began to bombard the atoms of heavy elements like gold and light elements like nitrogen. Drawing on these observations, Rutherford proposed the planetary concept of the atom.

The solar system serves as the model for the planetary atom. Centrally located and dominating the solar system is the sun, whose mass is approximately seven hundred times that of all the planets and their satellites combined. Far away from the sun the nine planets revolve around; the nearest (Mercury) being 36 million miles away and the most remote (Pluto) 3670 million miles away from the sun. Therefore, the solar system consists mostly of empty space. Centrally located in the atom is a compact nucleus which consists of positively charged particles called protons, which are about 1800 times heavier than the electrons; hence most of the mass of the atom is in its nucleus. Far away from the nucleus revolves a cloud of electrons whose number is equal to the number of the protons. The orbits in which the various electrons revolve about the nucleus are circular or elliptical. The number of electrons or the number of protons is designated as the *atomic number*. The space occupied by the nucleus and the electrons is very small as compared to the total size of the atom; therefore the atom, like the solar system, contains within its boundaries a great deal of empty space. The dimensions of the two systems illustrate a problem of science. The diameter of the solar system is 1.2×10^{15} centimeters and that of the atom is in the order of 2×10^{-8} centimeters, a ratio of 5×10^{22} to one.

THE NUCLEUS

The experimental evidence which suggested to Rutherford about 1910 the concept of a compact heavy positively charged nucelus involved the bombardment of gold, silver, or platinum foils by means of alpha particles from radium *C*. (Refer to Figure 22–7.) A beam of alpha particles from the source was deflected by means of a magnetic field (so as to separate it from beta and gamma rays) and directed toward a thin gold foil. Beyond the foil the alpha particles were allowed to fall on a fluorescent screen of zinc sulfide. Each alpha particle, on striking the screen, produced a tiny flash of light. It was observed that the glow on the screen was in line with the alpha particle beam. This indicated that nearly all the alpha particles passed directly through the foil without deflection. A few of the particles, however, were scattered at wide angles from their path, and occasionally an alpha particle was turned at an angle of nearly 180°, that is, sent back in the direction from which it came.

Several conclusions were drawn from the passage and scattering of alpha particles through metal foils. First, since most of the alpha particles pass through the metal foil without deflection, the atoms must be largely empty space. The second inference drawn by Rutherford was that the occasional deflections of the alpha particles were caused by their approach near the positive centers of the atoms; since this deflection occurred only once for every 200,000 undeflected passages, the inference is that the positive *kernel* or *nucleus* is compact and concentrated in a small space or at the center of the atom. This early work of Rutherford indicated further that the magnitude of the positive charge of the nucleus was equal to

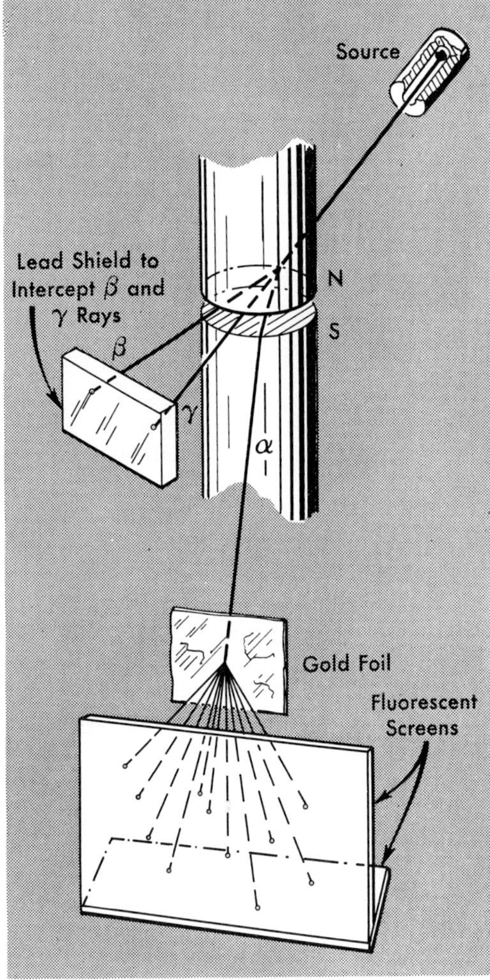

Fig. 22–7 *Scattering of alpha particles by a gold foil.*

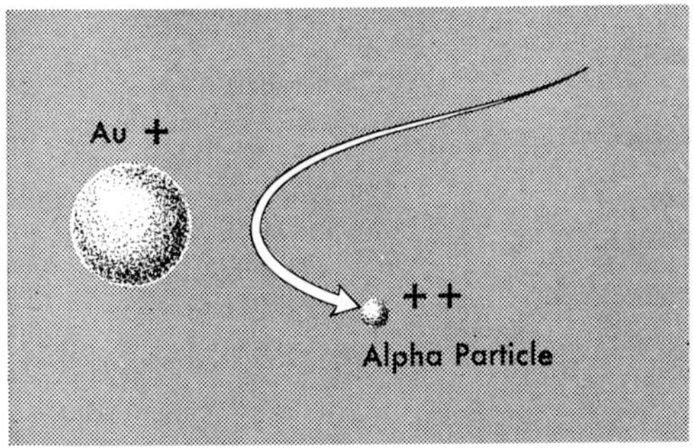

Fig. 22–8 *Repulsion of an alpha particle by the positive nucleus.*

approximately half of the atomic weight. Obviously then there must be other particles in the nucleus to make up the total mass of the atoms.

In the early days of speculations about atomic structure, the other particles were assumed to be protons and electrons so enmeshed as to neutralize their charges. This was not far from the nature of neutrons, which were discovered later.

STABLE ATOMIC PARTICLES

Before proceeding to the multitude of other atomic particles which have been demonstrated during the past twenty years as a result of the probing of the atoms by all types of projectiles, it should be noted that for the purpose of our discussion we can divide the atomic particles into two general categories. One of these comprises the stable particles, *electrons, protons,* and *neutrons,* which are summarized in Table 22–1, and these we shall consider here. The particles in the second category will be discussed in the next section. As noted in Table 22–1, the neutron is an uncharged particle of about the same mass as the proton and residing in the nucleus. Its discovery and properties are given on page 360.

The term *stable* is relative and merely indicates that we shall use these particles in discussing only the *low-energy* reactions of the atoms which comprise all the chemical reactions. Thus, our picture of the atom as developed up to this point consists of a centrally located compact nucleus made up of protons and neutrons. The nucleus is positively charged; the number of protons designates the atomic number of the atom. The number of protons plus neutrons gives the mass of the atom. Far away from the nucleus is a cloud of electrons whose number is equal to the number of protons in the nucleus. The difference between atoms of different elements is the difference in the number of protons, neutrons, and electrons, and the difference in the arrangement and motions of the electrons around the nucleus.

Table 22–2 lists particles used as projectiles in nuclear reactions. The first two are radioactive fragments. It was soon discovered that these natural projectiles could be used to produce other particles, which in turn could be accelerated to produce high-energy particles and used to smash other atoms. One of the most important of these particles is the deuteron, an outgrowth of the discovery of the heavy hydrogen isotope, ${}^{2}_{1}H^{-}$, which is often referred to as deuterium, ${}^{2}_{1}D$. Heavy water, D_2O, is the corresponding compound to ordinary water, H_2O, when the hydrogen isotope 1 is replaced by isotope 2. Deuterium is prepared by electrolysis of D_2O. When solutions of sodium hydroxide are repeatedly electrolyzed, ordinary hydrogen is evolved more readily than deuterium. The deuterium is readily ionized by collision with alpha particles or by a beam of electrons.

$$\underset{\text{Deuterium}}{{}^{2}_{1}D} + \text{Energy} \rightarrow \underset{\text{Deuteron}}{{}^{2}_{1}D^{+}} + \underset{\text{Electron}}{e^{-}}$$

TABLE 22–1 STABLE ATOMIC PARTICLES

PARTICLE	SYMBOL	MASS BASIS (electron = 1)	MASS (oxygen = 16.0000 a.m.u.)*	CHARGE	PART OF ATOM	DISCOVERED
Electron	e^{-}	1	0.000548	−	Outside nucleus	1896 Thomson
Proton	p,H^{+} ${}^{1}_{1}H$	1845	1.00758	+	Nucleus	1896–1910 Thomson, Rutherford
Neutron	${}^{1}_{0}n$	1845	1.00897	0	Nucleus	1932 Chadwick

* a.m.u. = atomic mass units.

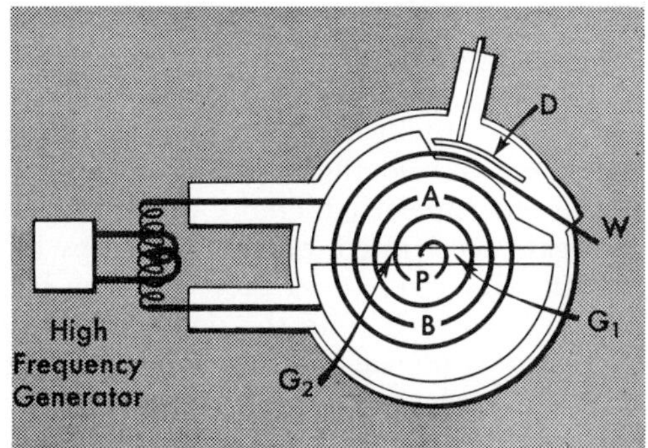

Fig. 22–9 *Principle of the cyclotron.*

The energy of the positively charged deuterons (heavy hydrogen nuclei) can be increased tremendously by accelerating them through application of large potentials in accelerating machines, of which the best known is the cyclotron.

The first cyclotron was devised by an American Nobel prize winner, Ernest O. Lawrence, at the University of California. In effect, the cyclotron is a mechanical slingshot for deuterons or other particles. Two large hollow D-shaped plates, called "dees" (*A* and *B* in Figure 22–9), are placed between the poles of a powerful electromagnet. Provision is made for charging these plates positively and negatively by connecting them to a rapidly oscillating electric current at a potential of 100,000 volts. Gaseous deuterium (heavy hydrogen) is ionized at the center *P* by exposure to a hot filament. It is characteristic of ions to travel in circular paths in crossing a magnetic field. Hence the ionized deuterium

Fig. 22–10 *Cyclotron emitting a beam of deuterons. (University of California Radiation Laboratory)*

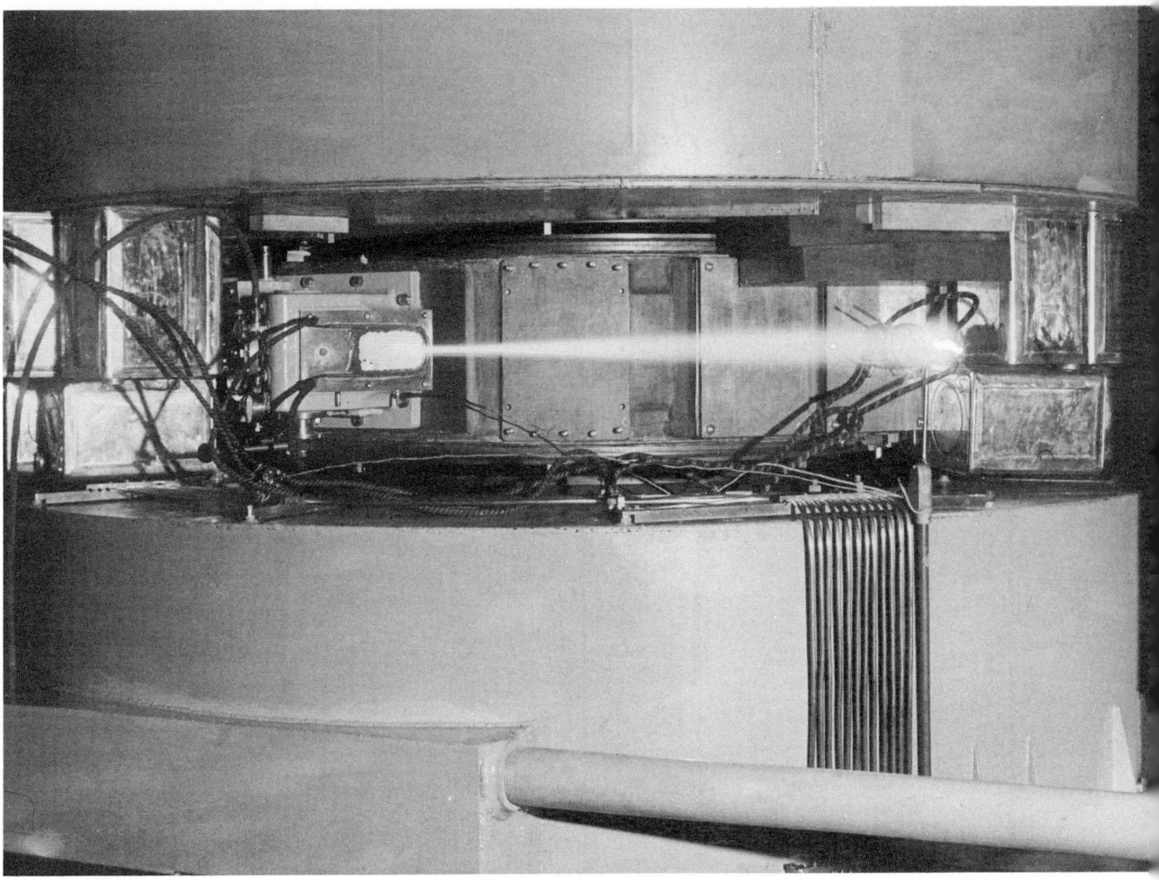

($^2_1H+$) produced at *P* starts traveling in a circular path. While the dee *B* is negative and *A* is positive, the deuterons are accelerated across the gap G_1 toward *B*. After they have crossed the gap G_1 the polarity of the dees is reversed. Hence the deuterons are again accelerated, being repelled by the positive charge on *B* as they cross the gap at G_2. Thus each time the deuterons cross the gap — twice each revolution — they receive an increment of energy and the speed is increased as a result of proper timing of the oscillating electric current. The charged particles travel in ever-widening circles with ever-increasing velocity. When they reach the periphery they are deflected to a window *W* by a negatively charged plate and emerge as a beam of deuterons (Figure 22–10) with velocities of 25,000 miles or more per second to form projectiles with the greatest energy per unit of mass of any produced by man. The cyclotron will likewise accelerate protons and alpha particles.

The limiting energy of the deuterons in a cyclotron depends upon the number of times they can be given a "kick" as they cross the gap between the dees. This depends in turn upon the radius of the pole pieces of the electromagnet.

The best known of the cyclotrons is the 184-inch instrument at the University of California. This dimension refers to the size of the pole pieces. The huge electromagnet weighs over 4000 tons and cost $1,500,000. Research with such a cyclotron requires the cooperation of many skilled workers, electronic and electrical engineers, physicists, and chemists. The energy of the emergent deuterons in terms of energy per unit of mass is so large that they serve as exceedingly useful packets of energy for the scientist. These high-energy particles have made possible the modern methods for transmuting elements.

OTHER ATOMIC PARTICLES

These are of importance in considering nuclear or *high-energy* reactions. For the purpose of discussion, they are divided into two groups as listed in Tables 22–2 and 22–3. The particles listed in Table 22–2 are well understood and are used extensively as projectiles in the transformation of one element into another. Table 22–3 gives a partial list of transitory particles which are imperfectly understood at present, but which are of importance in balancing the equations for high-energy reactions.

The positron has the same mass as the electron, but it has a positive charge. It appears when cosmic rays coming from outer space encounter matter. It has only a

TABLE 22–2 FUNDAMENTAL PARTICLES OF SIGNIFICANCE IN NUCLEAR REACTIONS

PARTICLE	CHARGE ($e^- = 1$)	MASS (a.m.u.)	SOURCE OR PRODUCTION OR ACCELERATION
Alpha Particle	++	4.00276	Radioactive elements
Beta Particle	−	0.000548	Radioactive elements
Proton	+	1.00758	By collision of hydrogen or hydrogen compounds with alpha particles
Deuteron	+	2.01417	By ionization of heavy hydrogen with alpha or gamma rays and acceleration in cyclotron
Neutron	0	1.00897	Bombardment of light elements with alpha particles or heavy water with deuterons. Also obtained in atomic piles.
Electron	−	0.000548	From bombardment of many substances, with alpha particles, gamma rays, and X-rays
Photon (gamma)	0	0	High-energy (nuclear) changes

TABLE 22–3 SOME TRANSITORY PARTICLES IN NUCLEAR REACTIONS

PARTICLE	CHARGE	MASS IN e^- UNITS	AVERAGE LIFE OF DECAY (seconds)	PRODUCTS OF DECAY	INTERACTIONS WITH OTHER PARTICLES	
					Particle	*Product*
Positron	+	1	Stable	....	Electron	Two photons
Meson (Muon)	+ or −	207	10^{-6} to 10^{-8} second	Neutrinos or Positrons or Electrons	Atomic nucleus	Excitation or disruption
Pion	+, − or 0	264–273	10^{-8} to 10^{-16}	.....	.....	.....
Neutrino	0		Stable	.....	.....	.....

transitory existence, since in encountering an electron, the particles interact and annihilate each other with the appearance of an equivalent amount of energy, according to Einstein's equation, $E = mc^2$. The reverse process, that is, the creation of particles out of energy, is possible, so we may think that energy can condense into material particles.

The mesons are intermediate particles between protons and neutrons on the one hand, and electrons and positrons on the other. Their mass is roughly one-tenth of the former particles and 200 times the mass of the latter particles. Their life span is measured in billionths of a second, and they undergo spontaneous disintegration into other particles and radiant energy. The mesons are observed in cosmic rays and have been produced in large particle accelerators. The pions and neutrinos are nonmaterial particles of radiant energy, and may be regarded as creations of the scientist in order to balance high-energy reactions.

In considering the current theories of electrically charged particles, it should be noted that the trend is to have for each particle a counterpart of the opposite charge. For example, for the electron e^- we have the positron e^+. In fact, the existence of the positron was postulated by theory before it was discovered. Accordingly, we should have an antiproton which would have the same mass as the proton but a negative charge. As yet no experimental evidence has been found for the existence of this particle.

TRANSMUTATION OF ELEMENTS

Alchemists of the Middle Ages tried to transmute base metals into gold, but they never succeeded. Lavoisier and Dalton, the founders of chemistry, convinced scientists that elements could never be transmuted from one into another because the individual atoms could not be changed. This view prevailed throughout the nineteenth century. Then suddenly, in 1919, Rutherford did transmute one element into another. He bombarded nitrogen atoms with alpha particles from radium and observed a very unexpected result. When an alpha particle collided with a nitrogen atom, an atom of oxygen-17 and a hydrogen atom appeared, and both the nitrogen atom and the alpha particle disappeared. This event was in reality the first induced transmutation of matter, though in quantities too small to be recovered. A partial explanation of the transmutation process is shown in Figure 22–11. (See also Figure 22–12.) A further aspect of this reaction will be discussed later in connection with the relationship between matter and energy.

The full significance of the transmutation experiment of Rutherford was that it indicated the steps that had to be followed to bring about transmutations of elements. A transmutation required a change in the nucleus of an atom. What was needed, then, was some particle with energy sufficient to penetrate into the nucleus and thus change the composition of the nucleus. The first projectile particles used for this purpose were alpha particles from radium. With

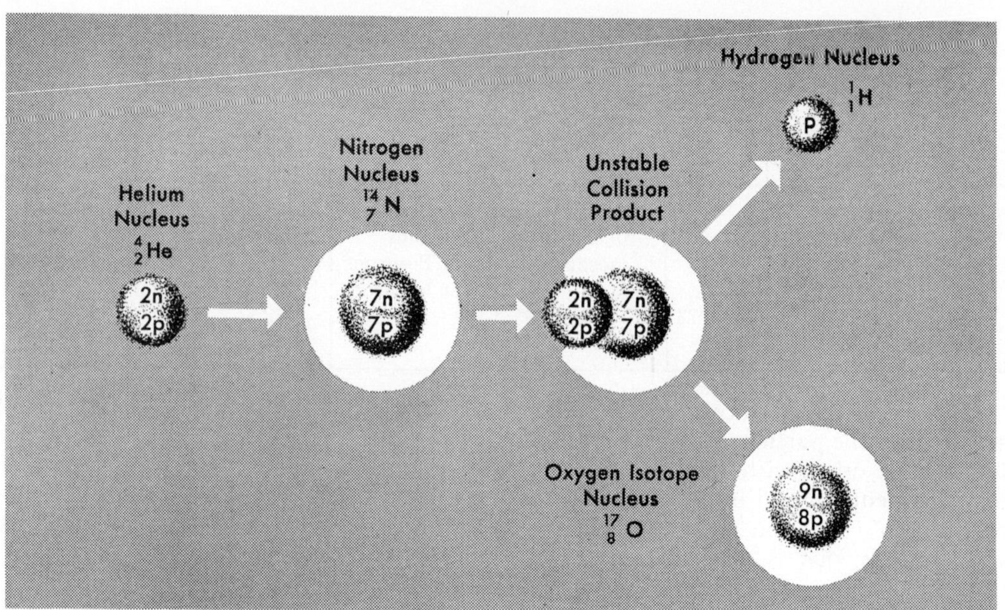

Fig. 22–11 *A schematic representation of transmutation of nitrogen into oxygen by bombardment with high-velocity alpha particles.*

Fig. 22–12 *Cloud chamber photograph of transmutation of a nitrogen nucleus by collision with an alpha particle. Heavy branch of forked track was formed by new oxygen isotope nucleus; fine branch, by hydrogen nucleus.* (*Photo by P. M. S. Blackett, Imperial College, London*)

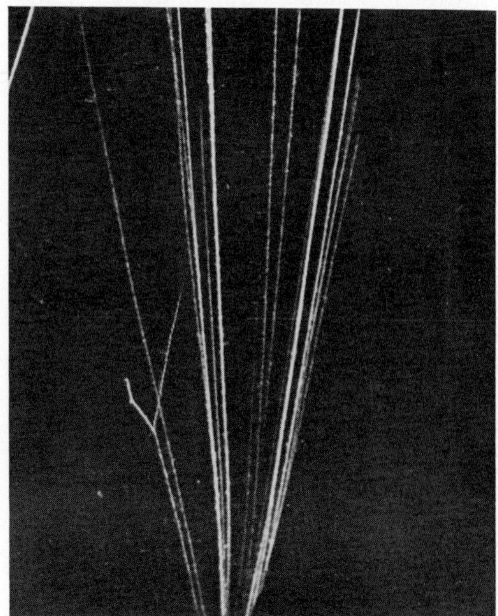

alpha particles, nitrogen atoms were converted to oxygen atoms according to the following equation:

$$^4_2\alpha + ^{14}_{7}N \rightarrow ^{17}_{8}O + ^1_1H$$

Many other light elements were converted into other elements by this type of nuclear reaction. However, the disadvantage of this method for producing new elements was the relatively small amounts of alpha particles that could be made available from radium. Radium is rare and very expensive. Physicists and electrical engineers therefore designed and built huge particle accelerators such as *cyclotrons*.

CONCEPT OF ATOMIC NUMBER

Our understanding of the nature of visible light, X-rays, and gamma rays as a form of energy will be presented in a later chapter (Chapter 36). But briefly, the energy of X-rays formed in an X-ray tube depends upon the metal in the anode. (Refer to Figure 22–1, page 347.) It was found that upon the application of a large potential to the X-ray tube, electrons move with great velocity to the anode. Upon collision with the target, X-rays are formed which readily travel through the glass wall to the outside. The *energy* of the X-rays depends upon the material in the anode target. The energy of the X-rays can be given in terms of ergs or of either "wave length" or "frequency." But the discussion of these latter methods for measuring energy must await a discussion of wave motion in Chapter 36.

A young scientist, H. G. J. Moseley (Britain, 1887–1915), working with Rutherford, systematically studied the energy of the X-rays emitted by many different elements. He was able to show that the energy in these X-rays differed in a *regular* manner. For the purpose of this comparison, the energy of the X-rays from different elements is expressed in ergs (the dyne-centimeter; refer to page 284). In Figure 22–13, the square roots of the energies of the X-rays from six common elements are plotted first against their atomic weights. Refer to Curves A. It is impossible to draw a meaningful single curve through all the experimental points. At best there is a discontinuity between two separate curves. Moseley inferred that there must be a more fundamental property for each element than its atomic weight. This he called the *atomic number* or *Z number*. His concept that the nuclei of different elements must differ from each other stemmed, of course, from Rutherford's nuclear concept of the atom. Moseley assumed that the *nuclear charge* – a whole-number multiple of the charge of a proton – was the atomic number. In Moseley's own words, "there is in the atom a fundamental quantity, which increases in regular steps as we pass from one element to the next. This quantity can only be the charge on the central positive nucleus, of the existence of which we already have definite proof." In other words, Moseley stated that the atomic number of any element can be determined by studying the energy of its X-rays.

The atomic numbers assigned to the elements manganese to zinc are given in Table 22–4. Curve B of Figure 22–13 was obtained by plotting the square root of energy of X-rays against their atomic number. Curve B definitely shows that the progressive change of the energy of the X-rays from different elements depends upon the atomic number. The smooth curve with no discontinuities indicated to Moseley that the

Fig. 22–13 *Relation of energy of X-rays to the atomic number.*

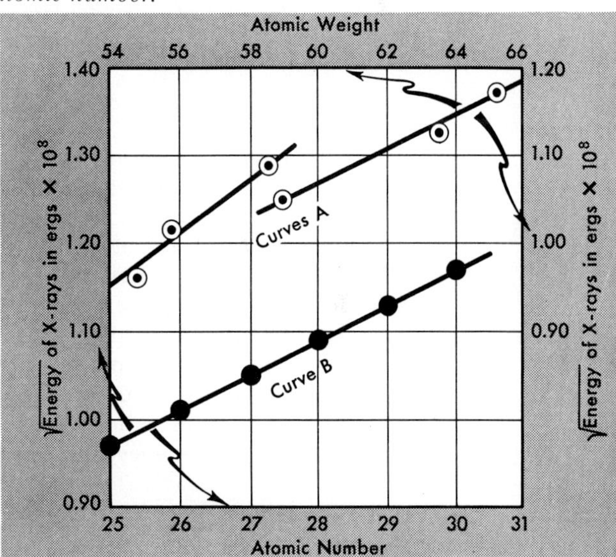

TABLE 22–4 ENERGY OF X-RAYS OF SOME COMMON ELEMENTS

ELEMENT	SYMBOL	ATOMIC WEIGHT (a.m.u.)	ENERGY OF X-RAYS (ergs × 10^8)	ATOMIC NUMBER	$\sqrt{\text{ENERGY}}$
Manganese	Mn	54.93	0.939	25	0.970
Iron	Fe	55.85	1.02	26	1.01
Cobalt	Co	58.94	1.10	27	1.05
Nickel	Ni	58.69	1.19	28	1.09
Copper	Cu	63.54	1.28	29	1.13
Zinc	Zn	65.38	1.37	30	1.17

nuclear charge or atomic number is a much more fundamental property of an atom than its atomic weight. As will be shown later, this is the most fundamental property of an element.

DISCOVERY OF THE NEUTRON

As stated on page 354, in the early hypotheses of atomic structure it was assumed that the nucleus contained some other particles beside protons. For example, the only way to account for the structure of carbon with an atomic mass of 12 and atomic number of 6 was to assume (as below) that

p pe p
pe p pe
p pe p
pe p pe

Carbon atom nucleus

$$12p + 6e \rightarrow 6p$$

the nucleus contained 12 protons but also 6 electrons enmeshed in some way so as to neutralize the charge of 6 protons. There was some evidence from radioactive disintegrations which indicated that electrons may reside in the nucleus. For example, as shown on page 351, radium *B* and radium *C* disintegrate with the emission of beta particles which are known to be energetic electrons originating within radioactive nuclei. The theory of proton-electron pairs,

Fig. 22–14 *Alpha particles from polonium bombarding a beryllium foil eject neutrons; these passing through a cloud chamber leave no tracks since they have no charge. However, when neutrons collide with an atom they are absorbed by the nucleus, which is transmuted into another kind of atom and often disrupts into two stable nuclei giving rise to two tracks.*

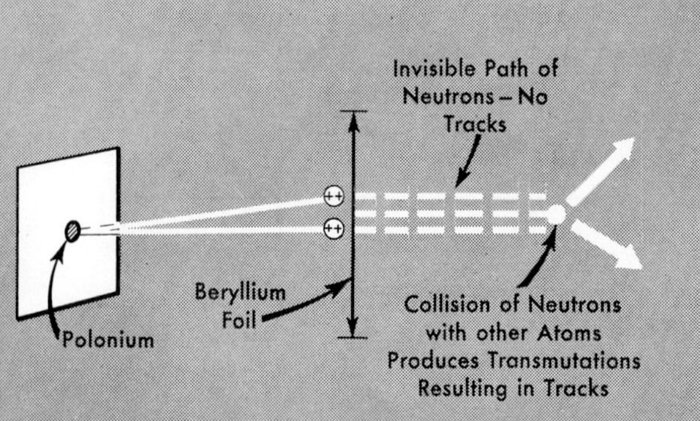

therefore, sounded very plausible. In fact, by 1920 some nuclear scientists came to accept the existence of a proton-electron pair and called it a neutron. But proof of the existence of neutrons did not come until 1932 with the work of James Chadwick (Britain, 1891–). The neutron of Chadwick, however, was not simply a proton-electron pair. Instead it was a very unusual particle with zero charge and approximately unit mass. Having no charge, it easily penetrated all forms of matter. It is now recognized as one of the fundamental particles present in all atomic nuclei except ordinary hydrogen.

The following representation gives a simple picture of the composition of some atomic nuclei.

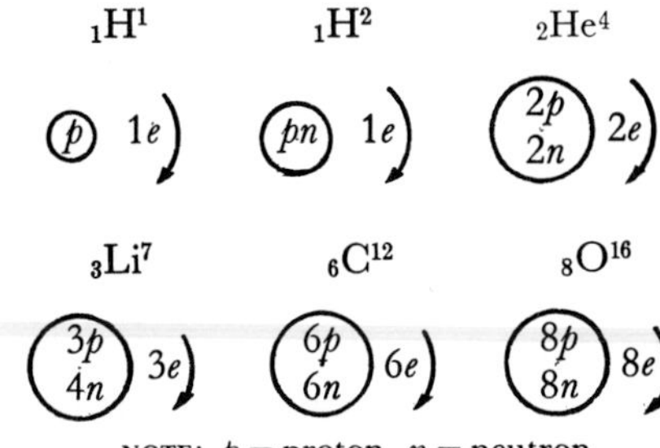

It employs the symbolism used to show the composition of atoms. Thus the symbol

$$[^{12}_{6}\mathrm{C}\ 6\ e]^0$$

indicates that the atom of carbon has a nucleus of 6 protons and a mass number of 12 due to 6 neutrons in the nucleus. The nucleus is surrounded by 6 planetary electrons. The whole atom is electrically neutral. The discussion of atom structure with particular attention to the arrangement of the electrons outside of the nucleus will be continued in the next chapter.

In concluding this discussion of atomic particles, it should be pointed out that their discovery is the product of investigations conducted within the past seventy years, and that much of the evidence for their discovery consisted of lines or fog-trails on photographic plates and the ideas of a few persons as to the meaning of these lines.

The alchemist's dream of the transmutation of elements persisted for nearly two thousand years, but the alchemist had neither a method nor the instruments to detect its reality. Under the compulsion of controlled and scientifically oriented curiosity observations were made, instruments were constructed, data were collected and correlated, inferences were drawn and hypotheses were elaborated to explain the observations and data. As new data were accumulated, the hypotheses were either modified or discarded. Mistakes were made also, but as Niels Bohr has pointed out, there is no progress without mistakes. Even the present concept of the structure of the atom, as described in this chapter, is provisional. It will be elaborated in the following one, and used to explain the chemical changes which the materials of the world undergo.

SUMMARY

1. The structure of the atom was elaborated from studies of electrical discharge in vacuum tubes and of radioactive changes.
2. Radioactivity, a unique property of many elements, was discovered by Becquerel.
3. In radioactive changes the nucleus of the atom undergoes disintegration, giving an atom of lower mass and either positively charged particles (alpha particles) and intense radiation (gamma rays), or negatively charged particles (beta particles) and gamma radiation.
4. The products of radioactive transformations may undergo further disintegration until stable atoms are formed. In the natural disintegration of radium the ultimate product is lead.
5. The discovery and study of radium by Marie and Pierre Curie inaugurated the nuclear age.
6. The instruments employed in the study of charged particles and of nuclear changes are the electroscope, the Geiger counter, the cloud chamber, and the cyclotron.
7. The modern nuclear theory of the atom had its inception in the work of Rutherford.
8. The atom consists of a compact nucleus containing most of the mass of the atom. The nucleus contains protons and neutrons; the sum is called the mass number (A) of the atom. Outside of the nucleus and a great distance from it a swarm of electrons revolves about it. The number of electrons is equal to the number of protons.
9. The number of protons in the nucleus of an element is called the atomic (Z) number of that element. The experimental procedure for determining the atomic number was developed by Moseley.
10. Elements consist of atoms of the same atomic number.
11. The important particles involved in nuclear or radioactive changes are the alpha particle, the beta particle, neutrons, protons, deuterons, positrons, and gamma rays or photons.
12. Elements can be transformed into other elements by bombarding their nuclei with high-energy atomic particles. Capture of an atomic particle by the nucleus may result in instability and emission of another particle in order to become stabilized.

STUDY EXERCISES

1. The following are instruments or apparatus used in connection with the development of the structure of the atom. Give briefly the basis for the operation of each instrument, and the purpose for which it is used: (*a*) electroscope; (*b*) cathode ray tube; (*c*) cloud chamber; (*d*) Geiger counter; (*e*) cyclotron; (*f*) a cathode ray tube provided with a metallic anode on which the electrons strike.
2. Give a simple method to determine whether a material is radioactive.
3. What experiments indicate that the positive charge in an atom is concentrated into the nucleus?
4. Summarize the experimental evidence which indicates the existence in atoms of elements: (*a*) negatively charged particles; (*b*) positively charged particles; (*c*) neutral material particles.

5. What particle or particles are now believed largely to account for the mass of an atom? For example, how can you account for the atomic weight of carbon ${}^{12}_{6}C$, oxygen ${}^{16}_{8}O$, sodium ${}^{23}_{11}Na$, chlorine-35 ${}^{35}_{17}Cl$, and chlorine-37 ${}^{37}_{17}Cl$?
6. What is the distinction between the atomic weight and the mass number of an element?
7. What is true of the number of electrons revolving around the nucleus of an atom and its atomic number?
8. An atom is always electrically neutral even though it contains protons, neutrons, and electrons. How can this be accounted for?
9. What simple rule enables you to determine the number of neutrons in the nucleus of an atom? Consider such examples as ${}^{12}_{6}C$, ${}^{23}_{11}Na$, ${}^{197}_{79}Au$, ${}^{226}_{88}Ra$.
10. At the right is a list of the particles often mentioned in discussing the modern theory of matter. Match by number each particle with the descriptions given:

1. Positron
2. Electron
3. Alpha particle
4. Neutron
5. Hydrogen atom
6. Deuteron
7. Proton

a. Has unit mass and unit positive charge. . . . .

b. Has a mass the same as the electron and unit positive charge. . . . .

c. The particle which consists of one electron revolving around a single proton. . .

d. The particle of unit mass and zero charge. . . . .

e. The element which is an isotope of hydrogen and consists of one electron in an orbit about a nucleus of one proton and one neutron. . . . .

f. A particle of mass four and charge of plus two which is emitted by many elements that undergo radioactive disintegration. . . . .

g. A particle with a mass of 1/1850 the mass of the proton, with unit negative charge. . . . .

h. A particle with a mass of 2 and charge of 1+. . . . .

FOR FURTHER READING

1. MARKHAM, E., C., and S. E. SMITH, *General Chemistry*. Boston: Houghton Mifflin Company, 1954.
   Chapter 12 deals with electrons and ions, and Chapter 15 with atomic nuclei.
2. PAULING, LINUS, *General Chemistry*. San Francisco: W. H. Freeman and Company, 1953.
   Chapter 3 deals with the electron and the nucleus.
3. Paperback: HABER, H., *Our Friend the Atom*. Dell, 35¢.
4. Paperback: DE BROGLIE, LOUIS, *Matter and Light*. Dover, $1.75.
5. Paperback: BRAGG, WILLIAM, *Concerning the Nature of Things*. Dover, $1.35.
   Chapter 1 gives a simple treatment of atomic structure. The best parts of the book are the chapters devoted to the nature of crystals.

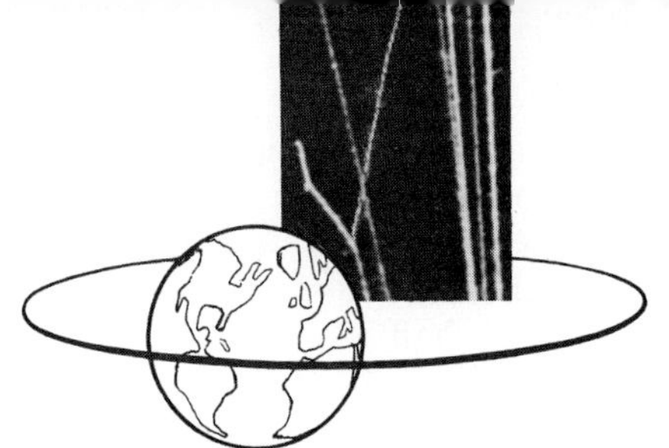

23

MODERN ATOMIC THEORY

ADVANCES IN SCIENCE at times come in spurts. The discovery of X-rays and of radioactivity, the isolation of radium, the determination of the characteristics of the electron, the planetary concept of atoms consisting of nuclei surrounded by electrons, the perfection of the method for the determination of the nuclear charge — all came within the small span of the two decades from 1895 to 1915. These were truly fundamental discoveries that were to start the physical sciences off in new directions. The new ideas and concepts being born were to shake the sciences that had been so long dominated by Newton and Dalton. In 1894, Albert A. Michelson (United States, 1852–1931), the first Nobel prize winner in the western hemisphere, said, "It seems probable that most of the grand underlying principles [of the physical sciences] have been firmly established, . . . that the future truths are to be looked for in the sixth place of decimals." In other words, Michelson was saying that future advances would be limited to making measurements with much greater precision than that hitherto attained.

It is no discredit to the great Michelson that he could not then foresee that Newtonian science had reached its apex and that a new physical science based upon radically new concepts was being born. This new science was to be associated with the names of Roentgen, Curie, Rutherford, Einstein, Planck, Bohr, Heisenberg, Pauli, Fermi, and many others. Much of the rest of this volume will be devoted to the developments, particularly with respect to the so-called quantum theory, associated with these scientists. In this chapter, we shall be concerned with the problem of the structure of the electrons around nuclei of atoms, the solution of which was the contribution of Niels Bohr (Denmark, 1885–). Dalton's hypothetical atoms were tiny ball-like objects. Beginning with Bohr, atoms were shown to have knowable dimensions and definite structure.

Rutherford's nuclear concept of the atom came in 1911. Moseley's methods for the determination of the nuclear charge came in 1913. About that same time, Niels Bohr, as a young man of 27, had set for himself the task of finding a satisfactory model for the hydrogen atom, and in 1913 he published his answer.

Bohr started with the assumption that the hydrogen atom with an atomic number of 1 consisted of a nucleus of one proton with one electron in a definite orbit around the nucleus. (Refer to Figure 23–1.) There is, of course, a force of attraction between the + charge of the nucleus

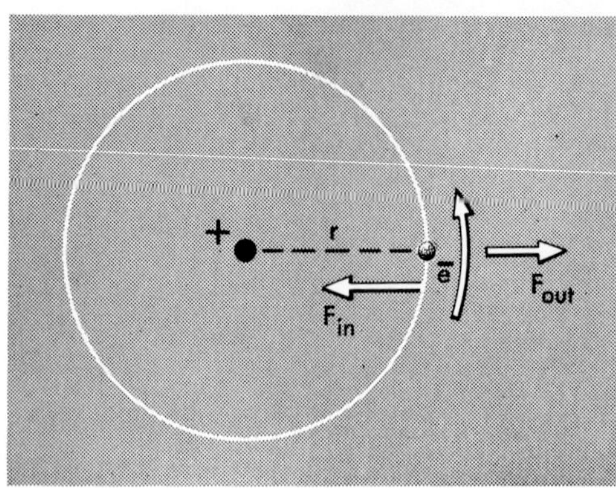

Fig. 23–1 *Bohr's concept of the orbital hydrogen atom. F_{out} is a centrifugal force due to electron of mass m moving in circular motion of radius r which is fixed. F_{in} is a coulomb force of attraction between charge on proton nucleus (+) and negative electron (−).*

and the − charge of the electron, but the electron is also moving at a *constant* velocity in a circular orbit. Try whirling a weight on the end of a string in a circular path. There is also a force acting outward from the center called a *centrifugal* force. The force outward (F_{out} = centrifugal force) just balances the electrical force (F_{in}) directed toward the center. Since these two forces are balanced, the electron moves with constant speed in an orbit of fixed radius. Hence, the electron never spirals into the nucleus.

But Bohr also hypothesized a large number of orbits around the nucleus. Four are shown in Figure 23–2. These have definite radii, which are in the ratio

$$\begin{aligned} r_1 : r_2 : r_3 : r_4 &= 1^2 : 2^2 : 3^2 : 4^2 \\ &= 1 : 4 : 9 : 16. \end{aligned}$$

These orbits were assigned so-called quantum numbers, n_1, n_2, n_3, and n_4. It should be observed that the radii of the orbits are proportional to the square of the quantum number, or $r \propto n^2$. Any one atom of hydrogen has only one electron, but this can be in *any* one of a large number of orbits depending upon the energy it possesses. It will have the least energy in the first orbit $n = 1$. This is called the ground state of the atom. Bohr was able to predict the velocity of the electron in each orbit. The velocity v in the innermost orbit was 1/137 the velocity of light. In the second orbit, the velocity was only half as great, and in the third orbit, one third as great, and so on.

The orbit for the lone electron in the hydrogen atom, according to Bohr, depends entirely on the amount of energy it possesses. By supplying a definite quantity of energy ($+E_1$) called a *quantum* of energy, the electron can be made to jump from orbit $n = 1$ to the orbit $n = 2$. Another quantum ($+E_4$) would take it to orbit $n = 3$. Or a larger single quantum ($+E_2 = +E_1 + E_4$) would take the electron directly from the first to the third orbit. (Refer to Figure 23–3.) Conversely, an electron can jump from outer orbits to inner orbits and release energy. Note that a "$+E$" means a *gain* of energy for an atom while a "$-E$" means a *loss* of energy. Thus an electron could jump from orbit $n = 4$ to orbit $n = 3$, or to orbit $n = 2$, or to orbit $n = 1$. The energy $-E_3$, for example, would be equal to $[E_6 + E_4 + E_1]$. This energy is emitted in some form of light, visible light, infrared, or ultraviolet. The kind of light emitted by hydrogen atoms is shown in Figure 23–4. The discussion of the nature and energy of light will be postponed to Chapter 36. A mercury vapor sun lamp is rich in ultraviolet light. Infrared light is emitted by an ordinary toaster. The energy

Fig. 23–2 *Scale diagram of the four Bohr circular orbits.*

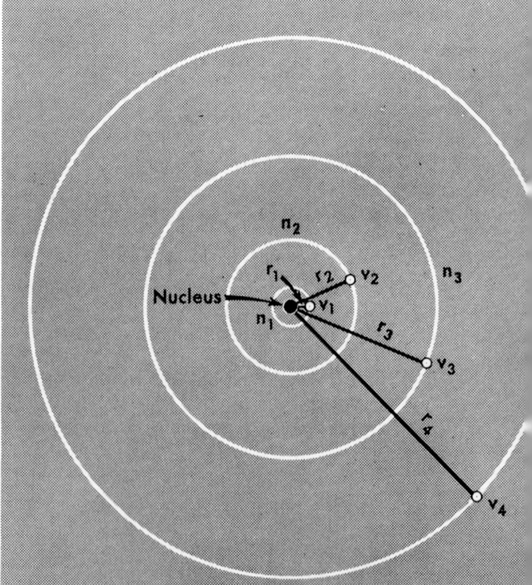

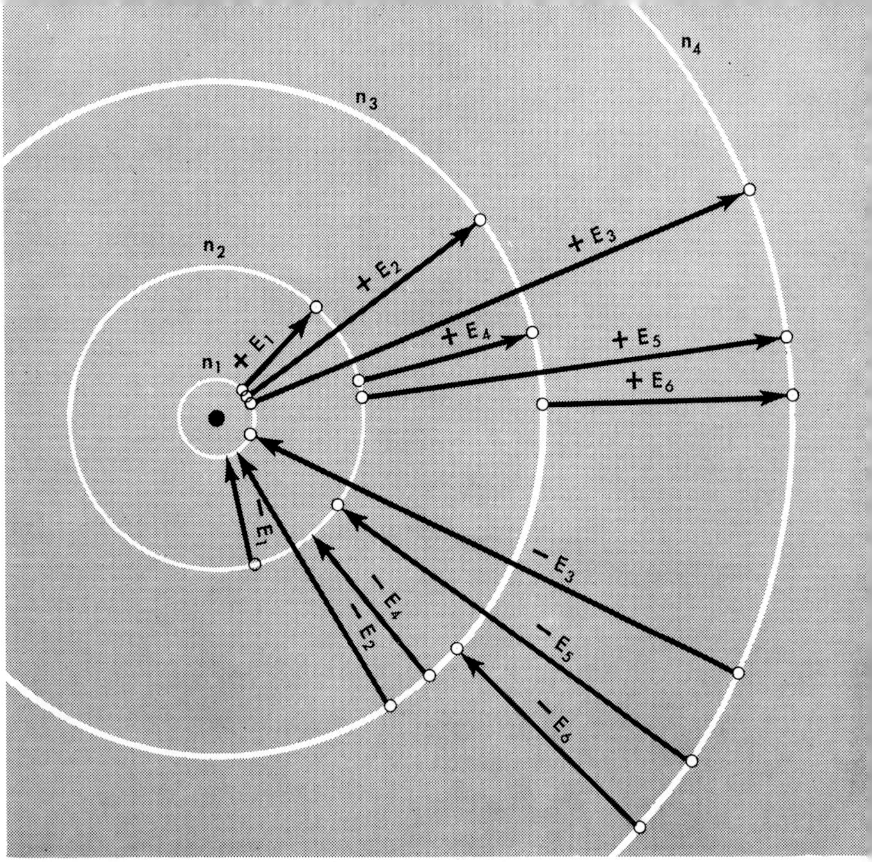

Fig. 23–3 *Electron jumps in the hydrogen atom according to Bohr.*

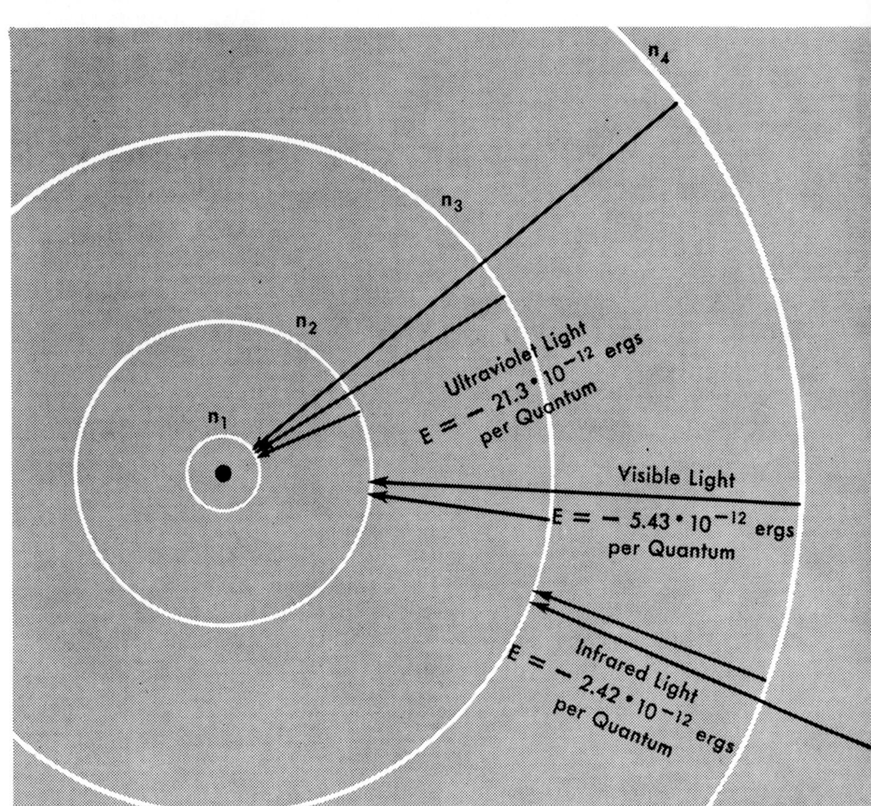

Fig. 23–4 *Energy and kind of light emitted by hydrogen atoms as electrons drop into the first, second, or third orbits.*

emitted by electrons which jump from outer orbits to the innermost orbit n_1 is ultraviolet light. If the electron jumps to orbit $n = 2$, the energy is emitted as visible light, while only infrared light is emitted if the electron jumps into the third orbit $n = 3$. The concept of electron jumps came from quantum theory. An electron is, for example, in orbit $n = 1$. If supplied with a quantum of energy sufficient to place it in orbit $n = 2$, it *disappears* from orbit $n = 1$, and *appears* in orbit $n = 2$. It spends no time in intervening space.

QUANTUM THEORY

The laws of motion and energy which had prevailed since the time of Galileo and Newton could not account for the behavior of the hydrogen atom. Quantum mechanics, originated by Max Planck (Germany, 1858–1947), was a relatively new science in 1913, but the success of Bohr in applying the quantum theory to a model for the hydrogen atom which accounted for the properties of hydrogen gained many adherents for the theory. It is now a fundamental part of modern physical science. Newton believed that light consisted of corpuscles. Quantum theory supports the same view but calls the particles of light *quanta*. They represent minute packages of light with a definite energy content. The electron jumps postulated by Bohr (Figure 23–3) are due to absorbing or emitting energy as energy quanta. Heat energy is emitted from the hot gas flame in all directions having quanta of many different sizes. In Figure 23–5 quanta traveling in only one direction are shown. The electron in orbit n_1 absorbs a quantum of energy E_3 which is just sufficient to lift the electron to the fourth (n_4) orbit. This electron may subsequently drop down to orbit n_2 to give off a quantum of energy $-E_5$, which happens to be visible light. The difference between $(+E_3 - E_5)$ is the energy that remains with the electron in the second orbit. A sample of hydrogen will consist of many atoms behaving in a similar

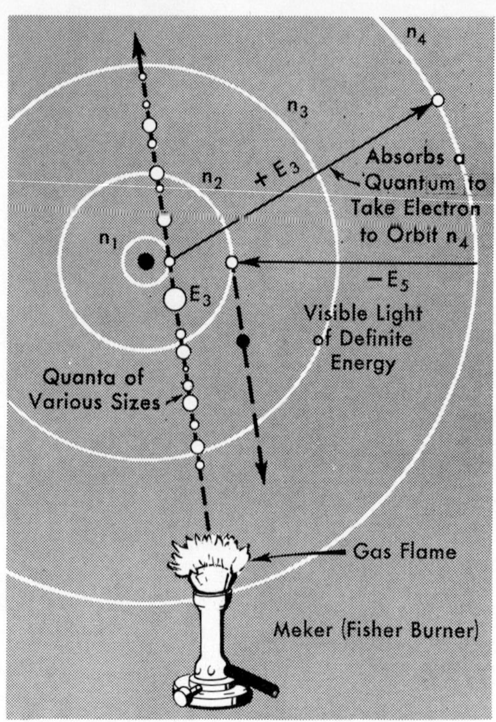

Fig. 23–5 *Quanta with varying energy from gas flame.*

fashion. The result will be a visible glow from the hydrogen tube due to the continuous emission of light quanta in the visible range. In a later chapter, we shall refer again to quantum theory. It has become one of the principal foundation stones of modern science.

Bohr's theory with uncanny accuracy accounted for many of the properties of hydrogen. In addition, it successfully helped in predicting certain properties that were unknown before the advent of the Bohr theory. While it is true that the simple model of Bohr had to be modified before it could be applied to the atomic structure of more complex atoms, it is rightly considered to be one of the greatest triumphs of the human mind.

ATOMS, MOLECULES, AND IONS

During the first two decades of this century the concepts concerning atoms and molecules were changing very rapidly. An atom was recognized as the ultimate particle of an element. Atoms formed various aggregates called molecules. These were the ultimate particles of any pure substance. Thus iron, oxygen, and iron oxide (a component of ordinary rust) are pure substances. Iron and oxygen are elements but iron oxide is a compound. All three are pure substances each with a fixed composition. Iron, if pure, is 100 per cent iron, but iron oxide contains 69.94 per cent iron and the balance is oxygen. The ultimate particles which determine the properties of any pure substance — element or compound — are called molecules. In general, molecules are more complex than atoms. Molecules usually have two or more atoms, but some molecules have hundreds or even thousands of atoms. The latter are giant molecules. A moment's reflection shows that molecules of elements consist of the same kind of atoms, but that molecules of compounds consist of atoms of different elements. These ideas are illustrated schematically in Figure 23–6.

The work of Rutherford and Bohr definitely showed that atoms consist of various aggregates of atomic nuclei, which consist of protons and neutrons, and plan-

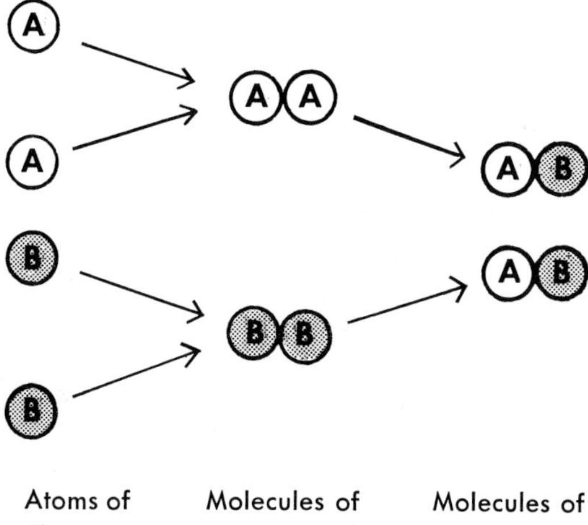

Fig. 23–6 *Schematic representation of atoms of elements, molecules of elements, and molecules of compounds. A_2 and B_2, and AB, are pure substances.*

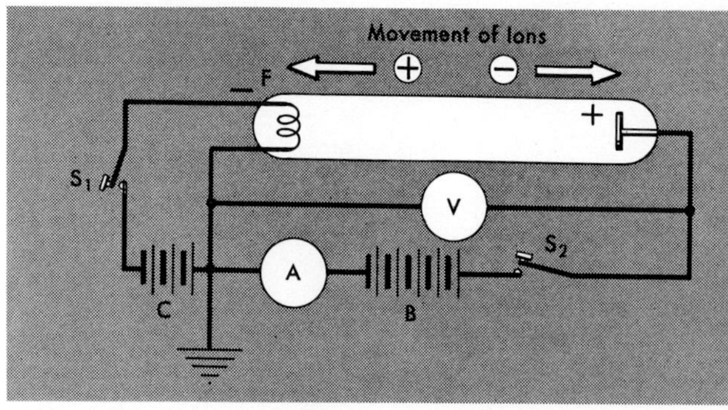

Fig. 23–7 *Ionization, by impact, of nitrogen atoms by high-speed electrons.*

etary electrons. Molecules, then, consist of various aggregates of these atoms. Atoms and molecules can be partially disintegrated to form ions which are positive and negative. Ions may be considered shattered molecules carrying an electric charge; they are common and are important particles because they do carry electrical charges. Ions can be formed, for example, by literally knocking electrons out of atoms. Neutral nitrogen atoms are poor conductors of electricity since they are electrically neutral. Refer to Figure 23–7: When the switch S_1 is closed, an electric current from battery *C* heats the filament red hot; the heated filament then acts as a source of electrons, that is, some electrons evaporate from the filament into the surrounding space. These can be given a high velocity by applying a high potential from the battery *B*. The electrons travel to the + electrode. The current flowing through the ammeter *A* is negligible when the switch S_2 is open. When the switch is closed, however, there is an appreciable current due to the movement of + ions in the tube to the − electrode and of − ions (electrons) to the + electrode.

The mechanics of ionization are explained in Figure 23–8. An energetic electron approaching an electron in an orbit of a nitrogen atom literally repels it out of its orbit into surrounding space. The nitrogen atom having lost one electron now carries one positive charge. It is a positive ion and migrates to the − electrode. This process

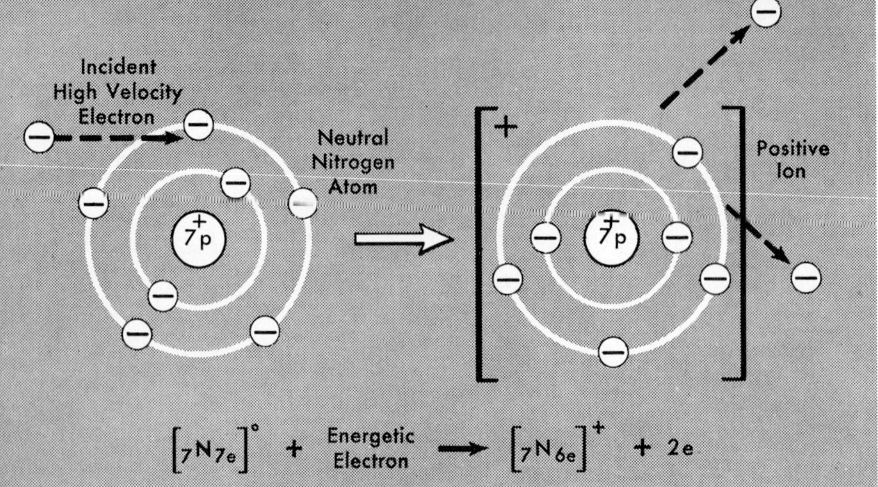

Fig. 23–8 *Ionization by collision. Schematic diagram to indicate how a neutral nitrogen atom can form a positive ion by loss of an electron following impact with a high-speed electron.*

is called ionization by collision. Note that an ion pair consists of an electron and a positively charged atom. The phenomena described in Figure 23–7 are responsible for the red-orange color in a neon sign. A lightning discharge during a storm is the result of the production of gaseous ions on an enormous scale. Ion pair formation can occur with either atoms or molecules. Ordinary oxygen, for example, consists of diatomic molecules O_2; by detaching an electron the molecule becomes the $(O_2)^+$ ion.

Ionization of gaseous substances can be brought about in a variety of ways: by (1) light – the photoelectric effect; (2) heat; (3) X-rays or γ-rays; (4) exposure to radiation as α-rays; and (5) application of high-speed electrons. For example, an electroscope is easily discharged by passing a flame near the ball-like terminal (see Figure 23–9). The particles which form air, as a result of being subjected to the high temperature, have their kinetic energies suddenly increased. In the violent agitation which results from the sudden heating, some of the electrons become detached from their atoms. The resulting atom then becomes an ion with one plus charge – if only one electron is lost. Some of the free electrons attach themselves to other neutral oxygen atoms to form negative oxygen ions. Thus, the air in the vicinity of the electroscope contains both positive and negative ions. The positive charge on the electroscope is then immediately neutralized by some of the negative ions in the air and the leaves of the electroscope collapse. Of course, the same result is obtained if the electroscope leaves are carrying a negative charge, since the ionized air contains positive ions to neutralize the negative charge on the electroscope.

THE MASSES OF IONS, ATOMS, AND MOLECULES

A very significant application of the fact that atoms and molecules can be made into ions was the perfection of a method for the determination of their masses – the method of mass spectrography. With the mass spectrograph, determinations of the masses of atoms of the order of 1×10^{-24} gram are made with great precision. Our knowledge of the fine structure of atoms and molecules would be impossible without the mass spectrograph.

A mass spectrograph determines the mass of an atom by converting molecules containing the atom into positive ions. These ions, then, by the use of an intense electric field, can be made into a fast-moving positive ray. As illustrated in Figure 23–10, in the chamber *C* the gas being studied is converted into positive ions, using alpha particles from radium. The cathode *A* is circular with a small opening. An accelerating potential is applied at *kl*. Some of the rapidly moving positive ions, because of their own inertia, form a narrow beam moving from left to right. These pass into the chamber at the right, which is evacuated, and between the charged plates + and −. If there is no applied potential, the rays make an impression on the photographic film at *a*. If there is an applied potential, the positive rays will be bent from their original path and strike at *b*. The amount of bending of the positive ray beam depends upon three factors, namely:

1. The applied potential — the bending increases with the applied potential.

2. The charge on the ion — the bending increases with the positive charge on the ion.

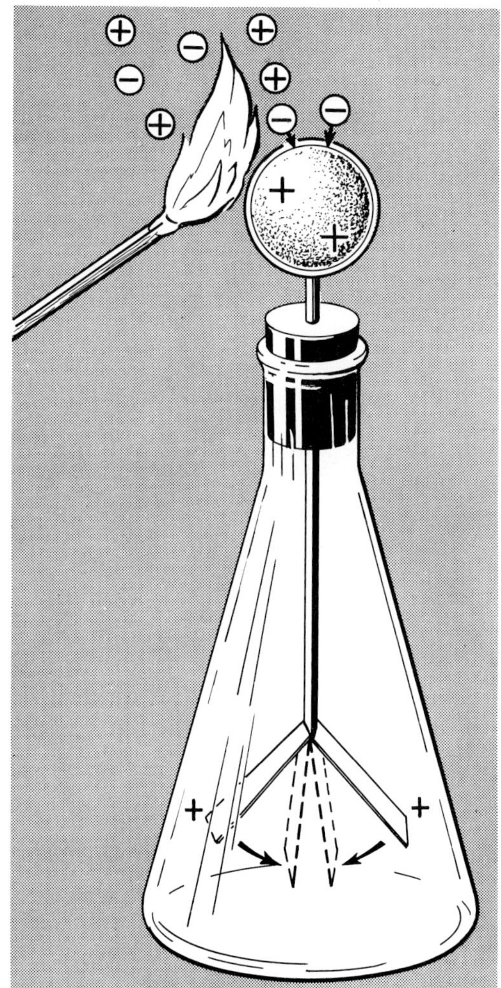

Fig. 23–9 *Ionization of air by a flame. Negative ions produced by the flame discharge the electroscope. The same result is obtained if the electroscope is charged negatively. Why?*

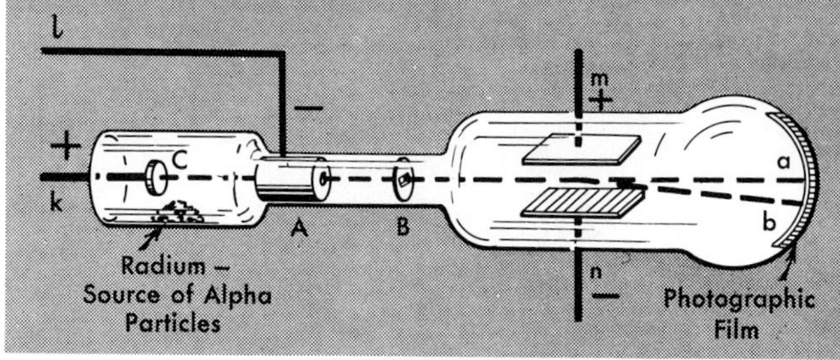

Fig. 23–10 *The principle of positive ray analysis.*

3. The mass of the ion — the bending decreases with an increase in mass of the particle.

Dropping balls of different masses from a bridge when there is a side wind illustrates the application of the principle. (Refer to Figure 23–11.) If no wind is blowing, the balls will fall vertically to the ground. If there is a side wind, the balls will have displacements *m* and *n*. The lengths of the displacements will depend upon the force of the wind. Because of the greater mass of the baseball, the displacement *m* will be less than that of *n* for the ping-pong ball. By appropriate applications of principles of physics, the relative masses of a baseball and a ping-pong ball can be determined by this procedure.

The mass spectrograph employs also an intense magnetic field to further sort out and focus the different kinds of positive rays that may be present. (Refer to Figure 23–12.) Magnets are surrounded by so-called magnetic fields. Just as an electric field produces motion of an isolated positive charge, so does a magnetic field produce motion in an isolated magnetic north pole. Just as the intensity (E) of an electric field is the force in dynes exerted on unit positive charge, so the intensity of a magnetic field (H) is the force in dynes exerted on a unit magnetic north pole. These concepts will be studied further in Chapters 31 and 32.

The whole apparatus is in a chamber which can be evacuated and then filled with a gaseous compound of the atom to be studied. Ionization of this gas is accomplished by a stream of electrons moving under high potential from the cathode *C* to the anode *A*. Positive ions of the atom are produced which, under the repulsion of *A*

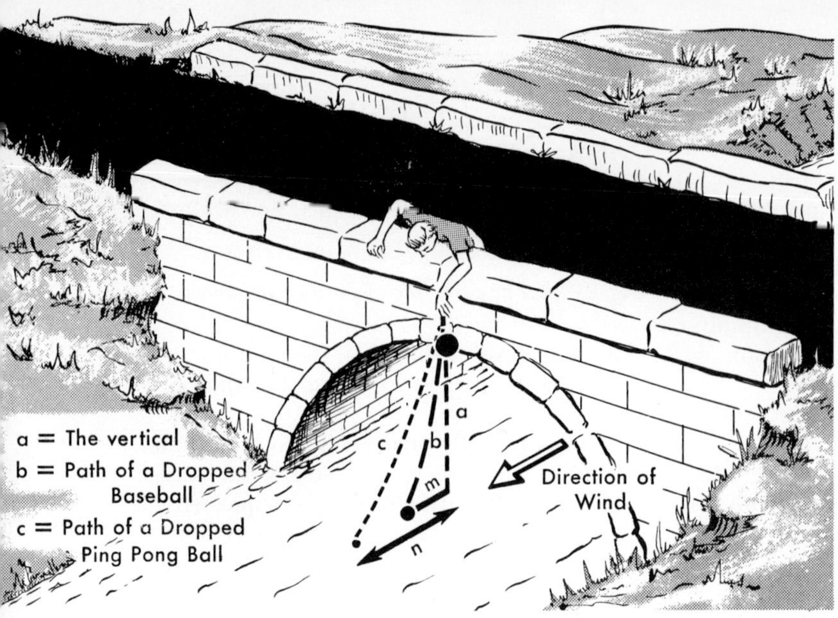

Fig. 23–11 *A side wind sorts out balls of different masses.*

and the attraction of *C*, are accelerated toward *C*. These positive ions, because of their inertia, pass through the narrow canal in *S* to form a narrow beam of positive rays. These rays are deflected in an electric field between the velocity selector plates P_1 and P_2, which are connected to a suitable high electrical potential. This part of the apparatus is between the poles of a powerful electromagnet. The beam of positive rays, then, behaves like an electric current surrounded by a magnetic field. Because of the action of the powerful magnetic field between the poles of the electromagnet, the beam of positive rays is again bent and at the same time focused. The amount of bending of the rays depends upon the charge q divided by the mass m of the ion. As the charge of the ion increases, the bending increases; as the mass of the ion decreases, the bending increases. The net effect is the sorting out of the positive particles according to mass and charge (q/m). When they impinge upon the photographic plate they produce a line somewhat analogous to the spectral line produced with a spectroscope. Since the position of the line on the plate is determined by the mass of the positive particles, the instrument itself is referred to as a mass spectrograph. Typical photographs taken with the mass spectrograph are shown in Figure 23–13.

THE DISCOVERY OF ISOTOPES

A postulate of Dalton's atomic theory (Chapter 20) stated that all atoms of a given element are alike and have identical masses. The intensive study of the composition of elements in the early part of this century cast doubt on this concept. For example, by 1914, lead from certain ores was

Fig. 23–12 *The principle of a mass spectrograph.* (*Adapted from H. E. White,* Classical and Modern Physics. *Copyright 1940, D. Van Nostrand Co., Inc., Princeton, New Jersey.*)

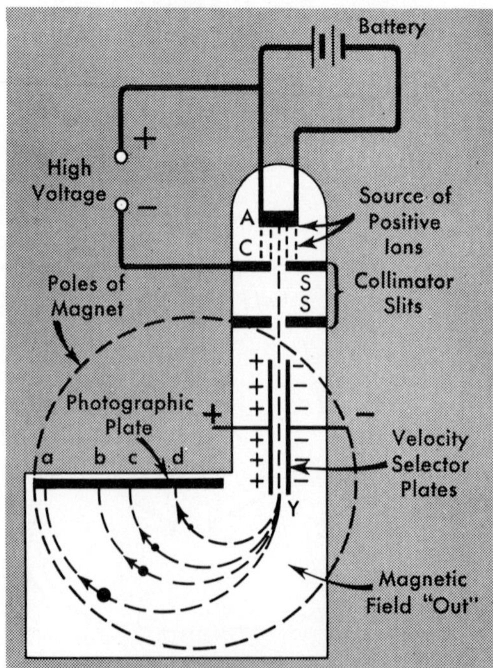

found to have atomic weights as low as 206.01 and as high as 207.9. The accepted value for lead in an atomic weight table is 207.21. The atomic weight of neon, for example, is 20.183. By 1918–1920, A. J. Dempster (United States, 1886–1950) and F. W. Aston (Britain, 1877–1945) showed definitely that it was a mixture of atoms of approximate weights 20 (90.5%), 21 (0.3%), and 22 (9.2%). In 1932, to the amazement of the entire scientific world, Harold Urey (United States, 1893–) proved the existence of heavy hydrogen, which is hydrogen-2. Thus hydrogen, one of the commonest of elements, was shown after a hundred and fifty years of study to be a mixture of isotopes. The hydrogen-2 isotope was named deuterium from a Greek word meaning "second place."

Different forms of the *same element* are called *isotopes*. They are characterized by the same nuclear charge (atomic number or *Z* number) due to protons. The different masses are attributable to varying numbers of neutrons in the nucleus. Thus, the isotopes of neon are accounted for as follows:

$_{10}Ne^{20}$	$_{10}Ne^{21}$	$_{10}Ne^{22}$
10*p* 10*n* — 10*e*	10*p* 11*n* — 10*e*	10*p* 12*n* — 10*e*

It is now known that there are three isotopes of hydrogen, $_1H^1$, $_1H^2$, and $_1H^3$. The nuclei are identical in that they all contain one proton surrounded by one electron.

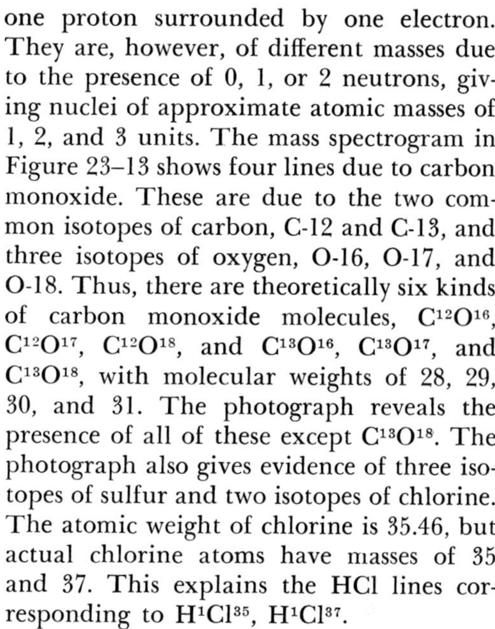

They are, however, of different masses due to the presence of 0, 1, or 2 neutrons, giving nuclei of approximate atomic masses of 1, 2, and 3 units. The mass spectrogram in Figure 23–13 shows four lines due to carbon monoxide. These are due to the two common isotopes of carbon, C-12 and C-13, and three isotopes of oxygen, O-16, O-17, and O-18. Thus, there are theoretically six kinds of carbon monoxide molecules, $C^{12}O^{16}$, $C^{12}O^{17}$, $C^{12}O^{18}$, and $C^{13}O^{16}$, $C^{13}O^{17}$, and $C^{13}O^{18}$, with molecular weights of 28, 29, 30, and 31. The photograph reveals the presence of all of these except $C^{13}O^{18}$. The photograph also gives evidence of three isotopes of sulfur and two isotopes of chlorine. The atomic weight of chlorine is 35.46, but actual chlorine atoms have masses of 35 and 37. This explains the HCl lines corresponding to H^1Cl^{35}, H^1Cl^{37}.

THE OCCURRENCE OF ISOTOPES

It is now known that nearly all elements occur in isotopic forms. Only about one-fifth of the elements occur in atoms of only a single atomic mass. These include fluorine, sodium, aluminum, phosphorus, and gold. It is interesting to note that all these elements have an odd atomic mass. Ordinary oxygen consists of O-16, O-17, and O-18. Tin occurs in as many as ten isotopic forms.

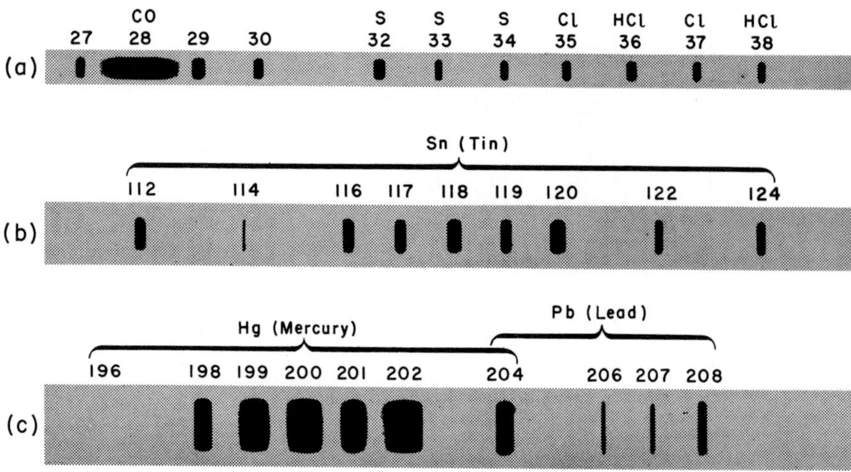

Fig. 23–13 *Typical mass spectrograms: (a) Carbon monoxide, sulfur, and chlorine lines (after Aston). (b) and (c) Isotopes of tin, mercury, and lead (after Bainbridge and Jordon). (Adapted from H. E. White,* Classical and Modern Physics. *Copyright 1940, D. Van Nostrand Co., Inc., Princeton, New Jersey.)*

TABLE 23–1 STABLE ISOTOPES, LISTED IN ORDER OF ABUNDANCE

ATOMIC NUMBER	ELEMENT	ATOMIC WEIGHT	MASS NUMBERS
1	H	1.0080	1, 2
2	He	4.003	4, 3
3	Li	6.94	7, 6
4	Be	9.02	9
5	B	10.82	11, 10
6	C	12.01	12, 13
7	N	14.008	14, 15
8	O	16.000	16, 18, 17
9	F	19.00	19
10	Ne	20.183	20, 22, 21
11	Na	22.997	23
12	Mg	24.32	24, 25, 26
13	Al	26.97	27
14	Si	28.06	28, 29, 30
15	P	30.98	31
16	S	32.06	32, 34, 33, 36
17	Cl	35.457	35, 37
18	A	39.944	40, 36, 38
19	K	39.096	39, 41, 40
20	Ca	40.08	40, 44, 42, 48, 43, 46
21	Sc	45.10	45
22	Ti	47.90	48, 46, 47, 49, 50
23	V	50.95	51
24	Cr	52.01	52, 53, 50, 54
25	Mn	54.93	55
26	Fe	55.85	56, 54, 57, 58
27	Co	58.94	59
28	Ni	58.69	58, 60, 62, 61, 64
29	Cu	63.57	63, 65
30	Zn	65.38	64, 66, 68, 67, 70
31	Ga	69.72	69, 71
32	Ge	72.60	74, 72, 70, 73, 76
33	As	74.91	75
34	Se	78.96	80, 78, 76, 82, 77, 74
35	Br	79.916	79, 81
36	Kr	83.7	84, 86, 82, 83, 80, 78
37	Rb	85.48	85, 87
38	Sr	87.63	88, 86, 87, 84
39	Y	88.92	89
40	Zr	91.22	90, 92, 94, 91, 96
41	Cb	92.91	93
42	Mo	95.95	98, 96, 95, 92, 94, 97, 100
44	Ru	101.7	102, 101, 104, 100, 99, 96, (98)
45	Rh	102.91	103, (101)
46	Pd	106.7	106, 108, 105, 110, 104, 102
47	Ag	107.88	107, 109
48	Cd	112.41	114, 112, 111, 110, 113, 116, 106, 108
49	In	114.76	115, 113
50	Sn	118.70	120, 118, 116, 119, 117, 124, 122, 112, 114, 115
51	Sb	121.76	121, 123
52	Te	127.61	130, 128, 126, 125, 124, 122, 123, 120
53	I	126.92	127
54	Xe	131.3	132, 129, 131, 134, 136, 130, 128, 124, 126
55	Cs	132.91	133
56	Ba	137.36	138, 137, 136, 135, 134, 130, 132,
57	La	138.92	139
58	Ce	140.13	140, 142, 136, 138
59	Pr	140.92	141
60	Nd	144.27	142, 144, 146, 143, 145, 148, 150
62	Sm	150.43	152, 154, 147, 149, 148, 150, 144
63	Eu	152.0	153, 151
64	Gd	156.9	156, 158, 155, 157, 160, 154, 152
65	Tb	159.2	159
66	Dy	162.46	164, 162, 163, 161, 160, 158
67	Ho	164.94	165
68	Er	167.2	166, 168, 167, 170, 164, 162
69	Tm	169.4	169
70	Yb	173.04	174, 172, 173, 176, 171, 170, 168
71	Lu	174.99	175
72	Hf	178.6	180, 178, 177, 179, 176, 174
73	Ta	180.88	181
74	W	183.92	184, 186, 182, 183, 180
75	Re	186.31	187, 184
76	Os	190.2	192, 190, 189, 188, 187, 186, 184
77	Ir	193.1	193, 191
78	Pt	195.23	195, 194, 196, 198, 192
79	Au	197.2	197
80	Hg	200.61	202, 200, 199, 201, 198, 204, 196
81	Tl	204.39	205, 203
82	Pb	207.21	208, 206, 207, 204
83	Bi	209.00	209
90	Th	232.12	232
92	U	238.07	238, 235, 234

A listing of stable isotopes as determined with mass spectrographs is given in Table 23–1.

MASS NUMBERS AND TRUE ATOMIC WEIGHTS

The mass of an atom is due principally to its protons and neutrons. The *mass number* with the symbol *A* is merely the sum of the protons and neutrons in the nucleus. The true atomic weight is the actual weight of an atom as determined by the use of a mass spectrograph. This implies of course a unit for atomic masses. The masses of atoms revealed by the mass spectograph are all relative to that of the most abundant isotope of oxygen, O-16. Oxygen is a mixture of three isotopes which occur in the following ratios, O-16 : O-17 : O-18 = 2550 : 1 : 5. Chemists have long assigned 16.0000 as the atomic weight of ordinary oxygen, but this referred to the mixture of the three isotopes as they occurred in nature. All three isotopes are easily identified in a mass spectrograph. It is worthy of note that the heavier isotopes of oxygen are assigned masses of 17 and 18 with reference to the most abundant lighter isotope *assigned a value of 16*. Hence, the standard for *all* atomic weight determinations by mass spectrograph is O-16. This is often referred to as the *physical scale*. This is 0.26 per cent lighter than the natural mixture of oxygen isotopes, which is called 16.0000 on the chemist's scale. The natural mixture of oxygen, therefore, has an apparent atomic weight of 16.0044 on the physical scale. Hence the two atomic weight scales are in the ratio

$$\frac{\text{Chemical atomic weight}}{\text{Physical atomic weight}} = \frac{16.0044}{16.0000} = \frac{1.00027}{1}.$$

Because of the precision of modern mass spectrographs and their relative ease of operation, atomic and molecular weights are now usually based upon the physical scale.

THE ATOMIC MASS UNIT

The abbreviation a.m.u. or symbol *amu* (atomic mass unit) is now frequently in use. This is one-sixteenth of the mass of the atom of the most abundant oxygen isotope O-16. Its mass is so small (1.66×10^{-24} gram) that the actual mass in grams is seldom used. Thus the atomic weight of sulfur, for example, is 32.06 a.m.u., of gold 197.2 a.m.u., etc. The symbol for the unit is often omitted for convenience but it should not be omitted in the mind of the user.

THE MOLE

It is impossible, for all practical purposes, to work with individual atoms. One cannot weigh out on ordinary balances even a million oxygen atoms — a mass of $16 \times 1.66 \times 10^{-24} \times 1{,}000{,}000$ or 26.6×10^{-18} gram. Hence, it has become customary to work with a standard large number of atoms or molecules of a substance called a *mole*. This is the weight in grams that corresponds to the number which expresses the atomic or molecular weight of a substance.

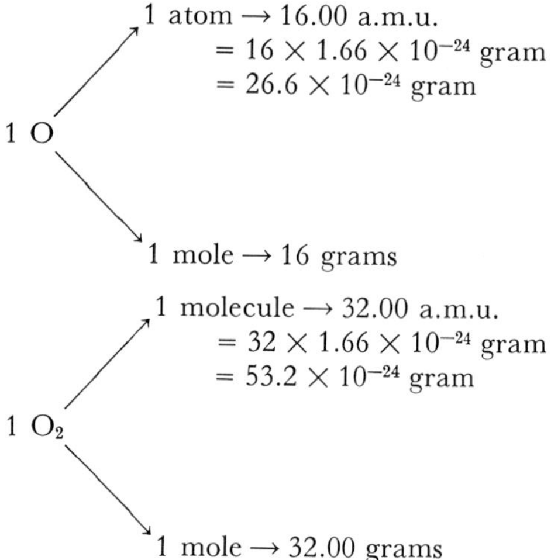

It is comparatively simple to weigh out 16.00 or 32.00 grams of oxygen. When this is done we have weighed out *one mole* of oxygen atoms or one mole of oxygen molecules. Table 23–2 should help to clarify the concept of a mole.

TABLE 23–2

WEIGHT FOR ONE MOLE OF SOME COMMON SUBSTANCES

SUBSTANCE	FORMULA	ATOMIC OR MOLECULAR WEIGHT (a.m.u.)	GRAMS FOR ONE MOLE
Hydrogen	H_2	2.016	2.016
Gold	Au	197.2	197.2
Water	H_2O	2.016 + 16.000 18.016	18.016
Ethyl alcohol	C_2H_5OH	46.07	46.07

As we learned in Chapter 20, Avogadro's law stated that equal volumes of all gases under the same conditions of temperature and pressure contained the *same number* of molecules, and gave rise to a method for determining the actual number of molecules in a given volume. A convenient volume of any gas is the molar volume — the volume in liters of a mole of a gas at standard temperature and pressure (STP). This quantity is nearly constant, as shown in Table 23–3; hence, 22.4 liters[1] of a gas at STP is *one* mole.

By Avogadro's law, 22.4 liters of any gas (STP) must contain the same number of molecules. This is Avogadro's number, which is frequently symbolized by N. This number can be easily calculated since, for a gas such as oxygen, both the molecular weight and molar weight are known, as well as the atomic mass unit expressed in grams. (Refer to page 373.) It follows, therefore, that

$$N \frac{\text{molecules } O_2}{\text{mole}} \times 32.000 \frac{\text{a.m.u.}}{\text{molecule}} \times 1.66 \times 10^{-24} \frac{\text{grams}}{\text{a.m.u.}} = 32.000 \frac{\text{grams}}{\text{mole}}.$$

Hence,

$$\begin{aligned} N &= \frac{1.000}{1.66 \times 10^{-24}} \\ &= 0.602 \times 10^{24} \\ &= 0.602 \times (10^6)^4 \\ &= 0.602 \text{ million million million million.} \end{aligned}$$

The importance of this number lies in the fact that 0.602×10^{24} particles (atoms, molecules, or ions) represent the quantity of *one mole*. If the substance is a gas, the volume at STP is 22.4 liters. Philosophically, the number is important because it vastly simplifies our knowledge of all substances.

[1] The interested student can study ideal and real gases for the significance of the small departures of this volume for many gases from the ideal value of 22.414 liters.

TABLE 23–3 THE CONCEPT OF THE MOLAR VOLUME (22.4 LITERS OF A GAS)

SUBSTANCE	FORMULA	MOLECULAR WEIGHT (a.m.u.)	MOLAR WEIGHT (grams)	WEIGHT 1 LITER (S.T.P.)	VOLUME FOR ONE MOLE
Hydrogen	H_2	2.016	2.016	0.0899 g	$2.016 \text{ g} \times \frac{1 \text{ liter}}{0.0899 \text{ g}} = 22.4$ liters
Oxygen	O_2	32.00	32.00	1.429 g	$32.00 \text{ g} \times \frac{1 \text{ liter}}{1.429 \text{ g}} = 22.4$ liters
Neon	Ne	20.18	20.18	0.9002 g	$20.18 \text{ g} \times \frac{1 \text{ liter}}{0.9002 \text{ g}} = 22.4$ liters
Nitrogen	N_2	28.016	28.016	1.2506 g	$28.016 \text{ g} \times \frac{1 \text{ liter}}{1.2506 \text{ g}} = 22.4$ liters

SUMMARY

1. The quantum theory of Planck states that many physical changes involving atoms and molecules depend upon energy absorbed or emitted intermittently in discrete quantities called quanta.
2. Present atomic theory is based upon quantum theory and states:
   a. Elements consist of particles called atoms.
   b. An atom is a particle consisting of a nucleus with a definite charge and mass, which depends upon the number of protons and neutrons in the nucleus, surrounded by an equal number of electrons arranged in definite energy levels.
   c. The chemical properties of atoms depend upon the arrangements of the electrons in the various energy levels.
   d. Atoms of the same atomic number (Z number) are of the same element.
   e. Atoms of the same atomic number and different mass numbers (A numbers) are called isotopes.
   f. The atomic weight of an element is the weighted average of all the isotopes of that element as they occur in nature.
3. The Bohr theory of the hydrogen atom assumes that the electron in any one atom is located in a definite orbit as to energy and radius, which is identified by a definite quantum number. By absorption of discrete quanta of energy, the electron may jump to an orbit of higher quantum number. Conversely, the electron may jump from a higher to a lower orbit and release a definite amount of energy.
4. Electrons which jump from outer orbits to the third orbit ($n = 3$) emit energy as infrared heat rays; if they jump to the second orbit ($n = 2$), they emit energy as visible light; if they jump to the first orbit ($n = 1$), they emit energy as ultraviolet light.
5. The detachment of electrons by any process from atoms or molecules produces positive ions and electrons. This is called ionization.
6. Ionization can be accomplished by light (the photoelectric effect), heat, X-rays, alpha, beta, or gamma rays, or by high-speed electrons.
7. The mass spectrograph utilizes positive rays of elements to determine atomic masses.
8. The physical atomic weight scale is based upon the mass of the atoms of the most abundant oxygen isotope, oxygen-16.
9. The atomic mass unit is one-sixteenth of the actual mass of an atom of oxygen-16.
10. A mole of an element or compound is the weight in grams that is numerically equal to the molecular weight of the substance.
11. A mole of any gas at standard temperature and pressure (STP) is 22.4 liters.
12. A mole of any substance contains 0.602×10^{24} particles – atoms, molecules, ions.

STUDY EXERCISES

1. Distinguish between an atom, a molecule, and an ion. Explain with examples.
2. Describe some common phenomena that depend upon the ionization of gases.
3. What is the distinction between the atomic weight and the mass number of an element? Give examples.
4. Describe the elements listed below by filling out a table that has the following headings: atomic number (Z); mass number (A); atomic weight; composition of nucleus in protons and in neutrons; electrons.

   Elements
   Carbon-12
   Oxygen-8
   Sodium-23
   Chlorine-35
   Chlorine-37

5. How can you account for the similarity of the chemical properties in isotopes of the same element?
6. Ordinary chlorine consists of Cl-35 and Cl-37. The atomic weight of natural chlorine is 35.46. What per cent of ordinary chlorine consists of the Cl-35 isotope?
7. What process is taking place in a neon sign in operation which accounts for the red-orange glow?
8. Oxygen and hydrogen consist of isotopes. Write the formulas of all the possible kinds of water molecules (H_2O). Refer to Table 23–1.

9. The "chemical atomic weight" of aluminum is 26.97. The atomic weight on the "physicist's scale" is 26.99. State the meaning of these figures and account for the difference between them.

FOR FURTHER READING

1. WHITE, HARVEY E., *Classical and Modern Physics*. New York: D. Van Nostrand Company, 1940.

   A discussion of isotopes and the principles and use of mass spectrographs, with excellent illustrations, is presented in Chapter 29. An excellent discussion of the Bohr theory is in Chapter 35.

2. HOLTON, GERALD, *Introduction to Concepts and Theories in Physical Science*. Cambridge, Mass.: Addison-Wesley Press, 1952.

   Chapter 25 has a very complete presentation of the Bohr theory. Discusses quite completely some of the consequences of the theory.

3. PAULING, LINUS, *General Chemistry*. San Francisco: W. H. Freeman and Co., 1953.

   The subject of the electron and the nucleus is admirably treated in Chapter 3. Quantum theory and the hydrogen atom according to Bohr are considered on pages 173–180.

24

ATOMIC STRUCTURE

THE SUCCESS of Bohr in determining the structure of hydrogen atoms stimulated a tremendous interest in other atoms. Attempts were immediately made to work out the structure of such atoms as helium, lithium, and carbon, with atomic numbers of two, three, and six, and with two, three, and six electrons in orbits around the nuclei. What were the electron energies and what kind of orbits were involved? The problem was immensely complicated; progress at first was discouragingly slow. The problem could not be solved by constructing models built upon the classical principles of mechanics that we owe to Galileo and Newton. A new physical science, the quantum mechanics of Max Planck (Germany, 1858–1947) and Albert Einstein (Germany and United States, 1879–1955), had to be applied. Even new mathematical techniques such as matrix algebra had to be invented. So numerous and so complicated were the ramifications of the new science that scientists had to specialize in small separate areas of the total problem. Some concentrated on studying the nuclei of atoms and the methods of transforming one kind of nucleus to another. These workers were frequently called nuclear scientists. Others concentrated on the arrangement of the electrons around the nucleus and their relation to the physical and chemical properties of the atoms. These studies resulted in modern chemistry. It is the purpose of this chapter to indicate some of the principal developments in each of these areas, with major attention given to the concept of the arrangement of the electrons around the nucleus.

THE ARRANGEMENTS OF THE PLANETARY ELECTRONS

As we have seen, the number of electrons around the nucleus of an atom is the same as the nuclear charge. In oxygen ($^{16}_{8}O$) there are eight electrons outside the nucleus. Are they arranged as a swarm around the nucleus, or are they arranged in definite orbits? These were the questions that had to be answered. The complexity of the problem can be appreciated when it is pointed out, for example, that iron ($_{26}Fe$) has 26 electrons outside the nucleus. It was inferred that, since the properties of all iron atoms are constant, these electrons must have some definite arrangement or structure with respect to the nucleus. The possibilities for the arrangements of the 26 elec-

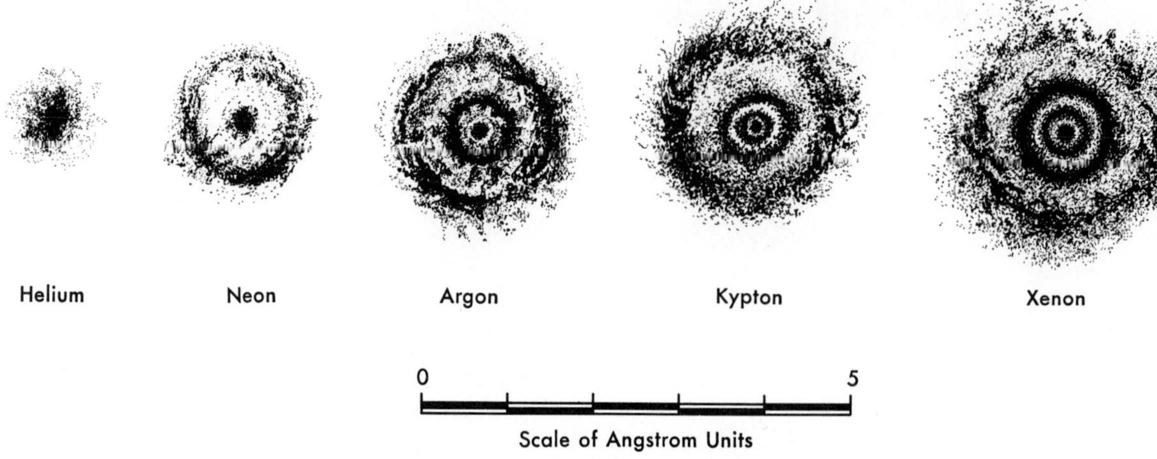

Fig. 24–1 *"Electron cloud" concept of the distribution of electrons in atoms. This is not an actual cloud. The depth of shading is an indication of the relative probability of electron (s) being found in a given region around an atom. (After* College Chemistry, *Second Edition, by Linus Pauling. San Francisco: W. H. Freeman and Company, 1953.)*

trons in space around a nucleus are manifold. Our present understanding of atomic structure was not achieved until scientists accepted certain simplifying assumptions.

The orbits postulated by Bohr in his theory of the atom seemed to call for definite orbits for the electrons in all orbits. But W. Heisenberg (Germany, 1901–) in 1927 pointed out that this called for an impossible solution. From certain theoretical considerations involving both classical physical theory and quantum theory, Heisenberg showed that it was impossible to know *exactly both the velocity and the position* of an electron in its orbit. One or the other must be to a certain degree uncertain. This is the *uncertainty principle* which has become an essential part of modern thought. We have reconciled ourselves to the idea that certain kinds of information can never be obtained. As a result, chemists started thinking in terms of electron clouds and not in terms of electrons in definite orbits. In the hydrogen atom a given electron has a random motion in space around the nucleus with a certain average speed and a certain average radius from the nucleus. This is thought of as an electron cloud. The concept of electron clouds simplified the task of finding the arrangements of electrons outside the nucleus. (Refer to Figure 24–1.)

A second important development was the establishment of the fact that the electrons are arranged in not over seven main energy levels, called shells. The successive shells are designated both by letters and numbers:

K	*L*	*M*	*N*	*O*	*P*	*Q*
1	2	3	4	5	6	7

The numbers 1 to 7 are called the *principal quantum* numbers, indicated by n. It was found that up to the fourth level (N shell) the maximum number of electrons that can occupy any shell is given by the formula $2n^2$. Thus in the K shell ($n = 1$), the maximum number of electrons is 2. In the L shell, $2n^2 = 8$ electrons, in the M shell $2n^2 = 18$ electrons, with a maximum of 32 electrons in the N shell. The $2n^2$ rule would call for 50 electrons in the fifth shell. However, the rule no longer applies, for there are never enough electrons to fill the shell to the capacity indicated by the rule. For this reason the maximum number of electrons possible in the fifth and sixth shells tapers off to 18 and 8, respectively.

The unraveling of the mysteries of the actual arrangement of the electrons in atoms was a problem of extraordinary difficulty. The neon atom, for example, has ten electrons, and conceivably these might have ten different kinds of motion around the nucleus. The final solution of the problem required the invention of a new principle in science, the *exclusion principle,* which was due to W. Pauli (Switzerland, 1900–). This principle operated by *excluding* large numbers of possible arrangements of the electrons. It is an extension of the "common-sense" principle that no two objects can occupy the same place at the same time. Pauli in effect extended this principle by showing that no two electrons in an atom could have precisely the *same energy* or *motion.* What does this mean in the case of helium, which has two electrons? They are in the same level or *K* cloud. They are alike in all respects except that they are *spinning* in opposite directions. That is, if one is spinning clockwise, the other is spinning counterclockwise. The two electrons are thus a pair of electrons with opposite spins. Pauli thus established the maximum population of electrons in the *K* level as two.

The Pauli exclusion principle led naturally to another useful conclusion, namely, that the electrons in main levels after the *K* level always were in sublevels with not more than two electrons in each sublevel and again with opposite spins. Thus the *L* level with 8 electrons could have only four separate electron clouds each with two electrons with opposite spins. In the *M* level, with 18 electrons, there could be only 9 sublevels; and in the *N* level there could be just 16 sublevels with a maximum of 32 electrons.

TABLE 24–1 ELECTRONIC CONFIGURATION OF ATOMS, ELEMENTS 1 TO 10*

ELEMENT	Z	K LEVEL 1s	L LEVEL 2s	L LEVEL 2p			NOTATION
H	1	(↑)					$1s^1$
He	2	(↑↓)					$1s^2$
Li	3	(↑↓)	(↑)				$1s^2 2s^1$
Be	4	(↑↓)	(↑↓)				$1s^2 2s^2$
B	5	(↑↓)	(↑↓)	(↑)			$1s^2 2s^2 2p^1$
C	6	(↑↓)	(↑↓)	(↑)	(↑)		$1s^2 2s^2 2p^2$
N	7	(↑↓)	(↑↓)	(↑)	(↑)	(↑)	$1s^2 2s^2 2p^3$
O	8	(↑↓)	(↑↓)	(↑↓)	(↑)	(↑)	$1s^2 2s^2 2p^4$
F	9	(↑↓)	(↑↓)	(↑↓)	(↑↓)	(↑)	$1s^2 2s^2 2p^5$
Ne	10	(↑↓)	(↑↓)	(↑↓)	(↑↓)	(↑↓)	$1s^2 2s^2 2p^6$

Energy of electons increases
from inner to outer sublevels

*The notations s and p for the various sublevels are in universal use. The numeral superscript indicates the number of electrons in the indicated sublevel. The numerals 1 and 2, preceding the letters s and p, refer to the K and L main levels, respectively.

Lithium ($Z = 3$) has 3 electrons in each atom. The third electron is excluded by Pauli's principle from the *K* level; it must go into the next higher level. The regular manner in which the subshells are filled in the first ten elements (that is, in order of ascending atomic number) is shown in Table 24–1. In this table the convention (↑↓) is used to indicate a pair of electrons of opposite spins, while (↑) indicates an unpaired electron. Note the regularity of the build-up of the electronic structures. In the *L* level there are, for example, only four permissible sublevels. In nitrogen, there are enough electrons to occupy all three *p* orbitals, but with only one electron in each of the orbitals. Oxygen, with one more electron, has only two unfilled *p* orbitals, while fluorine has one unfilled *p* orbital, but neon has all the orbitals filled. No more electrons can be accepted in these two sublevels. Note that the order of filling the orbitals is from the innermost orbital outward. That is also the order of the total energy of the electrons in these atoms.

A summary of the composition of the sublevels within the first four energy levels when completely filled is given in Table 24–2. The letters *s, p, d,* and *f* are used by universal agreement to designate the various kinds of sublevels, and they have no added significance. The chemistry texts of a generation ago had many diagrams intended to picture atoms; this practice has been abandoned, for the uncertainty principle indicates that true pictures of atoms will forever be impossible. However, the arrangements of the electrons within sublevels and main levels can be determined, and this knowledge has definite predictive value. It becomes important, therefore, to learn of these arrangements and the simple methods of notation that are in common use.

ELECTRON PAIRS AS BONDING FORCES

A concept chemists have found useful is that a shared pair of electrons of opposite spins acts as a bonding force between atoms. How can this be explained? A very qualitative explanation based upon Figure 24–2 is as follows: Two different objects often form stable complexes by rotating (in elliptical orbits) about each other. Thus the earth and moon, and an electron about a positive nucleus, constitute such systems. The electron e_1 originally belonged to nucleus A, and electron e_2 belonged to nucleus B. When the two nuclei approach each

TABLE 24–2 SUBSHELLS OF ELECTRONS

MAIN LEVEL	QUANTUM NUMBER	SUBSHELLS	NUMBER	TOTAL ELECTRONS	NOTATION
K	1	$1s^2$	1	2	$1s^2$
L	2	$2s^2$	1	2	
				8	$2s^22p^6$
		$2p^2$	3	6	
M	3	$3s^2$	1	2	
				8 18	
		$3p^2$	3	6	$3s^23p^63d^{10}$
		$3d^2$	5	10	
N	4	$4s^2$	1	2	
				8	
		$4p^2$	3	6 18 32	$4s^24p^64d^{10}4f^{14}$
		$4d^2$	5	10	
		$4f^2$	7	14	

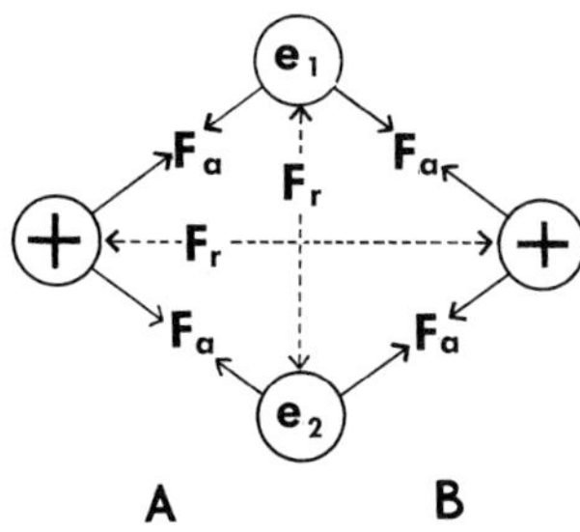

Fig. 24–2 *An electron pair is a bonding force within a molecule.*

other, there will be an electrostatic attraction between e_1 and e_2 and the two nuclei. These are the forces F_a in Figure 24–2. Thus the two nuclei tend to approach each other. As the nuclei and the electrons approach each other, they begin to repel each other because of their like charges. These are the forces F_r in Figure 24–2. At the same time the electrons and the nuclei are rotating about each other under the influence of centrifugal forces outward. Eventually there is reached a stable dynamic equilibrium where A and B form a particle called a molecule because of a rotating system of two electrons which are always somewhere between the two nuclei. To represent the bonding force between the two atoms A and B, conventions such as the following are in common use:

$$A(\uparrow\downarrow)B \quad \text{or} \quad A{:}B \quad \text{or} \quad A{-}B$$

WHY DETERMINE ATOMIC STRUCTURES?

Man in his constant effort to understand and control nature must understand the structure, properties, and behavior of the particles called atoms, molecules, and ions that make up all matter. The chemist does this by use of the electron theory of the structure of atoms and their various aggregates. In doing this he works with mental images of atoms or diagrams of atoms on paper which to him are very real. And yet at the same time, the electron theory makes no pretense of actually portraying atoms and molecules.

In Chapter 20 we learned that Dalton thought the particles of elements consisted of a single atom. Avogardo made use of his theory (page 328) to prove that elements consisted of particles which we call molecules, which in the case of gases such as fluorine, oxygen, and nitrogen could not be simpler than two atoms per molecule, or F_2, O_2, and N_2. The explanation for this came with the electron theory of the elements. Reference to Table 24–1 shows that the atom of fluorine contains 3 pairs of electrons ($2s^22p^22p^2$) and one unpaired electron ($2p^1$) in its *L* level. Hence, two atoms of fluorine can combine to form a molecule through a shared electron pair. This can be represented

$$F(\uparrow) + F(\uparrow) \rightarrow F(\uparrow\downarrow)F,$$

$$\text{or} \quad F{:}F, \quad \text{or} \quad F{-}F, \quad \text{or} \quad F_2.$$

It is the shared electron pair *between* the two atoms which is the bonding force that forms the molecule F_2. The oxygen atom has two unpaired *p* electrons. Hence, two oxygen atoms also form a diatomic molecule but with two bonding pairs:

$$O(\uparrow)(\uparrow) + O(\uparrow)(\uparrow) \rightarrow O(\uparrow\downarrow)(\uparrow\downarrow)O,$$

$$\text{or} \quad O{::}O, \quad \text{or} \quad O = O, \quad \text{or} \quad O_2.$$

The nitrogen atom has three unpaired electrons. Again two atoms can bond together but with a so-called triple bond between the atoms:

$$2\ N(\uparrow)(\uparrow)(\uparrow) \rightarrow N(\uparrow\downarrow)(\uparrow\downarrow)(\uparrow\downarrow)N,$$

$$\text{or} \quad N{:::}N, \quad \text{or} \quad N{\equiv}N, \quad \text{or} \quad N_2.$$

The electrons in the orbital regions of atoms possess energy, potential energy with respect to the nucleus and kinetic energy because they have mass and motion. Chemists early learned that the chemical properties of elements depended upon changes in the outer electrons. In some cases elements were reactive because they lost some of the outer electrons. In other cases the atoms gained electrons into the outer shells. These outer electrons are called the *valence electrons*. For example, consider the burning of magnesium in oxygen, which was discussed on page 322. Let us compare the electron arrangement of the atoms of magnesium and oxygen with that of neon:

$$\begin{array}{ll} {}_{12}\mathrm{Mg} & 1s^2,\ 2s^22p^6,\ 3s^2 \\ {}_{10}\mathrm{Ne} & 1s^2,\ 2s^22p^6, \\ {}_{8}\mathrm{O} & 1s^2,\ 2s^22p^4 \end{array}$$

Atoms of magnesium, then, if they lose two electrons per atom would form an ion with an electron structure similar to that of neon. Atoms of magnesium are accordingly said to possess two valence electrons which they tend to lose. This is indicated by the shorter notation $\dot{\dot{\mathrm{M}}}\mathrm{g}$. Atoms of oxygen, on the other hand, must gain two electrons to gain an electron structure similar to that of neon. The notation $:\ddot{\underset{\cdot\cdot}{\mathrm{O}}}$ indicates this. When atoms of magnesium react with atoms of oxygen, there is a transfer of electrons from magnesium to oxygen,

$$\ddot{\mathrm{M}}\mathrm{g} + :\ddot{\underset{\cdot\cdot}{\mathrm{O}}} \rightarrow \mathrm{Mg^{++}O^{=}}$$
(more conveniently written $Mg^{++}O^{=}$)

to form magnesium oxide (Mg^{++} $O^{=}$). If the chemical reactivity, then, of elements depends upon the arrangements of the outer valence electrons, it is important to find the structure of these outer electrons. One method is to determine their ionization energies.

It requires energy to detach an electron in the process we have termed *ionization.* The amount of energy required to detach an electron is called the *ionization energy* of the atom. This energy can be in the form of heat or electricity. The helium atom ($_2$He) is electrically neutral because of two electrons in its $1s^2$ orbital. These are held very tightly because of the small size of the helium atom. It is, however, possible to remove one electron if sufficient energy is supplied to produce a He^+ ion.

$$\mathrm{He} + 93.7 \times 10^{-20}\ \mathrm{cal.} \rightarrow \mathrm{He^+} + e^-$$

To remove the second electron requires even more energy,

$$\mathrm{He^+} + 208 \times 10^{-20}\ \mathrm{cal.} \rightarrow \mathrm{He^{++}} + e^-$$

The energy of ionization is the energy required to ionize one atom of helium. A mole of helium (about 4.0 grams) is a relatively small amount of helium. But the energy needed to ionize this would be $N(0.602 \times 10^{24})$ times larger or 56.5×10^4 calories. This is an enormous quantity of heat. Helium, then, is a very stable and inert element. Lithium, an important metal, has a relatively low ionization energy – 20.6×10^{-20} cals/atom for the first electron. It is much easier to detach an electron; lithium, therefore, will be very different in its chemical behavior from helium. It is a very reactive element.

Figure 24–3 shows that ionization energies of the elements rise and fall in a *periodic* manner with increase in atomic number. The ionization energies are very low with lithium, sodium, potassium, rubidium, and cesium. In a later chapter we shall learn that all these are very soft and very reactive metals with similar properties. The peaks in the curve give the ionization energies of the inert gases, helium, neon, ar-

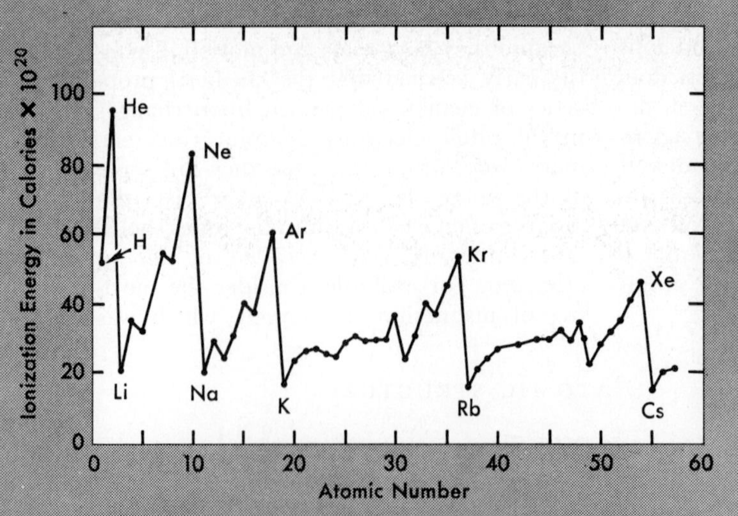

Fig. 24–3 *The ionization energies per atom for the first electron in elements 1 to 60.*

TABLE 24–3 IONIZATION ENERGIES PER ATOM OF THE 1ST, 2ND, 3RD, AND 4TH ELECTRONS IN THE LIGHTER ELEMENTS

Z	ELEMENT	ARRANGEMENTS OF ELECTRONS						*IONIZATION ENERGY IN CALORIES × 10^{20}			
		1s	2s	2p	3s	3p	4s	1st	2nd	3rd	4th
1	H	1						52.0			
2	He	2						93.7	208.0		
3	Li	2	1					20.6	289.0	416.0	
4	Be	2	2					35.6	69.6	586.0	830.0
5	B	2	2	1				31.8	96.0	145.0	990.0
6	C	2	2	2				43.0	93.0	183.0	246.0
7	N	2	2	3				57.5	113.0	181.0	300.0
8	O	2	2	4				52.0	134.0	210.0	296.0
9	F	2	2	5				66.5	134.0	240.0	383.0
10	Ne	2	2	6				82.3	157.0	244.0	382.0
11	Na	2	2	6	1			19.6	181.0	274.0	378.0
12	Mg	2	2	6	2			29.2	57.5	306.0	419.0
13	Al	2	2	6	2	1		22.9	72.0	108.5	459.0
14	Si	2	2	6	2	2		31.1	62.5	128.0	172.0
15	P	2	2	6	2	3		42.0	75.1	115.0	196.0
16	S	2	2	6	2	4		39.6	89.4	134.0	181.0
17	Cl	2	2	6	2	5		49.6	91.0	151.5	204.0
18	A	2	2	6	2	6		60.0	105.5	156.0	228.0
19	K	2	2	6	2	6	1	16.5	Very high	Very high	Very high
20	Ca	2	2	6	2	2	2	23.2	45.1	Very high	Very high

* To obtain actual ionization energies, multiply numbers in these columns by 10^{-20}.

gon, krypton, and xenon. These inert gases are all very much alike.

The data tabulated in Table 24–3 show that the chemical behavior of elements depends upon the ease of detachment or attachment of electrons in outer orbits. This table illustrates the great mass of information that chemists have accumulated on just the first twenty elements. Similar data are known for all the elements. The deductions leading to our ideas of atomic structure are firmly established relative to the outer electrons in all the elements. Only a few general observations will be made here.

1. Helium, neon, and argon are similar in that they have atoms with very high ionization energies and are accordingly nonreactive. Hence these elements are said to be stable and inert.

2. Lithium, sodium, and potassium are similar in that each has an *s* electron (2*s* in Li; 3*s* in Na, 4*s* in K) with a very low ionization energy. Hence ion formation to form Li^+, Na^+, or K^+ occurs with relative ease, and these elements are very reactive. Note also that the ease of ion formation, and thus chemical reactivity, increases as the atomic number increases. The *valence,*

TABLE 24–4 SOME IONIZATION ENERGIES PER ATOM IN CALORIES $\times 10^{20}$

METAL	IONIZATION ENERGY	NUMBER OF ELECTRON SHELLS BENEATH OUTER ELECTRON	METAL	IONIZATION ENERGY
Group I			Group II	
$_3$Li	20.6	*K*	$_4$Be	35.6
$_{11}$Na	19.6	*K, L*	$_{12}$Mg	29.2
$_{19}$K	16.5	*K, L, M*	$_{20}$Ca	23.2
$_{37}$Rb	15.9	*K, L, M, N*	$_{38}$Sr	21.7
$_{55}$Cs	14.8	*K, L, M, N, O*	$_{56}$Ba	19.8

a measure of the capacity for combining with other elements, is said to be +1.

Metals can be compared with each other on the basis of their relative tendency to lose the outer valence electrons. It is noteworthy that the tendency of the metals lithium, sodium, and potassium to lose electrons increases in that order. That is, lithium is the least reactive, and potassium is the most reactive. This is to be expected from the ionization energies of these metals. (Refer to Table 24–4.) Note that the ionization energy – the energy needed to detach the outermost electron – *decreases* with increase in atomic number. A partial explanation for its effect is based upon the relationships suggested in Figure 24–4. Let us assume that the average radii of the *K, L,* and *M* levels follow those postulated by Bohr for the hydrogen atom. That is,

$$r_K : r_L : r_M \text{ as } 1^2:2^2:3^2, \text{ or as } 1:4:9.$$

Thus, the outer electron in sodium is at a significant distance beyond the *K* and *L* electron clouds. The positive nucleus of 11+ is surrounded by an electron cloud of 10− charges. Thus the kernel of the atom has a net charge of +1. Since the electrons are uniformly distributed around the nucleus, this net charge of +1 can be considered to be in the nucleus. Let us now apply Coulomb's law of electrostatic attraction:

$$F_{\text{attraction}} = \frac{q^+ \cdot q^-}{d^2} = \frac{q \text{ nucleus} \cdot q^-}{d^2}$$

The value of the numerator term (q nucleus $\cdot\, q-$) will be the same for sodium and potassium. Hence this is not the factor which explains the much lower ionizing energy of potassium. But the $(1/d^2)$ term will be much less for potassium than for sodium. Thus, the force of attraction between the net charge on the nucleus for the outer electron will be much less for potassium than for sodium.

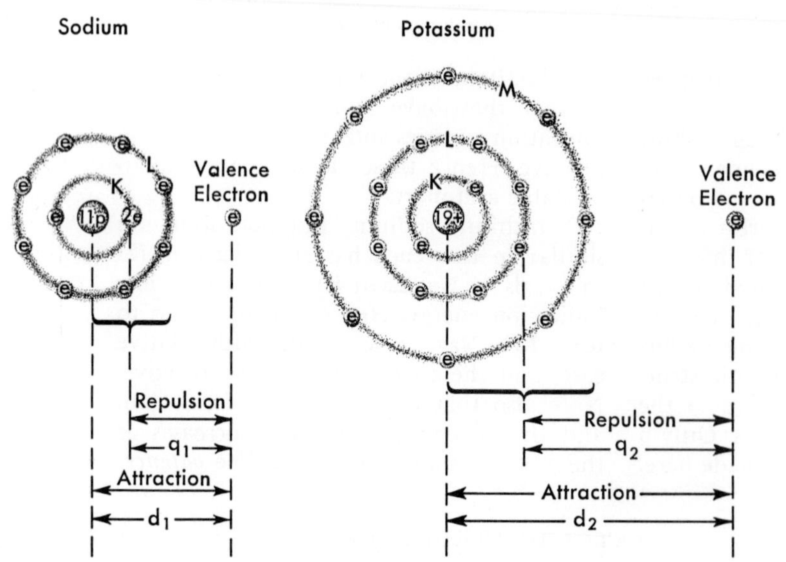

Fig. 24–4 *Relative effects of nuclear charge and atomic size on the tendency to lose by ionization an outer electron. The tendency to lose the valence electron is the greatest in potassium.*

THE GROUPING OF ELEMENTS

Table 24–3 reveals many similarities and regularities among the twenty elements listed. Thus helium, neon, and argon are very inert elements. Lithium, sodium, and potassium (alkali metals) have one outer electron each that is very easily detached as compared with the rest of the electrons in the atom. Note the much larger ionization energy for the second electron in each of these elements. It has become customary to indicate the above behavior by writing the symbols of these elements thus:

$$_{3}Li\cdot \quad _{11}Na\cdot \quad _{19}K\cdot$$

This is a convenient notation to indicate that these elements when they react with other substances lose one electron per atom to form the ions:

$$Li^{+} \quad Na^{+} \quad K^{+}$$

Note that the following elements have similar structures for the outer electrons:

$\cdot\dot{B}\cdot$ and $\cdot\dot{Al}\cdot$

$\cdot\underset{\cdot}{\dot{C}}\cdot$ and $\cdot\underset{\cdot}{\dot{Si}}$$\cdot$

$:\underset{\cdot\cdot}{\ddot{O}}$ and $:\underset{\cdot\cdot}{\ddot{S}}$

$:\underset{\cdot\cdot}{\ddot{F}}\cdot$ and $:\underset{\cdot\cdot}{\ddot{Cl}}\cdot$

Be: and Mg: and Ca:

We shall learn later how these structures make these elements have similar chemical properties. What we call the "outer electrons" are in the s and p sublevels of the outer main shells. Thus the "outer electrons" in aluminum are $2s^2$ and $1p$ electrons, $2s^2$ and $2p^2$ electrons in carbon, but $3s^2$ and $3p^2$ electrons in silicon. The importance of these regularities in electron structure will be pointed out in later chapters.

UNIQUENESS OF INERT GASES

As we shall see in the next chapter, the elements whose electron shells are full are the elements with atomic numbers 2, 10, 18, 36, 54, and 86. They are the inert or "noble" gases, helium-2, neon-10, argon-18, krypton-36, xenon-54, and radon-86. Our study of the rest of the elements will always be based upon a comparison of their structures with those of the inert gases. Because these elements are rather rare, chemically inert, and do not form compounds, they were not discovered until near the end of the last century. The first indication of the existence of such substances on this planet, however, was recorded by Henry Cavendish (England, 1731–1810) in 1785. Cavendish found that nitrogen could be removed from the air by oxidation with an electric spark discharge. The acid oxide of nitrogen was removed by a base, and the surplus oxygen which had been added was removed by combustion, but still a small inactive residue which "stood its ground" and which "was not more than 1/120 of the whole" remained. This recorded fact stimulated no further investigation at the time and remained unnoticed for a hundred years.

In 1868 J. Janssen, a French astronomer, observed in the spectrum of the sun's chromosphere, during an eclipse, a yellow line which did not correspond to the spectrum of any known element. It was concluded by J. N. Lockyer and E. Frankland that the yellow line was due to a new element, which Lockyer named *helium* (*helios,* sun). Twenty-six years after Janssen's observation, terrestrial helium was discovered by Sir William Ramsay, who obtained it by heating cleveite and similar minerals.

Shortly before the discovery of terrestrial helium, Lord Rayleigh observed that the density of nitrogen obtained from the atmosphere by the removal of the other known components was 1.2572 grams per liter, while that of nitrogen obtained by the decomposition of its compounds was 1.2505 grams per liter. This difference, together with the certainty that all impurities had been removed from the latter sample, led to the inference that the nitrogen obtained from the air contains another gas of higher density than nitrogen. The clue found by Cavendish, over a hundred years before,

TABLE 24–5 THE INERT GASES

GAS	MOLECULAR FORMULA	ATOMIC NUMBER	DENSITY, GRAMS PER LITER, S.C.	BOILING POINT, °C.	MELTING POINT, °C.
Helium	He	2	0.1785	−268.9	−272.2
Neon	Ne	10	0.9002	−245.92	−248.52
Argon	A	18	1.7836	−185.85	−189.52
Krypton	Kr	36	3.743	−152.9	−156.6
Xenon	Xe	54	5.896	−107.1	−111.5
Radon	Rn	86	9.97	−62.	−71.

now took on real significance. To test this hypothesis, Ramsay, who collaborated with Rayleigh, carefully removed all the known gases from the air and obtained a gaseous residue (about one per cent of the air by volume) with an atomic weight of 39.9. This he named *argon* (*argos,* idle, lazy) because of its chemical inertness. In the next few years Ramsay found helium in the atmosphere, and by fractional distillation of air obtained two new gaseous elements with atomic weights of 82.9 and 130.2, which he named *krypton* (hidden) and *xenon* (strange), respectively. The last element of this group, radon-86, was discovered by Rutherford.

The unique properties of the inert gases make them useful for certain special purposes. Helium is used for balloons and dirigibles because it gives great lifting capacity without danger of explosions. It is also used in medicine and in certain kinds of welding. Neon, helium, and krypton are used in electric signs; argon and krypton, in certain kinds of electric light bulbs to make them more efficient. The physical properties of the inert gases are shown in Table 24–5. Because of the complete electronic structure of the atoms, molecules of the inert gases are monatomic, that is, contain only one atom. The very low boiling and melting points of these gases is due largely to the weak attractive forces between the molecules.

The electron shells of the inert gases are shown in Table 24–6. These gases have such stable electron shells that they resist ionization. They simply lack chemical properties. For all practical purposes they never react to form compounds among themselves or with other elements; their molecules, as noted above, are monatomic.

TABLE 24–6 ELECTRON SHELLS OF THE INERT (NOBLE) GASES

ELEMENT	AT. NO.	MAIN LEVELS					
		K	*L*	*M*	*N*	*O*	*P*
He	2	2					
Ne	10	2	8				
A	18	2	8	8			
Kr	36	2	8	18	8		
Xe	54	2	8	18	18	8	
Rn	86	2	8	18	32	18	8
Sublevels		$1s^2$	$2s^2\ 2p^6$	$3s^2\ 3p^6\ 3p^{10}$	$4s^2\ 4p^6\ 4p^{10}\ 4f^{14}$		

SUMMARY

1. The Heisenberg uncertainty principle states that it is impossible to know both the speed exactly and the location exactly of any one electron outside a nucleus. Scientists have therefore substituted the concept of electron clouds for electron orbits.
2. Electrons within atoms can travel within spherical clouds or elliptical clouds, and also have two kinds of spin, clockwise and counterclockwise. The total energy of an electron results from a combination of the energies of all these motions.
3. The Pauli exclusion principle states that no two electrons in any atom have exactly the same kind of motions and energies.
4. The Pauli exclusion principle limits the number of electrons in each main (quantum) level by establishing the maximum permissible number of electrons in the sublevels. This excludes an enormous number of possible theoretical arrangements of the electrons outside the nucleus. The principle is based upon experimental observations. It is basic to establishing the electron structure of the atoms of elements.
5. The chemical properties of an element depend upon its electronic configuration as compared with an inert gas.
6. The arrangements of electrons in different kinds of atoms have been inferred from the varying ionization energies of the outer electrons.
7. The composition of the electron shells in the inert gases is basic to an understanding of the chemical behavior of the elements. (Refer to Table 24–5.)
8. A shared pair of electrons of opposite spins is a principal bonding force between atoms within molecules. This is symbolized,

$$A(\uparrow\downarrow)B \quad \text{or} \quad A{:}B.$$

9. A knowledge of the electron theory of the structures of the atoms of the elements provides explanations for the following:
   a. the structures and properties of the molecules of elements and their compounds,
   b. the chemical behavior of the elements,
   c. the observed similarities in certain groups of elements,
   d. the observed properties of elements of contrasting properties such as metals and nonmetals, and
   e. the unusual properties of the inert gases.

STUDY EXERCISES

1. Deduce the electronic configuration of the following elements, using the notation used in Table 24–1:

$${}_{3}Li,\ {}_{16}S,\ {}_{9}F,\ {}_{11}Na,\ {}_{17}Cl,\ \text{and}\ {}_{8}O.$$

   Predict which of these elements could be expected to have similar chemical properties.
2. Contrast the electron configuration of neon and argon, using the *s* and *p* notation for the various sublevels. What is true of the properties of these gases? Do they have common uses?
3. Try to predict whether the elements fluorine, oxygen, nitrogen, and carbon should form compounds with hydrogen. Consider the hydrogen to be monatomic or H· .
4. What is Heisenberg's uncertainty principle? How has the principle influenced our concept of atoms? Has this principle gained acceptance in areas other than chemistry?
5. Deduce the electron structures of atoms described by the following notations:

$$1s^22s^22p^63s^23p^1,$$
$$1s^22s^22p^63s^23p^4,$$
$$1s^22s^22p^63s^23p^6,$$

   and identify the elements.
6. Account for the fact that ${}_{3}Li^6$ and ${}_{3}Li^7$ have very similar properties. What term is used to refer to these elements?
7. Contrast as completely as you can the concept of an atom of oxygen as viewed by Dalton and the modern concept based upon its electron structure. Point out the usefulness of the modern electron theory.

FOR FURTHER READING

1. MARKHAM, E. C., and S. E. SMITH, *General Chemistry*. Boston: Houghton Mifflin Company, 1954. Chapter 17.
2. PAULING, LINUS, *General Chemistry*. San Francisco: W. H. Freeman and Company, 1953. Pages 87–97.

25

PERIODIC CLASSIFICATION OF ELEMENTS

IN THE two preceding chapters the modern concepts of the structure of the atoms were discussed in detail. The object of the present chapter is to consider the classification of the 92 naturally-occurring elements.

The basis of any scientific classification is similarity in one or more characteristics. The earliest classification of elements was made largely on the basis of physical properties. If an element was heavy and had a sheen or luster and certain mechanical properties, it was classified as a metal. Elements that were light and brittle and did not have the properties of metals were considered nonmetals. Later the rare or inert gases were added. This threefold classification, though old and at times difficult to apply, is useful for many purposes, one of these being its great adaptability as a guide for the beginner.

Elements are now classified on the basis of their atomic patterns. Elements which have related electronic configurations are arranged in the same group. The properties of the elements listed in each group are similar, though there is a gradation from the elements having relatively simple structure to the more complex. In this classification, as the elements are arranged according to increasing atomic numbers, a regular repetition of certain properties appears which is related to a kind of rhythmical repetition of electronic structure; it is consequently known as the *periodic classification* of the elements.

METALS AND NONMETALS

Of the 92 naturally-occurring elements, 70 are metals, 16 are nonmetals, and 6 are inert gases. Twenty-one of the elements exhibit natural radioactivity and have 50 different isotopes. Over 800 synthetic isotopes of the 92 elements have been produced by nuclear reactions, but we are concerned here only with the elements occurring in nature, and particularly with those which are abundant or important to life and to our present civilization.

The different characteristics of elements can be illustrated if we choose aluminum and copper to represent the metals, sulfur and chlorine to represent the nonmetals, and helium and neon to represent the inert gases. Aluminum and copper are solids which can be highly polished to a mirror-like surface. The density of aluminum (one of the lightest metals) is a little under 3 g/ml, and that of copper a little under 9 g/ml. The density of sulfur is about 2 g/ml. Chlorine is a gas, and both helium and neon are light gases. Free aluminum and copper are crystals made of atoms held together by strong forces which permit extensive distortion and bending without rupture, while the crystals of sulfur consist of molecules held together by weak forces. Thus, rods of aluminum or copper are relatively hard and can be bent, while a rod of sulfur is brittle, that is, it breaks when struck with a hammer and cannot be bent. Chlorine, helium, and neon are gases at room temperature. Chlorine has diatomic molecules; neon and helium have monatomic molecules. Copper and aluminum are excellent conductors of heat and electricity; sulfur is a poor conductor of heat and an insulator for electric charges; chlorine, helium, and neon do not conduct electricity unless their molecules are activated. Copper melts at 1083°C. and boils at 2582°C.; aluminum melts at 658°C. and boils at 2330°C.; sulfur melts at 114°C. and boils at 444°C.; chlorine melts at −101.6°C. and boils at −33.6°C. The melting and boiling points of helium and neon are not very far from absolute zero.

There is a difference in the ways metals and nonmetals combine with other elements. Aluminum and copper as a rule combine by losing electrons and forming *positive ions;* sulfur and chlorine react by gaining electrons and forming negative ions. Both metals and nonmetals, however, can combine by other types of union. But the trend suffices to serve as a contrast. It should be stressed that the transition between metals and nonmetals is gradual and not abrupt. The inert gases, as their name indicates, do not combine. The classification of Table 25–1 is made on the basis of differences in physical characteristics and chemical behavior.

PERIODIC CLASSIFICATION

The basis of the periodic classification may be stated in the form of a generalization known as the *periodic law. The properties of the elements are periodic functions of their atomic numbers.* This, of course, is an abbreviation of the statement that when the elements are arranged according to increasing atomic numbers they fall into eight groups, each with similar properties. In other words, if we place the elements one by one in the order of their atomic numbers in a table with eighteen columns (Table 25–2, pages 392–393) we shall find

TABLE 25–1 PHYSICAL CHARACTERISTICS AND CHEMICAL BEHAVIOR OF METALS, NONMETALS, AND INERT GASES

PROPERTY	METALS	NONMETALS	INERT GASES
State	Usually shiny solids	Brittle solids or gases	Gaseous
Structure of free element	Usually crystalline	Usually molecular	Exist as single atoms
Density	High	Low	Low
Melting point	High	Low	Very low
Boiling point	High	Low	Very low
Thermal conductivity	Good	Poor	Poor
Electrical conductivity	Good	Poor	Poor
Tensile strength	High	Low	Low
Hardness	High	Low	Low
Ductility and malleability	Good	Poor	Poor
Chemical activity	Usually lose electrons to form positive ions	Usually gain electrons to form negative ions	Do not combine—inert

a general similarity in physical and chemical properties among the elements listed in each column. For example, fluorine, chlorine, bromine, and iodine (Group VII A) are all nonmetals, are generally prepared by similar methods, combine with metals to form compounds having similar color and crystal structure, and so on. Similar properties recur after a certain increase in the positive charges of the nucleus; this recurrence is related to the arrangement of the outer electrons. For example, all the halogens have seven electrons in the outer shell and exhibit related chemical properties. The physical and chemical properties of an element depend upon the mass (nucleus) of the atom and the arrangement of electrons outside the nucleus, and according to the periodic law, the recurrence of a pattern in the structure of the nucleus and outer electrons produces the similarities in physical and chemical properties.

THE PERIODS

Originally the Periodic Table had seven groups divided into A and B families and Group VIII consisting of three families of elements. Later a zero group was added, making a total of nine groups. In the modern version of the table this division is retained, but the B families are arranged separately, so instead of nine columns in the table there are eighteen.

Table 25–2 gives a modern version of the Periodic Table. Hydrogen, atomic number 1, is listed separately, being a simple atom with a single *s* electron. Helium, atomic number 2, has two *s* electrons in the *K* shell. Since the potential required to ionize atoms of helium is high, and also because helium shows inertness toward uniting with other elements, a *K* shell with two *s* electrons (or $1s^2$) is regarded as extremely stable.

Lithium, atomic number 3, has two *s* electrons in the *K* shell and one *s* electron in the *L* shell ($1s^2$, $2s^1$). The energy required to remove the one *s* electron in the *L* shell is 1/10 to 1/20 that required to remove the two *s* electrons in the *K* shell; hence, the inner two electrons have the same configuration as the two *s* electrons in the helium atom. Further, there is a tendency in lithium to lose the *s* electron in the outer shell and thus form a positive ion. Indicating the outer *s* electron by a single dot, we can write:

$$\text{Li}\cdot \rightarrow \text{Li}^+ + e^-$$

The next element is beryllium with atomic number 4; the *K* shell (helium shell) is the same; that is, two *s* electrons in the *K* shell; it also has two *s* electrons in the *L* shell. The energy required to remove the *L*-shell electrons is less than 1/10 that required to remove the *K*-shell electrons. Hence, the trend for beryllium is:

$$\text{Be}: \rightarrow \text{Be}^{++} + 2\,e^-$$

Boron, atomic number 5, has two *s* electrons in the *K* shell and two *s* and one *p* in the *L* shell ($1s^2$, $2s^1$, $2p^1$). In the next four elements, carbon, nitrogen, oxygen, and fluorine, the *s* electrons in the *K* and *L* shells are the same as in beryllium and boron, and the only increase in electrons occurs in the *p* subshell. Thus, carbon: ($1s^2$, $2s^2$, $2p^2$); nitrogen: ($1s^2$, $2s^2$, $2p^3$); oxygen: ($1s^2$, $2s^2$, $2p^4$); fluorine: ($1s^2$, $2s^2$, $2p^5$). With the tenth element, neon, the *p* subshell has six electrons and is filled. As shown in Chapter 24, when the configuration of the *L* shell is 2 + 6, the element has great stability, and neon appears in the table below helium; both are inert gases. Thus, the first series or period of the Periodic Table has been completed.

The next period begins with sodium, element 11, and ends with argon, element 18. Sodium is below lithium; since the *L* shell was filled with neon, the next electron enters the *M* shell ($1s^2$, $2s^2$, $2p^6$, $3s^1$). Thus, sodium, like lithium, has in the outer shell one electron which belongs to the *s* subshell. In magnesium, aluminum, silicon, phosphorus, sulfur, and chlorine, the electrons entering the *M* level fill up first the *s* subshell and then enter the *p* subshell, so that chlorine has the configuration ($1s^2$, $2s^2$,

$2p^6$, $3s^2$, $3p^5$). With the next element argon, the *p* subshell has six and is filled. Argon, element 18, is another inert gas and falls directly below neon, thereby completing the second period of the table.

In the next period, element 19, potassium, is listed below sodium. The single electron enters the 4*s* subshell. Thus, lithium, sodium, and potassium have similar properties and similar electronic configurations, with respect to the outer electronic shell. Calcium, element 20, has two electrons in the 4*s* subshell. Beginning with element 21, scandium, the electrons enter the 3*d* subshell (*M* shell and *d* subshell) until the number of *d* electrons reaches 10 or until the *M* shell has a total of 18 electrons in copper. The increase in electrons beyond copper goes into the *N* shell until the 4*p* subshell has filled up in element 36, krypton. It will be noted that the shell configuration of krypton is 2–8–18–8. Krypton has the same number and subshell arrangement of the outer electrons as argon and neon do. This periodic recurrence of the electronic pattern accounts for the similarity in properties.

The fourth period, like the third, has 18 elements. It begins with element 37, rubidium, and ends with element 54, xenon. The increase in electrons in rubidium (37) and strontium (38) occurs in the 5*s* subshell, as in elements 19 and 20. The nine elements 39 to 48 resemble elements 21 to 30 in that the successive electrons are added to the *d* subshell. These two groups of elements plus elements 57 to 80 form the *transitional* or *subgroup* elements. The fourth period ends with xenon which has an electronic configuration like that of the other inert gases (2–8–18–18–8).

The long fifth period of 32 elements begins with element 55, cesium. Elements 56 and 57 resemble in properties and electronic structure elements 38 and 39 respectively, as well as elements 20 and 21. Thus, the outer electrons of the cesium and barium atoms are in the 6*s* subshell. However, from cesium on (element 58), the successive electrons are added to the 4*f* subshell until the number of 14 is reached in element 71, making a total of 32 electrons in the *N* (4) main shell. The whole group of elements 57 through 71 is listed as a separate series at the bottom of the table. These 15 elements, called the rare earths, bear some resemblance to the series of elements 89 through 102, which includes the transuranium elements synthesized by nuclear reactions. The fifth period ends with radon, an inert gas, whose electronic structure is similar in the structure of the outer shell to the other inert gases.

The last period is incomplete. Thus, the periodic arrangement results in six periods: two short periods of 8 elements each; two long periods of 18 elements each; a long period of 32 elements and an incomplete period of 7 elements. If the 10 transuranium elements which have been synthesized are added, the last period comprises 17 elements and is nearly complete.

THE GROUPS

The periodic arrangement shown in Table 25–2 and discussed in the preceding section resolves into groups or families elements which have the same number of electrons in the outer shell and show many similar properties. Inspection of Table 25–2 shows: (*a*) one group of inert gases called the zero group; (*b*) seven groups of elements called *main* or *A* groups; (c) seven groups of elements called *B* groups or subgroups, which with Group VIII are often called the transitional elements.

Group zero contains the *inert gases* which do not react to form any stable compounds. The elements of Groups I A and II A are often called the *alkali* and *alkaline earth* metals, respectively. They are *light reactive metals,* and their atoms readily "lose" electrons to form positive ions with stable electronic structures like those of the nearest inert gas. Group III A contains boron and the aluminum metals; boron has some transitional properties and in some respects resembles silicon. Group IV A, as shown in the table, is divided by a heavy line into carbon and silicon, which are classified as

TABLE 25-2

PERIODIC TABLE

(REVISED

LIGHT METALS (I A, II A) — HEAVY METALS — INERT GASES — BRITTLE

0	I A	II A	III B	IV B	V B	VI B	VII B	VIII
n 1.009								1 — 1 H 1.0080
INERT GASES								
2 — 2 He 4.003	2,1 — 3 Li 6.940	2,2 — 4 Be 9.013						
2,8 — 10 Ne 20.183	2,8,1 — 11 Na 22.991	2,8,2 — 12 Mg 24.32						
2,8,8 — 18 Ar 39.944	2,8,8,1 — 19 * K 39.100	2,8,8,2 — 20 Ca 40.08	2,8,9,2 — 21 Sc 44.96	2,8,10,2 — 22 Ti 47.90	2,8,11,2 — 23 V 50.95	2,8,13,1 — 24 Cr 52.01	2,8,13,2 — 25 Mn 54.94	2,8,14,2 — 26 Fe 55.85
2,8,18,8 — 36 Kr 83.80	2,8,18,8,1 — 37 * Rb 85.48	2,8,18,8,2 — 38 Sr 87.63	2,8,18,9,2 — 39 Y 88.92	2,8,18,10,2 — 40 Zr 91.22	2,8,18,12,1 — 41 Nb 92.91	2,8,18,13,1 — 42 Mo 95.95	2,8,18,13,2 — 43 Tc s (99)	2,8,18,15,1 — 44 Ru 101.1
2,8,18,18,8 — 54 Xe 131.30	2,8,18,18,8,1 — 55 Cs 132.91	2,8,18,18,8,2 — 56 Ba 137.36	57-71 See Lanthanide Series	2,8,18,32,10,2 — 72 Hf 178.50	2,8,18,32,11,2 — 73 Ta 180.95	2,8,18,32,12,2 — 74 W 183.86	2,8,18,32,13,2 — 75 Re 186.22	2,8,18,32,14,2 — 76 Os 190.2
2,8,18,32,18,8 — 86 * Rn 222	2,8,18,32,18,8,1 — 87 * Fr (223)	2,8,18,32,18,8,2 — 88 * Ra 226.05	89-96 * See Actinide Series					

LANTHANIDE SERIES (Rare Earth Elements)	2,8,18,18,9,2 — 57 La 138.92	2,8,18,19,9,2 — 58 Ce 140.13	2,8,18,20,9,2 — 59 Pr 140.92	2,8,18,22,8,2 — 60 Nd 144.27
ACTINIDE SERIES	2,8,18,32,18,9,2 — 89 * Ac 227	2,8,18,32,19,9,2 — 90 * Th 232.05	2,8,18,32,20,9,2 — 91 * Pa 231	2,8,18,32,21,9,2 — 92 * U 238.07

s = synthetic elements

* = radioactive elements

Atomic weights in parentheses are approximate values for the isotope of the longest half-life.

OF THE ELEMENTS

DECEMBER 1957)

DUCTILE | LOW MELTING | NON METALS

VIII	VIII	I B	II B	III A	IV A	V A	VI A	VII A
				2 3 **5** **B** 10.82	2 4 **6** **C** 12.011	2 5 **7** **N** 14.008	2 6 **8** **O** 16.000	2 7 **9** **F** 19.00
				2 8 3 **13** **Al** 26.98	2 8 4 **14** **Si** 28.09	2 8 5 **15** **P** 30.975	2 8 6 **16** **S** 32.066	2 8 7 **17** **Cl** 35.457
2 8 15 2 **27** **Co** 58.94	2 8 16 2 **28** **Ni** 58.71	2 8 18 1 **29** **Cu** 63.54	2 8 18 2 **30** **Zn** 65.38	2 8 18 3 **31** **Ga** 69.72	2 8 18 4 **32** **Ge** 72.60	2 8 18 5 **33** **As** 74.91	2 8 18 6 **34** **Se** 78.96	2 8 18 7 **35** **Br** 79.916
2 8 18 16 1 **45** **Rh** 102.91	2 8 18 18 **46** **Pd** 106.4	2 8 18 18 1 **47** **Ag** 107.880	2 8 18 18 2 **48** **Cd** 112.41	2 8 18 18 3 **49** **In** 114.82	2 8 18 18 4 **50** **Sn** 118.70	2 8 18 18 5 **51** **Sb** 121.76	2 8 18 18 6 **52** **Te** 127.61	2 8 18 18 7 **53** **I** 126.91
2 8 18 32 17 **77** **Ir** 192.2	2 8 18 32 17 1 **78** **Pt** 195.09	2 8 18 32 18 1 **79** **Au** 197.0	2 8 18 32 18 2 **80** **Hg** 200.61	2 8 18 32 18 3 **81** **Tl** 204.39	2 8 18 32 18 4 **82** **Pb** 207.21	2 8 18 32 18 5 **83** **Bi** 209.00	2 8 18 32 18 6 **84** * **Po** 210	2 8 18 32 18 7 **85** * **At** s (210)

2 8 18 23 8 2 **61** **Pm** s (145)	2 8 18 24 8 2 **62** * **Sm** 150.35	2 8 18 25 8 2 **63** **Eu** 152.0	2 8 18 25 9 2 **64** **Gd** 157.26	2 8 18 26 9 2 **65** **Tb** 158.93	2 8 18 28 8 2 **66** **Dy** 162.51	2 8 18 29 8 2 **67** **Ho** 164.94	2 8 18 30 8 2 **68** **Er** 167.27	2 8 18 31 8 2 **69** **Tm** 168.94	2 8 18 32 8 2 **70** **Yb** 173.04	2 8 18 32 9 2 **71** **Lu** 174.99

2 8 18 32 22 9 2 **93** * **Np** s (237)	2 8 18 32 23 9 2 **94** * **Pu** s (244)	2 8 18 32 25 8 2 **95** * **Am** s (243)	2 8 18 32 25 9 2 **96** * **Cm** s (248)	2 8 18 32 26 9 2 **97** * **Bk** s (247)	2 8 18 32 27 9 2 **98** * **Cf** s (251)	2 8 18 32 28 9 2 **99** * **Es** s (253)	2 8 18 32 29 9 2 **100** * **Fm** s (253)	2 8 18 32 30 9 2 **101** * **Md** s (256)	? **102** * **No** s [?]

Adapted with permission from chart published by Merck & Co.

nonmetals and have some unique properties in forming compounds. Carbon is the basic structural element of the living world, while silicon is the basic element of the rocks of the earth. The remaining three elements of Group IV A (germanium, tin, and lead) are metals. The elements of Groups V A (nitrogen family), VI A (oxygen and sulfur family), and VII A (halogen family) comprise the most important nonmetals, and their atoms "gain" electrons to form negative ions with stable structures like those of the adjacent inert gases.

Groups I B to VII B and Group VIII contain all of the heavy metals and most of the important metals such as iron, nickel, or copper; they are characterized by relatively high tensile strength and often by ductility and malleability. The relation of the properties to the electronic structure of these metals is discussed on page 478.

The subgroup elements have few properties in common with the main-group elements except that they have the same number of electrons in the outer shell. However, as will be shown later, the subgroup elements can lose electrons from *both* the outer and the next to the outer energy levels (see page 479).

Elements 57–71, which are shown at the bottom of the Periodic Table on pages 392–393, are grouped together and called the *rare earths* or *lanthanide series*. It will be noted that the outermost shell in all the members of the series remains the same. Similarly, the radioactive elements 89–102, which include the synthetically produced transuranium elements of atomic numbers 93 to 102, are grouped together as the *actinide* series.

GRADATION OF PROPERTIES WITHIN PERIODS AND GROUPS

Within each period there is a periodicity in physical properties. This is shown in Figure 25–1. The repetition of peaks and depressions in the curves, with the maxima occurring in those elements which have atomic numbers one unit larger than those of the inert gases, are good examples of the periodicity.

Within each period, the metallic properties decrease and the nonmetallic properties increase from left to right, that is, with increasing atomic numbers within the period. For example, in the first period there is a gradual change from lithium, an active metal, to fluorine, an active non-

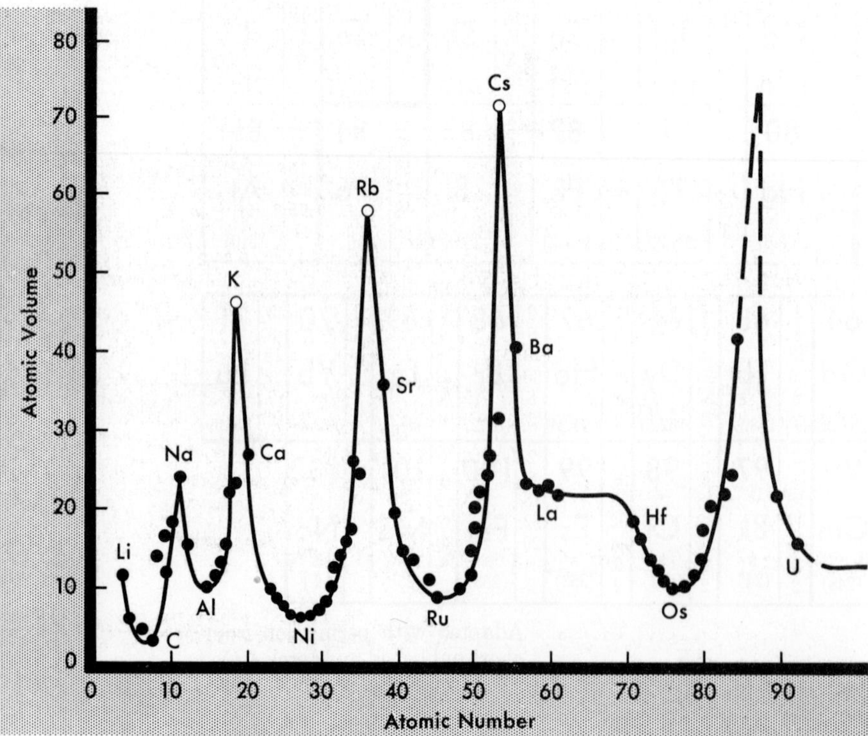

Fig. 25–1 *Variation of atomic volume (atomic weight divided by density) with atomic number.*

TABLE 25–3 ELECTRONIC CONFIGURATION OF ELEMENTS IN GROUP I A

ELEMENT	SYMBOL	ATOMIC NO.	ELECTRONIC SHELL					
			K	*L*	*M*	*N*	*O*	*P*
Lithium	Li	3	2	1				
Sodium	Na	11	2	2,6	1			
Potassium	K	19	2	2,6	2,6	1		
Rubidium	Rb	37	2	2,6	2,6,10	2,6	1	
Cesium	Cs	55	2	2,6	2,6,10	2,6,10	2,6	1

TABLE 25–4 SOME PROPERTIES OF ELEMENTS OF GROUP I A

PROPERTY	Li	Na	K	Rb	Cs
Density	0.53	0.97	0.86	1.53	1.90
Melting point, °C.	179	97	63	39	28
Boiling point, °C.	1,367	892	779	679	690
Ionizing potentials volts	5.3	5.1	4.3	4.1	3.9
Reaction with Cl_2	Formation of white salts [Me^+Cl^-] all cubical except cesium chloride				

metal. The same gradation appears in the second period from sodium to chlorine. The gradual change manifests itself in the transitional elements which have both metallic and nonmetallic properties; they are called *metalloids* or *semimetallic* and in chemical behavior are both metallic and nonmetallic (*amphoteric*). Antimony in its physical properties has a number of distinctly metallic characteristics, but in chemical behavior it exhibits amphoteric properties.

The general trend in the main groups is for the metallic properties to become more pronounced with increase in atomic number or as the atomic radius increases. For example, in Group V A, nitrogen and phosphorus are definitely nonmetallic, arsenic and antimony are metalloids, and bismuth has definitely metallic properties. In Group VII A, the halogens are all nonmetallic; nevertheless, iodine does exhibit a trend toward some chemical properties characteristic of the metals, being the least active of the group.

The ease with which atoms of various elements react chemically is called activity. *The activity of the elements in any main group increases, if the elements are definitely metallic, with increase in atomic radius;* thus, lithium is the least active and cesium the most active in Group I A. Conversely, the *activity decreases with increase in atomic radius if the group is definitely nonmetallic;* thus, fluorine is the most active and iodine the least active of the elements in Group VII A.

To illustrate the relation between the periodicity of properties and the recurrence of electronic structure patterns, a comparison of some of the properties of the alkali metals, Group I A, will be useful. Table 25–3 gives the electronic configuration of the alkali metals, and Table 25–4 lists a few of the properties of the elements.

All the metals are soft and silvery-white when cut by a knife; the bright surface is rapidly tarnished as it reacts with oxygen and moisture in the air. The density increases with the atomic number, while the melting and boiling points decrease. The metals are all very reactive, the reactivity increasing from lithium to cesium. Lithium and sodium react vigorously with water; potassium, rubidium, and cesium react still more vigorously and catch fire a few seconds after they come in contact with water. The electronic configurations of lithium 2–1 and potassium 2–8–8–1 indicate that the orbits of the outer electrons of the two atoms are at different distances from the nucleus. Hence, potassium can lose its electron more easily and react more readily than lithium. This was developed in great detail in the preceding chapter (page 384).

USES OF THE PERIODIC TABLE

The Periodic Table has served both as a guide to the discovery of unknown elements and as a means of assigning correct atomic weights for newly discovered elements. For example, in the latter part of the nineteenth century the atomic weight of indium was given as about 76. This value was assigned on the basis that 38 grams of the element combined with 8 grams of oxygen. However, it could be either $2 \times 38 = 76$ or $3 \times 38 = 114$. If indium were assigned an atomic weight of 76, it would fall between arsenic (75) and selenium (79.2) where its properties would not fit. But if it were assigned to the gap between cadmium (112.4) and tin (118.7), its general properties would fit better. Investigations later proved that the atomic weight of indium was 114.7 and the position assigned to it by use of the Periodic Table was the correct one.

Another use of the Periodic Table is as a tool in new investigations. Many examples can be cited from both theoretical and applied research in the development of new drugs, accelerators, refrigerants, and thousands of compounds developed for specific uses within the past fifty years. If, say, it is found that traces of platinum accelerate the speed of a particular reaction, other and less expensive metals of Group VIII to which platinum belongs – iron and nickel, for example – are tested for the same action. In general, if an element shows a particular activity or a desirable effect, related elements of the same group and also of the same series (those to the right and left) are usually investigated.

A striking recent example of the great usefulness of the Periodic Table was its application in the determination of the properties of the transuranium elements 93–102. The discovery and the determination of the properties of these elements would have been much delayed without the Periodic Table, because these elements were at first available in tiny traces. Much of the early work on plutonium, for example, was carried on with less than half a milligram of the element. The general relationships revealed in the Periodic Table constantly guided the early research with these elements. Were these elements similar to uranium or quite different? The evidence as it accumulated gradually indicated that the transuranium elements had structures which made elements 92, 93, 94, 95, and 96 analogs of the rare earth elements 60, 61, 62, 63, and 64. Compare the structure of americium, for example with that of europium (Table 25–5). The structures of the *Q*, *P*, and *O* energy levels of americium are similar to the *P*, *O*, and *N* levels in europium. Hence, the chemical properties of americium were assumed to be similar to those of europium, and this was demonstrated to be true. In fact, it was this similarity which suggested that element 95 be

TABLE 25–5 STRUCTURES OF AMERICIUM AND EUROPIUM COMPARED

	K	*L*	*M*	*N*	*O*	*P*	*Q*
				s p d f	*s p d f*	*s p d f*	*s*
$_{63}$Eu	2	8	18	2 6 10 6	2 6 1 –	2 – – –	–
$_{95}$Am	2	8	18	2 6 10 14	2 6 10 6	2 6 1 –	2

TABLE 25–6 NEWLANDS' OCTAVES

OCTAVE	1	2	3	4	5	6	7
I II III	H Fl Cl	Li Na K	Be Mg Ca	B Al Cr	C Si Ti	N P Mn	O S Fe

named americium for the Americas as element 63 was named europium for Europe. In the same way, the chemical properties of element 96 were found to be similar to those of element 64. The Periodic Table is an extremely valuable system of correlated classification of the elements and their compounds for the mature scientist as well as for the beginner.

THE DEVELOPMENT OF THE PERIODIC TABLE

The concept of the unity of all matter arose very early and persisted through periods in the development of thought when all available evidence was against such an assumption. Shortly after Prout (England, 1785–1850) proposed his speculative hypothesis that the atoms of all elements were built up of hydrogen atoms, isolated attempts were made to discover relations between the properties and the atomic weights of the elements. Döbereiner (Germany, 1780–1849) suggested in 1829 that many elements could be arranged in triads, in which the order was determined by atomic weight. The middle element of each triad differed from the other two by approximately the same number of atomic weight units and possessed properties which were intermediate between the first and the third. For example, in the first triad, bromine differed by 45 atomic weight units from the first element of the triad and 47 from the third. Bromine is less active than chlorine but more active than iodine; further, the physical state of bromine (liquid) is intermediate between that of chlorine (gas) and iodine (solid). In the second triad, the metal strontium differed from calcium by 47 atomic weight units and by 50 from barium. The three elements form analogous compounds with many elements and appear in the same group (II A) of the modern periodic chart.

Döbereiner's Triads

Cl (35) — Br (80) — I (127)
difference 45 47

Ca (40) — Sr (87) — Ba (137)
difference 47 50

Döbereiner's efforts attracted little attention; no more did those of De Chancourtois, who wrote that the properties of elements are a function of numbers, a close approximation to the present periodic law.

The first attempt to classify the elements in one system of ascending atomic weight into a series by which related groups are obtained was made by Newlands in 1865. As shown in Table 25–6, each series consists of seven elements, and every eighth element has some similarities to the elements that occupy corresponding positions in succeeding series. The elements lithium, sodium, and potassium fall into the same groups; beryllium, magnesium, and calcium comprise another. The ideas of Newlands were not accepted and were even ridiculed as an attempt to bring back the Pythagorean notion of the "music of the spheres." For Newlands' classification suggests that certain elements should be related in a fashion somewhat similar to the notes in successive octaves in music. For example, related properties should be found among elements 1, 8, and 15; 2, 9, and 16; and 3, 10, and 17. There were, however, many difficulties in Newlands' arrangement, for it grouped rather unsimilar elements together, hydro-

TABLE 25–7

COMPARISON OF PREDICTED PROPERTIES FOR EKA-SILICON AND THOSE OF GERMANIUM

MENDELEEF'S PREDICTION, 1871	OBSERVED PROPERTIES OF GERMANIUM, 1886
Atomic weight: 72	Atomic weight: 72.6
Element Es will be prepared by reduction with sodium of EsO_2 or K_2EsF_6.	Ge is prepared by reduction of K_2GeF_6 with sodium.
Element will be a dark gray metal.	Ge is grayish-white.
Density: 5.5	Ge has a density of 5.4 g/cm^3.
On heating Es, an oxide EsO_2 will be formed which will have a density of 4.7 and a high melting point.	Ge unites with oxygen to form GeO_2 a white powder having a density of 4.70 g/cm^3 and a melting point of 1100° C.
The effect of acids on Es will be slight and of alkalies more pronounced.	Ge is not attacked by HCl; NaOH solution has no action. Reacts with concentrated HNO_3 and molten KOH.
The chloride $EsCl_4$ will be a liquid boiling below 100° C. and having a density of 1.9; the fluoride EsF_4 will not be a liquid.	$GeCl_4$ boils at 86.5° C. and has a density of 1.887 g/cm^3; pure GeF_4 is unknown but $GeF_4 \cdot 3H_2O$ is a crystalline solid.

gen with fluorine and chlorine, for example, and oxygen with iron. The reasons for these difficulties are apparent to us today, namely, that there were many elements still undiscovered and the atomic weights of those known had not yet been accurately determined.

Though Newlands' attempts received little recognition by his contemporaries, they stimulated thought in the proper direction and influenced the derivation of the Periodic Law of the Elements by Mendeleef (Russia, 1834–1907) and Lothar Meyer (Germany, 1830–95), working independently. Both men announced their arrangement of the elements about the same time (1869), but Mendeleef's bold predictions as to the properties of unknown elements, which years later were discovered, won him more recognition, and his name is usually associated with the periodic arrangement of the elements. Though Mendeleef himself regarded his Periodic Law as a purely empirical statement of fact, there is no doubt that he was profoundly influenced by the work of his predecessors: the ancient concept of the unity of matter, the attempts of Döbereiner, De Chancourtois, and particularly the arrangement of Newlands.

Mendeleef's table did not include the inert gases (zero group) and had many other imperfections which are of interest to students of the history of science. However, one of the important contributions of Mendeleef was his recognition of the gaps in his arrangement and his assignment of these empty spaces to the positions of undiscovered elements. In several cases, he predicted by bold deductive reasoning the properties of the undiscovered elements. For example, he found in series 4 that calcium (atomic weight 40) was followed by titanium (atomic weight 48). This atomic weight interval was longer than usual; further, if titanium were placed after calcium it would fall under aluminum to which it does not bear much resemblance, being more like silicon. On the other hand, if a blank is left after calcium, both titanium and the elements following it fall under elements which they resemble. Mendeleef named the element to fill this blank *eka-boron*. Similarly he left two blank spaces in series 5 after zinc and named them eka-aluminum and eka-silicon. Further, he predicted on the basis of the periodic relationships the properties of the undiscovered elements and their compounds. The discovery of these elements came within about fifteen years. De Boisbaudran (France, 1838?–1912) discovered eka-aluminum in 1875 and named it *gallium* after the Latin name for his country; Nilson (Sweden, 1840–99) discovered eka-boron in 1879 and called it *scandium* after Scandinavia; and Winkler discovered eka-silicon in 1886 and named it *germanium* after his country, Germany. The extent of agreement between the predicted properties of the hypothetical elements and those found by measurements by their discoverers is shown in Table 25–7 for germanium.

The validity of the Periodic Table in providing spaces for new elements was tested late in the nineteenth century when two inert gases, argon and helium, were found in the earth's atmosphere. The original table of Mendeleef had no places for these two elements. It was inferred that they were members of an unknown family of inert gases and that they might be found in the atmosphere in very small quantities. This inference stimulated Ramsay and Travers to investigate the lighter fractions of liquid air for a gaseous element to fill the gap between helium and argon and from the heaviest fractions to find gases which would enter in places below argon. Thus, *neon, krypton,* and *xenon* were discovered. Since the gases were found to have no ability to combine with ether elements they were placed in a "zero" group to the left of Group I. When this was done it found that the elements fell into correct positions with respect to their atomic weights. For example, the atomic weight of helium is below that of lithium, and the atomic weight of neon below that of sodium.

SUMMARY

1. The chemical properties and most of the physical properties of the elements are periodic functions of their atomic numbers. This is the modern statement of Mendeleef's Periodic Law.
2. The periodic arrangement of the 92 naturally-occurring elements results in two short series of 8 elements each, two long series of 18 elements each, a long series of 32 elements, and an incomplete series of 7 elements.
3. The vertical groups of the periodic arrangement are: one group of inert gases; seven main or *A* groups; and seven *B* groups or subgroups, which together with Group VIII are called transitional elements.
4. The main or *A* group in each vertical group consists of elements which lose or gain electrons to form an ion with an outer shell of eight electrons similar to that of an inert gas. The charge on the ion depends upon the number of electrons gained or lost.
5. The *B* subgroup in each vertical group consists of elements with much more complex electronic structures. These elements not only lose electrons from the outer shell, but from the next to the outside shell as well, and possess properties different from those of the *A* group.
6. The various horizontal series in the Periodic Table reveal a gradual transition in many properties from left to right in the Periodic Table.
7. Characteristic groups of elements within the Periodic Table are: (*a*) the inert gases, (*b*) the light metals, (*c*) the heavy metals, (*d*) the nonmetals, (*e*) the elements carbon and silicon, (*f*) the transition elements, (*g*) the radioactive elements, and (*h*) the actinide series.
8. There is a distinct trend in the change from metallic to nonmetallic, from left to right, within a horizontal series in the Periodic Table.
9. For the main elements within a vertical group of the Periodic Table, metallic character increases with increase in atomic number, i.e., from top to bottom. With nonmetals, the most nonmetallic are found at the top of the groups.
10. The Periodic Table correlates and systematizes the immense amount of factual information concerning all the elements and their compounds, and it serves as a guide in research seeking to discover new applications of the elements and their compounds.

STUDY EXERCISES

1. Give a statement of the periodic law and indicate the experimental evidence upon which the atomic numbers are based
2. Explain in terms of theory the present views as to the recurrence of properties in the groups of elements as they are arranged in the periodic chart.
3. Listed below are properties of elements, some metallic and some nonmetallic. Indicate with a + or — sign which properties are associated with metals and which with nonmetals.

Properties	*Metals*	*Non-metals*
a. Conduct heat readily.	......	......
b. Often very ductile.	......	......
c. Conduct electricity readily.	......	......
d. Often malleable.	......	......
e. Often brittle.	......	......
f. Have a common characteristic luster.	......	......
g. Readily gain electrons.	......	......
h. Readily lose electrons.	......	......

4. (In answering these questions, refer to the Periodic Table on pages 392–393.) The properties of the elements vary in a regular manner within a *series* or within a *group.* Indicate how each property listed below varies within the Periodic Table: whether from left to right (*LR*), right to left (*RL*), top to bottom (*TB*), or bottom to top (*BT*). For nearly all, two answers should be given; for example (Question *a*), the atomic number increases from left to right and from top to bottom.
   a. Atomic number increases ....
   b. Atomic weight increases ....
   c. Number of valence electrons increases ....
   d. Tendency to lose electrons increases ....
   e. Tendency to gain electrons increases ....
   f. Metallic character increases ....
   g. Tendency to become radioactive increases ....
   h. Number of electronic shells increases ....
   i. Nonmetallic character increases ....
5. After each item place the letter(s) of the groups or areas which best fit the description. Refer to the Periodic Table on pages 392–393 in answering.

A. Group I A	K. Group O
B. Group I B	L. Upper left corner of table
C. Group II A	M. Lower left corner of table
D. Group II B	N. Along diagonal
E. Group III A	O. 5th period of elements
F. Group IV A	P. 6th period of elements
G. Group V A	Q. 1st period of elements
H. Group VI A	R. Transitional groups
I. Group VII A	S. Lanthanides
J. Group VIII	T. Actinides

(*a*) Halogen family .....; (*b*) inert gases .....; (*c*) alkali metals .....; (*d*) most active metal .....; (*e*) most active nonmetal .....; (*f*) groups containing most heavy metals .....; (*g*) the elements in this area are mostly metals .....; (*h*) the elements in this area are mostly nonmetals .....; (*i*) the elements in this area are mostly metalloids .....; (*j*) the elements of these groups exhibit a tendency to lose electrons .....; (*k*) the elements of these groups exhibit a tendency to gain electrons .....; (*l*) the elements with the lowest melting points will be found in this group .....; (*m*) the rare earths are found in this period .....; (*n*) most radioactive elements are found in these periods .....; (*o*) the element which most readily forms negative ions is found in .....; (*p*) most of the synthetic elements will be found in .....; (*q*) the periods which have elements with electrons in the *d* subshell .....; (*r*) the period with elements having electrons in the *f* subshell .....; (*s*) the period with elements having electrons only in the *s* and *p* orbits .....; (*t*) the metals used in greatest quantities belong to this group .....; (*u*) elements which form the greatest number of known compounds are in this group .....; (*v*) the most expensive metals (dollars per pound) are found in this group .....; (*w*) metals or alloys with good tensile strength and low density are made of the elements found in ......

6. Construct a table with the name of the person listed, giving his chief contribution toward the development of the present system of the classification of elements. List in

chronological order of contribution: Newlands, Mendeleef, Döbereiner, Prout.

7. What explanation can be offered to account for the difficulty that has been encountered in finding elements 85 and 87?
8. Tungsten (74) is used to make filaments in electric light bulbs. Under certain conditions it is ductile and has a melting point of 3370°C. Would you venture an opinion that tantalum (73) might also be used for making bulb filaments? Explain.
9. Using the Periodic Table, predict as many properties as possible for elements 87 and 103.
10. Taking as an example Group VII A, construct a table which will show the similarities in properties and another table to indicate the similarities in electronic structure. Which of the two sets of data are facts, and which are assumptions based on inferential evidence?

FOR FURTHER READING

1. MARKHAM, E. C., and S. E. SMITH, *General Chemistry*. Boston: Houghton Mifflin Company, 1954.
   Chapter 18 deals with electron configurations and the periodic law.
2. PAULING, LINUS, *General Chemistry*. San Francisco: W. H. Freeman and Company, 1953.
   Chapters 5 and 6 deal with chemical elements and the periodic law.
3. Paperback: EDITORS OF SCIENTIFIC AMERICAN, *New Chemistry*. Simon and Schuster, $1.45.
   Part 3 (pages 89–126) gives an excellent treatment of the rare earths and the synthetic elements.

26

INTERACTION OF ELEMENTS

THE MODE by which elements combine to form compounds has been an intriguing subject from the earliest days of chemical science. At first a force called affinity was assumed to attract and hold atoms together. Later it was correctly guessed that this chemical affinity was electrical in nature. As more was learned about the capacity of each atom to combine with atoms of different elements, this combining affinity was called *valence.* The present theories of chemical combination are based on the interaction of atoms and redistribution of their *outer valence electrons* to form a more stable structure.

MODERN THEORY OF CHEMICAL BONDING

Departure of the structures of the various atoms from the structure of inert gases, which were discussed in Chapter 24, gave rise to the theory of chemical bonding.

The present theory of chemical combination or *chemical bonding* may be summarized as follows: *The force that holds the atoms together is called the chemical bond. The bonding forces in the interaction of atoms are provided by the outermost (valence) electrons. In the formation of the chemical bonds there is a redistribution of the valence electrons of the reacting atoms in such a manner as to enable each atom to attain the electronic configuration of the inert gas closest to it.*

COVALENT BONDS

The atoms *A* and *B* may unite by each contributing one electron to form an electron pair, which by being shared between them becomes the bond. Atoms which unite by sharing *pairs of electrons* or *covalent bonds* form molecules (Figure 26–1). The electrons shown in the figure can be represented by dots, and the formation of the covalent bond between *A* and *B* is simplified:

$$A\cdot + \cdot B \rightarrow A{:}B$$

The tendency to form covalent bonds is greatest among atoms which have similar or

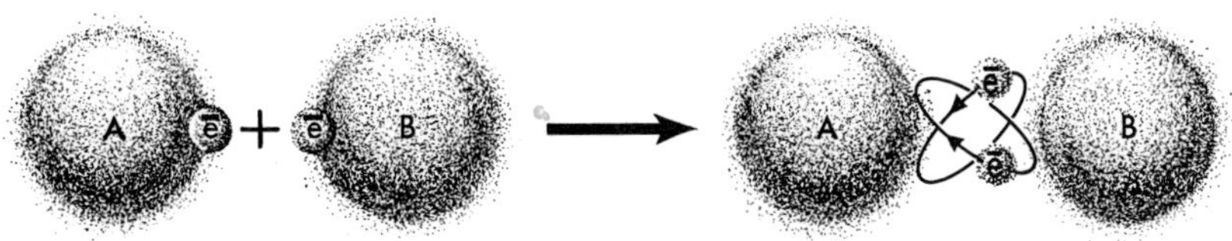

Fig. 26–1 *Atoms uniting through sharing of a pair of electrons or formation of a covalent bond.*

closely related electronic structures and have *four or more electrons in the outer shell.* Thus, two atoms of chlorine unite by forming a covalent bond (Figure 26–2).

A better insight into the nature of the covalent bond may be obtained by considering the covalent hydrogen molecule, H_2. The molecule consists of two hydrogen atoms each of which in turn consists of a proton plus one 1*s* electron. When the two atoms combine to form the molecule of hydrogen, the electron cloud of each atom interpenetrates that of the other, so that the two electrons move about both nuclei which act as a combined nucleus having a charge of +2 and hence hold the electrons more firmly than would a nucleus with a charge of +1. Now the energy levels which the two electrons occupy in the molecule are not exactly the same as in the isolated atoms but an energy level which is a hybrid of the two and is called a *molecular orbital.* According to Pauli's principle (page 379), when two electrons occupy the same orbital their spins must be opposed or paired, and such a pair furnishes the bonding force holding the two nuclei of the hydrogen atoms together. Thus the electron pair forming the covalent bond may be pictured in an elementary manner as a pair of negatively charged particles rotating in orbits around each other with opposed spins. In this manner, the electron pair of the covalent bond provides not only an electrostatic attraction for the positive nuclei but also magnetic fields generated by their motions which also serve as bonding forces.

Although it is not possible to determine the precise position of the electron pair, the greatest probability is that it will be between the two nuclei; hence, the electronic structure for the hydrogen molecule is given by the symbol H:H. If it is desired to indicate the opposed spins of the bonding pair of electrons, the following structure can be written, H:H(↑↓).

The pairing of electrons between atoms of more complex structures than hydrogen to form covalent bonds is difficult to explain without the use of concepts beyond the scope of this work. However, the union of oxygen with hydrogen to form water will be briefly discussed in order to illustrate some of the difficulties involved.

Hydrogen and oxygen gases even when mixed in a ratio of two volumes of hydrogen to one of oxygen do not react, unless we pass a spark or bring a flame close to the mixture. The spark or flame activates a few of the molecules into atoms which react, releasing energy which activates other atoms, and the reaction is propagated rapidly so that an explosion results. Therefore, we can attempt to explain the reaction in terms of the interaction of oxygen and hydrogen atoms to form water molecules. The normal oxygen atom $_8O = 1s^2, 2s^2, 2p^4$ has two electrons in the 1*s* subshell, two electrons in the 2*s* subshell, and four in the 2*p* subshell. However, not all of the four 2*p* electrons are the same. Two of these are paired, and we can call them $2p_x$(↑↓), while the other two are unpaired and are designated as $2p_y$(↑) and $2p_z$(↑). According to theory, only the latter two unpaired electrons are involved in the formation of the two covalent bonds by uniting with the two 1*s* electrons of the hydrogen atoms to form bonds between the two hydrogen and one oxygen atoms and produce the water

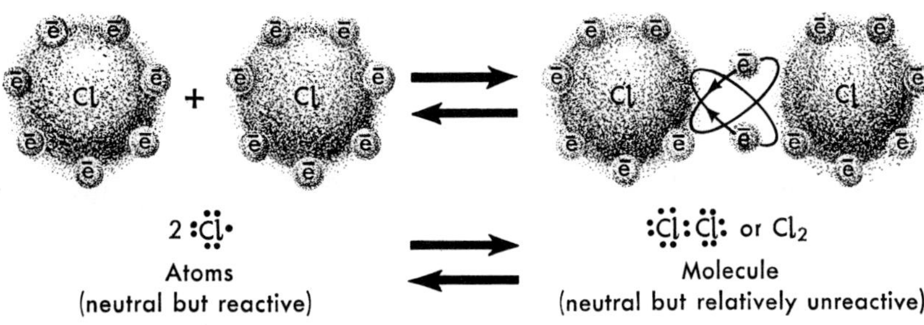

Fig. 26–2 *Formation of a covalent bond between two atoms of chlorine.*

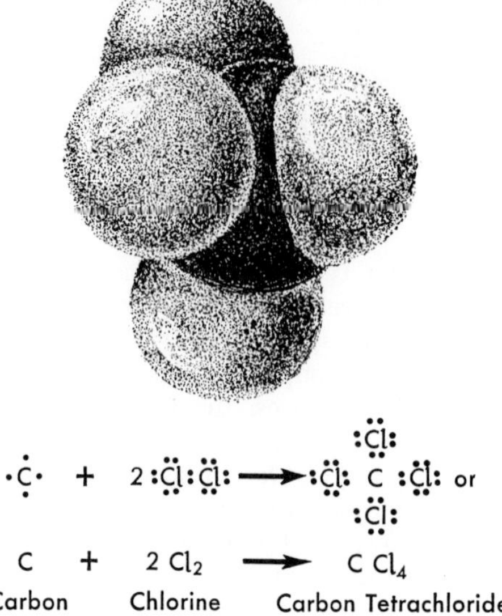

Fig. 26–3 *Formation of 4 covalent bonds between a carbon atom and 4 chlorine atoms.*

molecule. In such a molecule the covalent bonds are nearly at right angles to each other. As shown in Figure 26–13 (page 411), the bond angle in the water molecules is 105° instead of nearly 90° mostly because of the slight repulsions between the two positive hydrogen nuclei.

This elementary discussion of the energy levels that the electrons occupy in the molecule (molecular orbitals) shows that such considerations are complex. Therefore for most subsequent discussions we will assume a simpler picture, namely, that two or more atoms which combine by covalent bonds to form molecules do so by each atom donating electrons to form pairs having opposed spins, the arrangement of electrons in the molecule being such that each atom acquires the electronic configuration of the inert gas nearest to it. Thus one atom of carbon which has four electrons in the outer shell (two paired and two unpaired) unites with four atoms of chlorine each of which has seven outer electrons. Each chlorine atom contributes one electron and each carbon atom four electrons to form a molecule with *four covalent bonds* (Figure 26–3). In such a molecule each atom has eight electrons arranged around it, thus attaining the stability of the inert gas structure. The molecules of oxygen, hydrogen, nitrogen, and many other elements and the vast number of compounds of carbon are assumed to have covalent bond structures.

ELECTROVALENT OR IONIC BONDS

The atoms *A* and *B* may unite by electron transfer. Atoms of A lose one electron per atom to form positive ions; the atoms of B gain electrons (one each) to form negative ions. This transfer of electrons is shown in Figure 26–4. In the solid state, the ions of opposite charge are held together by electrostatic forces. Compounds formed by this type of union consist of *ionic aggregates,* and the bond is called an *ionic* or *electrovalent bond.*

The tendency to form ionic compounds is greatest among the elements of Groups I, II, VI and VII A. Elements of Group I A, such as lithium and sodium, tend to lose one electron and attain the electronic configuration of the preceding inert gas structure:

Na·	→	Na^+ + e^-
2–8–1		2–8
Sodium atom (neutral particle)		Sodium ion similar in structure to neon atom (charged particle)

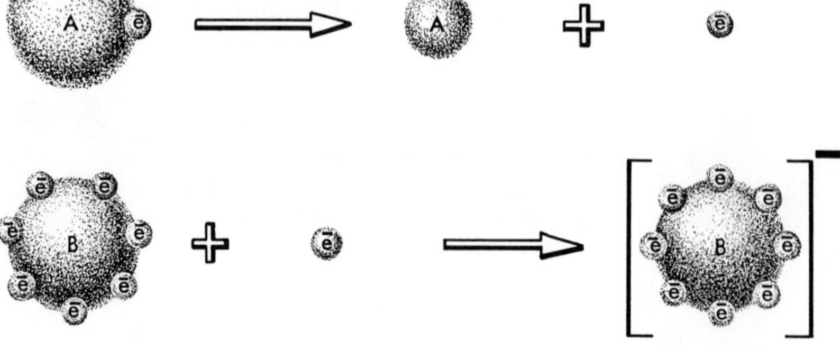

Fig. 26–4 *Formation of positive and negative ions from neutral atoms.*

On the other hand fluorine, chlorine, and other elements of Group VII A with seven electrons on the outer shell tend to acquire one electron per atom forming negative ions with eight electrons and the stability of the inert gas which follows. For example, an atom of fluorine with an electronic structure of 2–7 gains one electron and forms a negative ion with an electronic structure 2–8, which is similar to that of neon:

$$:\ddot{\underset{\cdot\cdot}{F}}\cdot \; + \; e^- \; \rightarrow \; :\ddot{\underset{\cdot\cdot}{F}}: \quad \text{or} \quad F^-$$

Fluorine atom (neutral particle) — Fluorine ion; similar in structure to neon atom (charged particle)

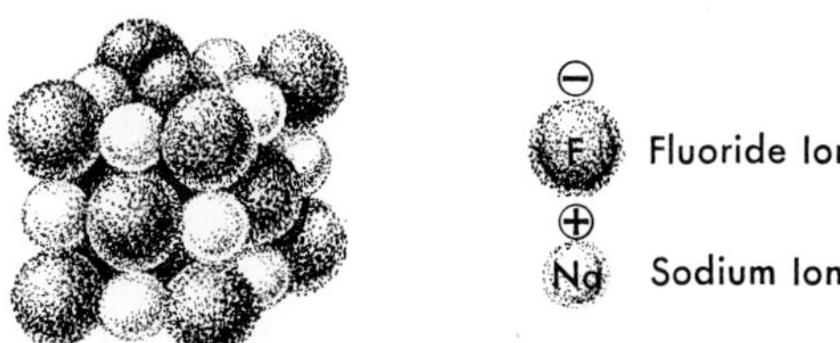

Fig. 26–5 *Unit of sodium fluoride crystal. Sodium and fluoride ions are arranged in a cubic pattern.*

Thus sodium fluoride Na^+F^- is composed of sodium and fluoride ions held together by the electrostatic forces of oppositely charged bodies (Figure 26–5). The ionic type of chemical bonding is characteristic of the majority of the common substances known as salts. For example, consider the burning of magnesium in air, discussed on page 322. There is an actual transfer of electrons from magnesium atoms to oxygen atoms forming magnesium ions (Mg^{++}) and oxide ions ($O^=$). The product is an aggregate of ions. These are distinct electrical forces of attraction between the ions of opposite charge. The positively charged magnesium ion has achieved a neon-like structure

$$[_{12}Mg\ 1s^2,\ 2s^22p^6]^{++}$$

The oxygen ion also has a neon-like structure

$$[_{8}O\ 1s^2,\ 2s^22p^6]^=$$

but with a negative charge of −2.

It is possible to demonstrate experimentally that there is an actual loss of electrons in the formation of magnesium oxide. (Refer to Figure 26–6.) A large sheet of clean magnesium (*A*) is dipped in a water solution of sodium hydroxide. The magnesium serves as an electrode. The second electrode (*B*) is a strip of platinum selected because it is chemically inert. The sodium hydroxide is an ionic compound, so the solution contains sodium (Na^+) and hydroxyl (OH^-) ions. When the switch is closed, these ions carry an electric current in the solution. The following series of changes occur:

At Mg electrode:

$$\ddot{Mg} + H_2O \rightarrow Mg^{++}O^= + 2H^+ + 2\,e^-$$

At Pt electrode:

$$2H^+ + 2\,e^- \rightarrow H_2 \text{ (gas)}$$

Net over-all effect:

$$\ddot{Mg} + H_2O \rightarrow MgO + H_2 + \text{electric current}$$

The reactive Mg atoms in contact with water form magnesium oxide (MgO) by losing two electrons. If the switch is closed, the electrons flow through an external circuit of copper wire to the platinum electrode. These combine with hydrogen ions (H^+)

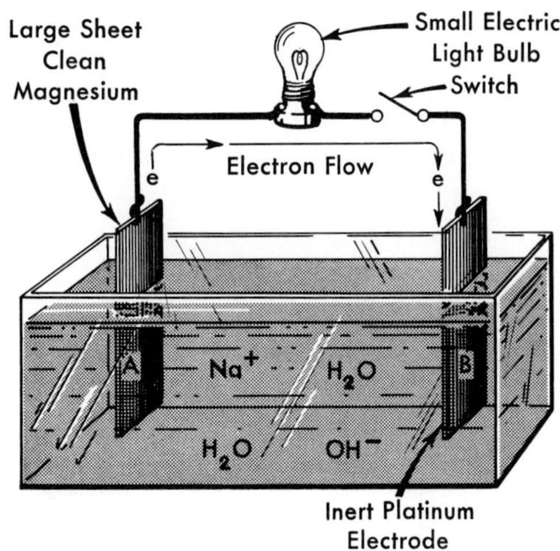

Fig. 26–6 *The formation of magnesium oxide involves an actual transfer of electrons.*

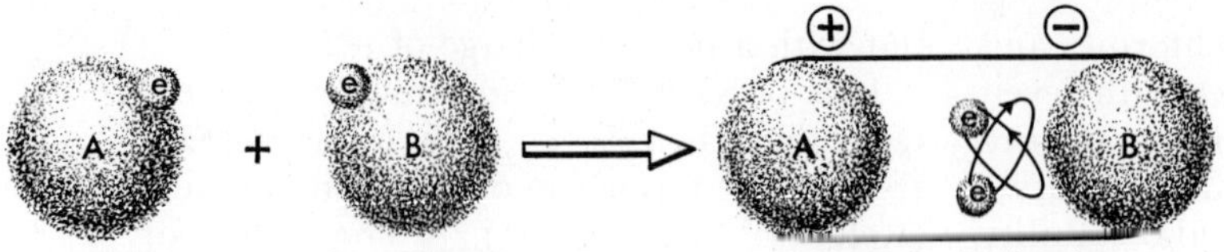

Fig. 26–7 *Schematic representation of the formation of a dipolar molecule.*

to form hydrogen gas. Thus the electrons are diverted to form an electric current. The evidence for this is the glowing of the small electric light bulb.

Chemical reactions involving metals to form electrovalent compounds are very common. The rusting of iron to form iron oxide, for example, is an electrochemical process. Many of the metals, such as zinc chloride ($ZnCl_2$), copper sulfate ($CuSO_4$), silver nitrate ($AgNO_3$), limewater ($Ca(OH)_2$), and hundreds of others are compounds with electrovalent bonds.

INTERMEDIATE BONDS

Intermediate bonds between the ionic and the covalent are formed when two atoms *A* and *B* have different attractions for electrons. If, for example, *B* has a greater electron attraction than *A,* the electron pair of the covalent bond will be displaced closer to *B* than to *A,* thus forming an unsymmetrically charged molecule; one end of such a molecule (area of *B*) will have a small negative charge, while the other will have a small positive charge. Such molecules are called *dipolar molecules* or polar molecules (Figure 26–7). The molecules which have a symmetrical distribution of charges, such as those of chlorine, hydrogen, or carbon tetrachloride, are called nonpolar. An example of the formation of a polar molecule may be cited in the reaction between hydrogen and chlorine to produce hydrogen chloride (Figure 26–8). The electronic equation as written indicates that when hydrogen combines with chlorine to form the compound hydrogen chloride the resulting combination consists of molecules in which the distribution of electric charges is not symmetrical. Further, the *bonding* pair of electrons is closer to chlorine than to hydrogen, and hence the molecule has a slight positive charge at one end and a slight negative charge at the other. As we shall see, this displacement can be further increased by the environment, and under appropriate conditions the molecule of hydrogen chloride can be dissociated into *ions* or become *ionized.* From this point of view, we can assume that between the clear-cut character of the covalent bonds of the nonpolar molecules and the electrovalent bonds of the ionic salts, the large majority of compounds have chemical bonds which possess some properties of the covalent bond and some properties of the electrovalent bonds.

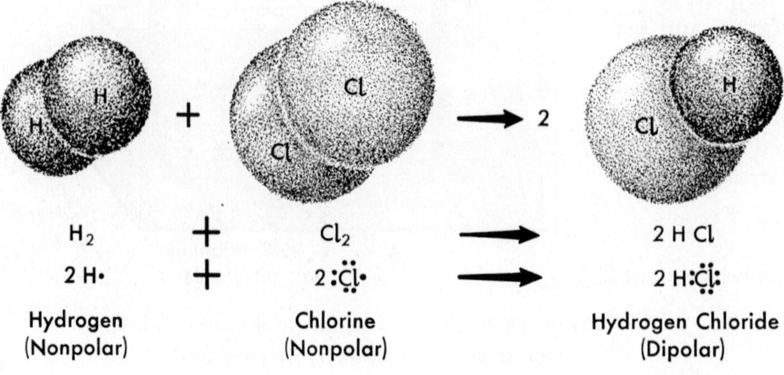

Fig. 26–8 *Reaction between a molecule of hydrogen and a molecule of chlorine (both nonpolar) to form two polar molecules of hydrogen chloride.*

BONDS AND PROPERTIES

Of the two common compounds, sodium chloride (ordinary table salt) and carbon tetrachloride, one is a hard brittle solid and the other is a liquid at room temperature. From the previous discussion, we saw that sodium chloride is formed by ionic bonds and carbon tetrachloride by covalent bonds. In order to examine further the relation between the type of bonds and the properties of the compound, we tabulate some of the physical and chemical properties of the two compounds as shown in Table 26–1.

The properties of sodium chloride can be related to the type of bonds formed when sodium atoms combine with chlorine atoms:

$$\underset{\text{Sodium (atoms)}}{2\,Na} + \underset{\text{Chlorine (molecules)}}{Cl_2} \rightarrow \underset{\text{Sodium chloride (ions)}}{2\,NaCl}$$

$$2\,Na\cdot + :\ddot{\underset{\cdot\cdot}{Cl}}:\ddot{\underset{\cdot\cdot}{Cl}}: \rightarrow 2\,Na^+[:\ddot{\underset{\cdot\cdot}{Cl}}:]^-$$

Accordingly, the sodium chloride crystals consist of the positive sodium ions and negative chloride ions held together by the electrostatic attraction of unlike charged bodies. A single crystal of sodium chloride is a cubical lattice having alternate positive ions and negative chlorine ions, as diagrammatically shown in Figure 26–9. Experimental evidence for such a structure is obtained by study of the crystals with X-ray methods. Not only the crystal structure can be determined but also the effective size of the sodium and chloride ions.

TABLE 26–1

SUMMARY OF PROPERTIES OF SODIUM CHLORIDE AND CARBON TETRACHLORIDE

PROPERTY	SODIUM CHLORIDE NaCl	CARBON TETRACHLORIDE CCl_4
State at room temperature	Solid	Liquid
Melting point of solid	801° C.	− 22.8° C.
Boiling point of liquid	1413° C.	76.8
Density (D_4^{20})	2.165	1.595
Electrical conductivity of liquid	Good (melted)	None
Solubility in water (g/100 ml) at room temperature	Good (35.7 g)	Insoluble (0.08 g)
Electrical conductivity of aqueous solution	Good	None
Reaction with silver nitrate solution ($AgNO_3$)	Immediate—with formation of silver chloride (AgCl) precipitate	No immediate reaction

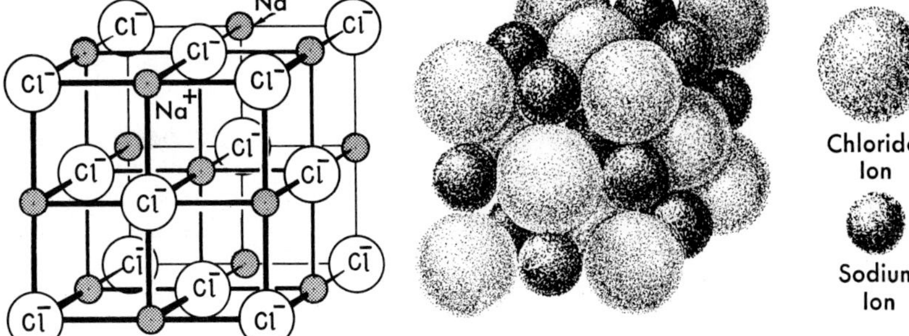

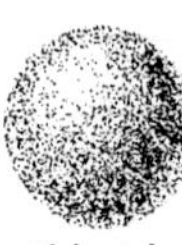

Fig. 26–9 *Structure of sodium chloride crystal.*

The properties of sodium chloride summarized in Table 26–1 can be explained on the basis of such structure. The force between the unlike charged ions is strong, and hence a great deal of heat energy must be employed to separate the ions in the crystal. As the solid is heated, the vibratory motion of the ions increases until the bonding force is overcome, and the crystal melts to form an ionic liquid of sodium chloride; hence the temperature at which sodium chloride melts is high (801° C.). The ionic liquid or molten sodium chloride consists of ionic aggregates which, while being charged, will migrate under a potential or conduct electric current; further, since the interionic forces in the liquid are strong, the velocity of the ions is low and the heat required to vaporize them is very high. Therefore sodium chloride and other ionic solids are not readily transformed to the gaseous state.

When solid sodium chloride dissolves in water, the bonding forces are overcome by the polar water molecules and thus ions pass into the solution. A solution of sodium chloride consists of sodium ions and chloride ions surrounded by water molecules. Such a solution, containing positive and negative ions, conducts an electric current. Finally, when silver nitrate is added to a solution of sodium chloride, a chemical reaction involving ions takes place. The ions of silver and chlorine unite to form the solid silver chloride, which being much less soluble than sodium chloride separates out as a curdy precipitate:

$$\underset{\text{Sodium chloride Ions}}{Na^+Cl^-} + \underset{\text{Silver nitrate Ions}}{Ag^+NO_3^-} \rightarrow \underset{\text{Solid silver chloride precipitate}}{Ag^+Cl^- \downarrow} + \underset{\text{Ions}}{Na^+NO_3^-}$$

Since the sodium ions and nitrate ions do not react but merely are spectators, the chemical reaction leading to the formation of silver chloride can be written as:

$$\underset{\text{Ion}}{Ag^+} + \underset{\text{Ion}}{Cl^-} \rightarrow \underset{\text{Solid settles out of solution}}{Ag^+Cl^- \downarrow}$$

In solution

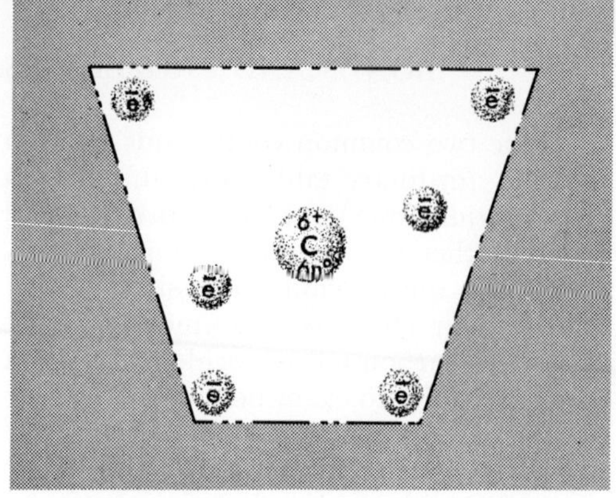

Fig. 26–10 *Schematic diagram of the carbon atom with an electronic structure of 2–4. The bonding forces of the four outer electrons are shown as directed at the four corners of an imaginary tetrahedron.*

Sodium chloride (and ionic compounds in general) are solid at room temperature, have high melting points, and on melting form ionic liquids of low volatility and high boiling points. The ionic liquids as well as the solutions of ionic compounds in water are conductors of electricity and react rapidly with other ions.

The properties of carbon tetrachloride (and other covalent compounds) can also be explained by their structure. In the structure of carbon tetrachloride the carbon atom with an electronic structure of 2–4 is important. (Refer to Figure 26–10.)

Experimentally it is observed that carbon atoms do not readily lose electrons to form positive ions like metals, nor gain electrons to form negative ions like typical nonmetals. That is, ions such as C^{4+} and C^{4-} are never observed to form under ordinary conditions. This can in part be attributed to the small size of carbon atoms. The carbon atom can most easily attain the inert gas structure 2–8 by forming four covalent bonds. In the case of chlorine, which has *seven* electrons in the outer shell, it takes *four* chlorine atoms to form covalent bonds with the four electrons available from one carbon atom. In the case of oxygen, which has *six* electrons, it requires *two* oxygen atoms to form covalent bonds with one carbon atom.

$$\cdot\dot{\underset{\cdot}{C}}\cdot \; + \; 4\,:\ddot{\underset{\cdot\cdot}{Cl}}\cdot \; \rightarrow \; :\ddot{\underset{\cdot\cdot}{Cl}}:\ddot{\underset{\cdot\cdot}{C}}:\ddot{\underset{\cdot\cdot}{Cl}}: \text{ (with } :\ddot{Cl}: \text{ above and below C)}$$

Carbon Chlorine Carbon tetrachloride

$$\cdot\dot{\underset{\cdot}{C}}\cdot \; + \; 2\,:\ddot{\underset{\cdot\cdot}{O}} \; \rightarrow \; \ddot{\underset{\cdot\cdot}{O}}::C::\ddot{\underset{\cdot\cdot}{O}}$$

Carbon dioxide

The resulting structure is a *neutral molecule* composed of atoms held together by covalent bonds. The electron pairs forming the covalent bond must be thought of as a pair of negatively charged particles spinning and rotating in orbits around each other, thus providing not only an electrostatic attraction for the positive nuclei of carbon and chlorine, but also magnetic fields which serve as bonding forces. The magnetic fields are generated by the motion of the negatively charged electrons and their spins. (Figure 26–11.)

A liquid such as carbon tetrachloride, if shaken with a solution of silver nitrate, fails to give a precipitate of silver chloride. Even after the mixture is boiled for several hours only a faint opalescence results; carbon tetrachloride does not form chloride ions readily. This tendency of nonpolar molecules to retain their structure and not undergo either temporary or permanent displacement of the electric charges (polarization) accounts for their relatively low rates of reaction as compared to ionic compounds. It also accounts for the fact that compounds formed by covalent bonds and consisting of nonpolar covalent bonds are not conductors of electricity. In general, therefore, compounds formed by covalent bonds *have a molecular structure* and *are gases or liquids* at ordinary temperature, if the molecular weight is not high. Molecular liquids are nonconductors and have relatively high volatilities and low boiling points. Covalent compounds with high molecular weights are solids at room temperature, but these solids melt at low temperatures, usually below 300° C. The reactivity of the molecular compounds is low, and in order that any appreciable reaction may take place, it is necessary to cause a polarization of the molecule, that is, a displacement of the electric charges.

STRUCTURE AND PROPERTIES OF POLAR MOLECULES

In the previous discussion on the types of chemical bonds it was stated that between the two extremes of equal sharing and complete displacement of the valence electrons *intermediate* bonds are formed. These are essentially covalent bonds with the electron pairs displaced closer to the more *electronegative atom.* The result is a *polar molecule.* Thus hydrogen chloride gas is assumed to consist of molecules which are slightly unsymmetrical with reference to the distribution of electric charges, one being slightly positive, the other slightly negative. Since the attraction of the atoms for electrons varies (depending on the charge on the nucleus and the radius of the atom), it follows that the displacement of the covalent bonding pairs will vary. For example,

Fig. 26–11 *Diagram of a molecule of carbon tetrachloride showing the nature of the covalent bonds. Molecule as a whole is nonpolar.*

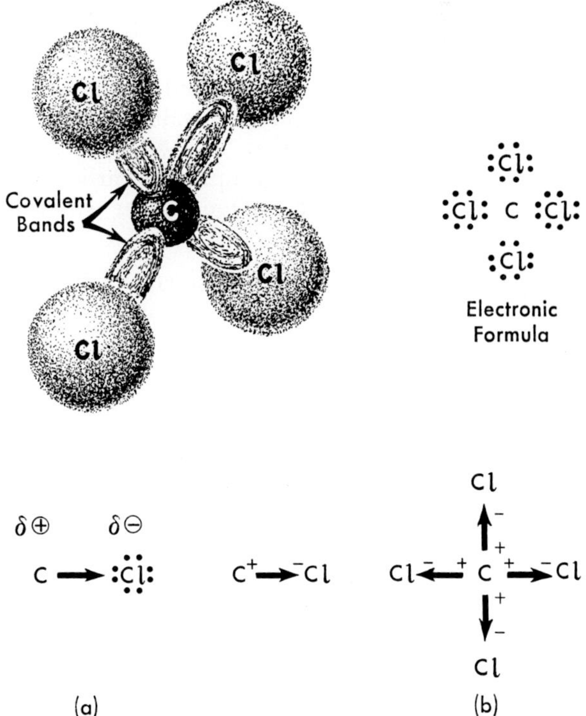

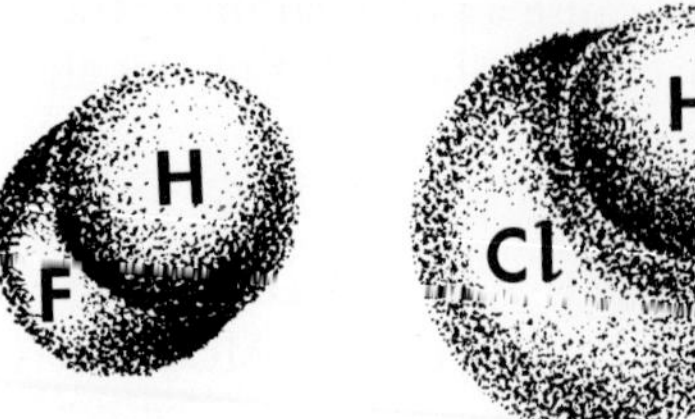

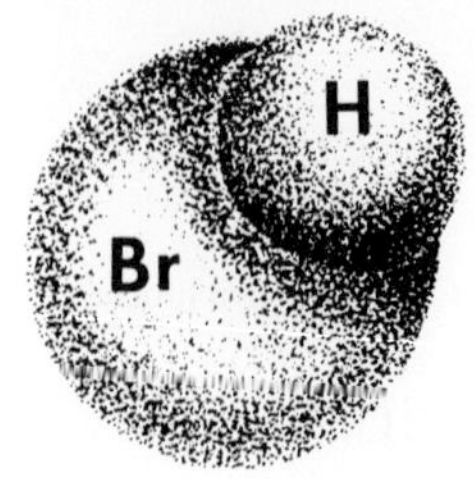

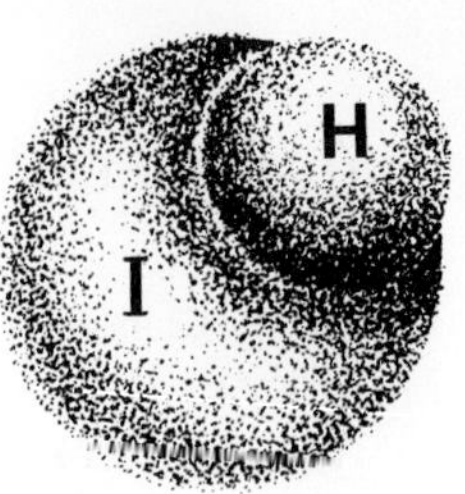

Fig. 26–12 *Hydrogen compounds of fluorine, chlorine, bromine, and iodine.*

consider all the hydrogen compounds of fluorine, chlorine, bromine, and iodine (Figure 26–12). The bonds between the hydrogen and the other elements are covalent. All the molecules are polar. Fluorine is the most electronegative since it has the smallest radius among the halogens. The *bond strength* depends not only on the relative displacement of the electron pair, but also on the bond distance between the centers of the two atoms that are covalently bonded together. For example, in the four molecules listed above, the bond strength is weaker in HI than in HF because the bond distance (as shown in Figure 26–12) in HI is more than twice that of HF.

The bond between carbon and chlorine is not a symmetrical one with respect to the distribution of electric charge. The affinity of chlorine for electrons with a structure 2–8–7 is greater than that of carbon with a structure 2–4; that is, chlorine is more electronegative than carbon. Hence the electron pairs will be attracted closer to the chlorine atoms, and the covalent bonds will have a polarity that is a small positive charge in the area occupied by carbon and a small negative charge at the chlorine atoms (Figure 26–11*a*). But when all four bonds are considered with five atoms lying on the same plane it will be seen that the bond polarities are in opposite directions and counterbalance each other (Figure 26–11*b*). The molecule as a whole is *nonpolar* or neutral. Such neutral molecules will have little attraction for each other; hence if the number of atoms is not large, that is, if the molecular weight is not high, the nonpolar covalent compound is usually a liquid or a gas. For example, consider the compounds of carbon shown in Table 26–2. It will be noted that carbon tetrabromide and tetraiodide are solids at ordinary temperature. With carbon tetrachloride (which is a liquid), if the temperature is lowered, ultimately the motion of the nonpolar molecules is sufficiently reduced so that molecular crystals are formed. A temperature of below −22.8° C. must be attained before it solidifies. In such a molecular crystal the forces between the individual molecules in the lattice are often weak; they are gravitational forces similar to those attracting any two neutral objects. As a consequence, an input of only a small amount of energy will separate the molecules and melt the crystal.

TABLE 26–2 PROPERTIES AND STRUCTURE OF SEVERAL SIMPLE COMPOUNDS OF CARBON

NAME	METHANE	CARBON DIOXIDE	CARBON TETRAFLUORIDE	CARBON TETRACHLORIDE	CARBON TETRABROMIDE	CARBON TETRAIODIDE
Formula	CH_4	CO_2	CF_4	CCl_4	CBr_4	CI_4
Normal state	Gas	Gas	Gas	Liquid	Solid	Solid
Molecular wt.	16	44	88	153.8	331.7	519.7
Melting pt.°C.	−184.	−56.5	−184	−22.8	48.4	171
Boiling pt.°C.	−161.5	−78.5	−128	76.8	189.5	dec.

The molecular liquids have high volatilities; that is, since there are weak attractive forces between molecules, they evaporate readily and, as a rule, have relatively low boiling points as compared to ionic compounds.

The hydrogen halides, HF, HCl, HBr, and HI, are all gases; when compressed and cooled, they become liquids which have a low electrical conductivity as would be expected of molecular liquids having some polarity. However, when the gaseous halides are dissolved in water, their solutions exhibit large conductivities, indicating that an appreciable number of molecules on dissolving in water have been pulled apart into ions. This is confirmed by adding to a sample of the aqueous solution of hydrogen chloride (called hydrochloric acid) a solution of silver nitrate when a precipitate of silver forms instantaneously:

$$H^+Cl^- + Ag^+NO_3^- \rightarrow \underset{\text{solid}}{Ag^+Cl^-} \downarrow + H^+NO_3^-$$

These and other facts indicate that polar molecules undergo ionization when they are dissolved into a solvent such as water which itself is composed of polar molecules. The structure of the water molecules has an important bearing in understanding solutions of solids in water and the reactions which take place in aqueous systems.

THE STRUCTURE OF WATER

As noted on page 404, the direction of the bonds in the water molecule are at an angle of 105°. Since the oxygen atom has a larger nuclear charge and a greater electron attraction, the bonding pairs are closer to oxygen than to hydrogen atoms; the two hydrogen atoms lie at a distance of 0.97 angstrom units from the oxygen atom at an angle of 105° as shown in Figure 26–13. The resulting structure is an asymmetrical molecule with the oxygen end negative and the end at which the two hydrogens are located positive.

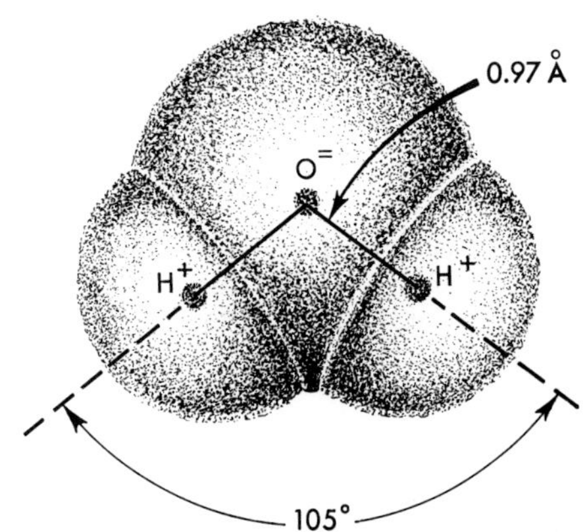

Fig. 26–13 *Schematic diagram showing structure of water.*

A number of consequences can be deduced from the structure of water molecules. For example, the dipolar molecules of water can attract each other by means of their oppositely charged ends. The two unshared pairs of electrons about the oxygen atom provide another point of association of the water molecules by means of hydrogen bridges or bonds, so that a water molecule is not H_2O but $(H_2O)_n$, where n at room temperature is a small number. Such a structure may be represented as

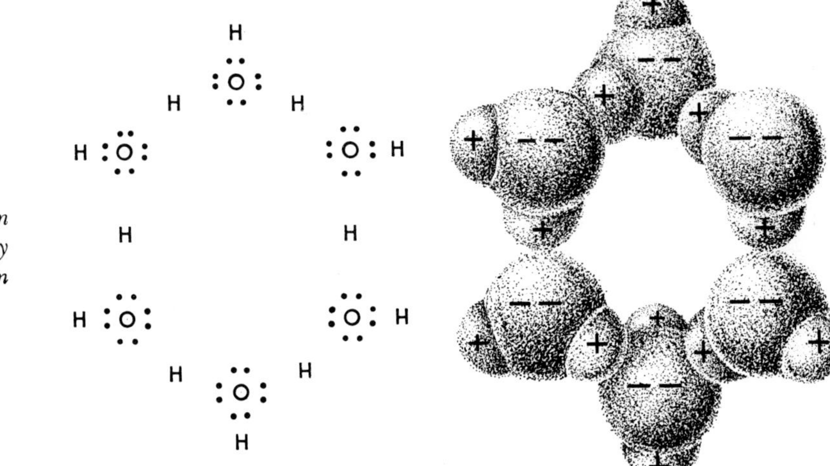
Fig. 26–14 *Association of water molecules by means of hydrogen bonds.*

TABLE 26–3 SOME PHYSICAL PROPERTIES OF THE HYDROGEN COMPOUNDS OF THE OXYGEN FAMILY OF ELEMENTS

NAME OF COMPOUND	FORMULA	MOLECULAR WEIGHT	STATE AT ROOM TEMP.	B.P. °C.	M.P. °C.
Water (hydrogen oxide)	H_2O	18	Liquid	100	0
Hydrogen sulfide	H_2S	34	Gas	−61.8	−82.9
Hydrogen selenide	H_2Se	81.2	Gas	−42	−64
Hydrogen telluride	H_2Te	129.5	Gas	−4	−51

shown in Figure 26–14. The abnormalities water exhibits in its physical properties as compared with other hydrogen compounds of the oxygen family or elements of Group VI A of the Periodic Table suggests that there is considerable association of water molecules in the liquid state. Table 26–3 lists a number of these properties. The table shows that water has the lowest molecular weight; hence it should also have the lowest boiling point since, in the other compounds, the boiling and melting points increase with the molecular weight. However, as we see from the table, water boils 104° C. above the hydrogen compound of tellurium, which has a molecular weight more than seven times that of water. This anomaly is explained on the basis of association of the water molecules by means of hydrogen bonds. The amount of heat required to pull the molecules apart and then impart to them enough kinetic energy to overcome the pressure of the atmosphere is considerable; hence water boils more than 160° C. higher than it would boil if it were not associated.

SOLUTIONS

A dispersion of one kind of molecule among other molecules is called a *solution.* The component present in larger amount is called the *solvent;* the smaller amount is the *solute.* Thus when a teaspoonful of sugar (about 5 grams) is stirred into a glass of water (about 150 milliliters) the solid particles disappear, and the resulting mixture is called a solution of sugar in water. In the same manner, when carbon dioxide or hydrogen chloride is bubbled in water and dissolved, the resulting mixture is a solution. However, the molecules of sugar in dispersing among the water molecules undergo no essential change. The same is true of all covalent compounds whose molecules are essentially nonpolar. Such solutions do not conduct current and generally react chemically with other substances at a slow rate.

A solution of hydrogen chloride in water is called hydrochloric acid. The so called "concentrated acid" contains about 36 per cent by weight of the compound dissolved in water, and it is one of the most common acids. It is an excellent conductor of electric current, and it reacts with active metals, giving off hydrogen. These properties are explained if we first consider the process of solution of hydrogen chloride molecules in water. These molecules are already polar and, as they are surrounded by dipolar water molecules, they become dissociated into hydrogen and chloride ions (Figure 26–15). The hydrogen ion is immediately associated with one or more water molecules, thus producing *hydronium ions* which are *characteristic* of all acid solutions. The chloride ion (chlorine atom carrying an extra electron) moves about the solution surrounded by water dipoles. Thus, a solution of hydrogen chloride seems to be composed of "hydrated" ions. The solutions of ionic compounds such as sodium chloride, potassium bromide, or calcium hydroxide consist of hydrated ions. In other words, the process of solution of solid ionic compounds involves essentially the surrounding of the solid crystals which consist of ions by water dipoles and the dispersion of the hydrated ions in solution. There is evidence to show that the positively and negatively charged hydrated ions move about the solution with velocities which are related to the mass of the ion and the degree of hydration.

The high conductivity of solutions of polar molecules, such as hydrogen chloride and hydrogen bromide, and of ionic compounds is readily explained by the attraction of the ions to the electrodes of opposite charge. As will be shown later, the ions on reaching the electrodes undergo chemical reactions. Therefore the conductance is evidence of the presence of ions. This also explains the rapid rate of reactions by solutions which contain ions as compared with solutions of substances which contain molecules. For any molecular substance to react chemically, there must be a displacement of the electrical charges within the molecule so as to produce charged particles or ions. As a result, solutions of sugar, glycerol, and others of the vast number of organic (carbon) compounds do not conduct current and react sluggishly. In order that they may react, the molecules have to be activated, that is, in some part of the molecules the electrons have to be disturbed by heat or other chemical reagents so as to produce even slight charges. This topic will be discussed in greater detail in the next chapter.

Fig. 26–15 *Hydrochloric acid is an aqueous solution of hydrogen chloride and contains hydronium ions, hydrated chloride ions, and water molecules.*

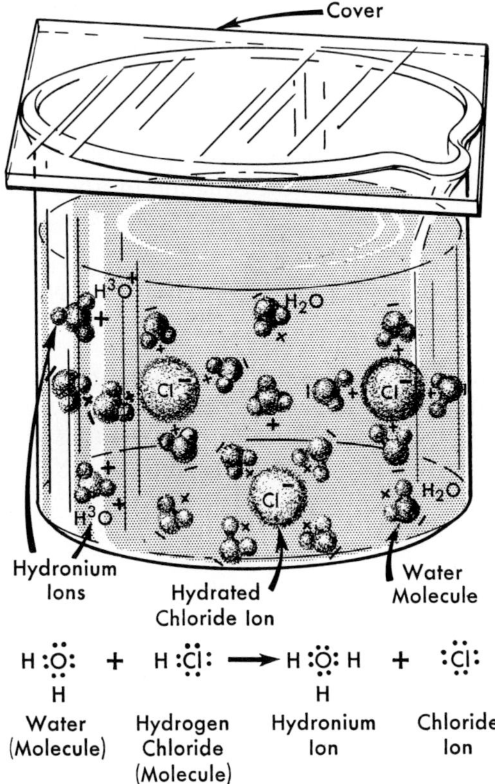

ACIDS AND BASES

The words *acid* and *base* are intimately connected with the behavior of elements and compounds and particularly the aqueous solutions of compounds. We speak of sodium, potassium, and calcium and most metals as *basic elements* and of sulfur, phosphorus, and most nonmetals as *acidic elements*. The reason is that when the metals combine with oxygen the resulting oxides dispersed in water solutions exhibit basic properties, while nonmetals give oxides which have acidic properties. Therefore it is necessary to consider the general aspects of acidic and basic properties.

In the modern definition, an *acid* is *a substance which donates a proton* and a *base* is *a substance which accepts a proton*. The solution of hydrogen chloride is accordingly represented thus:

HCl	+	H_2O	$\rightleftarrows$	H_3O^+	+	Cl^-
Hydrogen chloride molecule		Water molecule		Hydronium ion		Chloride ion
$Acid_1$		$Base_2$		$Acid_2$		$Base_1$

It will be noted that a chloride ion is considered as a base since it can accept a proton to form a molecule of hydrogen chloride. On the other hand, a hydronium ion is an acid since it can donate a proton to the chloride ion; also the water molecule, in accepting a proton, acts as a base. A solution of sodium hydroxide in water gives rise to sodium ions and hydroxide ions (hydrated).

$$NaOH \rightarrow Na^+ + OH^-$$

Sodium hydroxide ionic compound → Sodium ions + Hydroxyl ions

The hydroxyl ions are bases since they readily accept protons to form water molecules:

$$H^+ + OH^- \rightarrow HOH$$

(*Equation 26–1*)

$$H_3O^+ + OH^- \rightarrow HOH + HOH$$

Hydronium ions + Hydroxyl ions → Water molecules

$$\text{Acid}_1 + \text{Base}_2 \qquad \text{Acid}_2 + \text{Base}_1$$

(*Equation 26–2*)

The reactions represented by Equations 26–1 and 26–2 are essentially what occurs when an acidic solution, such as hydrochloric acid, reacts with a basic solution, such as sodium hydroxide. The process is called *neutralization* in the old terminology. This reaction will be discussed again in the next chapter. For the present, we have learned that the acid-base system is a *conjugate;* such a conjugate, when dissolved in water, gives rise to a new acid and a new base, which have different strengths. For example, the molecular acid HCl is a conjugate acid-base system, since when it dissolves in water it forms by reaction the *cation acid* H_3O^+, or hydronium ion, and the *anion base* Cl^-. Hydronium ions have strong acidic properties, while hydroxyl ions have strong basic properties. Hence solutions containing a large number of hydronium ions, H_3O^+, are strongly acidic, and those containing a large number of hydroxyl ions, OH^-, are strongly basic. Such solutions are commonly tested by the change in color of certain substances called *acid-base indicators.* Thus acidic solutions change the color of litmus paper to red and bases to blue. It is possible by using a series of indicators to determine approximately the relative degree of acidity or basity of a solution. Thus hydrochloric acid (HCl), sulfuric acid (H_2SO_4), and nitric acid (HNO_3) are strong acids; even dilute solutions will injure human tissues. On the other hand, acetic acid (CH_3COOH) is a weak acid, and as vinegar, a solution of about 5 per cent, is used in foods; boric acid (H_3BO_3) is feeble, and a solution of 5 to 8 per cent is used as an eyewash. Of the common bases, sodium hydroxide (NaOH), potassium hydroxide (KOH), calcium hydroxide ($Ca(OH)_2$), and trisodium phosphate (Na_3PO_4) are strong bases, while ammonia (NH_3) and sodium bicarbonate ($NaHCO_3$) are weak bases.

ATOMIC GROUPINGS OR RADICALS

Before concluding the discussion of atomic chemical bonds and their relation to the properties of the resulting combinations, the behavior of compounds containing ionic and covalent bonds and intermediate bonds should be explained.

When we write the equation for the solution of nitric acid in water, we represent it as follows:

$$HNO_3 + H_2O \rightarrow H_3O^+ + NO_3^-$$

Nitric acid + Water → Hydronium ion + Nitrate ion

Similarly we consider the solution of silver nitrate as consisting of silver (Ag^+) and nitrate (NO_3^-) ions. In representing the behavior of the nitrogen-oxygen (NO_3^-)

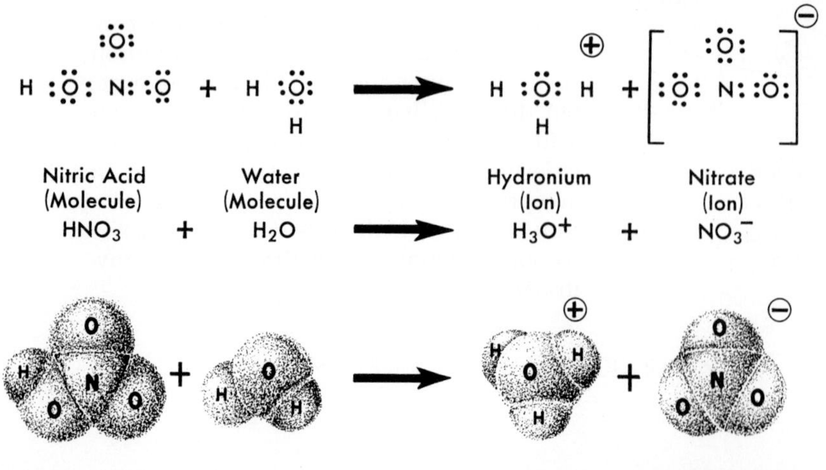

Fig. 26–16 *Structure of nitric acid and nitrate ion.*

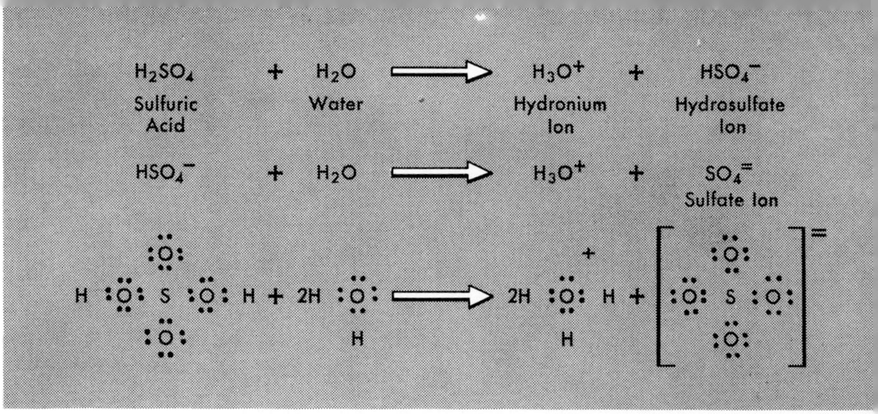

$$H_2SO_4 \ (\text{Sulfuric Acid}) + H_2O \ (\text{Water}) \longrightarrow H_3O^+ \ (\text{Hydronium Ion}) + HSO_4^- \ (\text{Hydrosulfate Ion})$$

$$HSO_4^- + H_2O \longrightarrow H_3O^+ + SO_4^{=} \ (\text{Sulfate Ion})$$

Fig. 26–17 *Structure of sulfuric acid and sulfate ion.*

combination in this manner it is implied that it is stable and remains unchanged in many reactions. The explanation of this behavior is to be found in the type of bonds by which the various atoms in a compound are united. For example, in silver nitrate ($Ag^+NO_3^-$) or nitric acid (HNO_3), the bond between oxygen and nitrogen is mostly covalent and is not readily disrupted. On the other hand, the silver atom tends to form an ionic bond, which water readily disrupts. Similarly hydrogen, with one electron in its outer shell, forms with elements of Groups V, VI, and VII bonds having considerable polarity; in water they undergo large or small dissociation. The electronic structure of nitric acid and the nitrate ion may be represented as shown in Figure 26–16. It should be noted that the nitrate grouping has an extra electron. As shown above, the NO_3^- grouping or radical within the brackets has 24 electrons instead of 23 which it would have if uncharged (5 from nitrogen and 6 from each of the 3 oxygen atoms). The extra electron from the hydrogen atom therefore gives the nitrate radical a single negative charge.

The same reasoning can be applied to showing that the sulfate $SO_4^{=}$ is stable. Both S and O are close together in the Periodic Table, that is, they have similar electronic structures (2–6 and 2–8–6). They unite by covalent bonds which are not easily disrupted, as shown in Figure 26–17. The sulfate radical has 32 electrons instead of 30 (4 oxygen atoms and 1 sulfur with 6 electrons each) and therefore it has 2 extra electrons represented by a double negative charge.

Atomic groupings which in solution and chemical reactions stick together are called *radicals*. However, it should be pointed out

TABLE 26–4 SOME COMMON RADICALS AND COMPOUNDS IN WHICH THEY EXIST

RADICAL NAME	FORMULA	EXAMPLE OF COMPOUND CONTAINING RADICAL	FORMULA
Acetate	$C_2H_3O_2^-$	Acetic acid	$HC_2H_3O_2$
Bicarbonate	HCO_3^-	Sodium bicarbonate (baking soda)	$NaHCO_3$
Borate	$B_2O_7^{4-}$	Sodium borate (borax)	$Na_4B_2O_7$
Carbonate	$CO_3^{=}$	Calcium carbonate (limestone)	$CaCO_3$
Chromate	$CrO_4^{=}$	Potassium chromate	K_2CrO_4
Dichromate	$Cr_2O_7^{=}$	Potassium dichromate	$K_2Cr_2O_7$
Nitrate	NO_3^-	Potassium nitrate (saltpeter)	KNO_3
Phosphate	$PO_4^{\equiv}$	Phosphoric acid	H_3PO_4
Sulfate	$SO_4^{=}$	Copper sulfate	$CuSO_4$
Sulfite	$SO_3^{=}$	Sodium sulfite	Na_2SO_3
Silicate	$SiO_3^{=}$	Sodium silicate (waterglass)	Na_2SiO_3
Thiosulfate	$S_2O_3^{=}$	Sodium thiosulfate (hypo)	$Na_2S_2O_3$

that the stability of these groupings or radicals (nitrate NO_3^-, sulfate $SO_4^=$, and the like) varies. They can be disrupted in reactions which involve migrations of electrons. Table 26–4 lists some common radicals and an example of a substance in which the radical is found.

SUMMARY

1. Inert gases are assumed to have stable configurations and hence do not react chemically. Any element which reacts tends to lose or share electrons so as to attain the electronic configuration of the inert gas closest to it.
2. Elements combine by means of their outer or valence electrons, which thus act as the force that holds the atoms together, the *chemical bond.*
3. Metals ordinarily have less than four electrons in the outer shell; they react by losing the *s* electrons to form positive ions and generally form ionic bonds. However, by means of their *p* electrons they can form covalent bonds.
4. Nonmetals usually have more than four electrons in the outer shell. The very active nonmetals such as the halogens and sulfur tend to gain electrons and form negative ions and ionic bonds. The other nonmetals tend to form covalent bonds.
5. Elements which have similar or closely related electronic structures usually combine by sharing electrons and form covalent bonds. These bonds involve shared pairs of electrons of opposite spins.
6. Compounds with ionic bonds are composed of ions; in the liquid state or in solution they are conductors of electric current and generally react rapidly. Covalent compounds do not conduct current and generally react slowly.
7. Compounds formed by covalent bonds have a molecular structure and are composed of either nonpolar (electrically symmetrical) molecules or polar molecules (electrically asymmetrical). Polar molecules result when the combining atoms have a noticeably different attraction for the electron pairs and form asymmetrical molecules.
8. Water is a highly polar molecule and tends to form hydrogen bonds readily. These factors account for many of its physical and chemical properties, such as its abnormally high boiling point and its solution and dissociation effects on ionic compounds.
9. Solutions are dispersions of one species of molecules among the molecules of another. The component in larger amount is the *solvent;* the other component is the *solute.*
10. *Acids* are substances which donate protons. *Bases* are substances which accept protons.
11. Stable atomic groupings or radicals are formed by means of covalent bonds. Many of the common acids such as HNO_3, H_2SO_4, and H_3PO_4 contain relatively stable radicals, which form ions.

STUDY EXERCISES

1. After each of the substances listed, write *I* if the bonds are ionic; *CN* if the bonds are covalent and the molecule nonpolar; *CP* if the bonds are covalent and the molecule polar; *M* if both ionic and covalent bonds are present.
   a. H_2 ....
   b. H_2O ....
   c. Br_2 ....
   d. LiCl ....
   e. $MgBr_2$ ....
   f. CCl_4 ....
   g. KNO_3 ....
   h. N_2 ....
   i. CH_4 ....
   j. KNO_3 ....
   k. $NaHCO_3$ .....
   l. Fe_2O_3 ....
   m. $Ca_3(PO_4)_2$ ....
   n. H_2S ....
   o. NH_3 ....
2. An element Q belongs to the II A group of the periodic system and is situated in an upper period. Write the formulas of the bromide, phosphate, carbonate, and nitrate. (Consult Table 26–4.)
3. An element Y has an atomic number 15 and atomic weight 31. Write its structure and give the formulas of its compound with oxygen, hydrogen, and chlorine. Indicate the type of bonds in each compound (consult the Periodic Table).
4. Underline the word or phrase in parentheses which makes each statement true.
   a. A covalent compound is one which is formed when electrons are (shared by two atoms, gained by two atoms, trans-

ferred from one atom to another, lost by two atoms).

b. An atom which has 6 electrons in its outer shell is likely to (lose, gain) (0, 1, 2, 3, 4) electrons and form (positive, negative) ions.

c. An atom which has 8 electrons in its outer shell is likely to (gain, lose, keep) (0, 1, 2, 3, 4) electrons and form (positive, negative, neutral, no) ions.

d. Two substances which easily lose electrons (are, are not) likely to combine.

e. Two substances which easily gain electrons (may, may not) combine. If they do combine, they probably form (ionic, nonionic) compounds by (sharing, transferring) electrons.

f. Two substances, one of which gains while the other loses electrons, form compounds by (sharing, transferring) electrons.

5. Underline the formula which results from the combination of the two elements whose valence electrons are given:

   a. X 2; Y 7; the compound will be (XY, X_2Y, XY_2).

   b. X 3; Y 6; the compound will be (XY, X_2Y_3, XY_2).

   c. X 1; Y 6; the compound will be (XY, X_2Y, XY_2).

   d. X 4; Y 7; the compound will be XY_4 X_2Y, XY_2).

6. The following is a list of ions of elements. Place after each ion the name of the inert gas whose electronic configuration it resembles.

a. Li+	*f.* K+ . . . .
b. Na+	*g.* Ca++ . . . .
c. F−	*h.* Br− . . . .
d. Mg++	*i.* Al+++ . . . .
e. Cl−	*j.* I− . . . .

7. Consider the compounds CH_4, CH_3Cl, CCl_4, and CO_2. Indicate the types of bonds in each and whether each of the molecules is polar or nonpolar. Give reasons for your statements.

8. After each of the following compounds, write *C* if it conducts electric current well either in the liquid state or when dissolved in water; *P* if it is a poor conductor; *N* if it is a nonconductor.

a. CH_3OH	*d.* HI . . . .
b. $C_6H_{12}O_6$	*e.* $SiCl_4$ liq . . . .
c. $CaBr_2$	*f.* CH_3COOH . . . . .

9. Indicate which of the following oxides will be acidic (*A*) and which basic (*B*).

a. K_2O	*d.* MgO . . . .
b. N_2O_5	*e.* CO_2 . . . .
c. P_2O_5	*f.* SiO_2 . . . .

10. Write the electronic structure of each of the following compounds: NaBr; NH_3; SiO_2; H_3PO_4; $BaCO_3$.

11. Summarize the important properties of water which can be explained by its molecular structure.

12. In the list below are given the electron structures of atoms of several elements. In the blank space after each exercise item place the letter which designates the electron structure of the element to which the item refers.

    A. 2–8–18–18–8–1
    B. 2–8–18–18–8–2
    C. 2–8–18–18–6
    D. 2–8–18–18–7
    E. 2–8–18–32–18–8

    a. This element is a halogen . . . .
    b. This element is an inert gas . . . .
    c. This element is an alkali metal . . . .
    d. This element is like sulufur . . . .
    e. This element forms no compounds . . . . .
    f. This element forms negative ions most easily . . . .
    g. This element forms positive ions most easily . . . .
    h. This element may form a compound with chlorine of the type MCl_2 . . . .
    i. The structure of this element resembles the structure of a halide ion . . . .

FOR FURTHER READING

1. MARKHAM, E. C., and S. E. SMITH, *General Chemistry*. Boston: Houghton Mifflin Company, 1954.

   Chapter 17 deals with atomic structure and chemical bonds.

2. PAULING, LINUS, *General Chemistry*. San Francisco: W. H. Freeman and Company, 1953.

   Chapters 9 and 10 deal with covalent and electrovalent bonds.

27

STUDY OF CHEMICAL REACTIONS

A NUMBER of chemical reactions have already been considered in connection with the development of chemical concepts. For example, the burning of magnesium and carbon in air was considered in Chapter 26, and shown to be reactions between the atoms of magnesium and oxygen, and carbon and oxygen. Similarly in the last chapter the reaction of silver and chloride ions to give the solid silver chloride was briefly discussed; also mentioned was the reaction of a strong acid and a strong base as involving essentially reactions between hydronium (H_3O^+) and hydroxyl (OH^-) ions. In the present chapter, having obtained a general foundation of atomic structures, we shall systematize and study the important types of chemical reactions in an attempt to discover how chemists predict and control the course of chemical reactions. In general most chemical reactions proceed *in the direction which will give the reacting system a greater stability than it possessed before the reaction.* Thus the rusting of an iron fence involves a complex reaction in which the atoms of metallic iron are slowly converted into a mixture of hydrated iron oxides ($Fe_2O_3 \cdot n\ H_2O$), because these oxides represent more stable configurations in nature than metallic iron.

CLASSIFICATION OF CHEMICAL REACTIONS

The classification of chemical reactions used in the present study is based on the total mechanism of the reaction: not only on what takes place, but how? By these criteria, most reactions fall into two categories, those in which ions or protons are transferred and those in which electrons are transferred. When sodium chloride reacts with silver nitrate, the equation of the reaction shows that it involves an exchange of ions. The reaction belongs, therefore, to one very large category of chemical reactions which may be grouped under the general term of *ionic* reactions, or reactions which *involve ion or proton transfer or exchange.* In some cases, the substances undergoing ionic reactions are already dissociated in ions, as in the reaction of sodium chloride and silver nitrate:

$$Na^+Cl^- + Ag^+NO_3^- \rightarrow Ag^+Cl^- \downarrow + Na^+ + NO_3^- \quad (\textit{Equation 27–1})$$

Sodium chloride · Silver nitrate · Silver chloride solid · Sodium nitrate ions in solution

In other cases, the ion or group exchange may take place between molecules which under the conditions of the reaction form ions. For example, methyl chloride reacts to water this way:

$$H_3C\overset{+\ -}{\rightarrow}Cl + H\rightarrow OH \rightarrow H_3C\overset{+\ -}{\rightarrow}OH + H^+Cl^- \quad (\textit{Equation 27–2})$$

Methyl chloride · Water · Methanol · Hydrogen chloride

The equation as written assumes that methyl chloride and water react by the formation of ions. However, this type of reaction involves at the very start a shift of the electron pair of the covalent bonds as shown by the arrows in the formulas for the molecules of methyl chloride and water. Therefore, though the net result appears to be exchange of ions, the mechanism also involves a shift of electron pairs in covalent bonds.

The second large category of chemical reactions includes those which *involve a shift or transfer of electrons.* For example, the burning of magnesium can be written as:

$$2\,Mg + O_2 \rightarrow 2\,MgO$$

Magnesium (atoms) · Oxygen (molecule) · Magnesium oxide (ionic compound)

(*Equation 27–3*)

However, on the basis of the electronic structure of the initial reactants and final product, it is better explained in the steps:

$$2\,Mg\!: \rightarrow 2\,Mg^{++} + 4\,e^-$$

Magnesium atoms · Magnesium ions · Electrons

$$:\ddot{O}:\ddot{O}: \xrightarrow{\text{dissociates}} 2\,:\ddot{O}$$

Oxygen molecule · Oxygen atoms

$$2\,:\ddot{O} + 4\,e^- \rightarrow 2[:\ddot{O}:]^=$$

Oxide ions

$$2\,Mg^{++} + 2\,:\ddot{O}: \rightarrow 2\,Mg^{++}\,:\ddot{O}:^= \text{ or } 2\,MgO$$

Magnesium oxide (ionic compound)

(*Equation 27–4*)

It will be noted that in Equation 27–4 the net result of the reaction is loss of electrons by the magnesium atoms and gain of electrons by the oxygen atoms. Generally, those atoms or groups which lose electrons are called *reductants,* those which gain electrons are called *oxidants,* and the over-all change is known as a *redox reaction.*

DIRECTION OF CHEMICAL REACTIONS

Before considering in detail the various subdivisions of the two large classifications of chemical reactions, it may be well to consider the direction in which chemical reactions take place.

In considering the direction of chemical reactions it should be noted that those which occur in nature without the intervention of man take place usually unnoticed and at measurable rates. The growth of plants and animals, the reactions which occur on a grand scale on the face of the earth, the weathering of rocks, the precipitations in small and large bodies of water, and even the rusting of metals, take place rather quietly as compared with the burning of coal and oil to produce energy, or the reduction of metallic ores in furnaces to produce metals, or the burning of magnesium in air and the burning of aluminum in chlorine to demonstrate to students the types of chemical reactions. There are many exceptions to this general observation. Lightning, for example, in passing through the mixture of nitrogen and oxygen which is air, causes these elements to combine by dissociating the relatively stable molecules to atoms:

$$O_2 + N_2 + \text{heat} \rightarrow 2\,NO$$

Oxygen · Nitrogen · Nitric oxide

Further observations show that the most active elements which are commonly employed to illustrate chemical reactions in lectures and laboratories are not found free in nature. For example, *sodium, magnesium, aluminum,* and *chlorine* are never found free but in *a combined state.* Even iron, which is used in construction because it is relatively inactive, ultimately acquires the configuration of ferrous and ferric ions and is found in nature as deposits of iron oxides. Therefore the general trend in all chemical reactions is to *give rise to products of the most stable configurations.* For example, chlorine is never found free in nature, but as chloride ions in sea water. To produce free chlorine, an electron must be removed from each chloride ion. This is shown by the following steps.

$$n:\ddot{\underset{\cdot\cdot}{\mathrm{Cl}}}: + \underset{n\,e^-}{\overset{\text{agent to}}{\text{remove}}} \rightarrow \tfrac{1}{2}n:\ddot{\underset{\cdot\cdot}{\mathrm{Cl}}}:\ddot{\underset{\cdot\cdot}{\mathrm{Cl}}}: \quad \text{or} \quad Cl_2$$

Chlorine molecules

Chlorine gas reacts with gain of $n\,e^-$ forming (arrow back to $n:\mathrm{Cl}:$)

(*Equation 27–5*)

Brine containing chloride ions is treated with an agent to remove one electron from each chloride ion to produce chlorine atoms, which combine to form molecules of chlorine gas, which is then compressed to liquid chlorine and stored in cylinders. Most of the 1,500,000 tons of chlorine produced annually in the United States is used for its oxidant property, that is, the tendency of chlorine molecules to combine with other molecules by gaining electrons and revert to its most stable configuration, namely, the chloride ion. Therefore, we do work first to remove electrons from chloride ions and obtain a system of high potential energy (elementary chlorine). Then when we wish to disinfect water or bleach paper pulp or produce an insecticide, we add free chlorine which combines with, for example, the impurities and releases part or all of the stored potential chemical energy of the sytem to obtain ultimately the most stable configuration of chlorine, the chloride ion.

TABLE 27–1 ELECTRONIC STRUCTURE OF ALKALI AND HALOGEN FAMILIES OF ELEMENTS

I A–ALKALI METALS		VII A–HALOGENS	
SYMBOL	ELECTRONIC CONFIGURATION	SYMBOL	ELECTRONIC CONFIGURATION
Li	2–1	F	2–7
Na	2–8–1	Cl	2–8–7
K	2–8–8–1	Br	2–8–18–7
Rb	2–8–18–1	I	2–8–18–18–7
Cs	2–8–18–18–8–1	At	2–8–18–32–18–7

RELATIVE ACTIVITY OF ATOMS

The principle of the general trend of chemical reactions described in the preceding section does not give detailed information which can be used in the study of the reactions of individual substances. The problem of trying to develop generalizations about chemical reactions can be visualized if we realize that we are trying to discover how 92 different types of atoms react with each other and how the several thousands of compounds resulting from combinations of these atoms react in turn. In spite of the complexity of the problem, there are a number of principles that are employed in predicting the course of chemical reactions. Many of these are complex and beyond the scope of the present study, but a few of the simpler ones can be used as examples. One such principle is the relative activities of the atoms; that is, similar groups of elements can be arranged in such a manner as to indicate the relative order of chemical reactivity.

By *activity* we mean the ease with which atoms react chemically. For example, Table 27–1 lists the alkali metals and the halogen family of nonmetals, that is, Groups I A and VII A of the periodic system. The facts about their activities, of course, are first obtained by observations and experiments,

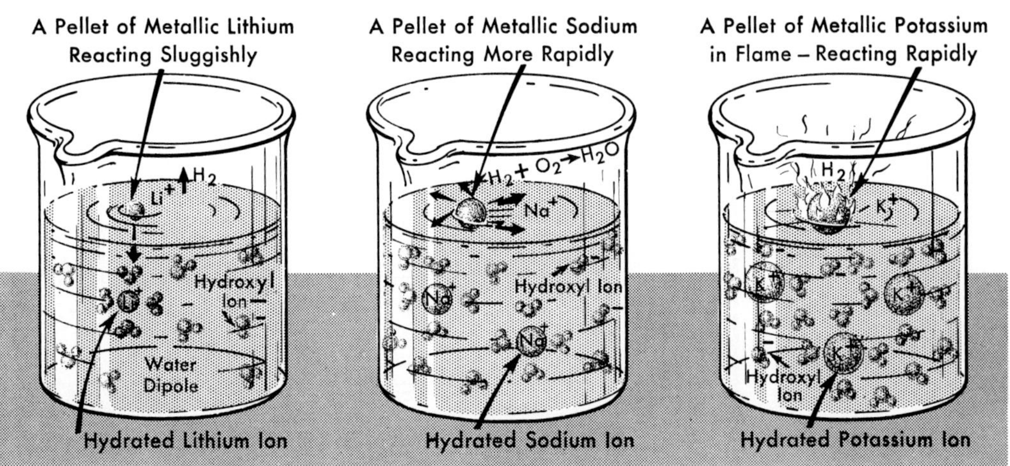

Fig. 27–1 *Three beakers showing reaction of pellets of lithium, sodium, and potassium with water.*

and these are correlated with their electronic structure. For example, the activity of lithium, sodium, and potassium can be tested by dropping small pellets of the metals (the size of grape seeds) in water which contains the acid-base indicator phenolphthalein. As the metallic pellet hits the water it begins to react. The metallic atoms lose electrons which are accepted by hydronium ions from water to yield hydrogen gas and hydroxyl ions. (See Figure 27–1.)

$$2\,Li\cdot \rightarrow 2\,Li^+ + 2\,e^-$$

$$2H_2O + 2\,H_2O \rightarrow 2\,H_3O^+ + 2\,OH^-$$

$$2\,H_3O^+ + 2\,e^- \rightarrow 2\,H\cdot + 2\,H_2O$$

$$2\,H\cdot \rightarrow H{:}H \text{ or } H_2\uparrow$$

$$\overline{2\,Li + 2\,H_2O \rightarrow 2\,LiOH + H_2}$$

(*Equation 27–6*)

Since the hydroxyl ions are basic, the phenolphthalein indicator turns red. The lithium pellet reacts sluggishly; the sodium pellet reacts more rapidly; the potassium pellet reacts so rapidly that the hydrogen evolved, mixing with the oxygen of the air surrounding the pellet, ignites instantly and the whole metallic mass burns. On the basis of these experiments and the electronic configuration of the atoms in Group I A of the periodic system, one can predict that rubidium will react more vigorously than potassium, and cesium still more vigorously than rubidium, because as shown in Equation 27–6 reactivity means loss of electrons by the metallic atoms. As the atomic radius increases, the force by which the valence electron is held by the nucleus is decreased; hence the potassium atom with an electron configuration of 2–8–8–1 will lose its electrons more readily than the lithium atom of configuration 2–1. Also, the inner electrons act to some extent as a screen; hence, the more inner electrons, the more weakly the outer electrons are held. Generally, therefore, in the active metals (Groups I A, II A, and III A) the activity increases with the atomic radius. Equation 27–6 shows that the over-all reaction is a *redox* one, since lithium atoms lose electrons (act as reductants) and hydronium ions from water gain electrons (act as oxidants); second, the last part of the equation shows the reason for referring to such reactions in the older nomenclature as *displacement reactions.* The lithium displaces part of the hydrogen in the water molecules, and this is evolved as a gas, leaving lithium hydroxide.

Table 27–1 also shows that the reverse of the above trend should be among the halogens. In these atoms reactivity means ability

TABLE 27–2

REPLACEMENT SERIES OF SOME IMPORTANT ELEMENTS

ELECTRON DONORS	Oxidation → ELECTRONS ARE LOST ← Reduction ELECTRONS ARE GAINED	ELECTRON ACCEPTORS
Cs·	⇄	$Cs^{+} + e^{-}$
K·	⇄	$K^{+} + e^{-}$
Ba.	⇄	$Ba^{++} + 2\,e^{-}$
Ca:	⇄	$Ca^{++} + 2\,e^{-}$
Na·	⇄	$Na^{+} + e^{-}$
Mg:	⇄	$Mg^{++} + 2\,e^{-}$
Al⁝	⇄	$Al^{+++} + 3\,e^{-}$
Zn:	⇄	$Zn^{++} + 2\,e^{-}$
Fe:	⇄	$Fe^{++} + 2\,e^{-}$
Sn:	⇄	$Sn^{++} + 2\,e^{-}$
Pb:	⇄	$Pb^{++} + 2\,e^{-}$
H:H	⇄	$2\,H^{+} + 2\,e^{-}$
Cu:	⇄	$Cu^{++} + 2\,e^{-}$
$2\,I^{-}$	⇄	$I_2 + 2\,e^{-}$
Hg:	⇄	$Hg^{++} + 2\,e^{-}$
Ag·	⇄	$Ag^{+} + e^{-}$
$2\,Br^{-}$	⇄	$Br_2 + 2\,e^{-}$
$2\,Cl^{-}$	⇄	$Cl_2 + 2\,e^{-}$
Au·	⇄	$Au^{+} + e^{-}$
$2\,F^{-}$	⇄	$F_2 + 2\,e^{-}$

to gain electrons; those with the smallest radius, therefore, are the most active. Thus fluorine with a configuration of 2–7 is more active than chlorine with a configuration of 2–8–7. Hence the table shows that the most active metal is cesium and the most active nonmetal is fluorine.

The activity of atoms to gain or lose electrons is measured by more precise methods than the qualitative procedure described in the case of the alkali metals. Table 27–2 gives a partial list of the activities of some of the more common atoms. The metals above hydrogen are those which are able to donate electrons to hydronium ions (that is, liberate hydrogen gas from acids); those which are not sufficiently active are below hydrogen. Thus, the strongest electron donors (reductants) are at the top of the column on the right and the strongest electron acceptors (oxidants) at the bottom. The table is so arranged that a reductant will give electrons to any oxidant below it, and an oxidant will take electrons from any reductant above it. Thus zinc will give electrons to a copper ion, that is, displace copper from solutions of its salts:

$$Zn\!: + Cu^{++} \rightarrow Zn^{++} + Cu\!:$$

while copper will not react with solutions of zinc salts:

$$Cu\!: + Zn^{++} \rightarrow \text{no reaction}$$

Table 27–2 shows that the sodium atom loses only one electron to form an ion with a charge of 1+ and aluminum three elec-

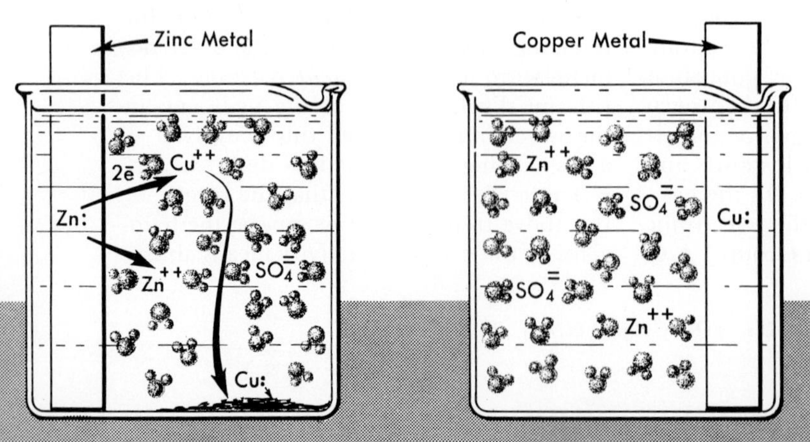

Fig. 27–2 *Zinc metal displaces copper from its salts (reduces cupric ions to the metallic state). Copper will not react with solutions of zinc salts.*

trons to form an ion with a 3+ charge. Similarly, chlorine gains one electron to form an ion with 1− charge. This relative positive or negative charge that atoms acquire when they combine is called the *oxidation number* of the element. As will be shown in Chapter 30 (Table 30–3), many atoms exhibit a variable valence and hence more than one oxidation state. For example, iron may acquire an oxidation state of 2+ as in ferrous oxide FeO, and a 3+ as in ferric oxide Fe_2O_3; there are also a few compounds such as barium ferrate, $BaFeO_4$, in which the iron atom takes part in the formation of the negative ion (that is, it acts as a nonmetal) and exhibits the oxidation state of 6+. However, the 2+ and 3+ oxidation states are the most common.

CHARACTERISTICS OF CHEMICAL REACTIONS

The speeds at which chemical reactions occur vary widely. Some are fast and others slow. The reactions which liberate large amounts of energy are very rapid and usually take place with the intervention of man. For example, the combustion of active metals, the burning of fuels, or the reaction of ions such as hydronium and hydroxyl or silver and chloride takes place very rapidly. On the other hand, the rusting of metals under atmospheric conditions or the weathering of rocks is a very slow process. Most reactions in the living cells of plants or animals, if they are attempted in the laboratory at the same temperatures as employed by living organisms, are found to take place at extremely slow rates, or not at all.

Another characteristic of chemical reactions, besides their speeds, is *reversibility* or *irreversibility*. For example, the burning of magnesium is called an irreversible reaction:

$$\underset{\text{Magnesium}}{2\,Mg} + \underset{\text{Oxygen}}{O_2} \rightarrow \underset{\text{Magnesium oxide}}{2\,MgO} + \text{heat}$$

(*Equation 27–7*)

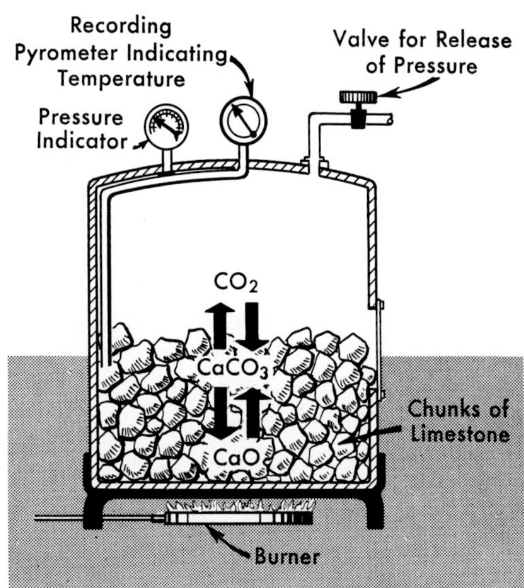

Fig. 27–3 *Decomposition of calcium carbonate in a closed vessel. The reaction attains equilibrium at 910° C.*

That is, once it has been initiated the reaction will proceed to completion. Similarly, we can consider the burning of limestone as an irreversible reaction:

$$\underset{\text{Calcium carbonate}}{CaCO_3} \xrightarrow[910°\,C.]{+\text{heat}} \underset{\text{Calcium oxide}}{CaO} + \underset{\text{Carbon dioxide}}{CO_2\uparrow}$$

(*Equation 27–8*)

However, suppose we do not let the gaseous carbon dioxide escape. If, for example, we heat calcium carbonate in a closed vessel at 910° C., the reaction will stop before all the calcium carbonate has been changed to lime. Hence we conclude that the reverse reaction is taking place, that carbon dioxide is combining with calcium oxide to form calcium carbonate:

$$CaO + CO_2 \rightarrow CaCO_3$$ (*Equation 27–9*)

Equation 27–9 is simply the reverse of Equation 27–8; they can be written as one equation by using the double arrow to denote the reversibility:

$$CaCO_3 \underset{910°}{\overset{910°}{\rightleftarrows}} CaO + CO_2$$

(*Equation 27–10*)

The reaction attains equilibrium at 910°C. Thus the decomposition of calcium carbonate in a closed vessel becomes a *reversible reaction,* that is, a reaction in which the products react among themselves to reform the original substances. It is to be expected that in such reversible reactions there will not be a completion either in the forward or in the reverse direction, but eventually the forward velocity will equal the reverse velocity. Such a state is known as *dynamic equilibrium.*

CHEMICAL EQUILIBRIUM

A very large number of reactions initiated under what we may call ordinary conditions exhibit reversibility. In order to obtain a general expression for the state of chemical equilibrium, we will designate the reacting substances as A and B and the products as C and D. The forward reaction is written as:

$$A + B \xrightarrow{S_1} C + D \quad (\textit{Equation 27–11})$$

The rate or speed at which A and B react is designated by the symbol S_1. As the reaction proceeds and the number of molecules of A and B decreases, since they react, the speed S_1 must diminish. At the same time, however, C and D are formed and begin to react with each other to form A and B:

$$C + D \xrightarrow{S_2} A + B \quad (\textit{Equation 27–12})$$

The rate S_2 is initially small since only a few molecules C and D are present, but increases steadily as the reaction of A and B proceeds. As S_1 diminishes steadily, and S_2 increases, ultimately the *two opposing rates* become equal. In other words a state of dynamic equilibrium has been reached:

$$A + B \underset{S_2}{\overset{S_1}{\rightleftarrows}} C + D \quad (\textit{Equation 27–13})$$

When the condition of equilibrium has been reached, the quantities of A, B, C, and D remain unchanged. However, the reactions of Equations 27–11 and 27–12 have not ceased; they just proceed at equal rates.

EQUILIBRIUM YIELD

When we reflect on this state of dynamic equilibrium there are several questions which we should like to ask: (*a*) How fast (or at what rate) is this state of equilibrium reached? What factors affect the rate? What can we do to accelerate it or retard it? (*b*) Is equilibrium reached when 50 per cent of A and B have reacted? In other words, if we start with one mole (one molecular weight expressed in grams) each of A and B, what will be the yield of C and D when equilibrium is reached? If the yield is 0.99 moles of C and D, we can say the reaction has gone to completion. Yet, on the other hand, equilibrium may be reached when only 0.05 moles of C and D have been formed, and in such cases we may feel justified to say that the reaction does not take place.

The answers to these questions are not easy. The *rate at which equilibrium is reached and the yield at equilibrium* are very different, though they are related. Assume, for example, that we start with one mole each of A and B and that S_1 at a temperature T_1 is 1000 times faster than S_2. By the time equilibrium is attained, A and B will have almost disappeared; that is, the equilibrium point will be at the extreme right in Equation 27–13, and the rightward reaction for all practical purposes is said to "have gone to completion." On the other hand, let it be assumed that S_2 at the same temperature T_1 is 1000 times faster than S_1. Then when A and B are mixed and any C and D are formed they will react very rapidly to form A and B. Hence equilibrium will be reached when only small amounts of C and D are present, the yield at equilibrium will be at the extreme left, and for all practical purposes the reaction of A and B to form C and D is considered "not to take place." However, both the speeds of S_1 and S_2 and the equilibrium yield are affected by temperature and other conditions which will now be considered.

Nature of Reactants. When two substances are mixed will they react, and if so at what speed? This question has many facets and cannot be answered by any series of direct statements. The first qualified statement is that the fact of reaction or nonreaction depends on the nature (atomic or molecular structure) of the substances. In the case of elements, active metals react rapidly with active nonmetals by forming ions; two elements, such as oxygen and nitrogen, which have similar electronic structures can combine only by sharing electrons, and under ordinary conditions the speed of reaction is negligible. In the case of compounds, the ionic compounds as a rule act at faster rates than the molecular covalent. In the covalent compounds those with polar structures react faster than those with nonpolar. The latter require *considerable activation* in order to produce some asymmetry or polarity in the molecule. In general, something must be done to activate molecular compounds to accelerate their slow rates of reaction.

Effect of Temperature. Another factor that profoundly influences the rate of reactions is temperature; the fact that heat promotes the speed of reactions is too well known to need detailed discussion here. Generally a rise of 10° C. approximately doubles the speed of most chemical reactions. Conversely, lowering the temperature will decrease the rate. A fire, for example, can be extinguished by lowering the temperature of the mixture undergoing combustion.

Effect of Catalysts. The rates of a large number of reactions are increased or decreased by the presence of small amounts of other substances, called *catalysts,* which apparently remain unchanged in the process. A striking example of catalytic effect is the generation of oxygen from hydrogen peroxide (3 per cent) used as an antiseptic and as a bleaching agent. The compound has low stability and readily decomposes into water and oxygen:

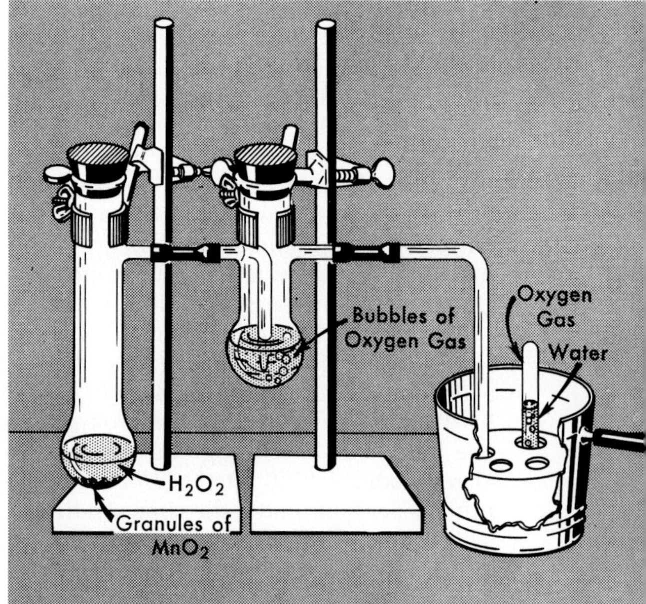

Fig. 27–4 *Laboratory apparatus for generating oxygen from hydrogen peroxide.*

$$\underset{\text{Hydrogen peroxide}}{2\,H_2O_2} \rightleftarrows \underset{\text{Water}}{2\,H_2O} + \underset{\text{Oxygen}}{O_2} + 47{,}800 \text{ cal}$$

(*Equation 27–14*)

The equation shows that there are two rates, one to the right for decomposition, and the other to the left for formation or prevention of decomposition. Both rates may be catalyzed, that is, accelerated by the presence of other substances. For example, the rate of decomposition can be accelerated by manganese dioxide. The apparatus shown in Figure 27–4 consists of an 8-inch test tube containing 10 milliliters of 3 per cent hydrogen peroxide. About 0.5 gram of powdered manganese dioxide is added and the rubber stopper is placed on the mouth of the tube, thus connecting it to the assembly for the collection of gases. Oxygen is evolved without heating and collected by water displacement.

Living tissues contain a catalyst which behaves exactly like manganese dioxide. This can be demonstrated by gargling with a solution of hydrogen peroxide. The foam produced is caused by the generation of oxygen. The antiseptic properties of hydrogen peroxide when used as a gargle or when placed on wounded tissues are due to the formation of atomic oxygen (which is the active germicidal agent) by the effect of *catalase,* a catalyst elaborated by living tissues and called an *enzyme.* The multitude of chemical reactions involved in digestion, synthesis, and production of energy in living organisms is brought about by means of enzymes. Enzymes are prodigiously efficient in promoting chemical reactions. One milligram (0.001 gram) of manganese dioxide added to the hydrogen peroxide at 0° C. will hardly produce 10 milliliters of oxygen in one hour, but one milligram of pure catalase produces 2740 liters (2,740,000 milliliters) per hour under the same conditions.

The rate of decomposition may be retarded as well as accelerated; small amounts of acids or organic compounds (for example, a compound like acetanilide) can retard the rate to the right. Such catalysts are called *inhibitors.* Inhibitors are used, for example, in the manufacture of rubber tires. The rubber of automobile tires becomes warm in operation due to friction, and under these conditions rubber reacts with oxygen, tends to become less elastic, and eventually hardens and cracks. The addition of small amounts of certain catalysts inhibits or slows the speed of this reaction between rubber and oxygen; such additive antioxidants have increased the life of tires by five to ten thousand miles.

The mechanism of catalysts is intriguing; it seems strange that the presence of a minute amount, sometimes a mere trace, of a catalyst has such a striking effect on the rate of reaction. For example, it was repeatedly pointed out that a mixture of hydrogen and oxygen does not react at room temperature. However, if the mixture is allowed to pass through a small tube containing asbestos on which a minute amount of finely divided palladium or platinum has been deposited, the gases react rapidly. The activation of hydrogen molecules by a palladium catalyst is shown diagrammatically in Figure 27–5. The effect of the catalyst is shown to consist in the following: (*a*) As hydrogen is passed over finely divided platinum or palladium the gas is *adsorbed* on the surface of the catalyst. (*b*) The molecules adsorbed on the metallic crystal lattice become "strained"; their bonds undergo distension with the formation of hydrogen atoms which react rapidly. Thus, one way by which catalysts act is to adsorb molecules at the surface and activate them by straining or breaking the bonds, thus forming reactive atoms or ions.

Another way by which a catalyst acts is to unite with one of the reactants and form an *unstable intermediate* compound. Assume that A and B react very slowly and catalyst X is added. Now catalyst X can react with B to form an unstable compound BX which then reacts rapidly with A:

$$A + B \xrightarrow{\text{slow}} C + D$$

$$X + B \xrightarrow{\text{fast}} BX$$

$$A + BX \xrightarrow{\text{fast}} C + D + X$$

(*Equation 27–15*)

Thus X is regenerated and reacts again with B to form BX. In this manner a small amount of catalyst X suffices to accelerate the speed of reaction between A and B and remains apparently unchanged in the process.

Effect of Subdivision. Another factor which affects the rate of reactions is the state of dispersion of the reactants. If the reacting substances are in the solid state, the reaction proceeds slowly. To accelerate the speed of the reaction, solids may be changed to the liquid or gaseous state by heating. In solids the motion of molecules or ions is mainly vibration within the boundaries of the crystal; hence, molecular or ionic collisions are not frequent. In the liquid, and particularly in the gaseous state, the motion of molecules is in all directions; as a result there are frequent collisions. More often, however, solids are dissolved in a medium which will produce molecular or ionic dispersions. In general, the finer the subdivision, the greater the speed; molecular or ionic subdivision is attained in the liquid and gaseous states or in solutions.

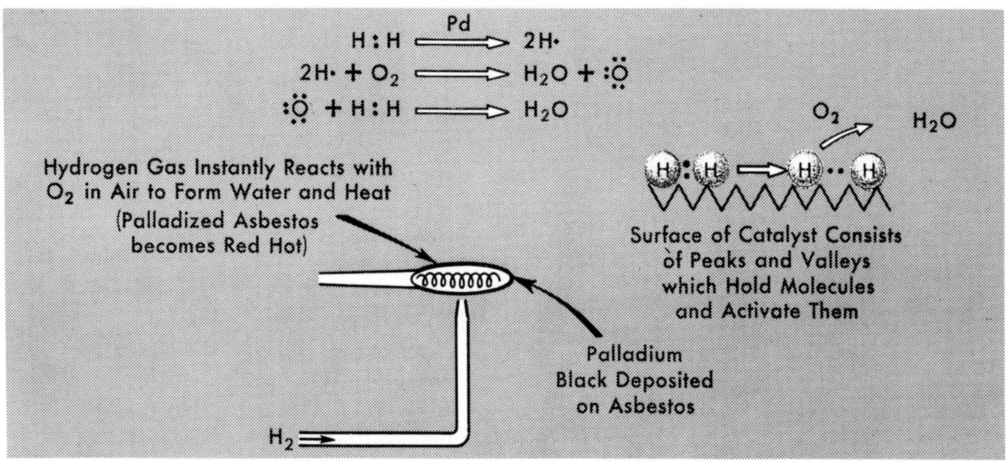
H : H —Pd→ 2H·
2H· + O₂ → H₂O + :Ö
:Ö + H : H → H₂O
O₂
H₂O
Hydrogen Gas Instantly Reacts with
O₂ in Air to Form Water and Heat
(Palladized Asbestos
becomes Red Hot)
Surface of Catalyst Consists
of Peaks and Valleys
which Hold Molecules
and Activate Them
Palladium
Black Deposited
on Asbestos
H₂

Fig. 27–5 *Activation of molecular hydrogen by adsorption on the surface of palladium or platinum black (finely divided particles of the metal).*

Subdivision does not have any effect on the equilibrium point of a reversible reaction.

Effect of Molecular Concentration and Methods of Increasing the Equilibrium Yield. The molecular concentration of a substance in a reaction mixture is defined as the weight of the substance *expressed in moles per unit volume.* If the number of reacting molecules within a given volume is increased, it follows that the number of collisions per second and hence the speed of the reaction will be increased. For example, to return again to the generalized reversible reaction of Equation 27–13, it is possible after the reaction of one mole of A and B has been going for five minutes to add another mole of A to the reacting mixture. The chances of B's colliding with A will then increase; hence, the speed S_1 will increase. Similarly if, instead of adding one mole of A, we add one mole of C, the leftward velocity S_2 is increased.

Increase in the concentration of one of the components of a reaction mixture affects not only the rate of the reaction but also the equilibrium yield. For example, consider the reaction of one mole of ethanol with one mole of acetic acid:

When the reaction is allowed to proceed until equilibrium is reached, it is found by analysis for unreacted acetic acid that 0.335 moles of unreacted acid remain in the mixture; hence 0.665 moles of ethyl acetate (C) and water (D) have been formed. Now suppose we add 0.5 moles of ethanol to the equilibrium mixture. It is obvious that since we increase the concentration of A (Equation 27–16) more of B will react with it and more of C and D will be formed. It is possible to calculate the increase by methods which need not enter this discussion. The increase is found to be roughly 12 per cent. In other words, the equilibrium yield of ethyl acetate will rise from 0.665 moles to about 0.78 moles. Thus increase in the molecular concentration of ethyl alcohol (A) or acetic acid (B) will increase the equilibrium yield of the products (C and D), that is, ethyl acetate and water.

Another way to increase the equilibrium yield is to remove one of the products, C or D, in Equation 27–13. Let us assume, for example, that a dehydrating agent is added to the equilibrium mixture in Equation 27–16. This will remove the water produced in

$$\underset{\substack{\text{Ethanol}\\ \text{A}}}{CH_3CH_2OH} + \underset{\substack{\text{Acetic acid}\\ \text{B}}}{HOCOCH_3} \rightleftharpoons \underset{\substack{\text{Ethyl acetate}\\ \text{C}}}{CH_3CH_2OCOCH_3} + \underset{\substack{\text{Water}\\ \text{D}}}{H_2O}$$

(*Equation 27–16*)

the reaction and cause more of the ethanol and acid to react (*A* and *B*) to form more ethyl acetate (*C*) and water (*D*). By calculation it is found that this increases the yield of ethyl acetate to 0.82 moles or roughly 16 per cent. Therefore by removing the water continuously it is possible to obtain almost complete reaction in a system that gave an equilibrium yield of about 66 per cent and left 33 per cent of unreacted substances.

Returning to the consideration of the equilibrium shown by Equation 27–16, conditions may be chosen under which the equilibrium can be reached within a few hours instead of months if the reaction is allowed to take place at room temperature. For example, the mixture may be heated to 50–60° C. and a small amount of sulfuric acid added. The sulfuric acid acts as a catalyst to accelerate the rate of reaction and also removes some of the water formed by combining with it to form a hydrate. Thus both the rate and the equilibrium yield of the reversible reaction may be increased by a judicious use of concentration, temperature, and catalysts.

REACTIONS INVOLVING TRANSFER OF IONS

After the preceding discussion of the general nature of chemical reactions it is now possible to return to the detailed discussion of the two main classes of chemical reactions. Those which involve transfer of ions will be considered first. This class in turn will be subdivided for the purpose of discussion into two parts: (*a*) acid-base reactions, and (*b*) ionic reactions in which there is a separation of a phase, that is, evolution of a gas or formation of a precipitate.

ACID–BASE REACTIONS

According to the conjugate acid-base system, sulfuric acid dissolving in water loses two protons in steps:

$$\underset{\text{Sulfuric acid}}{H_2SO_4} + H_2O \rightleftarrows \underset{\text{Hydronium ion}}{H_3O^+} + \underset{\text{Hydrosulfate ion}}{HSO_4^-}$$

(*Equation 27–17*)

$$\underset{\text{Acid}_1}{HSO_4^-} + \underset{\text{Base}_2}{H_2O} \rightleftarrows \underset{\text{Acid}_2}{H_3O^+} + \underset{\text{Base}_1\ (\text{sulfate ion})}{SO_4^=}$$

(*Equation 27–18*)

The length of the arrows indicates the equilibrium point; that is, sulfuric acid dissolved in water becomes hydronium ions and hydrosulfate and sulfate ions. The hydrosulfate is a weak anion base since the reverse reaction (acceptance of protons) does not occur readily.

Another type of a base is ammonia, NH_3, which when dissolved in water accepts protons from water to form the ammonium ion:

$$\underset{\text{Acid}_1}{H_2O} + \underset{\text{Base}_2}{NH_3} \rightleftarrows \underset{\text{Acid}_2}{NH_4^+} + \underset{\text{Base}_1}{OH^-}$$

(*Equation 27–19*)

In this reaction water acted as an acid, but in Equations 27–17 and 27–18 it acted as a base. Water is called, therefore, an *amphoteric substance* or simply an *ampholyte*. That is, water molecules can take protons from each other:

$$\underset{A_1}{\mathrm{H\!:\!\ddot{\underset{..}{O}}\!:\atop H}} + \underset{B_2}{\mathrm{H\!:\!\ddot{\underset{..}{O}}\!:\atop H}} \rightleftarrows \underset{A_1}{\left[\mathrm{H\!:\!\ddot{\underset{..}{O}}\!:\!H\atop H}\right]^+} + \underset{B_2}{\mathrm{:\ddot{\underset{..}{O}}\!:\!H^-}}$$

or

$$H_2O + H_2O \rightleftarrows \underset{\text{Hydronium ion}}{H_3O^+} + \underset{\text{Hydroxyl ion}}{OH^-}$$

(*Equation 27–20*)

The extent to which the rightward reaction takes place at 25° C. is extremely small; in other words, pure water at 25° C. exists almost entirely as molecules and only about one out of 550,000,000 ionizes as indicated in Equation 27–20. The amounts of hydronium and hydroxyl ions, though very small, are equal, and this gives a definition of a neutral solution: one in which the

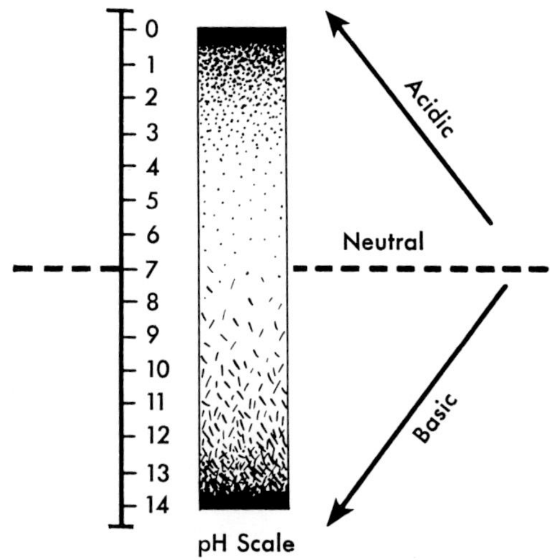

Fig. 27–6 *Schematic representation of pH scale, expressing relative acidity and basicity.*

H_3O^+ and OH^- ions are equal in *number*. This number is measured as 1×10^{-7} moles per liter, and for convenience it is expressed on an arbitrary scale by the symbol pH 7.0. Just as we have a thermometric scale in which water at 98.6° F. (37° C.) means body temperature, 120° F. means warm water, 140° F. means hot, and 190° F. scalding hot, so we can express relative acidity or basicity on a pH scale. In this scale pH 7.0 is the neutral point; pH 6.0 means an increase of 10 times in the concentration of hydronium ions H_3O^+ and pH 5.0 an increase of 100 times. A pH of 1 is a million times and pH 0 is 10 million times greater in acidity or concentration of hydronium ions than pH 7.0. Similarly pH 8 is a tenthfold decrease in the H_3O^+ concentration or a tenthfold increase of the OH^- ion. Therefore an aqueous solution of pH 14 is 10 million times more basic than water. To show the application of this concept, let us consider three common acids, hydrochloric, acetic, and boric. Suppose we take three beakers, each containing 100 milliliters of water and dissolve in each the amounts of acid indicated under each beaker in Figure 27–7 so as to obtain a solution of each acid.

Hydrochloric acid reacts with water completely, and acetic acid and boric acid to a very slight extent because of their structure. In the acetic acid structure, as shown in the electronic formula of the acid, only one of the four hydrogen atoms is attached to an oxygen and can to a small degree ionize to react with water.

Fig. 27–7 *Difference in strengths of acids.*

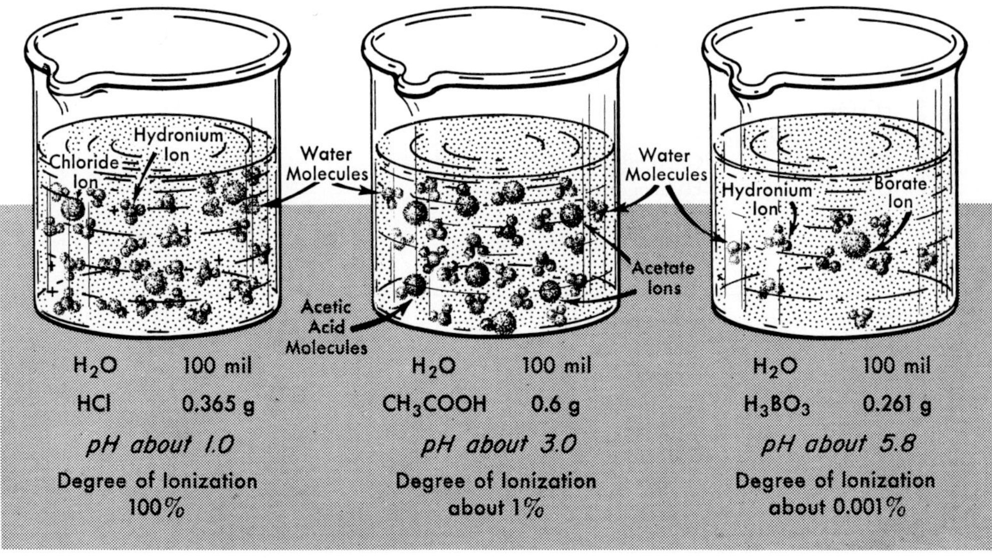

$$\begin{array}{ccc} \begin{array}{c} \mathrm{H}\ \ \ \ddot{\mathrm{O}}: \\ \mathrm{H}:\underset{\cdot\cdot}{\overset{\cdot\cdot}{\mathrm{C}}}:\overset{\cdot\cdot}{\mathrm{C}}:\underset{\cdot\cdot}{\overset{\cdot\cdot}{\mathrm{O}}}:\mathrm{H} \\ \mathrm{H} \end{array} & \rightleftharpoons & \left[\begin{array}{c} \mathrm{H}\ \ \ \ddot{\mathrm{O}}: \\ \mathrm{H}:\underset{\cdot\cdot}{\overset{\cdot\cdot}{\mathrm{C}}}:\overset{\cdot\cdot}{\mathrm{C}}:\underset{\cdot\cdot}{\overset{\cdot\cdot}{\mathrm{O}}}: \\ \mathrm{H} \end{array} \right]^{-} + \mathrm{H_3O^+} \\ \text{Acetic acid} & & \text{Acetate ion} \qquad \text{Hydronium ion} \end{array}$$

(*Equation 27–21*)

Moreover, two or more acetic acid molecules may combine with each other or associate, thus inhibiting ionization. In general most acids and bases are weak. Of the total number of acid-base systems known only a few are strong. The strength of the bases is expressed in the same manner. A dilute solution of sodium hydroxide, NaOH, or potassium hydroxide, KOH, has a pH of about 13, that is, 100 per cent ionized; on the other hand, ammonia has a pH of about 10 and is 1 per cent ionized.

Table 27–3 lists a number of acids and bases and their approximate strengths. It will be noted that the common mineral acids, HCl, H_2SO_4, and HNO_3, are strong acids while their conjugate bases, that is, the ions Cl^-, HSO_4^-, and NO_3^-, are *feeble*

TABLE 27–3 LIST OF COMMON ACIDS AND BASES AND APPROXIMATE STRENGTH OF THEIR DILUTE SOLUTIONS

	ACIDS (FORMULA)	NAME	pH RANGE OF DILUTE SOLUTIONS	BASES	
STRONG	HCl	Hydrochloric	0	Cl^-	FEEBLE
	HBr	Hydrobromic		Br^-	
	HI	Hydriodic		I^-	
	HNO_3	Nitric	1	NO_3^-	
	H_2SO_4	Sulfuric		HSO_4^-	
	$HClO_4$	Perchloric		ClO_4^-	
	H_3O^+	Hydronium ion		H_2O	
INTERMEDIATE	H_2SO_3	Sulfurous	2	HSO_3^-	WEAK
	HSO_4^-	Hydrosulfate		$SO_4^=$	
	H_3PO_4	Phosphoric		$H_2PO_4^-$	
	HF	Hydrofluoric		F^-	
	HNO_2	Nitrous		NO_2^-	
	$H(CH_3COO)$	Acetic	3	CH_3COO^-	
	H_2CO_3	Carbonic		HCO_3^-	
	H_2S	Hydrogen sulfide		HS^-	
	HSO_3^-	Hydrogen sulfite ion		$SO_3^=$	
	$H_2PO_4^-$	Dihydrogen phosphate ion		$HPO_4^=$	
	H_3BO_3	Boric	7	$H_2BO_3^-$	
WEAK	NH_4^+	Ammonium ion		NH_3	INTERMEDIATE
	H_2SiO_3	Silicic	10	$HSiO_3^-$	
	HCO_3^-	Bicarbonate ion		$CO_3^=$	
FEEBLE	$HSiO_3^-$	Hydrogen silicate ion	12	$SiO_3^=$	STRONG
	$HPO_4^=$	Hydrogen phosphate ion		$PO_4^=$	
	HS^-	Hydrosulfide ion		$S^=$	
	H_2O		14	OH^-	
				[NaOH, KOH, $Ca(OH)_2$, $Ba(OH)_2$]	

bases because their tendency to accept protons is negligible. On the other hand, the hydroxides of the alkali and alkaline earth metals such as NaOH, KOH, $Ca(OH)_2$, and $Ba(OH)_2$ which are extensively ionized in solution are *strong bases* since their solutions contains the OH^- ion which is a strong proton acceptor.

The relative acidity and alkalinity or the pH of a system has a profound effect on the rates of most chemical reactions. For example, most metals corrode more rapidly in acid pH than in alkaline. The enzymes of the stomach are most active at pH about 3.0 and those of the small intestine at about 8.0; the pH of the blood is maintained at 7.2. The pH of distilled water, although it should be 7.0, is actually 5.8 because carbon dioxide from the air dissolves in the water to give it a slight acidity. When distilled water is boiled, the CO_2 is expelled and the pH rises near 7.0. On the other hand, tap water is about 8.0 because in its passage through rocks and soils rain water has acquired small amounts of basic ions.

Reaction of Strong Acids and Bases. We can study the reaction of an acid with a base by adding an indicator to the acid (phenolphthalein, for example) and then adding the base slowly until a pink color is obtained which indicates that the neutralization or proton transfer from acid to base is complete. The chemical reaction can be written as in Equation 27–22 below, which shows that the driving force in the reaction is the quantitative transfer of protons from a strong acid (A_1) to a strong base (B_2) to form a stable feeble acid (A_2) and a stable feeble base of (B_1). The equilibrium point, as indicated by the length of the arrow, is to the extreme right since A_2 and B_1 in reacting will furnish equal amounts of H_3O^+ and OH^- ions. Thus, in the reaction of a strong acid with a strong base approximate neutrality is reached. The reaction is called *protolysis* in the modern nomenclature and *neutralization* in the older.

Reaction of Weak Acids and Bases. If instead of hydrochloric acid in the reaction shown in Equation 27–22 acetic acid is used, the approximate point of neutrality pH 7 to 8 will not be reached. After the exact amount of sodium hydroxide has been added, the pH is close to 9. The reaction is written as in Equation 27–23 below. It will be noted that the neutralization is not as complete as in Equation 27–22. The product of this neutralization is the anion base acetate ion CH_3COO^- which has some basic strength of its own (Table 27–3). This can be shown by dissolving a solution of sodium acetate $CH_3COO^- Na^+$ in water. The acetate ion reacts appreciably to form molecular acetic acid and hydroxyl ions (Equation 27–24 below). Hence a solution

$$\underset{\substack{\text{Hydronium}\\ \text{ion}\\ A_1}}{H_3O^+} + \underset{\substack{\text{Hydroxyl}\\ \text{ion}\\ B_2}}{OH^-} \rightleftarrows \underset{\substack{\text{Water}\\ A_2}}{H_2O} + \underset{\substack{\text{Water}\\ B_1}}{H_2O} + 13{,}700 \text{ cal}$$

(*Equation 27–22*)

$$\underset{\substack{\text{Acetic acid}\\ \text{(weak)}\\ A_1}}{CH_3COOH} + \underset{\substack{\text{Sodium}\\ \text{hydroxide}\\ \text{(strong)}\\ B_2}}{(Na^+)OH^-} \rightleftarrows \underset{\substack{\text{Sodium acetate}\\ \text{(weak)}\\ B_1}}{CH_3COO^-(Na^+)} + \underset{\substack{\text{Water}\\ \text{(feeble)}\\ A_2}}{H_2O}$$

(*Equation 27–23*)

$$\underset{\substack{\text{Acetate ion}\\ B_2}}{CH_3COO^-} + \underset{\substack{\text{Water}\\ A_1}}{H_2O} \rightleftarrows \underset{\substack{\text{Molecular}\\ \text{acetic acid}\\ A_2}}{CH_3COOH} + \underset{\substack{\text{Hydroxyl}\\ \text{ion}\\ B_1}}{OH^-}$$

(*Equation 27–24*)

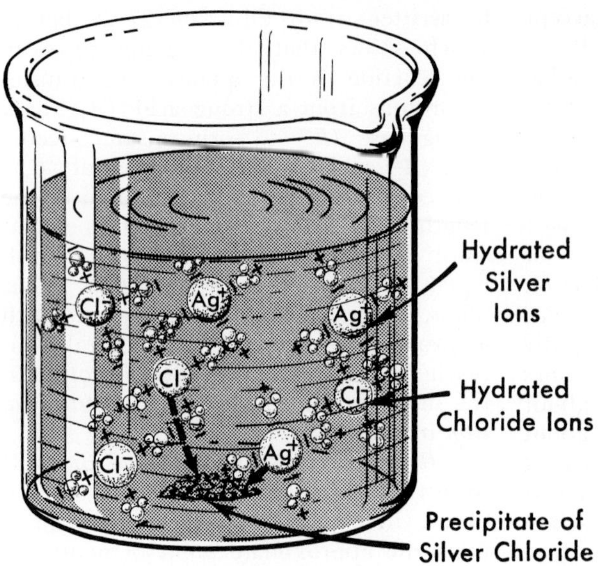

Fig. 27–8 *Precipitation of silver chloride when silver and chloride ions meet in solution. The hydrated ions, attracted momentarily to a small dust particle or a sharp edge of the beaker or vessel, leave the solution state and form unit cubical cells of silver chloride; these repeat to form crystals, and many crystals unite to form agglomerates which settle out as a precipitate.*

of sodium acetate in water is slightly basic, about pH 8.8.

By similar reasoning it can be shown that a solution of a weak base such as ammonium hydroxide added to an equivalent amount of a strong acid such as hydrochloric will yield a slightly acidic solution that is about pH 5.0.

$$\underset{B_2}{NH_4^+OH^-} + \underset{A_1}{H^+Cl^-} \rightleftarrows \underset{A_2}{NH_4^+Cl^-} + \underset{B_1}{H_2O}$$

(*Equation 27–25*)

The ammonium ion, NH_4^+, has a significant strength of its own to shift the equilibrium somewhat. If pure ammonium chloride is dissolved in water, the solution is distinctly acidic:

$$\underset{\substack{A_1 \\ \text{weak}}}{NH_4^+(Cl^-)} + \underset{\substack{B_2 \\ \text{feeble}}}{H_2O} \rightleftarrows \underset{\substack{B_1 \\ \text{weak}}}{NH_3} + \underset{\substack{A_2 \\ \text{strong}}}{H_3O^+} + (Cl^-)$$

(*Equation 27–26*)

In short, acids and bases react completely if the products are feeble acids and bases, but otherwise incompletely. The salts of strong acids and bases in water solutions give feeble bases and acids and hence are neutral. The salts of weak acids and strong bases yield in solutions bases of intermediate strength and hence are *basic* while the salts of weak bases and strong acids yield acids of intermediate strength and hence are *acidic.*

IONIC REACTIONS INVOLVING A SEPARATION OF A PHASE

The precipitation reactions have already been discussed in Chapter 26. The following experiment further explains the formation of precipitate. Each of five beakers contains 10 milliliters of water and 10 milligrams of silver ion (Ag) or 1 mg/ml. To the first beaker is added 1 ml of solution containing 5 mg of chloride ion; to the second, 1 ml of solution containing 5 mg of bromide ion; to the third, 1 ml of solution containing 5 mg of iodide ion; to the fourth, 1 ml of solution containing 5 mg of sulfate ion; to the fifth beaker only water is added to serve as a control in comparing the various beakers. A separation of a solid phase from the solution, or precipitate, takes place in the beakers in which chloride (Figure 27–8), bromide, and iodide are added, but no separation of solid takes place when sulfate or water is added to silver ion. The reactions are represented by the following equations:

$$Ag^+ + Cl^- \rightleftharpoons Ag^+Cl^- \text{ solid} \downarrow$$

(*Equation 27–27*)

$$Ag^+ + Br^- \rightleftharpoons Ag^+Br^- \text{ solid} \downarrow$$

(*Equation 27–28*)

$$Ag^+ + I^- \rightleftharpoons Ag^+I^- \text{ solid} \downarrow$$

(*Equation 27–29*)

$$2\ Ag^+ + SO_4^= \rightleftharpoons Ag_2^{++}SO_4^=$$

(*Equation 27–30*)

Equation 27–30 represents a reversible reaction (the arrows are given as equal lengths). The concentrations of the silver and sulfate do not exceed the solubility of silver sulfate. However, in Equations 27–27 to 27–29 the length of arrows indicates that the equilibrium is shifted to the right and that a solid phase separated out. In other words, the concentration of silver and chloride ions (in Equation 27–27) exceeds the solubility of silver chloride, and the driving force for the separation of the solid is the relatively low solubility of silver chloride. Hence, when silver and chloride ions meet, precipitation of silver chloride will take place until the concentration of the two ions is equal to that permitted by the solubility of silver chloride at that temperature. *Generally, when the ions of a sparingly soluble substance meet, precipitation will tend to take place if the concentration of these ions exceeds the value permitted by the solubility of the substance.*

Another type of reaction in which a separation of phase occurs (gaseous) is the addition of an acid such as hydrochloric and a saturated solution of sodium bicarbonate:

$$\underset{\text{Sodium bicarbonate}}{NaHCO_3} + (H_2O) \rightleftharpoons Na^+ + \underset{\text{Bicarbonate ion}}{HCO_3^-}$$

(*Equation 27–31*)

$$HCl + H_2O \rightleftharpoons H_3O^+ + Cl^-$$

(*Equation 27–32*)

The hydronium ions and bicarbonate ions react to produce the weakly ionized carbonic acid, which in turn may decompose to carbon dioxide and water:

$$\underset{\text{Hydronium ion}}{H_3O^+} + \underset{\text{Bicarbonate ion}}{HCO_3^-} \rightleftharpoons \underset{\text{Carbonic acid}}{H_2CO_3} + H_2O$$

(*Equation 27–33*)

$$\underset{\text{Carbonic acid}}{H_2CO_3} \rightleftharpoons \underset{\text{Carbon dioxide}}{CO_2 \uparrow} + H_2O$$

(*Equation 27–34*)

With the addition of the first drop of acid the equilibrium shown in Equation 27–33 will not be shifted to the right. As the addition of acid continues, however, due to the increased concentration of H_3O^+ the equilibrium is shifted considerably to the right; this disturbs the equilibrium shown in Equation 27–34. Eventually the solubility of CO_2 at that temperature is exceeded and the gas escapes from the solution. Generally, the addition of a strong acid to solutions of carbonates or bicarbonates evolves carbon dioxide.

REACTIONS INVOLVING TRANSFER OF ELECTRONS

The chemical reactions in which there is a transfer or displacement of electrons will be subdivided for the purpose of this discussion into the following four groups: (*a*) combination of elements leading to synthesis of compounds; (*b*) reductions of ions to elements; (*c*) reactions between molecules involving displacement of electrons; (*d*) electrolytic reactions, involving transfer of electrons between ions. The object is not to enumerate all types of chemical reactions but to discuss the general types and relate them to the principles for predicting the course of a reaction and controlling it.

COMBINATION OF ELEMENTS

We are already familiar with several examples of the reaction between atoms leading to the formation of ionic bonds. The reactions between sodium and chlorine, magnesium and oxygen, are examples. These reactions, once they are started, evolve a large amount of heat, and hence the reaction proceeds to completion. For example, calcium metal, when heated in oxygen or air, forms calcium oxide:

$$2\,Ca{:} + {:}\ddot{O}{:}\ddot{O}{:} \rightarrow 2\,Ca^{++}[{:}\ddot{O}{:}]^{=} + 303{,}600 \text{ cal}$$

Calcium metal (atoms); Oxygen gas (molecules); Calcium oxide (ions)

The equations represent the union of two molecules of hydrogen with one molecule of oxygen to form two molecules of water. A mixture of oxygen and hydrogen in the volume ratio of 2:1 can be mixed at room temperature without any noticeable reac-

This reaction, once started by heating the metal for a short time, proceeds with vigor until all the calcium has reacted because, as shown in the equation, a tremendous amount of heat is liberated. As previously noted, the metallic atom is the reductant; it loses electrons, becoming a positive ion. The oxygen atom is the oxidant; it accepts electrons, becoming a negative oxide ion. The over-all change may be called a *redox reaction* (*ox*idation-*red*uction). The driving force of the reaction is the trend of the calcium atoms to change the electronic configuration from 2–8–8–2 to 2–8–8 (argon configuration) and of the oxygen atoms to change from 2–6 to 2–8 (neon configuration). The large amount of energy evolved is related to these electronic changes and the interaction of the ions to form the ionic bonds.

This type of combination can be generalized for all the reactions of typical metals and nonmetals:

$$Zn{:} + {:}\ddot{S} \rightarrow Zn^{++}[{:}\ddot{S}{:}]^{=}$$

Zinc metal (reductant); Sulfur nonmetal (oxidant); Zinc sulfide (positive) (negative) (ions)

It should be pointed out, however, that this type of combination of elements may also involve the formation of covalent bonds instead of ionic. The burning of hydrogen and carbon in air are examples of displacement of electrons to form covalent bonds:

$$2\,H_2 + O_2 \rightarrow 2\,H_2O + 136{,}000 \text{ cal}$$

$$2\,H{:}H + {:}\ddot{O}{:}\ddot{O}{:} \rightarrow 2\,H{:}\ddot{O}{:}H$$

Hydrogen (reductant); Oxygen (oxidant); Water or Hydrogen oxide (polar molecules)

tion taking place. The mixture will remain inert until it is heated or ignited by means of a flame or a spark; then combination takes place with explosive violence. The explosion occurs because the large amount of heat indicated in the equation above is liberated at once. The heated gases expand with explosive violence. The flame or spark which initiates the reaction activates a few molecules which break into atoms. The atoms ejected from molecules bombard other molecules, dissociating them and accelerating the reaction. As the molecules of hydrogen and oxygen disrupt, the resulting atoms combine. In such combination there is *interpenetration* between two hydrogen atoms and one oxygen atom with the formation of two covalent bonds; the electron pairing to form the two covalent bonds was discussed on page 403. Since oxygen is more electronegative, the two electron pairs migrate closer to oxygen in the formation of the water molecules. Hence, oxygen is considered the oxidant and hydrogen the reductant.

The combination of carbon and oxygen to form carbon dioxide is involved in the burning of coal, gasoline, and other commercial fuels:

$$C + O_2 \rightarrow CO_2 + 96{,}500 \text{ cal}$$

$$\cdot\dot{C}\cdot + {:}\ddot{O}{:}\ddot{O}{:} \rightarrow {:}\ddot{O}{::}C{::}\ddot{O}{:}$$

Carbon (reductant); Oxygen (oxidant); Carbon dioxide (polar molecule)

The combustion of carbon to form carbon dioxide is also a redox reaction in which carbon is considered as the reductant. Though the electrons in carbon dioxide are shared between oxygen and carbon, the oxygen is regarded as negative with respect to the carbon. The carbon-to-oxygen bonds have polar characteristics indicating that there has been a shift of the four electrons of carbon closer to oxygen; hence, carbon is considered as the reductant. However, despite the polar characteristics of the four bonds, the molecule of carbon dioxide as a whole is neutral or nonpolar because, as shown in Figure 27–9, the bond polarities counterbalance each other since they are in opposite directions.

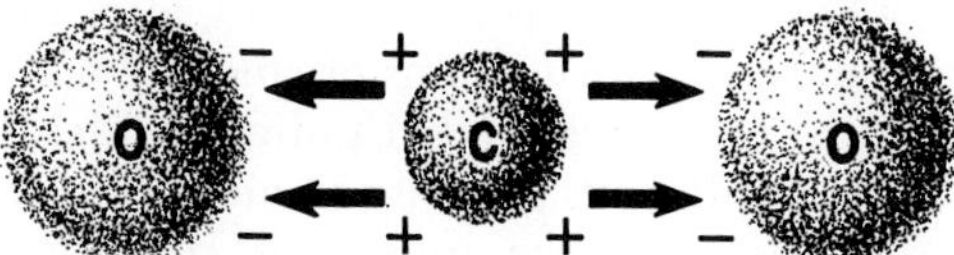

Fig. 27–9 *Diagram of CO_2 molecule showing bond polarities.*

REDUCTION OF IONS

When a silver ion, Ag^+, is furnished an electron it becomes a metallic atom:

Ag^+	+	e^-	$\rightarrow$	$Ag\cdot$
Silver ion		electron		Silver atom

The gaining of electrons is called *reduction of the ion*. As shown in Table 27–2, the silver and copper ions will gain electrons more readily than sodium and potassium ions. We could write, for example:

$$Na^+ + e^- \leftrightarrows Na\cdot$$
$$K^+ + e^- \leftrightarrows K\cdot$$
$$Cu^{++} + 2\,e^- \rightleftarrows Cu:$$
$$Ag^+ + e^- \rightleftarrows Ag\cdot$$

The length of the arrows indicates the normal direction of the equilibrium. The driving force of such reactions is the amount of energy involved. In the case of sodium and potassium the activity of the metallic atoms is high and a large amount of energy is evolved in losing electrons to become ions; hence the ion is the more stable form. For copper and silver it is the reverse. The trend to lose electrons is low, the metals do not corrode readily and the ions revert to a metallic state (gain electrons) readily.

The reduction of metallic ions to metals is the basis of all metallurgical processes for the large-scale production of the metals indispensable in modern technology. (See Chapter 30.) The oxides of metals which are found as deposits in the crust of the earth are heated in furnaces with a reducing agent which furnishes the electrons. For example iron ore is converted to iron by heating with carbon monoxide.

$2\,C$	+	O_2	$\rightarrow$	$2\,CO$		
Coke		Oxygen		Carbon monoxide		
$3\,CO$	+	Fe_2O_3	$\rightarrow$	$2\,Fe$	+	$3\,CO_2$
Carbon monoxide (reductant)		Iron oxide		Iron		Carbon dioxide

The reduction of iron oxide may be also accomplished by heating with a metal which is more active (see Table 27–2) than iron, for example, magnesium or aluminum:

$Fe_2^{3+}O_3^{=}$	+	$2\,Al\vdots$	$\rightarrow$	$Al_2^{3+}O_3^{=}$	+	$2\,Fe$
Iron oxide (oxidant)		Aluminum (reductant)		Aluminum oxide		Iron

Another example of reduction of ions to elements is the so-called replacement reaction when an acid attacks a relatively active metal. For example, hydrochloric acid will not attack copper or silver (see Table 27–2), but will attack aluminum, zinc, or iron, giving off hydrogen:

$2\,HCl$	+	$Zn:$	$\rightarrow$	$Zn^{++}Cl_2^-$	+	$H_2\uparrow$
Hydrochloric acid		Zinc atoms		Zinc ion		Hydrogen molecules

The term *replacement* originated out of the apparent replacement of hydrogen in HCl by Zn. However, the reaction involves transfer of electrons from the zinc atoms to the hydrogen ions. The steps may be pictured thus:

$$2\,HCl + 2\,H_2O \rightarrow 2\,H_3O^+ + 2\,Cl^-$$
$$Zn: \rightarrow Zn^{++} + 2\,e^-$$
$$2\,H_3O^+ + 2\,e^- \rightarrow 2\,H\cdot + 2\,H_2O$$
$$2\,H\cdot \rightarrow H:H \text{ or } H_2\uparrow$$

Zn	+	$2\,HCl$	$\rightarrow$	Zn^{++}	+	$2\,Cl^-$	+	$H_2\uparrow$
Active metal atoms (reductant)		Hydronium ions of acid (oxidant)		Zinc ions		Chloride ions		Hydrogen molecules (gas)

REACTIONS BETWEEN MOLECULES

The third group of reactions which involve migration of electrons comprises the collision of molecules resulting in changes of bonds and as a consequence a small or large degree of electron pair shift. In order that any molecular substance may react, that is, enter into a chemical reaction, there must be a displacement of the electrical charges within the molecules so as to produce *polarization,* that is, a *charge on some parts of the molecule.* Nonpolar molecules are relatively inert until they become activated or polarized. For example, methane, CH_4, is composed of nonpolar molecules. When mixed with chlorine in the dark, no appreciable reaction takes place over a period of months. If, however, the mixture is illuminated by diffused light, a reaction takes place whereby atoms of hydrogen are detached and combine with chlorine to form hydrogen chloride, while chlorine atoms take the place formerly occupied by the hydrogen atoms:

$$\underset{\text{Methane}}{CH_4} + \underset{\text{Chlorine}}{Cl_2} \rightarrow \underset{\text{Methyl chloride}}{CH_3Cl} + \underset{\text{Hydrogen chloride}}{HCl}$$

The illumination produces activation of a few chlorine molecules which become dissociated into atoms:

$$\underset{\text{molecule}}{:\overset{..}{\underset{..}{Cl}}:\overset{..}{\underset{..}{Cl}}:} \xrightarrow{\text{energy}} 2\ \underset{\text{atoms}}{:\overset{..}{\underset{..}{Cl}}\cdot}$$

The atoms having an incomplete outer shell of seven electrons are very active, and as they collide with methane molecules they form hydrogen chloride and a neutral structure, the methyl radical:

$$\underset{\text{Methane molecule}}{H:\overset{H}{\overset{..}{\underset{\underset{H}{..}}{C}}}:H} + \underset{\text{Chlorine atom}}{:\overset{..}{\underset{..}{Cl}}\cdot} \rightarrow \underset{\text{Methyl radical}}{H:\overset{H}{\overset{..}{\underset{\underset{H}{..}}{C}}}\cdot} + \underset{\text{Hydrogen chloride}}{H:\overset{..}{\underset{..}{Cl}}:}$$

The methyl radical resulting from this collision is very reactive because it has an odd number of electrons. It can react either with an atom of chlorine to form a molecule of methyl chloride or by colliding with a chlorine molecule it acquires an atom of chlorine and leaves another free chlorine which in turn can collide with a methane molecule and thus propagate a *chain reaction:*

$$\underset{\text{Methyl radical}}{H:\overset{H}{\overset{..}{\underset{\underset{H}{..}}{C}}}\cdot} + \underset{\text{Chlorine molecule}}{:\overset{..}{\underset{..}{Cl}}:\overset{..}{\underset{..}{Cl}}:} \rightarrow \underset{\text{Methyl chloride}}{H_3C:\overset{..}{\underset{..}{Cl}}:} + \underset{\text{Chlorine atom}}{:\overset{..}{\underset{..}{Cl}}\cdot}$$

Thus a few chlorine molecules, after they are activated, form atoms of chlorine which in turn form free methyl radicals which in turn by collisions give rise to more chlorine atoms, so that the process is continuous and proceeds by a chain reaction. This type of change is characteristic of many reactions of organic molecules.

After the initial shift of the electrons in covalent bonds, the collision of molecules may result in the formation of ions. This is characteristic of molecular collisions in solutions, while the formation of neutral atoms or free radicals is characteristic of molecular collisions in the gaseous state. As pointed out on page 419 and in Equation 27–2 (the reaction of methyl chloride molecules with water to form methanol and hydrogen chloride), though the net result appears to be an exchange of ions between the methyl chloride and water molecules the initiation of the reaction starts with a shift of the electron pair forming the covalent bond between the carbon and chlorine atoms.

There are more complex reactions of organic molecules than those which have been discussed. However, the study of these changes are beyond the scope of this text and in general most of the reactions of organic molecules can be assumed to take place either by a free radical or by an ionic mechanism.

ELECTROLYTIC REACTIONS

The passage of current through a solution or a molten mass of a compound in-

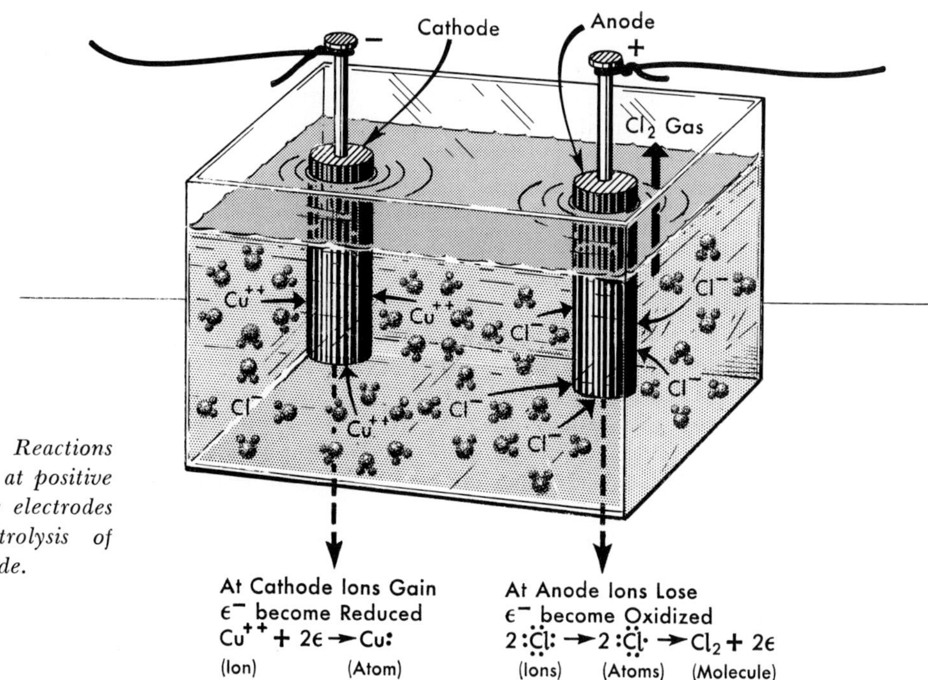

Fig. 27–10 *Reactions taking place at positive and negative electrodes during electrolysis of cupric chloride.*

volves transfer of electrons. Whether the cell is a small automobile battery, or a large electrolytic cell for the production of aluminum, or an electroplating bath employed for the production of a "chrome-finish," there occurs transfer of electrons at both positive (anode) and negative (cathode) electrodes. The over-all reactions in any electrolytic cell, no matter for what it is used, involve *redox changes.*

A simple illustration of the redox reactions taking place at the positive and negative electrodes of an electrolytic cell is shown in Figure 27–10 which shows the electrolysis of cupric chloride. From a battery or other source of direct current electrons flow to the cathode or negative plate of the cell, which dips into the solution of the salt $CuCl_2$. The hydrated cupric ions, Cu^{++}, are attracted to the cathode where each gains two electrons, becoming reduced to a metallic copper atom, which then deposits as a film on the negative plate or cathode. The negatively charged hydrated chloride ions migrate to the positive plate or anode. Since at the anode there is a deficiency of electrons, each chloride ion gives up one electron, thus becoming oxidized to chlorine atoms; two chlorine atoms (having seven electrons each) unite to form a covalent bond, thus producing a molecule of chlorine which then rises upward as gaseous chlorine. The over-all reactions are summarized in Figure 27–10.

The relatively simple electrolytic cell described in the preceding paragraph may be used to explain all electrolytic reactions. In electroplating, for example, the articles to be plated form the cathode, while at the anode we may place the metal which we wish to plate – copper, nickel, silver, and the like. The solution is usually a complex salt. Copper or nickel or silver enters the solution as ions and is then deposited as an adhering metallic film on the objects which serve as the cathode.

SUMMARY

1. Chemical reactions are classified into two large groups: (*a*) ionic reactions which involve ion or proton transfer or exchange, and (*b*) redox reactions which involve transfer or shift of electrons.
2. Chemical reactions proceed in the direction which will give the reacting system a greater stability than it possessed before the reaction.

3. The general trend of a chemical reaction can be predicted if detailed information is available on the electronic structure of the reacting substances; for example, if the electronic configuration of the atom of an element and its position in the Periodic Table is known, one can predict its activity.
4. Reactions which are accompanied by a large evolution of energy are usually regarded as irreversible. However, under ordinary conditions most reactions reach an equilibrium at which there is a balanced activity between reactants and products.
5. The extent to which a reaction proceeds toward completion depends upon the final state of equilibrium.
6. Increase in concentration and temperature, fine subdivision, or the presence of catalysts may increase the rate at which equilibrium is reached.
7. Temperature and concentration may be varied so as to change the equilibrium yield, which is equivalent to changing the direction of the reaction.
8. Ionic reactions are subdivided into (*a*) acid-base reactions, and (*b*) reactions in which there is a separation of a phase, such as evolution of a gas or formation of a precipitate.
9. Acids are conjugates which donate protons to a base giving rise to a new acid and the conjugate base.
10. The pH of a solution indicates the relative acidity or basicity; pH 7.0 is neutral, below 7.0 acidic, and above 7.0 basic.
11. The reaction of an acid with a base is called protolysis in the modern system and neutralization in the older. Acids and bases react completely with each other if the products are feeble acids and bases, but otherwise incompletely.
12. Salts are ionic compounds whose ions in water may act either as acids or as bases.
13. The separation of a phase (evolution of a gas or formation of a precipitate) in the reaction of ions depends (*a*) on the solubility and stability of the compound which can be formed by the interaction of the ions, and (*b*) on the concentration of the reacting ions.
14. Redox reactions which involve transfer or displacements of electrons include: (*a*) combination of elements to form ionic or covalent substances; (*b*) reduction of ions by metals (replacement) and other reductants; (*c*) reactions between molecules; and (*d*) electrolytic reactions. Molecular reactions are initiated by shifts in the covalent electron pairs to form either ions or free radicals.
15. In simple combination of elements the metallic atoms lose electrons or act as reductants; the nonmetallic atoms gain electrons and act as oxidants.
16. In all electrolytic reactions, at the cathode (negative) ions gain electrons and become reduced, and at the anode (positive) ions lose electrons and become oxidized.

STUDY EXERCISES

1. The following statements represent definite chemical changes. In the blank space following the item, write *A* if it is a reaction involving transfer or shift of electrons (redox), or *B* if it is an ion transfer or exchange (ionic).
   a. Calcium metal, when heated in air, burns and forms calcium oxide. . . . .
   b. Sodium metal added to water evolves hydrogen and forms Na^+ and OH^- which pass into the solution. . . . .
   c. When a sodium sulfate solution (Na_2SO_4) is added to a solution of barium chloride ($BaCl_2$), a white solid, $BaSO_4$, settles out. . . . .
   d. Carbon when burned in air forms CO_2. . . . .
   e. Sodium carbonate added to dilute acetic acid (vinegar) evolves CO_2. . . . .
   f. Copper when heated with sulfur turns black, forming Cu_2S. . . . .
   g. Hydrogen (H_2) passed over hot iron oxide (Fe_2O_3) forms Fe and H_2O. . . . . .
   h. When potassium bromide is added to a solution of silver nitrate a white solid, AgBr, forms. . . . .
2. Refer to the replacement series and select the most probably correct answer.

a. Of the metals listed, the one which will react rapidly with dilute hydrochloric acid is: Pb; Hg; Mg; Fe; Ca.

b. Of the following ions, the one which will not be reduced by magnesium metal is: Sn++; Fe+++; Ba++; Cu++; Zn++.

c. Of the following oxides, the one that is most difficult to reduce by passing hydrogen over it while heating the oxide is: CuO; Ag_2O; Fe_2O_3; Al_2O_3; PbO.

3. Below is given a series of possible reactions. After each, write *A* if a reaction will take place, or *B* if no reaction is expected. All ions, acids, and salts (NaCl, etc.) are assumed to be in dilute aqueous solutions. (Use Table 27–2 as a guide in answering.)

a. Zn: + H_3O^+ ....

b. Fe: + Zn++ ....

c. Mg: + HCl ....

d. Hg: + Ag+ ....

e. $\dddot{Al}$ + NaCl ....

f. $\dddot{Al}$ + Fe_2O_3 ....

g. H_3O^+ + Cu: ....

h. Na· + $AlCl_3$ ....

i. Na· + HCl ....

j. $MgCl_2$ + Ca: ....

k. Na· + HOH ....

l. Zn: + H_2S ....

m. Ca: + HBr ....

n. Cl_2 + HI ....

4. In the following exercises select the best completion of the statement.

a. Equilibrium is (1) a condition no chemical reaction reaches; (2) a method for activation of molecules in order that they may unite; (3) the midpoint of every chemical reaction; (4) a condition in which two opposing reactions are taking place at equal velocities so that the concentrations of the reacting substances remain constant.

b. The speed of a chemical reaction may be accelerated by (1) cooling; (2) pressure; (3) use of an appropriate catalyst; (4) dilution with an inert solvent.

c. A catalyst is a substance that (1) affects the equilibrium; (2) is produced by living matter; (3) alters the speed at which equilibrium is reached; (4) always displaces the equilibrium yield.

d. The equilibrium yield can be increased by (1) cooling; (2) heating; (3) use of an appropriate catalyst; (4) increasing the concentration of the reactants and removing one of the products; (5) diluting with an inert solvent.

e. Enzymes are (1) composed of protoplasms; (2) organic substances that aid digestion; (3) organic catalysts produced by living tissues; (4) organic catalysts which affect the equilibrium of reaction in living tissues.

5. Consider the following equilibrium:

$$\begin{array}{lcccc} & A + & B \rightleftarrows & C + & D \\ \text{B.P.} & 110^\circ & 320^\circ & 130^\circ & 72^\circ \end{array}$$

The boiling point (°C.) of each reactant or resultant is given under it. The reaction is carried at 50°C. by mixing 1 mole of *A* and 1 mole of *B*. After equilibrium is established it is found that only 0.4 moles of *C* is formed. How many moles each of *A, B,* and *D* are present in the equilibrium mixture? Give two methods by which the equilibrium yield of *C* can be increased to about 0.8 moles or more.

6. After each of the following items write *A* if the substance is an acid, *B* if the substance is a base, *C* if it is an ampholyte (can act both as an acid or a base). Consult Table 27–3.

a. H_2O ....

b. HNO_3 ....

c. HCO_3^- ....

d. $CO_3^=$ ....

e. H_3O^+ ....

f. H_2SO_4 ....

g. HSO_4^- ....

h. OH^- ....

i. NH_3 ....

j. Cl^- ....

k. NH_4^+ ....

l. H_3PO_4 ....

m. $PO_4^{\equiv}$ ....

7. For each of the following *dilute* solutions, give the approximate pH and indicate by the symbols *SA, IA, WA* and *SB, IB,* and *WB* whether the substance is a strong, intermediate, or weak acid or base. (Consult Table 27–3.)

a. HCl ....

b. H_2SO_4 ....

c. KOH ....

d. CH_3COOH ....

e. NaOH ....

f. NH_4OH ....

g. $Ca(OH)_2$ ....

h. H_3BO_3 ....
i. H_3PO_4 ....
j. H_2O ....
k. $NaHCO_3$ ....
l. Na_2CO_3 ....
m. Na_2S ....
n. NH_4Cl ....
o. Na_3PO_4 ....

8. Each acid in column I is reacted with the base listed on the same line of column II. In column III state whether after complete reaction of equimolar solutions of acid and base the solution will substantially be *neutral, acidic* or *basic.*

I	II	III
HCl	NaOH	....
CH_3COOH	KOH	....
HCl	NH_4OH	....
H_2SO_4	$Ca(OH)_2$	....

9. The following groups of compounds are dissolved in water. After each, write *A* if the solution will be below pH 6 (acidic) ; *B* if above 8 (basic) ; and *N* if between pH 6 and pH 8 (neutral) .
   a. Oxides of nonmetals ....
   b. Oxides of metals ....
   c: Hydrogen compounds of halogens .....
   d. Hydrogen compounds of nitrogen .....
   e. Hydrogen compounds of sulfur or selenium ....
10. After each of the following materials, write the approximate pH range.
    a. Soda water ....
    b. Distilled water ....
    c. Tap water ....
    d. Sea water ....
    e. Boiled distilled water ....
    f. Blood serum ....
    g. Gastric juice ....
    h. Lemon juice ....
11. The following represent reactions which take place in solution. Using the material of this chapter, write after each item the probable products. (It is not necessary to write a balanced equation.)
    a. $Ag^+ + Zn$: ....
    b. $Hg^{++} + Sn$: ....
    c. $Ca^{++} + CO_3^=$ ....
    d. $H_2SO_4 + CaCO_3$ ....
    e. $ZnO + Al$ ....
    f. $Fe + S$ ....
    g. $PbS + Fe$ ....
    h. $Pb^{++} + S^=$ ....
    i. $Zn + H_2SO_4$ ....
    j. $Fe + HCl$ ....
    k. $NaCl \xrightarrow[\text{fused}]{\text{D. C.}}$ ....
    l. $MgCO_3$ + heat ....
12. Briefly indicate how each of the following can be determined:
    a. Whether a sample of city water has been chlorinated.
    b. Whether a compound which contains chlorine in combination with other elements is ionic or nonpolar covalent.
    c. Whether a metal has strong reductant properties.
    d. Whether an oxidant is strong or weak.
    e. Whether an acid is strong or weak.

FOR FURTHER READING

1. MARKHAM, E. C., and S. E. SMITH, *General Chemistry.* Boston: Houghton Mifflin Company, 1954.
   A discussion of chemical equilibrium will be found in Chapter 24. Important chemical changes, redox reactions, and acids and bases are discussed on pages 195–204, 220–227, and 230–237.
2. PAULING, LINUS, *General Chemistry.* San Francisco: W. H. Freeman and Company, 1953.
   Redox reactions are discussed in Chapter 11; chemical equilibrium, in Chapter 20; acids and bases, in Chapter 21.
3. Paperback: EDITORS OF SCIENTIFIC AMERICAN, *New Chemistry.* Simon and Schuster, $1.45.
   A good article on free radicals is given on pages 32–43.

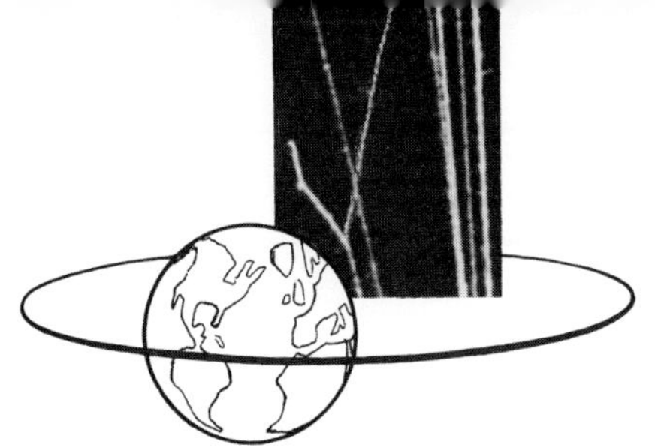

THINGS OF THIS WORLD: I 28

CULTURES can be measured in many ways. We often speak of "primitive," "backward," or "underdeveloped" countries, implying that our own social structure is more advanced than any other that exists at present over the face of the earth and, by inference, better than any other that has existed at any time in the past. It should be pointed out, however, that our pride grows from comparisons based on the number of automobiles that move over our roads, the machines that fill our factories, the gadgets that fill our homes, and all the implements which are employed to increase our capacities and lessen our burdens. If we were to use as a standard of measurement such criteria as the amount of willingness to participate in all the duties of our society, disinterested pursuit of knowledge, the number of serious books read per capita per year, and intellectual productivity, we might not then rate our way of life so highly as when machines are used as criteria. What we really mean by our high "standard of living" is that we have a highly developed and complex technological social structure which differs radically not only from that of a primitive jungle society, but also from the existing social structures in many places in the Middle East, Africa, and Asia. In the final analysis, the fundamental difference is the quantity of matter and energy consumed or expended per individual. This does not mean food alone but every conceivable form of matter which man collects and possesses, all the forms of matter which he uses to alter the conditions of his environment and to extend his capacities. Therefore, the object of this and the next two chapters is to survey the most important materials which are collected, processed, synthesized, and used in our complex social structure.

SOURCES OF ENERGY

Behind all the activity of the 2.5 billion people who move about the face of the earth is the physical effort for living and for "the pursuit of happiness" toward which energy (human, animal, and mechanical) must be expended. In primitive societies only the effort exerted by human beings and draft animals needs to be measured and it can be expressed as so many "man hours" or "horse days" of work. In technological societies like our own we have to measure energy from diverse sources, wood, coal, oil, wind, falling water, and even from the

TABLE 28–1

ENERGY UTILIZED IN THE WORLD (163 COUNTRIES)

	BILLION KG CAL
(*a*) Coals	101,000
(*b*) Liquid fuels	31,000
(*c*) Gaseous fuels	7,750
(*d*) Firewood	15,500
(*e*) Foods (human power)	16,330
(*f*) Feeds (animal power)	26,700
(*g*) Hydroelectric	1,720
(*h*) Nuclear, sun, wind, and heat of the earth	Negligible
(*i*) Total irreplaceable	155,250
(*j*) Total replaceable	44,750
(*k*) Total consumption $(i + j)$	$200{,}000 \times 10^9$ kg cal
Per cent replaceable (j/k)	22.3 per cent
Per cent irreplaceable (i/k)	77.7 per cent
Human energy (e/k)	8.2 per cent
Animal energy (f/k)	13.2 per cent

Department of State, Publication 3248, Washington, D.C., 1949.

"slow explosions" of nuclear fuels. Therefore we must employ a common unit in order to understand and compare our figures. We can use either the small calorie (page 308) or the kilowatt-hour (page 541). The latter would seem more suitable because it is larger (1 kilowatt-hour = 8,600,000 calories), but we can conveniently use the kilocalorie[1] (1000 calories) since the energy of fuels is more readily visualized as heat than electricity is. Table 28–1 gives a summary of the energy utilization in 163 countries of the world. From this table two striking facts are evident. The first is that of the total consumption of energy, only about 8 per cent is furnished by direct human work; animals furnish another 13 per cent, so that the total contribution of human beings and animals is about one-fifth of the total. The second striking fact is

[1] Called also kilogram calorie and often written *Calorie* (large calorie).

Fig. 28–1 *Per capita consumption of energy in different countries.*

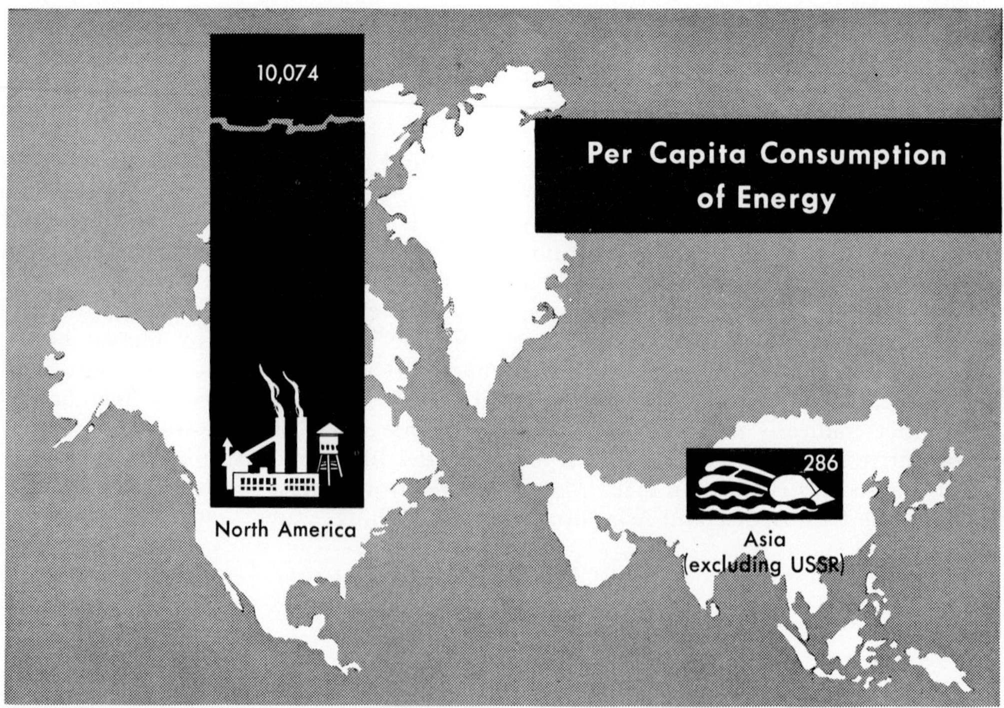

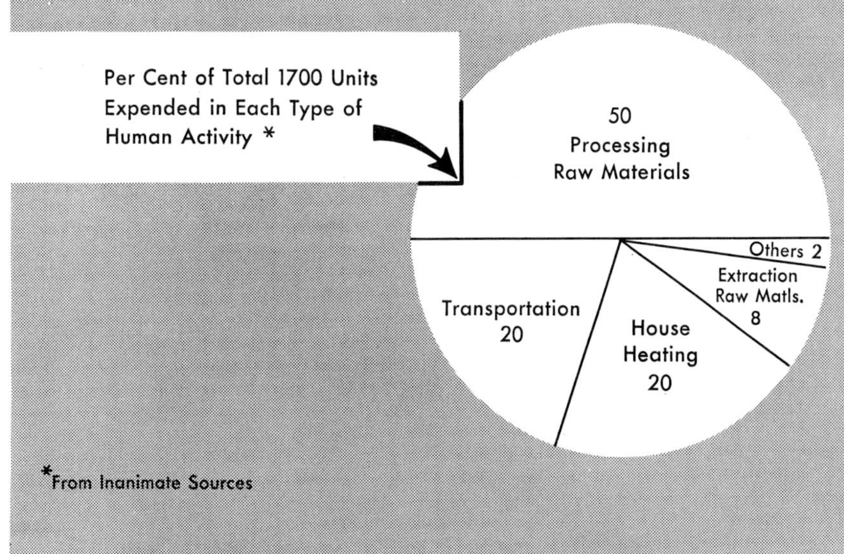

Fig. 28–2 *Utilization of energy for various purposes.*

that about four-fifths of the total energy consumed comes from irreplaceable sources, that is, coal, oil, and gas. Therefore, the statement which is often made that we are drawing for the most part on energy resources accumulated in the past is substantially correct.

PER CAPITA CONSUMPTION OF ENERGY

Let us assume that the supply of food the world over is about the same and also that the average per capita consumption of energy derived from fuels and other inanimate sources is also the same. So that we can deal with small numbers we will use as a unit 10^4 kg cal (10,000 kilogram calories). With this unit the energy output of man derived from his own body is 100 units, while the total consumption is about 1800 units. In other words, of the average per capita consumption of energy, close to 95 per cent is derived from sources other than the human body.

When we examine the per capita consumption in various countries, some vast differences appear, which are shown graphically in Figure 28–1. At one extreme of the scale is the United States (the "haves"), utilizing over 10,000 units per capita. At the other extreme are the countries of the Middle East and Asia (the "have nots") where the average per capita consumption is less than 300 units and in some countries 125–150 units. This gives a quantitative picture of difference in the standard of living and points to the underlying reasons for the "unstable" and "volcanic" human areas of our world.

UTILIZATION OF ENERGY

Disregarding the vast differences in the average per capita consumption of energy and taking the 1800 units ($\times 10^4$ kilocalories) as the per capita average the world over, we wish to inquire in what fields of human activity this expended energy is utilized. Of course, about 5 per cent is utilized for the human machine to live and move about. Leaving this energy out of consideration, and considering the 1700 units from outside sources, we can obtain a breakdown shown graphically in Figure 28–2. The significant fact emerges that 50 per cent of the outside energy is expended for changing the raw materials obtained from nature by cooking or manufacturing. If we take out the 20 per cent utilized to alter the effects of climate (house heating), then 8 per cent of the total is employed to obtain raw materials and 70 per cent to change them in order to satisfy our material wants. These statistics give a picture of our technology.

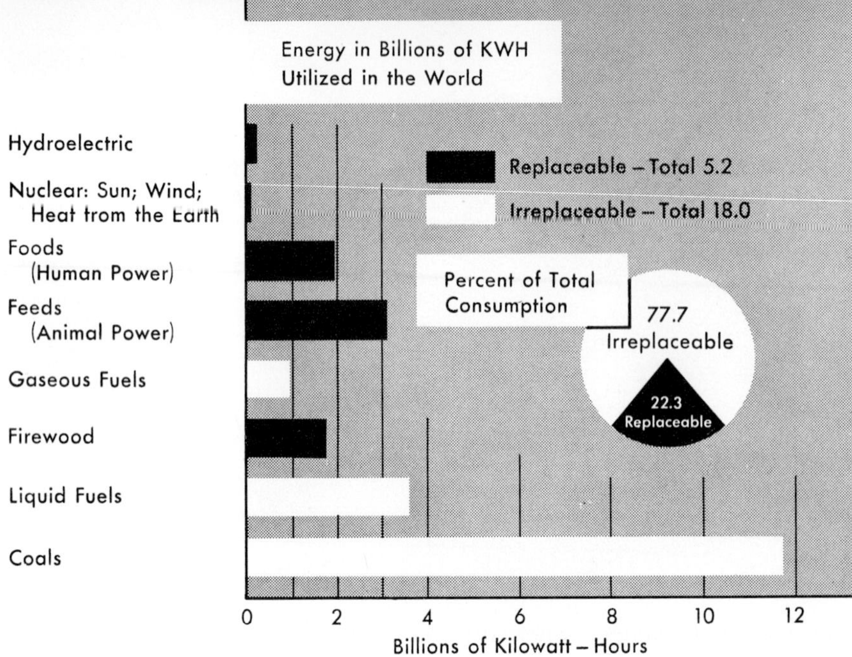

Fig. 28–3 *Sources of energy.*

The demand for energy all over the world is certain to rise in the future, partly because of increasing populations and partly because of the upward trend in technological development in the so-called underdeveloped countries.

SOURCES OF ENERGY IN THE UNITED STATES

Figure 28–3 and Table 28–1 summarize the principal sources of energy in the world and the proportion yielded by each source. The first six sources listed in the table account for 99 per cent of the total energy used. This huge portion is derived entirely from compounds of carbon. Another striking fact is that only foods and wood represent sources which are being produced at the present; 70 per cent of the total energy requirement is drawn from coal, oil, and gas, which are accumulated energy reserves inherited from the past. At the present rate of consumption, the question how long our coal and oil will last has a real significance. As the accumulated resources dwindle, future generations will turn their attention to other sources of energy.

Here we shall consider in some detail the nature of the principal fuels (coal, oil, and gas), and particularly the nature of foods, the fuel of the human engine. No matter how rich a society may be in deposits of fuels, its well-being is primarily based on its ability to produce and distribute economically an adequate supply of food. Industry is a desirable development, but agriculture comes first.

Coal, oil, gas, and foods are all essentially compounds of carbon. Hence, before any intelligent discussion of the nature, production and processing of coal, oil, gas, and foods can be given, it is necessary to consider the general nature and properties of carbon compounds.

ORIGIN OF CARBON COMPOUNDS

Carbon and hydrogen compounds are the structural elements of living matter. The reason for so designating them is based on the following considerations. Living organisms are composed of molecular structures of greater complexity than is found in minerals and rocks, which are designated as *inorganic*. Analysis shows that these complex molecular structures contain the element carbon associated for the most part with only a few elements: hydrogen, oxygen, and nitrogen. Further, it appears that the most

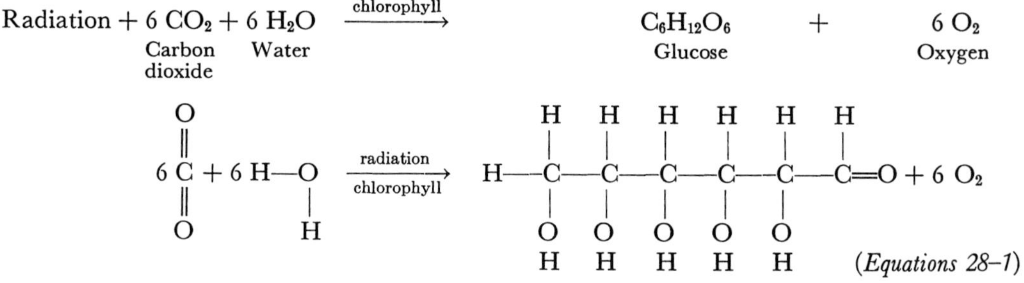

$$\text{Radiation} + 6\,CO_2 + 6\,H_2O \xrightarrow{\text{chlorophyll}} C_6H_{12}O_6 + 6\,O_2$$

(Equations 28–1)

important function of the *carbon-hydrogen* system is to furnish the energy of life.

Of the living organisms, animals are unable to synthesize organic compounds directly from inorganic matter. All animals depend directly or indirectly on green plants; these perform on a vast scale the chemical synthesis which forms the basis of life on the earth, and through which the energy of life is supplied by the sun. The vast scale of this silent synthesis can be visualized if we consider that each year the plants of the earth utilize about 150 billion tons of carbon dioxide and release about 400 billion tons of oxygen, and that 80 to 90 per cent of this large-scale reduction of carbon dioxide to produce organic compounds is performed under the surface of the ocean by the lowly algae.

The over-all chemical reaction involved in the synthesis of organic compounds by plants, called *photosynthesis,* may be written as in Equations 28–1, above.

As the equations show, oxygen is set free, and carbon dioxide is reduced to a complex carbon compound containing carbon-hydrogen and carbon-carbon bonds. Energy is absorbed, since the product glucose, $C_6H_{12}O_6$, can be burned with evolution of heat. Hence, in photosynthesis, completely oxidized molecules (carbon dioxide and water) undergo chemical changes to produce substances with higher energy content which is released in living organisms by rupture of the C–C and C–H bonds to supply the energy of life.

The microscopic laboratories in which photosynthesis takes place are the tiny bodies in the cells of the leaves called *chloroplasts,* composed mostly of a green pigment called *chlorophyll,* which as shown in Equations 28–1 plays an important role in the over-all reaction. Photosynthesis is not completely understood, but enough information has been accumulated during the past two centuries to give a general outline of the reaction. First, radiation or light of low intensity is required. Second, during irradiation, there is an activation of chlorophyll, which in turn initiates the reduction of carbon dioxide. This involves pulling hydrogen atoms from water and forming carbon-hydrogen bonds and liberating oxygen. Though the exact intermediates are not known, the hypothetical step shown in Diagram 28–2 may be supposed.

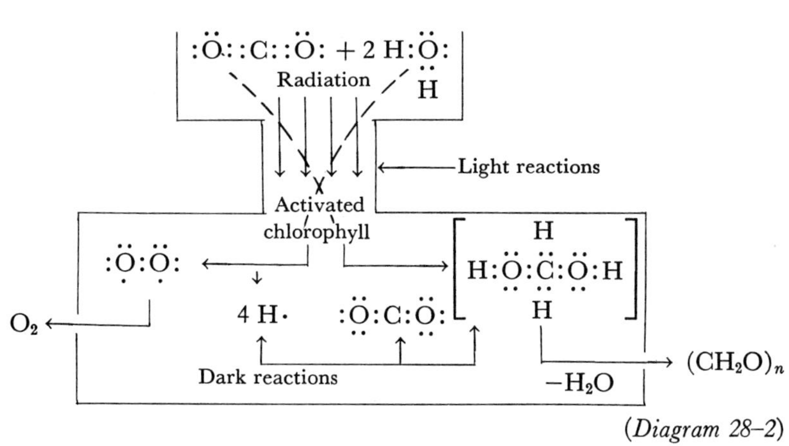

(Diagram 28–2)

There is no direct evidence that the compound shown in the brackets is formed, but compounds having the –COOH group, organic acids, have been shown to form immediately after irradiation in the presence of carbon dioxide labeled with C^{11} carbon. The "dark reactions" in the diagram shows that the hydrogen atoms are "pulled out" from the water molecules and that the oxygen set free comes from water and not from carbon dioxide. This fact has been shown by experiments with water containing the isotope of oxygen $^{18}_{8}O$. All the oxygen liberated in photosynthesis comes from water and none from carbon dioxide.

After irradiation there follows a "dark period" reaction which is not affected by light. This conclusion is based on the following considerations. First, as the intensity of radiation is increased, the rate of photosynthesis, measured by the volume of oxygen produced, increases until further increase in the intensity of light has no effect. Second, the liberation of oxygen continues for an interval in the dark. This evidence suggests that in the irradiation stage chlorophyll is activated and unstable intermediates are formed and during the dark stage these unstable intermediates, indicated in the diagram as (CH_4O) and $(CH_2O)_n$, are stabilized by their final conversion through enzymatic reactions to glucose, $C_6H_{12}O_6$, and oxygen, O_2.

Returning to Diagram 28–2, it will be noted that the unstable intermediate in brackets (that is, partially reduced carbon dioxide) has acquired two C–H bonds which have increased the potential chemical energy of the system since energy could be released by their cleavage: the intermediate could be burned to give carbon dioxide and water.

As glucose is formed in the cells, it is converted by enzymes to starch which is stored in the leaf.

$$\underset{\text{Glucose}}{nC_6H_{12}O_6} \rightleftarrows \underset{\text{Starch}}{C_6H_{10}O_5} + nH_2O$$

(*Equation 28–3*)

During the night the excess starch stored in the leaf is reconverted to sugar, passed down to the stem and roots, and is there reconverted into starch. The plant cells utilize the sugar molecules to build the other compounds necessary for the living functions. For example, *cellulose,* the hard fiber of plant tissues, is built up by symmetrical combination of glucose molecules. Starch and cellulose therefore have the same chemical composition; both yield glucose on hydrolysis. The difference in the arrangement of the glucose "blocks" accounts for the difference in their properties.

Most of the sugars, starches, and celluloses have a general composition which may be expressed by the general formula $C_x(H_2O)_y$, and hence they are called *carbohydrates,* that is, hydrates of carbon. From the carbohydrates (the initial products of photosynthesis) the living cells by enzymatic chemical reactions synthesize other organic compounds required in the various functions of the cells. Two important classes of compounds are recognized, *fats* and *proteins.* Fats, like carbohydrates, are primarily fuels and contain carbon, hydrogen, and oxygen. The proteins contain nitrogen in addition to carbon, hydrogen, and oxygen, and sometimes they also contain small amounts of sulfur and phosphorus. The nitrogen, sulfur, and phosphorus are derived from the various inorganic ions (NO_3^-, $PO_4^{\equiv}$, $SO_4^=$, etc.) which are taken in solution from the soil. Thus the living cell, working primarily with four elements (carbon, oxygen, hydrogen, and nitrogen), is able to build up the many organic compounds in plants and animals.

THE ENERGY CYCLE OF LIFE

The animal body is not unlike a machine. It obtains energy by the oxidation of carbon compounds — mostly carbohydrates and fats which have a higher energy content than the resultant products of the oxidation, carbon dioxide and water. For example, the carbohydrates in digestion are converted to glucose, which passes through the intestinal wall into the lymph and blood and is taken to the liver, where it is changed to glycogen (animal starch).

About 0.1 per cent of glucose remains in the blood, which is the circulating medium. In the various tissues, heat energy is produced by enzymatic oxidation using the oxygen transported from the lungs by the hemoglobin "carrying" system. As more glucose is required, glycogen is changed to glucose. The over-all process is called respiration and the burning of glucose in the tissues is analogous to the burning of glucose in a calorimeter:

$$C_6H_{12}O_6 + 6\ O_2 \rightarrow 6\ CO_2 + 6\ H_2O + 675\ \text{kg cal}$$

(*Equation 28–4*)

The combustion shown in Equation 28–4 releases a large amount of heat energy and is the reverse of the equation (28–1) of photosynthesis. The burning of glucose, then, is somewhat analogous to the combustion of gasoline in the automobile engine. Both are fuels, both contain carbon compounds, and both undergo oxidation to give carbon dioxide, water, and heat. The combustion in the metallic engine is explosive and at a high temperature; the oxidation in the "protein converter" is quiet, and in the human body proceeds at a temperature of 37° C. (98.6° F.).

Respiration in plants involves oxidation of carbon compounds by living cells. During the oxidation changes, carbon dioxide and water are produced as in the animal tissues; these waste products are eliminated chiefly through the leaves. In plants, respiration takes place day and night, but photosynthesis only in light; in animals only respiration takes place. Therefore, respiration covers all the complex chemical changes in living cells in which atmospheric oxygen is used, organic compounds are oxidized, and carbon dioxide and water are formed, accompanied by the transformation of definite amounts of chemical energy to the kinetic energy which makes life possible. The cycle is completed by photosynthesis. The products of respiration — carbon dioxide and water — are consumed, radiant energy is transformed into potential (chemical) energy; carbon dioxide is reduced and C–C and C–H bonds are formed resulting in organic compounds; and oxygen is set free.

Thus, the cycle of the energy of life may be described as the instantaneous capture in the microscopic plant cell laboratories of the radiation energy streaming through 93 million miles of space from the sun and the storing of this energy in the form of C–C and C–H bonds; then these bonds are slowly broken by the living organisms to liberate this borrowed energy, to live, reproduce their species, and eventually die. The greatest fantasies elaborated in fiction pale to insignificance before the factual realities of this cycle of which we are all a part.

METHANE AND THE CARBON–HYDROGEN BOND

Photosynthesis, then, involves essentially the reduction of carbon dioxide with the formation of carbon-hydrogen, C–H, and carbon-carbon, C–C, bonds. Hence it is advisable to study in some detail the molecules which result by the formation of such bonds. The first one to be considered is methane, the simplest compound of carbon and hydrogen.

Carbon dioxide, CO_2 is a colorless gas with an acid taste and a faint, pungent odor. It is produced in the burning of all carbonaceous fuels, in heating of limestone (for the production of lime, see page 423), and in fermentations. It is used in refrigeration (dry ice), in carbonated beverages, and as a fire extinguisher. The latter use definitely suggests that it cannot be oxidized further. It can, however, be reduced to carbon monoxide either by passing it over hot coals or by heating it with hydrogen:

$$\underset{\text{Carbon dioxide}}{CO_2} + \underset{\text{Carbon}}{C} + 40.8\ \text{kg cal} \rightarrow \underset{\text{Carbon monoxide}}{2\ CO}$$

(*Equation 28–5*)

$$CO_2 + H_2 \xrightleftharpoons{\text{catalyst}} CO + H_2O$$

(*Equation 28–6*)

The electronic structure of carbon monoxide

$$:C:\ddot{\underset{\cdot\cdot}{O}}: \quad \text{or} \quad :C::\ddot{\underset{\cdot\cdot}{O}}$$

indicates a reactive molecule since both structures show carbon with less than eight electrons and also with an unshared pair of electrons. This reactivity accounts for the high toxicity of the gas even in small quantities. Air containing 100 to 500 parts per million (p.p.m.) will cause death in a few minutes. The toxicity is due to the fact that, even in low concentrations, air containing carbon monoxide coming in contact with the blood in the lungs will produce two equilibria:

$$\underset{\text{Hemoglobin}}{Hb} + \underset{\text{Oxygen}}{O_2} \rightleftarrows \underset{\text{Oxyhemoglobin}}{HbO_2}$$

(*Equation 28–7*)

$$\underset{\text{Hemoglobin}}{Hb} + \underset{\text{Carbon monoxide}}{CO} \rightleftarrows \underset{\text{Carboxyhemoglobin}}{Hb{:}CO}$$

(*Equation 28–8*)

The equilibrium shown in Equation 28–8 has a greater rate than the equilibrium shown in Equation 28–7, due to the higher reactivity of the carbon monoxide and the greater stability of the Hb:CO complex. As a result, the amount of HbO_2 is reduced and asphyxiation results.

When one volume of carbon monoxide and three volumes of hydrogen are mixed and passed over a nickel catalyst at 200 to 250° C., carbon-hydrogen bonds are formed and *the simplest compound of carbon and hydrogen or hydrocarbon,* methane, CH_4, results:

$$\underset{\text{Carbon monoxide}}{CO} + \underset{\text{Hydrogen}}{3\,H_2} \xrightarrow[\text{Ni}]{200^\circ} \underset{\text{Methane}}{CH_4} + \underset{\text{Water}}{H_2O}$$

(*Equation 28–9*)

Methane has a high content of potential chemical energy since it readily undergoes combustion with the evolution of a large quantity of heat, as shown by the following equations:

$$CH_4 + 2\,O_2 \rightarrow CO_2 + H_2O + 212.8 \text{ kg cal}$$

$$H{:}\overset{\textstyle H}{\underset{\textstyle H}{\ddot{\underset{..}{C}}}}{:}H + 2\,{:}\ddot{O}{:}\ddot{O}{:} \underset{\text{red.}}{\overset{\text{oxid.}}{\rightleftarrows}} {:}\ddot{O}{::}C{::}\ddot{O}{:} + 2\,H{:}\underset{\textstyle H}{\ddot{\underset{..}{O}}}{:}$$

(*Equation 28–10*)

The electronic formulas of methane and carbon dioxide indicate that the transition from the former to the latter involves a shift of electrons away from the carbon atom; and further, that reduction involves a shift of the bonding electrons closer to the carbon atom, that is, *an increase in the electron density of the carbon atom.* Thus the stepwise conversion of carbon dioxide to carbon monoxide, then to methane (Equations 28–5, 6, and 9), and the formation of the C–H bonds involves: (*a*) reduction of the carbon atom, that is, an increase in its electron density; (*b*) raising of the potential chemical energy of the system from zero to a high level (212.8 kilocalories/moles). Finally the combustion of methane (Equation 28–10) shows a release of this potential energy by breaking of the C–H bonds and the formation of C–O and H–O bonds.

The above considerations give the underlying basis for the large-scale use of hydrocarbons as fuels. Natural gas contains 85 to 95 per cent methane; gasoline, fuel oil, and all petroleum products consist of mixtures of liquid hydrocarbons.

LARGE-SCALE PRODUCTION OF HYDROCARBONS

Equation 28–9 shows that methane may be produced by the catalytic reduction of carbon monoxide with hydrogen. The reaction mixture (CO and H_2) is often called "water gas" because it is formed when steam is passed through hot coal:

$$\underset{\text{Carbon (coal)}}{C} + \underset{\text{Water (steam)}}{H_2O} \rightarrow \underbrace{\underset{\text{Carbon monoxide}}{CO} + \underset{\text{Hydrogen}}{H_2}}_{\text{Water gas}}$$

(*Equation 28–11*)

TABLE 28–2 COMPOSITION OF TYPICAL AMERICAN NATURAL GAS

NAME OF COMPONENT	AMOUNT %	BOILING POINT °C.	COMPOSITION		MOL. WT.	FORMULA
			C%	H%		
Methane	85–90	−161	75	25	16	CH_4
Ethane	5–10	−88	80	20	30	C_2H_6
Propane	1–5	−44	81.8	18.2	44	C_3H_8
Butane		−0.5	82.7	17.3	58	C_4H_{10}
Pentane		36	83.3	16.7	72	C_5H_{12}
Nitrogen	2–5	−195.8	...	...	28	N_2

This reaction is one of the important large-scale processes for producing the manufactured gas that is piped into homes and factories for cooking and heating purposes. In many localities this manufactured *water gas* is admixed with *natural gas,* which is obtained by drilling wells in gas-producing sedimentary strata, as, for example, in the Gulf of Mexico area. The composition of a typical sample of American natural gas is shown in Table 28–2. It will be noted in the last column of the table that the four hydrocarbons following methane differ each from the next one by a CH_2 group; all may be represented by the general formula C_nH_{2n+2}.

The first four hydrocarbons listed in Table 28–2 are gases, whereas pentane is liquid at room temperature (b.p. 36° C.). Other hydrocarbons of the series C_nH_{2n+2} are obtained either by distilling petroleum or by passing the water gas mixture through a catalyst:

$$n\,CO + (2\,n + 1)\,H_2 \xrightarrow[\text{catalyst}\ 200°]{\text{Co}} C_nH_{2n+2} + 2\,n\,H_2O + \text{heat}$$

(*Equation 28–12*)

The reaction represented in Equation 28–12 is known as the Fischer-Tropsch process and was developed in Germany between 1923 and 1930, for the production of synthetic liquid motor fuels. The process, as further developed in this country, can be placed in commercial production, if the necessity arises. Since the reaction gives off heat and a reduction of volume occurs in converting a gaseous to a liquid mixture, low temperature and elevated pressure will favor a shift of the equilibrium to the right. Pressures of about 10 atmospheres are employed. In this country the mixtures of hydrocarbons known as *gasoline, kerosene, fuel oil,* and *lubricating oils* are obtained by distillation of petroleum or rock oil.

The first four hydrocarbons listed in Table 28–2 are used primarily as gaseous fuels and to a limited extent to produce more reactive hydrocarbons (unsaturated) for the synthesis of plastics and rubbers. Natural gas consists mostly of methane, and the so-called bottled gas mostly of propane and butane. Gasoline is a mixture of saturated hydrocarbons which have six to ten carbon atoms, while kerosene contains hydrocarbons with more than ten carbon atoms.

The large-scale production of these mixtures can be visualized from the following facts. The first oil well was drilled in 1859 at Titusville, Pennsylvania. By 1930 the production of petroleum was about 10 million gallons daily; today the figure is close to 400 million gallons. In the short time of a century the use of these mixtures as fuels has made possible the internal combustion engines of automobiles, trucks, Diesel locomotives, tractors, and airplanes, and has altered the social structure of a large part of the world. Mechanization has meant an ever-increasing demand for energy-producing fuels.

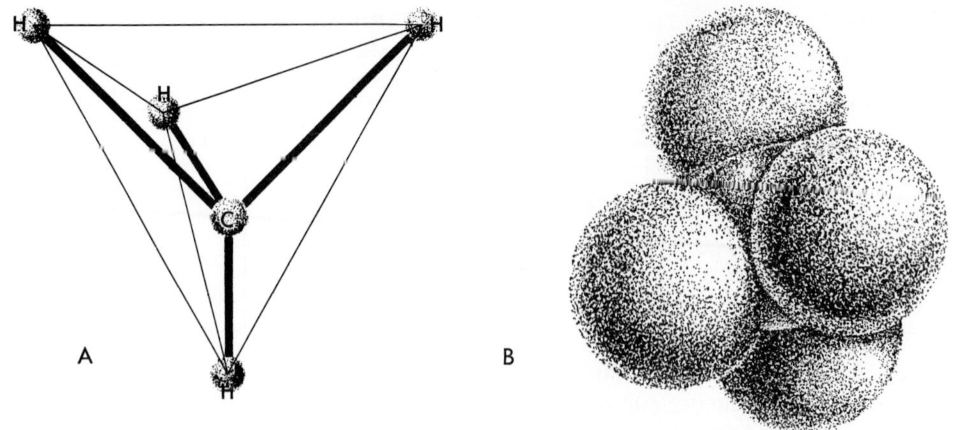

Fig. 28–4 *Architecture of methane molecule.*

THE ARCHITECTURE OF HYDROCARBON MOLECULES

The formula of methane as previously indicated may be represented in different ways, thus:

```
            H                   H
            |                  ••
  CH4     H-C-H              H:C:H
            |                  ••
            H                   H
  (1)      (2)                 (3)
```

Formula (1) gives only the composition of the molecule, namely, that it has one carbon and four hydrogen atoms and thus a molecular weight of 16 $(12 + 4)$ and a composition of 75 per cent (12/16) carbon and 25 per cent (4/12) hydrogen. Formulas (2) and (3) indicate that the carbon atom is joined to four hydrogen atoms by covalent bonds which are represented either by a short dash or by a pair of electrons.

A three-dimensional picture of the methane molecule is shown in Figures 28–4*A*

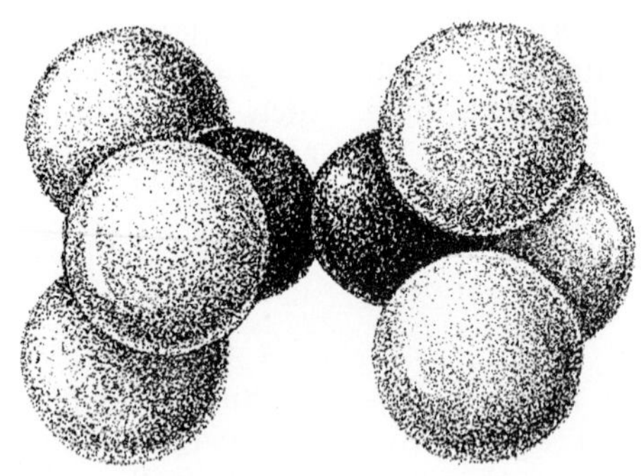

Fig. 28–5 *Architecture of ethane molecule.*

```
   H   H                  H  H
   |   |                  •• ••
 H—C—C—H               H :C :C: H
   |   |                  •• ••
   H   H                  H  H
```

and 28–4*B*. In Figure 28–4*A* the carbon atom is situated at the center of an imaginary tetrahedron with the four hydrogen atoms arranged symmetrically at its four corners, the heavy lines representing the covalent bonds. Figure 28–4*B* shows a space contour model of the structure in Figure 28–4*A*. In the same manner Figure 28–5 shows the structure of ethane composed of two carbon and six hydrogen atoms.

The abbreviated structural formula for ethane is usually written CH_3CH_3; similarly, the formula for propane is written $CH_3CH_2CH_3$. However, with butane C_4H_{10} we are presented with a new phenomenon. There are two hydrocarbons which by analysis and molecular weight determination have the formula C_4H_{10}; it can be shown that both are pure substances and not mixtures; one boils at −10° C. and the other at −0.5° C. Moreover, they have different melting points, densities, and other physical properties. Compounds which differ in properties but have the same kind and number of atoms are called *isomers*. Each kind of butane molecule has four carbon atoms and ten hydrogen atoms. To account for the difference in properties it is assumed that they have different architecture in their molecules; in other words, they have different arrangements of the four carbon and ten hydrogen atoms. These differences are most simply shown in Figure 28–6. The structural theory of organic chemistry predicts only two possible arrangements for molecules which contain four carbon and ten hydrogen atoms. Isobutane differs from *n*-butane in that it has one carbon atom joined to three other carbon atoms. This agrees with the existence of only two butanes, C_4H_{10}. Similarly there are only three pentanes (C_5H_{12}) known, and the structural theory also predicts only three possible arrangements:

$$CH_3CH_2CH_2CH_2CH_3$$

n-Pentane (b.p. 36°)

$$CH_3—\overset{\displaystyle H}{\underset{\displaystyle CH_3}{C}}—CH_2CH_3$$

Isopentane (b.p. 27.95°)

$$CH_3—\overset{\displaystyle CH_3}{\underset{\displaystyle CH_3}{C}}—CH_3$$

Neopentane (b.p. 9.5°)

As the number of carbon atoms per molecule increases, the number of possible isomers rises rapidly. Thus there are five possible isomers of hexane (C_6H_{14}); there are eighteen for C_8H_{18}, thirty-five for C_9H_{20}, and over 100,000 for $C_{20}H_{42}$.

ceding section, such as methane (CH_4), the butanes (C_4H_{10}), pentanes (C_5H_{12}), and

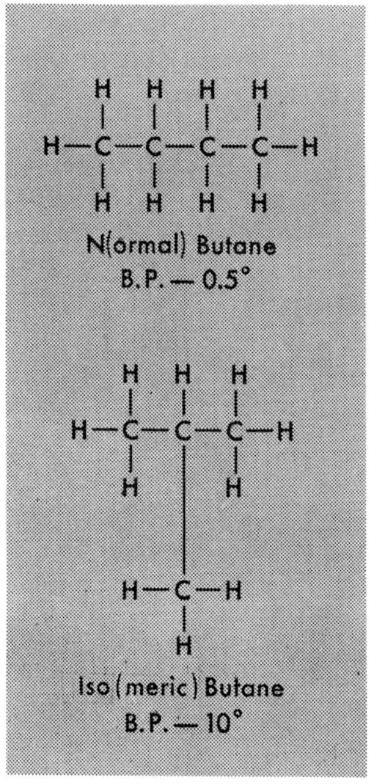

Fig. 28–6 *Architecture of n-butane and isobutane molecules.*

the like, are called *saturated hydrocarbons.* They react slowly with the common chemical reagents at room temperature; for example, they are not oxidized when shaken with one per cent solution of potassium permanganate and do not decolorize bromine water. Similarly, they react very slowly with concentrated sulfuric and nitric acids at room temperature.

From petroleum distillates it is possible to separate small amounts of hydrocarbons in which the proportion of hydrogen in the molecule is less than in the saturated hydrocarbons. Their composition is represented by the general formulas C_nH_{2n}, C_nH_{2n-2}, etc. They are called *unsaturated* hydrocarbons. Compared with the saturated they show a striking reactivity: they are oxidized easily by permanganate, and decolorize bromine water readily with the formation of definite compounds. This unsaturation, or smaller hydrogen content, is directly connected with this striking reactivity. The first member of the unsaturated hydrocarbons, *ethene* (C_2H_4), is related to ethane, which when heated decomposes as follows:

$$\underset{\text{Ethane}}{C_2H_6} + \text{Heat} \rightleftarrows \underset{\text{Ethene}}{C_2H_4} + H_2$$

The reversible reaction shows that ethene contains two hydrogen atoms less per molecule than ethane. If ethene is heated under pressure with hydrogen it is converted to ethane. Since the two hydrogen atoms were removed from the ethane molecule to produce ethene, there are two possibilities: (*a*) the hydrogen atoms were removed from a single carbon atom as shown in formula (1) below; (*b*) the hydrogen atoms were removed from the *two adjacent carbon atoms* as shown in formula (2).

It can be shown by appropriate experiments that the formation of unsaturation is best represented by formula (2), namely, that the elimination of the hydrogen takes place from each of two *contiguous carbon atoms.* Further, the two odd electrons, shown as short dashes in formula (3) and produced by the elimination of the two hydrogen atoms, form a pair of electrons that is shared by the two carbon atoms in addition to the single covalent bond of ethane. The two dashes, called a *double bond,* shown in formula (4), indicate the sharing of two pairs of electrons; one is the normal covalent bond, and the other a special or more reactive chemical bond. For example, if bromine is added to ethene it is immediately decolorized with the *addition* of two atoms of bromine per molecule of ethene:

$$\underset{\text{Ethene}}{\begin{matrix} H & H \\ HC & \!\!=\!\! & CH \end{matrix}} + \underset{\text{Bromine}}{Br_2} \rightarrow \underset{\text{Ethene bromide}}{\begin{matrix} H & & H \\ HC & - & CH \\ | & & | \\ Br & & Br \end{matrix}}$$

Under similar conditions bromine has no action on ethane; if heat is applied in the presence of a catalyst a reaction takes place, but it is unlike addition, for the reaction is very slow and hydrogen bromide is given off:

$$\underset{\text{Ethane}}{\begin{matrix} H & H \\ HC - & C \\ H & H \end{matrix}}\!\boxed{H + Br}\!\underset{\text{Bromine}}{-Br} \rightarrow \underset{\text{Ethyl bromide}}{\begin{matrix} H & H \\ HC - & C - Br \\ H & H \end{matrix}} + HBr$$

It will be noted that the reaction involves *substitution* of one hydrogen atom by a bromine atom. From this brief discussion it is evident that molecules of saturated hydrocarbons react with bromine or chlorine through *substitution* of the halogen atoms

---

$$\underset{(1)}{\begin{matrix} H & H \\ HC - & C\boxed{H} \\ H & \boxed{H} \end{matrix}} \quad \text{or} \quad \underset{(2)}{\begin{matrix} H & H \\ HC - & CH \\ \boxed{H} & \boxed{H} \end{matrix}} \rightarrow \underset{(3)}{\begin{matrix} H & H \\ HC - & CH \\ | & | \end{matrix}} \quad \text{or} \quad \underset{(4)}{\begin{matrix} H & H \\ HC = & CH \end{matrix}}$$

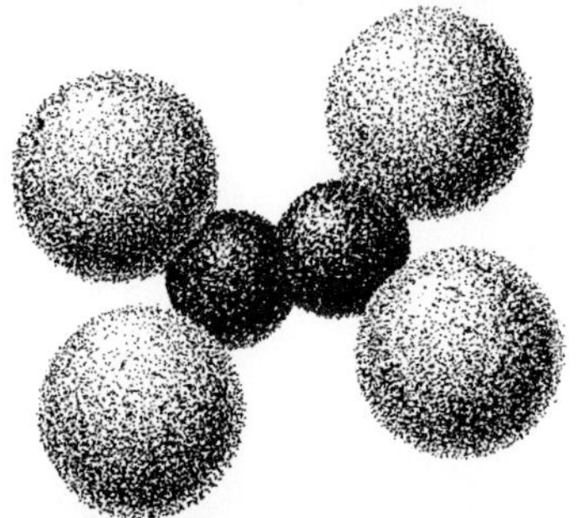

Fig. 28–7 *Architecture of ethene molecule.*

```
   H  H                         H  H
   |  |                         ..  ..
H—C=C—H                      H :C::C: H
```

for hydrogen, while those with *double* bonds (unsaturated hydrocarbons) can form reaction products by process of *addition.* Therefore, the notation of a double bond in any organic compound denotes a special type of chemical bond – unsaturation – between two contiguous carbon atoms. The structural representation of the double bond in both two-dimensional and three-dimensional space is shown in Figure 28–8. Unsaturated hydrocarbons and generally compounds which have one or more double bonds exhibit a large number of reactions. One of the most useful is self-addition or polymerization, which is discussed and illustrated at the end of Chapter 30.

CYCLIC HYDROCARBONS

Another class of hydrocarbons differs from the two thus far considered in that the structure is cyclic. For example, *n*-hexane, C_6H_{14}, can be converted under appropriate conditions to cyclohexane:

```
                                                              H2
                                                              C
                                                            /   \
CH3CH2CH2CH2CH2CH3 → CH2CH2CH2CH2CH2CH2   or            H2C     CH2
    n-Hexane          |_______________|                  |       |     + H2
                         Cyclohexane                    H2C     CH2
                                                            \   /
                                                              C
                                                              H2
```

The formation can be assumed to involve the elimination of one hydrogen atom from each of the two end carbon atoms and union of the latter to form a *cyclic ring,* represented as a hexagon structure in the formula. Though cyclohexane, C_6H_{12}, has the general formula, C_nH_{2n}, it does not exhibit any unsaturated properties; this is in accordance with the cyclic structure assigned to it which shows no double bonds. Cyclohexane, however, can be converted by an appropriate reaction to cyclohexene which shows unsaturated properties:

```
        H2                      H
        C                       C
      /   \                   /   \\
   H2C     CH2             H2C     CH
    |       |       →       |       |    + H2
   H2C     CH2             H2C     CH2
      \   /                   \   /
        C                       C
        H2                      H2
    Cyclohexane             Cyclohexene
```

There is another class of cyclic unsaturated hydrocarbons which differs radically

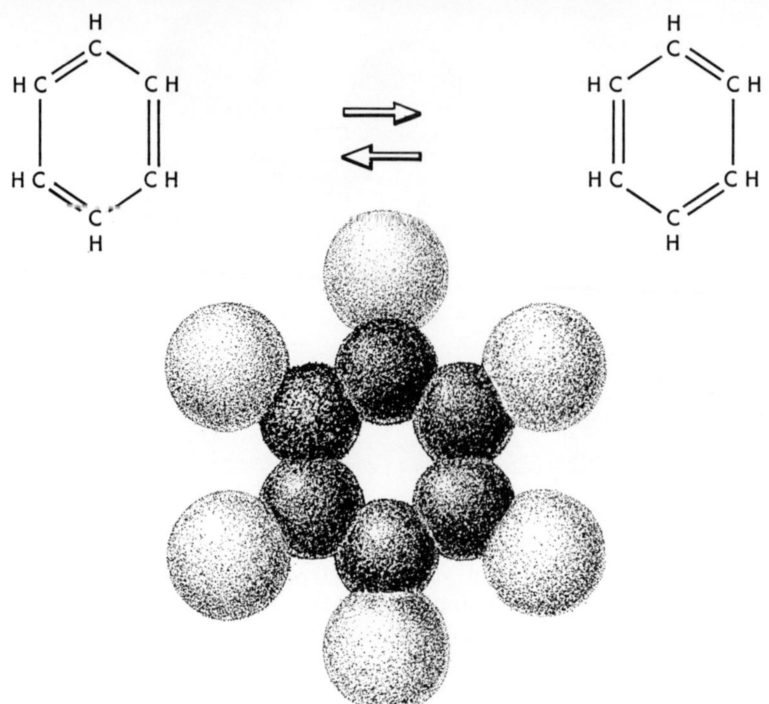

Fig. 28–8 *Architecture of benzene molecule.*

from cyclohexene in that its members do not show great reactivity. The simplest hydrocarbon of the class is benzene, C_6H_6, which is obtained from coal tar. Its relation to cyclohexane is shown by the following formulas.

```
        H2                      H
        C                       C
       / \                     / \\
   H2C     CH2             HC     CH
    |       |      ⇄       ||      |    + 3 H2
   H2C     CH2             HC     CH
       \ /                     \ //
        C                       C
        H2                      H
   Cyclohexane               Benzene
                         (Cyclohexatriene)
```

The formulas indicate that cyclohexane is converted to benzene by removal of hydrogen (dehydrogenation) and benzene can add hydrogen to form cyclohexane (hydrogenation). Figure 28–8 shows a contour model of the benzene molecule. The model as drawn shows equal distances between the centers of the carbon atoms to indicate that six bonds in the ring are equivalent. Though the structure of benzene shows three double bonds, it exhibits under ordinary conditions substitution reactions instead of addition:

$$\underset{\text{Benzene}}{C_6H_6} + \underset{\text{Bromine}}{Br_2} \xrightarrow[60^\circ]{\text{Fe}} \underset{\text{Bromobenzene}}{C_6H_5Br} + HBr$$

Under special conditions, as for example in presence of peroxides, benzene does show addition reactions, thus proving that it has an unsaturated structure:

$$\underset{\text{Benzene}}{C_6H_6} + \underset{\text{Chlorine}}{3\ Cl_2} \xrightarrow{\text{Cat.}} \underset{\text{Benzenehexachloride}}{C_6H_6Cl_6}$$

The addition product has been found useful as an insecticide, particularly toward flies which have developed immunity to DDT. Benzene hydrocarbons, however, are mostly useful for their substitution reactions. For example, benzene with nitric acid is converted to nitrobenzene, which on treatment with reducing agents gives aniline:

$$C_6H_6 \xrightarrow{HNO_3} C_6H_5NO_2 \xrightarrow{3H_2} C_6H_5NH_2 + 2\,H_2O$$

Benzene — Nitrobenzene — Aniline

The reactions given above are of considerable interest and importance, for they are pertinent in the study of a large number of compounds related to hydrocarbons and form the starting point in the synthesis of many useful products such as dyes and drugs.

LIQUID FUELS

As noted in the preceding pages, the commercial products known as gasoline, kerosene, fuel oil, and lubricating oils are mixtures of hydrocarbons obtained from petroleum. The daily production of petroleum in the United States has been steadily rising. In the first part of 1956 it reached a high peak of 7.3 million barrels per day. Of this huge volume, 42 per cent was produced in Texas, about 14 per cent in California, and 11 per cent in Louisiana. Thus, of the twenty-five producing states, three contribute about 67 per cent, and six (Illinois, Kansas, and Wyoming, with the three above) about 82 per cent of the total. Most of these oil fields are in Paleozoic and Mesozoic formations. The composition of the crude product varies with its source, but the general composition is essentially the same, namely, a mixture of hydrocarbons.

Petroleum is always found in rock beds which have marine strata, never in igneous rocks; it contains, in small amounts, derivatives of chlorophyll, haemin, and hormones, all of which are unquestionably of organic origin. Petroleum, therefore, is assumed to be formed in muds, clays, and shales from the decomposition of animal and vegetable matter. The products, together with gas and salt water, diffuse into porous sandstones and limestones. In order for petroleum to be obtained from oil-bearing strata, a natural separation must have taken place through faulting or folding. In other words, geologic changes in the region have caused the gas to migrate to the top of the fold with the oil below it, and finally with the water at the lower level. The wells are drilled after geological studies, so they top the upper part of the folds.

REFINING OF PETROLEUM

Petroleum as obtained from the ground is a viscous liquid with a greenish fluorescence. The color ranges from pale yellow to black. Crude petroleum must be refined, for it cannot be used as a motor fuel or an illuminant without removing its many impurities. The refining of petroleum is accomplished by fractional distillation and subsequent chemical purification of the distillate. Fractional distillation is the separation of a liquid mixture into several portions by distilling and collecting different fractions as

TABLE 28–3 PRIMARY DISTILLATION OF CRUDE PETROLEUM

FRACTION	NAME	BOILING RANGE °C.	COMPOSITION [1]	YIELD % [2]	USES
I	Gasoline	35–225	6–10	25	Motor fuel
II	Kerosene	225–300	10–12	12	Fuel
III	Fuel oil	300–400	10–14	37	"Cracked" to gasoline [3]
IV	Lubricating oils	400–450	12–16	7	Lubricants
V	Residue	....	14 and above	19	"Cracking" operations

[1] Number of carbon atoms in the hydrocarbon molecules found in the fraction.
[2] Average yield based on the volume of crude oil used in the distillation.
[3] This fraction may be refractionated to obtain various solvents, used for paints and the like.

the temperature rises. The composition of the fractions depends largely on the origin of the crude oil. In general practice the fractions indicated as I and II in Table 28–3 are separated; the constituents of gasoline boil off first, then kerosene. After removal of these two fractions the distillation may be discontinued at this point and the remaining crude oil (topped crude) used as fuel oil in industrial and domestic heating. The distillation may be continued, however, to obtain fractions III and IV; the lubricating oils are used to minimize resistance between the moving metallic parts of machines. After distillation and upon cooling, the oils deposit a solid which is known as *paraffin.* Certain types of lubricating oils are decolorized by careful treatment with sulfuric acid, fuller's earth, decolorizing carbon, or other agents to a water-white liquid known as *mineral oil.* It is used extensively for the preparation of cosmetic "cold cream," and as a laxative in medicine. Another product of the refining of petroleum is petroleum jelly, or vaseline, a white, butterlike mass used in the preparation of ointments. Petroleum jelly consists mainly of paraffin hydrocarbons.

Cracking. Table 28–3 shows that fractions III and V add up to more than 50 per cent of the original crude oil. The combined fractions III and V are used to produce more gasoline. The fundamental difference between the gasoline fraction (I), for which there is a large demand, and the higher boiling fractions is that the constituents of the latter have larger molecular weights, that is, they have more carbon and hydrogen atoms per molecule. Therefore, to convert these high-boiling fractions into gasoline it is necessary to "break down" the molecules of high molecular weight to molecules of lower molecular weight. In the older processes the high-boiling fractions were subjected under pressure to temperatures above those employed in ordinary distillation of petroleum. Under these conditions hydrocarbons of high molecular weight underwent rupture or *cracking* to smaller molecular fragments similar to those which occur in gasoline. In the modern processes, the cracking is accomplished catalytically. The crude oil is vaporized and preheated and is then blown through a bed of finely divided solid catalyst at a rate so controlled that each particle of the catalyst is surrounded by the vapors of the crude oil. The bed of the solid catalyst thus becomes a "mobile fluid" and boils off like a liquid. This "fluidized" action greatly promotes the "thermal cracking" of the crude oil into low molecular weight compounds or "cracked gasoline."

In the cracking operations, besides the saturated hydrocarbons of low molecular weight which are used as gasoline, there is always produced in addition to hydrogen a considerable amount of *unsaturated* hydrocarbons of low molecular weight. These must be removed from the cracked gasoline, since their presence leads to gum formation in the gasoline lines and orifices of the motor car and to increased vaporization losses. In the early days of the petroleum industry the unsaturated hydrocarbons were utilized as fuel in the distillation of petroleum. Today they are utilized to produce synthetic gasoline, synthetic rubber, and a variety of plastics. Several examples of this type of reaction will be found at the end of Chapter 30.

SOLID FUELS

The term *coal* is applied to several types of carbonaceous fuels. Table 28–4 lists the various types of coal in order of age. Below wood is peat, which is considered to be the first step in the alteration and consolidation of deposits of plant tissues to coal. The last stage is anthracite or hard coal.

The evidence on which our present theories of coal formation are based is rather extensive. Lignite and bituminous coals usually occur in beds alternating with beds of clay or shales. Both in the coal seams and in the adjoining clay beds, impressions of leaves, roots, and even stumps of trees are found, offering evidence of the nature and mode of formation of coal. Most coal shows a tendency under the impact of a hammer to break into small blocks or very small particles approaching dust. When examined closely, most pieces of soft coal show divisional planes indicating the effect of pressure.

As is well known, when wood decays, exposed to the atmosphere, it is slowly decomposed by fungi and bacterial enzymes and apparently disappears. A decomposing log or branch is a familiar sight in the woods. But when wood undergoes decay submerged in water, as in swampy regions, with the air partly excluded, it is slowly changed to a brown, pasty, compact mass known as *peat*. The changes are brought about by bacterial enzymes, and during this process there is a progressive loss of oxygen and hydrogen, with the production of water, carbon dioxide, and methane. When peat is buried deep, it is slowly changed to a low-grade coal called *lignite*. The changes are brought about by geologic factors and are similar to the processes by which sediments are changed into rocks. When peat changes to lignite, there is an increase in the percentage of carbon; if subjected to increased pressure by being more deeply buried, lignite is changed to *bituminous* coal. When bituminous strata have been repeatedly folded and squeezed, hard coal or *anthracite* results. In the foothills of the Appalachian region in Ohio the coal-bearing strata are horizontal, and the coal is more closely related to that found in Illinois than to the beds a little to the east in Pennsylvania, where the coal beds in the mountainous regions are highly folded and consist almost entirely of anthracite.

The coal found in the Illinois, Kentucky, and Pennsylvania regions was formed prior to the elevation of the Appalachian Mountains during the latter part of the Paleozoic Era. The conditions during the geologic periods of extensive coal-making swamps must have been a warm, moist climate, a luxuriant forest growth in swampy lowlands along rivers, and a relatively unstable continent. As the continent subsided, the plant material that had accumulated in swamps was buried by sediments of sand and mud (clay). When the region was reelevated, a new forest grew on these sediments, which after an interval of several thousand years were again covered by mud and clay. In this manner the alternating strata of coal and shale came into existence. Occasionally the subsidence was extensive, and the region was covered by shallow seas with a deposition of limestone.

TABLE 28–4 COMPOSITION OF WOOD AND VARIOUS TYPES OF COAL

SAMPLE	WATER	VOLATILE MATTER	CARBON	ASH	APPROXIMATE COMPOSITION OF DRIED SAMPLES EXCLUDING WATER AND ASH			HEAT VALUE (B.T.U. PER LB.)
					Carbon	Hydrogen	Oxygen	
Wood	11.5	....	...	0.3	50.0	6.0	44.0	4,500
Peat	15.0	50.0	25.0	10.0	59.0	5.0	36.0	4,500
Lignite	32.0	30.0	29.0	9.0	67.0	6.0	27.0	6,500
Bituminous coal	4.0	35.0	53.0	8.0	80.0	5.0	15.0	14,000
Anthracite	3.3	3.0	91.0	2.7	95.0	2.5	2.5	15,500

Table 28–4 shows that lignite and bituminous coals contain a high percentage of volatile matter. When they are heated about a third of their weight is given off as a black, smoky, gaseous mixture. A part of this smoky, gaseous mixture burns when bituminous coal is used for the production of heat in homes and factories. However, a substantial part is exhausted in the atmosphere as smoke and soot through the chimneys. About 50 to 60 per cent of the soot and tarry products which pollute the air of

large cities like New York, Chicago, or Los Angeles are contributed by the furnaces of apartment houses and private dwellings.

When bituminous coal is subjected to heat in the absence of air, so that the volatile matter is driven off, the carbonaceous residue is known as *coke*. It contains about 80 to 85 per cent carbon, 0.5 per cent hydrogen, and 13 to 15 per cent ash, and gives about 14,000 B.T.U.'s per pound. Coke is produced on a large scale for the conversion of iron ore to iron. The gaseous components of the volatile fraction (coal gas) consist mainly of methane and hydrogen, with smaller quantities of carbon monoxide and higher hydrocarbons. By cooling the gases, water, ammonia, and a viscous liquid known as coal tar are obtained. The latter on fractional distillation yields mostly benzene hydrocarbons. Thus, "coal tar drugs" and "coal tar dyes" are so called because they are manufactured from benzene hydrocarbons derived originally from coal tar.

SUMMARY

1. Man differs from other animals in that he uses a large amount of energy produced outside of his body in order to change his physical environment. Of the total energy consumed in the world, only 8 per cent is furnished by direct human work and 13 per cent by animals; about four-fifths comes from fuel resources accumulated in the past — coal, oil, and gas.
2. The average per capita consumption of energy in the world is about 1800×10^4 kilocalories; about 5 per cent of this is utilized by man simply for living, 20 per cent for changing the effects of climate, and about 50 per cent for changing the raw materials of the world to satisfy his material wants.
3. The oil (petroleum) industry in the United States is important because it supplies about 45 per cent of the total energy demand.
4. About 90 per cent of the sources of energy of the United States are compounds of carbon.
5. Carbon is unique among the elements in that it forms a large number of compounds with hydrogen, oxygen, and nitrogen. In forming compounds, carbon atoms also unite with themselves to form long chains or complex ring structures.
6. The carbon-hydrogen system is considered to be the energy carrier of life. The changes involved in the processes of photosynthesis and respiration are essentially oxidation-reductions of the carbon-hydrogen system. During photosynthesis C–H and C–C bonds are formed and the energy from the sun is stored. During respiration those bonds are broken and energy is released.
7. Photosynthesis occurs only in plants and involves absorption of energy and partial reduction of carbon dioxide to organic compounds.
8. Respiration occurs in both plants and animals; it involves oxidation of organic compounds and transformation of the chemical potential energy to heat.
9. Hydrocarbons contain carbon and hydrogen and are the components of most carbonaceous fuels. They can be synthesized from carbon monoxide and hydrogen (water gas), but are mostly obtained from the distillation of petroleum and from coal.
10. Coal is altered plant débris from previous geological ages. The transformation of wood to coal takes place in stages: peat, lignite, bituminous coal, and anthracite. In the transformation the percentage of volatile matter decreases and fixed carbon increases.
11. Petroleum is a complex mixture of hydrocarbons derived from sedimentary strata; it is separated or refined by fractional distillation into light fractions of gasoline and kerosene and heavy fractions of fuel oil and lubricating oils. The higher fractions when heated under pressure are "cracked," or partially converted into lighter fractions. In such processes, hydrocarbons of high molecular weight are converted to smaller molecular fragments.
12. The general structure of the saturated hydrocarbons is C_nH_{2n+2} and of unsaturated hydrocarbons C_nH_{2n}. The former are generally unreactive while the latter are very reactive. Benzene hydrocarbons, though they

are unsaturated, possess special stability.

13. Isomers are compounds which have the same kind and the same number of atoms in their molecules, but have different arrangements of the various atoms.
14. In all carbon compounds the carbon atoms form covalent bonds with other atoms (including other carbon atoms) with the valence electrons tetrahedrally arranged in space.

STUDY EXERCISES

1. Of the total energy used per capita in the world, how much is replaceable and how much irreplaceable?
2. Assuming that the average per capita energy consumption in the United States is 10,000 units (10^4 kg cal) per year, compare it with that of one of the so-called "underdeveloped" societies. What conclusions can you draw?
3. What evidence can you propose for each of the following statements:
   a. Heat energy is constantly produced in the animal body.
   b. Carbon compounds are oxidized by animals and plants.
   c. Carbon dioxide and water are utilized in photosynthesis.
   d. The end products of photosynthesis contain higher potential energy than the initial products.
   e. The oxygen liberated in photosynthesis comes from water.
   f. C–H and C–C bonds are formed in photosynthesis and these are broken in respiration.
   g. In photosynthesis there is a series of reactions which take place in presence of light and a series of reactions which take place in dark.
   h. Probably most of the oxygen of our atmosphere was formed by photosynthesis.
   i. The carbon-hydrogen system is the energy carrier of life.
4. Show how a mixture of hydrocarbons of the general formula C_nH_{2n+2} can be synthesized by drilling holes into young beds of coal (lignites), setting the coal on fire, then pumping steam into the burning coal seams.
5. Given 6 carbon atoms and 14 hydrogen atoms, write condensed formulas (see Figure 28–6) of as many different molecular structures of isomeric hexanes as you can.
6. Write the structural formulas and names of all the saturated hydrocarbons which contain 1, 2, 3, and 4 carbon atoms.
7. How does ethane differ from ethene?
8. What are the chief uses of the following: (*a*) saturated hydrocarbons with 1 to 4 C atoms; (*b*) saturated hydrocarbons with 5 to 10 C atoms; (*c*) unsaturated hydrocarbons; (*d*) benzene hydrocarbons.
9. How can it be demonstrated that benzene (C_6H_6) has an unsaturated structure, though it exhibits great stability?
10. Write the reaction between ethene and bromine.
11. What evidence exists that there are three isomeric pentanes (C_5H_{12})?
12. Draw a diagram to show the progressive change of wood into anthracite. Indicate (*a*) the type of geologic processes which brought about each change; (*b*) the nature of chemical changes in each stage — that is, which elements were diminished or increased. (Refer to Table 28–4.)
13. In what type of strata is petroleum sought? Draw a rough diagram showing the operations of petroleum refining. Give the various fractions and their uses.

FOR FURTHER READING

1. MARKHAM, E. C., and S. E. SMITH, *General Chemistry*. Boston: Houghton Mifflin Company, 1954.
   The chemistry of hydrocarbons is discussed on pages 555–566.
2. PAULING, LINUS, *General Chemistry*. San Francisco: W. H. Freeman and Company, 1953.
   An introduction to the chemistry of organic compounds will be found on pages 569–580.
3. Paperback: EDITORS OF SCIENTIFIC AMERICAN, *The Physics and Chemistry of Life*. Simon and Schuster, $1.45.
   An excellent discussion of photosynthesis is given on pages 27–47.

29

THINGS OF THIS WORLD: II

THE PRECEDING CHAPTER discussed the general nature of the hydrocarbons, which are liquid and solid fuels essential to our technological society. In the present chapter, to discuss foods — the fuels of the animal engine — it becomes necessary to consider other groups of carbon compounds, such as the *alcohols,* the *amines,* the *aldehydes* and *carboxylic acids.* All of these may be considered as derivatives of the hydrocarbons; in other words, the hydrocarbons may be formally considered as the parent substances of all organic compounds. It does not follow that all organic compounds are always prepared by procedures which start with a hydrocarbon, or with a compound which was derived from a hydrocarbon. For purposes of relationship, however, all organic compounds may be considered as derived from hydrocarbons by the removal of one or more hydrogen atoms from a hydrocarbon and the substitution for it of one or more reactive groups called functional groups.

FUNCTIONAL GROUPS OF ORGANIC COMPOUNDS

Let us consider the hydrocarbon ethane CH_3CH_3. Assume that we replace a hydrogen atom by a hydroxyl group $-OH$; the resulting compound as shown in formulas 29–1 and 29–2 is the alcohol ethanol:

```
 H   H                      H   H
 |   |                      |   |
H—C—C—H                    H—C—C—OH
 |   |                      |   |
 H   H                      H   H
```

Ethane (Hydrocarbon) $C_2H_5—H$ (29–1)

Ethanol (Alcohol) $C_2H_5—OH$ (29–2)

```
 H   H
 |   |
H—C—C—NH2
 |   |
 H   H
```

Ethylamine (Amine) $C_2H_5—NH_2$ (29–3)

Similarly substitution of the amino group $-NH_2$ for a hydrogen atom gives an amine, shown in formula 29–3. The formulas show that if a hydrogen atom is removed from ethane the remaining part of the molecule, C_2H_5-, is the same in both ethanol (29–2) and ethylamine (29–3). This grouping of atoms, C_2H_5-, is called the *ethyl radical.* By joining the radical with various reactive or functional groups such as Cl, OH, or NH_2, the simpler types of organic compounds, halogens, alcohols, or amines are obtained. Table 29–1 gives a partial list of the simpler organic compounds and the functional groups joined to the ethyl radical.

As stated above, not every class of organic compounds is always prepared directly from the hydrocarbons. However, it is possible to relate each compound listed in Table 29–1 to the parent hydrocarbon ethane. For example, chlorination of ethane yields ethyl chloride, which on hydrolysis yields ethanol or on reaction with ammonia yields ethylamine:

$$\underset{\text{Ethane}}{CH_3CH_3} \xrightarrow{[Cl_2]} \underset{\text{Ethyl chloride}}{CH_3CH_2Cl} \begin{cases} \xrightarrow{[H_2O]} \underset{\text{Ethanol}}{CH_3CH_2OH} \\ \xrightarrow{[NH_3]} \underset{\text{Ethylamine}}{CH_3CH_2NH_2} \end{cases}$$

Ethanol on mild oxidation yields ethanal (acetaldehyde) which, on further oxidation, yields acetic acid:

$$\underset{\text{Ethanol}}{CH_3CH_2OH} \xrightarrow{[O]} \underset{\substack{\text{Ethanal} \\ \text{(Acetaldehyde)}}}{CH_3CHO} \xrightarrow{[O]} \underset{\substack{\text{Ethanoic acid} \\ \text{(Acetic acid)}}}{CH_3COOH}$$

As shown in Table 29–1, the functional group of aldehydes (and ketones) is the carbonyl, CO; and the carboxyl, COOH, the functional group of carboxylic acids. Ethyl ether is obtained by removal of one molecule of water from two molecules of ethanol:

$$\underset{\text{Ethanol}}{CH_3CH_2O\boxed{H + HO}CH_2CH_3} \xrightarrow{(H_2SO_4)} \underset{\text{Ethyl ether}}{CH_3CH_2\text{—}O\text{—}CH_2CH_3} + H_2O$$

The ester ethyl acetate is obtained by removal of a molecule of water from a molecule of acetic acid and a molecule of ethanol:

$$\underset{\text{Acetic acid}}{CH_3CO\boxed{OH}} \boxed{+ H}\underset{\text{Ethanol}}{OC_2H_5} \xrightarrow{(H_3O^+)} \underset{\text{Ethyl acetate}}{CH_3COOC_2H_5} + H_2O$$

With this relatively elementary knowledge of organic compounds it is possible to consider the chemical nature of foods.

NATURE OF FOODS

The essential nutritive requirements of a balanced human diet are: *water, salts*

TABLE 29–1 SIMPLE DERIVATIVES OF ETHANE

CLASS OF COMPOUNDS	NAME AND FORMULA OF DERIVATIVES	FUNCTIONAL GROUP ATTACHED TO CH_3CH_2- RADICAL	
Monohalogens	Ethyl chloride CH_3CH_2Cl	Chloride	—Cl
Alcohols	Ethanol CH_3CH_2OH (Ethyl alcohol)	Hydroxyl	—OH
Amines	Ethylamine $CH_3CH_2NH_2$	Amino	$-NH_2$
Ethers	Ethyl ether $CH_3CH_2-O-CH_2CH_3$	Oxide	—O—
Aldehydes	Ethanal CH_3CHO (Acetaldehyde)	Carbonyl	$>C{=}O$ *
Carboxylic acids	Ethanoic acid CH_3COOH (Acetic acid)	Carboxyl	—COOH*
Esters	Ethyl acetate $CH_3COOC_2H_5$	Carboxylic ester	$-\overset{\overset{O}{\parallel}}{C}-O-$

* The carbonyl and carboxyl functional groups are obtained by oxidation of the $-CH_2$ part of the ethyl radical CH_3CH_2-.

(*or minerals*), *carbohydrates, fats, proteins,* and *vitamins.* Table 29–2 lists the chemical composition of a number of common foods.

The table shows that the ash (mineral salts) is a very small component while water makes a very large part of the total. Fats and proteins are found predominantly in meat products; carbohydrates occur chiefly in plant and vegetable products.

CARBOHYDRATES

As shown in the preceding chapter, carbohydrates are the first products of photosynthesis. They include sugars, starches, and the celluloses. The sugars and starches serve essentially as fuels in the human diet. The sugars are sweet crystalline substances which are widely distributed in nature, particularly in fruits and vegetables. *Glucose,* or *dextrose,* occurs in appreciable amounts in the juice of grapes and other fruits and is probably the most important *simple* sugar. Other simple sugars are *fructose* (fruit sugar), which occurs in honey and fruits, and *galactose,* which results when *lactose* (milk sugar) is hydrolyzed. The chemical composition of these three simple sugars is expressed by the formula $C_6H_{12}O_6$; each contains one carbonyl and five hydroxyl groups arranged differently. The following formulas show, for example, that the difference between glucose and fructose is in the position of the carbonyl group:

```
  H  H  H  H  H  H
  |  |  |  |  |  |
H-C--C--C--C--C--C
  |  |  |  |  |  ||
  O  O  O  O  O  O
  H  H  H  H  H
```

Glucose

```
  H  H  H  H     H
  |  |  |  |     |
H-C--C--C--C--C--C-H
  |  |  |  |  || |
  O  O  O  O  O  O
  H  H  H  H     H
```

Fructose

The more complex carbohydrates result from unions of the simpler sugars. For example, a molecule of glucose and one of fructose combine to form a molecule of a more complex sugar, *sucrose* (cane sugar or beet sugar, which are identical). Conversely, when sucrose is heated with acidified water or treated with saliva, it breaks down into a molecule of glucose and a molecule of fructose:

$$\underset{\text{Sucrose}}{C_{12}H_{22}O_{11}} + H_2O \xrightleftharpoons[\text{or enzymes}]{\text{HCl}} \underset{\text{Glucose}}{C_6H_{12}O_6} + \underset{\text{Fructose}}{C_6H_{12}O_6}$$

Glucose and galactose unite in the same way to form lactose (milk sugar), which is found to the extent of from three to five per cent in the milk of mammals.

The complex carbohydrates are built up by the union of simple sugar molecules, just as cane and milk sugar are built up. For example, all the starches found in corn, wheat, rice, and potatoes are built up of glucose units. Thus, the molecule of starch is believed to be built up of from twenty-five to thirty glucose units; this would assign a molecular weight of about 5000 to starch, the molecular weight of glucose being 180. With an increase in the size of the molecule there is a decrease in the solubility and reactivity. Thus starch does not dissolve in water but forms a dispersion; it does not react with the same ease as the simple sugars. In the animal body the starches and complex sugars are converted by the enzymes of the digestive juices to simple sugars such as glucose. The process is essentially hydrolysis, as shown in the following equation:

$$(C_6H_{10}O_5)_n + n\,H_2O \rightleftarrows n\,C_6H_{12}O_6$$

The simple sugars are absorbed through the intestinal wall into the lymph and the blood stream. In the muscles and liver the simple sugars are polymerized to animal starch or glycogen, leaving in the blood stream 0.1 per cent of glucose. Whenever the body needs more glucose for fuel, it is drawn from the glycogen in storage.

TABLE 29–2 AVERAGE COMPOSITION OF SOME FOODS

FOOD	WATER %	PROTEIN %	FAT %	CARBOHYDRATES %	REFUSE %	ASH %	CALORIES PER POUND
Beef shoulder	57.9	16.0	10.1	0	15.2	0.8	735
Bacon smoked	10.4	9.5	66.9	0	8.7	4.5	2685
Chicken broiler	43.7	12.8	1.4	0	41.4	0.7	295
Fish Mackerel edible portion	73.4	18.3	7.1	0	....	1.2	645
Eggs boiled	67.5	14.5	16.6	0.5	....	0.9	975
Butter	11.0	1.0	85.0	0	....	3.0	3605
Cheese American	31.6	28.8	35.9	0.3	....	3.4	2055
Milk whole	87.0	3.3	4.0	5.0	....	0.7	325
Corn meal	12.5	9.2	1.9	75.4	....	1.0	1655
Wheat flour	11.4	13.8	1.9	71.9	....	1.0	1675
Bread whole wheat	38.4	8.7	0.9	49.7	....	1.3	1140
Rice	12.3	8.0	0.3	79.0	....	0.4	1630
Cabbage fresh	91.5	1.6	0.3	5.6	....	1.0	145
Peas dried	9.5	24.6	1.0	62.0	....	2.9	1655
Potatoes boiled	75.5	2.5	0.1	20.9	....	1.0	440
Apples edible portion	84.6	0.4	0.5	14.1	....	0.4	290
Oranges edible portion	86.9	0.8	0.2	11.6	....	0.5	240

FATS

Fats are esters of the trihydroxy alcohol, glycerol, and long-chain carboxylic acids, also known as fatty acids. The composition can be demonstrated by boiling fats with sodium hydroxide, when glycerol and the sodium salts of the fatty acids (soaps) are formed:

$$\begin{array}{l} H_2C-O-CO-(CH_2)_{16}-CH_3 \\ \quad | \\ HC-O-CO-(CH_2)_{16}-CH_3 + 3\,NaOH \rightarrow \\ \quad | \\ H_2C-O-CO-(CH_2)_{16}-CH_3 \\ \text{Glyceryl tristearate} \\ \text{(Fatty ester or fat)} \end{array} \quad \begin{array}{l} \rightarrow 3\,CH_3(CH_2)_{16}COO^-Na^+ \\ \text{Sodium stearate} \\ \rightarrow H_2C-OH \\ \quad | \\ HC-OH \\ \quad | \\ H_2C-OH \\ \text{Glycerol} \end{array}$$

It will be noted that the soap molecules contain a long nonpolar hydrocarbon chain and a polar group, the carboxylate ion, $-COO^-$. This structure can explain to a large extent the cleansing action of soaps. If, for example, one has grease or a fatty substance on the hands, water will not remove it since these materials are not soluble in water. If, however, a small amount of soap is added, the long hydrocarbon chain of the soap molecules orients and associates itself with the hydrocarbon molecules of the grease; the carboxylate ion end of the soap molecules, since it is polar, associates with the water molecules thus forming a "bridge," so to speak, between the two nonmiscible materials, grease and water, as shown diagrammatically in Figure 29–1.

In animal digestion, the fats are broken down by digestive enzymes to glycerol and organic acids; after absorption through the intestinal wall, the fragments are resynthesized into the fats which are characteristic of each animal. A small amount of fat is left in the blood, and the rest is stored under the skin and around many organs. Like the carbohydrates, fats serve as fuels and undergo enzymatic oxidation to give carbon dioxide, water, and heat. Besides being important sources of energy, fats have other functions: they are necessary constituents of tissues of the body and also act as regulators of food intake. This regulatory function depends on the slow rate of digestion of fats as compared with that of carbohydrates and proteins. Since they digest slowly, fats delay the sensation of hunger. Low fat content in food causes an abnormal feeling of hunger a few hours after meals. Finally, fats are necessary for the absorption of certain vitamins (A, D, E, and K).

Fig. 29–1 *Cleansing action of soap.*

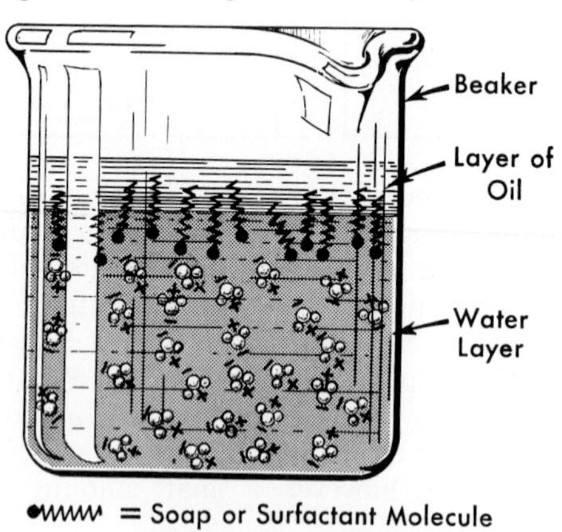

PROTEINS

Proteins serve as the essential parts of the animal engine in which carbohydrates and fats burn; they are the basic constituents of all tissues, perform and coordinate the functions of the body, and transmit heredity. The number of proteins is very large; among the most common are casein from milk and albumen from eggs or blood. Proteins differ from carbohydrates and fats in that they contain nitrogen (16 to 17 per cent), besides carbon, hydrogen, and oxygen. They have a very complex structure; their molecular weights vary between 36,000 and 5,000,000.

On digestion with enzymes, proteins yield the simpler parts of which their molecules are built. These smaller fragments are called amino acids. The simplest amino acid, glycine (or aminoacetic acid), may be thought to be derived from acetic acid by the removal of one hydrogen from the CH_3^- group and replacement with the amino group:

$$\begin{array}{cc} \text{H} & \text{H} \\ \text{HC—COOH} & \text{HC—COOH} \\ \text{H} & | \\ & \text{NH}_2 \\ \text{Acetic acid} & \text{Glycine} \\ & \text{(Aminoacetic acid)} \end{array}$$

About thirty different amino acids have been obtained from proteins and their structure can be expressed by the general formula R–$CHNH_2COOH$, where R represents various organic radicals. It is assumed that the amino acids combine with each other to form the proteins, which in turn combine to form tissues. The union of amino acids, which may be likened to the union of the letters of the alphabet to form words, is assumed to take place through the amino and carboxyl groups, which are present in every amino acid. For example, two amino acids may combine as follows:

$$\underset{\underset{\textstyle \mathrm{NH_2}}{|}}{\mathrm{CH_2}}\mathrm{CO}\boxed{\mathrm{OH + H}}\overset{\mathrm{H}}{\mathrm{N}}\text{—}\underset{\underset{\textstyle \mathrm{CH_3}}{|}}{\mathrm{CH}}\mathrm{COOH} \rightarrow \underset{\underset{\textstyle \mathrm{NH_2}}{|}}{\mathrm{CH_2}}\text{—}\mathrm{CO}\text{—}\mathrm{NH}\text{—}\underset{\underset{\textstyle \mathrm{CH_3}}{|}}{\mathrm{CH}}\mathrm{COOH}$$

Amino acids　　　　　　　　Peptide

The product of this chemical union is called a *peptide.* By the union of many amino acids through combination of the carboxyl group of one with the amino group of anther, a large molecule of the resulting protein is formed.

It is assumed that the amino acid residues in the form of peptide chains are coiled in the form of a helix into precise patterns which are maintained by intermolecular linkages of hydrogen bonds between the CO and NH groups of adjacent helixes. The regularity in protein structure is related to the specificity of the enzymes, since these so-called moving parts of the protoplasmic engine are elaborated from protein fragments. The pattern of the protein in turn is controlled by a giant molecule called desoxyribonucleic acid, or DNA for short. This giant molecule is a component part of all chromosomes, the transmitters of heredity. As shown in Figure 29–2, DNA is composed of three different basic chemical units: phosphoric acid, sugar, and an organic base. The structural model shown in the figure is composed of two DNA chains wound as a double helix around a central axis. Unwinding results in two complementary chains which are able to pick up from the materials within the cell the precursor fragments of the DNA and thus produce two new helixes. In this manner DNA is able to duplicate itself and control the development of the other parts of the cells in a specific way.

In the digestive tract, through the action of several kinds of enzymes, proteins are hydrolyzed to amino acids which pass through the intestinal wall to the lymph and blood. From the circulating blood, each cell selects

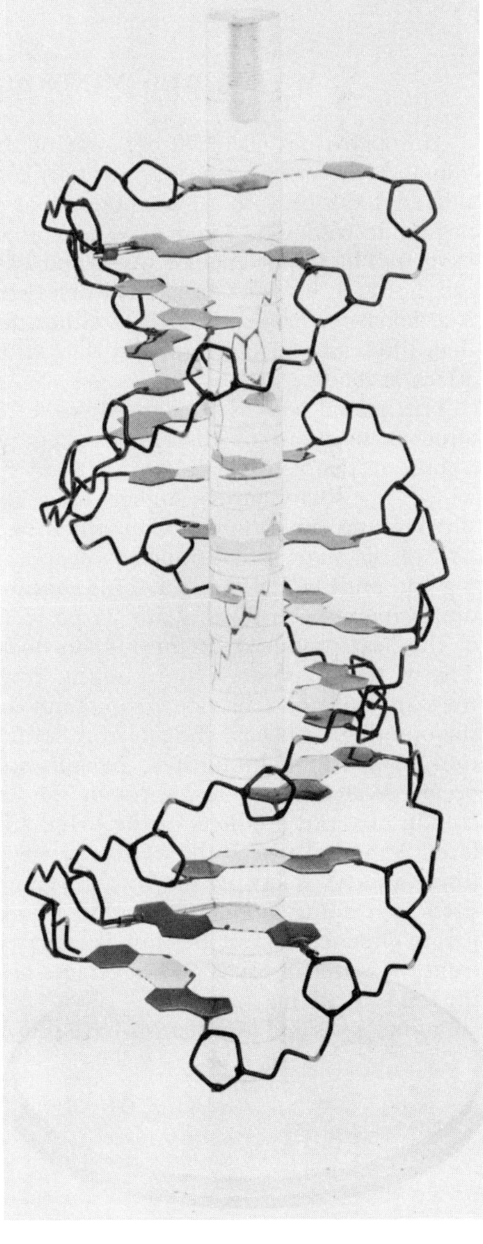

Fig. 29–2 *Structural model of DNA (desoxyribonucleic acid). This giant molecule consists of three basic units: (a) a five-carbon sugar unit, represented in the model as white pentagons, (b) a cyclic (five or six atoms) organic base represented as shaded hexagons or pentagons, and (c) a phosphoric acid unit represented as links joining the sugar units. The model shows a pair of DNA chains wound as a double helix.* (Scientific American)

and removes the amino acids it needs to build up its particular proteins. The amino acids which are not required for tissue-building are broken down by the cells and utilized as energy sources. The human body is able to synthesize some of the amino acids but not all. Obviously, those that cannot be manufactured must be obtained from food. It is therefore important that the diet should include proteins which contain these essential amino acids. A variety of both meat and vegetable proteins in the diet insures a supply of the required amino acids. Deficiency in the required amino acids leads to serious disturbances both of growth and of health.

WATER AND MINERALS

Although from 60 to 70 per cent of the human body is water, this is not usually considered food because it is obtained at a negligible cost. The same may be said of oxygen. The importance of water and oxygen, however, becomes apparent when there is a deficiency or a total lack of either, for then life ceases far more rapidly than from a lack of foods.

The animal body is a balanced system of aqueous solutions or dispersions, kept at a constant temperature (37° C., or 98.6° F.) which is usually much higher than the surrounding environment. Consequently, a part of the water is continuously evaporating and must be replenished. This continuous evaporation utilizes about 25 per cent of the heat produced by the human body. The water evaporates continuously from the skin, and when the rate is rapid and the surrounding air is near the moisture saturation point (high humidity), perspiration occurs. Water is also lost through the excretion of waste products in the urine and feces. A total of two to three liters of water (three quarts) is lost per day by an average-sized man doing moderate work in a temperate climate. Part of the loss is replaced from the water in foods and beverages and the rest by drinking.

Physiologists and biochemists have shown that an appreciable amount of inorganic ions, such as magnesium, Mg^{++}, and calcium, Ca^{++}, must be supplied to plants for growth and normal functions. Likewise, inorganic ions are necessary to animal life. Some of the inorganic ions that must be supplied for normal human nutrition are calcium, Ca^{++}, phosphate, $PO_4^{\equiv}$, chloride, Cl^-, sodium, Na^+, potassium, K^+, magnesium, Mg^{++}, iodide, I^-, ferric, Fe^{+++}, cupric, Cu^{++}, and manganous, Mn^{++}. They are often called *minerals.* The first two are the prime builders of bones, the chassis of the animal engine. The chloride ion is involved in the secretion of hydrochloric acid in the stomach; iodine is essential to the function of thyroid glands; iron is necessary for hemoglobin formation; and copper and manganese, together with iron, are involved in the oxidative processes of the body.

Most of the inorganic ions are present in the plant and animal tissues of foods; there are some, however, particularly Ca^{++}, $PO_4^{\equiv}$, and Fe^{+++}, which are not in great abundance, so that certain diets may lead to deficiencies in these elements and give rise to grave disorders, such as stunted growth, rickets, anemia, and goiter. Protection against such deficiencies is of greater importance during the period of growth, when the diet should include foods rich in these elements.

VITAMINS

The term *vitamin* is used to designate certain nutritive organic compounds which must be present in small amounts in the diet of animals for normal development and functioning. Deficiency or absence of a vitamin from the diet leads to disturbances in some specific function and ultimately leads to bodily derangement or disease. For example, deficiency of vitamin A causes night blindness; deficiency of vitamin D causes rickets; and deficiency of nicotinic acid — a constituent of the complex vitamin B — causes pellagra.

The knowledge of vitamins was elicited almost entirely through controlled nutritional experiments, mostly through the use of the lowly and despised rat. In 1913 American investigators noticed that rats could not grow normally if fed with diets which contained purified fats, but that their condition was improved when butter fat and cod liver oil were added. The conclusion was reached that certain fats carry a small amount of a required nutrient; this factor was named fat-soluble A, and is now known as vitamin A. The entire research on vitamins has been guided by experiments of this type: first, to find a food rich in the particular vitamin; next, to control the concentration of a food extract that is rich in the vitamin; and finally, to standardize the vitamin concentrate. Because the chemical nature of a vitamin in the beginning is unknown, the vitamins are designated by letters (A, B, C, D, and so on). In many cases, what was originally thought to be one vitamin (for example, vitamin B), was progressively found by continued research to contain several factors or different substances, B_1, B_2, B_3, and so forth. Vitamin B_1 is also known as thiamin, and B_2 was renamed vitamin G or riboflavin. In fact, from the vitamin B complex more than ten distinct vitamins have been isolated whose structures are known, and undoubtedly a few more essential food factors remain to be discovered. When a sufficient amount of a vitamin has been prepared in the pure state, the problem of its chemical structure is taken up, so that in a comparatively short time the nature of the vitamin is determined. In this manner the synthesis of vitamins has been accomplished. Formulas 29–4 and 29–5 show the structure of thiamin (B_1) and ascorbic acid (C). It will be noted that the latter is related to sugars; its synthesis usually begins with glucose.

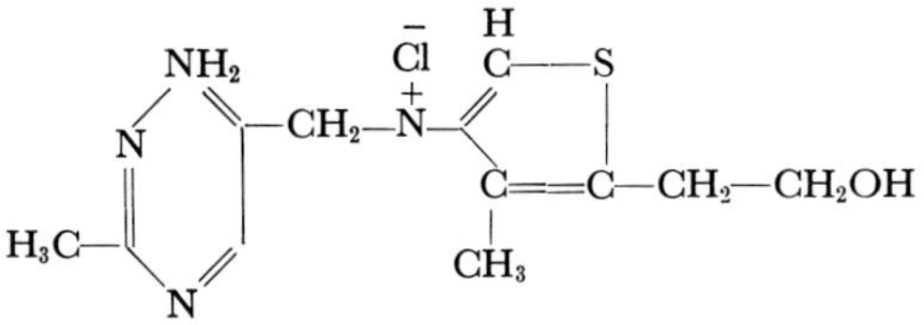

```
                 -    H
      NH2        Cl   C———S
     /   \       +   //    |
    N     ——CH2—N—<        |
    ‖     |          \     |
H3C—      |           C==C—CH2—CH2OH
     \   //           |
      N               CH3
```

Vitamin B_1
(Thiamin)
(29–4)

```
        O
        ‖
        C———
        |   |
   HO—C    |
        ‖   O
   HO—C    |
        |   |
    H—C———
        |
   HO—C—H
        |
        CH2OH
```

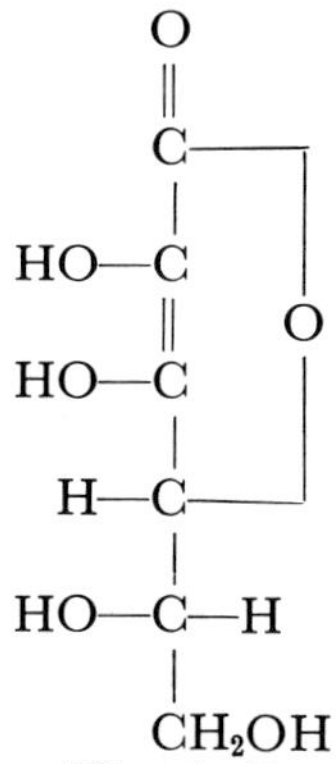

Vitamin C
(Ascorbic acid)
(29–5)

The sources of vitamins are common foods, so that by a selection, it is possible to obtain the amounts needed for normal functioning. There is evidence that a number of vitamins (including thiamin and ascorbic acid) can be used in therapeutic and preventive medicine. This, however, is not a license for the indiscriminate addition of an excess of vitamins to the diet. There is a tendency in the advertising of foods to cite the alleged vitamin content as a sure protection against one or more diseases. Needless to say, such claims should be viewed with suspicion.

PRODUCTION OF ENERGY IN THE ANIMAL BODY

Through the process of digestion, the complex molecules of carbohydrates, fats, and proteins are hydrolyzed to the simple sugars, amino acids, and simple organic acids. These, together with water and inorganic ions, finally pass through the intestinal walls to the blood and lymph and, together with the oxygen taken through the lungs, are carried to all the tissues and are therefore the nutrients of the cells. Through complex chemical reactions the protoplasm of the cells utilizes these simpler substances to build the characteristic tissues of the animal body and produce the energy by which life is sustained. These complex

TABLE 29–3 LIST OF A NUMBER OF VITAMINS

VITAMIN	CHEMICAL NAME	FUNCTIONS*
Vitamin A Group		Promote growth; help maintain normal resistance to infection; maintain visual adaptability to dim light, integrity of epithelial cells. Deficiency leads to serious eye disease.
A_1	Axerophthol	
A_2		
Vitamin B Group		Promote growth; involved in oxidation changes; essential to normal functioning of nerves; anti-pernicious anemia factor. Deficiency of B vitamins causes serious disturbances, among them neuritis, beriberi, pellagra.
B_1	Thiamin	
B_2 or G	Riboflavin	
B_3 or B_x	Pantothenic acid	
B_4	Choline	
B_5	Nicotinic acid (Niacin)	
B_6	Pyridoxine	
B_7 (H)	Biotin	
B_8	Inositol	
B_c (M)	Folic acid (Pteroylglutamic acid)	
B_{12}	Cyano-Cobalamin	Proper maturation of red blood cells.
B_{12}a	Hydroxo-Cobalamin	
B_{12}b	Cobalamin (Aquo)	
B_{12}c	Nitrito-Cobalamin	
B_{12}d		
Vitamin C	Ascorbic acid	Essential to formation and maintenance of teeth, bones, and blood vessels; increases resistance to infection and hemorrhage; important in oxidation and reduction reactions in the body. Deficiency causes scurvy.
Vitamin D Group		Important in the utilization of calcium and phosphorus, and hence in the building and maintenance of bones and teeth; prevent rickets.
D_2	Calciferol	
D_3	Activated 7-dehydrocholesterol	
Vitamin E Group	Tocopherols (α, β, γ, δ, ϵ, ζ, η)	Involved in cell maturation and differentiation and in reproductive processes.
Vitamin H (B_7)	Biotin	Involved in fat metabolism.
Vitamin K Group		Necessary for normal blood coagulation.
K_1	2-methyl-3-phytyl-1,4-naphthoquinone	
K_2	2-methyl-3-farnesyldigeranyl-1,4-naphthoquinone	
K_3		
K_4	2-methyl-1,4-naphthalenediol diacetate	
K_5	4-amino-2-methyl-1-naphthol hydrochloride	
K_6	2-methyl-1,5-naphthalene-diamine-2-hydrochloride	
Vitamin P	Esculin, Rutin, Citrin	Involved in maintaining normal function of small blood vessels.

* Described only in general terms for each vitamin group.

chemical reactions are included under the term *metabolism.*

The over-all reactions of metabolism can be written thus:

$$\left.\begin{matrix} C\text{—}C \\ \text{and} \\ C\text{—}H \end{matrix}\right\} \text{bonds} + \xrightarrow[\text{enzymatic oxidation}]{[O]} CO_2 + H_2O + \text{energy}$$

The reaction as written above, however, is a great oversimplification of the complex steps involved in such biological oxidations. There are a very large number of intermediate steps. For example, glucose or glycogen, when oxidized, first unites with a phosphate ion to form glucose–6–phosphate which is then converted to a three-carbon carboxylic acid, pyruvic acid, $CH_3COCOOH$. From here on, the path of oxidation differs depending on whether oxygen is present or not. In primitive cells like yeasts, oxidation of pyruvic acid can take place in the absence of oxygen (*anaerobic oxidation*) to alcohol and carbon dioxide, a process called fermentation. This same type of anaerobic oxidation takes place in liver and muscle tissues to yield lactic acid, $CH_3CHOHCOOH$. A more efficient oxidation of pyruvic acid, however, takes place in the presence of oxygen (*aerobic oxidation*) through a complex series of stepwise chain oxidations which involve a number of enzymes and carriers related to two vitamins of the B group (nicotinic acid and riboflavin) and the cytochromes which are related to hemoglobin. Hence, aerobic oxidation is often referred to as *cytochrome oxidation.* For each step, for each link in the chain, a specific enzyme is necessary. In this manner, instead of an explosive combustion of glucose, $C_6H_{12}O_6$, to 6 CO_2 and 6 H_2O which would be a wasteful release of energy, the oxidation takes place by a series of intermediary processes. The cleavage of C–H and C–C bonds takes place so that the energy is transferred to a form from which it can be released when needed. The energy liberated by the cleavage of bonds is stored in a relatively simple compound resulting from a combination of the amine adenosine and phosphoric acid known as ATP (adenosine triphosphate). As energy is required for muscle contraction, thermal requirements of the body, transmission of nerve impulses, and synthetic functions of the cells, ATP transfers its energy to the proper cells.

The final oxidation products of carbohydrates and fats are carbon dioxide and water; in proteins the end products are carbon dioxide, water, and ammonia. While most of the carbon dioxide is carried through the blood stream and exhaled through the lungs, the ammonia is eliminated through a process involving the conversion of ammonia and carbon dioxide into a compound called urea. The reaction can be written thus:

$$\underset{\text{Carbon dioxide}}{CO_2} + \underset{\text{Ammonia}}{2NH_3} \rightarrow \underset{\text{Urea}}{H_2N\text{—}CO\text{—}NH_2} + H_2O$$

However, the enzymatic synthesis of urea involves three distinct steps in which three related amino acids are involved, thus providing a cycle which essentially performs the synthesis shown in the equation above. The urea passes into the blood stream, and is eliminated through the excretory system as a dilute water solution (urine).

ENERGY REQUIREMENTS OF THE HUMAN BODY

It is possible by means of a respiration calorimeter to measure the heat evolved by an individual at rest. By means of such an instrument the amount of oxygen intake and the carbon dioxide and nitrogen output are measured. From these figures it is possible to calculate the amount of heat produced and also the amount of carbohydrate, fat, and protein metabolized. An individual who has fasted for about twelve hours before undergoing a calorimeter measurement and who remains in a state of complete rest during the measurement will generate an amount of heat which tends to be constant, and represents the energy required by the individual for the internal processes required to sustain life.

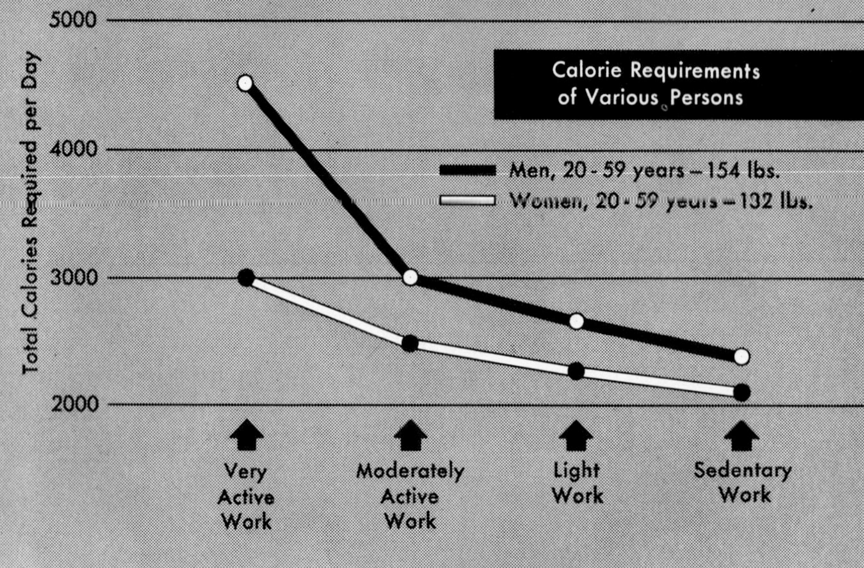

Fig. 29–3 *Energy requirements of the human body.*

This energy expressed in kilocalories (Calories) is called the *basal metabolism.* Though basal metabolism is expressed in Cal/m²/hr, for comparative purposes it can be expressed in Calories per kilogram of body weight (2.2 pounds) per hour. Thus it has been found that an average adult weighing 150 pounds (68 kilos) has a basal metabolism of 68 Calories per hour or about 1600 Calories for 24 hours.

We can assume that any given individual in health has a constant basal energy requirement. However, for all other activities, which involve movements of the body (exercise, work, eating), additional energy is required. Figure 29–3 shows the average daily caloric requirements for men and for women in activities ranging from very active to sedentary work. Walking upstairs, surprisingly, requires twice as much energy as the hardest work. But walking upstairs is very hard work – it is lifting the entire weight of one's body against gravity. Similarly, it is possible to estimate from the physical circumstances of the job the total calorie requirements for any given type of work. Children need more calories per pound than middle-aged adults to meet the demands of growth and greater physical activity. The activity of a boy eleven to fifteen years old requires as many calories as heavy work. Old people need even less than the middle-aged.

A balanced diet should contain: (*a*) a sufficient amount of carbohydrates and fats to furnish the caloric requirements – for an adult doing light work, 400 g (14 ounces) of carbohydrates and 50 g (1.8 ounces) of fats suffice; (*b*) a sufficient amount of mixed proteins (minimum 60 to 70 g, or 2 ounces) per day; (*c*) the required amount of inorganic ions (1 g of Ca, 0.9 g of P, and 0.2 g of Fe); and (*d*) the required amount of vitamins, water, and fibrous material for normal functioning. It is possible by an application of the knowledge obtained from nutritional studies to meet all the requirements for a balanced diet and at the same time satisfy all psychological factors such as individual likes, dislikes, and whims.

The energy requirement of an adult does not appear very large compared with the heat energy derived from fuels. One gram of coal liberates about six Calories and one gram of gasoline about ten Calories. Thus the heat from one pound of gasoline is more than sufficient for the daily requirements of an adult. It has been shown (Chapter 19), however, that only a fraction of the heat produced by the combustion of fuel is converted to useful work. Steam engines have an efficiency (at best) of about 10 per cent; and a gasoline engine, of 20 to 25 per cent. The efficiency of the animal body compares very favorably with that of the gasoline engine. When a new automobile and a young man or a young steer are compared, the results are in favor of the animal converter. The animal converts 35 per cent of the energy of the fuel into work as compared with the 25 per cent converted by the gasoline engine.

SUMMARY

1. The simpler organic compounds, alcohols, amines, aldehydes, acids, and esters may be formally regarded as derived from hydrocarbons by replacement of one or more hydrogen atoms with functional groups.
2. Functional groups are the reactive parts of organic molecules such as OH, NH_2, CO, or COOH. Each functional group imparts to the molecules distinct properties.
3. Alcohols are organic compounds having the hydroxyl (OH) functional group. Similarly, amines have the NH_2 group; aldehydes, the CO group; carboxylic acids, the COOH group; and esters, the $-COO-$ group.
4. The essential nutrients present in foods are water, salts or minerals, carbohydrates, fats, proteins, and vitamins.
5. Carbohydrates include starches and sugars and compose about one-half of the average diet. Most carbohydrates used in diets are built up of glucose units. Glucose is a complex hydroxy-aldehyde; fructose is a complex hydroxy-ketone. Cane sugar and starch yield mainly glucose and fructose on digestive hydrolysis.
6. Fats are esters of glycerol and long-chain acids. When hydrolyzed in the body they produce glycerol and fatty acids and as they are absorbed they are synthesized into the fats of the animal. When fats are boiled with alkalis, they give glycerol and the alkali salts of the fatty acids known as soaps. The cleansing action of soaps is due to the presence of a polar group and a long hydrocarbon chain.
7. Proteins are complex compounds of high molecular weight formed by union of many amino acid molecules. In the body, proteins are converted by digestive hydrolysis into amino acids.
8. Water makes up the largest part of anim. tissues. It provides a medium for the complex reactions of the living cells.
9. The inorganic ions necessary to animal life are sulfate, phosphate, chloride, iodide, sodium, potassium, magnesium, calcium, ferric, cupric, and manganous.
10. Vitamins are complex organic compounds required in very small amounts in the diet of animals for normal development and functioning.
11. *Metabolism* designates the complex chemical reactions through which living cells utilize the simple nutrients supplied in foods to obtain the energy by which life is sustained. The amount of energy (measured in kilocalories) required for body functions (aside from work and normal activity) is the *basal metabolism.*
12. Generally there are two types of biochemical oxidations by which carbon compounds are oxidized and energy is released. One is the primitive *anaerobic type* and the other the *cytochrome aerobic type.* In both processes one of the intermediates is pyruvic acid, but otherwise, the steps of aerobic and anaerobic oxidations differ. Each step requires a specific enzyme. The ultimate end is the cleavage of C–H and C–C bonds with release of energy which is stored in a simple molecule known as adenosine triphosphate (ATP.) As energy is required for muscle contraction, transmission of nerve impulses, and other body functions, ATP transfers its energy to the proper cells.

STUDY EXERCISES

1. Classify the following compounds (that is, name the group to which each belongs).
   a. CH_3CH_2CHO ....
   b. CH_3NH_2 ....
   c. CH_3OCH_3 ....
   d. $CH_3CH_2CH_2CH_2COOH$ ....
   e. $CH_3CH_2COOCH_3$ ....
   f. CH_3CHNH_2COOH ....
   g. $CH_3(CH_2)_{12}COOK$ ....
2. Indicate the main products of the following complex substances after boiling with an acid and water.

a. Olive oil ....
b. Butter ....
c. Straw ....
d. Corn ....
e. Bread ....

3. In each of the following, select the item that best completes the statement.
   a. Of the following elements the one not found in any quantity in proteins is (1) C; (2) H; (3) S; (4) Se; (5) N. ....
   b. Of the following, the one compound not present in natural gas is (1) CH_4; (2) CO; (3) C_2H_6; (4) C_3H_8; (5) C_4H_{10}. ....
   c. The compound that is not likely to be found in protein hydrolyzates is (1) NH_3; (2) CH_2NH_2COOH; (3) CH_3CH_2OH; (4) CH_3CHNH_2COOH; (5) $C_6H_5CH_2$-$CHNH_2COOH$. ....
   d. Silica, SiO_2, is most likely to be present in the following part of the human body: (1) bones; (2) blood; (3) nails; (4) eye; (5) brain. ....
4. Identify by letter the item or items from the following list that apply to each of the statements given below.

   A. $CH_3CH_2CH_2CH_2CH_2CH_3$
   B. $CH_2(OH)CH(OH)CHO$
   C. $C_{12}H_{22}O_{11}$
   D. $CH_3CH(NH_2)COOH$
   E. CH_3CH_2OH
   F. $CH_3(CH_2)_{16}CH_3$
   G. $CH_3(CH_2)_{16}COOH$
   H. $CH_3CH(CH_3)CH_2CH_2CH_3$
   I. CH_3–O–CH_3
   J. $(CH_3)_2$–CH–CH–$(CH_3)_2$
   K. H–COOH
   L. $(C_6H_{10}O_5)_n$
   M. CH_3CHO
   N. $C_6H_5CH_2CH(NH_2)COOH$
   O. $CH_2(OH)CH(OH)CH_2(OH)$

   a. This compound gives glucose on hydrolysis. ....
   b. These compounds are aldehydes. ....
   c. These pairs of compounds are isomers. ....
   d. These compounds in biochemical oxidation will yield urea. ....
   e. This compound has the highest heat of combustion of those listed. ....
   f. This compound has the lowest heat of combustion. ....
   g. These two compounds when combined in proper ratios will yield a fat. ....
   h. The alkali salt of this compound will have cleansing action. ....
   i. On oxidation it yields carboxylic acids.
5. Why is it possible to use hay and straw as foodstuffs for livestock and not for human beings? Can powdered straw be treated so that it may be used as food? Explain.
6. Assume that you are doing hard work for four hours per day and light work for the remainder of your waking time. Calculate your weekly calorie requirements. Base the calculations on your body weight.
7. On the basis of the figure obtained in Exercise 6, calculate the amount of (*a*) carbohydrates, (*b*) fats, and (*c*) proteins that you need. Give the amounts in grams of dry weight and also in ounces.
8. Compare the combustion of hexane, C_8H_{14}, in an automobile engine with the biochemical oxidation of glucose, $C_6H_{12}O_6$, in the human body with respect to the following: (*a*) which of the two oxidations will give more calories of heat per mole; (*b*) the possible steps (as far as your knowledge permits) in the oxidation of each; (*c*) the end products of each oxidation; (*d*) the efficiency of work obtained from the same input of calories; (*e*) if one mole of each substance is burned in the calorimeter, which will give the larger quantity of heat.

FOR FURTHER READING

1. MARKHAM, E. C., and S. E. SMITH, *General Chemistry*. Boston: Houghton Mifflin Company, 1954.
   A discussion of organic compounds will be found on pages 567–581.
2. PAULING, LINUS, *General Chemistry*. San Francisco: W. H. Freeman and Company, 1953.
   A discussion of organic compounds and biochemistry will be found on pages 588–617.
3. Paperback: EDITORS OF SCIENTIFIC AMERICAN, *The Physics and Chemistry of Life*. Simon and Schuster, $1.45.
   For articles on proteins and structure of hereditary materials, see pages 58–117; for articles on the production of energy by enzymatic reactions, pages 151–180 and 223–248.

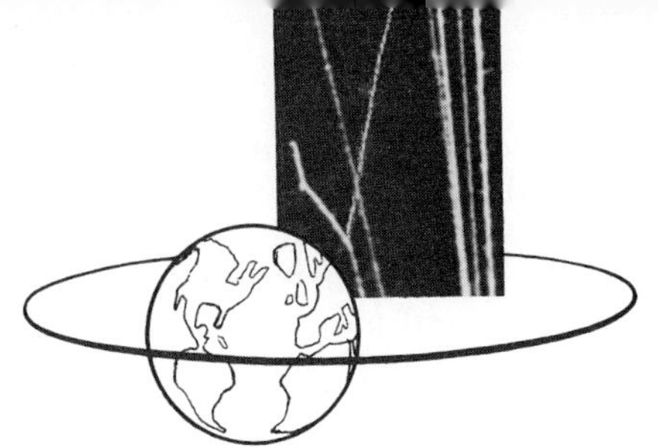

30

THINGS OF THIS WORLD: III

THE PRECEDING two chapters dealt with the two most important classes of materials employed in our society, foods and fuels. In our attempt to obtain a summary of the materials which our society is busily engaged in collecting, processing, changing, storing, and utilizing, we selected fuels and foods on the basis of the tonnage in which they are produced annually. An estimated summary is shown in Table 30–1. The table shows that more than 70 per cent of all the materials produced each year in the United States are fuels and foods, or compounds of carbon. Under "inorganic construction materials," which comprise 20 per cent, are included sand, gravel, stone, cement, plaster, and various other materials used in the construction of houses, factories, office buildings, and roads, most of which contain the element silicon. Metals comprise 5 per cent of the total; about 90 per cent of this 5 per cent consists of iron and its alloys. The balance, which comprises the multitude of all the forms of matter which we use in our everyday life, makes up only 3.6 per cent.

It should be pointed out, however, that a statistical appraisal of this nature may lead to false conclusions. A material may well be produced and used in relatively small quantities as compared to the total tonnage, and yet it may be indispensable in our kind of society. For example, under the classification of "luxuries" in Table 30–1 are included cosmetics, stimulants (alcoholic and nonalcoholic beverages, coffee, tea, and the like), tobacco, confectionery, and ice cream. It can be well argued that ice cream and candy are foods and indeed they are; however, one may live a normal life without the necessity of using either as foods. On the other hand, the amount of chlorine produced in the United States and included under "process chemicals" is less than 0.1 per cent of the total tonnage of the materials we produce each year. Yet without chlorine, we could not keep up our present sanitation arrangements that permit a high density of population in many areas of our country.

We shall select for the purpose of our discussion certain aspects of the production of metals, the production of salt (sodium chloride) and chlorine, and a few examples of synthetic polymers.

METALS

It was pointed out in Chapter 28 that our society differs from those of preceding centuries in that it uses vast amounts of energy obtained by the burning of solid and liquid fuels. The use of these vast amounts of energy to alter the conditions of our environment would be impossible without tools and machines – that is, the arrangement of "moving metallic parts" by which energy is generated and transferred. Our automobiles, the Diesel engines which pull trains on miles of steel tracks, our factories, tractors, and plows are evidence of the fact that we are living today in a "metal age."

The use of metals dates back over a period of about five thousand years. The first metals to be discovered and used were those which are found in the uncombined or chemically free state, that is, the less active metals – gold, silver, and copper. Native copper was probably the first metal to be used widely; admixed with tin it forms an alloy known as *bronze.* Both copper and bronze tools were common five thousand years ago. It is quite probable that the first iron used was of meteoric origin, for the ability to separate iron and other metals from compounds found in the earth's crust (ores) was not achieved until about a thousand years before the Christian era.

Of the 92 elements that occur in nature, about 70 are classified as metals. Of these, about 31 find extensive use in our society; and of these 31, about 95 to 98 per cent of the tonnage used is accounted for by five metals: *iron, copper, zinc, lead, aluminum,* and their alloys, and most of this by iron. Table 30–2 lists the more important metals. As the table shows, the atomic numbers of most of the important metals are below 30, and most of the metals are subgroup or transition elements. The significance of these facts to a consideration of the general properties of the metals listed in Table 30–2 is more extensively discussed in a subsequent section.

TABLE 30–1 ESTIMATED TONNAGE, VARIOUS CLASSES OF MATERIALS PRODUCED ANNUALLY IN U.S.

MATERIAL	MILLIONS OF TONS
Fuels	950
Foods	350
Inorganic construction materials	350
Metals	90
Process chemicals	35
Luxuries	15
Plastics	10
Textiles and leathers	5
Total	1805

The importance of metals is based on the extent to which they are used either in their pure form or as alloys. Therefore it is necessary to examine the factors which determine their uses. Though the various uses of the metals are so diverse as to preclude a general rule, certain factors are of primary significance in determining whether a particular metal can be used on a large scale:

(1) *Abundance or availability and cost of production* are chief considerations. For example, iron, which accounts for 90 to 95 per cent of the total quantity of metals used, is relatively abundant and is being produced at a comparatively low cost. Iron comprises about 5 per cent of the earth's crust (see page 64); aluminum about 8 per cent; copper, lead, and zinc, less than one per cent. However, the amounts in percentages do not give a true picture of the extent of the actual workable deposits. For example, aluminum is present mostly in clay and other silicates, and though in terms of percentage it is abundant (8 per cent), the actual availability is limited because the extraction of aluminum from clay or other complex silicates is not economical. At present, only aluminum oxide (bauxite) deposits are suitable for the production of aluminum metal.

(2) *Desirable physical and mechanical properties* are also important considerations in determining the use of a particular metal. For example, a metal suitable for the construction of an automobile spring should have a high tensile strength, high

TABLE 30–2 PRODUCTION OF IMPORTANT METALS

METAL	ATOMIC NO.	PERIODIC GROUP	APPROXIMATE PRODUCTION IN THOUSANDS OF TONS		APPROXIMATE PRICE (U.S.A.)*
			World	U.S.A.	Dollars/lb.
Iron	26	VIII B	330,000	138,000	0.05
Copper	29	I B	2,250	760	0.30
Zinc	30	II B	1,800	600	0.13
Lead	82	IV B	1,500	400	0.14
Aluminum	13	III A	1,300	600	0.19
Manganese (ores)	25	VII B	4,530	1,100	....
Chromium (ores)	24	VI B	1,900	....	....
Tin	50	IV A	162	....	1.21
Nickel	28	VIII B	146	1	0.56
Sodium	11	I A	90	70	0.16
Antimony	51	V A	34	10	0.39
Magnesium	12	II A	22	12	0.25
Molybdenum	42	VI B	13	12	3.00
Tungsten	74	VI B	3	2	6.00
Cadmium	48	II B	6	4	2.10
Silver	47	I B	6	1	12.14
Mercury	80	II B	4	0.4	2.45
Titanium	22	IV B	....	....	....
Cobalt	27	VIII B	3	0.3	2.40
Vanadium	23	V B	2	1.0	....
Bismuth	83	V A	2	....	2.25
Gold	79	I B	1	0.06	510.30
Platinum	78	VIII B	0.02	....	1,355.00
Others: Pd, Ir, Ta, Ca, U					

* Average price over last five years.

elastic limits, resistance to fatigue, and, if possible, low density. To a very large extent the diversified applications of metals depend on their physical and mechanical properties rather than on their chemical properties, though the latter (described in the following section) can be important. Desirable physical and mechanical properties can often be obtained by mixing two or more metals to produce an *alloy*. For example, pure aluminum has nearly one-third the density of steel; its tensile strength, however, is low (9000 lb/in^2). By introducing

Fig. 30–1 *Testing experimental alloys for tensile strength. The alloy sample is placed in a stretching machine that heats it while attached weights tug at it with tremendous force. Alloys scoring well in the tests are potential materials for uses requiring tough, heat-resistant metals.* (*Ford Motor Co.*)

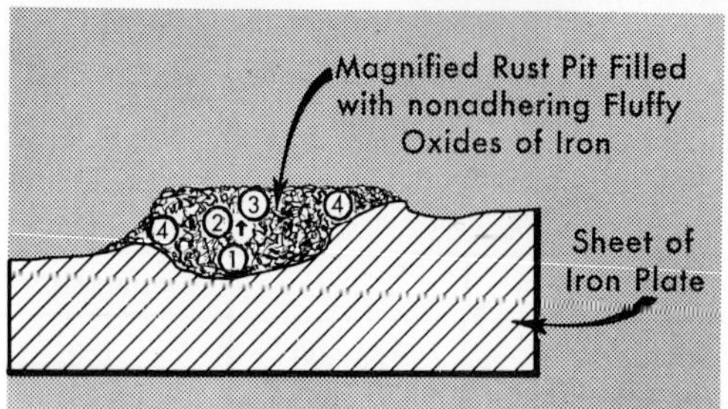

Fig. 30–2 *Schematic diagram of reactions occurring on the surface of a sheet of iron plate. (1) Area of rusting iron which is corroding, the concentration of* O_2 *being low: main reaction,* $Fe \rightarrow Fe^{++} + 2e^-$. *(2) Diffusion of* Fe^{++} *and* OH^- *ions to form* $Fe(OH)_2$ *or* $FeO{\cdot}n\,H_2O$. *(3) Oxidation of* Fe^{++} *to* Fe^{+++} *or* $FeO{\cdot}n\,H_2O = O_2 = Fe_2O_3{\cdot}n\,H_2O$. *(4) The changes taking place at the anodes of the pit:*

$$2\,H_2O + 2\,H_2O = 2\,H_3O^+ + 2\,OH^-$$
$$2\,H_3O^+ + 2\,e^- = H_2 = 2\,H_2O$$
$$2\,H_2 + O_2 = 2\,H_2O$$

small quantities (total 4 to 5 per cent) of copper, magnesium, manganese, and silicon, an alloy called Duralumin is obtained which can develop a maximum tensile strength equal to that of low carbon steel (60,000 pounds per square inch). Thus for the manufacture of airplanes, in which low density combined with relatively high tensile strength and toughness are essential, the requirements are met by changing some of the properties of a metal which has one or more of the desirable properties, in this case, low density.

(3) *Resistance to corrosion* under the conditions of use is the third important factor in determining the suitability of a particular metal. This property, of course, is directly connected with the chemical activity of the metal and the nature of the oxide. For example, aluminum is much more active than cast iron or steel, and, exposed in air, aluminum corrodes rapidly. But its oxide adheres and prevents further corrosion by sealing off the surface of the metal. Under the same conditions, the corrosion of iron is more rapid and presents a more serious problem, because iron rust "peels off," exposing a new surface for attack.

Often one or two of the factors enumerated above are so favorable that others are not taken into consideration. For example, iron has a very low cost of production and is relatively abundant. At the same time, some of its properties, such as high density and high rate of corrosion, are undesirable. Yet on balance, though it has been estimated that at least 50 to 60 per cent of the annual production of iron is for replacement, its cost is so low, and our technology so well-rooted in iron and steel, that iron is by far the most important of the metals.

In special instances the cost of a metal may be initially high but its rate of corrosion so low as to render its long-term use economical. Consider, for example, a steam coil used to heat a slightly acidic solution containing ammonium chloride. If the coil is made of iron, lead, or even stainless steel, these are rapidly corroded so that the coil has to be changed every few weeks. To make such a coil, tantalum, even at a cost of forty dollars a pound, is cheaper in the long run.

PROPERTIES AND ELECTRONIC STRUCTURE OF METALS

The characteristic physical properties of metals which can serve to distinguish them from nonmetals and upon which their uses depend are these: high density, ductility, malleability, tensile strength, thermal and electrical conductivity, hardness, and metallic luster. The properties are shown by the various metals in different degrees, and any particular property may vary over a wide range. However, for most metals many of these properties are exhibited to a high degree.

Solid metals are crystalline, as shown by X-ray crystal analysis, and many of the physical properties depend on the type of crystal lattice or arrangement of the atoms, the atomic radius, electronic structure, and so on. An adequate treatment of this subject cannot be undertaken in this text, and only a few qualitative facts and ideas are mentioned. The atoms arrange themselves in such a way that in most metals each atom is in contact with either eight or twelve neighboring atoms. Because most metal atoms have a small number of outer valence electrons (one or two), there are not enough electrons to establish covalent bonds between each atom and the adjacent atoms, such as exist in crystalline carbon. A metal may therefore be regarded as an arrangement of positive ions in a cloud of electrons. The attraction of the ions and the electrons for each other holds the ions together. Since the electrons are rather loosely held, and are not permanently attached to any particular ion, they move freely through the metal. The ions, which are not linked to each other by specific covalent bonds, move relatively to each other when placed under a stress. Several of the physical properties of metals, such as electrical conductivity and malleability, may be explained (see below) by this concept.

Density is the mass per unit of volume, and is usually expressed in grams per milliliter. The density of a solid element depends not only on the mass of its atoms, but upon the number of atoms in a given volume. This is influenced by the electronic structure. In the atoms of the members of Group VIII, for example, there is an unusually compact electronic arrangement, and consequently low atomic volumes (the volume occupied by a gram atomic weight of a solid element). In this group the denser elements are found: platinum has a density of 21.45 g per ml; iridium, 22.4 g per ml; and osmium, 22.48 g per ml. On the other hand, the densities of magnesium and aluminum, both metals of considerable strength, are 1.74 g per ml and 2.7 g per ml respectively; hence these metals are used in airplane construction where a low density is vital.

Ductility is the property which permits a substance to be drawn into very fine wires. Platinum, for example, may be drawn into wires 1/200,000 cm in diameter, wires which are invisible to the naked eye.

Malleability, the property which permits a substance to be rolled into thin sheets, is closely related to ductility. Many of the transition elements are both very ductile and malleable, especially those in Groups I B and VIII. Gold has been hammered into sheets 1/38,000 cm in thickness. When the metal is drawn or rolled, the ions or kernels may be displaced with respect to their neighbors without destroying the binding forces of attraction between them and the electrons.

Tensile strength is the force required to break a rod or bar of the metal by a straight pull. Iron alloyed with vanadium, chromium, molybdenum, tungsten, nickel, or manganese forms steels of high tensile strength. This property is closely related to ductility, for it would be impossible to draw a very fine thread of a substance which does not have a high tensile strength.

Thermal and electrical conductivity, perhaps the most distinctive properties of metals, may be explained by the fast-moving free or mobile electrons. These electrons transmit heat energy from the hot portion of a metal to the ions in the cooler portion. Likewise, when the metal is connected in an electric circuit, the mobile electrons move faster in the direction of the electric field and their drift through the metal constitutes the electric current. The elements of Group I B, copper, silver, and gold, are all especially good conductors of both heat and electricity. Because of its high conductivity and lower cost, copper is extensively used in electric lines, radiators, and heating coils.

Hardness of metals is usually measured by the depth of the depression or indentation made by a steel ball under a given load for a given period of time. It is a desirable property in cutting steels and lathe tools. Of the elementary metals (not alloys), manganese is the hardest, while the metals of Group I B are very soft.

Other characteristics of metals which are factors in the determination of their uses are melting points and, as already noted, ability to resist corrosion. The transition metals of low melting points (all under 425° C.) are those in Groups I B, II B, and germanium, tin, and lead in Group IV A. A number of low-melting alloys made from tin, lead, cadmium, and bismuth are of commercial use in fire alarm systems, automatic sprinklers, and fuses for electric circuits. One of these, Woods's metal, melts at 60° C. Metals of very high melting points are found in Groups V B, VI B, VII B, and VIII, especially those of higher atomic numbers in each group. Tungsten, for example, has a melting point of 3370° C., and this property, together with its ductility, permits its use as an incandescent lamp filament.

The general chemical properties of the metals listed in Table 30–2 are the tendency to lose electrons and form positive ions; the oxides of these metals are only slightly soluble in water and form very weakly basic hydroxides. In combining, the metallic atoms which belong to subgroups exhibit variable valence or more than one oxidation state. For example, the sodium atom Na forms only a monovalent ion Na^+ in combining; similarly the calcium atom Ca forms only a divalent ion Ca^{++}; the iron atom Fe, however, forms both the ferrous Fe^{++} and ferric ion Fe^{+++} to make the black ferrous oxide, FeO, or the red ferric oxide, Fe_2O_3.

In order to explain and correlate the physical and chemical properties of the subgroup or transition elements (in which the most important metals belong) it is necessary to consider their electronic structures. Table 30–3 lists the electron configurations of the elements of the Periodic Table (page 392) beginning with calcium, number 20, and ending with gallium, number 31.

The Periodic Table and Table 30–3 show that in elements 21 to 30 inclusive the number of electrons in all shells except the third remains constant. It is significant that the number of electrons in the outermost shell, which increases with increase in atomic number, remains constant (in normal state). In the third shell, the number of electrons in the *d* subshell increases successively until it acquires its full quota of 10 electrons, thus raising the total number of electrons in this shell from 8 to 18. The Periodic Table shows that a similar series of elements begins with yttrium (39) and ends with silver (47) and another begins with lanthanum (57) and ends with gold (79). For elements 21 to 30 in Table 30–3 the atomic radius remains small and constant. Since their atoms are structured similarly, the elements exhibit a number of closely related physical and chemical properties.

The similarity in physical properties is shown by comparison of their melting points and densities as listed in Table 30–3. There is no sharp transition in passing from a lower to a higher atomic number as in

TABLE 30–3 ELECTRONIC STRUCTURE OF ELEMENTS, ATOMIC NUMBER 20 TO ATOMIC NUMBER 31

AT. NO.	SYMBOL	M.P. °C.	DENSITY g/c.c.	ELECTRONIC SHELL 1st	2nd		3rd			4th		ATOMIC RADIUS Å	OXIDATION STATES
				s	*s*	*p*	*s*	*p*	*d*	*s*	*p*		
20	Ca	851	1.5	2	2	6	2	6		2		1.97	2
21	Sc	1200	2.5	2	2	6	2	6	1	2		1.51	3
22	Ti	1800	4.5	2	2	6	2	6	2	2		1.49	2,3,4
23	V	1710	5.9	2	2	6	2	6	3	2		1.32	2,3,4,5
24	Cr	1800	7.1	2	2	6	2	6	5	1		1.25	2,3,6
25	Mn	1220	7.2	2	2	6	2	6	5	2		1.29	2,3,4,6,7
26	Fe	1535	7.9	2	2	6	2	6	6	2		1.26	2,3,6
27	Co	1490	8.9	2	2	6	2	6	7	2		1.26	2,3
28	Ni	1452	8.9	2	2	6	2	6	8	2		1.24	2,4
29	Cu	1084	8.9	2	2	6	2	6	10	1		1.27	1,2
30	Zn	419	7.1	2	2	6	2	6	10	2		1.31	2
31	Ga	30	5.9	2	2	6	2	6	10	2	1	1.33	1,3

TABLE 30–4

OXIDATION STATES OF IRON AND MANGANESE

NAME OF OXIDATION STATE	ELECTRONIC STRUCTURE OF ATOM BEFORE BONDING	OXID. STATE	COMPOUND
Ferrous	2–8–14–2	Fe^{++}	FeO
Ferric	2–8–13–3	Fe^{+++}	Fe_2O_3
Ferrate	2–8–10–6	Fe^{6+}	$BaFeO_4$
Manganous	2–8–13–2	Mn^{++}	$Mn(OH)_2$
Manganic	2–8–12–3	Mn^{+++}	$Mn(OH)_3$
Manganite	2–8–11–4	Mn^{4+}	MnO_2
Manganate	2–8–9–6	Mn^{6+}	K_2MnO_4
Permanganate	2–8–8–7	Mn^{7+}	$KMnO_4$

the main group elements. This close resemblance is most striking in iron, cobalt, and nickel.

In forming chemical bonds the transitional elements use both the electrons of the outer shell (4*s*) and also electrons from the next to the outer shell (3*d*). Thus in chemical bonding these elements exhibit various oxidation states. For example, iron and manganese may form compounds by bonding with electrons from the outer and the next to the outer shells as shown in Table 30–4. In the formation of these bonds it may be assumed that electrons move out from the inner (3*d*) to the outer (4*s*) subshell just before the atom combines, as shown in column 2 of Table 30–4. Of course, this kind of picture is merely an attempt to show how an atom exhibits variable valence.

Another similarity in the general properties of the transition elements is that their hydroxides do not split off hydroxyl, OH^-, ions as readily as the main group elements, and as a consequence they are weak or feeble bases. For example, both sodium (I A) and calcium (II A) form the strong bases $NaOH$ and $Ca(OH)_2$, while the hydroxides of iron, cobalt, nickel, chromium, and manganese are weak or feeble bases.

METALLURGY

Ores are rock masses from which a metal may be obtained *economically*. Native ores are those which contain the metal in the free state and include those of gold, silver, copper, mercury, bismuth, antimony, and the platinum metals. More often the ores contain *oxides, sulfides,* and *carbonates;* some *silicates* and *halides* are suitable ores for some metals. Table 30–5 shows the principal ores of some important metals. It will be noted that some pure minerals are listed in the table; they are invariably mixed with rocky material called *gangue.* Whether a rock mass containing these minerals can be considered an ore depends on several factors, among which are *the extent of the rock deposit* and *the percentage of metal that can be extracted from a ton of the ore.* The latter varies widely. Iron ores are rarely worth while unless they yield at least 40 to 50 per cent of their weight in metal, whereas some copper and zinc ores are worked and yield one per cent or less of metal. Gold ores with less than one ounce of metal per ton, however, are sufficient. Frequently an ore contains several metals; for example, lead ores usually contain ores of silver and zinc and often cadmium, antimony, bismuth, arsenic, manganese, iron, and nickel, along with other metals. As a consequence, the process for treating such ores must be adapted to the recovery of some of these metals, because they are valuable, and to the removal of others which affect the properties of lead adversely.

From the preceding discussion it follows that an ore must contain an appreciable amount of the metalliferous mineral. Such deposits are located either in igneous or sedimentary rocks. It was shown in Chapter 8 that mineral oxides and sulfides of the metals crystallize out first from molten magma. A very large number of ore de-

TABLE 30–5

ORES OF ECONOMIC IMPORTANCE

NATURAL STATE OF METAL	PRINCIPAL COMPONENT PRESENT	METAL EXTRACTED
(1) Free		Platinum, gold, copper
(2) As oxide, hydroxide, or carbonate	Hematite: ferric oxide, Fe_2O_3	Iron
	Limonite: hydrated ferric oxide, $Fe_2O_3 \cdot n\ H_2O$	Iron
	Magnetite: magnetic oxide of iron, Fe_3O_4	Iron
	Cuprite: cuprous oxide, Cu_2O	Copper
	Malachite: basic copper carbonate, $Cu(OH)_2 \cdot 2\ CuCO_3$	Copper
	Pyrolusite: manganese dioxide, MnO_2	Manganese
	Smithsonite: zinc carbonate, $ZnCO_3$	Zinc
	Bauxite: aluminum oxide, Al_2O_3	Aluminum
(3) As sulfide	Cinnabar: mercuric sulfide, HgS	Mercury
	Molybdenite: molybdenum disulfide, MoS_2	Molybdenum
	Sphalerite: zinc sulfide, ZnS	Zinc
	Galena: lead sulfide, PbS	Lead
	Chalcopyrite: cuprous sulfoferrite, $CuFeS_2$	Copper
	Stibnite: antimony trisulfide, Sb_2S_3	Antimony

posits have been formed by intrusion of magma between the cracks and fissures of older rocks. The most important known nickel deposits (in Sudbury, Canada) were formed in this way by intrusion of magma. About 90 per cent of the world's annual production comes from this nickel-bearing iron sulfide deposit.

Another way ore deposits were formed during the long geological eras is through water solution and deposition. Water coming through hot rocks and carrying minerals in solution percolated through cracks and fissures of the adjoining rocks and deposited the minerals as it cooled. In this way the so-called *vein-deposits* of silver, copper, lead, mercury, and zinc ore deposits were formed.

The iron ore deposits of the Lake Superior district (Mesabi range in Minnesota) were formed by differential weathering. Originally the ore was iron carbonate with some iron silicate. By weathering action this original ore was oxidized at or near the surface and then concentrated in part by removal of the silicates through the action of ground water. Thus the enriched ores are surfaced-mined today by steam shovels.

Two general methods are used to separate most of the gangue (nonmetallic or silicate part) from the ore with which it is mixed. The first method used to concentrate the ore is a *density separation*. The ore is finely ground, and the earthy material (with a density of about 3) is washed away in a water suspension. The more dense (density about 5) and faster settling metalliferous minerals remain. In the second method of concentration the finely ground ore is treated in such a manner that the heavier metalliferous particles are made to rise in a froth, while the lighter rock particles sink. The ore is mixed into a slimy mass with water containing a froth-producing substance and placed in a tank of water containing a small amount of pine oil. Air is blown into it, and the ore particles, to which the oil adheres, are carried to the top in the bubbles of foam. The earthy material, being wet by the water, settles out. By this *flotation process* metals may be profitably extracted from discarded ore dumps of earlier mining operations. After concentration, if the ores are sulfides or carbonates, they are often heated (roasted) to convert them to oxides.

The conversion of the ore, usually an oxide, to the metal is the reverse of the chemical reaction involved in the rusting or oxidation of the metal. Consider, for example, the natural process of rusting or oxidation of aluminum to form aluminum oxide, Al_2O_3. In reacting with oxygen, a metal usually loses electrons to the oxygen and forms positive ions:

$$Al \rightleftarrows Al^{+++} + 3\,e^-$$

To convert the ion in this case to the metallic state requires that three electrons be supplied to each aluminum ion under appropriate conditions, as shown by the reverse of the half-equation above. The final step of metallurgy is therefore a man-made process in which the metallic ions are *reduced* to metallic atoms, and is the reversal of the natural process of oxidation of metals.

The reduction of metallic ions under conditions which permit economical large-scale operation may be accomplished by one of three general methods:

(1) *Electrolysis.* The electrons are supplied by an electric current which is passed through a purified fused compound of the metal or through a water solution of a soluble salt of the metal.

(2) *Reduction by a more active metal.* A metal which is a stronger reducing agent than the metal whose ions are to be reduced may be used as a source of electrons. Potassium, sodium, magnesium, and aluminum are sometimes employed.

(3) *Reduction by carbon monoxide.* This substance, which is generated from charcoal or coke, is the reducing agent in the production of iron and other metals on a very large scale. One disadvantage is that the carbon dissolves and often combines with the hot metal, altering its properties.

METALLURGY OF ALUMINUM

The reduction of metal ions to the metal by electrolysis is illustrated by the production of aluminum. The most abundant metal, aluminum, was not prepared in the free form until early in the nineteenth century and was very costly ($113 per pound in 1855). Aluminum is an extremely active metal and a strong reducing agent. To prepare it from its oxide ore (bauxite) or from other compounds by a chemical process requires a more powerful reducing agent than aluminum. The metal was first prepared by the reduction of aluminum chloride with sodium or potassium, a difficult and costly process, for the metals employed had to be prepared by electrolysis of their fused salts.

An efficient and low-cost method of production, essentially the one in use today, was developed in 1886 by two young chemists in their early twenties, independently and about the same time, Hall in the United States and Heroult in France. Charles M. Hall, a graduate of Oberlin College, rented what we would call a small shack and went after a method to produce the metal electrolytically. Aluminum cannot be electrolytically deposited from water solutions of its salts. And aluminum oxide, which Hall was using, does not melt at a sufficiently low temperature for effective electrolysis. He therefore had to find a low-melting substance in which the oxide was soluble. After considerable search he found that the aluminum oxide dissolves in molten cryolite, an unusual ice-like fluoride of aluminum and sodium found only in Greenland. When he sent the electric current through this solution, he obtained metallic aluminum at the negative pole.

In the production of aluminum by this electrolytic process, cells of the type shown in Figure 30–3 are used. The positive electrode consists of carbon rods; the negative electrode is the iron box container; and the bath consists of a 10 to 20 per cent solution of purified aluminum oxide in fused cryolite. At the negative electrode, or cathode, the aluminum ions are reduced to

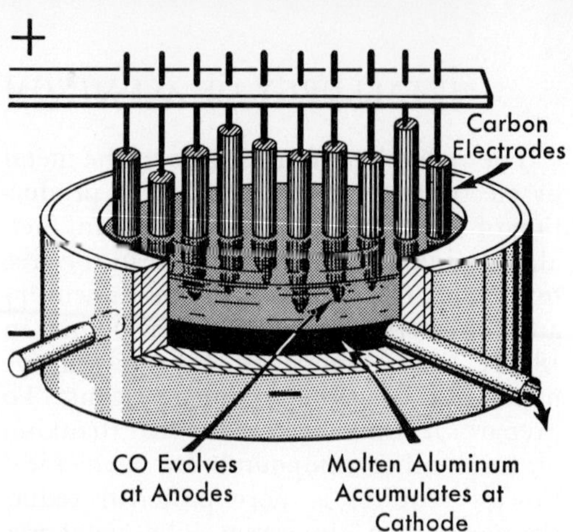

Fig. 30–3 *The electrolytic preparation of aluminum.*

the metal which collects on the bottom:

$$Al^{+++} + 3\,e^- \rightarrow Al$$

At the positive electrode, or anode, oxide ions give up their electrons (are oxidized), forming oxygen:

$$O^= \rightarrow O + 2\,e^-$$

The oxygen immediately combines with the hot carbon of the anode to form carbon monoxide, which burns to carbon dioxide as it escapes.

The present annual production of aluminum in the United States (1957) is about 800,000 tons, and the price of the ingot metal 18 to 20 cents per pound. The uses of aluminum (mentioned elsewhere) are based upon low cost, low density, high strength of alloys, and resistance to continued corrosion. Aluminum is self-protecting, for a thin transparent film of the oxide forms on a fresh surface of the metal and protects it from further action of the atmosphere.

REDUCTION BY METALS

Reduction of a metallic compound by a more active metal is illustrated by the production of titanium, a metal that has become important only during the last ten years for its use in the construction of jet engines. Titanium is a silver-white metal having high tensile strength and resistance to corrosion plus a relatively low density (see Table 30–3). Titanium ores are mostly oxides (TiO_2, for example). For the production of the metal the ores are "leached" with sulfuric acid, and then the dioxide, TiO_2, is precipitated out. The dioxide is converted to the chloride, $TiCl_4$, by mixing with carbon and passing chlorine over the heated mixture:

$$TiO_2 + C + 2\,Cl_2 \rightarrow TiCl_4 + CO_2$$

The chloride distills over and is further purified before it is reduced in a special furnace having an inert atmosphere (helium or argon) by means of magnesium metal:

$$TiCl_4 + 2\,Mg \rightarrow Ti + 2\,MgCl_2$$

Reduction of the dioxide by means of carbon is not feasible because at the temperature of reduction the metal readily forms carbides and nitrides. Reduction of the oxide by aluminum yields alloys of titanium and aluminum.

Another example of reduction of a metallic compound by heating it with a more active metal is the so-called *Thermit* welding process. Aluminum powder mixed with ferric oxide is placed between two iron joints to be united and then ignited. An enormous amount of heat is generated by the reaction:

$$2\,Al + Fe_2O_3 \rightarrow 2\,Fe + Al_2O_3 + \text{heat}$$

so that the iron set free is molten and will flow into the fracture to be welded.

REDUCTION BY CARBON MONOXIDE: METALLURGY OF IRON

Of all metals iron is by far the lowest in price and is produced in the largest quantities. The various oxides of iron – hematite, limonite, and magnetite – are the principal ores. The chief sources of ores in the United States are in the Lake Superior area and in Alabama. The ores are associated with various "earthy" materials, such as silica or silicates and alumina. The reduction of iron ore is carried out in blast furnaces, which can be seen on the horizon of many large industrial centers. The blast furnace is charged at the top with iron ore, coke, and limestone (see Figure 30–4). The coke performs two functions: (1) it supplies heat, since the reduction of ore takes place rapidly only at high temperatures; and (2) it forms carbon monoxide which is the reducing agent. A blast of preheated air, which enters at the base of the furnace, is also essential. There are four principal reactions involved in the formation of iron:

(1) Combustion of the carbon forms carbon dioxide and liberates heat:

$$C + O_2 \rightarrow CO_2 + 94{,}450 \text{ calories}$$

(2) The liberated heat raises the contents, including the unchanged carbon, to a high temperature. Under these conditions the carbon dioxide is reduced to carbon monoxide, CO, a gaseous and vigorous reducing agent:

$$C + CO_2 + 42{,}000 \text{ calories} \rightarrow 2\,CO$$

This reaction takes place in a zone slightly above the region where the combustion to carbon dioxide occurs.

Fig. 30–4 *A blast furnace for iron.*

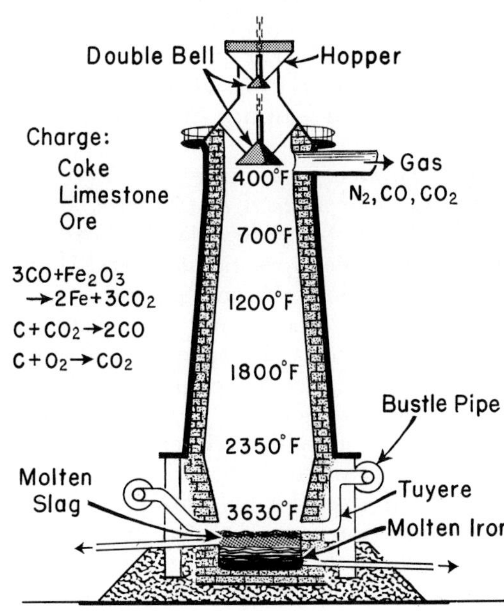

(3) The hot, gaseous carbon monoxide ascends through the furnace and reduces the iron oxide to metallic iron:

$$Fe_2O_3 + 3\,CO \rightarrow 3\,CO_2 + 2\,Fe$$

$$(Fe^{+++})_2[:\ddot{\underset{..}{O}}:]_3 + 3[:C:::O:] \rightarrow 2\,Fe + 3[:\ddot{O}::C::\ddot{O}:]$$

The iron accepts three electrons per atom to form neutral atoms of metallic iron.

(4) The limestone, which a metallurgist would call a *flux* or *slagging agent,* combines with the silica by forming calcium silicate or slag, useful in the preparation of Portland cement:

$$CaCO_3 + SiO_2 \rightarrow CO_2 + CaSiO_3$$

As the blast furnace operates, two liquid layers collect in the bottom of the furnace. The lower layer consists of *pig iron,* the upper layer of slag. The pig iron can be used in the crude state, but most of it is further refined and treated to form the *steels* of commerce.

PRODUCTION OF STEEL

The iron produced in the blast furnace contains many impurities and is weak and brittle. It cannot be hammered, rolled, or pressed. The liquid metal is poured into forms, such castings being known as *cast iron* or *pig iron.* The properties which are desirable – namely, bending without fracture (malleability), hardness, and high tensile stength – are obtained by treatments which convert the pig iron into steel. The difference in composition between these two types of impure iron is the degree to which the two main impurities, carbon and silicon, are present. Generally, one may define cast iron and steel on the basis of the carbon content. Cast iron contains above 2 to 4 per cent of carbon and other impurities such as silicon; steel contains 0.05 to 1.80 per cent of carbon. The principal change in effecting the conversion of pig iron to steel is the removal of the silicon and part of the carbon from the pig iron. The *open hearth* process is used to produce most of the steel.

In the open hearth process refining of the pig iron is accomplished by heating the molten pig iron with iron ore (Fe_2O_3), limestone, and steel scrap. The furnace is a rectangular brick structure usually having a capacity of 100 tons. The refining of the impure iron requires 10 to 11 hours per charge, and is therefore a controllable process. Samples of the metal and the slag are removed and tested in order to determine the degree to which silicon, manganese, sulfur, and phosphorus have been removed, and the desirable drop in the carbon content obtained. The essential reaction is between the iron oxides (from the ore and steel scrap) and the impurities resulting in the formation of a slag containing oxides, sulfides, phosphates, and silicates. When the desired composition has been reached, the metal is removed with ladles and poured into ingots. During this step other elements may be added to produce the various types of steels. Open hearth steel is used for structural work (buildings, bridges, cars, ships), springs, boilers, rails, and the many types of alloy steels.

ALLOYS

Only a few metals such as copper and tungsten are used in a pure form — metals are usually alloyed with other metals. Pure iron, for example, is seldom used outside of a chemical laboratory. What we speak of as iron and steel are mixtures or combinations of iron, carbon, and one or more metals, principally manganese, chromium, nickel, and tungsten. By melting together the components and then allowing the melt to solidify, there results an *alloy,* that is, a coherent metallic mass, a mixture, but homogeneous in appearance, and in many cases having some properties quite different from any one of the components. Classified by the manner in which the components blend, there are three types of alloys:

(1) The metals may form a *mechanical mixture,* in which crystals of one component may be buried in a matrix of the other substances. Alloys of this type usually have low melting points. Solder, an alloy of tin and lead; and Babbitt, a mixture of antimony and lead, are examples of this class.

(2) The components may dissolve in each other while in the molten condition, and remain in the same state of dispersion upon solidification. One of the brasses with a ratio of copper to zinc greater than 64 : 34 is an example of a *solid solution.* Where the solubility of one component in another is limited and it is present in excess, a mixture of the solid solution and a component may result.

(3) The components may react to form an *intermetallic* compound. The properties of such compounds are invariably different from those of the original metals. Copper and tin, for instance, can form a compound with the formula Cu_3Sn. The great hardness of bronze as compared to either copper or tin is due to the presence of this compound. Alloys containing intermetallic compounds may form either solid solutions or mechanical mixtures.

There are two principal reasons for alloying a metal with other metals:

(1) *To reduce the cost of production of an article.* Thus brass, an alloy of copper and zinc, costs less than pure copper, since zinc is considerably cheaper than copper. Aside from the introduction of cheaper metals, alloys are often cheaper to fabricate than pure metals. For instance, it is very difficult to make castings of pure copper or aluminum, but castings are easily made from their alloys.

(2) *To modify certain properties of the metal so as to make it more useful.* In alloys, desirable properties may be increased and undesirable properties decreased. Thus an alloy of copper, chromium, and a small amount of silver is harder than ordinary steel. Aluminum and magnesium are both structurally very weak, while an alloy of aluminum with four per cent magnesium has twice the strength of either metal alone.

In view of the definition that has previously been given for an alloy — a mixture of two or more metals which appears homogeneous to the eye — it may seem strange that steel should be referred to as an alloy.

TABLE 30–6 CHARACTERISTICS OF SOME COMMON ALLOYS

NAME	GENERAL COMPOSITION IN PER CENT		VALUABLE PROPERTIES AND CHARACTERISTIC USES
Aluminum casting alloy	Aluminum Iron and silicon Magnesium Copper	85–87 2.0 0.4 9–11	Light weight; relative high strength; pistons in automobile engines.
Duralumin	Aluminum Copper Magnesium Manganese	92 4 0.20–0.75 0.40–1	Can be rolled into sheets; very high tensile strength; desirable appearance; light in weight; used in airplane construction.
Brass	Copper Zinc	70 30	Cheaper than copper and superior to it in strength, ductility, and hardness; can be shaped by rolling, drawing, or casting; light fixtures, table lamps, gun cartridges, plumbing fixtures.
Bronze	Copper Tin Zinc	92–97 1–8 0–2	Very resistant to corrosion; easier to cast than copper; coinage, statuary.
Chromel	Nickel Iron Chromium	61 23 16	High electrical resistance; resistant to corrosion at high temperatures; a common heating element in electrical heating devices such as toasters.
Dowmetal	Magnesium Aluminum Manganese	88–96 4–12 0.1–0.30	The lightest structural metal yet available; can be shaped by extrusion or casting; various parts of airplanes.
Gold, jewelry	Gold Copper	75–84 24–16	Desirable color; resistance to corrosion; harder than pure gold.
Gold, white	Gold Nickel Zinc	75–85 8–10 2–9	Resembles platinum in appearance; used in jewelry.
Invar	Iron Nickel Carbon	64 36 0.2	Same coefficient of heat expansion as glass; used for the "lead-in" wires in electric light bulbs.
Iron, cast	Iron Carbon Sulfur Manganese Phosphorus Silicon	92–95 2–5 Varying (Sulfur, Manganese, Phosphorus, Silicon)	Very hard, brittle, non-elastic, relatively low melting point compared with pure iron; cheapest form of iron; cheap castings.
Sterling silver	Silver Copper	92.5 7.5	Desirable appearance; great resistance to corrosion; harder than pure silver; jewelry, silverware.
Steel, soft	Principally iron, with less than 0.8% carbon		Very ductile; resistant to shock; very soft; rather high tensile strength; wire, structural steel, rails.
Steel, hard	Principally iron, with more than 0.8% carbon		Very hard; high in tensile strength; can be heat-treated to make it very hard; tools, cutlery.
Steel, stainless	Iron Chromium Nickel Manganese Silicon	75–79 17–19 7–9 0.6 0.1–0.2	Very desirable appearance; very resistant to corrosion; very high tensile strength; lightweight construction of airplanes; high-speed trains; architectural purposes.
Steel, manganese	Iron Carbon Manganese	88–89 1–1.4 10	Unusually hard; burglar-proof safes, rail crossovers.
Steel, high-speed tool	Iron Tungsten Chromium Vanadium Carbon	74–75 18 4 1 0.7	Unusually hard and retains this hardness at red heat; used to make heavy-duty machine tools.
Steel, spring	Iron Silicon Manganese Carbon Chromium Vanadium	92–97 1.8–2.2 0.6–0.9 0.5–0.65 1.0 0.15	Very elastic; used to make railway-car and automobile springs.

However, the carbon combines chemically with the iron to form a compound called cementite, Fe_3C, a substance characterized by great hardness and brittleness. Hence steel can be considered an alloy of iron and a carbon compound of iron. The great difference in the properties of iron and steel can be attributed to the effect of the cementite.

Table 30–6 gives some of the more common alloys and a statement of their general composition, together with their significant properties and uses.

CORROSION OF METALS

A metal which has high chemical activity is usually attacked by the atmosphere, or corroded at a faster rate than a metal with a low activity. The environment to which metals are commonly exposed is the atmosphere, whose active chemical components are oxygen, water, and carbon dioxide. The rusting of an iron fence or bridge (a very common example of the corrosion of iron) is not a simple process of union of iron with oxygen to form iron oxides. The process is complex, requiring the presence of moisture and hydrogen ion, while the nonadhering iron rust is a mixture of various oxides and carbonates of iron. The general rule that chemically active metals corrode easily holds only if the oxide formed is nonadhering, that is, if the rust scales off to expose always a new surface to chemical action. Thus both copper and gold are low in the activity series and corrode slowly under ordinary atmospheric conditions. This relation does not hold if the rust adheres tenaciously to the metal. For example, aluminum and zinc are more active than iron, yet they corrode less readily than iron because the first fine film of oxide which forms on exposure adheres to the metallic surface and acts as a protective coating against further chemical attack. On the same principle there has been developed a method of protecting iron plate by dipping it in molten zinc, whereby "galvanized iron" is produced.

The annual monetary loss of metals by corrosion is estimated at 2.5 billion dollars. The economic importance of this loss has led to the development of numerous methods for checking corrosion, and to extensive research work for a better understanding of its mechanism. The attempt to develop alloys which are resistant to corrosion has met with some success. However, this is not a complete answer to the lowering of the corrosion rate of metals, since the cost of alloys is often higher than that of the principal metals. Moreover, alloys, including the so-called stainless steels, undergo corrosion at a slow rate.

At present the method most widely used to lower the rate of corrosion of metals such as iron is the use of protective coatings. The most common of these are: (*a*) certain metals, (*b*) metallic oxides or other adhering compounds, and (*c*) paints and

TABLE 30–7

PROCESS AND AGRICULTURAL CHEMICALS PRODUCED IN THE UNITED STATES

TYPE OF CHEMICAL	FORMULA	ANNUAL PRODUCTION IN MILLIONS OF TONS
Sodium chloride	$NaCl$	9.0
Sulfuric acid	H_2SO_4	6.0
Sodium carbonate	Na_2CO_3	2.5
Ethanol	C_2H_5OH	1.8
Sodium hydroxide	$NaOH$	1.0
Sodium silicate	Na_2SiO_3	0.6
Agricultural chemicals (fertilizers and insecticides)		8.1
Detergent chemicals (soaps, wetting agents, etc.)		2.0
Total		31.0

varnishes. Iron is coated by dipping it into molten tin to form "tin plate," into molten zinc to form "galvanized" iron, or into lead-tin alloy to form "terne plate." Metal coatings of nickel, chromium, cadmium, lead, copper, silver, gold, and other metals and alloys are made by electrodeposition (page 540). Other methods of applying metal coatings are by spraying the surface with molten atomized metal and by vaporizing the metal in a partially evacuated system. Aluminum may be coated with a film of its own oxide by a process called anodizing. The same process may be applied to magnesium and magnesium alloy castings. Iron is sometimes coated with an adhering magnetic iron oxide (gun blue coating) or with an insoluble phosphate.

Paints, varnishes, and baking enamels are the most widely used protective coatings, and their use is too widely known to need any elaboration. Enameled coatings, porcelain, or synthetic resins mixed with pigments find extensive application to refrigerators, stoves, table tops, and kitchen and bathroom utensils.

PROCESS CHEMICALS

Table 30–7 gives a summary of the process and agricultural chemicals produced annually in the United States. Ordinary salt makes up 28 per cent of the total tonnage; next to salt in volume is sulfuric acid; fourth is ethanol, the active component of all alcoholic beverages. The total tonnage of all sodium compounds is 42 per cent. The fact that sodium carbonate, sodium hydroxide, and sodium silicate are all derived from sodium chloride makes this simple material very important. Even in societies with no technological civilization, salt is one of the vital materials, not only because it preserves food but because it is essential in the diet of mammals. It is estimated that every person requires about twelve pounds per year. Animals, and particularly herbivores, will travel long distances in search of a salt lick. It seems probable that man first obtained salt from the same salt licks as the animals, but slowly developed a method of obtaining it first from sea water, then from deposits in the ground.

PRODUCTION OF SALT

Salt is found in the solid form, called *rock salt* or *halite,* in deposits that were formed from the evaporation of inland shallow seas in past geological ages. It usually contains impurities such as calcium, magnesium sulfate, and magnesium chloride. Salt can also be obtained from the ground at considerable depth in the form of brines or solutions containing a higher content of salt than sea water. In regions with long hot summers – California, for example – salt is obtained from the sea. Dikes are opened for sea water to run into shallow land basins. The heat from the sun evaporates the water and, as the solution becomes concentrated, the crystals of salt separate out.

If sea water is evaporated slowly, the least soluble salts crystallize out first. The first salts to precipitate out will be calcium and magnesium carbonate, then calcium and magnesium sulfate, then sodium chloride, and lastly the chlorides of potassium and magnesium. This ideal complete succession is found in the salt mines at Stassfurt, Germany, in which the beds of rock salt are over 1000 feet in thickness.

Of the total amount of salt utilized, about one-fourth is mined as rock salt; the remainder is produced by evaporation of artificial brines. Mining methods are similar to those used for the production of coal. Rock salt for the most part consists of large coarse gray granules; it is used for salting hides, obtaining low temperatures by mixing with crushed ice (as in the manufacture of ice cream), and for other industrial purposes.

Natural brines occur in southeastern Ohio and in West Virginia, on both sides of the Ohio River. The amount of dissolved solids in natural brines is not appreciable and hence the production of salt from these impure naturally occurring salt solutions is small. Most brines used to produce salt are obtained by drilling wells into salt deposits, usually to a depth of 1200 to 1500 feet and pumping fresh water down, then pumping or forcing upward the resulting saturated solution. The composition of these artificial brines varies somewhat with the district, but in general a brine contains 28 to 30 per cent of sodium chloride and 5 to 8 per cent of calcium sulfate, magnesium chloride, and sodium sulfate. Artificial brines may be used directly for the production of purified salt or for the industrial preparation of chlorine and sodium hydroxide by electrolysis. The annual world production of salt is 35 million tons; the United States produces about 25 per cent of the total.

INDUSTRIAL PREPARATION OF CHLORINE

Electrolysis of brine produces over 1,500,000 tons of chlorine annually in the United States. The principle of electrolysis is illustrated in Figure 30–5. The two graphite electrodes dipping in the solution of sodium chloride are connected to a source of electrons, such as a battery or a D. C. generator. In the solution there are water molecules, a few hydronium ions, H_3O^+, and a few hydroxyl ions, OH^-. All the salt is in the form of chloride, Cl^-, and sodium, Na^+, ions. As soon as the electrodes are connected to the battery a potential difference exists between them, and the chloride ions are attracted to the anode, which is positively charged or has a deficiency of electrons. The chloride ions give off electrons to become chlorine atoms; by union of atoms, molecular chlorine is formed:

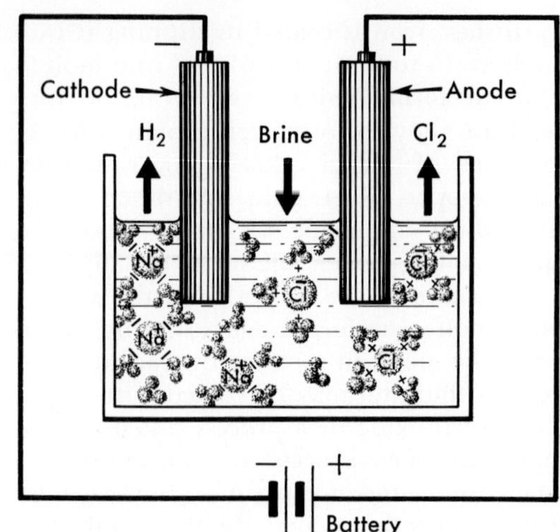

Fig. 30–5 *Electrolysis of solution of sodium chloride.*

As shown in the equations, the reverse reaction takes place at the cathode. That is, the hydronium ions (from water) are attracted to the cathode more readily than sodium ions, and gain electrons to form molecular hydrogen. As the hydronium ions are used up in the reaction, more are formed from dissociation of water:

$$\mathrm{H{:}\ddot{\underset{\displaystyle H}{\underset{..}{O}}}{:}} + \mathrm{H{:}\ddot{\underset{\displaystyle H}{\underset{..}{O}}}{:}} \rightarrow \left[\mathrm{H{:}\overset{\displaystyle H}{\overset{..}{\underset{\displaystyle H}{\underset{..}{O}}}}{:}}\right]^+ + \left[\mathrm{{:}\ddot{\underset{..}{O}}{:}H}\right]^-$$

The net result of the passage of current through the solution is the liberation of chlorine at the anode and of hydrogen at the cathode, and the accumulation of Na^+ and OH^- ions in the solution. Therefore, electrolysis involves definite chemical changes at the cathode (gain of electrons) and at the anode (loss of electrons).

$$\text{Anode}\quad 2\left[\mathrm{{:}\ddot{\underset{..}{Cl}}{:}}\right]^- \xrightarrow{\text{Anode}} 2\,e^- + 2\left[\mathrm{{:}\ddot{\underset{..}{Cl}}\cdot}\right] \rightarrow \mathrm{{:}\ddot{\underset{..}{Cl}}{:}\ddot{\underset{..}{Cl}}{:}}$$

Loss of e^- by ions — Chloride ions — Chlorine atoms — Chlorine molecule

$$\text{Cathode}\quad 2\left[\mathrm{H{:}\overset{\displaystyle H}{\overset{..}{\underset{\displaystyle H}{\underset{..}{O}}}}{:}}\right]^+ + 2\,e^- \xrightarrow{\text{Cathode}} 2\,\mathrm{H{:}\ddot{\underset{\displaystyle H}{\underset{..}{O}}}{:}} + \mathrm{H{:}H}$$

Gain of e^- by ions — Hydronium ions — Water molecules — Hydrogen molecule

The cell shown in Figure 30–5 cannot operate practically, since the chlorine will react with the sodium hydroxide. The industrial cells are equipped with porous diaphragms which separate the anode from the cathode but allow migration of the ions. Figure 30–6 shows a battery of these cells, called Hooker-type cells. They consist of graphite anodes and perforated cathodes close together but separated by sheets of asbestos which act as porous diaphragms to keep apart the products formed at the anode and at the cathode. Brine is piped into the cell from the brine feed line. Chlorine is liberated at the graphite anodes and passes to the overhead pipe collecting system. The solution seeps through the diaphragm to the cathode, and the hydrogen that is liberated passes into a separate collecting system. The solution of sodium hydroxide containing some sodium chloride is removed through a separate outlet. On evaporation, the sodium chloride, which is less soluble, separates out first and is removed; on further evaporation sodium hydroxide is obtained. The solid still contains some chloride. The chlorine passes into the main line, then to a compressor where it is liquefied and stored in steel cylinders or tanks for sale.

The principal uses of chlorine are for the treatment of drinking water, for bleaching wood pulp and textiles, and for the production of bromine from sea water. The bromine is used to prepare ethylene bromide for use with tetraethyl lead in motor fuels.

About one-half of the total annual production of chlorine is employed in the production of organic chlorine compounds. Chief among these are solvents such as carbon tetrachloride, CCl_4, and the like, and the chlorinated hydrocarbons such as DDT, Aldrin, and Dieldrin. These chemicals for insect control have been in use only about twenty-five years, yet in this short period they have helped greatly to eradicate malaria all over the world and to control insects in agriculture. Most of the insecticides contain more than fifty per cent of chlorine.

SYNTHETIC POLYMERS

The term *synthetic* means "making one out of two or more"; it is employed here to denote chemical compounds that are built out of simpler parts and that resemble in form and properties products formed by nature. The term *polymer* is applied to large molecular units formed by the union of simple units of low molecular weight. Hence, *synthetic polymers* are materials of high molecular weight produced by chemists from relatively simple molecules called *monomers.* They include the *plastics or synthetic resins* (resinoids), the *synthetic rubbers* (rubberoids or elastomers), and the *synthetic textile fibers* (fibroids.) The first polymer was prepared from styrene, $C_6H_5CH = CH_2$, by Simon in 1839; but not until the first decade of this century, when the plastic known as Bakelite was prepared by Baekeland (Belgium and United States, 1863–1944), did synthetic polymers receive any attention. Rapid advances have been made in the last twenty years, and today synthetic polymers have assumed an important place among the products of industrial chemical reactions.

Fig. 30–6 *Hooker electrolytic cell (Type S–3A) for the production of chlorine from salt solution. (Hooker Electrochemical Co.)*

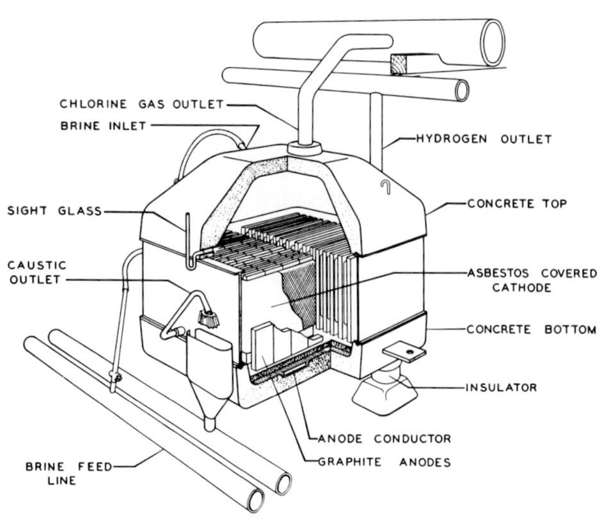

POLYMERIZATION

The term *polymerization* was mentioned under the reactions of unsaturated hydrocarbons as a reaction involving *the chemical union of a number of similar molecules to form a single complex molecule.* For example, when ethene, $CH_2{=}CH_2$, is treated with a catalyst under specified conditions, two molecules may combine to give butene, an unsaturated hydrocarbon with four carbon atoms:

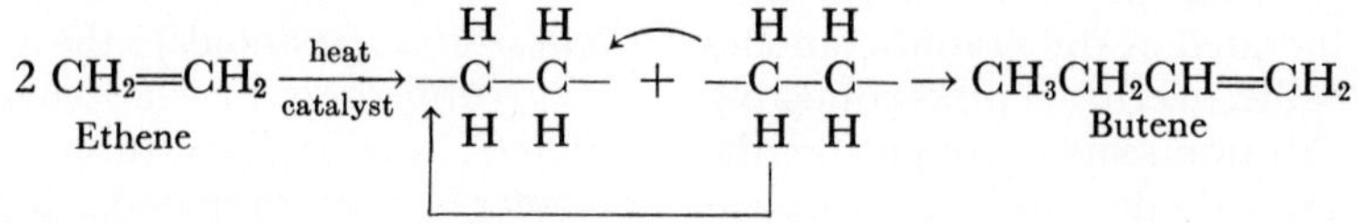

$$2\,CH_2{=}CH_2 \xrightarrow[\text{catalyst}]{\text{heat}} -\overset{H}{\underset{H}{C}}-\overset{H}{\underset{H}{C}}- + -\overset{H}{\underset{H}{C}}-\overset{H}{\underset{H}{C}}- \rightarrow CH_3CH_2CH{=}CH_2$$

Ethene — Butene

With a different catalyst and pressure the process of self-addition can be repeated to give molecules with several thousand carbon atoms. Ethene is a gas, but as the molecular weight increases during the reaction, it becomes a viscous oil, then a waxy and finally a hard translucent resin known as *polythene*:

$$n\,CH_2{=}CH_2 \xrightarrow[\text{heat}]{\text{catalyst}} (-CH_2-CH_2-)_n$$

Ethene (monomer) — Polythene (polymer)

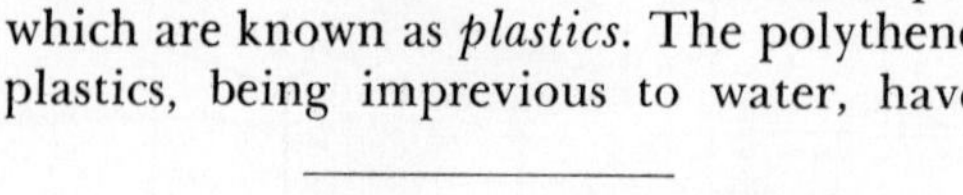

CH₂ CH₂ CH₂ CH₂ CH₂ CH₂ CH₂ CH₂ CH₂
CH₂ CH₂ CH₂ CH₂ CH₂ CH₂ CH₂ CH₂

The resin when heated becomes soft and can be extruded in the form of sheets or filaments, or molded into various shapes which are known as *plastics*. The polythene plastics, being imprevious to water, have been used to produce various articles such as bottles and jars, funnels, water resistant sheets, interior coatings for tanks, and the like.

The trend to polymerization of unsaturated compounds is shown by the following two examples. Styrene, $C_6H_5CH{=}CH_2$, may be regarded as derived from ethene, CH_2CH_2, by replacing one hydrogen atom with the phenyl C_6H_5- group. It undergoes polymerization much more readily than ethene; when heated to boiling, even in the absence of a catalyst, it changes first to a viscous oil then to a hard resin:

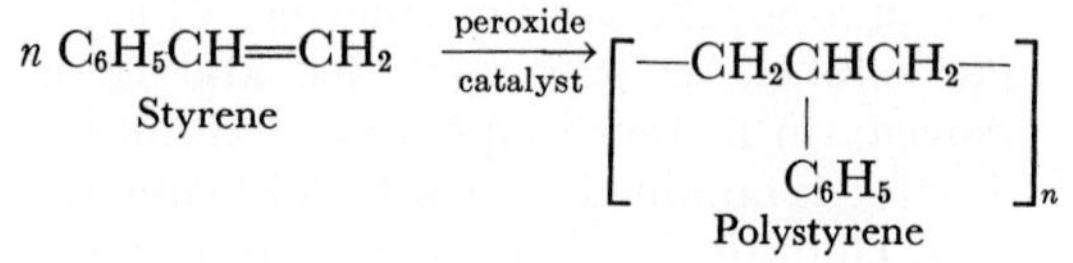

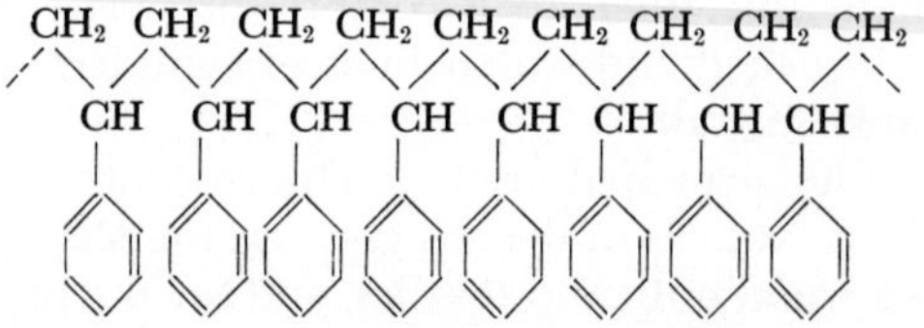

$$n\,C_6H_5CH{=}CH_2 \xrightarrow[\text{catalyst}]{\text{peroxide}} \left[-CH_2\underset{\underset{C_6H_5}{|}}{C}HCH_2-\right]_n$$

Styrene — Polystyrene

CH₂ CH₂ CH₂ CH₂ CH₂ CH₂ CH₂ CH₂ CH₂
CH CH CH CH CH CH CH CH

Besides unsaturated compounds which polymerize by *self-addition,* polymerization may take place between two *unlike* simple molecules having functional groups which can react with each other. For example, an aldehyde, $RCH{=}O$, can react with a hydroxy compound like phenol, C_6H_5OH, by splitting off a molecule of water, as shown below:

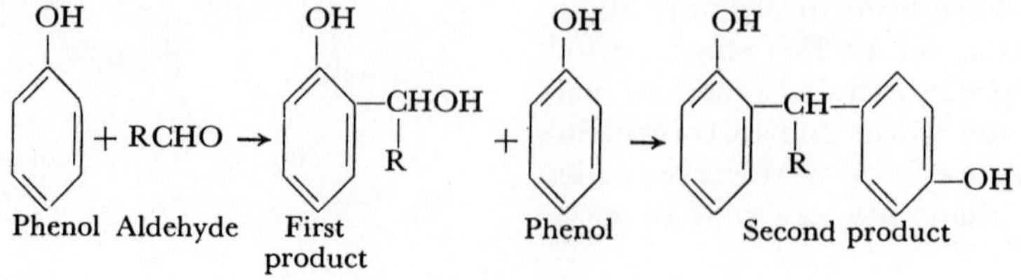

Phenol + RCHO (Aldehyde) → First product (C₆H₄(OH)–CHOH–R) + Phenol → Second product (HO–C₆H₄–CH(R)–C₆H₄–OH)

By successive reactions with more phenol and formaldehyde, larger molecules having a linear structure of 6 to 8 phenol residues are built. At this stage the product is still fusible — that is, it is plastic when heated, or *thermoplastic*. The following representation shows the phenol-formaldehyde intermediate thermoplastic polymer, with linear molecular structure and few cross-links between the molecules:

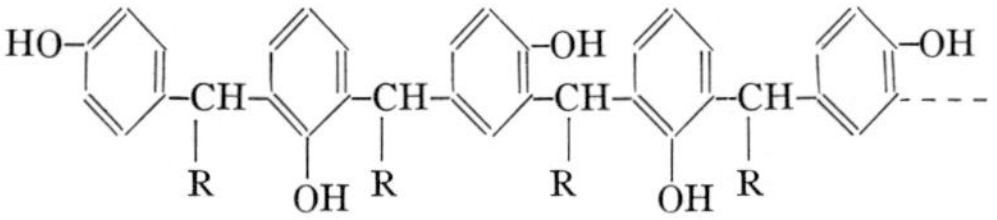

HO– –CH– –CH– –OH –CH– –CH– –OH - - - -
R OH R R OH R

However, when this intermediate is heated for a short time above 140° C. the resin hardens, becomes infusible, and can be machined like brass or wood, but cannot be molded any more. In other words, the resin has undergone a *thermosetting* stage which involves a change in the molecular structure: extensive cross-linkages develop which hold the linear molecules in a rigid three-dimensional structure:

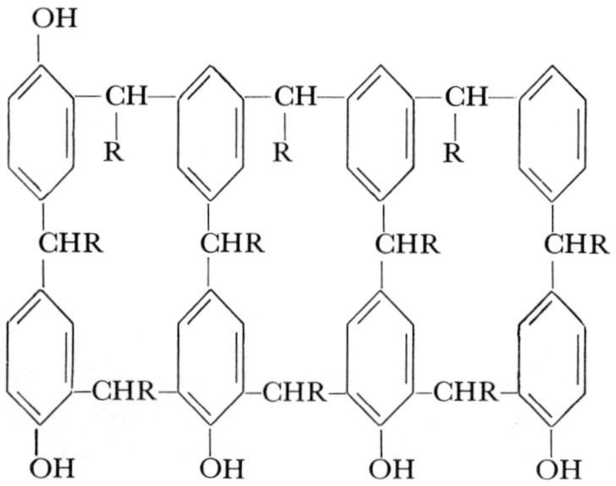

OH
–CH– –CH– –CH–
R R R
CHR CHR CHR CHR
–CHR– –CHR– –CHR–
OH OH OH OH

By using different aldehydes and phenols a variety of resins of this type can be produced. Mixed with fillers and pigments they are widely used for table tops and a multitude of molded or machined articles. Sheets of paper, textiles, or wood impregnated with the fusible resin, when pressed and cured, give a variety of *laminates,* that is, solids built up from layers (*lamina,* thin plate).

Since a great many unsaturated compounds can polymerize by self-addition and many compounds can polymerize by the reaction of two or more functional groups, the number of possible synthetic polymers is very large. Table 30–8 lists a few of the important groups of synthetic polymers. In Group I are listed the polythene, polystyrene, vinylite, and polyacrylate resins; they are all thermoplastic — they soften when heated. Also included in Group I are the alkyds and phenolics; these are thermosetting resins — at the molding temperature cross-links develop and the polymer becomes hard, rigid, and nonfusible. Group II comprises the synthetic rubbers or *elastomers,* that is, polymers which have rubber-like properties. In Group III are listed the polyamides and polyesters which are used to make textile fibers. The properties of the thermoplastic and thermosetting resins, and of the rubberoid and fibroid polymers are directly connected with their molecular structure.

ELASTOMERS OR RUBBEROIDS

Natural rubber comes mainly from the tree *Hevea Brasiliensis,* extensively cultivated in tropical countries. A milky exudate called *latex* is obtained when the bark is cut; this contains 30 to 35 per cent of dispersed rubber particles. When acid is added, the dispersed rubber is coagulated and pressed into sheets or balls. This is the natural rubber of commerce.

Rubber is used extensively in the manufacture of many familiar molded articles by milling it with various fillers. The outstanding property of rubber is its elasticity or its rebound on impact to acquire its original form. It is this property which accounts for its extensive use in tires, for example. Rubber, however, has also a number of undesirable properties. When cooled, it loses its elasticity and at about –80° C. becomes brittle; on exposure to sunlight, air, or heat, it hardens and cracks because of oxidation changes. To increase its resistance to these agents rubber is *vulcanized,* that is, heated with sulfur or sulfur compounds. This proc-

TABLE 30–8 IMPORTANT GROUPS OF SYNTHETIC POLYMERS

MONOMERS Name	Formula	POLYMERS Chemical Name	Trade Names
Group I	*Resinoids*		
Ethene	$CH_2{=}CH_2$	Polythene or polyethylene resin	
Styrene	$C_6H_5CH{=}CH_2$	Polystyrene resin	
Vinyl chloride	$CH_2{=}CHCl$	Polyvinyl chloride	Vinylite resins
Vinyl acetate	$CH_2{=}CHOCOCH_3$	Polyvinyl acetate	Vinylite resins
Methylmethacrylate	$CH_2{=}C(CH_3)COCH_3$	Polymethacrylate	Lucite, Plexiglass
Glycerol + Phthalic anhydride	$CH_2OHCHOHCH_2OH$ + $C_6H_4(COOH)_2$	Alkyd resins	Glyptals, Resyls, Aberlacs
Formaldehyde + Phenol	CH_2O + C_6H_5OH	Phenolic resins	
Group II	*Elastomers*		
Isoprene	$CH_2{=}C(CH_3){-}CH{=}CH_2$	Polyisoprene	Natural rubber
Chloroprene	$CH_2{=}C(Cl){-}CH{=}CH_2$	Polychloroprene	Neoprene rubber
Butadiene + Styrene	$CH_2{=}CH{-}CH{=}CH_2$ + $C_6H_5CH{=}CH_2$	Copolymer of Butadiene and Styrene	GR–S rubber
Group III	*Fibroids*		
Adipic acid + 1,6-Diaminohexane	$HOOC{-}(CH_2)_4{-}COOH$ + $H_2N(CH_2)_6NH_2$	Polyamide	Nylon
Ethylene glycol + Terephthalic acid	CH_2OHCH_2OH + $HOOC{-}C_6H_4{-}COOH$	Polyterephthalic ester	Dacron

ess decreases its plastic properties, but the rubber acquires greater resistance to oxidation.

About the middle of the last century chemists succeeded in isolating isoprene (2-methylbutadiene) among the products obtained from the destructive distillation of rubber. From that time on, the structure of rubber was exhaustively investigated; and from studies of the polymerization of isoprene under various conditions it was found, after research extending over a period of eighty years, that polymers almost identical with natural rubber are formed:

$$n\ \underset{\text{Isoprene (2-Methylbutadiene)}}{CH_2{=}\underset{\substack{|\\ CH_3}}{C}{-}CH{=}CH_2} \rightarrow \underset{\text{Polyisoprene rubber}}{\left[{-}CH_2\underset{\substack{|\\ CH_3}}{C}{=}CH{-}CH_2{-}CH_2{-}\underset{\substack{|\\ CH_3}}{C}{=}CH{-}CH_2{-}\right]_n}$$

$$\cdots CH_2{-}\underset{\substack{|\\ CH_3}}{C}{=}CH{-}CH_2{-}CH_2{-}\underset{\substack{|\\ CH_3}}{C}{=}CH{-}CH_2{-}CH_2{-}\underset{\substack{|\\ CH_3}}{C}{=}CH{-}CH_2{-}CH_2{-}\underset{\substack{|\\ CH_3}}{C}{=}CH{-}CH_2 \cdots$$

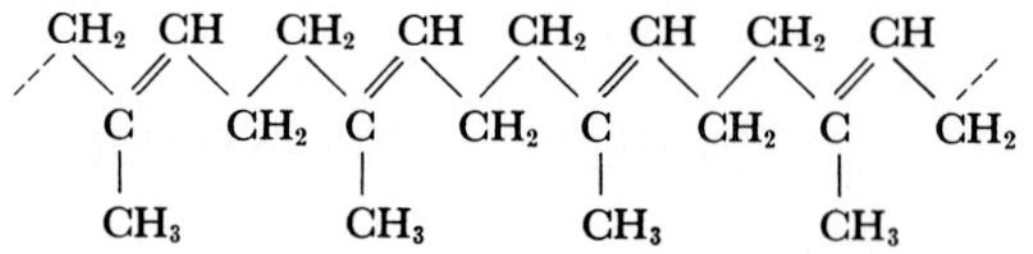

As shown schematically in the formulas the large molecules or *macromolecules* consist of long hydrocarbon chains arranged in a *linear* fashion and containing a number of residual double bonds. When rubber is vulcanized, sulfur reacts with some of the double bonds of the chains. However, some unsaturation is left, and even vulcanized rubber is susceptible to oxidation. The addition of small quantities of certain amines reduces the rate of oxidation (antioxidants) and greatly increases the life of rubber goods.

The consumption of rubber in the United States is over 1.5 billion pounds per year. Since we do not produce any natural rubber, numerous investigations have been undertaken toward the industrial production of synthetic elastomers. The first attempts (1908–12) in this country to produce industrially synthetic elastomers from isoprene were not successful because isoprene could not be synthesized economically on a large scale. Then over a period of years it was discovered that compounds containing the butadiene skeleton

$$\begin{array}{c}—C{=}C—C{=}C—\\ \;\;|\quad\;|\quad\;|\quad\;|\end{array}$$

yield elastomers when polymerized.

$$\underset{\substack{\text{Isoprene}\\\text{2-Methylbutadiene}}}{\overset{\qquad}{CH_2{=}\underset{\substack{|\\CH_3}}{C}—CH{=}CH_2}} \qquad \underset{\substack{\text{Chloroprene}\\\text{2-Chlobutadiene}}}{H_2C{=}\underset{\substack{|\\Cl}}{C}—CH{=}CH_2}$$

$$\underset{\text{Butadiene}}{H_2C{=}CH—CH{=}CH_2}$$

It will be noted that both isoprene and chloroprene are derived from butadiene by substituting a methyl group and a chlorine atom respectively for a hydrogen atom associated with the second carbon atom.

The first commercially available synthetic rubber was Neoprene, the result of a long series of researches on acetylene by Father Nieuwland (1878–1936) of the University of Notre Dame. Acetylene is produced either from calcium carbide or from the dehydrogenation of methane:

$$\underset{\substack{\text{Calcium}\\\text{carbonate}}}{CaCO_3} \xrightarrow[\text{heat}]{\text{carbon}} \underset{\substack{\text{Calcium}\\\text{carbide}}}{CaC_2} \xrightarrow{H_2O} \underset{\text{Acetylene}}{CH{\equiv}CH}$$

$$2\ CH_4 \xrightarrow[\text{heat}]{\text{catalyst}} CH{\equiv}CH + 3\ H_2$$

When acetylene is treated with cuprous chloride it forms a dimer vinylacetylene:

$$\underset{\substack{\text{Acetylene}\\\text{(monomer)}}}{CH{\equiv}CH + CH{\equiv}CH} \xrightarrow{Cu_2Cl_2} \underset{\substack{\text{Vinylacetylene}\\\text{(dimer)}}}{CH_2{=}CH—C{\equiv}CH}$$

Addition of hydrogen chloride to vinylacetylene yields chloroprene, which is then polymerized:

$$\underset{\text{Vinylacetylene}}{CH{\equiv}C—CH{=}CH_2} + HCl \rightarrow \underset{\text{Chloroprene}}{CH_2{=}\underset{\substack{|\\Cl}}{C}—CH{=}CH_2}$$

$$n\ \underset{\text{Chloroprene}}{CH_2{=}\underset{\substack{|\\Cl}}{C}—CH{=}CH_2} \rightarrow$$

$$\rightarrow \underset{\text{Neoprene rubber}}{\left[—CH_2—\underset{\substack{|\\Cl}}{C}{=}CH—CH_2—CH_2—\underset{\substack{|\\Cl}}{C}{=}CH—CH_2—\right]_n}$$

Meantime in Germany elastomers were produced industrially by polymerizing a mixture of about 75 per cent butadiene, $CH_2{=}CH{-}CH{=}CH_2$, with 25 per cent styrene, $C_6H_5CH{=}CH_2$. The product called Buna–S is a copolymer of the two unsaturated hydrocarbons. In the United States this type of synthetic rubber (now produced on a large scale) is called GR–S rubber since it was developed to a large extent by government sponsored research. The butadiene is obtained from butane and the styrene from ethyl benzene by dehydrogenation:

$$\underset{n\text{-Butane}}{CH_3CH_2CH_2CH_3} \xrightarrow[\text{heat}]{\text{catalyst}} \underset{\text{Butadiene}}{CH_2{=}CH—CH{=}CH_2} + 2\ H_2$$

$$\underset{\text{Ethylbenzene}}{C_6H_5CH_2CH_3} \xrightarrow[\text{heat}]{\text{catalyst}} \underset{\text{Styrene}}{C_6H_5CH{=}CH_2} + H_2$$

A

B

C

Fig. 30–7 *Some air-age uses of synthetic polymers. A. Polyester plastic core of antenna reflector for airborne radar (shown being removed from mold) solves problem of combining lightness, strength, and precise curvature. (Raytheon Mfg. Co., Waltham, Mass.) B. Portable hangar for plane or helicopter, with "skin" of Neoprene-coated nylon fabric, can be erected in minutes. (Official U. S. Marine Corps photo) C. Crash barriers of nylon save lives. (Official U. S. Air Force photo)*

The polymerization is effected by making an emulsion of the two hydrocarbons in water by the addition of soaps or other emulsifying agents and then adding a small amount of a peroxide catalyst and stirring the mixture. The milky latex which results from the reaction contains 30 to 40 per cent of dispersed elastomer, which is coagulated by the addition of salt or acid. Other unsaturated compounds may be copolymerized with butadiene. The copolymer with acrylic nitrile $CH_2{=}CHCN$ is known as Ameripol, in this country and as Perbunan in Germany.

FIBROIDS

The first synthetic fibroid, nylon, is a polyamide resinoid which is synthesized from relatively cheap materials (coke, lime, water, and air). Nylon was developed from a series of brilliant researches (1925–35) carried out by William Carothers and his collaborators at the research laboratories of E. I. du Pont de Nemours Company. Carothers' published papers on the structure of polyamides and polyesters still furnish excellent guide posts in the search for new fibroids.

Nylon is a generic term for all synthetic fibroids consisting of polymeric amides which have structural similarities to proteins such as silk and hair (see page 465). The polyamide is prepared by heating in an atmosphere of nitrogen a mixture of adipic acid and 1,6-diaminohexane:

$$\underset{\text{Adipic acid}}{HOOC{-}(CH_2)_4COOH} + \underset{\text{1,6-Diaminohexane}}{H_2N{-}(CH_2)_6{-}NH_2} \xrightarrow{218°C.} \underset{\text{Polyhexamethyleneadipamide or Nylon Polyamide}}{[-N{-}(CH_2)_6{-}[NHCO]{-}(CH_2)_4{-}CO-]_n}$$

It will be noted that the polyamide structure contains the [–NHCO–] polypeptide linkage that is characteristic of the union of amino acids in proteins (see page 465). The reaction mixture is poured in alcohol, which precipitates the polymer as a white, granular powder. Continuous filaments are made by heating the product to 230–240° C. and extruding it in an atmosphere of nitrogen. During the extrusion the fiber is stretched; this orients the molecules and lengthens the molecular chain, thus imparting high tensile strength and some elasticity. The polymer has a molecular weight of about 10,000 to 12,000. Since each repeating unit of the polyamide has a molecular weight of 225, the molecule of the polymer contains about 50 repeating units.

In general appearance, nylon closely resembles silk, but has a somewhat different feel and resilience. Under tests which drastically distort silk fabrics, nylon fabrics return to their original shape. Nylon is not inflammable, but if held in an open flame it melts to a transparent globule, then gradually blackens into a tar and disappears. It is resistant to moisture (does not swell), heat, and common solvents, but can be hydrolyzed to the original monomers (depolymerized) by boiling with strong acids. In some respects the synthetic fibroid has properties superior to silk and wool, to which it is relatively close in structure.

Other synthetic fibroids of commercial importance are Orlon, an acrylonitrile polymer, and Dacron, a polyester polymer from ethylene glycol and terephthalic acid.

STRUCTURE AND PROPERTIES OF POLYMERS

We have noted thus far three types of polymers: (1) the resinoids, of which polystyrene is an example; (2) the elastomers, of which natural and GR–S rubbers are examples; and (3) the fibroids, of which the nylon polyamide is an example. Since all these polymers consist of macromolecules arranged for the most part in a linear fashion, the question naturally arises: why do they exhibit vastly different properties? And further: what type of structure does the chemist attempt to build in "tailor-making" linear macromolecules for textile fibers?

A simplified answer to both questions is provided by studying the polymers by X-rays and correlating the patterns obtained with the chemical structure of the molecules, particularly the "polarity" and "bulk" effects of the various groups present in the macromolecules. Figure 30–8 represents the molecular structure of polystyrene resin.

Fig. 30–8 *Amorphous macromolecular structure as in polystyrene resin. The molecules resemble randomly placed coils.*

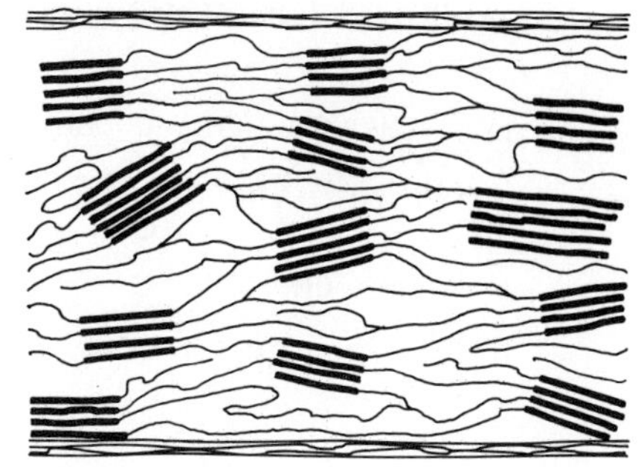

Fig. 30–9 *Oriented crystalline macromolecular structure as in nylon.*

The molecules resemble randomly placed coils or a heap of cooked spaghetti, since they are loosely entangled and wrapped around each other. This macromolecular structure is known as *amorphous.* Figure 30–9 represents an "oriented crystalline" macromolecular structure of fiber-forming polymers (such as nylon) which have been stretched under tension. The oriented areas, represented by dark lines, are called *crystallites;* these have been made parallel when the fiber was stretched. As the diagram indicates, the molecules are not completely crystalline but contain some amorphous areas. Figure 30–10 represents the structure of the polythene resin molecules, which are related to those in both Figures 30–8 and 30–9 since they contain both amorphous areas and crystallites. The chains appear to pass alternately from crystalline to amorphous areas; however, the crystallites are not oriented parallel to each other. Polythene is a wax-like resin consisting mainly of a linear arrangement of $-CH_2-$ (methylene groups) as shown in Figures 30–10 and 11. In the polythene structure the various chains are closely packed, but because there is no polarity in the $-CH_2-$ groups there is very little attractive force between the various chains. Hence the cohesive forces are low, and when stress is applied the molecules slip over one another and deformation occurs. On the other hand, in the polyamide chains, which are arranged in the same zig-zag fashion, there is a more ordered orientation due to the strong attraction between the polar groups of adjacent chains:

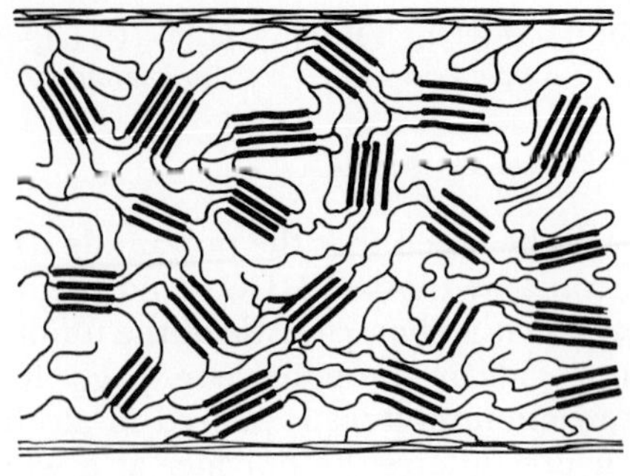

Fig. 30–10 *Mixed amorphous crystalline macromolecular structure as in polythene resin.*

Fig. 30–11 *Polythene structure.*

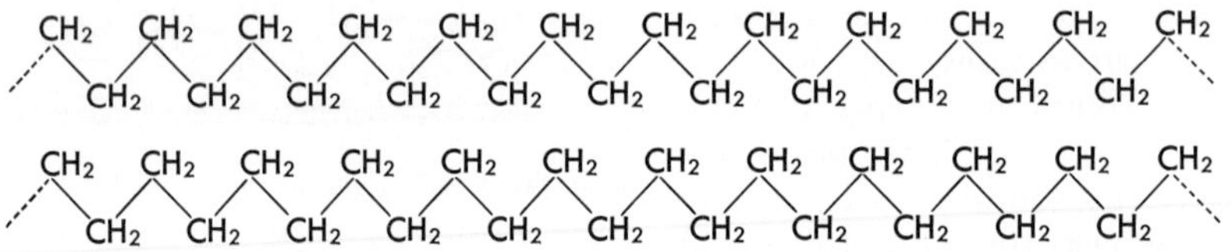

CH2 CH2 CH2 CH2 CH2 CH2 CH2 CH2 CH2 CH2 CH2 CH2
CH2 CH2 CH2 CH2 CH2 CH2 CH2 CH2 CH2 CH2 CH2

CH2 CH2 CH2 CH2 CH2 CH2 CH2 CH2 CH2 CH2 CH2 CH2
CH2 CH2 CH2 CH2 CH2 CH2 CH2 CH2 CH2 CH2 CH2

Fig. 30–12 *Polyamide structure.*

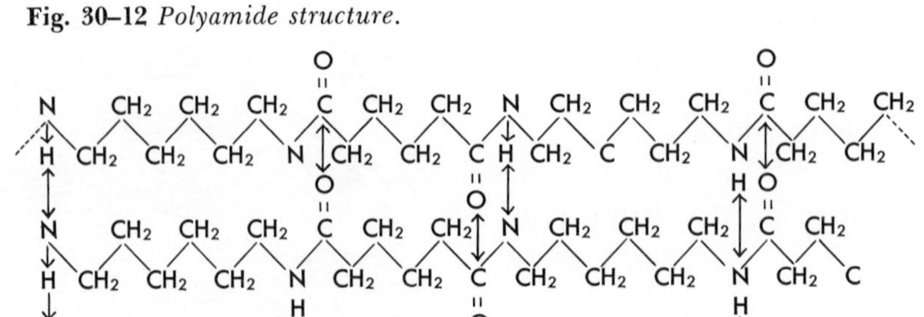

O O
N CH2 CH2 CH2 C CH2 CH2 N CH2 CH2 CH2 C CH2 CH2
H CH2 CH2 CH2 N CH2 CH2 C H CH2 C CH2 N CH2 CH2
O O H O
N CH2 CH2 CH2 C CH2 CH2 N CH2 CH2 CH2 C CH2
H CH2 CH2 CH2 N CH2 CH2 C CH2 CH2 CH2 N CH2 C
H O H

Fig. 30–13 *Dacron structure.*

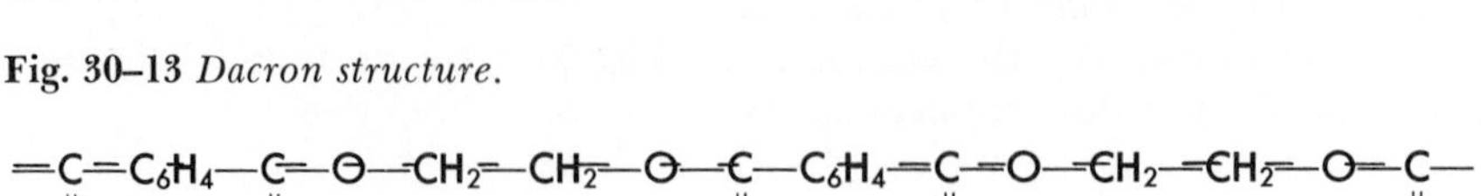

=C—C6H4—C—O—CH2—CH2—O—C—C6H4—C—O—CH2—CH2—O—C—
O O O O O

as shown by the arrows there is hydrogen bonding between the NH groups and CO groups of adjacent chains. Thus, the crystallinity of the linear polymer chains plus the polar attraction between functional groups in adjacent chains accounts for the high tensile strength of the polyamide fibers. The drawing and stretching tend to form an oriented pattern which is maintained by the dipolar forces of interchain functional groups.

The desirable fiber-forming properties of Dacron may also be explained by the crystallinity of the linear polymers and the strong polar forces developed between the C=O groups in adjacent chains (Figure 30–13). The tensile strength of the fibers is due to the symmetrical nature of the molecule and the strong polar forces between adjacent macromolecular chains, which prevent stoppage.

In considering the relation between the structure and the properties of elastomers, the following facts should be kept in mind. When rubber is cooled below −75° C. it becomes brittle, indicating that the macromolecular chains are held in fixed position with very little chance of free rotation. As the temperature is raised near 0° C., some elasticity returns. The highly coiled molecules are not attracted to their neighbors because there are no strong polar groups. When a stretching force is applied, the molecules uncoil and become more linear and more fixedly oriented. As the stretching force is diminished, the molecules return to the coiled condition in which there is more mobility; this accounts for the elasticity. During the stretching and rebound the residual double bonds (which are partially polar) act as rigid anchor points about which there is free rotation of the other carbon-to-carbon bonds. The introduction of sulfur atoms in vulcanization increases the number of cross-links between chains which serve as anchor points. By increasing the amount of sulfur and the time of heating, during the vulcanization, the number of cross-links can be increased to the point where the rigid three-dimensional structure of hard rubber, devoid of any elasticity, results.

SUMMARY

1. Next to fuels, foods, and materials of construction, metals are produced in largest tonnage. Metals are the backbone of our technological society.
2. Of about 70 metals which occur in nature, about 30 find extensive use; of these, iron accounts for about 90 per cent of the tonnage used, and copper, zinc, lead, and aluminum together for about 8 per cent.
3. The factors which determine the large-scale use of metals are: (*a*) availability and cost of production; (*b*) desirable physical and chemical properties (density, melting point, ductility, malleability, tensile strength, and hardness); (*c*) resistance to corrosion. Often one or two of these factors are so favorable that others are not taken into consideration. Iron, for example, has a high density, and its resistance to corrosion is poor, but the cost of production is low and many mechanical properties are favorable.
4. Often two or more metals are mixed in the molten state to produce an alloy that has more desirable properties than any of the alloying metals alone.
5. Ores are compounds which occur in nature and from which metals can be gleaned economically. Most ores are oxides, sulfides, or carbonates; the latter two by heating (roasting) are converted to oxides. Ores are concentrated by sedimentation and oil flotation processes. A few ores of inactive metals (copper, silver, gold, and platinum) contain the free metals.
6. All metallurgical processes for the conversion of the concentrated oxide ores to the metals involve reduction of the metallic ion; the electron source may be an electric current (as for aluminum or sodium), an active metal (as for titanium), or carbon monoxide (as for iron).
7. Most metals used on a large scale are subgroup or transitional elements; the number of *s* electrons (outermost shell) remains constant, and increase in atomic number results in increase in the *d* subshell (next to the outermost). Because of the similarity of the outermost electron shell: (*a*) the elements exhibit a number of related physical

properties; (*b*) in forming chemical bonds they lose electrons from the outermost shell (4*s*) and also electrons from the next to the outermost shell (3*d*) and hence form positive ions and exhibit variable valence—as, for example, Fe^{++} and Fe^{+++}; (*c*) they form weakly basic hydroxides.

8. Of the process chemicals, salt (sodium chloride) is produced in the largest tonnage; sulfuric acid is second. Most salt is obtained from brines made by circulating water through wells drilled into salt deposits.
9. The electrolysis of brine yields chlorine and sodium hydroxide, both of which are important process chemicals. In the electrolysis of brine the chloride ions are attracted to the cathode where they are discharged as molecular chlorine by removing electrons from their outer shells; the hydronium ions are attracted to the cathode where they are discharged as hydrogen gas through gain of electrons.
10. Synthetic *polymers* are materials of high molecular weight produced from relatively simple molecules called *monomers.* The process is called polymerization; it involves either addition of unsaturated molecules to each other or reactions between the functional groups of the monomers.
11. Polymers are usually divided into *synthetic resins* or *plastics, synthetic rubbers* or *elastomers,* and *synthetic fibers* or *fibroids.*
12. The properties of polymers are determined by: (*a*) the nature of the monomers; (*b*) the molecular weight and structure of the large molecules (*macromolecules*).
13. Plastics on the whole have linear molecules randomly arranged, amorphous in nature, and loosely entangled. When many cross-links develop between the macromolecules, the polymer acquires rigidity and loses its plasticity on heating; it is transformed from a *thermoplastic* to a *thermosetting* resin. Examples of important plastics are the polystyrenes, polythenes, polyacrylates, and phenolic resins.
14. The fibroids have a macromolecular structure of oriented "crystallites" with some amorphous areas. Examples of fibroids are the polyamides (nylons) and polyesters (Dacron and Orlon.) Their tensile strength is due to the strong attraction between the polar groups in adjacent chains.
15. The elastomers have linear and highly coiled macromolecules which on stretching become more linear and oriented; as the stretching is diminished the molecules return to the coiled condition and this mobility under distention accounts for the elastic properties of these polymers. Most elastomers are *polydienes.* Natural rubber is a *polyisoprene* and most synthetic rubbers are polymers or copolymers of butadiene and its derivatives.

STUDY EXERCISES

1. Define the following terms: ore, slag, active metal, transition metal, noble metal, metalloid, metallurgy.
2. Discuss the important factors which determine the extensive uses of a particular metal.
3. Cite specific examples of metals whose properties are profoundly altered by the presence of small amounts of other metals.
4. List the important ores used in the production of iron, aluminum, zinc, and lead; show how ores are pretreated before reduction to the metallic state.
5. Explain and illustrate the principal methods by which ores are reduced to metals.
6. Give three important relations between the transition metals and relate these to a similarity in electronic structure.
7. There is now considerable interest in large-scale production of the metal titanium. What are its general physical properties? The most extensive occurrence of titanium is as the oxide TiO_2. Starting from this, show how titanium chloride might be prepared and then reduced to the metal.
8. After each item listed below mark: *N,* if the statement is true of nonmetals only; *M,* if the statement is true only of metals; *B,* if the statement is true both of metals and nonmetals; and *I,* if the statement is true only of the inert gases.
   a. Are good conductors of heat and electricity. ....
   b. Form oxides which are acidic. ....
   c. Form oxides which are basic. ....
   d. Are malleable. ....

e. Are brittle if in the solid state. ....
f. Possess both positive and negative valences. ....
g. Form salts. ....
h. Have relatively few valence electrons. ....
i. Have complete valence shells. ....

9. The following is a list of certain properties of metals which determine many of their uses:

(A) Low density	(H) Low melting point
(B) High electrical conductivity	(I) Great resistance to corrosion
(C) High electrical resistance	(J) Attractive luster and color
(D) High ductility	(K) High thermal conductivity
(E) High tensile strength	(L) High melting point
(F) High coefficient of expansion	(M) High density
(G) Liquid at ordinary temperatures	(N) High fluidity when melted
	(O) A catalytic agent

Below are listed some of the common uses of familiar metals and alloys. Associate by letter, from the list above, the property or properties responsible for each of these applications.

a. Tungsten in electric light bulbs. ....
b. Copper for electrical power cables. .....
c. Aluminum for cooking vessels. ....
d. Aluminum for busbars on electric switchboards. ....
e. Aluminum alloys for constructing airplanes. ....
f. Nickel or nickel plate car bumpers and bathroom fixtures. ....
g. Bronze in statuary. ....
h. Mercury in thermometers. ....
i. Mercury in barometers. ....
j. Gold in jewelry. ....
k. Use of platinum in the manufacture of sulfuric and nitric acids. ....
l. Soft steel cables for suspension bridges.
m. Steel rails made by rolling. ....
n. Use of tinplate for "tin" cans. ....
o. Use of tin foil to preserve food. ....
p. Use of zinc to make galvanized iron. ....
q. Use of stainless steel for architectural decorative purposes. ....
r. Silver in silverware. ....
s. Chromium in stainless steel cutlery. ....
t. Use of pig iron (cast iron) to make an engine block for an automobile. ......
u. Use of a tin-lead alloy for soldering. ....
v. Application of both tin and zinc to iron sheets by dipping. ....

10. Why is ordinary salt indispensable in the diet of every mammal? How is salt obtained in a primitive civilization? How is it obtained today in the United States? Why is it such an important commodity commercially?
11. Taking the composition of sea water as 3.5 per cent sodium chloride by weight, how many tons of water must be evaporated by solar heat to produce 100 tons of salt?
12. Write an equation to show the reactions at the anode and cathode in the electrolysis of brine.
13. Which is more active, chlorine or bromine? If you pass chlorine into a solution containing bromide (Br^-) ion, what will happen? What large-scale process employs this reaction?
14. Can bromine be used in place of chlorine (in an emergency) for disinfecting drinking water? Is its continued use safe? How about fluorine?
15. Give an example of (*a*) thermoplastic resin; (*b*) thermosetting resin; (*c*) elastomer; (*d*) fibroid. In each case write an equation for producing the polymer, and give the structure of the macromolecules of each polymer and relate it to its properties.

FOR FURTHER READING

1. MARKHAM, E. C., and S. E. SMITH, *General Chemistry*. Boston: Houghton Mifflin Company, 1954.
   A discussion of metals will be found in Chapters 38 and 39.
2. PAULING, LINUS, *General Chemistry*. San Francisco: W. H. Freeman and Company, 1953.
   See Chapter 24 for the general nature of metals and alloys.
3. Paperback: ALEXANDER W., and A. STREET, *Metals in the Service of Man*. Pelican, 85¢.
4. Paperback: COUZENS, E. G., and E. V. YARSLEY, *Plastics in the Service of Man*. Pelican, 85¢.
5. Paperback: WILLIAMS, T. I., *The Chemical Industry*. Pelican, 50¢

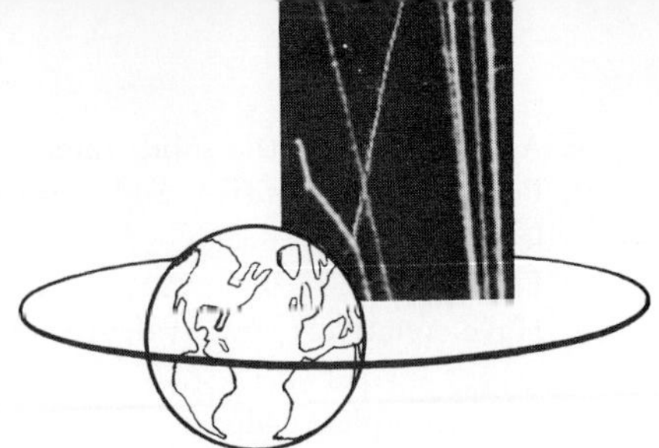

31

ELECTRICITY AND MAGNETISM: I

WE HAVE SEEN how studies of electric charges, at rest and in motion, gave much decisive data upon which modern theories of electricity and matter are built. The atomic character of electricity, indicated by Faraday's Laws of Electrolysis, was further verified by the separation of electrical particles from bulk matter. Atoms, regarded by Dalton as the ultimate particles of matter, "indivisible, indestructible and eternal," are now known to be complex aggregates of more fundamental particles, common to all. The mass of the atom is concentrated in the compact and generally stable nucleus, which is thought to consist of protons and neutrons. The nucleus is surrounded by an electron cloud, and it is the few outermost electrons that largely determine the chemical character of an element. The chemical union of atoms and the various types of chemical bonds which hold them together in more or less stable molecules are now interpreted in terms of these outer electrons.

It has been shown that our foods and many other so-called organic compounds originate in plant life. They are the product of an extraordinary series of chemical reactions which begin with photosynthesis and in which carbon dioxide (CO_2) undergoes a partial reduction. The food, in turn, is utilized in the body where much of it is oxidized to yield energy. In the complex compounds involved in these processes and in many other compounds, the atoms are bound together by the sharing of pairs of spinning electrons. In other chemical changes electrons move completely from one atom to another. An active metal, for example, gives electrons to a nonmetal, and the resulting positive and negative ions which comprise the compound are held together by the powerful forces of electrostatic attraction. If we wish to reverse the chemical reaction between the metal and the nonmetal, that is, to break the ion bond and obtain the original free elements, we must find a way to transfer the electrons from the negative to the positive ion. This change requires *energy,* and the *electric current* has been most successfully applied to the difficult cases. Sodium, aluminum, magnesium, chlorine, and many other elements are prepared by the process of electrolysis.

The subject of chemistry – the composition of matter, the changes it undergoes — thus requires us to consider further the subject so intimately allied to it, electricity. An over-all view of that subject was given in Chapter 21; we shall discuss in this and the two following chapters the various methods of producing an electric current, its effect on matter, and its uses. As we continue this study, bear in mind that *the electric current which readily causes chemical change was first produced by chemical reactions.*

CONCEPT OF ELECTRIC CURRENT

A flow of electrons constitutes an electric current. The rate of flow of the electricity past a point is the current — the quantity of charge passing a given point in one second. The universal symbol for electric current is *I,* standing for intensity of rate of flow. In symbols,

$$\text{Current} = I(\text{ntensity of flow of electricity}) = \frac{Q(\text{uantity passing})}{t\ (\text{in seconds})},$$

or

$$I = \frac{Q}{t}$$

The flow of electricity in a wire is analogous to the flow of water in a pipe. The water flowing through a pipe can be expressed as the total number of gallons which pass in a given time, say 100 gallons in 200 seconds, or in a rate — 0.50 gallon per second for 200 seconds. The two statements are equivalent if the rate is constant. In the same way, the passage of electricity can be expressed in the total number of coulombs that pass in a given time or as a rate, of say 0.10 coulomb per second. A flow of *one coulomb per second is one ampere of flow.* Hence, 0.10 coulomb per second is 0.10 ampere. Symbolically,

$$I\ (\text{amperes}) = \frac{Q\ (\text{coulombs})}{t\ (\text{seconds})}$$

(*Equation 31–1*)

The ampere is the practical unit of current flow. At times, it will be convenient to remember that a coulomb is equal to 3.00×10^9 e.s.u., or 6.24×10^{24} electrons. Statements may be made about either a rate of flow of electricity or the total quantity of electricity. Note that the following statements are equivalent to each other:

$$\text{Amperes} = \frac{\text{coulombs}}{\text{seconds}},$$

and

$$\text{Coulombs} = \text{amperes} \times \text{seconds}.$$

Thus a lamp drawing a current of 0.5 ampere for one hour utilizes

$$60\ \frac{\text{sec}}{\text{min}} \times 60\ \frac{\text{min}}{\text{hr}} \times 0.5\ \text{ampere} = 1800\ \text{ampere-seconds or coulombs.}$$

ELECTRICAL POTENTIAL

A flow of electrons through a conductor implies that there exists a "push" or force causing them to flow. This is referred to as a *potential difference,* which is measured in volts, and it is sometimes called an *electromotive force* or e.m.f. This electrical push is analogous to the pressure causing water to flow in a household water system. Water at a higher pressure has more energy per gallon than water at a lower pressure. The energy per gallon and the pressure depend on the height of the water column. Water will not flow from one region to another unless there is a difference in *head.* Thus *head* can be taken as a measure of the so-called difference in potential as water flows from a region of high potential to a region of lower potential. Similarly, electricity will flow if a difference in potential exists. Electrical differences in potential are measured in volts, which are analogous to feet of "head."

The concept of the volt can be derived as follows. Consider an electric field which exists between two plates, *A* and *B* in Figure 31–1. The field intensity *E* — the force in dynes on a unit positive charge — will be considered uniform. Consider the same posi-

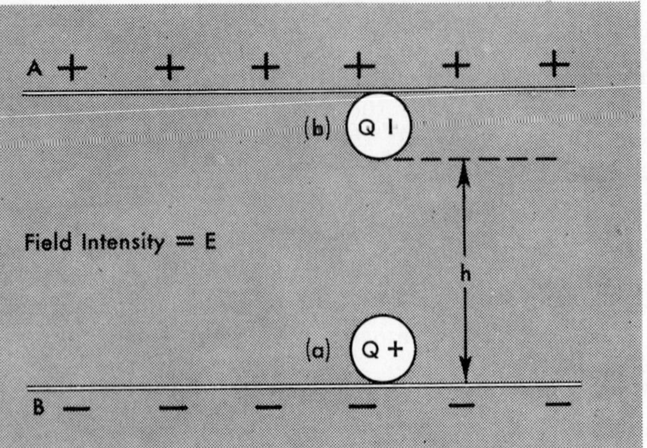

Fig. 31–1 *The concept of the volt as the unit of potential.*

tive charge $Q+$ in positions a and b. Obviously the potential energy of the charge will be a minimum at a and a maximum at b, because work is required to raise the charge against the electric field. The potential energy at b is the work expended in raising the charge a distance h against the electric field. This is also the work that is recovered as useful work when the charge returns to position a. The potential energy is readily calculated from Equation 21–4,

$$PE = W = \text{force} \times \text{distance} = Q \cdot E \cdot h$$

(*Equation 31–2*)

Then the potential by definition is the work per unit charge, or

$$P = W/Q = E \cdot h$$

(*Equation 31–3*)

Potentials are usually expressed in volts. Thus a charge of *one coulomb* possessing *one joule* of energy is said to be at a *potential* of *one volt*. In more general terms, the

$$\text{potential in volts} = \frac{\text{total joules of work}}{\text{total coulombs}}.$$

(*Equation 31–4*)

Thus in transferring Q coulombs from a higher potential to a lower potential, the electrical energy recovered is given by

$$\text{work in joules} = Q \text{ coulombs} \times \text{voltage}.$$

(*Equation 31–5*)

Since $Q = I \times t$, Equation 31–5 rearranges to another very useful equation,

$$\text{work in joules} = I \text{ amperes} \times t \text{ seconds} \times \text{voltage}.$$

(*Equation 31–6*)

As an example of the application of the last equation, consider this problem: a lamp operating on a 110-volt house circuit draws a current of 0.5 ampere for an hour. How much electrical energy was consumed?

$$\text{Energy in joules} = 0.5 \text{ ampere} \left(\frac{\text{coulombs}}{\text{sec}}\right) \times 3600 \frac{\text{sec}}{\text{hr}} \times 110 \frac{\text{joules}}{\text{coulomb}} = 198{,}000 \text{ joules}$$

ELECTRICITY AS ENERGY

The electric current, that is, the flow of electrons in a conductor or across an empty space, is a form of energy. It is generated by the expenditure of other forms of energy, chemical, thermal (heat), or mechanical. Conversely, the electric current is easily converted into other forms of energy: to heat by devices fitted with a high resistance wire (lamps, stoves, and the like), to mechanical energy by a motor, and to chemical energy by an electrolytic cell.

Our first problem, the generation of electric currents, may be broadly stated: how can each of the various forms of energy be used to produce and propel a stream of electrons?

ELECTRICITY FROM CHEMICAL ENERGY

A chemical reaction used to generate an electric current must involve the transfer of electrons from one substance to another, that is, oxidation-reduction (see Chapter 27). The substance which gives up the elec-

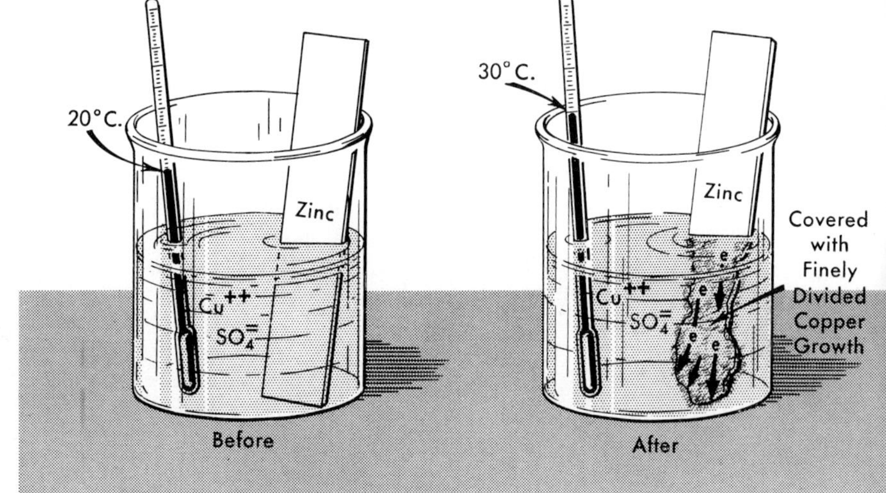

Fig. 31–2 *The metal zinc in a solution of copper sulfate results in a chemical change with a spontaneous liberation of energy as heat.*

trons is known as the *reducing agent* (reductant) and the one which receives the electrons as the *oxidizing agent* (oxidant). These substances may be free elements, ions, or compounds. Zinc metal, for example, is a reducing agent while copper (cupric) ion, a constituent of cupric salts, is an oxidizing agent. When a strip of zinc is placed in a solution of cupric sulfate (Figure 31–2), the zinc is gradually consumed, the blue color of the copper ion fades, and particles of metallic copper appear. The chemical change may be represented by the equation:

$$\overset{\curvearrowright 2e}{Zn + Cu^{++}} \rightarrow Zn^{++} + Cu + \text{heat}$$

Each zinc atom loses two electrons to a copper ion, that is, zinc reduces cupric ions to copper and is itself oxidized to zinc ions which pass into solution. The electrons move from the zinc directly to the copper ions in contact with it; no electric current is generated, but a rise in the temperature of the solution shows that chemical energy is converted to heat energy. In order to obtain an electric current the two substances must be physically separated but connected by an external conductor through which the electrons move. Such an arrangement is called a *cell;* a group of two or more connected cells is known as a *battery*.

Simple Cells. An experimental cell can be made by placing a strip of zinc in a beaker containing a solution of zinc sulfate and a strip of copper in another beaker containing a solution of copper sulfate

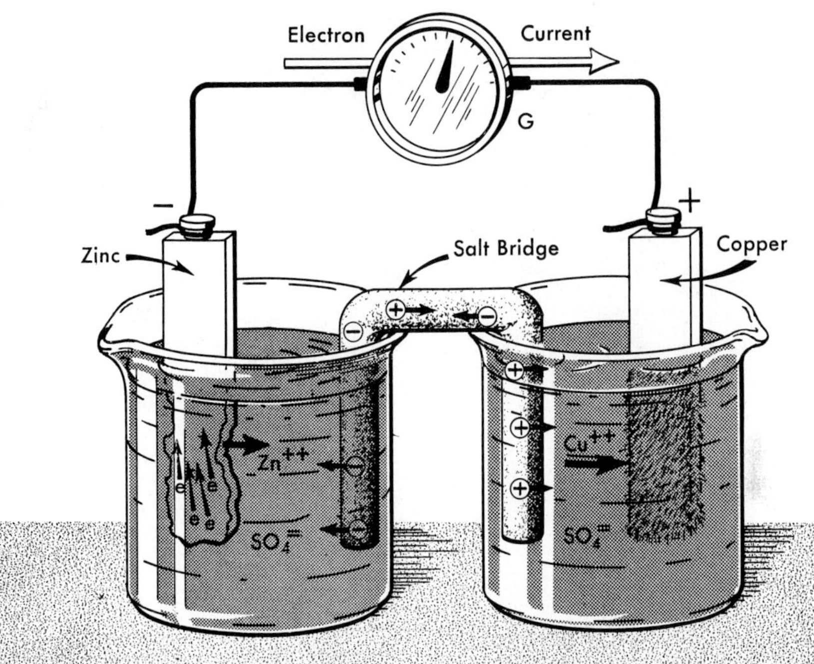

Fig. 31–3 *Electric energy from a chemical reaction. The reacting substances are the same as in Fig. 31–2. The electron flow (electric current) is from the zinc to the copper. Some of the zinc disappears in the zinc sulfate solution. Some copper is deposited upon the copper rod.* Positive *ions migrate through a salt bridge to the* right *and* negative *ions to the* left.

(Figure 31–3). Both of the metals, indeed all metals, have more or less of a tendency to lose electrons; their ions tend to gain electrons. Zinc is a stronger reducing agent (loser of electrons) than copper, and the cupric ion is a stronger oxidizing agent (gainer of electrons) than the zinc ion. Hence the reaction, shown by half-equations, proceeds:

$$Zn \rightarrow Zn^{++} + 2\,e^{-}$$

(*Equation 31–7*)

$$Cu^{++} + 2\,e^{-} \rightarrow Cu$$

(*Equation 31–8*)

The electrons lost by the zinc accumulate on the zinc plate, giving it a negative charge, and the Cu^{++} ion removes electrons from the copper plate, leaving it with a positive charge. Thus a potential difference is built up between the two plates, but it does not become very great, for an accumulation of electrons on the zinc tends to retard action (Equation 31–7), and the deficit of electrons on the copper prevents more cupric ions from receiving them, and thus action (Equation 31–8) is retarded. When the two plates are connected by a metal conductor and the solutions are joined by a salt bridge, electrons flow from zinc to copper and both reactions continue, thereby producing an electric current, which is indicated by the galvanometer *G* placed in the circuit. Thus, two chemical substances may react with each other at a distance, provided the reaction is one of oxidation-reduction; and such reactions may be utilized to produce an electric current. The total reaction involves Equations 31–7 and 31–8, and this time there is no rise in the temperature of the solution.

Fig. 31–4 *A gravity or Daniell cell. The zinc electrode in top solution decreases in weight; the copper electrode in bottom solution increases. The two solutions — zinc sulfate on top and copper sulfate in bottom — remain separated because of the greater density of the copper solution.* (*Redrawn from Kimball-Wold,* College Physics, *Fifth Edition, H. Holt & Co., Inc.*)

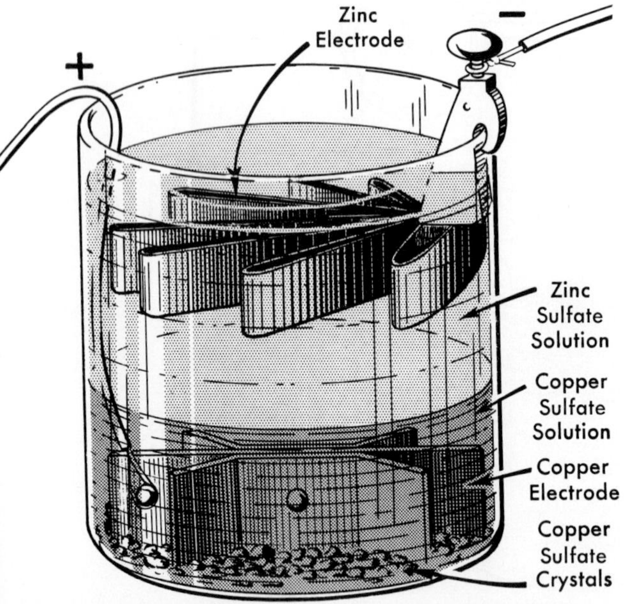

$$Zn + Cu^{++} \rightarrow Zn^{++} + Cu + \text{electric energy}$$

The salt bridge is also essential to the operation of the cell. It is filled with a solution of an ionic compound like sodium chloride which will not react with either the plates or the solutions and which serves to keep the solutions electrically neutral. The electric current flows between the beakers on the ions in the salt bridge.

In actual practice the plates and solutions may be placed in one container, and the metal ions kept more or less separate by a porous container around the zinc or by gravity, the heavier copper ions sinking to the bottom (Figure 31–4). This is exactly the type of cell developed by Daniell in England and formerly used for ringing doorbells. If we apply the principle of equilibrium to the reactions of Equations 31–7 and 31–8, it is apparent that, to get the highest potential, the zinc ions should be kept at a minimum concentration and the cupric ions at a maximum concentration. For practical purposes the concentrations are such that the potential difference between the plates is 1.1 volts.

A Generalized Cell. The rather full description of the Daniell cell may serve as a pattern for all other cells used for the conversion of chemical energy into electric energy and thus permit us to generalize. Such a cell must have a reducing agent which may serve as the minus electrode or plate, as does the zinc in the Daniell cell,

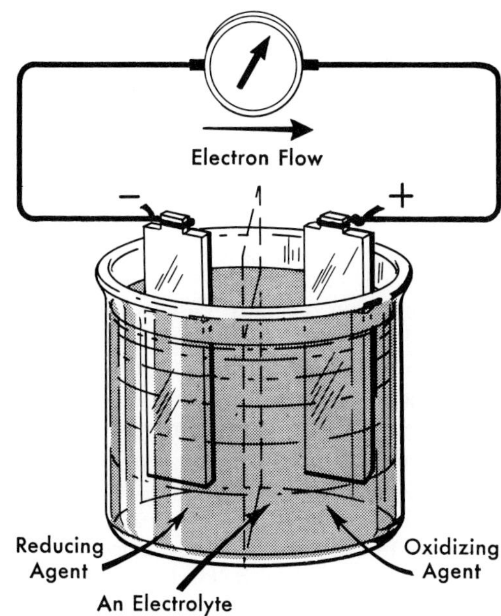

Fig. 31–5 *Generalized cell for production of current by chemical reaction.*

or which may be a part of the solution around this plate or even a gas absorbed on the surface of the plate. It must also have an oxidizing agent (Figure 31–5) which will serve as the positive plate. When the reacting chemicals are in solution around the plates, inactive electrodes like platinum or carbon are used. In all cases the electrons flow from the reducing agent to the oxidizing agent through the external wire until the connection is broken or one of the chemicals is completely used up in the reaction.

If one wishes to invent a new cell or battery, he cannot do so by a simple selection of any reducing agent as the electron source and any oxidizing agent as the electron receiver. Copper, for example, may act as a reducing agent under some circumstances, and the zinc ion as an oxidizing agent, but the two do not react with each other. In order to aid in the selection of suitable chemicals, a brief table, commonly called the activity or replacement series, may be referred to (page 422). The substances are arranged in two columns, one for the element in the reduced state, the other for the same element in the oxidized state. Sodium, for example, in the reduced state is the metal or free element, and is a very strong reducing agent. It is therefore placed near the top of the list of reducing agents. Its ion represents the element in the oxidized state, but it is not a good oxidizing agent, for it can take electrons only from better reducing agents than sodium. Sodium ions are, therefore, among the poorest of the oxidizing agents. On the other hand, silver is a very poor reducing agent, while silver ions are good oxidizing agents; hence, both are appropriately placed in the lower part of the table on the activities of some important elements.

In general, any substance in the reduced state will give electrons to any of those in the oxidized state below it in the table. Conversely, an ion or element in the oxidized state will take electrons from (oxidize) any item above it in the reduced state. Nickel reduces silver ions to silver, or, conversely, silver ions oxidize nickel to nickel ions. Such a table, which is the product of experiments with cells, tells us much about the relative activity of the various elements and compounds.

COMMERCIAL CELLS

Cells and batteries are useful tools for the experimenter, and two kinds are in everyday use — dry cells and storage batteries.

Dry cells. Dry cells are extensively used in radios, flashlights, and portable electronic devices. In the most common type, a zinc container serves as the negative electrode or electron source, and a carbon rod as the positive electrode. Packed between the electrodes is a moist mixture of chemicals, among which are manganese dioxide, zinc chloride, and ammonium chloride. A moist blotter-like cardboard separates the mixtures from the zinc electrode (Figure 31–6). In reality, therefore, the cell is wet. Upon discharge zinc loses electrons, which move through the wire and light a lamp or do some other work and are received by the manganese dioxide around the carbon rod.

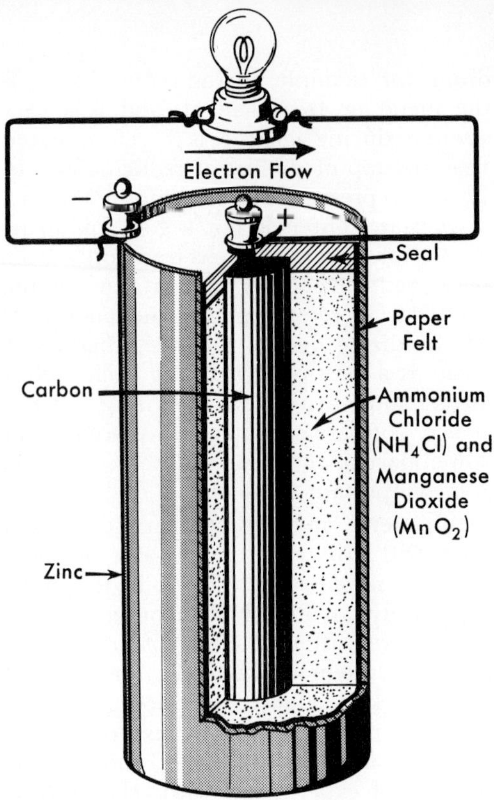

Fig. 31–6 *Essential parts of a common dry cell. The importance of dry cells is indicated by the fact that a large part of our total production of zinc (as metal) is used to produce them.*

The reactions are:

$$Zn \rightarrow Zn^{++} + 2\,e^-$$
$$2\,NH_4^+ + 2\,MnO_2 + 2\,e^- \rightarrow 2\,MnO(OH) + 2\,NH_3$$

This cell develops a potential of nearly 1.5 volts.

Another type of dry cell developed since World War II utilizes zinc as the electron source, mercuric oxide (HgO) as the oxidizing agent, and potassium hydroxide as the electrolyte. Miniature cells of this type are used in hearing aids.

The Lead Storage Battery. Unlike the primary cells described so far, the lead cell may be recharged. Electricity is not really stored as such, however. Chemicals which are consumed during discharge are merely produced again when a direct current from an outside source is sent through it in a direction opposite to that of discharge. The principle of the lead storage cell was discovered in 1860 by accident – one of those fortunate accidents which occur sometimes and are observed by alert scientists who quickly see their significance. Gaston Planté, a Frenchman, experimenting with a Daniell type of cell in the hope of eliminating certain defects, had connected the electrodes of the cell to two lead plates immersed in sulfuric acid. After the experiment he accidentally connected the lead plates to a galvanometer and the needle moved! Here was a reversible type of cell which was destined to be of great practical use.

The construction and operation of the lead storage cell may be understood by the use of a simplified cell somewhat like the one used by Planté. The charged cell consists of two plates of lead, one coated with lead dioxide, both immersed in a solution of sulfuric acid (Figure 31–7). The lead in the charged cell is the negative pole or electron source, and the lead dioxide the positive pole or receiver of electrons. During discharge, chemical reactions take place at the electrodes:

At the – pole: $Pb \rightarrow Pb^{++} + 2\,e^-$
At the + pole: $Pb^{++++} + 2\,e^- \rightarrow Pb^{++}$

The electrons move through the circuit to the Pb^{++++} in the lead oxide. The lead ions react with the sulfate ions to form insoluble lead sulfate; and the hydrogen ions of the sulfuric acid react with the oxide ions of the lead dioxide, forming water. The complete reaction is:

$$Pb + PbO_2 + 4\,H^+ + 2\,SO_4^{=} \underset{\text{charge}}{\overset{\text{discharge}}{\rightleftarrows}} 2\,PbSO_4 + 2\,H_2O$$

It should be noted that during discharge sulfuric acid is consumed and the plates tend to become alike, both coated with lead sulfate. When the battery is charged, the reverse reaction takes place: lead is restored to the one plate, lead dioxide to the other, and sulfuric acid is re-formed. When fully charged the potential of each cell is about 2.2 volts.

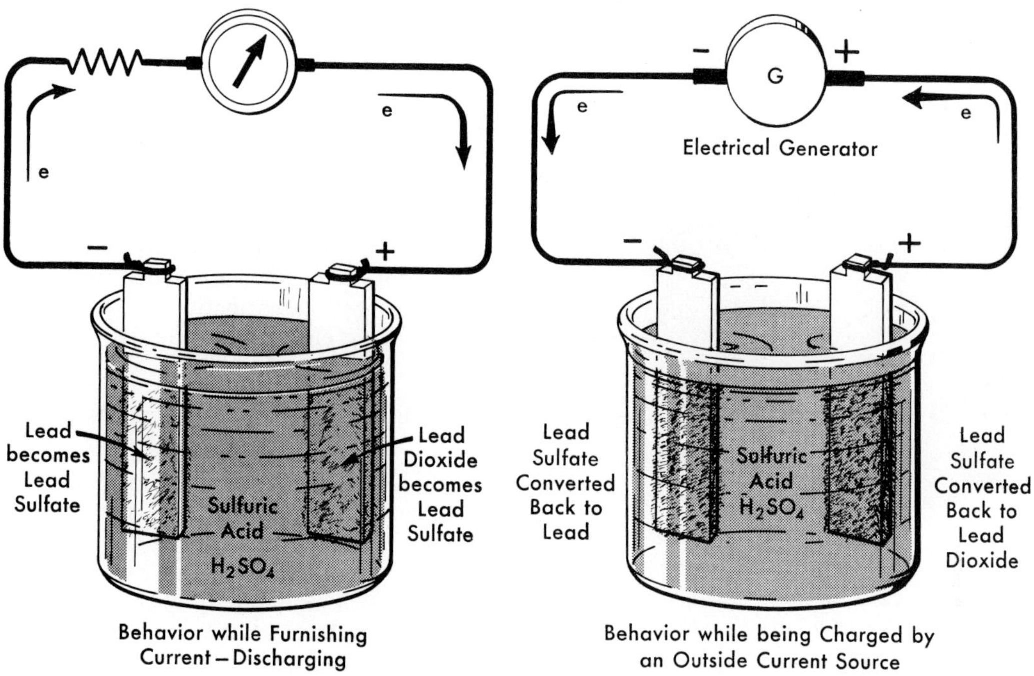

Fig. 31–7 *Simplified lead storage cell. On discharging, the + pole accepts electrons and becomes lead sulfate, and the − pole furnishes electrons and becomes lead sulfate. On charging the + pole furnishes electrons and is restored to lead dioxide and the − pole accepts electrons and is restored to lead. On discharging the specific gravity in the cell* decreases.

Commercial lead batteries, while reacting in precisely the same way, are more elaborate. More plates are used and are in the form of grids of an antimony-lead alloy in which are packed the respective materials, lead and lead dioxide. These plates are placed alternately close together with wood, glass-wool, or rubber separators between them. In each so-called cell all the like plates are joined together in one unit, while in a battery several cells are connected one after the other in series (Figure 31–8).

The great weight and the high rate of deterioration of the lead battery are serious disadvantages. A decided advantage, however, is the low internal resistance due to the great mobility of the hydrogen ions in the acid electrolyte and the close spacing of the electrodes. The lead battery readily supplies a very strong current. It is for this reason that the lead battery is universally used in the automobile – it can quickly supply the energy required to operate the starter. Until recently the three-cell (6-volt) battery was standard equipment in American automobiles; now many of the new models require a six-cell (12-volt) battery.

The Edison Storage Battery. The plates in the Edison cell consist of iron, which is the source of electrons, and a nickelic oxide (NiO_2). The electrolyte is potassium hydroxide. The Edison cell does not deteriorate upon standing, is of rugged construction, and is not damaged by overcharging or discharging. It is lighter than a lead cell of equal power, but owing to the type of the electrolyte used and the fact that the plates are farther apart, it has a higher internal resistance. Since it is more expensive and since it cannot supply quickly as large a

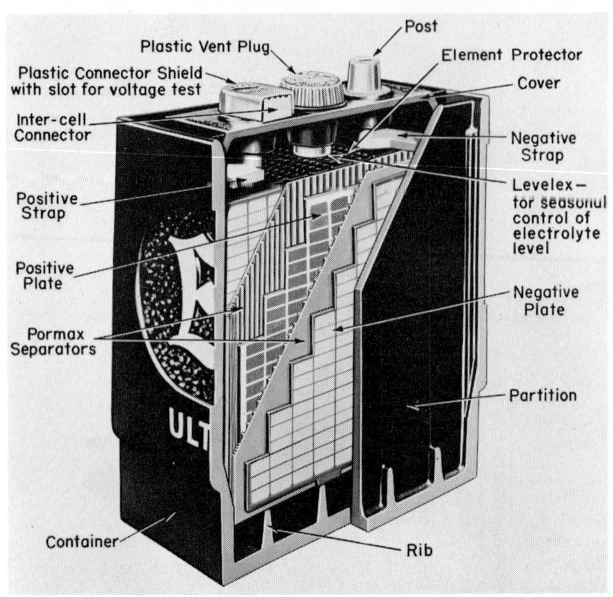

Fig. 31–8 *One cell of a 3-cell 6-volt automobile battery, cut away to show construction. (Exide Automotive Division, The Electric Storage Battery Company)*

current as the lead cell, it is not so widely used. The average discharge voltage is 1.2; hence a battery of five cells is required to furnish the six volts supplied by the three-cell lead battery.

The Cadmium Storage Battery. The negative plate or electron source in this battery is sponge cadmium packed in an iron grid. The positive plate (NiO_2) and the electrolyte (KOH) are the same as those in the Edison battery. The cadmium battery retains its charge when idle longer than other storage batteries, and it combines the high amperage delivery of the lead battery with the ruggedness and long life of the Edison type. It can be kept fully charged by a very small current and discharges efficiently even at low temperatures. It is more expensive than other types, and although there is some claim that it may be the "lifetime battery," it is not yet in general use in this country.

Other Batteries. Many kinds of batteries have been developed — all are applications of the principles outlined above. Three interesting combinations or uses may be noted:

1. The zinc-silver oxide (AgO) alkaline cell functions either as a primary cell or a storage cell. The current delivered per pound is one of the highest. It should be noted that the silver is divalent (Ag II).

2. A remarkable cell is the magnesium-silver chloride combination. It is manufactured as a really dry cell without any electrolyte, and can be stored almost indefinitely without deterioration. When water is added, the cell can function since magnesium can lose electrons to the silver in silver chloride:

$$Mg + 2\,AgCl \rightarrow MgCl_2 + 2\,Ag$$

It can be said to produce its own electrolyte.

3. An unusual battery was developed for use in the proximity fuse, one of the most effective devices of World War II. The battery consisted of three sections, each delivering current at a different voltage; it was rugged enough to withstand the terrific shock of a firing gun and small enough to fit into a space two and one-half inches by one and one-half inches. The electrolyte was kept in a sealed ampule which broke when the shell was fired.

ELECTRICITY FROM HEAT

If two wires of different metals, copper and iron, for example, are twisted together at their ends, the result is an electric generator for the direct conversion of heat to electricity. If the two junctions are the same temperature no current flows in the loop; if we heat (or cool) one of the junctions, electrons flow in the wires. This can be shown by inserting a galvanometer (a device for detecting an electric current — see Chapter 32) in the circuit (Figure 31–9). We do not obtain enough current to operate a motor or light an ordinary lamp, but the device, known as a *thermocouple,* is very useful for measuring temperatures. For a given thermocouple, the size of the current is proportional to the difference in the temperatures of the two junctions. Several such thermocouples connected in series increase the sensitivity and enable one to measure

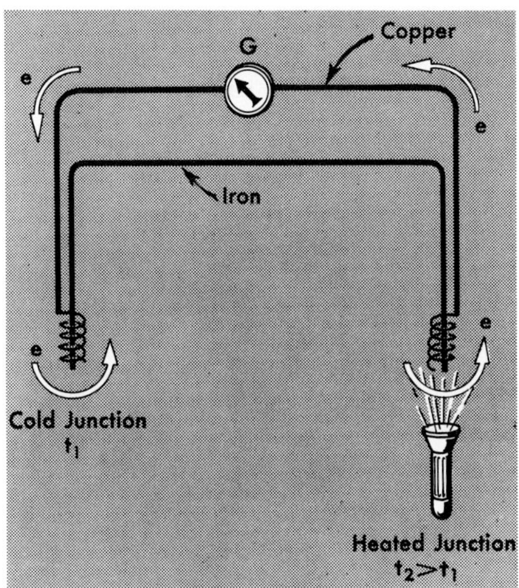

Fig. 31–9 *Principle of the thermocouple or thermel. There is a flow of electrons as long as there is a difference in temperature in the two junctions, or $t_2 > t_1$. The thermel current of e.m.f. registered on the meter G indicates the magnitude of the temperature difference $(t_2 - t_1)$.*

very slight changes in temperature. A couple consisting of platinum and a platinum-rhodium alloy can be used to measure temperatures as high as 1600° C. The electric meter has to be calibrated, and one junction must be kept at a constant known temperature.

MAGNETISM

We have seen how electrons can be put in motion by chemical reaction, and by heat. The bulk of our electric current, however, is generated by a third conversion — mechanical energy (motion) to electricity — which requires also a magnetic field. We therefore must first discuss the phenomenon of magnetism and its close relationship to electricity.

A piece of iron ore called *magnetite* (Fe_3O_4) shows a familiar but nonetheless extraordinary property; it attracts pieces of iron and, when freely suspended, orients itself in approximately a north-south direction. Its force operates at a distance as if an invisible arm pulled the iron to the magnetite; some force in the earth acts similarly to orient the suspended piece of magnetite. This phenomenon is known as *magnetism* and the body exerting the force is called a *magnet.* The earth is a huge magnet and magnetic forces are also at play around the sun and all of the stars.

The magnetite or *loadstone,* as it is called, may be used to make other magnets. A piece of steel, like a length of watch spring or a needle, stroked with the loadstone soon becomes magnetized and, freely suspended, orients itself in the north-south direction just as the natural magnet does. If the north-pointing end of a magnet is brought near the north-pointing end of a second magnet, the two repel each other. The two south-pointing ends also repel each other, but a north-pointing end of one and a south-pointing end of the other mutually attract (Figure 31–10). Each magnet, therefore, has two poles, a north-seeking or simply *north pole* and a south-seeking or *south pole.* When a magnet is carefully broken into two pieces, each fragment is a complete magnet

Fig. 31–10 *North-seeking poles repel other north poles but attract south magnetic poles.*

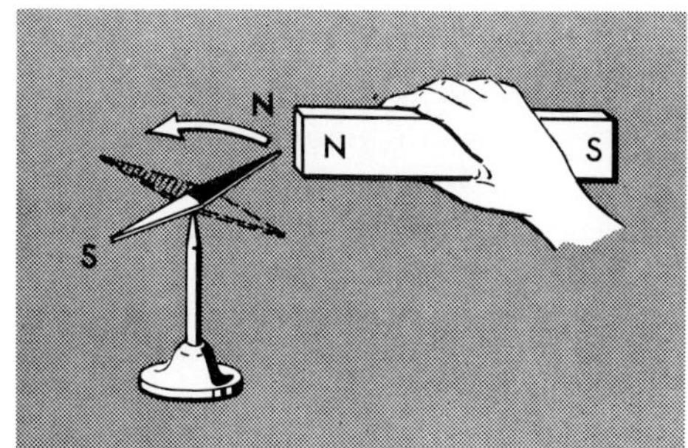

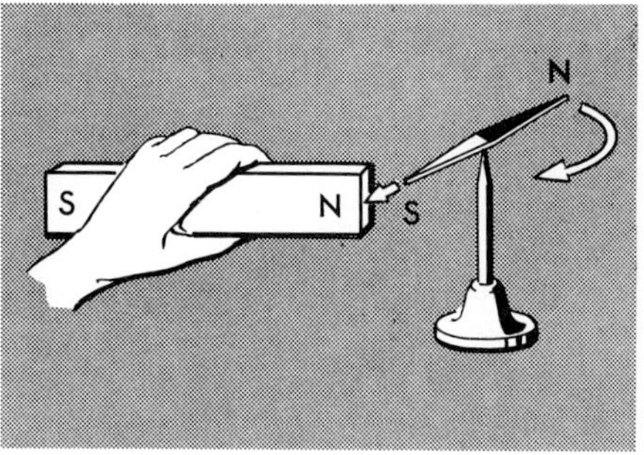

with a north and a south pole. These in turn can be broken into smaller and smaller lengths but each piece has the two poles. No one has yet made a magnet with only one pole (Refer to Figure 31–11.)

We can conclude, therefore, that *like magnetic poles repel and unlike magnetic poles attract each other.* The force of attraction or repulsion varies directly with pole strengths and inversely with the square of the distance between the poles. This induction, known as Coulomb's Law, is expressed by the equation:

$$F(\text{orce}) = \frac{m_1(\text{agnetic pole strength}) \times m_2(\text{agnetic pole strength})}{d(\text{istance})^2}$$

(*Equation 31–9*)

where the poles are separated by a vacuum or by air and the pole strengths are expressed in the appropriate system of units. The similarity of Coulomb's law for electric charges to Newton's law of universal gravitation should be noted.

Magnets attract iron, cobalt, and nickel very strongly — three elements that are closely related in the Periodic Table. Liquid oxygen is also similarly magnetic and many other elements show faint magnetic properties. Bismuth displays a surprising magnetic property — it is repelled. Soft iron does not retain its magnetism as well as a hard grade of steel. Strings of nails or tacks (soft iron) can be lifted by a magnet, each one becoming magnetized and holding on the one next to it. When the nail joining the magnet is removed, the others fall and separate. Only a small amount, if any, of residual magnetism persists.

Permanent magnets, that is, those that retain their magnetism, are made of very hard tool steel (compass needles, bar magnets, and horseshoe magnets for ordinary laboratory use). Much stronger magnets are now made from special alloys: *permalloy,* an alloy of iron and cobalt; *permivar,* containing nickel, cobalt, and iron; and *alnico,* a series of complex alloys of aluminum, cobalt, nickel, and copper, some of which can lift as much as one thousand times their own weight. Permanent magnets are used not only in compasses but in electrical measuring instruments, telephones, telegraph equipment, speedometers, magnetos, phonograph magnetic cartridges, and loud-speakers.

THE EARTH'S MAGNETISM

The earth's magnetic field is such that we may imagine it to be due to an internal magnet about four thousand miles long, the south pole of which at present lies beneath a point just north and east of Hudson Bay in 71° N. latitude and the north pole of which lies beneath a point south of Melbourne, Australia, in 70° S. latitude.[1] It has been known since the fifteenth century that the magnetic compass does not in general point toward the true, or geographical, north pole. Columbus observed this fact and also that the variation from the true north, known as the *magnetic declination,* changed from place to place. Knowledge of the magnetic declination at various points on the earth's surface is of great importance to navigators, for though a modern ship may carry a gyroscopic compass and may

[1] The magnetic pole in the north is a south magnetic pole; it attracts the north-seeking end of any free-swinging magnet.

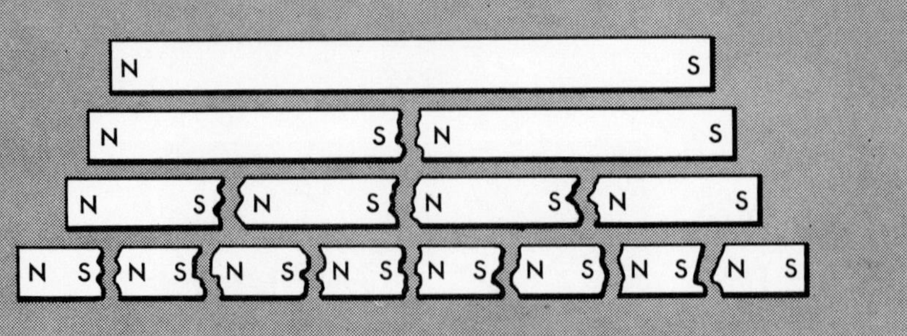

Fig. 31–11 *Magnetic poles always appear in pairs — north and south.*

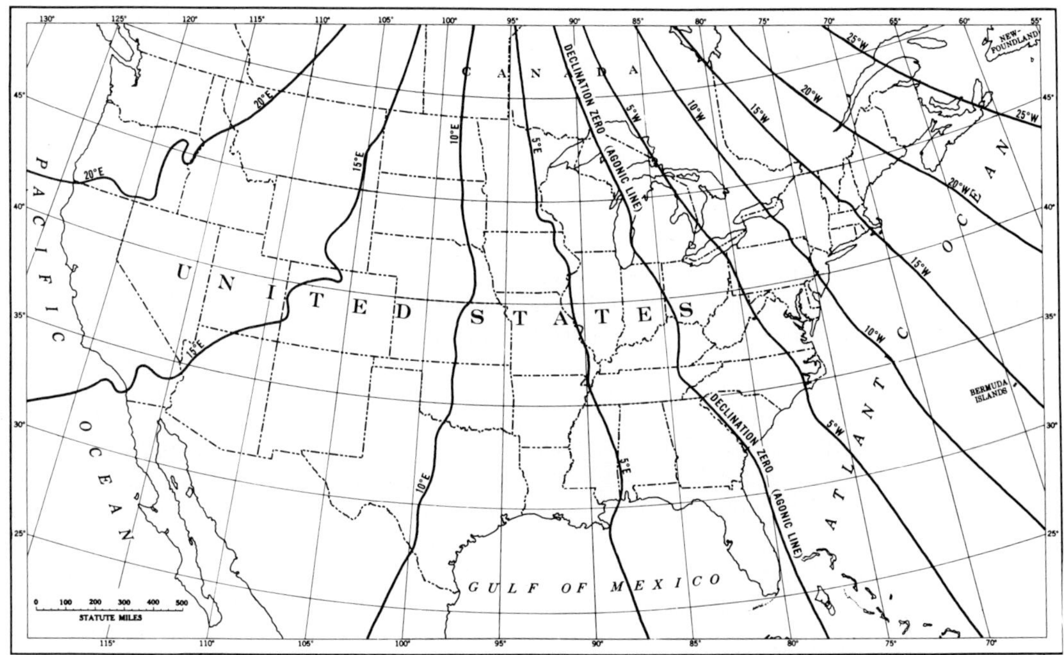

Fig. 31–12 *Magnetic map of United States showing isogonic lines.* (*U. S. Coast and Geodetic Survey*)

also make celestial observations, all ships carry a magnetic compass. Magnetic declination is measured on nonmagnetic ships that are constructed entirely of wood, bronze, and other nonmagnetic metals, even to the bolts, anchors, and cookstoves, to avoid any local attraction.

From the positions of the respective poles and the magnetic and celestial meridians, it is apparent that there are places on the earth with zero declination. The declination at New York (1957) is 11° west, so that there the compass needle points 11° west of true north; at Chicago it is 2° east, and at San Francisco 18° east. A line of zero declination, then, must run through this country a little to the east of Chicago (Figure 31–12).

The form of the earth's magnetic field is continually changing; the magnetic poles are shifting. There is a daily variation, and a much larger one extending over a long period. A careful record of such variations is kept and is referred to in studying old maps or surveys. Recently fragments of magnetite were uncovered in layers of sedimentary material laid down during the ice ages. They were in conformity with earth's magnetic field at that time in such a direction as to indicate that the northern magnetic pole was considerably west of its present position.

MAGNETIC EFFECT OF ELECTRICITY

Magnetism and electricity are unlike in some respects, yet there are striking similarities: attraction and repulsion, a field effect, and the transfer to certain other bodies of their peculiar properties. These similarities long led scientists to try to correlate the two phenomena.

Among those who investigated the relationship between magnetism and electricity was the Danish physicist, Hans Christian Oersted (1770–1851). Oersted was looking for some effect that would show this relationship, and, although he did not know how to obtain it or what it would be, he was quite prepared to recognize it when by accident he hit upon the method. In 1820 at the close of one of his lectures he placed a wire, carrying a current from a battery, above and parallel to a magnetic needle. The needle was deflected at right angles to the wire (Figure 31–13). He reversed the direction of the current, and the needle was deflected in the opposite direction. He changed the wire and found that the effect was independent of the material of the conductor.

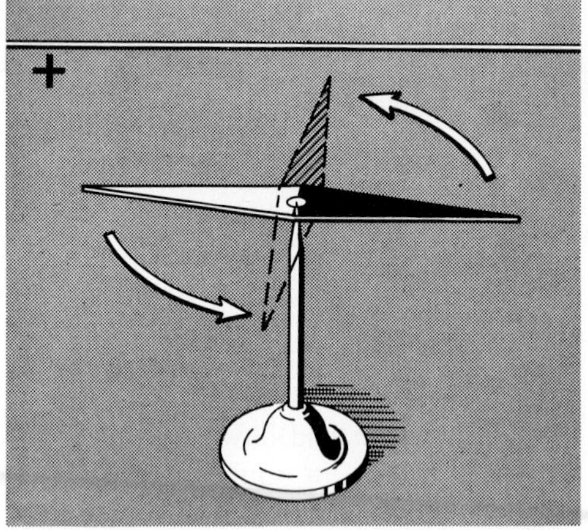

Fig. 31–13 *Oersted's experiment: production of a magnetic effect with an electric current.*

This discovery is of extreme importance. The electric current produces a magnetic effect; therefore, magnets which are supplied or excited by the electric current may be built. These may be powerful lifting magnets as used in industry or tiny magnets as used in many electrical devices. Motors, generators, measuring instruments, the telegraph, the telephone, and hundreds of other devices, some of which we shall discuss in the next two chapters, all require electrically excited magnets (*electromagnets*). In addition to the technological advances occasioned by this discovery was the great stimulus to further investigation which yielded more discoveries and a greater understanding of magnetic and electrical phenomena.

THE MAGNETIC FIELD

The region of influence around a magnet, like that around the earth or a charged body, is a field of force. The gravitational field is different from the electric field, and the magnetic field is different from either of the others. The magnetic field does not, for example, interfere with or exert any influence on the electric field around a charged body. Faraday, who introduced the field concept, devised a way to interpret or represent it. Around a magnet the force exerted at each point may be measured both as to magnitude and direction and may be represented by *lines of force*. In common practice we show the direction and to some extent the intensity of a magnet's field (but only in one plane) by placing magnetic compasses at different points, or, even more simply, by shaking iron filings on a piece of paper or glass placed over the magnet. In order to make the concept simpler, Faraday used the term *lines of force* and by convention regarded lines of force as leaving the north or "positive" pole of a magnet and extending through the space around the magnet into the south or "negative" pole (Figure 31–14).

If the single wire through which a current is flowing exerts a magnetic effect, then it too must have around it a magnetic field. Iron filings sprinkled on a piece of paper show a field which encircles the wire in the direction indicated (Figure 31–15). If the wire is grasped by the left hand with the thumb in the direction of the electron flow or current, the fingers point in the direction of the lines of force in the magnetic field around the wire (see Figure 31–17*a*). When the wire is bent into a loop, we get

Fig. 31–14 *The magnetic field around a bar magnet. The magnetic field consisting of lines of force is revealed by sprinkling iron filings on a glass plate over the bar magnet.*

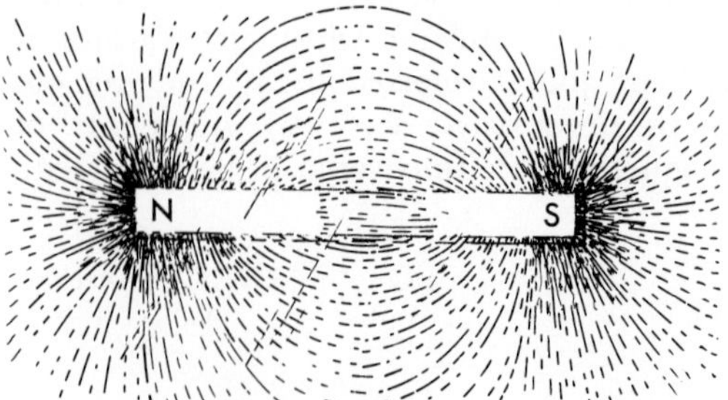

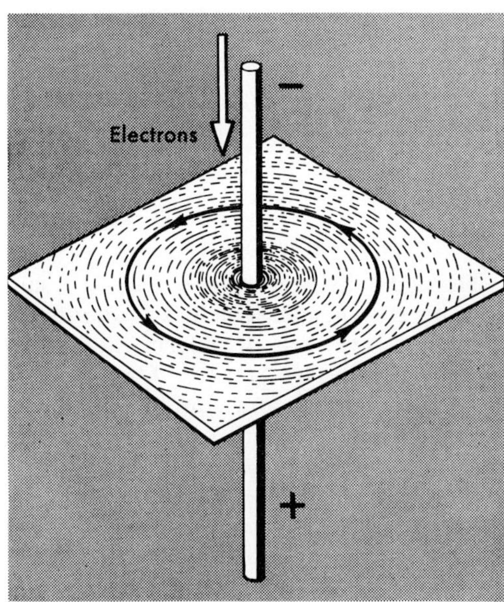

Fig. 31–15 *Magnetic field around a wire carrying current. Iron filings show lines of force, the direction of which is found by the left-hand rule. (See Fig. 31–17.)*

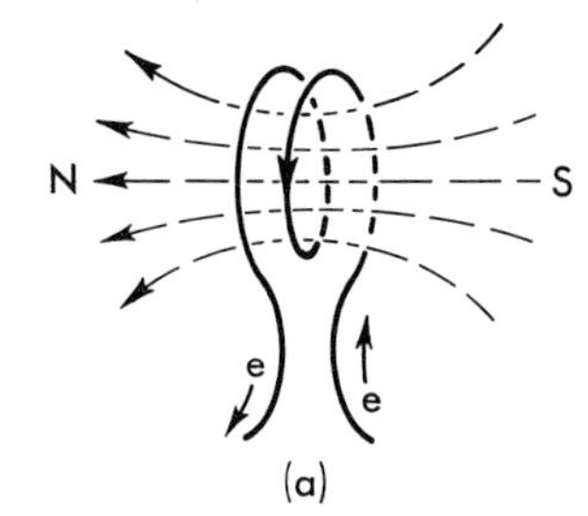

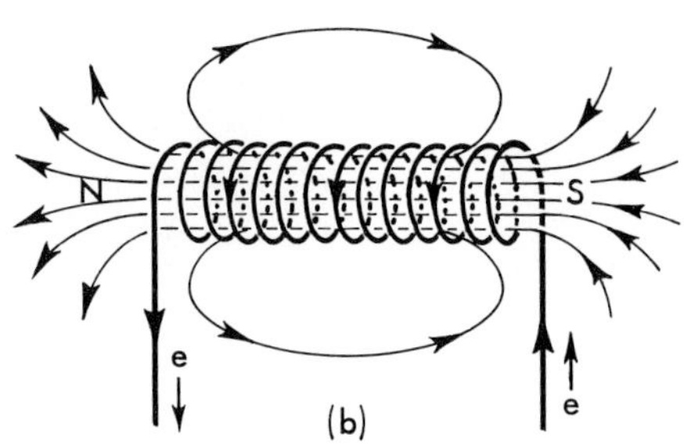

Fig. 31–16 *(a) Magnetic lines of force about a wire coil carrying an electric current. (b) Increasing the number of turns for a given current increases the magnetic effect.*

the same effect but with the lines of force leaving one end of the loop and entering by the other (Figure 31–16*a*). When the number of turns of wire is increased, the field becomes stronger, and is then represented by more lines of force (Figure 31–16*b*). A solenoid with many turns and with a soft iron core gives a much stronger field and is called an *electromagnet.* To the French scientist André Marie Ampère (1775–1836) we owe not only these discoveries but a rule for locating the poles. Modernized, this rule is as follows: when the coil is gripped in the left hand with the fingers around it pointing in the direction of electron flow, the thumb points to the north pole of the electromagnet or the direction of the emergent magnetic lines of force (see Figure 31–17*b*). The field of the solenoid, or electromagnet, is identical in character with that of the bar form of a permanent magnet. Their likeness further demonstrates the close relationship between electricity and magnetism; magnetism is thus one aspect or manifestation of electricity in motion.

ROWLAND'S EXPERIMENT

That the effect of the electric current on the compass needle is magnetic has been demonstrated by the identity of the fields produced by a permanent magnet and an electromagnet. The necessity of the electric current is shown by the utter absence of any effect of an electrostatic charge on the magnetic needle. Despite a demonstration by Wollaston that sparks from an electrostatic machine decompose water just as the electric current does, for a time there still existed some doubt of the relationship of static and current electricity.

This doubt was removed by a brilliant experiment performed by H. A. Rowland of the Johns Hopkins University. What Rowland did, in effect, was to whirl rapidly small bodies which carried static electric charges. A magnetic needle placed near them was deflected (Figure 31–18). What he rotated was a glass disc on the outer part of which were stuck pieces of tinfoil, all bearing static charges. Greater speed of rotation produced a greater magnetic effect.

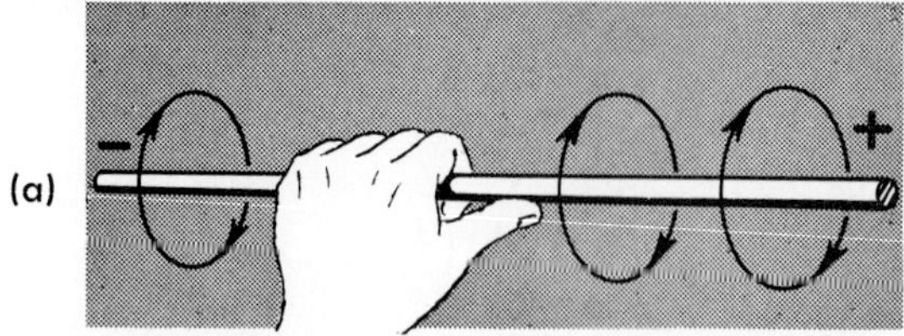

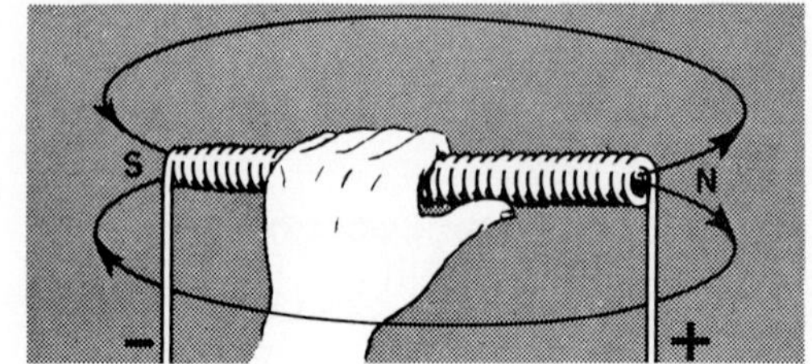

Fig. 31–17 *Left-hand rule (a) for a single conductor, (b) for a coiled conductor.*

Fig. 31–18 *(a) An electric charge at rest exerts no magnetic effect. (b) Rowland's famous experiment: an electric charge in motion is equivalent to an electric current and is surrounded by a magnetic field.*

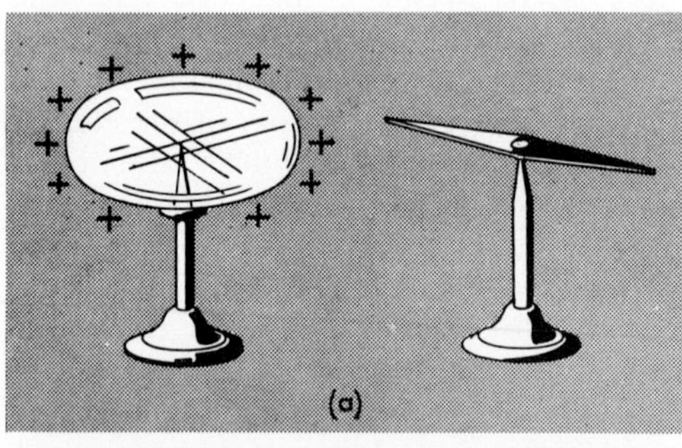

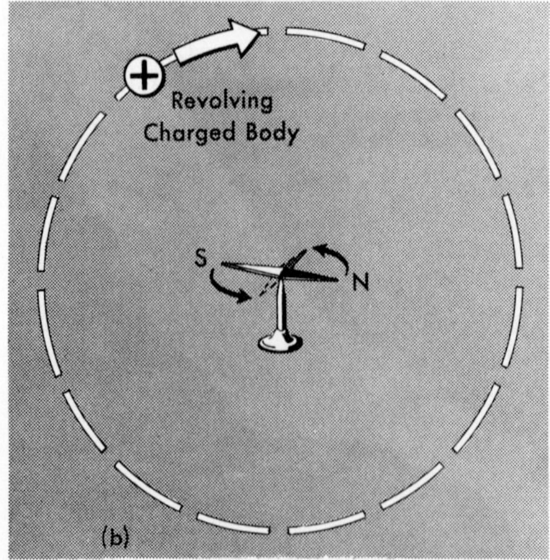

When he reversed the direction of rotation, the needle was deflected in the opposite direction. The moving charge is, in effect, an electric current.

THEORY OF MAGNETISM

Oersted's discovery that an electric current begets a magnetic field was almost immediately investigated, experimentally and mathematically, by Ampère. The magnetic properties of iron and similar (ferromagnetic) substances, Ampère theorized, were caused by electric currents within the atoms and molecules. This idea, which is basically the modern theory, was not accepted at the time and was developed and elaborated upon after the discovery of the electron and the formulation of our present concept of atomic structure.

A number of experimental facts supported Ampère's hypothesis that a magnetic needle, for example, was composed of an enormous number of tiny magnets all oriented so that their north poles pointed in the same direction. First, a steel needle can be magnetized by stroking with a magnet; it can be demagnetized by heating or hammering, which disrupts the alignment of the small units (Figure 31–19). Second, the magnetized needle can be broken into two magnets and these into four complete magnets and so on, until, in one's imagination, it is finally divided into the ultimate unit magnet – atoms or molecules. (Refer to Figure 31–11.) If the atoms are magnets because of electric currents, what is the source of the currents?

According to present theory, the ultimate magnetic unit is the spinning elec-

Fig. 31–19 *Ampère's theory of magnetism.*

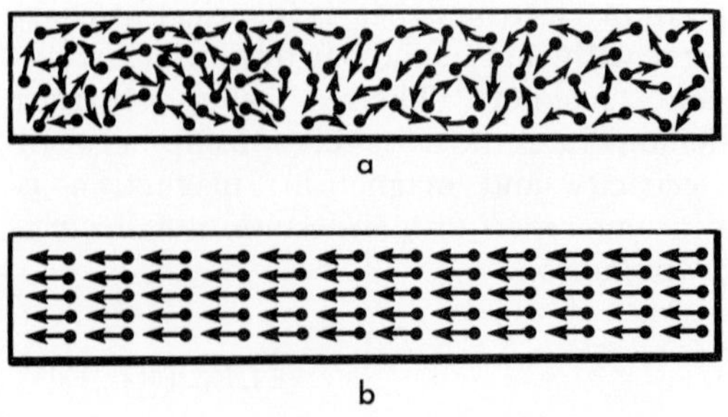

tron. We have seen that electrons revolve about atomic nuclei and that each electron is spinning about one of its diameters. It was also demonstrated by Rowland that a moving or spinning charge is, in effect, an electric current, and we know that an electric current produces a magnetic field. In a complete orbit or shell of any atom, electrons of opposite spins are paired and the net magnetic effect is zero. In iron and other ferromagnetic elements the third shell is incomplete and the unpaired electrons account for the magnetic properties. Many other elements, however, have unpaired electrons and do *not* show magnetic properties. It is thought that in ferromagnetic materials the magnetic fields of neighboring atoms are held in parallel positions by strong quantum mechanical forces (too complex to be discussed in this text). In other substances these quantum forces are thought to make the magnetic fields neutralize each other.

SUMMARY

1. The intimate relation between the sciences of chemistry and electricity is shown by the modern electron theory of matter.
2. Electric currents can be produced by chemical reactions in primary and storage *cells.* The electron flow is from the reducing agent, which is the − pole, through a conductor to an oxidizing agent, which is the + pole.
3. The ampere is the common unit of rate of flow of electricity or current strength. It is defined as a coulomb per second, or: amperes = coulombs/seconds.
4. The quantity of electricity flowing in an electrical circuit is given by: coulombs = amperes × seconds.
5. A flow of electricity means that a difference in electrical potential exists. The unit of potential is the volt. The volt is defined as one joule per coulomb.
6. The quantity of electrical energy used in an electrical circuit is given by
   joules = coulombs × volts,
   = amperes × seconds × volts.
7. In the *storage cell,* electrical energy is converted into chemical energy by reversing the current through the cell. Upon discharging, the chemical energy again becomes electrical energy. The process of discharging and charging can be repeated many times.
8. A *thermocouple* is a circuit of dissimilar metals which converts heat into electricity. For operation there must be a hot junction and a cold junction.
9. Natural magnets, loadstones, and certain forms of iron, have the ability to attract similar materials through empty space. This is the property of *magnetism.*
10. Natural magnets always have a north-seeking pole and a south-seeking pole. The space around a magnet contains a magnetic field with *lines of force* extending from the north to south pole.
11. Coulomb's law of magnetism: Like magnetic poles repel and unlike poles attract each other with a force which is directly proportional to the product of the pole strengths and inversely proportional to the square of the distance between the poles. The law is stated mathematically as,
$$F = \frac{m_1 m_2}{d^2}$$
12. Iron, cobalt, and nickel are the most magnetic natural substances. They are said to be *ferromagnetic.* (Substances which show weak magnetic properties are said to be *paramagnetic.*)
13. The earth is a huge magnet with a magnetic south pole (north of Hudson Bay) in the geographical north and a magnetic north pole (south of Australia) in the geographical south. The earth's magnetic poles are constantly changing position. The deviation of the magnetic compass from true north is known as the *magnetic declination.*
14. Oersted made the discovery that an electric current is surrounded by a magnetic field. Ampere developed the science of electromagnetism.
15. Magnetic fields may be produced either by permanent magnets or by electromagnets.
16. Our modern electron theory of matter attributes magnetic properties to unpaired electrons in the structures of atoms.

STUDY EXERCISES

1. Sum up all the facts so far considered which may be regarded as points of evidence to prove, or at least to indicate, that: (*a*) the electric current is a form of energy; (*b*) the electric current consists of electrons in motion.
2. A brief electromotive series is shown with the element or ion in the reduced state in the column at the left, below, and in oxidized state in the column at the right.

Reduced	Oxidized
K	K^+
Mg	Mg^{++}
Zn	Zn^{++}
Fe	Fe^{++}
Ni	Ni^{++}
H_2	$2H^+$
Cu	Cu^{++}
$2I^-$	I_2
Ag	Ag^+
$2Cl^-$	Cl_2
Au	Au^+
$2F^-$	F_2

If cells are made from each of the following combinations, which of the elements or ions listed above would be the source of electrons for the current (Column I)? Which element or ion would receive the electrons (Column II)?

I	II		
......	......	Zn, Zn^{++}	Cu, Cu^{++}
......	......	Ag, Ag^+	Fe, Fe^{++}
......	......	H_2, $2H^+$	Ni, Ni^{++}
......	......	$2Cl^-$, Cl_2	Mg, Mg^{++}

Write the reaction taking place at each electrode for one of these combinations, and indicate the reducing agent and the oxidizing agent.

3. Mark each of the statements as follows: *M* if true only of magnetism; *E* if true only of static electricity; *B* if true of both; *N* if true of neither.
   a. Like poles or charges repel and unlike poles or charges attract each other. .....
   b. Effect may be transferred to certain other bodies by induction. ....
   c. One kind of pole or charge cannot be developed without the other kind appearing simultaneously. ....
   d. One kind of pole or charge may be isolated from the other. ....
   e. Around a body which is electrically charged or magnetized is a field of force. ....
   f. The field at rest exerts an influence on a near-by magnet. ....
   g. The field at rest exerts influence on an electrically charged body. ....
   h. Phenomenon is due to transfer of electrons from one body or portion of a body to another. ....
   i. Phenomenon is thought to be due to spinning and revolution of electrons around molecules or atoms. ....
   j. Effect may be produced by electricity in motion. ....
   k. Property is retained by body in contact with grounded conductor. ....
4. Three types of cells or batteries in common use are listed. In the columns below answer each question by a single word (which may be yes or no).

	Dry Cell	Lead Storage Battery	Edison Storage Battery
May it be recharged?			
Is it a "wet" cell?			
What is the source of electrons?			
What is the oxidizing agent?			
Does the cell deteriorate upon standing?			
What is maximum voltage for each cell?			
If a storage battery, how many cells are usually grouped together?			
Which has the lowest internal resistance?			
What is the electrolyte?			

5. Describe two methods by which a piece of steel may be magnetized. How would it be demagnetized?
6. Write a *brief* discussion of the magnetic compass as an instrument of navigation, pointing out the lack of coincidence between the earth's magnetic and geographic poles and the need for data on magnetic declination at various points on the earth's surface.

7. Give the number of the word or phrase which *best* completes each of the following statements.
   a. Electromagnetism was discovered by: (1) Henry; (2) Faraday; (3) Volta; (4) Oersted. . . . .
   b. The earth's south magnetic pole is located (1) in 71° north latitude near Hudson Bay; (2) in 70° south latitude, south of Australia; (3) at the south geographic pole. . . . .
   c. Permanent magnets are used in (1) magnetic lifting cranes; (2) the telephone; (3) the doorbell. . . . .
   d. An electromagnet consists of a coil of wire around a core of (1) steel; (2) soft iron or a special alloy; (3) copper. . . . . .
   e. When a permanent magnet is broken into two pieces the result is (1) a magnet having only a north pole and another having only a south pole; (2) two complete magnets each with two poles; (3) demagnetization. . . . .
8. How does the field produced by a permanent bar magnet compare with that around an electromagnet of the same size and shape?
9. A magnet is broken into 100 pieces and yields 100 complete magnets. On the basis of Oersted's discovery, the present theory of atomic structure, and Rowland's experiment, extend the break-up in support of the theory that the molecule or atom is the ultimate magnet.
10. A magnet placed with its pole 4 cm from a nail exerts a force of 10 dynes on the nail. What force would it exert at a distance of 2 cm? At 8 cm?

FOR FURTHER READING

1. WHITE, HARVEY E., *Classical and Modern Physics.* New York: D. Van Nostrand Company, 1940.
   The concept of potential and the subject of electric cells are simply presented in Chapter 19.
2. LEMON, H. B., *From Galileo to the Nuclear Age.* Chicago: University of Chicago Press, 1946.
   The energy of electric fields, the concepts of the potential and the volt, and electric power are discussed in Chapter 25.
3. SKILLING, H. H., *Exploring Electricity.* New York: The Ronald Press, 1948.
   Chapter 9 is an interesting account of the lives of Michael Faraday and Joseph Henry. Chapter 10 is concerned with experiments dealing with the electromagnetism by Faraday and Henry.

32

ELECTRICITY AND MAGNETISM: II

WE HAVE SEEN how chemical energy is converted into electrical energy in cells and batteries. While these devices are of great value for many special purposes, they account for less than one per cent of the total electric current now consumed. The great bulk of our electricity is supplied by machines called *dynamos* or *generators* which convert *mechanical energy* into *electrical* energy. They vary in size from the small generators which are attached to an automobile engine to the huge machines in city power stations or in some of the hydroelectric installations. These machines have moving parts and produce current, that is, propel electrons through conducting systems, only when the parts are in motion. Some prime energy source is necessary to turn the generators. It may be a fuel (oil, coal, or fissionable materials) which supplies energy to an internal combustion engine or a steam turbine; in hydroelectric installations the prime energy is running water. First we shall consider how the generator converts the mechanical energy of motion into electricity; then we shall see how the electricity is distributed, measured, and used.

ELECTRICITY FROM MAGNETISM

If we were to examine a generator while it is being assembled or taken apart, we should find that it consists essentially of wires — many of them — and electromagnets. One or the other of these parts must be moved (rotated) in order to operate the machine. These machines are often enormous, but a small home-made generator — simply a coil of wire and a bar magnet — will show the principle. A galvanometer — not a part of the generator — connected to the ends of the coil detects the current. As the north pole of the magnet is thrust into the coil, a current is generated in the coil; the current is a momentary one continuing only as long as the magnet is in motion (Figure 32–1*a*). When the magnet is withdrawn, a current again flows in the coil but in the opposite direction (Figure 32–1*b*). If the magnet is held at rest and the coil thrust over it and then withdrawn, the results are the same. When the series of experiments is repeated with the south pole of the magnet entering and leaving the coil, the current in each instance is opposite in direction to that produced by the north pole. A

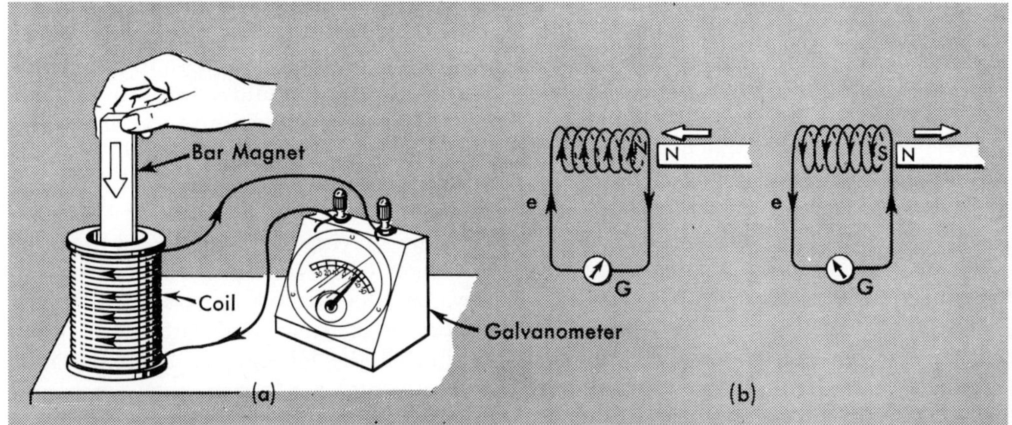

Fig. 32–1 *(a) Production of an electric current with a bar magnet and a wire coil. Presence of a current is indicated by a galvanometer. There is no current while bar magnet and coil are at rest with respect to each other. Motion of bar magnet produces a current. Likewise motion of coil produces a current. (b) Direction of current depends on the kind of motion. Thus, if bar magnet is moving down, top of coil becomes a north pole and electrons flow clockwise within coil.*

piece of unmagnetized steel produces no effect; if the ends of the wire are not connected through the galvanometer or otherwise, no effect is observed.

The current is developed only when the coil is in motion relative to the magnet or vice versa. There is no actual contact between the two, only the magnetic field, the strength of which varies inversely as the square of the distance from the magnetic pole. As the magnet is moved toward the coil, the number of lines of force or the magnetic flux passing through the coil increases; as it is moved away, the flux through the coil decreases. The current is therefore *induced* in the coil by the *changing* magnetic flux.

This hypothesis may be tested by several experiments. An electromagnet, which, as we have seen, possesses a magnetic field exactly like that of the permanent magnet, may be used. If either magnet or coil is moved, results identical with those described above are obtained. The electromagnet produces a magnetic field only while a current is flowing in its coils. When the circuit of the battery is closed, a magnetic field builds up around the coil, and

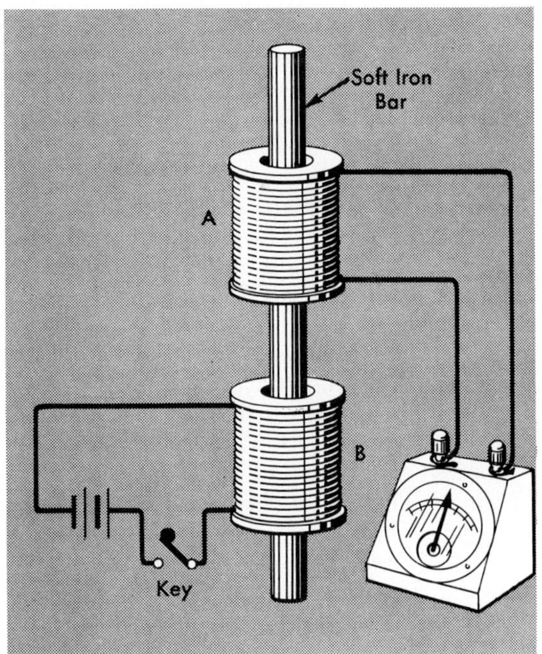

Fig. 32–2 *Electromagnetic induction. Current appears in A (1) if coil A is moved up or down while key is closed, (2) if coil B is moved up or down while key is closed, or (3) just after opening or closing key.*

when the circuit is opened, the magnetic field collapses; in either case the field is changing – expanding or contracting. Now we place our test coil, with the galvanometer, near the electromagnet, but move neither. The switch to the battery which supplies the electromagnet is closed (Figure 32–2*a*); a current flows in the coil for a brief moment. The switch is opened; a current again is registered by the galvanometer, but in the opposite direction (Figure 32–2*b*). At each "make" and "break" of the circuit in the electromagnet a current is induced in the coil. It does not matter which is moved; and if the field is moved, it makes no difference whether this is done electrically by the "make" and "break" or mechanically by moving the magnets. The phenomenon is known as *electromagnetic induction.*

THE DISCOVERY OF ELECTRO–MAGNETIC INDUCTION

Electromagnetic induction was discovered in 1831 by Michael Faraday. Prior to this outstanding addition to our knowledge of electricity and magnetism, several important facts had been observed and studied. The first was the attraction and repulsion between static electric charges; second, the attraction and repulsion between magnetic poles; third, the fact that electric charges could be put in motion, that is, that electric currents could be produced by chemical reaction; and fourth, the magnetic effect of the electric current, which definitely wedded magnetism and electricity and showed the former to be an effect of electricity. The last of these studies was made at just the right time to be taken up and carried forward by one of the greatest experimental scientists of all time – Faraday.

This gifted man began his career as a bookbinder's helper in London at the age of thirteen. He had very little formal education, but his employer, impressed by his burning desire for knowledge and by his intelligence, suggested that he read as much as possible so as "to know the insides as well as the outsides of books." Faraday studied books on science, particularly chemistry and electricity, performing such experiments as he could afford to buy apparatus for. An opportunity was given him to attend a series of lectures delivered by Sir Humphry Davy at the Royal Institution. He took complete notes of these lectures, and having carefully bound them, he sent them to Davy with a request for employment. As a result he was made Davy's laboratory assistant and later rose to be director of the laboratory. There Faraday spent his life, a life rich in research and discovery in many fields. He studied liquefaction of gases and combustion, discovered benzene, prepared steel alloys which anticipated modern developments, and made new optical glass of high refractive power, but he is best known for his work on electricity.

His greatest discovery was electromagnetic induction. If the electric current produces a magnetic field, reasoned Faraday, why not a reciprocal effect? Why not use the magnetic field to produce an electric current? Magnets, placed near wires, did not give the expected effect. By persistent experiment Faraday finally made the discovery that the magnetic field must be in motion relative to the wire in which the current is induced. For does not the electric charge in motion produce a magnetic field? Faraday's successful experiment, made in 1831, was essentially the same as that shown in Figure 32–3. He used an iron ring around which he wrapped two coils of wire. One coil, *A,* was connected to a battery *B* and had a switch *S;* the other coil, *C,* passed under a compass needle which was in effect a galvanometer. At the make and break of the switch *S,* momentary currents were induced in *C,* just as described in a previous section. In the course of about ten days of actual experimental work Faraday discovered and formulated the principles upon

Fig. 32–3 *Faraday's experiment by means of which he discovered electromagnetic induction.*

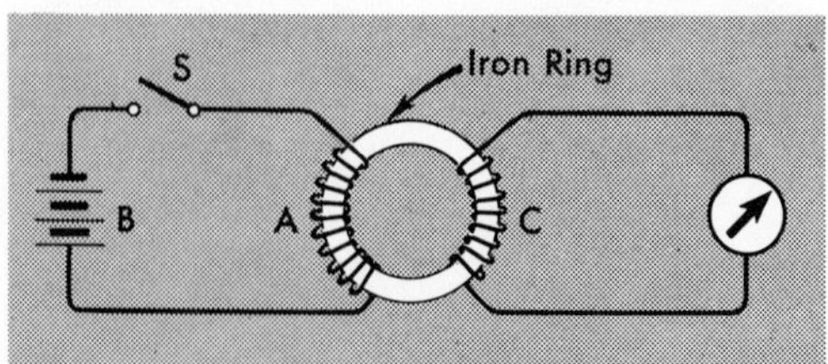

which the modern electrical industry is built. When asked, after a demonstration lecture, what was the practical value of his experiments, he is said to have replied, "Of what use is a newborn babe?" Thirty-one years later the first successful dynamo was built and used to supply current for arc-lighting. A method of producing an almost unlimited supply of electric current at a reasonable cost from cheaper energy had been found.

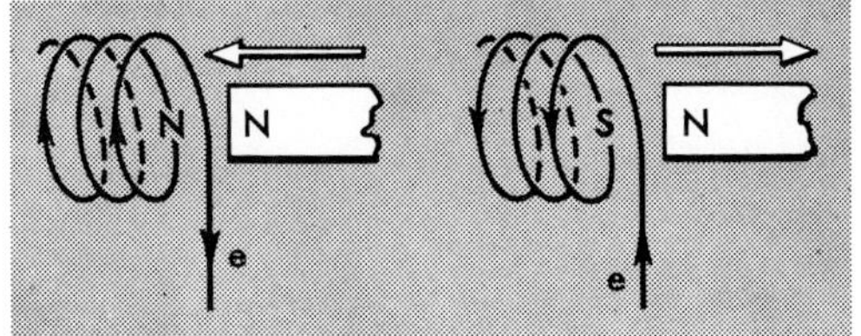

Fig. 32–4 *Lenz's law: the current induced is in such direction as to set up fields which oppose the motion or action producing it. The same conclusion may be arrived at by study of Fig. 32–1b.*

THE DIRECTION OF THE INDUCED CURRENT

In Figure 32–1 the direction of each current induced is indicated. It is determined by a principle which is in harmony with the principle of conservation of energy. In nature all changes require work, for nature resists change. The principle which was first specifically applied to induced currents by H. F. E. Lenz (1804–64), bears his name. *The direction of an induced current is such as to set up a magnetic field which opposes the motion producing it.* In Figure 32–4 the current in the coil sets up a magnetic field whose north pole is toward the north pole of the incoming bar magnet and tends to repel it (left-hand rule). When the bar is being withdrawn, the current induced in the coil is in the opposite direction. The magnetic field of the coil with the south end toward the retreating north pole of the bar magnet tends to hold it. The same rule is applicable whether permanent bar magnets or electromagnets are used and regardless of which one moves. It is likewise applicable, as we shall see in the next section, to the current induced, or generated, by the dynamo.

This principle also holds for even a single electromagnet, which may induce a current in its own coils. When an electric circuit is broken, a spark is usually produced. The collapsing magnetic field cuts across the wires and thus induces a current. In accordance with Lenz's law, the current is in the direction which tends to maintain the field. When the circuit is closed, the magnetic lines of force surge out and induce a current which opposes the flow of the established current. This phenomenon of self-induction may be regarded as "electric inertia." Self-induction was also discovered by a great American physicist, Joseph Henry (1797–1878), who was working on electromagnetic induction at the same time as Faraday and who independently made the same discovery.

GENERATORS

In accordance with the principles discussed in the preceding sections, a generator is a machine which can be so operated that the number of lines of force or the magnetic flux through a coil is constantly changing. To produce a continuous change in flux and therefore an uninterrupted current, one of the generator parts is rotated — either the coils or the magnets. Coils or loops of wire rotating in a magnetic field cut across the lines of force, or, if the magnets rotate, lines of force cut across stationary coils. The action of a generator can be better understood in terms of the above, that is, the "cutting" of lines of force by a conductor, whereas the results of the experiments involving the back and forth motions of magnet or coil, or the resurge and decay of a magnetic field across a coil are more appropriately interpreted by flux change.

If a single piece of copper wire is moved horizontally back and forth between the opposite poles of two horizontal magnets,

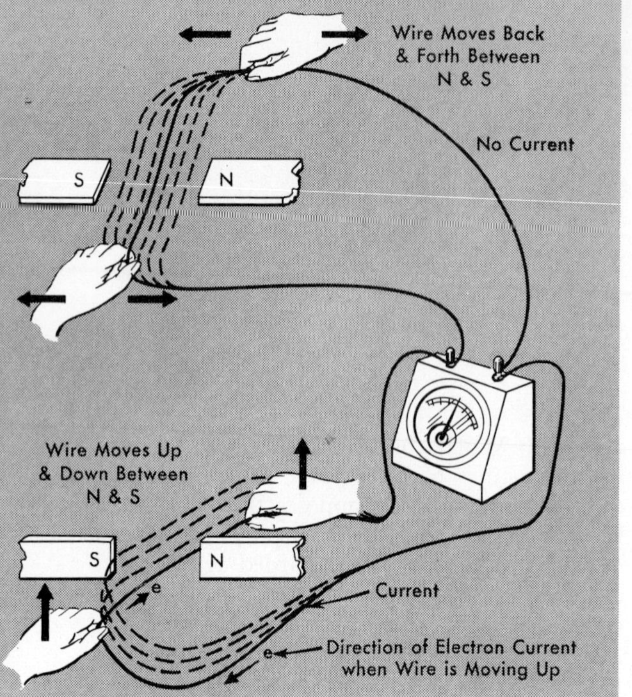

Fig. 32–5 *A moving conductor must move across magnetic lines of force to produce an electric current.*

no electromotive force is generated, for the motion is in the direction of the magnetic field (lines of force). When it is moved across the field, upward for example, the "free" electrons in the copper wire move clockwise (Figure 32–5), thus creating a potential. A current would flow if the ends of the wire were connected in a circuit. When the wire is moved downward, the flow of electrons is in the opposite direction, counterclockwise. The motion of the wire need not be perpendicular to the field; it can be at any angle, as long as it cuts across the lines of force. This experiment with a single wire shows how a generator works and suggests how one may be constructed. The underlying principle is, of course, that of electromagnetic induction and there are two significant facts which characterize this phenomenon and all generators. First, work must be done in order to move the wire (or the magnet), for the direction of the induced current always is such as to resist the motion which produces it. Second, the electrons are always given a sidewise motion relative to the plane established by the directions of the field and the motion of the conductor (Figure 32–6).

The essential parts of a generator or dynamo therefore are:

1. A magnetic field, which is supplied by *electromagnets.* A single pair of electromagnets is used for the demonstration generator, and several pairs arranged in a circle for a commercial machine. (In some generators, permanent magnets are used.)

2. A conductor, in which the current is induced and which is called the *armature.* For our experimental machine a loop of wire which rotates between the poles of the magnet is sufficient; but with a single loop of a few turns little electromotive force or current would be generated. The commercial armature consists of many coils of wire wound lengthwise, usually on a cylinder or drum. The body, or core, is made of iron, and the wires are embedded in grooves. In the direct-current generator, the commutator keeps the flow of current in one direction in the external circuit.

3. Collecting devices called *brushes,* which press against the split-ring commutator of a direct-current generator or the slip rings of an alternating-current generator which enable the current to enter and leave the armature.

DIRECT–CURRENT GENERATORS

An experimental direct-current generator which may be regarded as an elaboration of the single wire arrangement described above, is shown in Figure 32–7. Electromag-

Fig. 32–6 *Generation of an electric current, in the direction A to B, in a wire moving in the field of an electromagnet.*

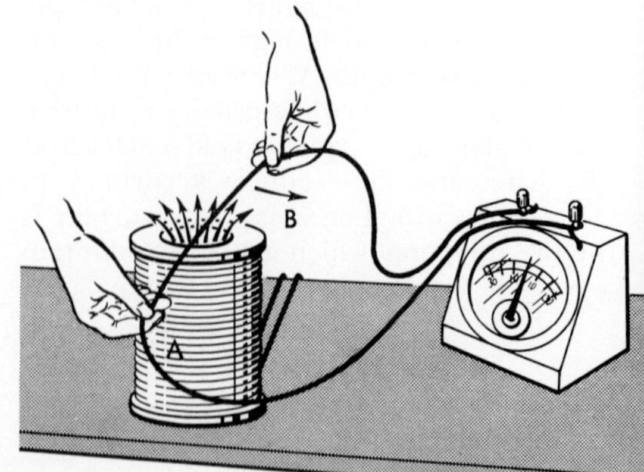

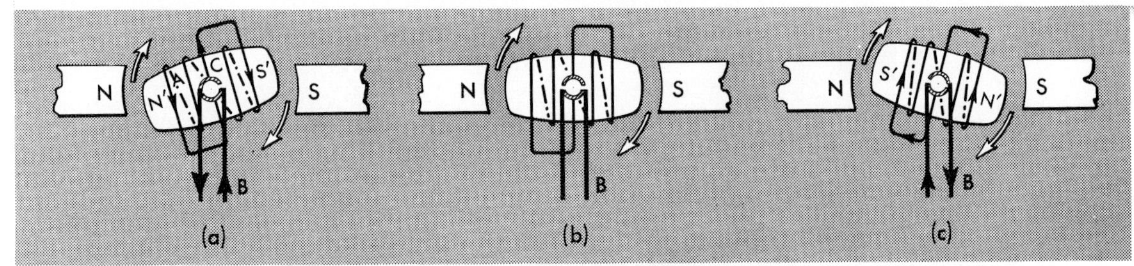

Fig. 32–7 *Simple direct-current generator. Outside energy which might come from a water-power turbine is used to rotate the armature A. The magnetic field within which the armature turns is produced by electromagnetic induction around the pole pieces N and S. Work is done to turn the armature against the opposing magnetic field. Most of the energy so expended appears as current.*

nets replace the bar magnets; the armature *A* consisting of a coil of insulated wire wrapped around an iron core is substituted for the single wire. It is made to rotate by outside force (energy) which might come from a water-power turbine, for example. A commutator *C* and collection brushes *B* are added necessary features. As the armature is rotated, the current induced in the coil creates magnetic forces that oppose those turning the armature. In position *a* the magnetic poles of the armature are of the same polarity (left-hand rule) as those which they are approaching. When the armature reaches position *c*, the direction of the induced current will have reversed and its poles are now of opposite polarity to those which they are leaving. The change in direction of the current comes as the coil passes through its vertical position (position *b*). As it approaches the vertical the top wires of the coil are cutting upward across the lines of force. At the vertical position it is moving in the direction of the lines of force, and, as it is cutting none, the induced current drops to zero. Beyond this point it cuts downward, and the induced current flows in the opposite direction. At 90° from position *b* it is cutting the maximum number of lines of force, and the induced electromotive force is greatest. Yet the current taken off by one brush and returned from the external circuit by the other is always in the same direction, for as the current in the coil changes its direction the brushes exchange their contacts with the two halves of the commutator.

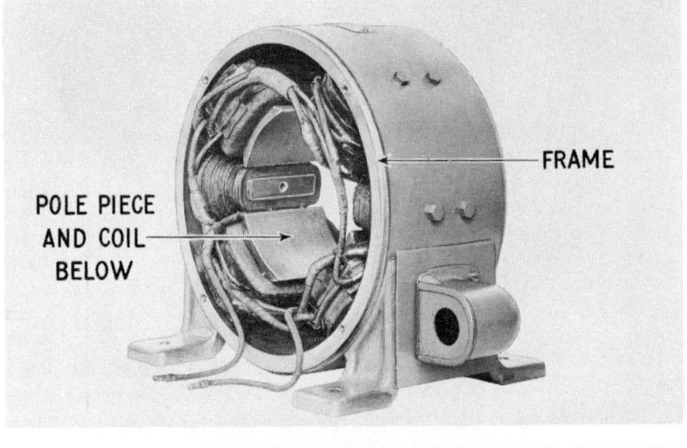

Fig. 32–8 *Direct-current generator or motor. It is a generator if it operates on outside energy to produce electricity. It is a motor if it uses electric energy to produce mechanical energy. (General Electric Co.)*

A commercial generator (Figure 32–8) is a further extension of the experimental model, and is designed to produce a greater current and voltage, in other words, to cut more lines of force in a given time. Obviously, this is achieved by increasing (1) the intensity of the magnetic field by means of more and stronger electromagnets, (2) the speed of rotation of the armature, and (3) the number of wires or conductors in the armature.

Fig. 32–9 *Low-speed A.C. generator with rotating field (rotor) at left and stationary armature (stator) at right.* (*General Electric Co.*)

ALTERNATING–CURRENT GENERATORS

Referring again to the drawings of a simple dynamo (Figure 32–7), we observe that the direction of the induced current reverses with every half turn, or twice for every rotation of the armature. If we replace the commutator with solid rings of metal connected to each end of the coil and against which the brushes rub, we obtain an alternating current. Electrons rush back and forth, and these reversals of the current in the coil are carried to the external circuit. The sixty-cycle current which we use in our homes flows through the lamps or the motors in the electric clock or refrigerator, reverses, and then flows in the opposite direction, changing one hundred and twenty times, or making sixty complete cycles, every second. Most small alternating-current generators have, in common with those producing direct current, a rotating armature and a fixed field piece. In power plants large currents are generated at very high voltages. To build the insulation necessary for such high voltages and to avoid the use of sliding contacts, the large alternating-current generators are constructed with stationary armatures and rotating field magnets (Figure 32–9). The coils of the fixed armature or stator are placed in a ring framework. Within the stator is placed the rotating part of the machine (rotor) with the electromagnets arranged in a circle and projecting outward. Direct current is required for the electromagnets and is supplied by a separate direct-current generator or exciter. The alternating current induced in the armature, no parts of which move, is led directly to a distribution switchboard.

MOTION FROM ELECTRICITY

We have seen how the generator converts energy of motion into electrical energy, and now we shall consider the opposite conversion, electrical energy into motion. In both of these transformations magnetic fields play an intermediary but necessary role. The discovery by Oersted that an electric current creates a magnetic field is the underlying principle of the latter conversion. The machine making the conversion is the *motor,* the action of which can be shown by a single wire in a magnetic field. When an electron current is sent through the wire (Figure 32–10*a*) from *A* to *B*, the interaction of the magnetic field thus created around the wire with the magnetic field between the poles of the magnet causes the wire to move leftward (32–10*b*). A similar arrangement can be used to demonstrate the action of a generator (32–10*c*). If the wire by outside force is moved to the right, an electron current (*A* to *B*) is generated within it which is in the same direction as the input current in the motor (32–10*a*). Figure 32–10*b* includes all the essential elements in an electric generator.

The force exerted on the wire, or the *motor effect,* as it is called, comes from the two magnetic fields. The field around a wire in which a current (electron flow) is circular is in a plane perpendicular to the wire. It is shown by the lines of force in Figure 32–10*a,* which appear in the field due to the permanent magnet. The combined fields appear in Figure 32–10*c*. The merged field is stronger to the right of this wire; the resultant force to the left accounts for the motion of the wire in that direction.

DIRECT–CURRENT MOTORS

As implied above, the direct-current motor consists of the same parts as a generator: electromagnets, armature, commutator, and brushes. Its performance can be interpreted in terms of combinations of systems of lines of force (above) or magnetic attractions and repulsions. Direct current flows in through the commutator to the coils of the armature (Figure 32–11*a*) in such a direction (left-hand rule) that its poles are each attracted by the opposite poles of the fixed or *field magnet* toward which they are moving. When the south pole of the armature coil is just opposite to the north pole of the field magnet, and vice versa, the coil would stop except for the switching device or commutator, which at exactly the right moment causes the direction of the current in the coil to reverse. The polarity of the armature also reverses, and the rotation continues, each of the poles now being repelled by the like poles of the field magnet (32–11*b*). At every half-rotation the current in the armature is reversed. All this occurs quickly and automatically; even with the single coil and magnet we may have a rapid rotation.

Fig. 32–10 (*a*) *Motion from electric energy — the motor effect. Wire loop is free to swing about supports pp′. When tapping key is closed, straight wire moves from right to left.* (*b*) *Motion converted into electric energy — the generator effect. Note that forced motion of wire AB is just opposite to that in a and an electric current is generated in AB.* (*c*) *Intensity of magnetic field is increased on right side of wire, and decreased on left side. Thus wire is pushed to the left.*

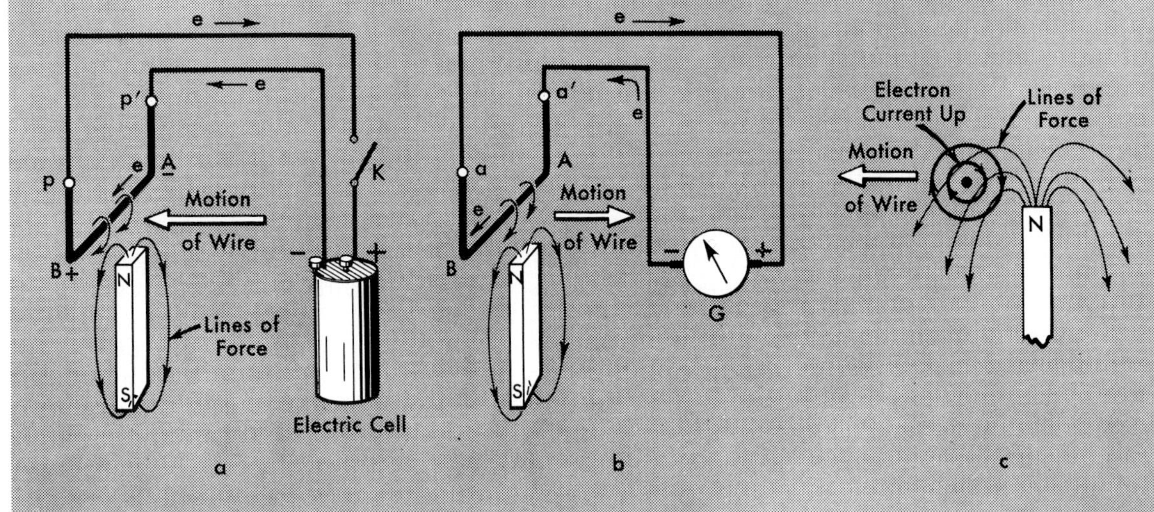

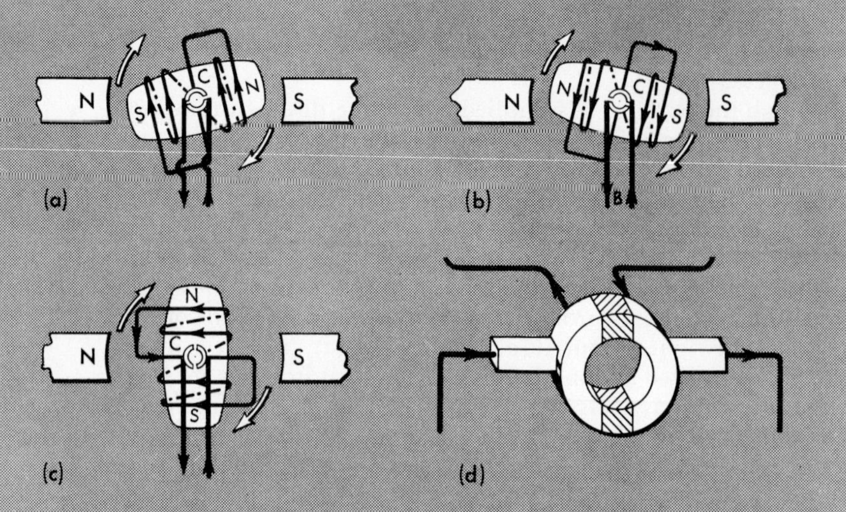

Fig. 32–11 *Simple motor. Interaction of magnetic field causes armature to rotate. Enlarged section of commutator with brushes is shown in diagram d.*

The motor described above is an aid in understanding the operation of commercial motors but would not do very much work and does not rotate steadily. Motors for practical use are multiples of the simple motor. The magnetic field is stronger and more nearly uniform and is furnished by electromagnets placed around the armature. These may receive the same current as the armature (*series wound*) or only a part of it (*shunt wound*). The armature consists of many turns of wire wound in slots lengthwise on a drum which has an iron core. Instead of two halves to the commutator there are many segments, each pair in contact at a given time with one of the coils (Figure 32–8). At any one moment one of the coils is receiving the greatest amount of mechanical force. The rotation is without jerks, just as a six-cylinder automobile is much smoother in doing its work than the one-cylinder engine. The electric motor is a very efficient machine. There is very little loss through heat. The heat which is generated is due to the unavoidable electrical resistance of the coils. There is little friction, for the armature turns on bearings and the brushes are very smooth.

From this description of the direct-current motor one can see that it is, in construction, identical with the direct-current generator (Figure 32–7). In fact, by turning the motor, it may be used as a generator. The current generated, however, flows in the opposite direction to that which would cause the armature to rotate in a given direction. Consequently, when used as a motor, the machine actually generates another current that opposes the current operating the motor. This electromotive counterforce accounts in part for the extremely low current which a motor draws when running at top speed without a load. When the motor is loaded to do work, the speed of rotation of the armature is less, the generator effect is correspondingly less, and consequently more current flows into it to do the extra work.

WHY USE DIRECT CURRENT?

Thus far we have discussed direct current, which is that produced by all cells and batteries and by generators fitted with commutators. Though in actual practice direct current is commonly confined to certain uses, these are very definite. It is indispensable for electroplating, other electrochemical processes, and battery charging. Indeed, for a strong and steady magnetic field, necessary in lifting magnets and magnetic brakes, and even for the magnetic field of the alternating-current generator, it is essential. Direct-current motors have several distinct advantages. They can run at variable speeds, are easy to control, and start under a heavy load. They are used in elevators, electric locomotives, automobile starters, streetcars, and other machines which require a very high initial torque (turning force) at low speed and a controlled higher speed. One type of direct-current motor used for blowers and in machine shops runs at nearly the same speed with full load as with little or no load.

The great difficulty with direct current is the matter of transmission. All transmission lines, whether of copper or aluminum, offer a considerable amount of resistance, which, as we have noted, increases with the length of the conductor. There is, therefore, a serious drop in potential ($E = IR$) when the current is conveyed over any great distance. To step up the direct-current voltage for transmission and to step it down to lower voltages for local use would each time require a motor to operate a generator delivering the required voltage. The use of direct current on a large scale is therefore restricted to the central areas of large cities and to buildings or factories or other localities where it is generated on the premises.

ALTERNATING-CURRENT MOTORS

Alternating-current motors are, with one exception, structurally unlike direct-current motors. The *induction motor,* for example, uses a rotating field which may be obtained with alternating current without mechanical rotation of the magnets. Within the rotating magnetic field is mounted the moving part of the motor. The rotor consists of heavy copper bars arranged in "squirrel cage" fashion and embedded in an iron core. Lines of force cut the copper bars and strong currents are induced in them. The currents are in such a direction as to oppose the motion of the field by magnetic attraction and the rotor is pulled around with the field. The rotor never moves quite so fast as the field, for then no lines of force would cut it. With a heavy load it moves more slowly and the necessary larger currents are induced.

It should be noted that in the induction motor no rings or brushes are necessary, for no current is supplied to the moving parts. The induction motor is widely used in household appliances, such as refrigerators and fans, and in shops and factories. It may be modified to give a high starting torque with low current.

The *synchronous motor* consists of a stator which usually contains the field magnets supplied with direct current and a rotor or armature which receives the alternating current. The armature pole pieces change their polarity with the frequency of the alternating current and must rotate in step with the alternations and at a constant speed. This speed is the same as or a multiple of that of the alternating-current generator which supplies the current. The electric clock is operated by a simplified form of this type of motor with a revolving permanent magnet. An electric clock is as accurate as the rate of alternation of the alternating current.

The *universal motor* in which the field coils and armature are supplied by the current (series wound) may be used with either direct or alternating current. The change in direction of the current changes the polarity of both the armature coils and the field coils, so that the reaction between the two fields is not changed. This type of motor, which in construction resembles the direct-current motor, is not very efficient and is rapidly going out of use except where small power is needed, as in sewing machines.

WHY USE ALTERNATING CURRENT?

As indicated in our discussion of the restricted use of direct current, most electric current is used in the form of alternating current. The reason for this is one of the chief reasons for using electric power at all — ease of transmission. In order to send the electric current through conductors over great distances without much loss, it must be at very high voltages. The loss in electrical energy is due to conversion to heat.

The heating effect is a function of both the resistance and the square of the current. That is, the heating effect of an electric current $= kRI^2$. (See page 538.) To reduce the heat loss, then, the current must be *reduced*. This is accomplished in a step-up transformer. Alternating current may be readily stepped up to extremely high voltages, sent over miles of high-tension transmission lines, and then stepped down to lower voltage for home or local use. These changes are brought about by a device known as a *transformer*. The principle of the transformer is that of electromagnetic induction. In Figure 32–2, it was shown that the opening or closing of the direct circuit of an electromagnet induced a current in a nearby coil. If for the direct-current circuit which is opened and closed by a switch, we substitute alternating current and discard the switch, we have a transformer. It has no moving parts save the growing and decaying magnetic field, which induces an alternating current in the coil across which it cuts. Transformers are inexpensive to use because they are so efficient; large ones are very nearly 100 per cent efficient.

The transformer, then, consists of two coils of wire which are wrapped around a continuous silicon-steel core (Figure 32–12). The core, which is built up of thin sheets of soft iron insulated from each other, may be in the form of a loop or otherwise and forms a continuous magnetic circuit. For a step-up transformer (Figure 32–12*a*), the primary coil *P* which receives the lower voltage alternating current must have fewer turns than the secondary *S* in which the high-voltage alternating current is induced. If we wish to multiply the voltage ten times, it is necessary to have ten times as many turns of wire in the secondary as in the primary. For the step-down transformer (Figure 32–12*b*) the reverse is true. In both transformers the lines of force of the magnetic field sweep out and back across the secondary, and then repeat in the reverse direction, thus inducing another alternating current. The two currents are entirely separate.

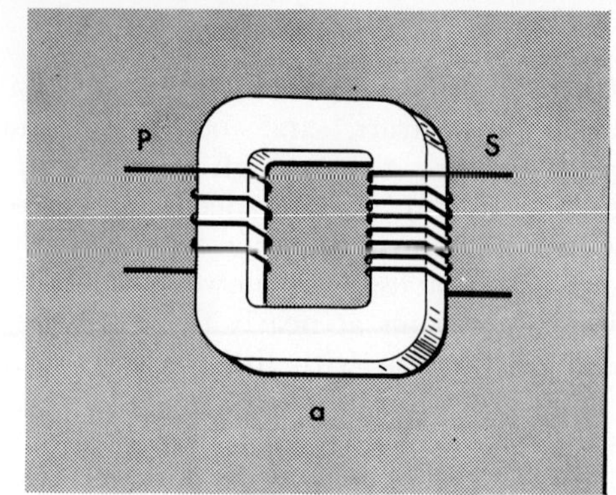

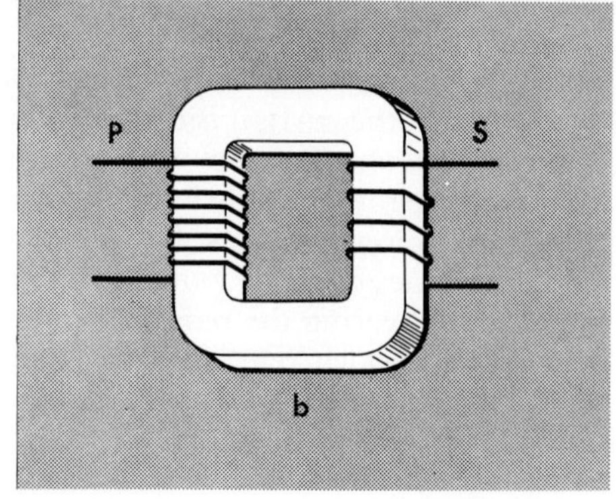

Fig. 32–12 *Transformers. Working on the principle of electromagnetic induction, the transformer is used to step up* (*a*) *or to step down* (*b*) *the voltage of alternating current.*

Here we have a means not only of transmitting the current, but of changing the voltage for any use we may wish to put it to, whether it be for a neon sign, a fluorescent lamp, a toy train, or an induction furnace. In the next chapter we shall see how the current is generated on a large scale, distributed, and used.

SUMMARY

1. An electric current is induced in a wire when a magnetic field, produced either by a permanent magnet or an electromagnet, is cut by the wire or cuts across the wire. This may be done mechanically, by motion, or electrically, by the make and break of the circuit of an electromagnet. The phenomenon is known as electromagnetic induction.

2. Electromagnetic induction was discovered by Joseph Henry in this country and by Michael Faraday in England. Faraday developed many of the important principles used in electric current generation.
3. The direction of an induced current is always such as to oppose the motion which generated the current (Lenz's law).
4. The left-hand rule for a single conductor relates the direction of the electron flow to the direction of the magnetic field.
5. The left-hand rule for a coiled conductor relates the direction of the electron flow to the north pole or the emergent field of the electromagnet.
6. A dynamo or generator consists of a magnetic field supplied by electromagnets, an armature in which the current is induced, and the collecting devices or brushes. A direct-current generator is equipped with a commutator.
7. Direct current is used in electrochemical industries and for variable speed motors with high starting torque. It cannot be efficiently transmitted very far.
8. In an alternating-current generator there is no commutator. The current reverses or alternates at a certain frequency. Large generators employ rotating field magnets (rotors) and a fixed armature (stator).
9. Most alternating-current motors utilize a rotating magnetic field, which is obtained without moving field coils.
10. Alternating current is extensively used because its voltage may be stepped up to high voltages for more efficient transmission and stepped down to various usable voltages. The transformer, consisting of two independent coils and with no moving parts, modifies the alternating-current voltage. It operates by electromagnetic induction.

STUDY EXERCISES

1. The diagram at the top of the next column represents a motor with field poles and the direction of rotation shown. Mark each of the following parts: brushes (*B*); commutator (*C*); armature (*A*). Indicate the direction of the electron current in the coil and in the wires leading to the brushes and the poles of the coil.

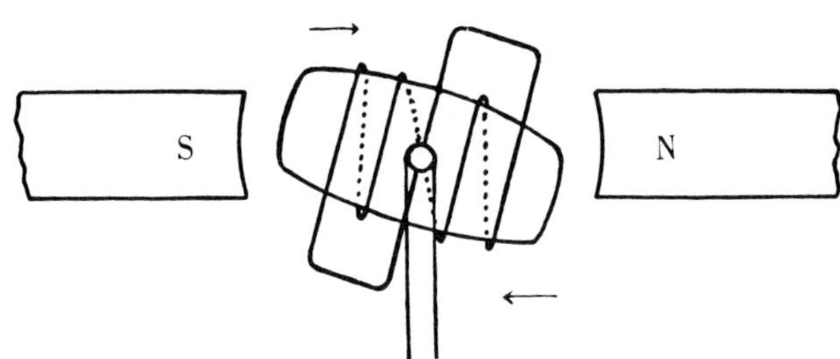

2. An electric current is induced in a conductor by a magnetic field under certain circumstances. Indicate whether a current appears in the following examples.
   a. The magnetic field and the nearby conductor are both at rest. ....
   b. There is relative motion of the conductor or field in any direction. ....
   c. Magnetic field and conductor are both moving at the same speed and in the same direction. ....
   d. There is motion of the conductor so that it cuts across the magnetic field. ....
   e. There is motion of the magnet so that its field cuts across the conductor. ....
   f. Both electromagnet and conductor are at rest but there is an alternating current in the electromagnet. ....
3. Make a general statement on electromagnetic induction, and describe how it may be demonstrated by the use of a straight wire, coil, or more complex armature winding, and a permanent magnet or electromagnet.
4. State Lenz's law and show how it may be applied to all cases of electromagnetic induction and to self-induction.
5. The diagram below represents a generator with field poles indicated.

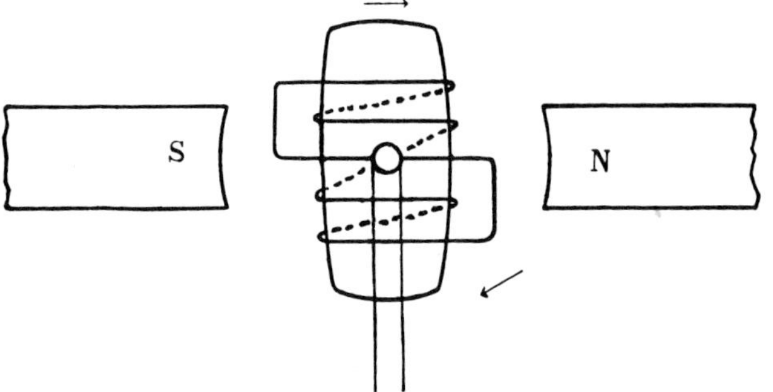

a. Is this machine for alternating or direct current? Explain.
b. Could this machine be used as a motor?
c. As a generator does it convert mechanical energy to electrical, or electrical energy to mechanical?
d. Does the rotating coil do work, or must work be done to rotate it?
e. Fill in the direction of the current in the wires and brush connections and indicate the poles of the coil.
f. Name the three essential parts of a generator and indicate them on the drawing.
g. List three ways in which the voltage output may be increased.

6. How would the generator shown in the diagram in the preceding question be modified in order to obtain alternating current?
7. List the advantages of alternating current over direct current.
8. List the advantages of direct current over alternating current for some purposes.
9. Mark *A* if the device operates only on alternating current; *D*, if it operates only on direct current; *E*, if it operates on either.

   a. Synchronous motor. ....
   b. Battery charger. ....
   c. Electrolytic cell. ....
   d. Transformer. ....
   e. Lamp. ....
   f. Cathode ray tube. ....
   g. Induction motor. ....
   h. Series wound motor. ....
   i. Streetcar. ....
   j. Elevator. ....
   k. Neon sign. ....
   l. Electric clock. ....
   m. Thermionic tube. ....
   n. Photoelectric cell. ....

10. Give the number of the one correct response completing each of the following.

   a. In a dynamo the magnetic field is supplied by (1) permanent magnets; (2) electromagnets fed by alternating current; (3) electromagnets fed by direct current. ....
   b. Direct current is produced by a dynamo equipped with (1) solid ring contacts from which the current is collected; (2) a commutator from which the current is collected; (3) a stator from which the induced current is drawn. ....
   c. Direct-current motors are used for streetcars, electrically driven locomotives, and elevators because (1) they run more smoothly; (2) they supply a greater starting torque; (3) no current is required for their moving parts. ....

FOR FURTHER READING

1. BRAGG, W. L., *Electricity*. London: G. Bell and Sons, Ltd., 1936.

   The author is a Nobel prize winner who likes to write for the general reader. The whole volume is devoted to electricity. The subject of magnetism and its relation to motors and dynamos is presented in Chapter III.

2. RINDE, C. A., *Electricity*. New York: Harcourt, Brace and Company, 1944.

   A "not-too-technical" nor too mathematical presentation of electricity, especially in its application to civil life. Chapter 10 is devoted to the generation of electrical energy by direct- and alternating-current generators. Motors and direct- and alternating-current transformers are discussed in Chapters 11 and 12.

3. TILDEN, WILLIAM H., *Famous Chemists*. London: George Routledge and Sons, 1921.

   Chapter XII deals with the life and work of Faraday, especially in electrochemistry.

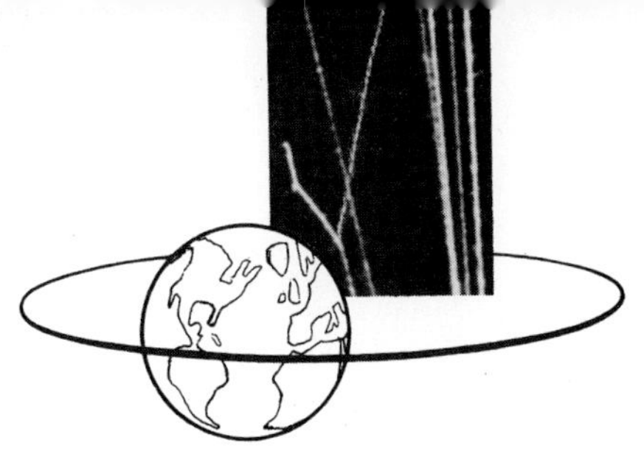

33

ELECTRICITY AT WORK

THE PRECEDING CHAPTER discussed the principles by which electric current is converted into work and vice versa. The motor in which electricity is converted to mechanical work (motion) operates solely because of the magnetic forces which an electric current creates around a conductor in which it is flowing. We shall continue our discussion of this important effect of electricity by applying it to some of the simpler measuring devices. We shall also consider two other effects of electricity on matter: its conversion to heat and light, and its use in bringing about chemical changes. The concept of electric power and energy, the prime energy sources from which our electrical energy is drawn, and the distribution and uses of electricity will be treated briefly.

But first we must review the common units of electricity which were introduced in Chapters 21 and 31.

ELECTRICAL UNITS

There are two fundamental systems of electrical units, the cgs (centimeter-gram-second) *electrostatic* system which begins by defining the unit charge in terms of the force of repulsion between like charges, and the cgs *electromagnetic* system which starts by defining the unit of current in terms of the force exerted by the magnetic field it produces. A so-called third system of *practical units,* primarily derived from the electromagnetic system and differing from that system by the factor 10 or some power of 10, is found to be more convenient. These units — amperes, volts, ohms, and so on — are now a part of the mks (meter-kilogram-second) *practical or absolute* system.

The *electrostatic* unit of charge (esu), the *statcoulomb,* is that charge which repels an identical charge one centimeter away with a force of one dyne. It is the only unit of this system which we shall employ; the charge of the electron (fundamental charge) is equal to 4.802×10^{-10} statcoulombs. Refer to page 343.

The operational definition of the mks unit of current depends upon the force of attraction between two parallel conductors with electric current flowing in both wires in the same direction. A single wire carrying an electric current is surrounded by a circular magnetic field. The fields about two parallel wires reinforce each other. (Refer to Figure 33–1.) The two heavy wires can be made of equal resistance so the current flowing in each branch is the same.

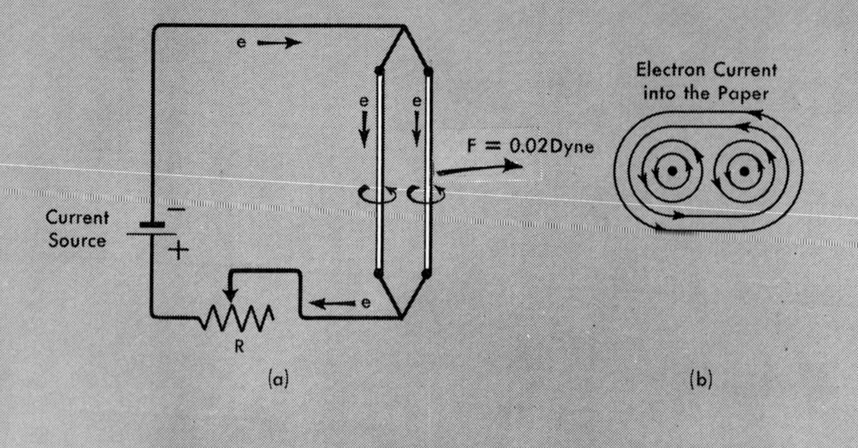

Fig. 33–1 *Operational definition of the unit of electric current — the ampere.*

The direction of the electron current is down ("into the page"). Application of the left-hand rule for the direction of the electron current indicates that the magnetic fields about each wire are counterclockwise. The lines of force are in opposite directions between the wires. The intensity of the magnetic field is less than on the outside of the two wires. Certain of the lines of force fuse and run completely around both wires (Figure 33–1*b*). Hence there is a force causing the wires to move *toward* each other. Thus a force must be applied to keep the wires at rest when a current is flowing. In Figure 33–1*a*, *R* is an adjustable resistance. This can be changed and thus vary the force *F* needed to keep the wires stationary.

The mks unit of current, the ampere, is the current which, if flowing in the same direction in each of two infinitely long parallel wires one meter apart in a vacuum, will cause the wires to attract each other with a force of 2×10^{-7} newton (.02 dyne) per meter of length. This is the force *F* in Figure 33–1*a*.

The mks unit of *charge* or *quantity* of electricity, the *coulomb,* is the amount of charge which in one second passes a point on a conductor in which there is a constant current of one ampere. It is an ampere-second and is equal to 3×10^9 statcoulombs.

The mks unit of *electrical potential* is the *volt.* It is the potential difference between two points if one *newton-meter* (joule) of work is required to move a charge of one coulomb from one point to the other.

The mks unit of *resistance,* the *ohm,* is discussed below.

CONCEPT OF RESISTANCE

All materials offer some resistance to the flow of an electric current. Some materials, such as silver, copper, and aluminum, offer very little resistance to the passage of electricity. They are good conductors. These are the materials used to make electric power lines and electrical machinery. Some materials, such as glass, certain plastics, sulfur, and paraffin, offer very high resistance. They are poor conductors. These are the substances used to prevent the passage of electricity.

The resistance of any conductor depends, however, upon the geometry of the conductor — the cross-sectional area and the length — as well as upon the material. Just as you would expect more water to flow through a large pipe than a small one, you should expect more electricity to flow through a large conductor than a small one. That is, the *resistance changes inversely* with the cross-sectional *area.* Also, for a given pressure, you would expect less water to flow through 100 feet of garden hose than through 10 feet. That is, the resistance to flow *increases* with the *length.* The same simple relationship applies to the resistance of various lengths of the same conductor;

that is, the resistance is directly proportional to the length. Hence, the *resistance of any conductor* is *proportional to its length, inversely proportional to its cross-sectional area,* and also *depends upon the substance in the conductor.* Symbolically, then,

$$R \propto \frac{l}{A}.$$

Introducing a constant of proportionality, R_s, we can write,

$$R = R_s \times \frac{l}{A}. \qquad (\textit{Equation 33–1})$$

The constant R_s is known as the specific resistance — the resistance in ohms of a centimeter-cube of material. It is a specific property of any substance. The specific resistance of some common materials is given in Table 33–1.

Equation 33–1 is very useful in computing the resistances of actual conductors, for example, the resistance of a copper wire with a diameter of 3 mm and 300 meters long:

$$R = R_s \times \frac{l}{A} = \frac{(1.7 \times 10^{-6}\ \text{ohm-cm})(300\ \text{m} \times 100\ \text{cm/m})}{\pi(0.3\ \text{cm}/2)^2} = 0.720\ \text{ohm}$$

TABLE 33–1 SPECIFIC RESISTANCES OF SOME COMMON MATERIALS

MATERIAL	SPECIFIC RESISTANCE IN OHM-CM
Silver	1.6×10^{-6}
Aluminum	2.8×10^{-6}
Copper	1.7×10^{-6}
Iron	10.0×10^{-6}
Mercury	95.8×10^{-6}
Platinum	10.0×10^{-6}
Glass	9.0×10^{13}
Quartz	5.0×10^{18}
Sulfur	1.0×10^{17}
Paraffin	5.0×10^{16}

OHM'S LAW

Any electrical circuit can be fully described in terms of the applied voltage (E) (electromotive force), the resistance (R), and the current (I). These are easily related. We have already learned that

$$I \propto E, \quad \text{and} \quad \propto \frac{1}{R}.$$

Introducing the constant of proportionality k, we can write,

$$I = \frac{k \cdot E}{R}. \qquad (\textit{Equation 33–2})$$

Equation 33–2 cannot be used without knowing the value of k. The scientists of a century ago arranged for the use of practical electrical units, which made k unity. This was easily done by arbitrarily defining the ohm as the resistance which would permit a current flow of one ampere under the applied voltage of one volt. The consequence of this arbitrary definition is that

$$k = \frac{R \cdot I}{E} = \frac{(1\ \text{ohm})\ (1\ \text{ampere})}{1\ \text{volt}}.$$

Hence, Equation 33–2 can be rewritten,

$$I = \frac{1\ \text{ohm-ampere}}{\text{volt}} \cdot \frac{E}{R}$$

or more simply,

$$I = \frac{E}{R}. \qquad (\textit{Equation 33–3})$$

This symbolic statement is known as Ohm's law. In using Equation 33–3, one should always remember that the complete statement in terms of ohms, amperes, and volts is implied. Ohm's law is constantly used in working with three variables: current, applied voltage, and resistance in *any* electric circuit. The student should recognize the law in any of its three equivalent forms.

$$I = \frac{E}{R}, \quad \text{or} \quad \text{Current} = \frac{\text{volts}}{\text{ohms}} \qquad (\textit{Equation 33–3})$$

$$E = RI, \quad \text{or} \quad \text{Volts} = \text{amperes} \times \text{ohms}$$
(*Equation 33–4*)

$$R = \frac{E}{I}, \quad \text{or} \quad \text{Ohms} = \frac{\text{volts}}{\text{amperes}}$$
(*Equation 33–5*)

SAMPLE PROBLEMS:

(1) An electric iron has a resistance of 22 ohms. What current does it use on a 110-volt circuit?

$$\text{Current} = \frac{\text{volts}}{\text{ohms}} = \frac{110 \text{ volts}}{22 \text{ ohms}} = 5 \text{ amperes}$$

(2) An electric light bulb has a resistance of 3 ohms. What voltage is necessary if the current is to be 0.5 ampere?

$$\begin{aligned}\text{Volts} &= \text{amperes} \times \text{ohms}\\ &= 0.5 \text{ ampere} \times 3 \text{ ohms} = 1.5 \text{ volts}\end{aligned}$$

(3) A light bulb draws 1.0 ampere under an applied voltage of 3 volts. What is its resistance?

$$\text{Ohms} = \frac{\text{volts}}{\text{amperes}} = \frac{3 \text{ volts}}{1 \text{ ampere}} = 3 \text{ ohms}$$

RESISTANCES IN SERIES AND PARALLEL

Conductors may be used in series or in parallel depending on circumstances. A series connection means a sequential connection, one right after the other, of a number of resistances. Consider, for example, a series connection of a "40-watt" and a "75-watt" light bulb in a 110-volt circuit. (Refer to Figure 33–2.) In a series circuit the current flowing in *all* parts of the circuit is the *same*. Thus the current through the 40-watt bulb is the same as in the 75-watt bulb. Symbolically, then,

$$R_{\text{series}} = R_1 + R_2 + R_3 + R_4 + \cdots$$
(*Equation 33–6*)

In Figure 33–2, then, the total series resistance is 302 ohms plus 161 ohms, or 363 ohms. Now applying Ohm's law, the total current flowing in the circuit is

$$I = \frac{E}{R} = \frac{110}{363} = 0.304 \text{ ampere.}$$

A 40-watt bulb is designed to operate on 0.36 ampere and a 75-watt bulb should have 0.67 ampere in a 110-volt circuit. Thus, neither bulb is being supplied sufficient current and both bulbs would be dim.

In a parallel connection, the resistances involved are "side-by-side." (Refer to Figure 33–3.) In this connection, the drop in potential across both lamps is 110 volts or E. Further, the current divides and only a part of the current, I_1 and I_2, passes through each lamp. Hence,

$$I = I_1 + I_2.$$

Then, applying Ohm's law as Equation 33–4, we can write,

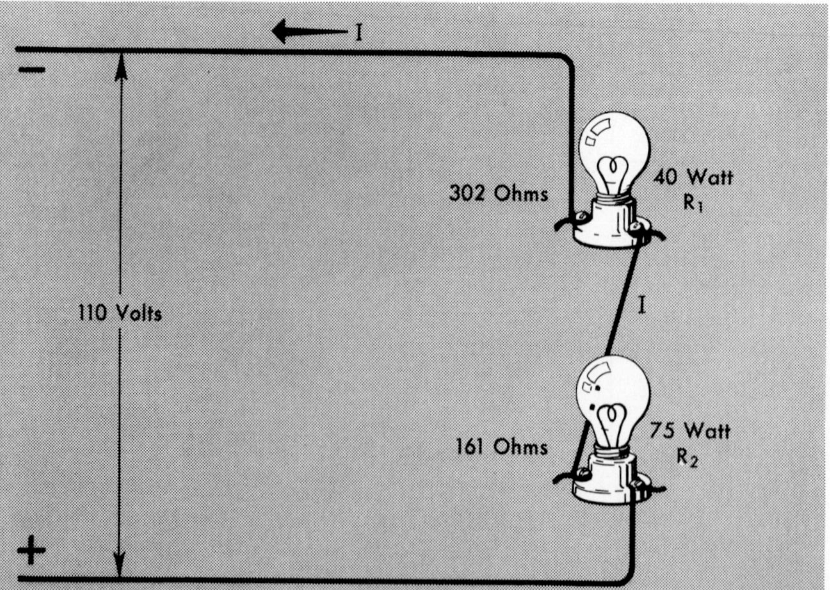

Fig. 33–2 *Series connection of a 40-watt and a 75-watt light bulb.*

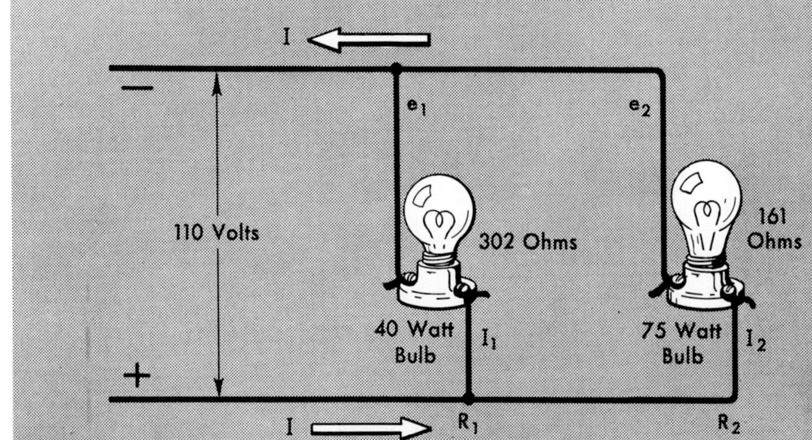

Fig. 33–3 *Parallel connection of a 40-watt and a 75-watt light bulb.*

$$E = R_T I_T = R_1 I_1 + R_2 I_2.$$

Then assuming an impressed voltage of unity, merely to simplify the arithmetic, we can write the equations,

$$I_T = \frac{1}{R_T}, \quad I_1 = \frac{1}{R_1}, \quad \text{and} \quad I_2 = \frac{1}{R_2}.$$

Since $I = I_1 + I_2$, we can write,

$$\frac{1}{R_T} = \frac{1}{R_P} = \frac{1}{R_1} + \frac{1}{R_2}. \qquad \textit{(Equation 33–7)}$$

Equation 33–7 is the law of parallel resistances. That is, the *reciprocal* of the total of resistances in parallel is the sum of the reciprocals of the individual resistances.

Solution of lamp problem: Using Equation 33–7, we can write,

$$\frac{1}{R_P} = \frac{1}{302} + \frac{1}{161} = 0.00331 + 0.00620$$
$$= 0.00951 \text{ ohm}^{-1}.$$

Hence,

$$R_P = \frac{1}{0.00951 \text{ ohm}^{-1}} = 105 \text{ ohms}.$$

Then, total current flowing by Ohm's law (Equation 33–3),

$$I_T = \frac{110}{105} = 1.05 \text{ amperes}.$$

To find out how the current divides, Ohm's law can be applied to each resistance separately. For

$$I_1 = \frac{E}{R_1} \quad \text{and} \quad I_2 = \frac{E}{R_2}.$$

Thus, $$I_1 = \frac{110}{302} = 0.36 \text{ ampere},$$

and $$I_2 = \frac{110}{161} = 0.68 \text{ ampere}.$$

The sum should agree for the first calculation of the total current, or

$$I_T = 0.36 + 0.68 = 1.04 \text{ amperes}.$$

This agrees with 1.05 amperes within the limits of accuracy of the problem.

There are two important advantages of the parallel connection. First, each lamp receives the amount of current it was designed for. Hence both lamps have their intended brightness. Second, the "burning out" of one bulb does not interrupt the burning of the other bulbs. It would be awkward indeed to have all the bulbs in a home on a series circuit, the way Christmas-tree lights are sometimes arranged. If one bulb burns out, all go out, and it is a time-consuming job to find which bulb should be replaced.

MEASURING INSTRUMENTS

The common measuring instruments may be looked upon as frustrated motors for, although they operate by the same principle as do motors, their moving parts are never permitted to make complete rotations. Gal-

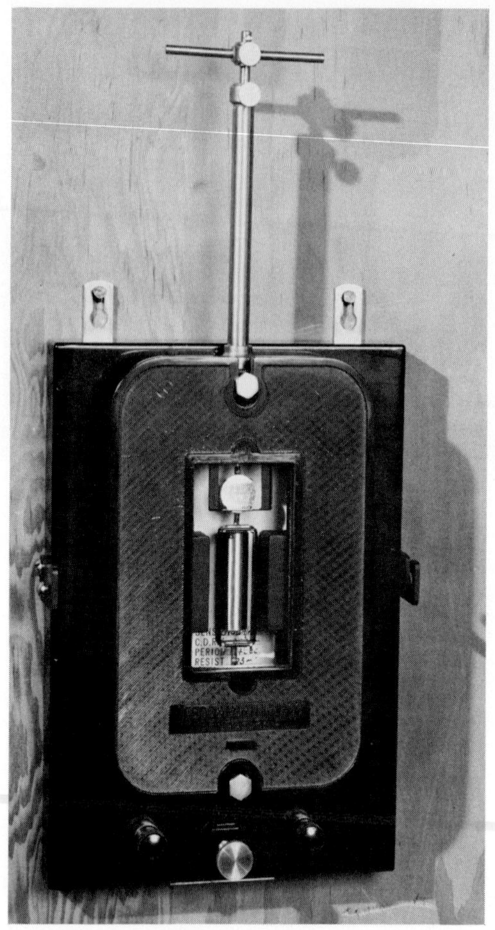

Fig. 33–4 *A sensitive moving coil galvanometer. (Leeds and Northrup Company)*

vanometers, ammeters, and voltmeters alike consist of a coil of wire suspended or mounted between the poles of a permanent magnet. A direct current flowing through the coil creates another magnetic field, and the reaction of the two fields causes the coil to rotate or swing through an arc. The swing is uniformly braked by springs, or the torsion of the suspension wire, to return the coil to its rest position when the circuit is broken. The coil would not make a complete rotation even if there were not arresting springs, for, unlike the motor, it is not equipped with a commutator.

Galvanometers are used to detect and to measure very small electric currents; they can be made so sensitive that they react to a current as small as one ten-billionth of an ampere. The coil of a galvanometer consists of many turns of fine wire wrapped around a soft iron core (Figure 33–4). It is suspended by a thin metal ribbon and so adjusted that the turning force exerted by the magnetic effect is proportional to the current passing through it. A tiny mirror attached to the suspension ribbon reflects a beam of light upon a fixed scale, thus indicating the twist of the coil. Galvanometers of this type are usually mounted on a wall.

A portable or *table galvanometer* has a moving coil mounted in jewel bearings between the poles of a permanent magnet bent in the shape of a horseshoe or of an arch (Figure 33–5). To insure a uniform magnetic field, soft iron pieces are attached to each pole of the magnet and the soft iron core and coil are mounted in the cylindrical space between. A pointer attached to the coil moves along a scale on which the appropriate units may be read.

The table galvanometer described above may be converted into an *ammeter* for meas-

Fig. 33–5 *A portable galvanometer. (Weston Electrical Instrument Corp.)*

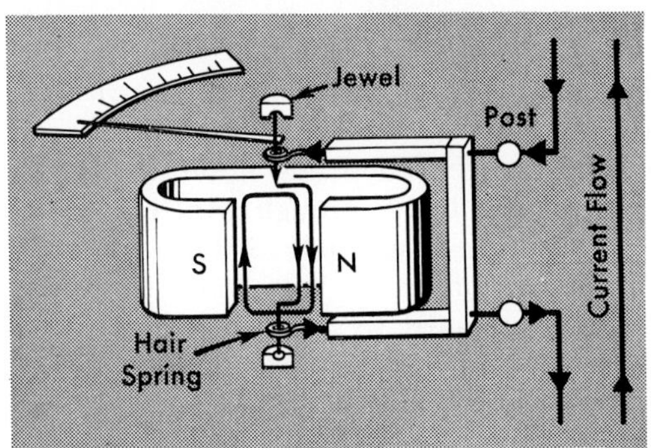

Fig. 33–6 *Path of current through an ammeter. Note that all the current goes through the instrument (a series connection) and that only a very small portion of the total current actually passes through the moving coil system in the ammeter.*

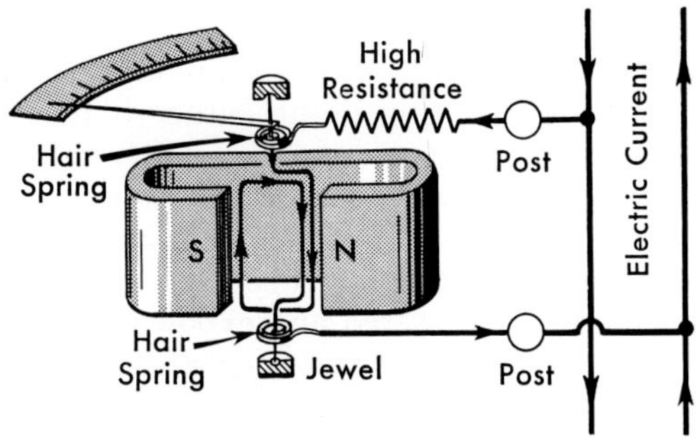

Fig. 33–7 *Construction and use of a voltmeter. The amount of current (actually very little) that passes through, and thus the potential in volts, depends on the potential difference between the two sides of the electrical circuit. Note that connection is "across" the circuit.*

uring larger currents by connecting a low resistance *shunt* across its terminals (Figure 33–6). An ammeter is always connected in *series,* that is, placed directly in the circuit so that all the current passes through the instrument. However, if all the current were to pass through the delicate coil, the fine, highly resistant wire would be fused or "burned out." The shunt prevents such damage by doing just what the name implies — it diverts most of the current across the terminals so that only a small but definite fraction of it passes through the coil.

The same instrument may be adjusted for use as a *voltmeter,* which measures the potential difference or potential drop between two points in a circuit. A high resistance is placed in series with the coil so that very little current passes through the instrument (Figure 33–7). Unlike the ammeter, the voltmeter is not placed directly in the circuit. It is connected to two points around the portion for which the potential drop is to be measured.

HEAT AND LIGHT FROM ELECTRICITY

It has been shown that all conductors, even the best, offer some resistance to the flow of electricity; there are no perfect conductors. The resistance of a metal, however, steadily decreases as its temperature is lowered and some metals, not all, display *superconductivity* when cooled to almost absolute zero. The resistance of tin, for example, suddenly drops to practically zero at –269.4° C. (3.8° absolute). A current induced in a ring of this metal at the above temperature continues to flow with very little loss for several days. When the temperature of the ring in which the current is flowing is permitted to rise, the metal recovers its resistance and the current suddenly stops; at this instant the ring moves slightly. When the flow of electrons (current) in the ring suddenly stops, the total angular momentum of the electrons is evidently transferred to the ring.

Superconductors, or even good conductors like copper or silver, are obviously not suitable for the conversion of electricity to heat. Conductors with fairly high resistances are used and the work or energy required to overcome the resistance is converted to heat. The electrons whose drift through the metal constitutes the current collide with atoms and molecules, which acquire more kinetic energy. The temperature, which is dependent upon the average kinetic energy of these particles, is thus raised.

The heating effect of the current is efficiently utilized for a number of practical purposes. The heat so generated is used for heating homes, where current is cheap, and for cooking. But the most important and extensive use is in the incandescent electric lamp. A filament for such a lamp must have a very high melting point; either it must have a high resistance if it is a fairly thick wire, or, if a good conductor, it must possess properties which permit it to be drawn into very fine wires. The first filament used was of platinum uncovered and exposed to air. While platinum does not react with any of the substances in air, it has not a sufficiently high melting point (1755° C.) to be an efficient converter of heat into light. Below this temperature only a small fraction of the heat is converted into visible light. It is to Thomas Edison that we owe the carbon filament lamp. Carbon has an extremely high melting point (3500° C.) but burns readily in air. Edison enclosed this filament in a bulb and pumped out the air. At about 2000° C., or a little below, the efficiency of the lamp in terms of heat converted into visible light was one per cent. At a few hundred degrees above this temperature the visible-light output is doubled, but the carbon soon disintegrates and the lamp "burns out." Lamps of this type, burning at about 2000° C., were in use for about twenty-five years.

On looking through the list of the elements, one finds very few of them with a sufficiently high melting point. Of all the metals, tungsten has the highest melting point, 3350° C., but it was only after W. D. Coolidge (United States, 1873–) developed a method of drawing it into a fine wire, that it came to be used. This metal offers a high resistance if in the form of a very fine filament. It is operated at a temperature of about 2800° C. and gives off whiter light with about five times the efficiency of carbon. In a vacuum it slowly sublimes, blackening the bulb, and burns out. Lamps as used at present are therefore filled with an inactive gas, such as argon or nitrogen, and this greatly retards the disintegration of the filament.

Certain alloys with a high resistance are used in electric irons, stoves, and cookers. Chromel, which contains 61 per cent nickel, 23 per cent iron, and 16 per cent chromium, and nichrome, which contains 75 per cent nickel, 12 per cent iron, 11 per cent chromium, and 2 per cent manganese, are typical. The quantity of heat developed by an electric current depends upon the resistance of the body through which it passes and upon the magnitude of the current. By our definition of the volt, work (joules) = volts × coulombs. By Ohm's law, E (volts) = I (current) × R (resistance); and by definition, Q (coulombs) = I (current) × t (seconds). Hence,

$$W \text{ (joules)} = E \times Q = IR \times It = I^2Rt.$$

Or, since 4.18 joules = 1 calorie,

$$H\text{(eat) per second} = \frac{I^2R}{4.18} \text{ calories in 1 second.}$$

In a lamp which requires two amperes and which has a resistance of fifty ohms, the heat generated is

$$H = \frac{I^2R}{4.18} = \frac{2^2 \times 50}{4.18} = 47.8 \text{ calories per second.}$$

These results assume that the circuit has a high resistance and that the electric energy is all converted into heat. Such a conversion is practically 100 per cent efficient, but this is not true of all heating devices. Carbon filament lamps now used as a source of infrared radiation (heat lamps) emit also considerable visible light.

If conducting wires are overloaded with appliances, or are short-circuited, the excessive current which flows may cause overheating. To protect instruments and appliances and to eliminate the fire hazard, fuses are placed in the circuit. The fuse, which serves as a safety valve, bridges the gap in the circuit with an alloy which melts or "blows out" when the current exceeds a certain value. The temperature at which the fuse wire melts is such that there is no danger of fire from drops of the molten metal. But because an arc and molten metal are produced, it is necessary to enclose the fuse wire in an asbestos tube or in a porcelain plug with a mica window (Figure 33–8). The size or kind of fuse wire determines how much current it may carry without melting.

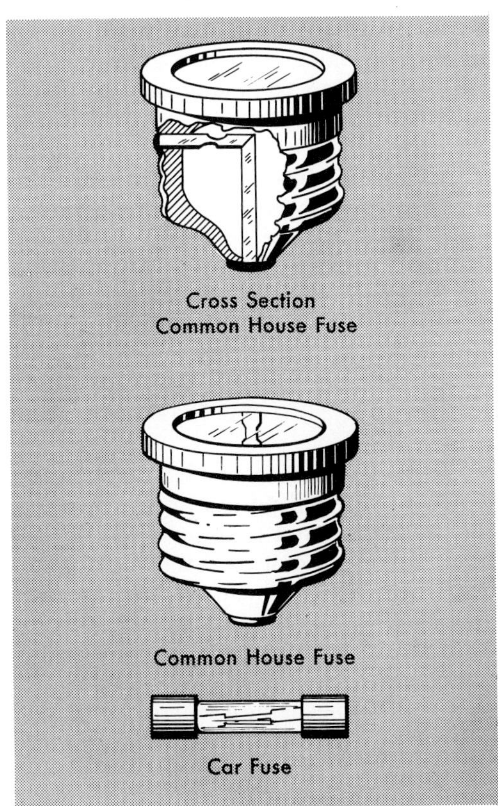

Fig. 33–8 *Electric fuses.*

THE CHEMICAL EFFECTS OF ELECTRICITY

The quantitative aspects of electrolysis embodied in Faraday's laws were treated in Chapter 21. We shall now discuss briefly the chemical changes that are brought about by the passage of an electric current through each of several solutions of ionic compounds. In all operations of electrolysis the electrodes which dip into the solution are connected to a source of direct current, either a battery or a generator. The current supplies electrons to the negative terminal of the battery or generator and removes electrons from the anode, which is connected to the positive terminal. The electrolytic cell contains the solution, nickel chloride ($NiCl_2$) in the first case we shall consider and sodium iodide (NaI) in the second. The electrodes are platinum, an inactive metal which does not undergo any change during the electrolysis. In all cases of electrolysis the ions migrate in accordance with the law of attraction and repulsion, the positive ions go to the cathode (−) and the negative ions go to the anode (+). At the anode, negative ions give up their surplus electrons and are oxidized; at the cathode, positive ions receive electrons and are reduced. It is not always the migrating ions, to which the solution owes its conductivity, that are oxidized and reduced. Thus the electric current is used to bring about chemical changes of oxidation-reduction whereas in the primary and storage cells (Chapter 31) chemical changes of oxidation-reduction are used to generate an electric current.

Electrolysis of Nickel Chloride. When the circuit is closed, nickel ions (Ni^{++}) move toward the cathode and chloride ions (Cl^-) toward the anode. The chemical changes taking place are:

At the anode: $2\ Cl^- \rightarrow Cl_2 + 2\ e^-$

At the cathode: $Ni^{++} + 2\ e^- \rightarrow Ni$

Chloride ions are oxidized to chlorine, which is liberated at the anode, and nickel ions are reduced to nickel, which is deposited on the cathode. The total effect is the decomposition of the compound, $NiCl_2$, into the two elements.

Electrolysis of Sodium Iodide. Sodium ions (Na^+) move toward the cathode, and iodide ions (I^-) toward the anode. Sodium ions are not as easily reduced as hydrogen ions (H^+) (see the Replacement Series in Table 27–2) which are also present due to the slight dissociation of water. Although the concentration of the hydrogen ions is very small, they are reduced while the sodium ions remain in solution. The reactions are:

At the anode: $2\ I^- \rightarrow I_2 + 2\ e^-$

At the cathode: $2\ H^+ + 2\ e^- \rightarrow H_2$

Since H^+ ions are removed, a surplus of hydroxyl ions (OH^-) from the water (H^+OH^-) remains in the solution. The products of the electrolysis are therefore hydrogen, iodine, and sodium hydroxide (Na^+, OH^-) in the solution.

Electroplating. From the process of electrolysis which has just been described we may formulate a general procedure for depositing a metal upon another metal by means of an electric current for protective or decorative reasons. Metals which are easily corroded or worn are coated with less active ones. Iron is frequently coated with copper, nickel, or chromium. Thus, the door hardware, the hub caps, and the bumpers on automobiles are given a thin coating of chromium superimposed on nickel, which in turn may be superimposed on copper. Tableware and other objects made of cheaper alloys of nickel or other metals are plated with silver. Chromium, which is used a great deal today, is applied in very thin layers, but these are porous and do not give full protection to the metal beneath. Hence, nickel is usually applied as a foundation for the chromium. In general, the object to be plated is placed in the electrolytic bath as the cathode, the metal with which it is to be plated is the anode, and the electrolyte is a salt of the same metal. For example, in silver plating (Figure 33–9) the tableware hung on a rack serves as the cathode, silver is the anode, and both are immersed in a solution containing silver ions.

In electrotyping plates for the printing of books, a wax mold is made by pressing a sheet of warm wax on the type, or "form," or the engraving. The wax mold or impression is coated with fine graphite (carbon), which is a conductor, and on this is electrolytically deposited a coating of copper or nickel. This duplicate is removed, or "stripped," from the mold and reinforced with a thicker backing of electrotype metal. Such a plate will withstand many printings without becoming worn or defective. Essentially the same process is used to prepare the molds for pressing phonograph records.

Fig. 33–9 *Silver plating. A complex salt of silver is used as the electrolyte. Silver from the anode enters the solution as silver ion and is deposited on objects which serve as a cathode.*

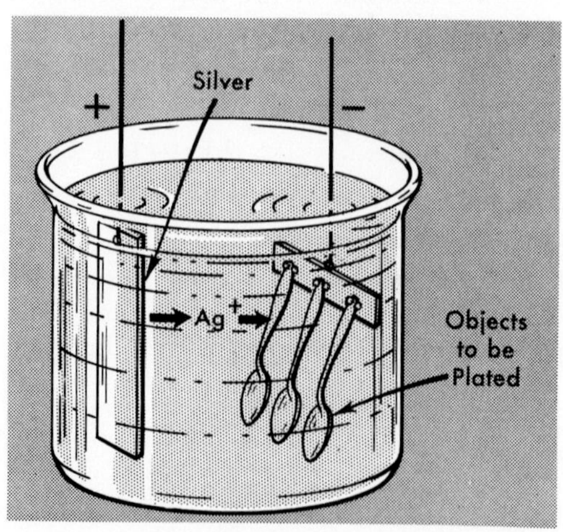

PAYING THE BILL

The uses we make of electricity in the home, the factory, and the various means of communication and transportation depend upon one or more of its three effects: magnetic, thermal, and chemical. When we buy electricity, we buy energy which is delivered to us and we pay for it in terms of energy (work) units, that is, kilowatt-hours. The cgs units of mechanical energy, ergs and joules, and the mks unit, the newton-meter, which is equal to 10^7 ergs or 1 joule, were discussed in Chapter 12. These units are no different when applied to electricity, but in order to calculate electric energy and power we must use certain electrical units, amperes, volts, and coulombs. From our definition of a volt,

$$\text{volts} = \frac{\text{newton-meters or joules}}{\text{coulombs}}$$

and newton-meters or joules = volts × coulombs, but since

$$\text{coulombs} = \text{amperes} \times \text{seconds},$$

$$\text{work (newton-meters or joules)} = \text{amperes} \times \text{volts} \times \text{seconds}.$$

Power is the time rate of doing work or the amount of work done in one second. The familiar unit in the British system is the horsepower. The unit of power in the metric system is the *watt,* named for James Watt who played an important role in the development of the steam engine. The watt is defined as one newton-meter or joule per second; and

TABLE 33–2

APPROXIMATE CONSUMPTION OF POWER AND ENERGY BY HOME ELECTRICAL EQUIPMENT

ARTICLE	WATTS OR H.P.	KILOWATT-HOURS PER MONTH
Blanket, automatic	65	15
Clock	2	1.5
Clothes dryer	4000	68
Dishwasher	400	30
Food freezer (13 cu. ft.)	$\frac{1}{3}$ H.P. motor	90
Iron	750	9
Percolator, automatic	400	6
Radio	30	4
Range	7,000–20,000	90
Refrigerator (10 cu. ft.)	$\frac{1}{7}$ H.P. motor	40
Roaster	1500	24
Room air conditioner	1 H.P. motor	250
Sewing machine	60–90	1
Television	150	15
Toaster	1000	3
Vacuum cleaner	400	4
Washing machine	250	3
Water heater	1000	310
Total estimate for family of four.		600–1200

$$P(\text{ower}) \text{ in watts} = \frac{W(\text{ork}) \text{ in newton-meters or joules}}{\text{seconds}} = \frac{\text{amperes} \times \text{volts} \times \cancel{\text{seconds}}}{\cancel{\text{seconds}}};$$

hence

$$\text{watts} = \text{amperes} \times \text{volts}. \qquad (\textit{Equation 33–8})$$

And since work = power × time, the work or energy of the electric current, which is expressed in kilowatt-hours, may be obtained by use of the equation

$$\text{kilowatt-hours} = \frac{\text{watts} \times \text{hours}}{1000}. \qquad (\textit{Equation 33–9})$$

Equations 33–8 and 33–9 may be used in the solution of a number of problems:

(1) How many amperes does a 75-watt lamp draw on a 110-volt circuit?

Since watts = volts × amperes,

$$\text{amperes} = \frac{\text{watts}}{\text{volts}} = \frac{75 \text{ watts}}{110 \text{ volts}} = 0.68 \text{ ampere}.$$

(2) A home uses twelve lamps, each consuming electricity at the rate of sixty watts and each burning on the average fifty hours per month. What is the cost at three cents per kilowatt-hour?

$$\frac{12 \times 60 \text{ watts} \times 50 \text{ hours}}{1000} = 36 \text{ kilowatt-hours}$$

$$36 \times 3 \text{ cents} = \$1.08 \text{ cost}$$

(3) An electric refrigerator is equipped with a one-seventh horsepower motor. At what rate does it consume electricity when running?

$$1 \text{ horsepower} = 746 \text{ watts}$$

$$\tfrac{1}{7} \times 746 \text{ watts} = 106.6 \text{ watts}$$

The refrigerator when running consumes only a little more electric power than two 50-watt lamps.

A 100-watt lamp is a more efficient light producer than two 50-watt lamps. That is, a greater percentage of the electrical energy is converted to visible light. Table 33–2 lists some common appliances with the average or probable wattage of each and the estimated energy consumption for a family of four.

ELECTRIC POWER GENERATION

The shock caused by the electric "eel" (actually a fish) and the discharge of atmospheric electricity, lightning, and St. Elmo's fire (the glow sometimes visible at the metal tips of ships' masts, steeples, and airplane wings), are some manifestations of natural electricity. Since neither lightning nor electric fish have been harnessed, we must generate our own electricity by drawing upon other natural forms of energy. There is an abundance of chemical energy in fuels (coal, oil, and gas); mechanical energy in running water and wind; radiant energy in sunlight; and the relatively new but promising nuclear energy may be used to generate heat (Chapter 38).

Wind offers neither constant nor concentrated power; it is used sometimes in remote areas to run battery-charging generators.

Solar radiation can be converted to electrical energy by two different processes. First, it causes certain substances to emit electrons (the photoelectric effect), but only 0.5 per cent of the absorbed radiation is converted to electrical energy. The solar battery (see Chapter 40) is more efficient, converting 10 per cent of the absorbed sunlight to electricity. Second, the energy of the sun's rays can be collected and converted to heat energy in a steam boiler, then to mechanical energy by a steam turbine, then to electrical energy by a generator. Although the earth receives from the sun in two days an amount of energy greater than that in our total reserves of coal and oil, the methods devised for utilizing this almost unlimited source of energy are still too costly. Nevertheless the search for more efficient and cheaper reflecting surfaces, focusing devices, and absorbing surfaces continues, especially in areas where there is a scarcity of fossil fuels.

Of the more than 650 billion kilowatt-hours of electricity consumed in the United States in 1957, about 90 per cent was generated in steam plants. Most of the energy is supplied by coal but some oil and gas are also used. The remaining 10 per cent of the energy is generated by running water.

COAL–BURNING POWER PLANTS

The first commercial central power station for the generation of electricity was opened in New York City in 1882. Edison built a constant voltage dynamo which had an efficiency of 90 per cent. The six dynamos in this plant were driven by reciprocating steam engines and produced direct current. This current was of low voltage and, for reasons discussed in the preceding chapter, could not be transmitted more than a few blocks from the station. A few years later the first power station generating alternating current was built at Greensburg, Pennsylvania.

The modern power station which supplies current for large cities converts the chemical energy of coal into electricity by a long series of energy transformations. Coal, which, as we have seen, obtained its energy from sunlight some three million years ago, is cheaper than the other fuels which might compete with it – petroleum and natural gas. It is burned, and its heat of combustion is used to convert water to steam. The kinetic energy of the steam molecules is converted to mechanical energy by a steam turbine connected directly to the rotor of the generator. With every energy transformation – chemical energy to heat, to steam, to mechanical energy, to electricity – there is loss of energy. Even with our most efficient methods of burning the coal and of utilizing steam, the loss is appallingly large – about 70 per cent.

The coal is crushed to a powder and very completely burned under boilers in which water is converted into steam. The steam, at temperatures of 900° F. and higher and at pressures up to 3200 pounds per square inch, enters the steam turbine. Here it is directed against curved blades on the edge of a wheel which is mounted on the shaft. From this section the steam exhausts into what is known as the reaction section, streaming through a set of blades which resemble, in action, a windmill, then to the next set of blades which is larger, and so on, with the steam thus being used many times. These sets of blades are mounted on the shaft and become progressively larger as the steam expands and its pressure falls. The steam, after it has done its work, passes to the condenser, where it is cooled and condensed to liquid water.

The shaft of the turbine, which may make as many as 3600 revolutions per minute, is joined directly to the moving part of the alternating-current generator at the end of which is attached a small direct-current generator, or exciter, which supplies current for the field magnets of the rotor. In general, the generator voltage for the supply of cities is 10,000 to 14,000 volts. Several turbine generators may operate in one station, feeding their current to a common main line or busbar, into which may also feed the current from other stations. From this line the current may go directly to a substation, where the voltage is reduced by a stepdown transformer to perhaps 2200 to 4000 volts (Figure 33–10). It is then distributed in this section of the city to smaller transformers, where it is stepped down to 110 to 125 volts for home use. High-voltage alternating current may be stepped down and by means of a rotary converter changed to direct current at 420 to 600 volts for streetcar use.

For a high-tension system – that is, for long-distance transmission – the generator voltage of possibly 22,000 to 33,000 volts is fed directly to transformers which may step it up to 330,000 or 340,000 volts (Figure 33–11). The alternating-current systems over a large section of the country, including cities, are connected in a network. Certain power houses are in operation at all times, but others supply current to the network only when needed. The current may be distributed where needed for peak loads at certain hours of the day or where, due to emergency situations, local power plants cannot handle the load.

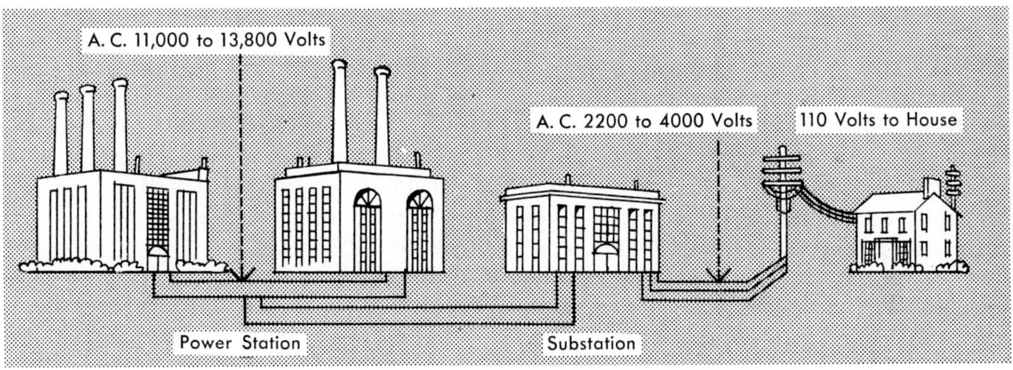

Fig. 33–10 *Elements in a typical city power system. Electricity from power stations is fed to the main line, then to substation transformers where voltage is reduced, and finally to pole transformers where it is reduced to usable voltages.*

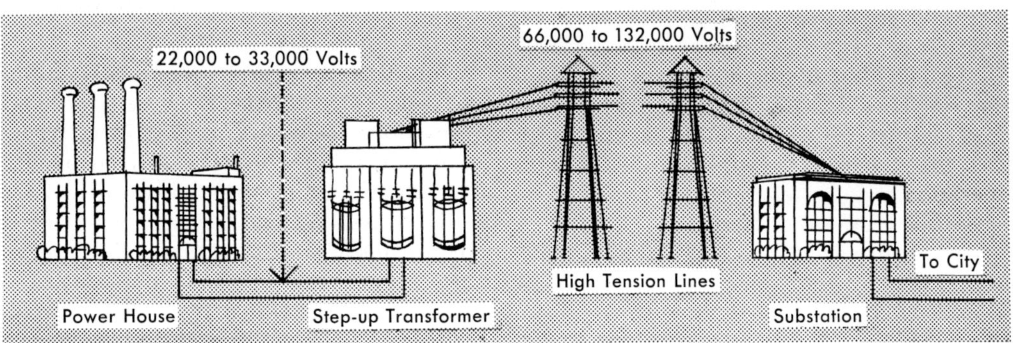

Fig. 33–11 *High-tension distribution of electricity. High-voltage current from power stations is delivered to a step-up transformer, and the voltage raised for long-distance transmission. Near place of use, voltage is reduced in steps.*

HYDROELECTRIC POWER STATIONS

Water power supplies at present about 10 per cent of the electricity sold to the American public. Here and in other parts of the world vast amounts of water power are going to waste. Fortunately, our government has recognized the great possibilities of this power source, which, unlike the dwindling supply of coal and other fuels, renews itself. Water runs downhill because of the force of gravity, is evaporated by the energy of the sun, falls as rain or snow, and the cycle continues to repeat itself. In order to utilize the energy of running water and to have it available at all seasons, dams are built. The water is held back in a reservoir or lake which fills up, rising above the former level of the river. Thus the water behind the dam has potential energy relative to the level to which it will fall when it is permitted to flow. This vertical difference in level, or the height through which the water falls, is known as the *head*. It may vary from a few feet to more than a thousand feet.

The energy of the water is utilized in a water turbine, which operates on the same principle as the steam turbine. A jet of water may be directed against blades, paddles, or bowls, causing rotation of the wheel of which they are a part. Others work not by the direct impulse or impact of the water but by the kickback, or reaction, of water leaving the blades. Connected directly to the shaft of the water turbine is the electric generator. The large units are mounted vertically, so that the generator is above the water turbine. The speed of rotation of the water turbine is not nearly as great as that of the steam turbine, but the efficiency is very high, ranging from 85 to 93 per cent. Once the dam is built and the machinery installed, the cost of operation is relatively small, for the forces of nature supply the energy.

Vast hydroelectric power plants have been built by the federal government in several sections of the country. In the Tennessee Valley great dams control the flood waters and harness their enormous energy. Industries, cities, and farms are supplied with power at low cost in an area which is almost as large as Great Britain and covers portions of seven states. At Hoover Dam the water of the Colorado River, operating at a head of 510 feet, runs twelve 82,500-kilowatt generators housed in the dam. Each generator requires a water turbine which delivers 115,000 horsepower. Electric power is supplied to industries and to cities as far away as Los Angeles. The water held by the dam is utilized in part for irrigation projects.

The Grand Coulee Dam (Figure 33–12) in the Columbia River Basin is the largest structure ever built by man, and behind it is the world's largest man-made lake. The lake site was formerly a fifty-mile-long canyon from which the dam got its name. A few million years ago a huge glacier diverted the course of the Columbia River, forcing it to cut a new channel through the adjacent rock. After the glacier receded, the river returned to its former course, leaving its rocky channel as the trenchlike canyon known as the Grand Coulee. The dam supplies not only electric power, but water for irrigation, and will so regulate the level of water in the river as to aid navigation. Two 10,000-kilowatt and eighteen 108,000-kilowatt generators have been installed with a total output of 1,964,000 kilowatts. This power is supplied to the cities of the Northwest, and is instrumental in the development of large industrial centers in the region.

MOVING POWER PLANTS

Not all electric power plants are stationary; some are on wheels, some are afloat. Many ships, freighters, luxury liners, battleships, and smaller craft, are driven by electric motors, which are more quickly and easily controlled and reversed and which operate more smoothly than Diesel or reciprocating steam engines. The electricity is, of course, generated by a Diesel engine or steam turbine. Diesel-electric motive

Fig. 33–12 *Grand Coulee Dam during the high-water season. The structures at the lower level house the water turbines and generators.* (*Bureau of Reclamation*)

power has been adopted by most railroads. Powerful Diesel engines are each coupled to direct-current dynamos to furnish the electric power to drive motors which are installed on the axles of the locomotive. High speed, absence of smoke, and much cheaper operating costs favor this type of power over the steam locomotive. Passenger trains with this kind of equipment are common today, and a number of railroads are now using powerful freight locomotives equipped with four 1350-horsepower Diesel engines, four generators, and sixteen motors. Such locomotives are capable of hauling more than three thousand tons of freight at a speed of seventy-five miles per hour. These trains must be propelled by an electric motor instead of by direct use of Diesel power because there is no clutch system which will stand up under the terrific force required to start the train. In order for the Diesel engine to develop enough power to move the train, it must burn sufficient fuel and must therefore run at a very high speed. To transmit this power directly to the axle or driving mechanism of the locomotive would require an involved system of gears with low speed for starting and higher speeds for pick-up and running. The use of electricity permits a fairly simple solution of the problem. At the start both the Diesel engine and the generator armatures are running at full speed. But unless the armature is turning in a magnetic field, no current to operate the motors is being generated. Hence the operating power is controlled, not by gears, but by regulating the current which supplies the magnetic field for the generator. As this current is increased, the field strength and therefore the current which is induced or generated and which operates the driving motors is increased; as the field current is decreased, less current is generated for the motors, and the locomotive may be brought to a stop.

ECONOMIC AND SOCIAL SIGNIFICANCE OF ELECTRICITY

Although we have recently been ushered into the nuclear or atomic era with its political repercussions, its dangers, and its potential benefits, we continue to live also in the age of electricity. With its offshoot, electronics, electricity has already brought about many changes that affect our daily lives. It has brought to the farm and rural towns many of the conveniences and comforts previously available only in cities.

Industries which formerly centered in city areas have spread to smaller communities. The number of farms using electric power increased from about 10 per hundred in 1932 to more than 90 per hundred in 1957. The use of machines powered by electricity and by internal combustion engines has lessened the burden of farm labor and increased the productivity per person, causing a population shift toward towns and cities.

A most significant trend in industry is toward *automation* or *continuous processing*. A part for an automobile engine, for example, may be made from a piece of steel by a series of operations, passing from one automatic machine to the next. The speeds of the various machines may be self-regulated by timing devices or photoelectric cells. Or the process may be "programmed" with central signals provided by a punched card or a magnetic tape. The work flows continuously and the machines correct their own errors without human direction. The key machines, essential to automatic processes of this type, are direct-current motors, for they run at various adjustable and controllable speeds.

AN HISTORICAL PERSPECTIVE

The developments in knowledge of atomic structure, in chemistry, and indeed in most of the physical sciences — developments that characterize the advance of modern science — could not possibly have occurred before methods of generating electric currents were found. It is therefore not surprising that the knowledge of electricity and magnetism possessed by the scientists of the eighteenth century differed very little from that of the ancients. The phenomena of magnetism and static electricity were known centuries before the Christian era. References are made to magnetism in the writings of Thales of Miletus, of Plato, of Pliny, and of the Roman, Lucretius Carus, who in his *De Rerum Natura* (first century B.C.) stated that the loadstone "had its origin in the hereditary bounds of the Magnetes," people who inhabited Magnesia in Thessaly.

Unlike the electric charge, magnetism was early put to a practical use — in the compass. The Chinese allegedly were the first to note the directive properties of the magnet; the first mention of a magnetic needle found in any literature was made by a Chinese mathematician and instrument maker, Shen Kua (1030–1093), who evidently used it only on land. (The invention of the magnetic compass has also been attributed to the Arabs, the Greeks, the Etruscans, the Finns, and the Italians.) In Europe the compass was in use as an instrument of navigation by the twelfth century, and the first detailed description of its use and properties was made by Petrus Peregrinus (1269), a French crusader. In 1600 William Gilbert (1540–1603), physician to Queen Elizabeth, published his classic book *De Magnete*. In this work he described the results of his own researches in magnetism and electricity and presented a carefully organized review of previous work and knowledge in these fields.

Other than the development of the Leyden jar (a condenser), the construction of friction generators, and the formulation of the law of attraction and repulsion, little progress was made in electricity until near the close of the eighteenth century. No use was made of electric charges except for purposes of entertainment, and electricity and magnetism were regarded as unrelated phenomena.

The second great revolution in scientific thought stemmed from the developments in electricity, magnetism, and radiation that took place during the nineteenth century. It was an Italian physicist, Alessandro Volta (1745–1827), who discovered a chemical method of generating electric currents, and in 1800 he announced by letter his most significant discovery — a source of continuous current, the Voltaic pile. With this new tool (electric current supplied by batteries) Oersted and Faraday soon made their brilliant discoveries, thus showing that magnetism and electricity are but different facets of the same thing. Later in the century John Clerk Maxwell developed the electromagnetic theory of radiation interpreting all light phenomena within the framework of electromagnetism (discussed in Chapter 36). The material benefits of this upsurge which brought us into the industrial age of electricity and electronics have been indicated and several of the crucial discoveries described. As with the scientific revolution of the sixteenth and seventeenth centuries (Chapter 14), a new framework was created and phenomena previously thought to be unrelated were unified. By the closing years of the nineteenth century great strides had been made in all areas of science, and a third revolution, the one that ushered us into the nuclear age, was under way.

SUMMARY

1. A working knowledge of electricity requires an understanding of the following practical electrical units:
   - Quantity: the *coulomb*
   - Current: the *ampere*
   - Potential (e.m.f.): the *volt*
   - Resistance: the *ohm*
   - Electrical energy: the *kilowatt-hour*
   - Power: the *kilowatt*
2. The relation between current, potential (e.m.f.), and resistance is given by Ohm's law:

   $$I \text{ (amperes)} = \frac{E \text{ (volts)}}{R \text{ (ohms)}}$$

   This expression is used to calculate any one of the three quantities when the other two are known.
3. An electric current may be used to do work by harnessing the forces developed between magnetic fields.
4. The magnetic effect of the electric current and the principle of magnetic repulsion and attraction are employed in these measuring instruments: (*a*) the galvanometer is used to detect and measure small currents; (*b*) the ammeter, used to measure current, is connected in series, but most of the current is shunted round its delicate coil; (*c*) the voltmeter, used to measure potential drop, is connected in parallel, but a large resistance permits only a small fraction of the current to pass through its coil.
5. Nonconductors, or insulators, are substances of low conductivity and high resistance, such as glass, rubber, and sulfur.
6. Work which is required to overcome resistance in a conductor is converted into heat. The heating effect of the current, which is due to impacts between the moving electrons of the current and atoms or molecules of the conductor, is utilized in the incandescent lamp, electric stoves, and the like.
7. The resistance of a given material increases with its length and decreases with an increase in cross-sectional area. It is independent of the current or voltage applied.
8. The heating effect, per second, in calories, of a current may be calculated by use of the equation

   $$H = \frac{I^2R}{4.18}$$

   where I is the current in amperes and R the resistance in ohms.
9. The passage of a direct current through solutions of ionic compounds or through molten substances results in electrolysis which includes (*a*) the ordered movement of ions and (*b*) chemical changes at each electrode — oxidation at the anode and reduction at the cathode.
10. Conductivity by metals is explained by the drift of electrons through the metal; that of gases and solutions in water, by the movement of ions.

11. Work must be done to produce electricity. Other forms of energy must, therefore, be transformed to electrical energy. Primary energy sources used are wind, coal, oil, and water power.
12. The distribution of electric power in a city and across country is accomplished by long-distance transmission at high voltages, substations, and an interlocking network.
13. The use of water power for the generation of electricity is being extensively developed in this country. Water power is cheap, but the sources are often remote from the great centers of population.
14. Trains, ships, automobiles, and airplanes all carry their power plants. Ships and trains may be electrically driven. Diesel power is used for the generation of electricity, which in turn operates motors connected to the propellers or the driving axle.

STUDY EXERCISES

1. Give an operational or practical definition of each of the electrical quantities listed in item 1 of the Summary, above.
2. How many electrons are required to reduce 100 atoms of silver ion to silver? How many copper ions (Cu^{++}) would be reduced by the same number of electrons? What law is illustrated by this relationship? Explain how this law suggested a relationship between matter and electricity and was the forerunner of our present theory of atomic structure.
3. An electric stove unit on a 110-volt circuit draws 10 amperes. Calculate the resistance of the heating unit. How many calories are produced per second?
4. A lamp on a 110-volt circuit draws 0.5 ampere. What is the resistance of the lamp? Calculate the number of calories of heat generated per second, assuming that all the electric energy is converted to heat.
5. Show by a single mathematical equation that the watt is a unit of power but that the kilowatt-hour is a unit of work or energy.
6. Calculate the current which a 75-watt lamp draws on a 110-volt circuit. What is the resistance of the lamp?
7. In a home there are the following devices operated by 110-volt 60-cycle alternating current: a one-fourth H.P. motor running 150 hours per month; six 40-watt lamps burning, on the average, 60 hours per month, four 75-watt lamps burning 80 hours per month. Calculate the monthly bill at three cents per kilowatt-hour.
8. What is the energy consumption per month (thirty days) of a 1.8-watt electric clock? What is the cost of operation per year at three cents per kilowatt-hour?
9. Make a list of energy sources, other than fuels, which might be used to operate an electric generator. Of these, which one is most used at present? Give reasons.
10. List all the reasons you can find for the adoption of locomotive electric power plants – that is, the Diesel electric system used by the railroads – in preference to the central power plant which feeds electricity to the train by an overhead trolley.
11. Why are the Diesel-powered trains run by electricity rather than by direct use of the Diesel power as are trucks and some boats? How is the speed of the Diesel electric locomotive controlled?
12. Mark *C* if the substance is a good conductor; *N*, if a poor conductor or an insulator.
    a. Copper ....
    b. Silver ....
    c. Sulfur ....
    d. Rubber ....
    e. Air ....
    f. Glass ....
    g. Carbon ....
    h. Amber ....
    i. Pure water ....
    j. Mica ....
    k. Paper ....
    l. Aluminum ....
    m. Paraffin ....
13. Check each correct statement.
    a. The resistance of a given substance –
    .... is proportional to the voltage applied to it.
    .... increases with an increase in length.
    .... increases with its cross-sectional area.
    .... increases with an increase in temperature.

b. A lamp filament must –

.... have a low resistance when drawn to a fine filament.

.... have a very high melting point.

.... not vaporize easily.

.... not react with oxygen at white heat.

c. In all cases of electrolysis –

.... ions migrate toward the electrodes carrying charges opposite to those on the ions.

.... oxidation takes place at the anode.

.... reduction takes place at the cathode.

.... the ions which migrate are always the ones which undergo oxidation or reduction.

14. How many amperes does a lamp with a resistance of 50 ohms draw on a 110-volt line?
15. An appliance whose resistance is 440 ohms draws 0.5 ampere. What is the voltage?
16. A 100-watt lamp draws one ampere on a 100-volt circuit. Calculate the resistance of the lamp.

FOR FURTHER READING

1. RINDE, C. A., *Electricity*. New York: Harcourt, Brace and Company, 1944.

   The interrelationships between voltage, current, and resistance series and parallel connections and applications of Ohm's law are discussed in Chapter 5.
2. BRAGG, W. L., *Electricity*. London: G. Bell and Sons, Ltd., 1936.

   Chapter IV discusses the development of our modern electrical generator and transmission systems. The discussion applies specifically to Britain, but the principles apply to this country as well.

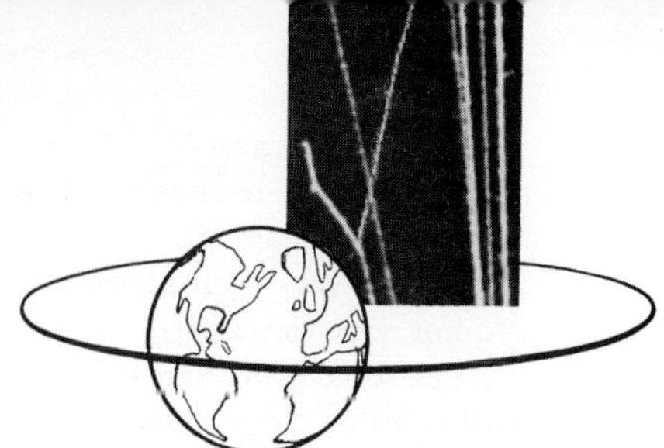

34

ENERGY THROUGH SPACE

THE MOST IMPORTANT source of energy for this planet is the sun. On the earth the sun's energy is absorbed and transformed in many ways. Water in the oceans, for example, is evaporated by heat from the sun. The water vapor is carried inland by air currents caused by the differential heating of the earth's surface by the sun; the vapor may then be precipitated as rain or snow in mountain regions. This rain or snow has associated with it potential energy, which becomes kinetic energy as the water flows downward to the sea. Some of this kinetic energy in passing through hydroelectric plants becomes electrical energy. Similarly, our coal deposits represent the operation of the process of photosynthesis in past geological ages. The chemical energy in the coal represents "solidified" solar energy. When we use electricity generated by burning coal or running water to operate a vacuum cleaner or a modern passenger train, we are operating with energy that came to us originally from the sun. The energy from the sun streams through 93 million miles of largely "empty" space at 186,000 miles per second. How does this energy travel? We call it radiant energy, but a label is not an explanation. Since the days of Sir Isaac Newton scientists have concerned themselves with questions pertaining to the nature of radiant energy. A completely satisfactory answer has not yet been found.

To explain complex natural phenomena, man often resorts to models which usually represent simple mechanical processes. By suitable models he can give explanations and make computations and predictions. Such models represent tentative guesses or hypotheses to be checked both experimentally and logically. If the model is successful it may become accepted as a sound scientific theory, but the final product is not something that will never undergo revision. New discoveries frequently compel revision of theories. Furthermore, theories do not always give complete answers. Nevertheless, a theory tends to be retained if it serves to organize a body of knowledge and enables man to make new discoveries.

The usefulness of scientific theories is demonstrated in the attempts that have been made to account for the transmission of energy through space with the speed of light. Newton believed that light traveled as particles — corpuscles, he called them. Christian Huygens (Netherlands, 1629–

1695), a contemporary of Newton, championed a wave theory. Both theories still prevail and, while they are not reconcilable with each other, have been responsible for many remarkable discoveries during the last century. The marvels of radio and television and our understanding of the atoms of all matter were made possible because of the wave and corpuscular theories of light.

SOME FACTS CONCERNING LIGHT

1. *Light is a form of energy.* Plants with chlorophyll in their leaves do not grow in the dark. In sunlight they absorb radiant energy to transform it into various forms of plant substance. The black soil within greenhouses absorbs radiant energy and converts it into ordinary heat, which is retained by the glass enclosure. Even in winter this process continues so that, even without any artificial heat, greenhouse temperatures are always much warmer than temperatures outside. A recent interesting development has been the perfection of a device which converts sunlight into electricity — the solar battery. The reader can suggest, no doubt, many other observations which show that radiant energy is readily converted into other forms of energy, proof enough that it is itself a form of energy.

2. *Light travels at an enormous and constant speed.* We are all prone to regard the velocity of light as instantaneous. It was so regarded by the ancients, but there have always been a few bold spirits who could not conceive of anything traveling in space from one point to another in "no time at all." Galileo unsuccessfully attempted to measure the velocity of light by sending a signal from a lantern on one hilltop to observers on a distant second hilltop, who returned another signal with another lantern. With the crude time-measuring devices available in Galileo's time it was impossible to measure the small interval of time required for the light to travel to and fro between the two stations. In any method for measuring the velocity of light, data for the following relationship must be used:

$$v(\text{elocity}) = \text{distance covered in one unit of time} = \frac{d(\text{istance})}{t(\text{ime})}$$

If the assumption is made that light travels with uniform speed and that it far transcends the velocities of any ordinary moving objects, there can be only two methods to measure the velocity of light experimentally. One possibility is to use ordinary methods for measuring time — common accurate clocks — and to get a measurable time interval by making the distance between two observation stations very large. The second method is to develop special, precise methods of measuring time intervals as small as 1×10^{-6} seconds, which will permit the use of observation stations relatively close together. Either procedure should be able to provide experimental data for the determination of the value of the ratio d/t, which is the velocity.

When time-measuring devices were relatively crude, only the first method could be

Fig. 34–1 *A solar battery: converts light into electricity.* *(Bell Telephone Laboratories)*

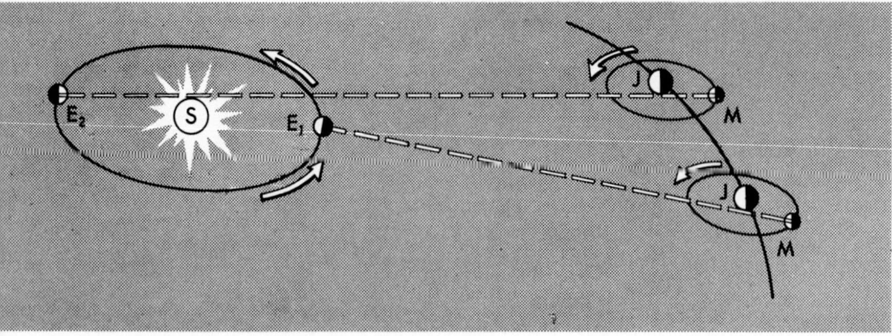

Fig. 34–2 *Roemer's method for measuring velocity of light.*

used to demonstrate that light has a measurable velocity. It was a brilliant young Danish astronomer, Ole Roemer (1644–1710), who first was keen enough to use observation and signal stations in astronomical space. The logic underlying his method should be apparent from Figure 34–2. In Roemer's method the observation station was on the earth, and the signal station was one of the moons of Jupiter. The time required for this moon to complete its orbit around Jupiter was known accurately. When the earth was in position E_1 with respect to the sun, the time that the moon would be eclipsed by Jupiter was carefully observed. Six months later the earth was in position E_2. If the velocity of light were actually instantaneous, the time that the same moon would be eclipsed could be accurately predicted. Actual observation showed, however, a time lag of about a thousand seconds between the predicted and the actual time of eclipse. Roemer correctly attributed this time lag to the additional time required for light to travel across the diameter of the earth's orbit, which we now know is 186,000,000 miles. Hence,

$$v = \frac{d}{t} = \frac{186{,}000{,}000 \text{ miles}}{1{,}000 \text{ seconds}}$$
$$= 186{,}000 \text{ miles/second.}^1$$

This corresponds to a distance of about seven and a half times the earth's circumference in one second. Many of Roemer's associates were inclined to be skeptical, but his data were amply confirmed when precise methods for the measurement of a very small time interval were finally devised by such experimenters as Fizeau, Foucault, and Michelson, who found it possible to measure the velocity of light between stations upon the earth itself.

The essence of Michelson's method is diagrammed in Figure 34–3. *A* is an oc-

Fig. 34–3 *Michelson's method for measuring velocity of light.*

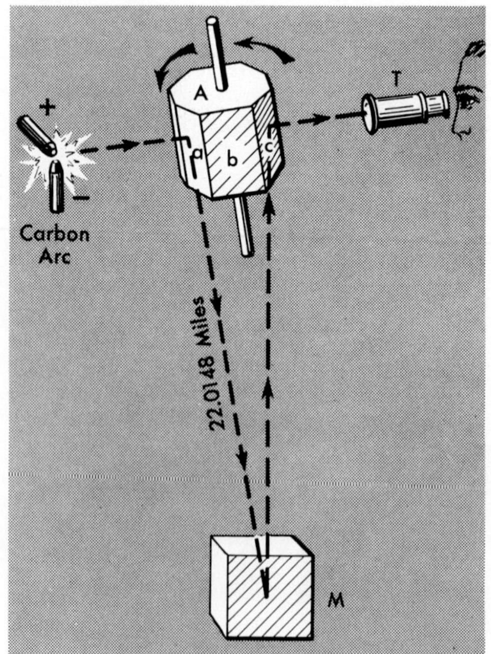

[1] This figure is not the one given by Roemer, but is based upon modern data. We now know that Roemer's result was 25 per cent too low because of errors in the data he had to use. However, the reasoning behind his method was sound, and his result was a first indication of the enormous velocity of light.

tagonally shaped wheel with a mirror in each face and with a provision for revolving at various constant speeds known in terms of revolutions per second. The mirror M is so placed on a distant mountain that light from the arc can be seen in the telescope T with A stationary. The wheel A is then set in rotation, and the light from the arc passes from the field of view in the telescope. As the speed of rotation is slowly increased, a point is reached where, while the light travels a distance of 2×22.0148 miles, the face b makes one-eighth of a turn and is in position c when the light beam returns. Under these precise conditions the light from the arc will again be seen in the telescope. Thus, the time interval needed for the light to travel between two stations and return could be found to a high degree of precision. The data from such an experiment read as follows:

Distance light traveled $= d = 2 \times 22.0$ miles
Revolutions per second $= 527.5$

$$\text{Time for light to travel to and fro} = t = \frac{1 \text{ sec}}{(8)(527.5)}$$

$$t = \frac{1}{4220} = .000237 \text{ second.}$$

Then,

$$v = \frac{d}{t} = \frac{2 \times 22.0 \text{ miles}}{.000237 \text{ sec}} = 186{,}000 \text{ mi/sec.}$$

After very careful attention to overcoming many experimental difficulties and after a lifetime of effort, Michelson attained for the velocity of light in a vacuum a final result of 186,245 mi/sec, or 299,776 km/sec. The latter quantity is thought to be precise to within 4 km/sec — a truly remarkable achievement. Michelson was awarded a Nobel prize (1907) for his achievement; he was the first American winner. For ordinary calculations involving the speed of light, the velocity is taken to be 186,000 mi/sec, or 3×10^{10} cm/sec.

3. *Light can be reflected.* Light in being reflected from any surface obeys a simple law: the angle of reflection is equal to the angle of incidence. In Figure 34–4 light

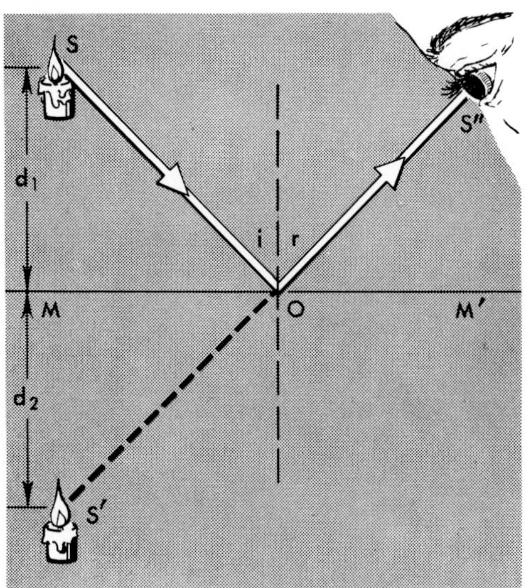

Fig. 34–4 *Law of reflection for light.*

rays from S make an angle i with the perpendicular to the surface of the mirror MM'. Experimentally it is found that the reflected rays OS'' make an angle r with the perpendicular, which is equal to angle i. The reflected light rays apparently originate at S' in the rear of the mirror. In reflection from a plane mirror the image appears to be as far behind the mirror as the object is in front of the mirror. The image, furthermore, is erect but reversed from right to left. Mirrors can therefore be used in interior decoration to produce an illusion of great depth and size.

4. *Light can be refracted.* Light rays, in passing obliquely from one transparent substance into another transparent substance of different density, always undergo a change in velocity and a change in direction. This phenomenon is known as *refraction.* Thus a straight stick partly immersed in water appears to be bent where it enters the water. Anyone can try the experiment with a pencil in a glass of water. In Figure 34–5 the fish appears to be at H and the bottom of the stream appears to be at I. Light rays FO, traveling from the fish, undergo a change in direction (OE) as they emerge into air. SO is a perpendicular to the surface of the water at O, where the

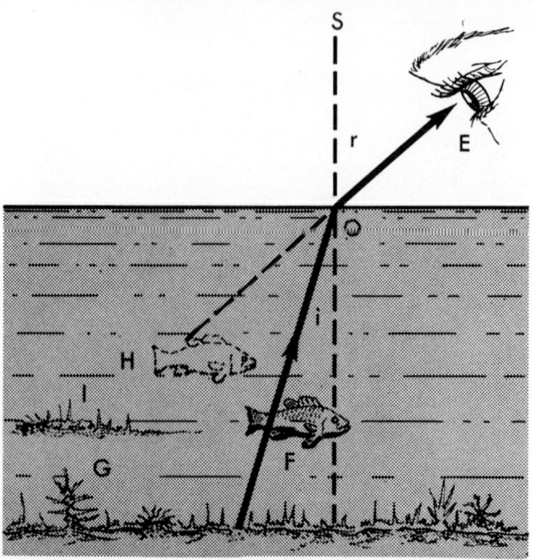

Fig. 34–5 *Refraction of light. Light rays from F are bent at surface of water.*

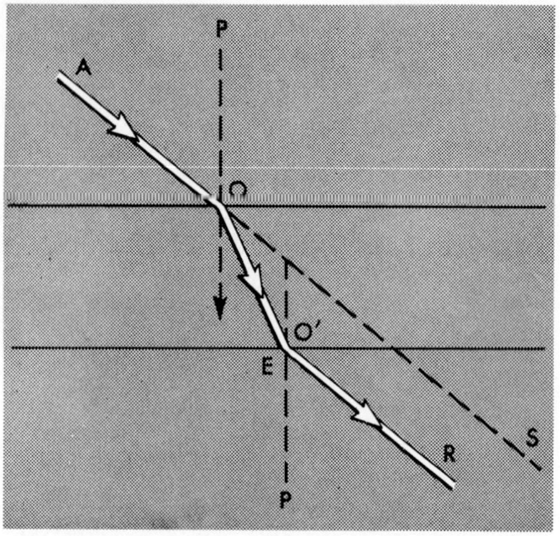

Fig. 34–6 *Refraction of light through plate glass.*

light ray emerges. The angle *i* is the angle of incidence, and the angle *r* made by the refracted ray *OE* and the perpendicular is the angle of refraction. Note that angle *r* is greater than angle *i* when light passes from the more dense medium, water, into air. In other words, under these circumstances the refracted ray is bent *away* from the perpendicular *SO*. Conversely, when light passes from air — the less dense medium — into water, the refracted ray is bent *toward* the perpendicular. Light rays that traverse a piece of plate glass are definitely displaced. In Figure 34–6 the light ray *AO* on entering the glass is bent toward the perpendicular; that is, *OE* approaches *PO*. When the ray *OE* passes from the glass into the less dense air, the emergent ray *ER* is bent away from the perpendicular *PO′*. If the sides of the glass are parallel, the ray *ER* is also parallel to *AO*.

5. *Light gives diffraction effects.* Light, when it goes by the edge of an opaque body, or is sent through small holes or slits, produces light and dark bands or prismatic colors. This phenomenon is known as *diffraction*. Diffraction effects with light are now known to be common: light will actually bend around corners and penetrate into a shadow. A common example of diffraction can be seen in the shadow of a needle behind a strong light. If light did not undergo diffraction, the shadow would have sharp, distinct edges. Instead, the edges of the shadow are fuzzy. A careful examination will reveal parallel light and dark lines within the shadow. Under certain circumstances it is possible to find a bright line through the middle of the shadow. (Refer to Figure 34–7.) An interesting variation of this experiment is to look at a bright, white surface or an open window through a narrow slit between two fingers held close to the eye. By properly varying the width of the opening, with the hand about four inches in front of the eyes, it is possible to see, not a single band of light, but alternate light and dark lines. These lines are the result of diffraction followed by interference. The discovery of diffraction phenomena in the behavior of light has strengthened the wave theory of light.

6. *Light shows interference and reinforcement effects.* In 1803, a young London physician Thomas Young (1773–1829), whose hobby was science, demonstrated that light can be used to obtain darkness. Some of his crucial experiments were extremely simple. For example, light from an intense light source *S* may be allowed to fall on a screen with a small opening (Figure 34–8). The resulting cone of light can be allowed to fall on a second screen *B* which has two small apertures *a* and *b*. The holes

Fig. 34–7 *Diffraction of light. The spreading of light around the edges of some common objects is clearly revealed in this photograph. These effects were caused by light passing through or around two narrow slits, four circular openings of various sizes, two small discs supported by thin wires, two needles, a pin, a wood screw, and the head of a needle. (From Frederick A. Saunders,* A Survey of Physics, *Henry Holt and Co., Inc.)*

a and *b* serve as two new independent sources of light waves, forming two new cones of light which will fall on the screen *C*. If the distance of screen C from screen *B* is properly controlled, the two cones of light will overlap. Where this happens, there will be observed alternate bright and dark lines, representing constructive and destructive interference.

LIGHT AS CORPUSCLES

Even in Newton's time there were two popular hypotheses to account for the properties of light, the corpuscular and the wave theories. Newton favored the corpuscular concept, that light consisted of particles emitted by the light source and traveling at enormous speeds. This guess is explained in

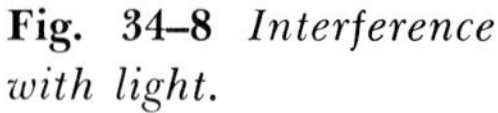

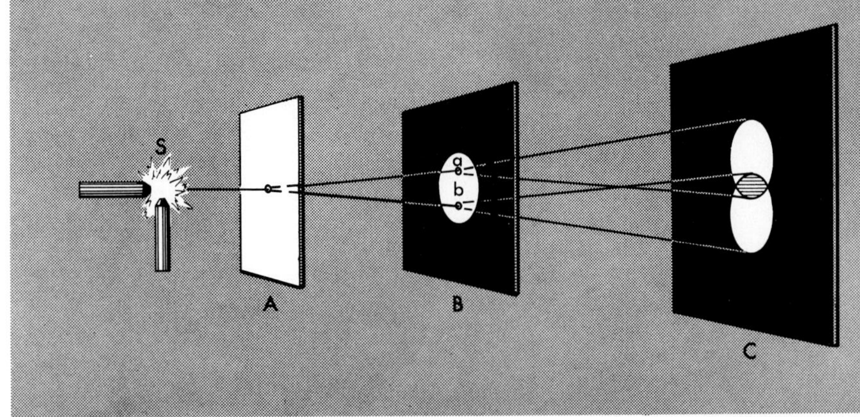

Fig. 34–8 *Interference with light.*

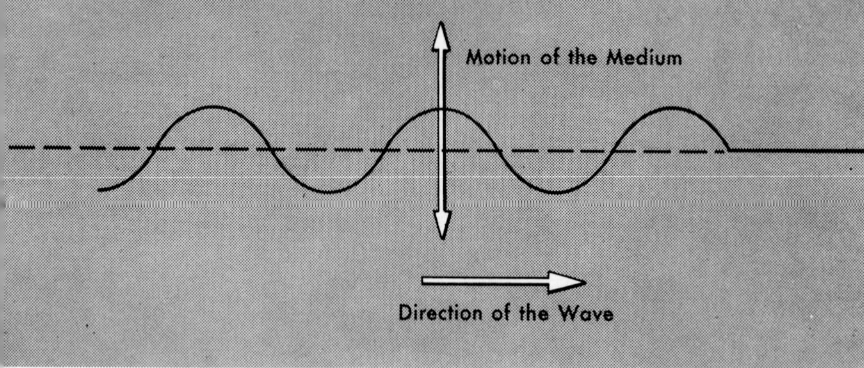

Fig. 34–9 *Characteristics of water waves — a transverse wave motion.*

great detail in the first comprehensive treatise on light, Newton's *Optics*. However, such questions as the mass and size of these light particles remained unanswered.

LIGHT AS WAVES

A Dutch contemporary of Newton's, Christian Huygens, argued for the hypothesis that light was a form of wave motion. The similarity to water waves is very striking. A disturbance like a dropped stone starts a train of waves in water. The water waves carry energy forward on the water which serves as the propagating medium (Figure 34–9). Later we shall show that light waves behave as a transverse wave motion just like water waves.

Historically the corpuscular and wave theories of light originated about the same time and they are still widely accepted and still in use. With very little pretense of consistency, modern scientists use both theories, for both are very useful. Scientists would like to have a single comprehensive theory for light, but lacking it they do not hesitate to use the particular theory that best serves their purpose in meeting an experimental or theoretical difficulty.

OSCILLATORY MOTION

Before considering wave motion it is necessary to study another form of motion. Thus far we have studied uniform, accelerated, and circular motion. Each form has certain characteristics which are conveniently expressed in neat mathematical statements. To these forms of motion, we now must add *oscillatory motion* or *simple harmonic motion.* An ordinary pendulum illustrates oscillatory motion (Figure 34–10). An expenditure of energy will raise the pendulum to position P_1. The system now possesses a definite amount of energy which is entirely potential. The bob is also under the influence of a restoring force due to the gravitational field of the earth. The force f of a component of the gravitational pull g is perpendicular to the support string. If

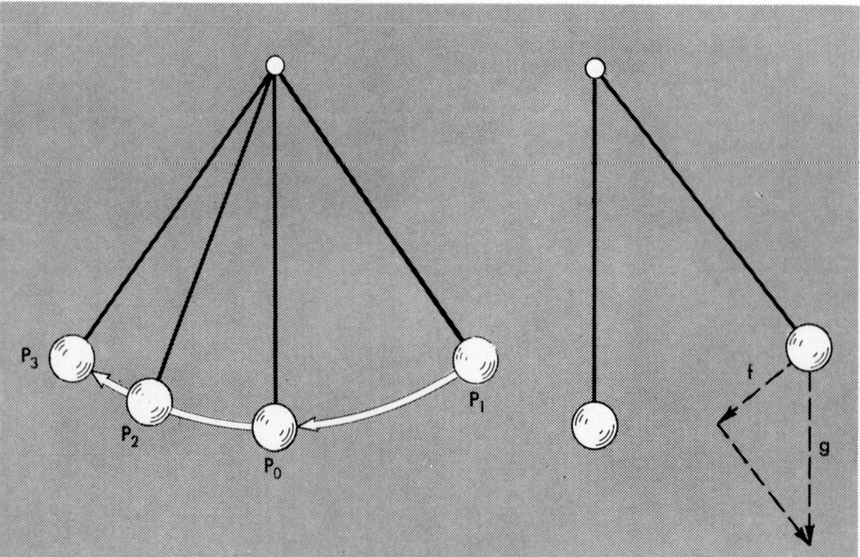

Fig. 34–10 *Oscillatory motion of a pendulum.*

the pendulum is released it starts to swing toward its original position P_0 because of the force f. At P_0 its energy is entirely kinetic. Its inertia carries it on to P_2 and P_3. After passing P_0 the bob comes under the influence of a restraining force which gradually brings it to rest at P_3 where the energy is again entirely potential and equal to its energy at P_1. Because the attractive force of the earth is acting continuously, the bob resumes its motion but in an opposite direction, which brings it back to P_0 and P_1. The bob now undergoes continuous oscillatory motion. If the pendulum did not lose energy as a result of pushing the air out of its path as it swings back and forth, and also lose some energy as heat in the string, the motion would continue forever.

The characteristics of the pendulum are described in terms of its *period,* the time necessary for a complete vibration. The *displacement* of the bob horizontally is called the *amplitude.* For short amplitudes *the period is independent of both the mass of the bob and the amplitude.* The energy of the oscillation system, however, does depend upon the amplitude. The *inverse of the period is called the frequency* or vibrations per second.

A child in a swing, the balance wheel of a watch, the vibration of a violin string, the up-and-down motion of a long bridge, the swaying in the air of a tall building are all examples of oscillatory motion. All require an initial expenditure of energy to start oscillation, but this energy tends to sustain the motion. It is the gradual loss of energy, due to various kinds of frictional loss, that eventually brings oscillatory systems to rest.

Another example of oscillatory motion is a vibrating mass on a stiff spring. This vibrating system can be fully described in the following terms:

Displacement = x (usually in centimeters)
Amplitude = $2x$
Period = t(ime) for one complete vibration from A to C to A (usually seconds/vibration)

$$\text{Frequency} = f = \frac{\text{vibrations}}{\text{second}} = \frac{1}{t}$$

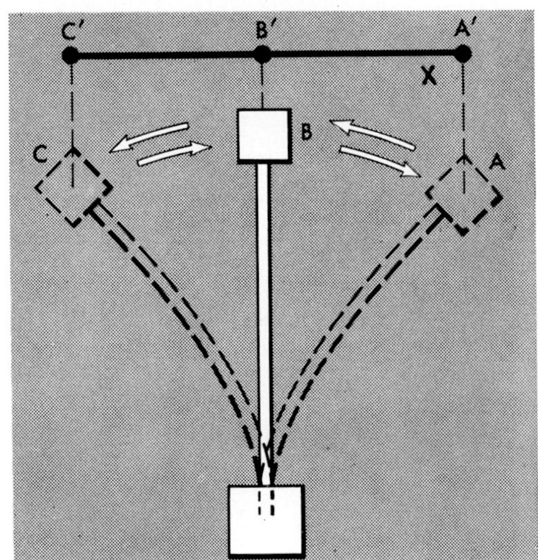

Fig. 34–11 *An example of oscillatory motion: vibrating mass on a stiff spring.*

The term *cycle,* rather than *vibration,* is usually used in describing oscillatory motions. Thus, frequency is usually given as cycles per second (cyc/sec).[1]

The restoring force which causes motion lies in the elasticity of the bent spring rod. The energy put into the system and thus the restoring force varies directly with the displacement x, or

$$\text{Energy} = kx.$$

Timing the vibration shows that the period and the frequency do not depend upon the amplitude. The frequency does, however, depend upon the characteristics of the vibrating support — its elasticity and other factors. Increasing the stiffness of the spring increases the frequency of vibration. Experimentally it can be shown that

$$\text{frequency} \propto \sqrt{\text{restoring force}}.$$

[1] This illustration should make clear the meaning of the terms *period* and *frequency*. Consider a child in a swing. Assume the child swings back and forth 8 times in 10 seconds. The "back-and-forth-and-back" motion constitutes one complete swing or cycle. Hence the period = time for one cycle =

$$\frac{10 \text{ seconds}}{8 \text{ cycles}} = 1.25 \frac{\text{sec}}{\text{cyc}},$$

and the frequency = cycles per second =

$$\frac{1}{1.25 \text{ sec/cyc}} = 0.80 \frac{\text{cycle}}{\text{second}}.$$

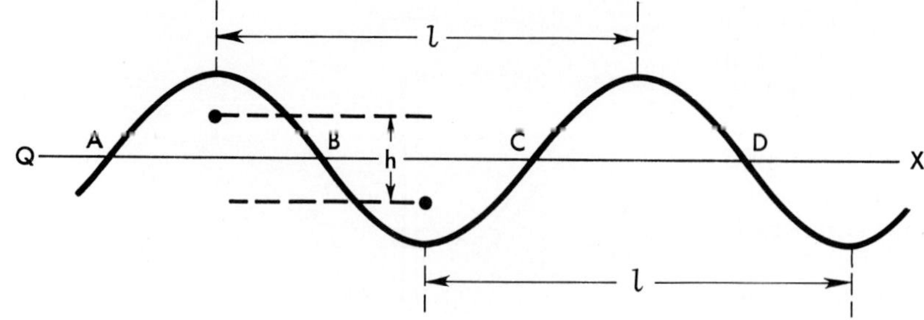

Fig. 34–12 *The form of small water waves.*

WATER WAVES AS TRANSVERSE WAVES

Ordinary water waves are typical examples of *transverse waves.* That is, the propagating medium undergoes an oscillatory up-and-down motion as the wave travels forward. The next time you are at the beach observe the behavior of any object floating in fairly deep water. It bobs up and down while many wave crests pass by, affording visible evidence that though the waves move forward, the water moves only up and down. A train of water waves can be set in motion by any disturbance that will transmit energy to a body of water. This disturbance can be, for example, anything that elevates or depresses the water at any point, such as a dropped stone. In Figure 34–12, QX represents the original surface of the water. After the disturbance the equivalent of the water in the trough BC is elevated into the crest AB. Let m be the mass of the water which will just fill the trough BC. Let h be the difference in height between the center of mass of the trough and the center of mass of the crest. (The center of mass is the point where all the mass of a body may be thought to be concentrated.) The energy expended in transferring the water from the trough to the crest will be mgh. The potential energy momentarily stored in the crest is thus mgh. This displaced water is now subject to the restoring force of gravity. It falls. Because of the inertia of the water it goes beyond its equilibrium position QX, and thus we have a continual oscillation due to gravitation. The disturbance tends to be maintained as a typical oscillatory motion. The surface of the water takes on a wave form that travels forward. Note that the wave form travels forward as the water medium undergoes a *transverse* motion.

The distance from crest to crest, or from trough to trough, is called the wave length, l. A train of waves must pass a point. The time for a mass of water to make a complete oscillation, the period in seconds/vibration, is the time necessary for the crest to move one wave length l (Figure 34–12). Hence the velocity of the crest which is the velocity of the wave, if the wave length is in centimeters, will be

$$v = \frac{l \text{ cm/cyc}}{t \text{ sec/cyc}} = \frac{l \text{ cm}}{t \text{ sec}}.$$

Since the frequency f is related to the period by $f = 1/t$ sec, it follows that

$$v = \frac{1}{t \text{ sec}} \cdot l \text{ cm} = \frac{f}{\text{sec}} \cdot l \text{ cm}.$$

In more general form, this is written

$$v = f \cdot l. \qquad \textit{(Equation 34–1)}$$

FUNDAMENTAL WAVE MOTION EQUATION

The equation $v = f \times l$ is the fundamental equation for *all* wave motions. Note that for any particular medium the velocity is constant and only the frequency and wave length can vary. These must vary in inverse ratio, since

$$f = \frac{v}{l}, \quad \text{or} \quad f \text{ varies as } \frac{1}{l}.$$

PROBLEM: At 0° C. and one atmosphere, sound travels with a velocity of 332.9 meters per second. A Middle C tuning fork has a frequency of 512 vibrations per second. What is the wave length?

SOLUTION: Using Equation 34–1,

$$l = \frac{v}{f} = \frac{332.9 \text{ m/sec}}{512 \text{ cyc/sec}} = 0.65 \text{ meter/cycle.}$$

PROBLEM: A certain radio station sends out a wave with a length of 517.5 meters. What is the frequency?

SOLUTION: Radio waves travel with the speed of light of 3×10^{10} cm/sec. Hence,

$$f = \frac{v}{l} = \frac{3 \times 10^{10} \text{ cm/sec}}{517.5 \text{ m/cycle} \times 100 \text{ cm/m}}$$

$$= 0.580 \times 10^{6} \frac{\text{cycles}}{\text{sec}}$$

$$= 580 \times 10^{3} \frac{\text{cycles}}{\text{sec}} \times \frac{1 \text{ kilocycle}}{1000 \text{ cycles}}$$

$$= 580 \frac{\text{kilocycles}}{\text{sec}}.$$

CORPUSCULAR VERSUS WAVE THEORY

In considering the velocity of light in water, the two theories led to divergent results. On the basis of Newton's corpuscular theory light ought to travel faster in the denser medium, whereas the wave theory of Huygens indicated that light should travel more slowly in the denser medium.

Fig. 34–13 *Light if corpuscular should travel faster in water due to attraction of the water.*

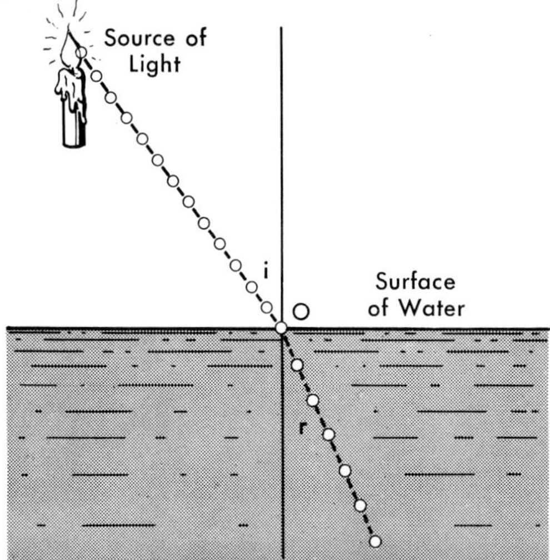

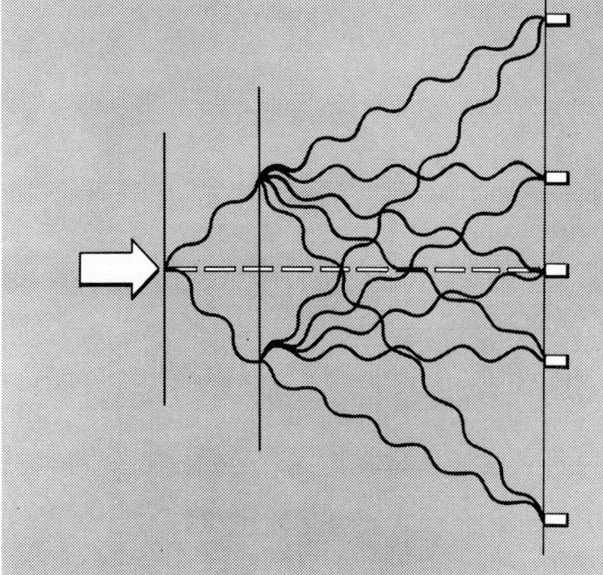

Fig. 34–14 *Conditions for reinforcement of light waves. Note reinforcement at places marked* ▭.

Here was need for a crucial experiment — the comparison of the velocity of light in water and in air — to decide between the two theories. Yet with the slowness that often marks the advancement of knowledge, over 150 years elapsed before the experimental values were finally determined. Fizeau (France, 1819–96) and Foucault (France, 1819–68) proved experimentally that the velocity of light in water is three-fourths of its velocity in air, and thus verified Huygens' expression for the index of refraction of water. By direct experiment Newton's corpuscular theory was thus finally refuted.

Young's experiment already described, in which he obtained darkness by combining light rays from two different sources (the phenomenon of reinforcement and interference), proved to be another crucial landmark in gaining acceptance for the wave theory. Refer to Figures 34–8 and 34–14; the intense bright lines represent regions of reinforcement of two separate trains of waves, and the black lines correspond to complete interference. In Figure 34–14 the arrow at the left represents an intense beam of parallel light rays. Some of these pass through a small opening in the first

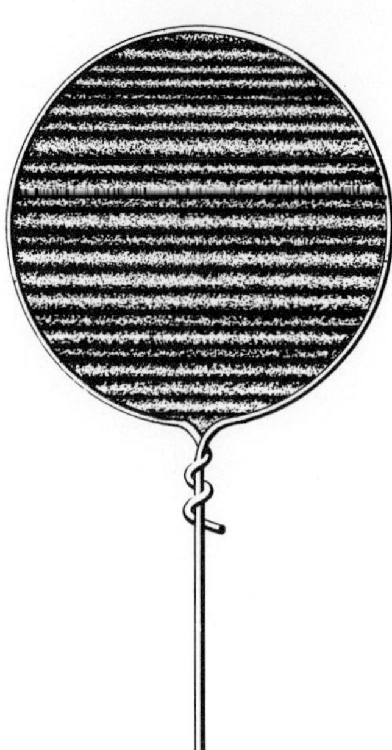

Fig. 34–15 *Interference and reinforcement of light with a soap film.*

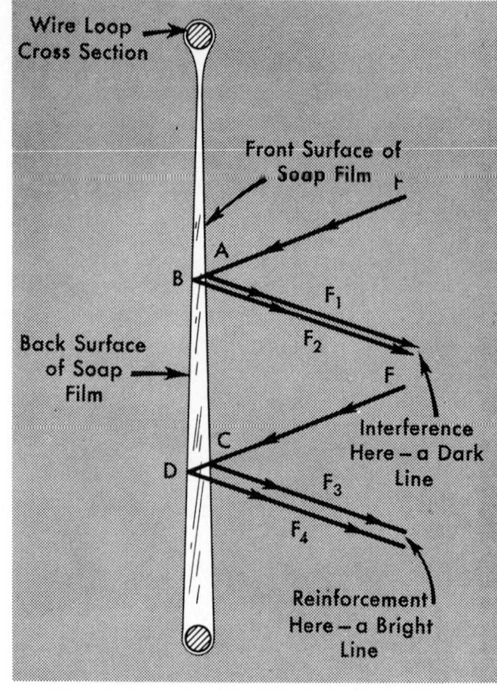

Fig. 34–16 *Interference and reinforcement of light with thin liquid films to form the alternate light and dark lines shown in Figure 34–15.*

plate. Diffraction (spreading) of the light occurs here. Some of these rays pass through small openings in the second plate; diffraction again occurs. The light rays, where they meet on the screen at the right, may reinforce or interfere with each other. The figure shows reinforcement at certain places on the screen; in these places the light is more intense. The regions in between will be dark because of interference.

An experiment very similar to Young's can be easily performed by the student. Place a soap film on a loop of wire and hold vertically to reflect light. In a short time the face of the film will show alternate bands of light and dark lines. These lines can be accounted for only on the basis of constructive interference (reinforcement) and destructive interference of light waves. When the film is held vertically, some of the liquid falls to make the film wedge-shaped, which permits reflection of light from the front surface of the film *AC* and also from the inside of the back surface *BD* (Figure 34–16). Thus there is the possibility of reflected waves from these surfaces being "in step" or "out of step." Some of the incident rays will be reflected at *A* and *C* as rays F_1 and F_3. However, a part of the incident rays will pass through to the rear surface and be reflected at *B* and *D* to form the reflected rays F_2 and F_4. If the difference in path length (FBF_2–FAF_1) is one-half of a wave length, the two reflected waves will destructively interfere with each other to form a dark line. If the difference in path length (FDF_4–FCF_3) is a full wave length, there will be maximum reinforcement and a bright line results. Thus the entire face of the film consists of alternate bright and dark lines. (Refer to Figure 34–15.) Experiments of this kind have been taken as convincing proof for a wave theory for light.

A similar illustration of constructive and destructive interference with light may be seen in the splotches of oil dropped on a wet pavement; these will reveal brightly colored alternate light and dark bands.

MAXWELL'S CONTRIBUTION

The reader has probably noted that there has been no discussion of the nature of the propagating medium. The early supporters of the wave theory invented the *ether,* a mysterious substance pervading all space where light was able to travel. They did not prove its existence but believed that its existence would eventually be proved. After all, waves had to travel on *something,* they reasoned, and this something was what they called ether.

James Clerk Maxwell (1831–79), a distinguished British scientist who contributed greatly to our present concepts of light and radiant energy, was intrigued by the experiments with electric and magnetic fields carried out by Faraday (Chapter 32). Maxwell believed with Faraday that "action at a distance" was possible because of electric and magnetic fields of force. He became convinced that electric charges traveling with oscillatory motion (that is, with continuously changing speeds) would generate electric and magnetic waves traveling with the velocity of light through all space.

Imagine *K, L,* and *M* to be copper wires parallel to one another (Figure 34–17). Assume that an electron *A* is moving with changing speed toward A_1. Electric lines of field, which always accompany an electric charge, are also in motion moving parallel with the moving electron. The moving electron is also surrounded by magnetic lines of force which are *perpendicular* to the conductor *K* and in circles around the wire. These lines of force cut the conductors *L* and *M*. By induction, an electric field appears in these wires. The moving electrons in *L* and *M* will move down and set up magnetic fields perpendicular to *L* and *M* which *oppose* the magnetic field around *K* (Lenz's law; see Chapter 32). The electron in *K* reaches its maximum displacement at A_1, where it momentarily is at rest. Simultaneously the electric and magnetic lines of force which accompany it *disappear.* As the generating electron in *K* starts moving down to position A_2, electric and magnetic lines of force (or fields) appear about *K,* but opposite in direction. Similarly, new electric and magnetic fields appear about *L* and *M* which are also reversed in direction. Thus the oscillating electron in *K* produces about itself and about *L* and *M* continuously fluctuating electric and magnetic fields. Since the intensity of electric and magnetic fields decreases with the square of the distance, the responses in and about *L* and *M* are considerably less than in the case of *K.* These fluctuating electric and magnetic fields travel through space with the enormous and characteristic velocity of 3×10^{10} centimeters per second or 186,000 miles per second, which is also the speed of visible light.

It is natural to ask what happens to the causative oscillating electron in *K.* There are two possibilities. First, the electron for any of a number of reasons may continuously maintain its oscillating motion. Then

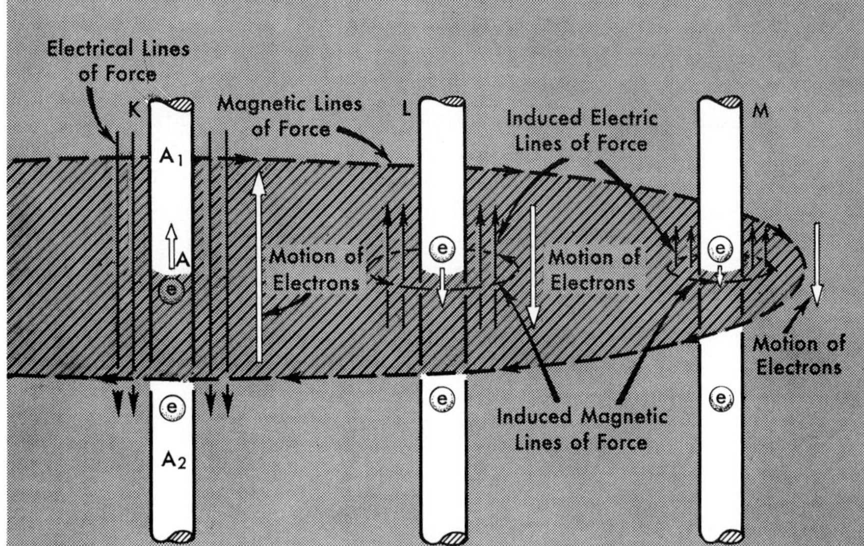

Fig. 34–17 *Changing electric and magnetic fields from an oscillating electron.*

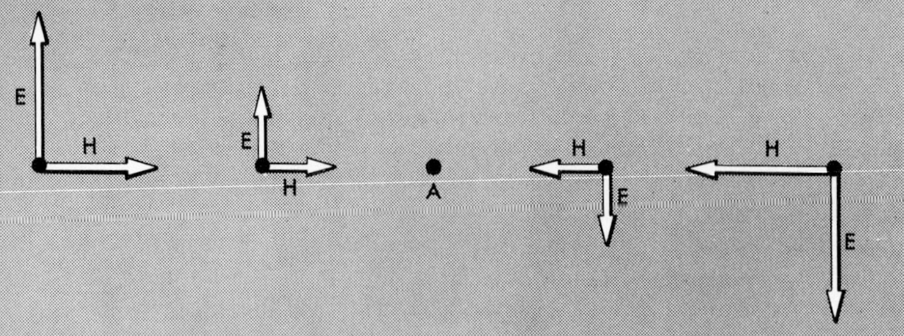

Fig. 34–18 *The change in intensity and direction of the electric and magnetic field vectors E and H.*

the induced and continuously varying electric and magnetic fields continue to stream out into space. The second possibility is that the electron gradually loses its energy. The appearance of moving electrons in *L* and *M* represents energy which came from the causative electron. Thus it is gradually sending its energy out into surrounding space, and the amplitude of oscillation therefore gradually decreases. It finally comes to rest when it has dissipated all its energy.

The intensity of the electric field *E* and of the magnetic field *H* about the point *A* continually changes in amount and direction. This can be represented by suitable vectors as shown in Figure 34–18.

The *combination* of the two kinds of fields traveling through space with a speed of 3×10^{10} centimeters per second constitutes an "electromagnetic wave." The reason for this is apparent from a plot of the electric field vectors as shown in Figure 34–19. This wave form can be described in terms of its wave length l or its frequency f, since

$$f = \frac{v \text{ (constant)}}{l}.$$

It should be apparent that this is a *mental picture,* and therefore entirely subjective, to account for certain observed results. Earlier experimenters, Huygens and Young, had pointed out that light behaved as if it consisted of waves. The contribution of Maxwell was the prediction of a definite velocity (3×10^{10} cm/sec), the same as for light, for the propagation of fluctuating electric and magnetic fields which travel as *transverse* waves through space and perpendicular to each other. These waves would behave just like visible light since they would undergo reflection, refraction, interference, and reinforcement, as visible light does.

The final bold step of Maxwell was to assert that visible light was also an electromagnetic phenomenon which differed from electric waves only in energy, wave length (or frequency), and in the fact that visible light affects the eye. Light originates in something containing oscillating electrons. The frequency of visible light is dependent upon the frequency of the electrons. The frequency range for visible light is about 4.3×10^{14} cycles per second for red light to 7.3×10^{14} cycles per second for violet light. The studies relative to electromagnetic waves were made by Maxwell principally in the years 1864–73. A very large number of experimental advances in electricity, magnetism, light, and radio came rapidly after the acceptance of Maxwell's electromagnetic wave theory. Almost simultaneously with the recognition that visible light was a form of wave motion came the recognition that there were also forms of invisible light. Thus any warm object, such as a flatiron, gives off radiation with wave lengths longer than that of red light. These are collectively referred to as the *infrared.* Similarly, there are forms of invisible light with wave lengths shorter than the visible violet called the ultraviolet. Neither infrared nor ultraviolet can be perceived by the eye, but they both produce definite physiological effects. The infrared are our common heat rays, while the ultraviolet can tan or burn the skin. The proof of the existence of ultraviolet and infrared light came after their existence had been predicted by the electromagnetic wave theory.

THE DOPPLER EFFECT

Because the frequency of light determines its color, changes in color from a source of known color indicate motion of the source. For example, the western side of the sun is rotating toward the earth. Thus light from this side of the sun, because it is moving toward the earth, apparently undergoes a decrease in wave length or an increase in frequency; the waves arrive more frequently on the earth than if the source were at rest. Hence the light from the western edge appears *bluer* than light from the middle. The eastern side of the sun, on the other hand, is moving away from the earth while emitting light. Thus the waves arrive less frequently, the frequency appears to decrease, and the wave length appears to increase. Hence the light from the eastern edge appears *redder* than light from the middle. The apparent change in the frequency and wave length of light due to motion of the source relative to the observer is called the *Doppler effect.* The same effect is observed with sound. Thus, a siren approaching the observer apparently increases in frequency or pitch. The importance of the Doppler effect lies in the fact that when observed it is evidence of motion of a light source with respect to an observer on the earth. The shift in color can be used to determine the speed with which luminous objects in space — stars, for example — are moving toward or away from the earth.

HERTZ AND RADIO WAVES

Eight years after the death of Maxwell in 1879, the German physicist Heinrich Hertz (1857–94) demonstrated the existence of radio waves. At the time of their discovery they were appropriately called Hertzian waves. It is not difficult to demonstrate that there are electromagnetic waves due to oscillating electrical charges. A glass bottle coated with tin foil on the outside and inside forms a so-called Leyden jar. If the outside of the jar is connected to the earth by a piece of wire, a large charge of electrons can be stored in the jar by connecting the inner coating to a source of electrons. (Refer to Figure 34–20.) The electrons in the outer coating are repelled and escape to the ground; thus a positive charge accumulates on the outside coating while an equal negative charge accumulates on the inside. Substantial charges of electricity can thus be stored in a Leyden jar, or condenser. If a metal knob *A* on a half-circle of steel wire is brought close to *B,* there is a spark discharge. This will occur at some critical distance depending upon the state of charge. When the spark occurs the electrons surge from the inner coating to the outer coating, leaving the inner coating positive. Momentarily the outer coating is negative. Then the electrons surge back to the inner coating and an oscillating electric circuit has been created. This gradually dies down because it radiates energy to the surroundings. (Refer to Figures 34–20 and 34–21.) Note that the conditions for the formation of both electric and magnetic

Fig. 34–19 *Charging a Leyden jar.*

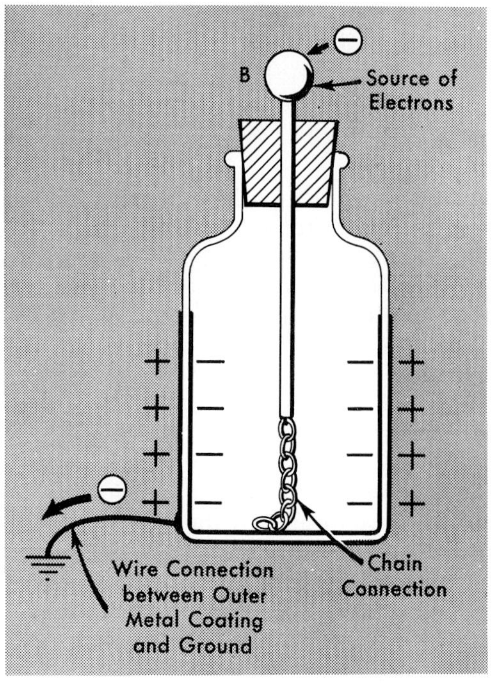

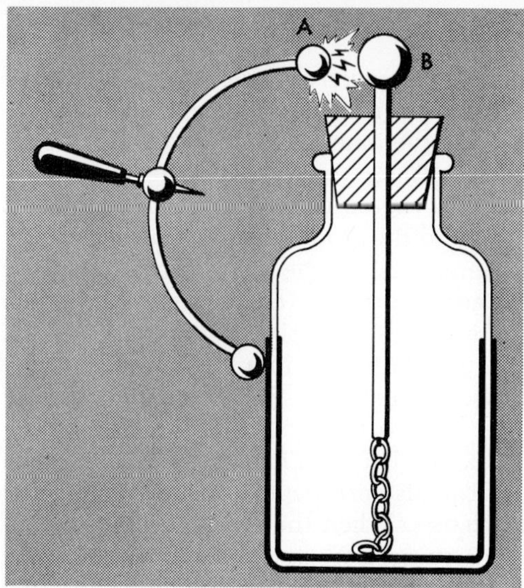

Fig. 34–20 *Production of an oscillating charge with a Leyden jar.*

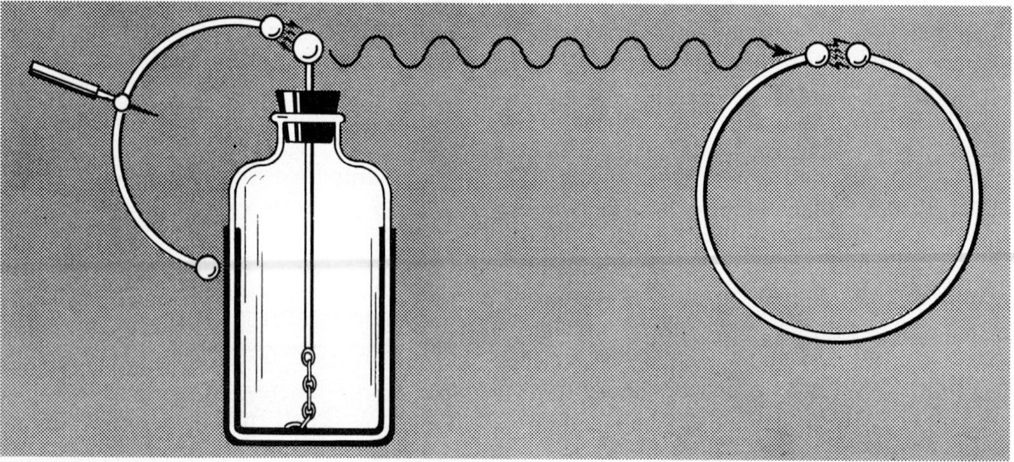

Fig. 34–21 *A simple radio "sender" and "receiver."*

fields exist in a rapidly oscillating electric charge. Hertz's receiver was extremely simple, a loop of stiff wire with a gap. By experimentation Hertz adjusted the size of the receiver and the size of the gap so the frequency of oscillation in each circuit was the same.

The discharging Leyden jar became a "sender," which sent out electromagnetic waves while discharging. Simultaneously an induced oscillating current appeared in the receiver as indicated by the spark discharge across the gap. Obviously a disturbance – an electromagnetic wave – had traveled through space. According to the theory of Maxwell, these waves were perpendicular to the oscillating charge in the sender. The waves were intercepted *only* when the receiver loop was in turn perpendicular to the waves. Thus Hertz proved that the waves were *transverse,* just as called for by Maxwell's theory. Furthermore Hertz proved that these Hertzian waves could be reflected and refracted like ordinary visible light. One thing he was not able to do, namely, measure the velocity of his radio waves. This had to be left for later experimenters.

WHAT ABOUT THE ETHER?

If an electromagnetic wave, including visible light, is a transmission of energy by transverse waves through space, what is the medium? All the early advocates of the ether theory hypothesized that a propagating medium had to exist. They named it *the ether* while hoping to prove its existence. But oscillating systems have frequencies which depend only upon their elasticity or restoring force and upon the mass. Thus if steel, water, and air are put in a state of compression, the restoring forces are in the elasticity of steel, water, or air. Sound is a wave motion. The velocity of sound varies with the elasticity, being greatest in steel. Light, however, travels in a vacuum. To account for the great velocity of light on the basis of an elasticity enormously greater than that of steel in a substance of no weight was not explainable. The two ideas are incompatible, and yet some scientists of the nineteenth century persisted in their belief in the existence of the ether and persisted in their efforts to find it.

Science has had to bury many working hypotheses and theories. It would be pointless to discuss here in detail the many experiments expressly designed to prove the existence of the ether which had negative results. Maxwell's equations applied even if no ether existed. The ether was not necessary for scientific thinking. It has therefore been abandoned, just as the hypothetical phlogiston and caloric of the previous century had been.

Scientists freely admit they do not know what electromagnetic waves "are." There is no demonstrated propagating medium. They represent energy traveling through largely empty space with a velocity of 186,000 miles per second. It appears that this energy travels as transverse waves. What the electromagnetic theory of radiation does is to give us a mechanical model which can be visualized and studied. The theory has been applied many times to advance our knowledge of light — visible and invisible. It serves as a coordinating concept for organizing all sorts of phenomena concerning light. It has been one of the most useful and fruitful of all scientific theories, even though it does not provide a "complete" explanation.

SUMMARY

1. Energy can be transferred through space by a process that is best described as a form of wave motion. There is no demonstrable propagating medium.
2. Water waves are the result of a disturbance (expenditure of energy) in a water surface, which causes an oscillatory up-and-down motion of the water, which in turn propagates the wave motion. The water remains stationary with respect to the forward motion of the wave.
3. In any regular oscillatory motion the time in seconds for one complete vibration, down and up (↓↑) or to and fro (⇆), is called the *period.*
4. In any regular vibratory motion, the number of complete vibrations per second is called the *frequency.* The frequency and the period (time) are related as follows:

$$f \propto \frac{1}{p} \propto \frac{1}{t}$$

5. The maximum displacement of a medium or body in oscillatory motion from its rest position is called its *amplitude.*
6. The frequency of an oscillating system is directly proportional to the elasticity of the substance (restoring force) and inversely proportional to the mass of the oscillating system. The exact nature of the restoring force depends upon the nature of the oscillating system.
7. The wave length of a water wave is the distance from a crest or trough to the next crest or trough.
8. The velocity of a wave is the distance that a given wave front will travel in a unit time. The velocity is related to the frequency and wave length as follows:

$$v = f \times l$$

9. The following characteristics are often used to identify a wave motion:
   a. Waves can be reflected.
   b. Waves can be refracted.
   c. Waves from different sources can reinforce or interfere with each other; that is, undergo constructive and destructive interference.

d. Waves can be diffracted.

e. Waves undergo the Doppler effect.

10. *Refraction* refers to a change in the direction of travel of a wave due to a change in its velocity.
11. The bending of a wave around corners or sharp edges is called *diffraction*.
12. A change in the wave length and frequency of a series of waves as a result of the source of the waves approaching or receding from the observer, or vice versa, is known as the *Doppler effect*.
13. Waves in which the movement of the medium is essentially perpendicular to the direction of travel are called *transverse* waves. These include water waves and visible light.
14. Roemer, a contemporary of Newton, devised the observational method which gave the first indication of the enormous velocity of light.
15. Michelson, an American, perfected a method for accurately measuring extremely small intervals of time, and thus he was able to measure with great precision the velocity of light between observation stations on the earth.
16. Light travels at the enormous velocity of 186,000 mi/sec or 3×10^{10} cm/sec.
17. Newton did not clearly recognize the phenomena of diffraction and interference in connection with light and therefore accepted a corpuscular theory of light which he thought adequately accounted for its reflection and refraction.
18. The final overthrow of Newton's corpuscular theory came during the middle of the nineteenth century, when, contrary to the prediction of Newton, light was found to travel more slowly in water than in air.
19. About 1800, Thomas Young and many others demonstrated that light can be diffracted and that light undergoes constructive and destructive interference. These findings led to the general adoption of the theory that light is a form of wave motion traveling upon a hypothetical medium called the ether.
20. The theory of light as waves traveling on ether had to be abandoned because no one could get any objective evidence for the existence of the ether.
21. Maxwell originated the conception of light as electromagnetic waves. Around an oscillating electrical current there coexist magnetic and electrical fields at right angles to each other. These expand and collapse, setting up a series of waves which travel with the velocity of light. Visible light consists of electromagnetic waves sent out by oscillating electrons in substances emitting light with a frequency range of 4.3×10^{14} to 7.3×10^{14} cycles per second for red to violet light, respectively.
22. Radio waves, infrared rays, and ultraviolet rays are forms of electromagnetic waves which differ from visible light in frequency and wave length and in their applications.
23. Electromagnetic waves have three common characteristcs: (*a*) they are produced by rapidly oscillating systems electrical in nature, (*b*) they all travel with the velocity of light, and (*c*) they all undergo the various phenomena characteristic of wave motion—reflection, refraction, diffraction, interference and reinforcement, and the Doppler effect.
24. The energy associated with electromagnetic waves is directly proportional to the frequency, or

$$E \propto f \propto \frac{1}{l}.$$

STUDY EXERCISES

1. Associate by number the terms from the following list with the appropriate descriptive phrases below.

1. Reflection	7. Amplitude
2. Refraction	8. Frequency
3. Diffraction	9. Period
4. Resonance	10. Elasticity
5. Interference	11. Wave length
6. Reinforcement	12. Doppler effect

a. The distance that a medium is displaced from its rest position, while transferring a wave motion. . . . .

b. The property of a substance which causes it to return to its original condition after being distorted by force. . . . .

c. The time required for one complete vibration of a substance or body in a regular oscillatory motion. . . . .

d. The length from crest to crest or from trough to trough in a series of water waves. ....

e. The change in the direction of travel of water waves as they approach shore as a result of an actual decrease in the velocity of the water waves. ....

f. The number of complete vibrations per second in any body or medium undergoing a regular oscillatory motion. ......

g. The light from a comet approaching the earth appears bluer than when it is receding from the earth. ....

h. A change in the direction of a wave motion in which the angle of incidence is equal to the angle of reflection. This illustrates what phenomenon? ....

i. The bending of waves around the corner of an obstacle. ....

j. A reduced displacement of the medium as a result of the union of two or more sets of waves of different wave lengths. ......

k. An enhanced displacement of a medium as a result of the union of two or more sets of waves of different wave lengths. ....

l. Properly timed pushes of a child in a swing soon cause a noticeable to-and-fro motion. ....

2. The following list gives the names of famous scientists who have contributed to our knowledge of light. Associate these names by number with the contributions noted below.

1. Newton	6. Hertz
2. Huygens	7. Fizeau
3. Young	8. Maxwell
4. Michelson	9. Faraday
5. Foucault	10. Roemer

a. Promulgated the electromagnetic theory of light. ....

b. Experimentally determined the present accepted value for the velocity of light. ....

c. First proved that a rapidly oscillating electric current sends out the waves predicted by Maxwell, which are now called radio waves. ....

d. First experimentally proved that light travels slower in water than in air, contrary to the prediction of Newton. ......

e. One of the first to get reliable observational evidence for the enormous velocity of light by making observations on one of the satellites of Jupiter. ....

f. Conceived the space about an electrically charged body to be filled with lines of force. ....

g. The first investigator to write exhaustively on the subject of light. ....

h. Originated the theory that light is a wave motion traveling through the ether. ......

i. The inventor of the corpuscular concept of light. ....

j. First proved that it is possible to get interference and diffraction effects which demand that light travel in transverse waves. ....

FOR FURTHER READING

1. WHITE, HARVEY E., *Classical and Modern Physics.* New York: D. Van Nostrand Company, 1940.

The unique methods which made it possible to measure the velocity of light are discussed on pages 319–324. Phenomena in light best interpreted on the basis of a wave theory are given on pages 329–340; diffraction and interference with light are treated on pages 377–390; and the photoelectric effect is discussed on pages 501–510.

2. HOLTON, GERALD, *Introduction to Concepts and Theories in Physical Science.* Cambridge, Mass.: Addison-Wesley Press, 1952.

Maxwell's electromagnetic theory of radiation is discussed on pages 501–515.

3. LEMON, H. B., *From Galileo to the Nuclear Age.* Chicago: University of Chicago Press, 1946.

The fundamentals of the electromagnetic theory of radiation are simply presented in Chapter 38.

35 SOUND AND THE INDIVIDUAL

AN EXCELLENT ILLUSTRATION of the great difference between subjective and objective information is found in answers to the question, "What is sound?" It is easy to start interminable arguments in any discussion group by raising the question, "If a tree falls in a distant forest with no person in the vicinity, is there any sound?" People who are concerned with the hearing mechanism and auditory sensation would answer, no. Physicists, however, who are primarily interested in the external disturbance itself, would promptly answer, yes. The physicist is aware of the imperfections of the human ear and knows that science has produced many devices which will hear sound that the human ear cannot hear. To the physicist, sound is a phenomenon that occurs externally to any possible observer and can therefore be described in objective terms.

It takes an expenditure of energy to produce sound, and this energy remains associated with the sound produced. It is, of course, a common experience that sound travels, which means that in discussing the subject of sound it is necessary to consider a process for transferring energy from one place to another as is done in the case of water waves. This suggests that sound is some kind of wave phenomenon. Modern knowledge of sound as a wave phenomenon has made possible the many methods by which we can transmit, preserve, and reproduce sound. "High-fidelity" records, microphones, and loudspeakers, for example, or the photographic recording of sound on film and the subsequent reproduction of that sound would be impossible without the modern knowledge of sound as a wave motion. Any wave motion exhibits a number of characteristics which are also shown by sound. Some of these will be mentioned.

1. *Sound requires an expenditure of energy for its production.* Thus, striking the keys of a piano, bowing the strings of a violin, "exploding" an inflated paper bag by suddenly crushing it between the hands, shooting a gun, all represent an expenditure of energy and produce sound.

2. *A medium is needed for the transmission of sound,* a substance which will return to its original condition after being distorted. In other words, the medium for

the transmission of sound must be elastic. Air, water, and such solids as concrete and steel, which are elastic, readily transmit sound. On the other hand, such materials as sponge rubber and cork have little tendency to resist changes of shape; that is, they are relatively inelastic. It is for this reason that sponge rubber and cork serve as excellent insulators against the transmission of sound.

Sound cannot be transmitted through a vacuum because there is no elastic medium. Thus, the ticking of a clock placed in an evacuated chamber cannot be heard. We are forever precluded from hearing events that occur in outer space, because most of astronomical space is empty. Our information respecting bodies in outer space can come to the earth only on beams of light, which is also a wave motion. Air is the usual medium for the transmission of sound, but water and many solids transmit sound with even greater efficiency and velocity. The Indian scout of frontier days would often detect the sound of approaching horses or marching men by listening with his ear to the ground.

3. *Sound travels with a definite speed,* which is determined by the nature of the medium. Thus, the speed of sound in air, water, and ice, all at a temperature of 0° C., is as follows:

Air:	331.4 m/sec	(1,087.1 ft/sec)
Water:	1450 m/sec	(4,750 ft/sec)
Ice:	3200 m/sec	(10,500 ft/sec)

The only factors affecting the speed of sound are the temperature and character of the medium. Loudness (the energy associated with a wave) and pitch (frequency) have no influence on velocity. Temperature very materially affects the speed of sound in air. The increase in speed in air amounts to about 0.6 meter, or two feet, per second for each degree Centigrade of rise in temperature. Thus the speed of sound in air at a temperature of 20° C. would be about 40 feet per second greater than at 0° C.

4. *Sound waves can be reflected* (*echo*). When sound waves strike a building, a hill, a cloud, or even a forest, they are reflected and returned to the sender, sometimes more than once. The distance to a far-off hill can be roughly determined by timing the interval between a sound and its echo. Half the elapsed time multiplied by 1100 ft/sec gives approximately the distance in feet. This same principle is used to determine ocean depths.

Fig. 35–1 *Sound cannot travel in a vacuum. Bell is easily heard when switch S is closed if bell jar is filled with air. When the vacuum pump is started, the intensity of the sound decreases as air is removed. The bell becomes inaudible when a large fraction of the air is removed.*

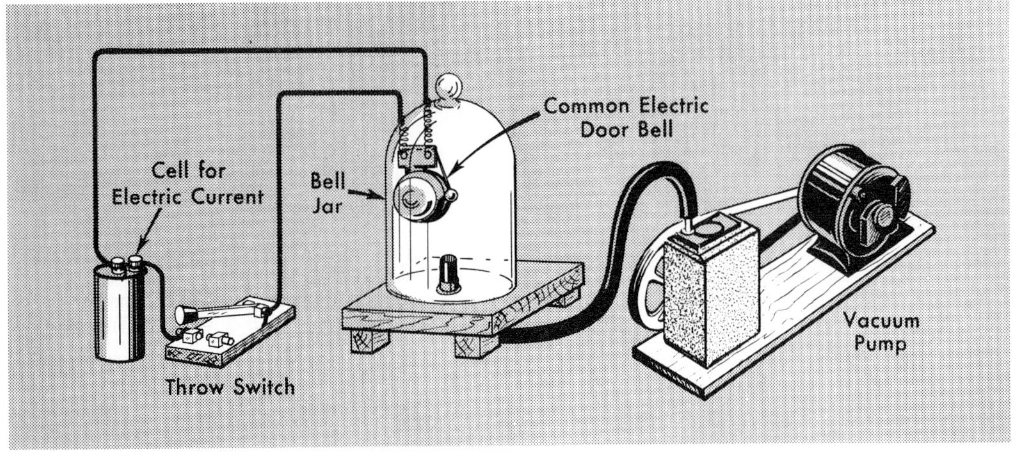

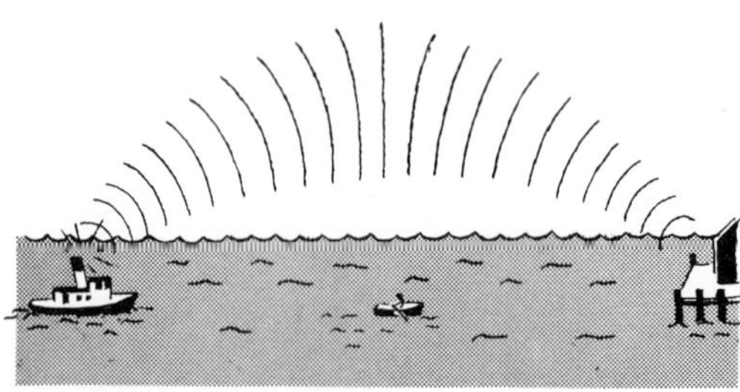

Fig. 35–2 *Refraction of sound waves.*

In public halls, excessive reflection from walls, floor, and ceiling, lasting over an appreciable length of time, interferes with hearing, an effect known as *reverberation.* To overcome excessive reverberation, use is frequently made of sound-absorbing surfaces, such as heavy draperies and acoustic tiles, which function by absorbing the sound as it strikes these surfaces and thus prevent excessive reflection.

5. *The direction of travel of sound may change (refraction).* The characteristics of air as a medium for transmitting sound change with temperature, sound traveling faster in warm air. Many persons have observed that sound seems to travel farther at night than in the daytime; the explanation is that the sound path is bent. In Figure 35–2 the air near the water surface is much cooler than the air above. Hence the upper end of the wave front travels faster and in this way the wave front returns to the surface of the earth again. Thus it happens that a person on a wharf can distinctly hear a boat whistle out on the water, while another person in a boat in an intermediate position may not hear the sound. In the daytime the conditions shown in Figure 35–2 would be reversed, in that the air near the surface of the water would be warmer than the air above. Hence the sound path would be bent *away* from the surface of the water and continually move away from it.

6. *The union of different sounds may result in either a decrease or an amplification in intensity.* The phenomena of constructive and destructive interference are common in connection with sound. For example, the popular percussion musical instrument, the marimba, consists of a series of wooden bars of graduated lengths. There is a definite mathematical relationship between the lengths of the hollow tubes and the various percussion bars. If Middle C, for example, is struck properly, a rich tone will result. If the experiment is repeated with a plug of cotton in the upper part of the tube, the volume of the tone will be markedly reduced. The tubes serve to amplify the tone and are called *resonators.* This illustrates the phenomenon of constructive interference. If the tubes for certain tone bars are interchanged, for example C and D, the effect is immediately noticeable when the bars are struck. The tone that is emitted by each tone bar is not nearly so loud, sounds harsh, and dies down in a short time. This illustrates destructive interference. The phenomenon of *beats* observed in music illustrates destructive interference of sound waves.

7. *The pitch of sound will vary if the source of sound moves toward or away from the hearer.* The sound from a skyrocket shooting into the air decreases in pitch or frequency. The sound from the siren of an approaching fire engine increases in pitch. The same effect is observed if the hearer approaches the sound source. This phenomenon is known as the *Doppler effect.* If the sound moves away from the hearer or if the hearer moves away from the sound source, there is a fall in the apparent pitch of the sound, because the sound waves arrive less frequently. Conversely, if the sound moves toward the hearer, sound waves arrive more frequently, and the pitch seems to rise. The Doppler effect can occur in any form of wave motion.

Fig. 35–3 *Resonance and non-resonance in a musical instrument.*

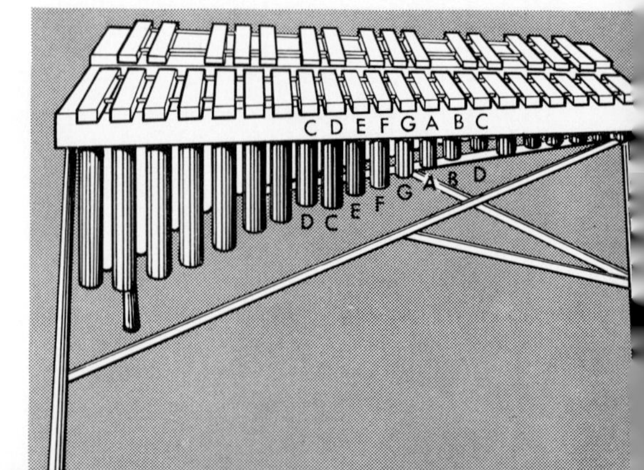

THE NATURE OF SOUND WAVES

These various phenomena pertaining to sound indicate that we are here concerned with a form of wave motion in which the movements of the medium are not easily discernible. However, it is not difficult to show that the medium is air undergoing a periodic motion. In water waves the visible up-and-down movement of the medium is perpendicular to the direction of travel of the waves. They are therefore referred to as *transverse waves* (Figure 35–4). Sound

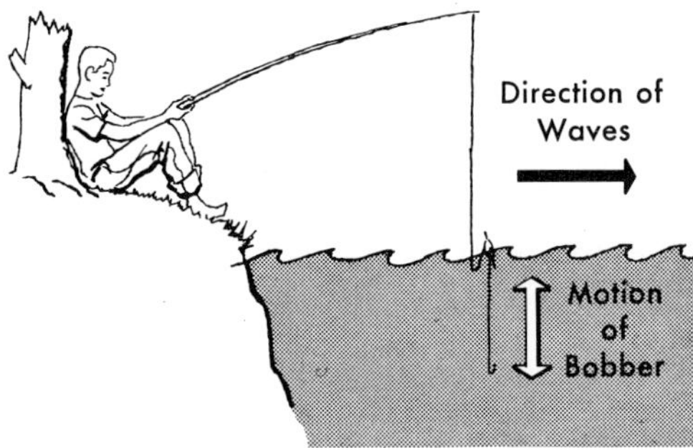

Fig. 35–4 *Water waves are transverse.*

waves, on the other hand, are of another type called *longitudinal* waves, in which the medium oscillates to and fro along a line *parallel* to the direction of travel of the wave; they are also referred to as *compressional* waves (Figure 35–5). A number of simple experiments serve to demonstrate this to-and-fro motion. For example, if a metal rod is clamped in the middle and rubbed lengthwise with a cloth dusted with rosin, a clear, ringing sound is produced (Figure 35–6). A pingpong ball suspended in such a way as to rest lightly against the end of the rod will swing out rapidly as the sound is produced in the rod. A "sound gun" (Figure 35–7) can be constructed out of a closed shipping carton by cutting a round hole in the middle of one side. It is easy to snuff out a candle with a sound wave by carefully aiming the box toward the candle. By sharply hitting the back of the box, a sound wave will be produced which can be made to hit the candle flame and snuff it out even at a distance of eight to

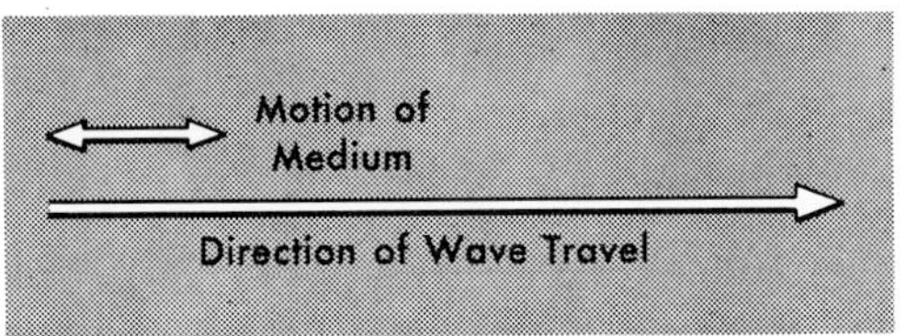

Fig. 35–5 *Motion of medium and direction of wave travel in longitudinal or compressional waves.*

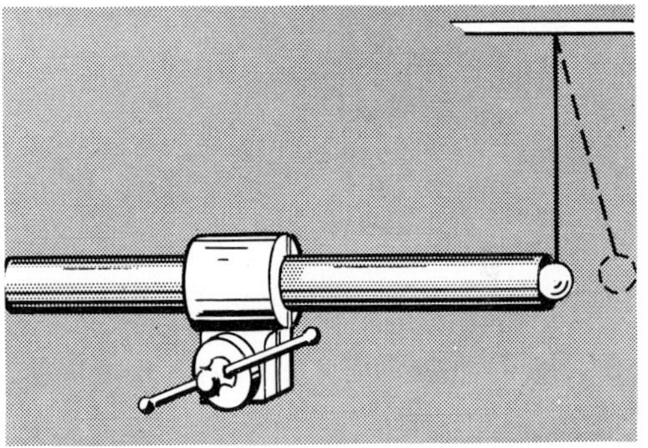

Fig. 35–6 *Longitudinal sound waves in a rod.*

ten feet. Just before the flame is extinguished, the vertical flame will assume a horizontal position, revealing the arrival of the wave front.

The mechanism involved in the propagation of a sound wave is not difficult to understand. In Figure 35–8, *A* represents a rapidly vibrating reed sending sound waves down the tube *B*. When the reed moves from position *M* to *N*, the molecules of air will be crowded closer together, forming a *condensation*. This momentary forward mo-

Fig. 35–7 *A sound gun utilizes compressional waves.*

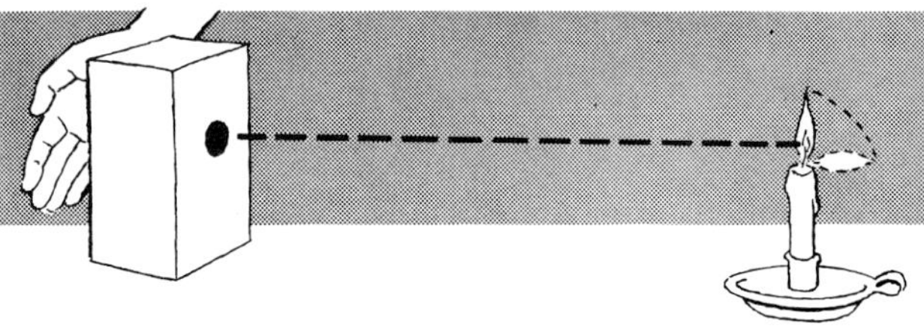

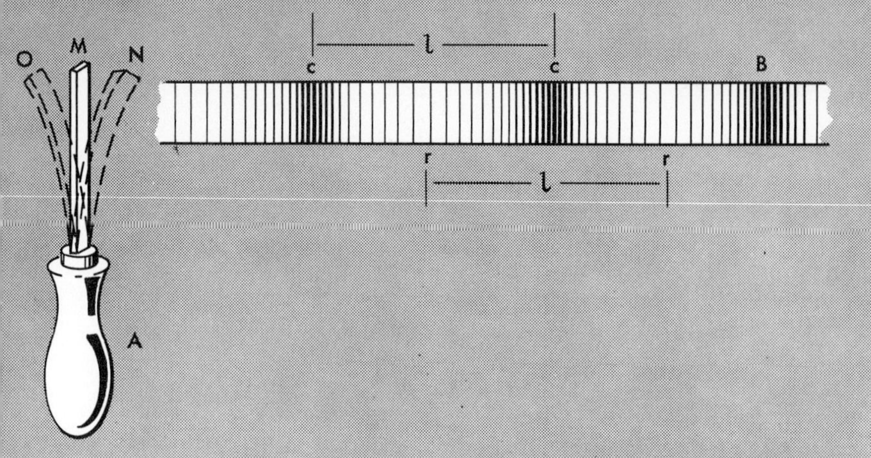

Fig. 35–8 *Sound waves consist of compressions and rarefactions.*

tion is then transmitted to the molecules in front of the united condensation, and thus it sends a disturbance (*wave front*) traveling down the tube. When the spring returns to *M* and continues on to *O,* because of its inertia, it will be followed by a *rarefaction,* or partial vacuum. In this rarefaction the molecules of air will be following the reed backward. When the reed starts moving toward *M* and *N* again, there will be formed another condensation to travel down the tube. Thus, throughout the tube there will be regions of condensation and rarefaction, which constitute the mechanism for the propagation of the sound wave through air. The disturbance or wave front progressively moves forward because of a minute vibratory motion of air particles, but no appreciable quantity of air is actually displaced from the tube. The vibratory motion of the air particles is longitudinal with respect to the motion of the wave.

The student is urged to study this mechanism carefully and to compare it with that involved in transverse waves. Note that a condensation corresponds to a crest, and a rarefaction to a trough, in transverse waves. The wave length is the distance between two successive condensations or rarefactions. The mechanism of the transmission of sound through liquids or solids is the same as through gases: that is, a transmission of energy from particle to particle in the medium with the wave front traveling forward as a condensation followed by a rarefaction. If the solid by its nature is relatively inelastic, then, as we have seen, it is incapable of transmitting sound. The actual velocity of sound in any medium is determined entirely by the properties of the medium itself. In general terms it is true that sound travels faster in liquids than in gases and considerably faster in solids than in liquids, because the resistance to distortion and thus the restoring force becomes progressively larger as we pass from gases to liquids and then to solids.

In the experiment described in Figure 35–8, it is found that substituting a reed with a different rate of vibration (frequency) changes the wave length of the sound wave in accordance with the relationship, $l \propto 1/f$. This must be true, since the velocity of the wave is constant for any particular substance and temperature. The relationship, $v = f \times l$, holds for the velocity of sound in any medium. Actually to apply this relationship, however, requires

Fig. 35–9 *Indirect measurement of the velocity of sound in air.*

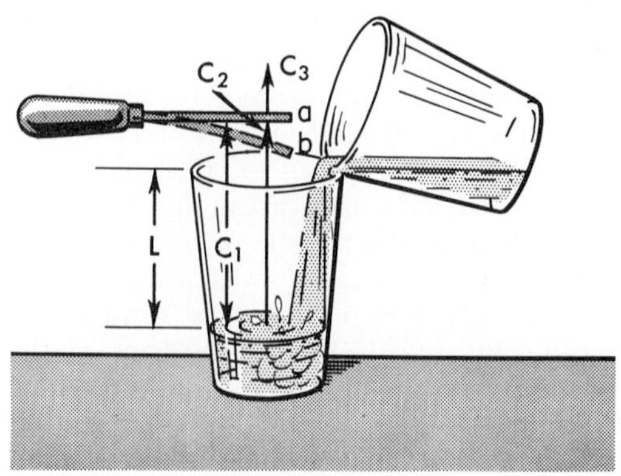

considerable ingenuity on the part of any investigator. This can be illustrated by an experiment which has for its object the verification of the velocity of sound in air. The experiment also illustrates that sound waves are subject to interference and reinforcement phenomena. If a vibrating reed is held over a vessel partly filled with water, it is found that the volume of the sound is markedly influenced by the level of the water. (See Figure 35–9.) As water is poured into a tall water glass the intensity of the sound gradually increases to a maximum and then dies down as the water level rises. This illustrates the phenomenon of *interference* (destructive interference) and *resonance* (constructive interference) in a vibrating air column.

Furthermore, the length of the vibrating air column L bears a simple relationship to the wave length l, the note emitted by the fork. For example, when the reed travels from a to b, a condensation c_1 is sent traveling down the tube. This, when it strikes the surface of the water, will be reflected as a condensation c_2. If this reflected condensation returns just as the reed has finished one-half of a vibration, the reed will be starting up from position a and sending out a condensation c_3. Under these conditions c_2 will have returned just in time to reinforce the vibration of the reed and thus increase the amplitude (energy) of the new condensation c_3, which is further increased by the energy associated with the reflected condensation c_2. There is thus a marked increase in the loudness of the emitted note – a resonance or constructive interference. Since the condensations c_1 and c_2 traveled down and up the tube during the course of one-half of a vibration, it follows that the distance 2 L corresponds to one-half the wave length l, or $\frac{1}{2}\,l = 2\,L$, and $l = 4\,L$. In other words, in a closed resonating air column the first position of resonance L corresponds to one-fourth of a wave length l.

It is still necessary to know the frequency of the vibrating reed. It is possible to attach a light stylus to the end of the vibrating reed and allow it to fall vertically and freely while vibrating, thus leaving a

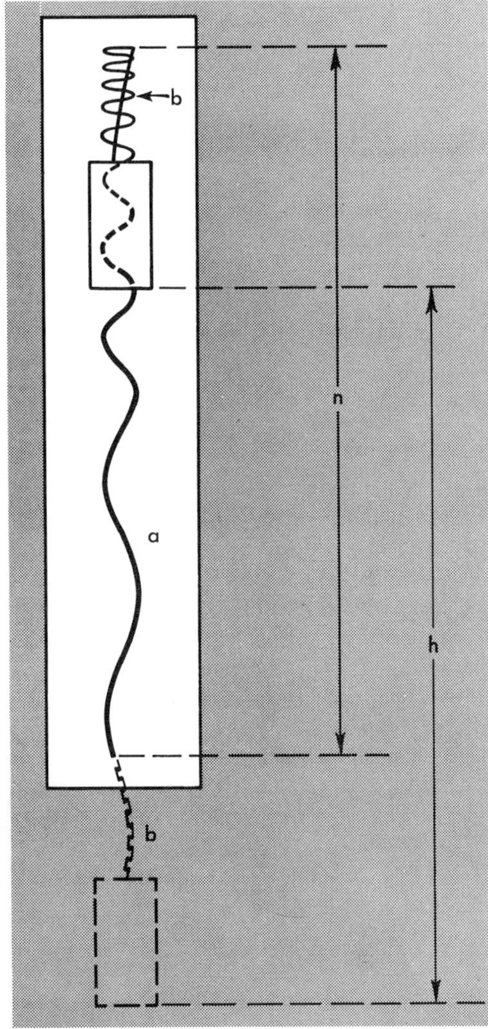

Fig. 35–10 *Determination of the frequency of a reed.*

wavy trace on a piece of smoked glass. (Refer to Figure 35–10.) The falling fork will leave a trace which indicates the number of vibrations n made by the vibrating reed while falling a vertical distance h. The time of falling t can, of course, be calculated from the laws of falling bodies. The data obtained in such an experiment were as follows:

L = 3.25 inches
h = 30 inches, or 2.5 feet
n = 405 vibrations

Then,

$$\text{wave length of sound} = l = 4\,L$$
$$= 4 \times 3.25 = 13 \text{ inches}$$
$$= 1.083 \text{ feet}$$

$$\text{Time for reed to fall} = t = \sqrt{2\,h/g},$$
$$= \sqrt{2 \times 2.5/32}$$
$$= \sqrt{2.5}/4 = 1.58/4,$$
$$= 0.40 \text{ sec}$$

$$f = 405(1/.40) = 1013 \text{ vibrations/second}$$
$$v = 1013 \times 1.083 = 1097 \text{ ft/sec}$$

MUSIC AND SOUND

Thus far our discussion of sound has been concerned entirely with its nature in an objective sense, but we are also interested in the relation of sound to hearing. Much of our knowledge comes to us by ear; much of our enjoyment in life we owe to music, which may vary in quality from the well-blended notes of the many instruments in a symphony orchestra to the swing effect of a jazz band. Music has a physiological and psychological basis as well as a physical one. A large part of the progress that has been made during recent years in recording and reproducing sound by the radio and phonograph is the result of our knowledge concerning the science of sound. Not all sound is audible, and the sensitivity and range of audibility of the human ear vary not only between individuals but also between one's right and left ear. The average audible range is found to lie between frequencies of 20 and 20,000 vibrations per second, though the ear is most sensitive to a frequency of about 2000. Young people usually have a higher limit of hearing than do old people. Sounds with frequencies greater than the audible limit are collectively referred to as ultrasonics (literally, beyond sounds). The sound frequencies of the human voice and of some common musical instruments are indicated in Figure 35–11.

Fig. 35–11 *Frequency ranges of some common musical instruments and of the human voice.*

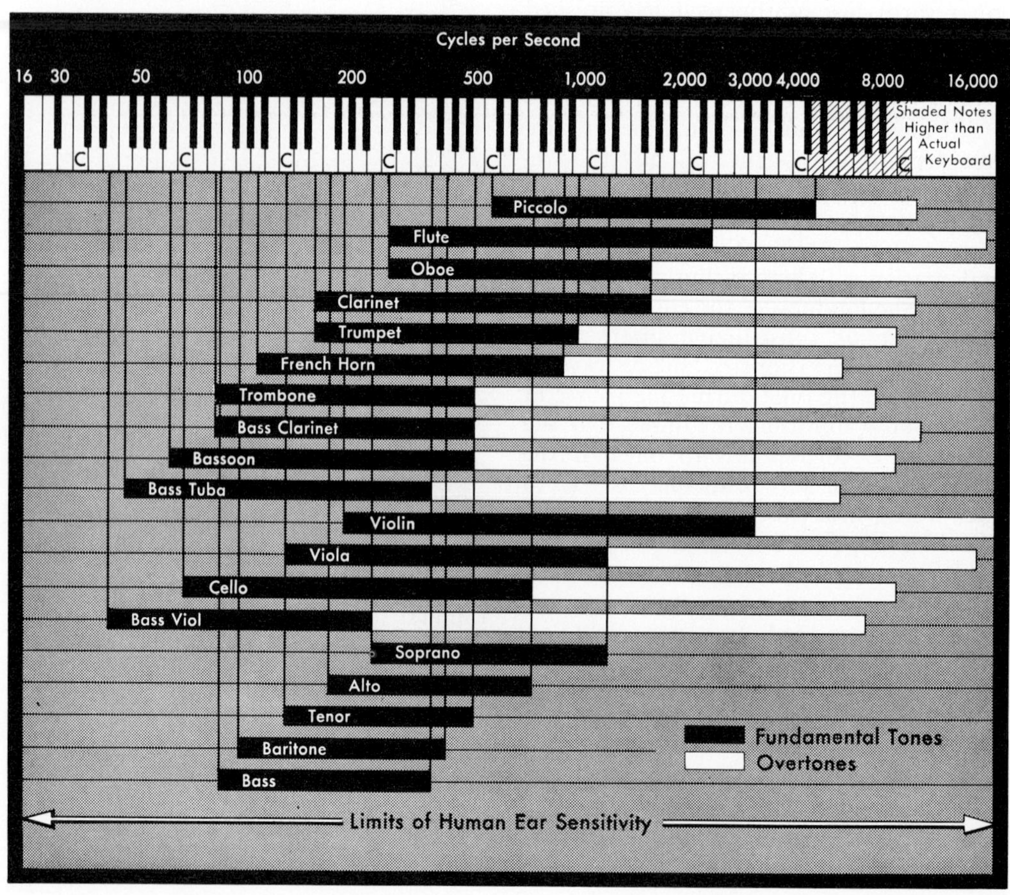

WHAT IS MUSIC?

There is a distinction between *music* and *noise*. The latter is not pleasing and consists of a jumble of many sounds of widely varying and continually changing frequencies. A pure tone in music, however, has a definite and constant frequency. A pure tone is difficult to obtain. The commonest device used to produce a definite pitch is the ordinary tuning fork. A properly constructed fork will have both its arms vibrating at the same rate, or frequency, and the tone from the vibrating fork will result from this single frequency. Because of differences in *quality* or *timbre,* the tones emitted by a violin are easily distinguished from those of a piano, even though they are of the same pitch. Timbre, pitch, and loudness are used to describe the characteristics of any musical tone. Pitch is determined by the number of waves striking the ear per second and refers to the dominating frequency of the note. The pitch known to musicians as Middle C is caused by 264 waves per second striking the ear, and that of Middle G by 396 vibrations per second. Loudness is a complex psychological reaction and is a measure of the sensation produced by sounds. It is due in part to the energy associated with the sound wave (which in turn is dependent upon the amplitude or energy of the vibrating source) and in part to the frequency of the tone.

The normal human ear is a remarkably sensitive instrument. Sound with a frequency of 2000 c.p.s. is audible if the energy of the waves exceeds 10^{-10} microwatts per square centimeter per second. (Refer to Figure 35–12.) The minuteness of this quantity of energy is brought out in the following illustration: A force of about one dyne can lift a mosquito. The energy expended in lifting the mosquito one centimeter, therefore, is

$$W = F \times d = 1 \text{ dyne} \times 1 \text{ cm} = 1 \text{ erg}.$$

Energy received at the rate of one watt corresponds to 10^7 ergs per second. Hence, energy received at the rate of 10^{-16} watts means

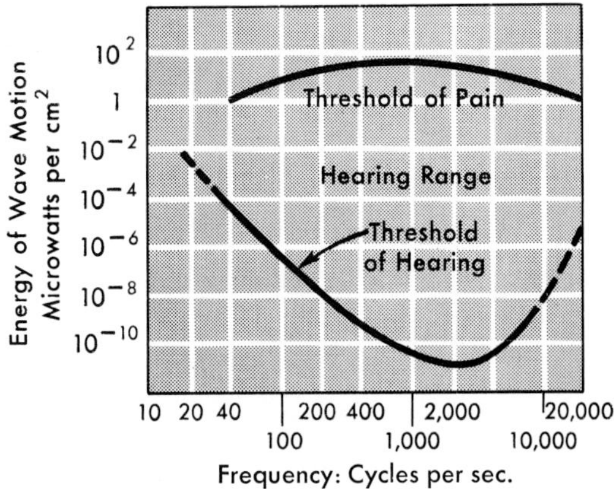

Fig. 35–12 *The relation of wave energy and frequency to audibility.*

$$10^{-16} \text{ watts} \times 10^7 \text{ ergs/(sec)(watt)} = 10^{-9} \text{ ergs per second.}$$

In order to accumulate enough energy at the latter rate to total one erg — enough to lift one mosquito one centimeter — it would have to be received continuously for

$$\frac{1 \text{ erg}}{10^{-9} \text{ erg/sec}} = 10^9 \text{ seconds,}$$

which is over thirty years. Figure 35–12 also indicates that sounds of frequency 100 and a power input of 10^{-8} microwatts per square centimeter would be inaudible, but would be audible if the power input were 10^{-4} microwatts. Likewise, Figure 35–12 shows that sounds of higher frequencies are more easily heard than those of lower frequencies. We say that they are *louder*. Loudness of a sound, therefore, depends upon two factors: the energy or intensity of the sound and the frequency. The high-pitched whistle of a referee at a hotly contested basketball game, for example, can be heard above the noise of the crowd, whereas a low-pitched whistle could not. Figure 35–12 shows that the hearing mechanism reacts best to frequencies of about two thousand vibrations per second. At this frequency the energy of the sound waves may be relatively low and still be heard. In order to be heard a sound with a frequency of forty cycles per second must have an energy con-

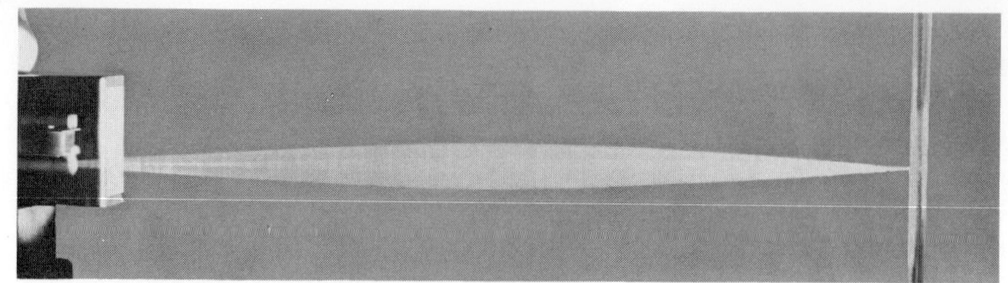

Fig. 35–13

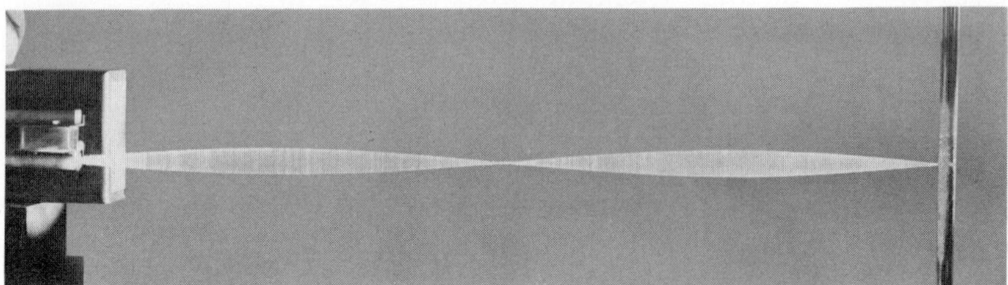

Fig. 35–14

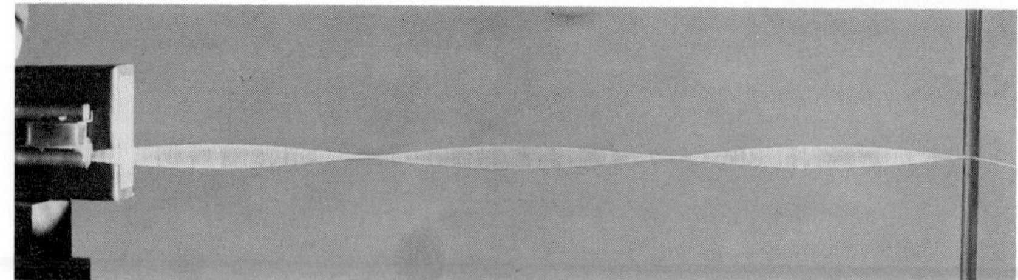

Fig. 35–15

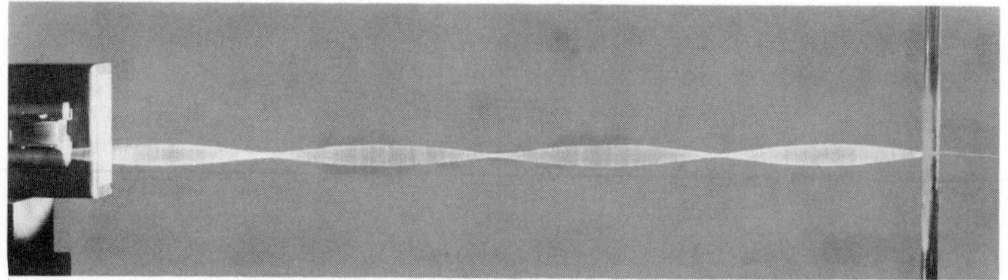

Fig. 35–16

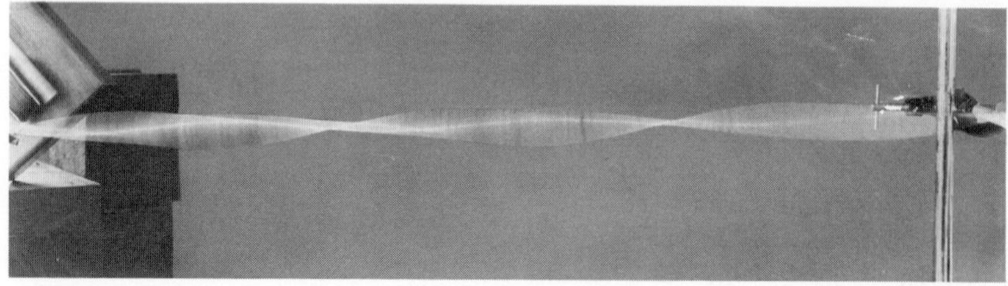

Fig. 35–17

Fig. 35–13 to **35–17** *A string vibrating in its fundamental and harmonic frequencies.*

tent a million times as large as the minimum required for an audible sound of 2000 frequency.

It is common knowledge that Middle C sung by a soprano, a tenor, a contralto, a baritone, and a bass singer will sound differently in each instance, though the singers are singing the same tone. This difference, as we have seen, is attributable to different quality or timbre of the voices. It is the different quality of the various instruments in the modern orchestra that makes each instrument indispensable for the ensemble effect. Actually, the vibrations of the human voice or of the various musical instruments are complex in nature because the foundation tone or *fundamental* is mixed with higher *harmonics* and lower *beat tones.* The harmonics, or overtones, have frequencies of two, three, four, or other simple multiples of the foundation tone. For example, if a string vibrates as a whole it will give out its fundamental frequency. But it can simultaneously vibrate in two segments, and the tone then will consist of the fundamental and the first overtone or second harmonic. The tones emitted by various musical instruments have their characteristic quality because of the presence of many harmonics in various degrees of prominence. (Refer to Figures 35–13 through 35–17.)

Thus far, the discussion has been limited to the characteristics of a single tone either with or without harmonics. Music, of course, is a combination of tones that follow certain patterns of harmony. As music is a cultural phenomenon it varies among different peoples and during different periods in their development. Music among primitive peoples is often based upon rhythm alone. The Indians of the Southwest still carry on their ceremonial dances with no other instrument than the tom-tom to accentuate the rhythm. Among such peoples the sense of rhythm is highly developed; some African tribes can even follow the individual pulsations of an automobile engine, something we can do only with elaborate instruments. Other cultures discovered that pleasant-sounding sequences of tones could be produced with strings of various length – the lyre – or with pipes of different length – the pipes of Pan. They played simple melodies on a single instrument or sang these individually or in unison. This step in the development of modern music is illustrated by the simple nursery rhymes set to music or the sacred music of the medieval church chanted in unison. The transition to music written in several parts and adhering to certain principles of harmony came slowly as the result of experimentation. By a long process of trial and error, tonal combinations which were pleasant were adopted and those which were unpleasant were discarded. The names of many great musicians – Johann Sebastian Bach, Handel, Mozart, Beethoven, Schubert, Schumann, Strauss, Liszt, Wagner, and others – are associated with the development of modern occidental music. Most people think of music as an art to be acquired by tedious practice and study. They forget that it is also a highly developed physical science.

When two tones are played simultaneously we get one of three principal results:

1. *The two tones may be in unison or the frequency of one may be a multiple of the other.* If so, the tones blend and reinforce each other. A variation of this experiment is to sing one tone only, say Middle C, close to a piano, with the sustaining pedal pressed down. It is found that Middle C or a multiple of Middle C on the piano will vibrate in response, since it has the same frequency or a multiple thereof.

2. *The two tones may interfere with each other to produce unpleasant beats.* They are then said to be dissonant. If two tuning forks with frequencies of 256 and 260 are in vibration simultaneously, the sound waves from these two forks will completely reinforce and interfere with each other four times per second; that is, in one-eighth of a second, while the slower fork is making 32, or 256/8 vibrations, the faster fork will make $32\frac{1}{2}$, or 260/8 vibrations. In other words, the faster fork has gained half a complete vibration and the two motions will be opposite in direction. At this point,

the two sound waves will destructively interfere. After another one-eighth of a second the slower fork will have completed 64 vibrations, while the faster fork will have gained another one-half vibration, and now the two waves will again be in step so as to have complete reinforcement. Thus there will be four intervals each second of complete reinforcement and interference of each sound — a phenomenon easily detected by the average ear. The alternate swelling and decrease in volume, occurring many times per second, produces the effect commonly referred to as beats. The number of beats per second is equal to the difference in frequencies of the two tones. Physiologically, beats, if few in number per second or erratic in character, have an unpleasant effect. Beats are most unpleasant occurring at the rate of 15 to 40 per second. Thus, C and D, and E and F, with frequency differences of 33 and $25\frac{1}{3}$, respectively, if played simultaneously, sound distinctly discordant.

3. *The two tones may serve to produce beat or difference tones which are pleasing to hear,* since they add to the quality or timbre of the combination. When frequency of the beats is sufficiently large, the result is pleasing. For example, the notes Middle C, E, G, and upper C (C′) on the piano have frequencies as follows:

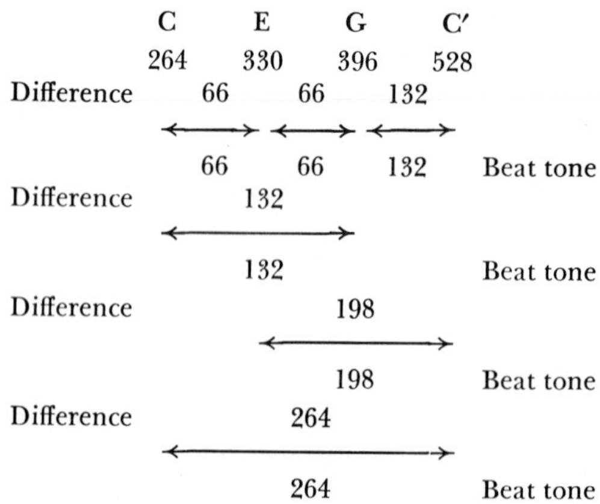

	C		E		G		C′	
	264		330		396		528	
Difference		66		66		132		
		66		66		132		Beat tone
Difference			132					
			132					Beat tone
Difference					198			
					198			Beat tone
Difference				264				
				264				Beat tone

If C and E are sounded simultaneously, there will be produced a distinct tone with a frequency of 66. That is, the diminuendo and crescendo effect due to complete reinforcement and interference 66 times per second itself produces a distinct tone. This third tone is as distinct as the two tones that produce it. It is technically called a *beat* or *difference tone.* Similarly, if C (264 c.p.s.) and G (396 c.p.s.) are played simultaneously, there will be a beat tone of 132, which is one octave below C. (Two tones which differ in frequency by a factor of two are said to be separated by an interval of one *octave.*) When E (330 c.p.s.) and C′ (528 c.p.s.) are played at the same time, a beat tone an octave below Middle G appears. If C, E, G, and C′ are sounded simultaneously on the piano, the ear will actually hear the C's one and two octaves below Middle C, and the G tone below Middle G. If C, E, G, and C′ are played with the "sustaining pedal" down, the strings one and two octaves below Middle C and the string one octave below Middle G will vibrate in sympathy.

The tonal effect of playing the four tones C, E, G, and C′ is not due entirely to the presence of beat tones. There will also be produced harmonics of all the tones actually sounded. In Figure 35–13, a string is vibrating in a single segment emitting a pure tone consisting of a foundation tone. In Figures 35–14, 35–15, and 35–16, a string is vibrating with two, three, and four loops, causing sounds having frequencies two, three, and four times that of the foundation tone. These sounds are often referred to as the second, third, and fourth har-

Fig. 35–18 *A violin tone includes a fundamental with many harmonics.*

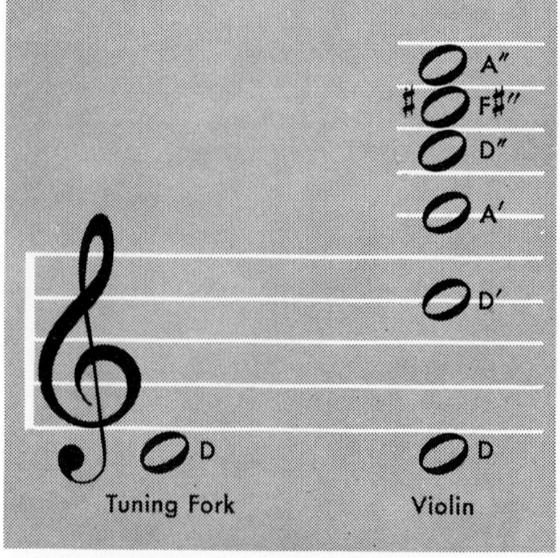

monics or the first, second, and third overtones. Figure 35–17 shows a complex vibration of a string simultaneously vibrating with several loop formations, thus sending forth composite sounds consisting of a foundation tone and a number of overtones. A specific illustration of this effect is to compare the sound of a D tuning fork with the note D played on a violin. (Refer to Figure 35–18.) The D tuning fork sends out a pure tone. The D string on the violin, however, not only sends forth its fundamental but also a number of overtones and harmonics in various degrees of prominence giving it tonal color. The combined effect, then, of playing the four tones C, E, G, and C′ together, is a fullness and richness in tone because of the presence of many beat tones and overtones. In the study of harmony it is called the *tonic chord.*

THE MAJOR DIATONIC SCALE

The distinctly pleasing combination of tones that has been discussed in detail has long been referred to by musicians as the *major triad,* C, E, G, or the *major tetrachord,* C, E, G, C′.

C	E	G	C′
264	330	396	528
4 :	5 :	6 :	8

The significant thing here is not the absolute frequencies of these tones, but the relative frequencies. Any four tones whose frequencies are in the ratio of 4 : 5 : 6 : 8, will be pleasing to the ear. The musical scale, the *do re mi* of our childhood days, is essentially a combination of major triads in the order shown in Table 35–1. The fundamental frequency used for the table is C = 264, but the fundamental tone in the musical scale can have any frequency; the musical scale is the result of establishing certain *relative frequencies* between the various tones. Manufacturers of musical instruments in the United States have now agreed to take A = 440 as the standard musical pitch in this country, and this is what gives Middle C a frequency of 264. The musical scale referred to above is called the *major scale.*

SCALE OF EQUAL TEMPERAMENT

The piano is considered the basic musical instrument. From one standpoint, however, it has a serious mechanical disadvantage. Its strings are fixed strings and there are only as many tones as strings. (Usually pianos are made with three adjacent strings for each tone.) If musicians could express all their ideas in the same musical scale based upon the same fundamental pitch of Middle C – that is, always play in the key of C – the keyboard on the piano could be in the major diatonic scale. However, the composer who wishes to produce certain effects often will build his scale on foundation frequencies other than that of Middle C, such as the key of E with E = 330 as a fundamental. Then, on these new fundamentals, he builds other major diatonic scales. This immediately makes it

TABLE 35–1

THE MAJOR DIATONIC SCALE

	G	A	B	C	D	E	F	G	A	B	C′	D′
				4		5		6				
							4		5		6	
	4		5		6			4		5		6
		220		264		330		396		495		594
	198		$247\frac{1}{2}$		297		352		440		528	
Ratio				1	$\frac{9}{8}$	$\frac{5}{4}$	$\frac{4}{3}$	$\frac{3}{2}$	$\frac{5}{3}$	$\frac{15}{8}$	2	
Interval					$\frac{9}{8}$ step	$\frac{10}{9}$ step	$\frac{16}{15}$ half-step	$\frac{9}{8}$ step	$\frac{10}{9}$ step	$\frac{9}{8}$ step	$\frac{16}{15}$ half-step	
				Do	re	mi	fa	sol	la	ti	do	

necessary to bring other pitches into the piano keyboard. However, it is mechanically impossible to build an instrument with fixed strings which is usable and which will allow the musician to play music written in any key he wants. This impasse led to a compromise, a new scale called the *scale of equal temperament.* Johann Sebastian Bach wrote "The Well-Tempered Clavichord" to demonstrate the new scale. In this scale the octave is divided into twelve equal intervals between thirteen keys. Each note has a frequency 1.0595 times that of the preceding note. The last note in the scale will have a frequency $(1.0595)^{12}$, or two times the fundamental making an octave. Figure 35–19 shows the relationship between these various keys on the piano keyboard. A comparison of the major diatonic and the equally tempered scales will indicate to what extent the piano keyboard is a musical compromise. Thus, the major diatonic scale consists of eight tones and seven intervals while the equally tempered scale consists of thirteen tones and twelve equal intervals. A violinist, or a vocalist, if singing alone, can render music in the *just tempered scale,* but the pianist must often use tones that deviate from the just tempered scale by nearly one per cent as indicated in Table 35–2. This difference is detectable by a trained musician, but hardly noticeable by the average person. Nevertheless, the piano is not included among the regular instruments of a symphony orchestra; it is brought in only for compositions that require it for certain effects.

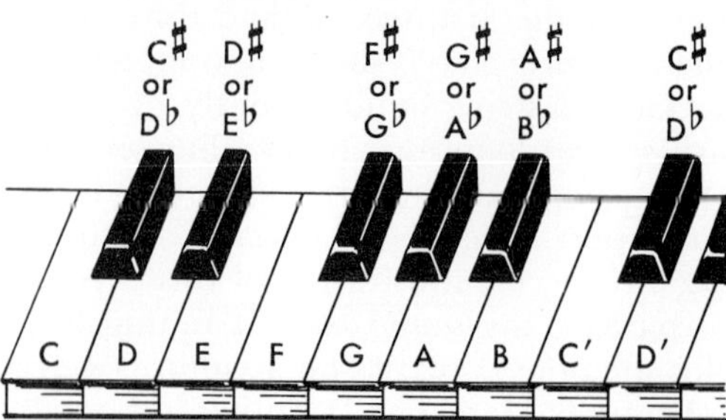

Fig. 35–19 *The piano keyboard in equal temperament.*

Sound can have unpleasant effects on an individual because of certain characteristics of the sound-emitting source. Thus music may be good or bad because of the manner of its production. Even the best of music as played, however, may be ruined for the hearer because of interference effects due to a poorly designed auditorium. A reflected sound wave when it returns to the hearer as a single sound is called an *echo.* In auditoriums of faulty design a particular sound wave may be reflected as many as a hundred times from various wall surfaces. The general prolongation of sound through a room due to multiple reflection is known as *reverberation.* For good audibility the time of reverberation in an auditorium should be from one to two seconds. If it is less than this, sound will often seem unnatural; if the period of reverberation is too great, sounds become unintelligible. To get this optimum period of reverberation, the auditorium itself must be designed for it and the materials used in the walls must be properly chosen.

Musical instruments have many differ-

TABLE 35–2 THE EQUALLY TEMPERED AND JUST TEMPERED SCALES COMPARED

	C	C♯ D♭	D	D♯ E♭	E	F	F♯ G♭	G	G♯ A♭	A	A♯ B♭	B	C
Equally tempered scale	264	279.7	296.3	314	332.6	352.4	373.4	395.6	419.6	444	470.4	498.4	528
Diatonic or just tempered scale	264	.....	297	...	330	352	.....	396	.....	440	.....	495	528

ent forms. They can be classified most conveniently into three different types: (*a*) percussion, (*b*) string, and (*c*) wind instruments. Within each type there are many designs to furnish all the desired frequencies. Thus the kettle drums, the snare drum, and the triangle found in every orchestra are percussion instruments with very different frequencies. The frequency of a vibrating string is determined by the length of the string, its tension, and its mass. The effect of these three factors can be summarized as

$$F(\text{requency}) \propto \frac{1}{l(\text{ength})} \propto \sqrt{\frac{t(\text{ension})}{m(\text{ass})}}.$$

In general there are three different ways to increase the frequency of a vibrating string: (*a*) reduce the length, (*b*) increase the tension, and (*c*) decrease the mass per unit of length. The frequency range of any particular stringed instrument is determined by the length and mass per unit length of the strings. After the instrument is once made and the length and weight of the strings fixed, tuning is then accomplished by controlling the tension on the strings. In the piano, for example, the high strings are made of short wires and thin cross sections under relatively great tension; the low strings are wound with wire to make them heavier; the piano is tuned by tightening or loosening the strings. To account for the frequency characteristics of wind instruments is more difficult. In general, air is set in vibration within an air column in a pipe or tube. The frequency of the sound from such a pipe *increases* as the length of the pipe *decreases.* Compare the length of a piccolo, for example, with that of a bass tuba. In most wind instruments the length of the vibrating air column can be controlled by the musician to change the frequency of the tones. In a trombone this is accomplished by means of a sliding tube; in a cornet, by valves. In the bugle or valveless trumpet the frequency depends entirely on the manner in which the air column is made to vibrate and this is controlled by the tension upon the lips.

NOISE

The combination of a nonharmonious group of audible frequencies is called *noise.* The significance of noise lies in the disturbing psychological and physiological effects. It lowers the morale and efficiency of workers. It is a frequent cause for impaired hearing or even deafness. The modern industry of sound-proofing is direct evidence of the reluctance of people to accept noise if it can be avoided. The intensity of noise is proportional to the squares of both the amplitude (energy) and the frequency. Thus the intensity of noise increases enormously with changes in amplitude and frequency. The units for measuring intensity of sound, the *bel* and the *decibel,* were devised to give relatively small numerical changes for the correspondingly enormous changes in intensity involved in common sounds.

If one sound is ten times the intensity of another, it is said to be one *bel* louder. The following data will serve as an illustration:

Relative energy	1 10^0	10 10^1	100 10^2	1000 10^3	10,000 or 10^4
Relative intensity in bels	0	1	2	3	4

Note that a sound of 4 bels intensity is 10,000 times greater than the reference sound of 0 bels.

The bel is too large a unit for most sound measurements, so a smaller unit, the decibel, is usually preferred. If a sound is one decibel louder than another, its intensity is about 26 per cent larger. This difference is just detectable by the human ear. The relative energy is shown below:

Relative energy	1	1.26	1.59	2.00	2.51
Relative intensity in bels	0	0.1	0.2	0.3	0.4
Relative intensity in decibels	0	1	2	3	4

The student familiar with logarithms will note that

$$\log 1.26 = 0.10$$
$$\log 1.59 = 0.20, \text{ etc.}$$

Furthermore, each level of intensity is 26 per cent greater (1.26 times) than the preceding level. That is,

$$2.00 = (1.26)\ (1.59)\,,$$
$$2.51 = (1.26)\ (2.00)\,.$$

The sound units, the decibel and the bel, become more meaningful by designating the intensity of sound at the threshold of hearing, which corresponds to about 10^{-10} microwatts per square centimeter, as *one decibel.* On this basis, the intensity of some common sounds is given in Table 35–3. Sound waves at the threshold of hearing have an amplitude of about 10^{-8} centimeters. Sound waves which cause pain have amplitudes in the range of about two millimeters.

HIGH–FIDELITY REPRODUCTION

The radio, which has become such an essential part of modern living, was originally developed only as a means for communicating information, most commonly in a coded form using but a single tone (Morse code transmission, for example). With the development of broadcasting systems, music became a prominent part of most radio programs. But music from the ordinary radio or phonograph is far from the "real thing," for many of the very high and very low frequencies are never reproduced. This is due to limitations of the equipment which are of little significance if the radio is thought of primarily as a device for communication. The relatively recent improvements in the recording of sound, and its subsequent reproduction with little loss of sound frequencies so that the resulting music is a faithful reproduction of the original music, is called *high-fidelity.* It means reproducing the full audio range of frequencies present in the original music with relatively little distortion. High-fidelity became possible when electronic engineers successfully fused the art of amplification of minute fluctuating electrical currents with our modern understanding of acoustics and music.

The human ear can hear musical tones with frequencies from as low as 16 cycles per second to as high as 20,000 cycles per second. (Refer to Figure 35–20.) The bass notes on a piano go as low as about 25 cycles per second. The high notes on a violin or a piccolo reach frequencies as high as about 16,000 cycles per second. The human ear covers a greater frequency range than that furnished by our musical instruments. Thus all the frequencies from a modern orchestra can be heard by the average human ear. (See Figure 35–11, page 574.) The very high frequencies often consist of higher harmonics or overtones of instruments, such as those of the flute, violin, or saxophone. Limitations of equipment which are relatively unimportant when the radio is used only to transmit code signals or speech make it impossible to transmit, by ordinary audio-modulated radio, musical tones with frequencies below about 50 or above 7500 cycles per second. Thus the very high and very low notes of music cannot be

TABLE 35–3

INTENSITY RATINGS OF SOME COMMON SOUNDS

	BELS	DECIBELS	REACTION OF HEARER
Jet plane	16	160	Extreme discomfort
	14	140	Pain in the ears
	12	120	Discomfort
Subway	9	90	
Heavy traffic	8	80	
Normal conversation	6.5	65	
Ticking of a watch	1.5	15	
Whisper	1	10	
Threshold of hearing		1	10^{-10} microwatts per cm^2, or 0.0002 dyne per cm^2
	0	0	Barely audible

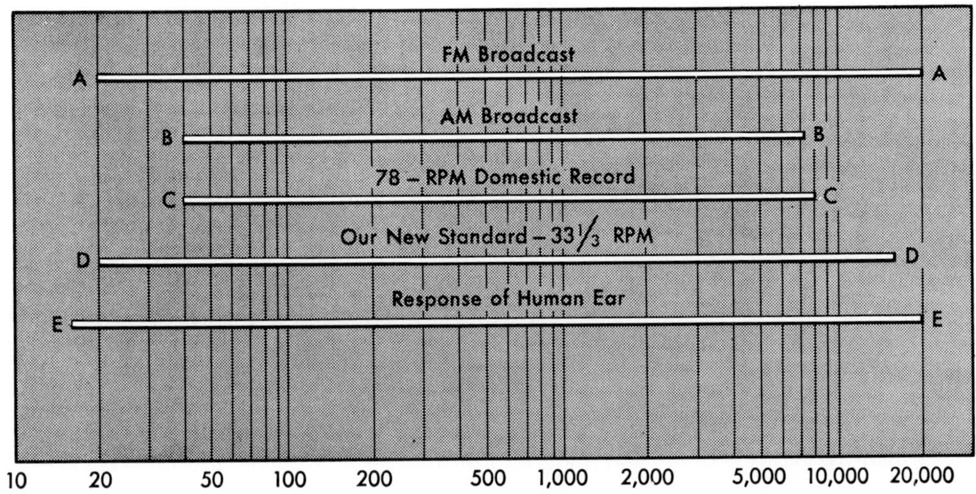

Fig. 35–20 *The frequency ranges of musical program sources. (From Harold D. Weiler,* High Fidelity Simplified, *John F. Rider, Publisher, Inc.)*

heard over radio. The 78 revolution-per-minute (r.p.m.) phonograph record of a decade ago had the same limitation. Lovers of good music naturally complained. Gradually the demand for good music from records became so persistent that a new standard for the recording and reproduction of music came to be accepted. This is the basis for *high-fidelity.* The new standard called for the reproduction of all frequencies from 30 to 15,000 cycles per second — a very acceptable compromise, for it means the loss of only the very lowest piano and organ pipe notes and of frequencies above 15,000 cycles per second. Thus only a few of the higher harmonics of instruments, such as the snare drum and the triangle, are lost. High-fidelity music is actually the result of a happy combination of at least six factors: (1) the acoustics of the room in which the music is recorded and of the room in which it is reproduced; (2) the faithfulness of the original recording; (3) the record player and the electromagnetic pick-up; (4) the preamplifier and amplifier; (5) the speaker; and (6) the speaker enclosure.

1. *Room Acoustics.* The room in which one listens to high-fidelity is an essential part of the reproducing instrument. Excessive reverberation due to reflections from hard wall and floor surfaces seriously reduces the quality of the music. On the other hand, a certain amount of reverberation is necessary — the time necessary for the sound to decrease about 60 decibels. Noise cannot be avoided, but the noise level must be kept as much below the music level as possible, say 40 decibels or below. To realize the above conditions closely, then, the listening room must not be too small, and the floors and walls should be covered with sound-absorbing materials such as carpeting or draperies. An acceptable arrangement can be found by experiment.

2. *The Faithfulness of the Original Recording.* The frequency and the amplitude of the sound to be recorded is impressed by a lateral movement in a master record with a tiny sharp stylus. (Refer to Figure 35–21.) A low-frequency note takes on the form shown in Figure 35–21*A*. A high-frequency note will be recorded as shown in Figure 35–21*B*. A combination of the two will give a complex form shown in Figure 35–21*C*. The recording engineer cannot escape noise. It must, therefore, be eliminated or reduced in intensity. This is done, at the time of recording, by deliberately *increasing* the recorded signal level for the higher frequencies and *decreasing* the recorded signal for the lower. Increasing the sound

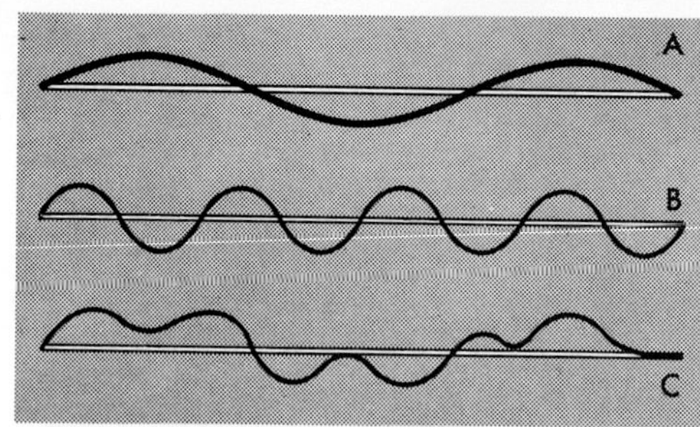

Fig. 35–21 *Low-frequency, high-frequency, and complex recorded wave forms. (From Harold D. Weiler,* High Fidelity Simplified, *John F. Rider, Publisher, Inc.)*

level of the higher frequencies to a decibel range which is greater than that of the noise means the elimination of much of the noise which would otherwise be heard. Decreasing the amplitude of the groove for recorded sounds of low frequencies makes it easier for the pick-up needle to follow the groove when the music is to be reproduced. The recording stylus is so small and the grooves are so close together that a standard $33\frac{1}{3}$ r.p.m. long-playing record actually has about 325 grooves per inch, and the long-playing characteristics of these records depend upon the small size of the grooves. High-fidelity can be achieved only if the lateral movement of the recording stylus faithfully follows in pattern the form of the music being recorded, but this is relatively easy to do.

3. *The Record Player and the Pick-up.* An essential part of a high-fidelity set is the "pick-up" with its diamond needle. It follows the microgroove of the record as it turns with (one hopes) uniform speed ($33\frac{1}{3}$ r.p.m.). This is the first step in obtaining music from the record. Most pick-ups are based upon electromagnetic effects. (Refer to Figure 35–22.) The moving part of the pick-up is a small mass of soft iron. This vibrates back and forth within a magnetic field provided by a permanent magnet, with the lateral movement of the diamond needle in the sound groove. The bar magnet as it vibrates induces an oscillating current in the coil surrounding it. The leads from this coil go to a preamplifier. The characteristics of this current match with varying degrees of fidelity the frequency characteristics of the recorded sound.

4. *The Preamplifier and Amplifier.* The current generated in an electromagnetic pick-up is extremely minute. It must be amplified millions of times before it has enough energy to operate a loudspeaker. This is the function of the preamplifier and amplifier. In addition, the preamplifier must preferentially amplify the energy of the low-frequency notes which were reduced in recording (see above). At the same time, the emphasis on the high frequencies must be reduced so the energy of low- and high-frequency notes as they go to the loudspeaker are as nearly like the original sound as possible. The preamplifier and amplifier are essential to any high-fidelity system.

5. *The Loudspeaker.* The output of the amplifier, a fluctuating electrical current of many frequencies and energies, is converted into audible music in an electromagnetic speaker. This, in essence, is a thin paper cone which is put in forced vibration by a fluctuating magnetic field generated outside a small electromagnet. The electromagnet is actuated by the fluctuating current from the amplifier. (Refer to Figure 35–23.) The vibrating cone generates the sound waves which become music.

Fig. 35–22 *Essential parts of an electromagnetic pick-up.*

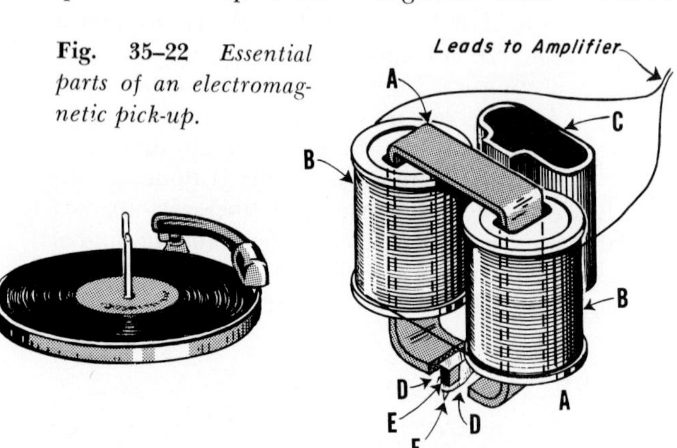

A Soft iron path to concentrate the magnetic lines of force of the permanent magnet C

B Small wire coils around upright parts of A with leads to amplifier

C Intense permanent magnet. Some of the magnetic lines of force outside the magnet carried in A

D Air gap with intense magnetic field

E Soft iron support for stylus which can vibrate laterally

F Jewel stylus (0.001 inch) which follows groove in LP record

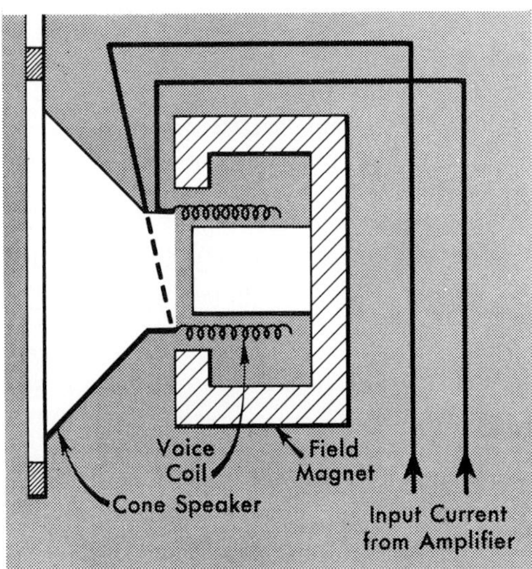

Fig. 35–23 *Principle of the cone loudspeaker.*

Our discussion has assumed only one speaker. Actually, no one speaker can efficiently reproduce notes of both high and low frequencies. Much better results are obtained by having at least two speakers, a so-called "tweeter" for the high frequencies, and a so-called "woofer" for the low frequencies. These may be separate speakers or mounted coaxially in the same speaker. The efficiency of producing the final sound can be further increased by dividing the sound spectrum into three or even four parts by use of three or four separate cones.

6. *The Speaker Enclosure.* A cone speaker in the open does not give good music reproduction. Sound waves are sent out from both the front and back of the vibrating cone, and they usually combine to cause undesirable interference effects. The easiest way to prevent these is to *absorb completely* the sound waves from the back of the cone. This can be most simply done by mounting the speaker in the side of a large box which is lined with sound-absorbing material. If the box is large enough – greater than 10 cubic feet – and well soundproofed on the inside, the sound waves from the back of the vibrating cone are completely absorbed. This type of enclosure is called an "infinite baffle."

Sound and electronic scientists and engineers, together with musicians, by thoroughly understanding these principal six factors necessary for the faithful recording and reproduction of music, have been responsible for modern high-fidelity. The sequence of changes from original music to reproduced music is a complex one, as shown in Table 35–4. High-fidelity is a good example of solving a problem by a thorough understanding and application of fundamental principles – in this case, of sound, electricity, and electronics.

TABLE 35–4 SEQUENCE OF CHANGES FROM ORIGINAL TO REPRODUCED MUSIC

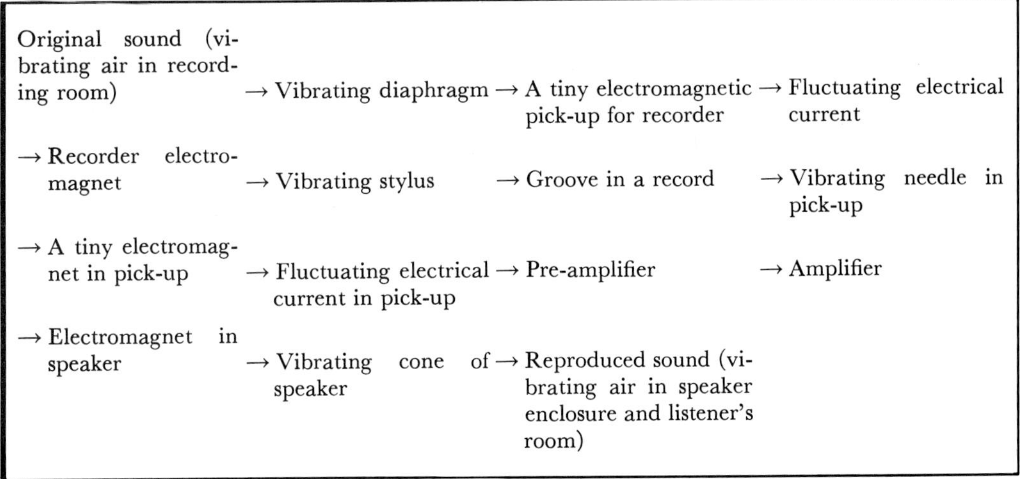

Original sound (vibrating air in recording room)	→ Vibrating diaphragm	→ A tiny electromagnetic pick-up for recorder	→ Fluctuating electrical current
→ Recorder electromagnet	→ Vibrating stylus	→ Groove in a record	→ Vibrating needle in pick-up
→ A tiny electromagnet in pick-up	→ Fluctuating electrical current in pick-up	→ Pre-amplifier	→ Amplifier
→ Electromagnet in speaker	→ Vibrating cone of speaker	→ Reproduced sound (vibrating air in speaker enclosure and listener's room)	

SUMMARY

1. Observations concerning sound which indicate that some form of wave motion is involved are the following:
   a. Sound requires an expenditure of energy for its production.
   b. A medium which resists distortion (possesses property of elasticity) is required for the propagation of sound.
   c. Sound travels in a given medium with a definite velocity which is determined by the characteristics of the medium – its elasticity and inertia.
   d. Sound waves under certain conditions undergo reflection, refraction, and diffraction.
   e. Sound waves can be made to interfere constructively and destructively.
   f. The Doppler effect takes place if the sound source continuously changes its position with respect to a hearer.
2. Sound waves are the result of very small longitudinal to-and-fro displacements of the molecules of an elastic medium. The waves consist of alternate regions of condensation and rarefaction.
3. Sound waves will not travel through an inelastic medium or vacuum.
4. Sound travels 1087 ft/sec at 0° C. in air.
5. The velocity of sound increases 2 ft/sec per degree Centigrade increase in temperature.
6. The frequency of a series of sound waves is the same as that of the vibrating body producing the sound.
7. The fundamental equation for any wave motion, $v = f \times l$, applies to sound.
8. The wave length of a sound wave is the distance from condensation to condensation or from rarefaction to rarefaction.
9. Whenever a sound source and a hearer approach each other, the wave length of sound waves intercepted by the hearer will be decreased and the frequency (pitch) will be increased. The opposite effect will be noted when the sound source and a hearer recede from each other. This is the Doppler effect in sound.
10. Noise consists of sounds of widely varying and continually changing frequencies.
11. A musical tone consists of sound of a single or predominant frequency in the audible range of the ear.
12. Three important characteristics of a musical tone are (*a*) pitch or frequency, (*b*) loudness, and (*c*) quality or timbre.
13. Loudness is a complex psychological reaction to sound and is a measure of the sensation produced on an individual by sound.
14. Loudness depends upon the simultaneous operation of two factors: (*a*) the energy carried by the sound waves to the ear, and (*b*) the frequency.
15. The average human ear is most sensitive to sounds with a frequency of about 2000.
16. The quality or timbre of a musical tone depends upon the number and prominence of overtones of the fundamental.
17. Music depends upon a blending of many tones of different frequencies. When two tones are played simultaneously, any of three principal results are possible:
   a. The two tones may be in unison or the frequency of one may be a multiple of the other. This result is pleasant.
   b. The two tones may result in beats which are unpleasant – dissonance. Beats are most unpleasant when they occur at the rate of 15 to 40 per second.
   c. The two tones may produce pleasant beats or difference tones.
18. A vibrating sound source – string, membrane, or air column – often vibrates in such a way as to send forth tones of frequencies 2, 3, 4, . . . *n* times the fundamental frequency. These are called harmonics or overtones.
19. Tones whose frequencies are in the ratio of 4 : 5 : 6 produce an especially pleasing effect on the ear because of a blending of many beat tones and overtones with the various foundation frequencies. This combination of frequencies is called the tonic chord or major triad.
20. A tone which is due to very frequent beats from two tones and whose frequency is a submultiple of one of the tones is called a beat or difference tone.
21. The major diatonic scale consists of eight tones and seven intervals with frequencies 9/8, 5/4, 4/3, 3/2, 5/3, 15/8 and two times the fundamental tone.

22. The scale of equal temperament consists of thirteen tones and twelve intervals all of which are alike. The scale of equal temperament is a musical compromise necessary to make the piano a practical instrument.
23. Musical instruments are classified as three principal types: (*a*) percussion, (*b*) string, and (*c*) wind.
24. The units for measuring the relative intensity of sounds are the *bel* and the *decibel.* Any sound that is 10^x times more intense than a reference sound is x bels or $10x$ decibels more intense.
25. A sound which is just at the threshold of hearing has an intensity of one decibel; normal conversation is about 55 decibels; sounds of 140 decibels are painful.

STUDY EXERCISES

1. Indicate whether the following statements are true (*T*) or false (*F*):
   - *a.* The audibility of a sound depends only upon the energy of the wave – amplitude of vibration. . . . .
   - *b.* The range of frequency of the human voice is from 20 to 20,000 vibrations per second. . . . .
   - *c.* The range of frequency of audible sound is 20 to 20,000 vibrations per second. . . . .
   - *d.* A musical tone consists of one or more sounds of regular and constant frequencies. . . . .
   - *e.* A noise consists of sounds that are of irregular and erratic frequencies. . . . .
   - *f.* The musical scale consists of notes that have frequencies that bear a definite relationship to some fundamental note, as Middle C = 264. . . . .
   - *g.* Two notes whose frequencies are in the ratio of 2 : 1 represent an interval of one octave. . . . .
   - *h.* It is possible for a violinist with a keen sense of pitch to play music in the major diatonic scale. . . . .
   - *i.* A skilled musician can play music in the major diatonic scale on an ordinary piano. . . . .
   - *j.* Musical tones of high frequency travel faster through air than notes of low frequency. . . . .
   - *k.* It is impossible to get a note of such high frequency that it cannot be heard. . . . . .
2. Associate by number the following terms with the appropriate statement given below.

1. Fundamental	6. Three notes whose vibration ratios are 10 : 12 : 15
2. Beats	7. Pitch
3. Beat tone	8. Sympathetic vibration
4. Overtone or harmonic	9. Dissonance
5. Three notes whose vibration ratios are 4 : 5 : 6	10. Consonance

   - *a.* Two notes which are unpleasant when sounded together illustrate . . . .
   - *b.* The major chord which is such a prominent part of all music consists of . . . .
   - *c.* A Middle C fork when sounded sets the Middle C string of a harp to vibrating. What does this illustrate? . . . .
   - *d.* A musical tone often represents a pleasing fusion of various sounds which have a definite frequency relationship to each other. What name is applied to the most prominent sound? . . . .
   - *e.* That term in connection with sound which corresponds to color in light. . . . .
   - *f.* Two notes which produce a pleasing combination when sounded together illustrate . . . .
   - *g.* That two notes are not quite in unison can be detected by listening for what? . . . .
   - *h.* A note with a frequency of 256 when sounded simultaneously with a note of frequency 384 will result in a note with a frequency of 128, the octave below 256. This is called a . . . .
   - *i.* Middle C (264), when sounded on a violin, consists of various sounds, among them a note with a frequency of 528. This is called . . . .
3. Certain numbered strings on a harp have frequencies as follows:

(1)	(2)	(3)	(4)	(5)	(6)	(7)
200	250	300	400	500	600	800

When various combinations of these strings are played simultaneously, certain sound effects are produced: Octave; Major chord; Beat tone; Consonance; and Dissonance. Which of the terms just given best describes the result that would be obtained by playing the following strings simultaneously:

a. 1 and 4 ....
b. 1, 2, and 3 ....
c. 4 and 5 ....
d. 2 and 5 ....
e. 4 and 7 ....
f. 4, 5, and 6 ....
g. 2 and 6 ....
h. 2 and 3 ....
i. 3 and 6 ....
j. 1 and 3 ....

4. A sound is 100 times more intense than a reference sound. What is the relative intensity in decibels?
5. How many times more intense is a low conversational sound (50 decibels) than a whisper (10 decibels)?

FOR FURTHER READING

1. LEMON, H. B., *From Galileo to the Nuclear Age.* Chicago: University of Chicago Press, 1946.

   The characteristics and properties of sound are entertainingly presented in Chapter 37.
2. WHITE, HARVEY E., *Classical and Modern Physics.* New York: D. Van Nostrand Company, 1940.

   The discussion of music and musical instruments in Chapter 16 is admirable.
3. MILLER, D. C., *The Science of Musical Sounds.* New York: The Macmillan Company, 1944.

   This is by one of the world's authorities on sound and music. There are many remarkable photographs of the effects of sound waves. Technical knowledge is not necessary to enjoy this work.

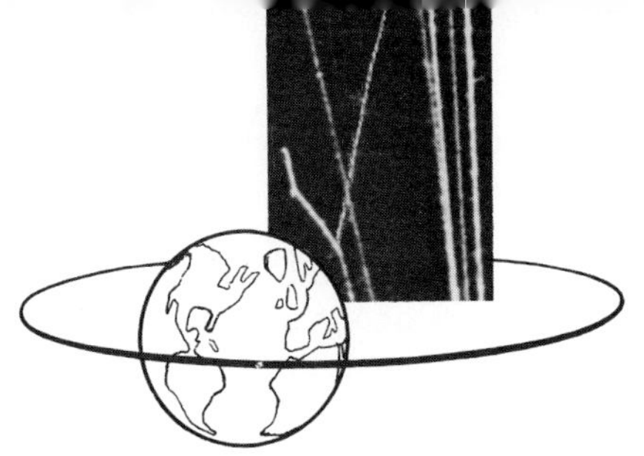

36

KINDS OF LIGHT

IN CHAPTER 34 we considered certain properties of visible light and the comprehensive theories that have been accepted to account for them. The wave theory of light states that light consists of transverse electromagnetic waves which originate in some oscillating electrical system and travel with a velocity of 3×10^{10} centimeters per second. The nature of the propagating medium, if any, is unknown. We have used the term *light* in its most general sense as any form of radiation traveling as transverse waves with the velocity of visible light. This includes not only visible light, but also ultraviolet, infrared, and radio waves. It is necessary now to extend this list to include X-rays, gamma rays, and cosmic rays. All these forms of light differ in their energy content, wave length, and frequency.

THE ELECTROMAGNETIC SPECTRUM

It can be shown that the wave length of visible light extends from about 7×10^{-5} cm for red light to about 4.1×10^{-5} cm for the visible violet light. The frequencies of these forms of light are:

For red light:

$$f = \frac{v}{l} = \frac{3 \times 10^{10} \text{ cm/sec}}{7 \times 10^{-5} \text{ cm}}$$
$$= 4.3 \times 10^{14} \text{ cycles per second.}$$

For violet light:

$$f = \frac{v}{l} = \frac{3 \times 10^{10} \text{ cm/sec}}{4.1 \times 10^{-5} \text{ cm}}$$
$$= 7.3 \times 10^{14} \text{ cycles per second.}$$

The range of frequencies for visible light corresponds, then, to just about one octave, or doubling the frequency: violet light has a frequency about twice that of red light. It is difficult to comprehend a frequency of 4.3×10^{14} cycles per second, but these frequencies have been verified by many different experimental procedures. A unique thing about visible light is that it can be perceived by the eye.

There are many forms of invisible light or radiation. One form, the infrared, had been discovered in the early part of the nineteenth century. We now know that infrared rays are electromagnetic in character, with wave lengths as much as seven hundred times greater than those of visible light. In fact, every warm flatiron or other hot object sends out invisible infrared rays which, when intercepted by the body, produce warmth. The picnicker has found from experience that frankfurters are more quickly roasted over a bed of glowing red coals than over a high smoky flame. The glowing coals are a rich source of infrared rays. Almost simultaneously with the discovery of the red rays came the discovery of another form of "black light" – ultraviolet. This is a portion of the electromagnetic spectrum with wave lengths about one-third (1.4×10^{-5} cm) as great as the visible violet. The sun and all objects at white heat send out ultraviolet rays, invisible to the eye, which result in definite physiological effects such as sunburn and tanning of the skin. The hot rays of the summer sun and of the mercury arc lamp are especially rich in ultraviolet.

In Chapter 34 we learned of the successful search by Hertz for invisible rays with wave lengths considerably greater than infrared rays. All oscillating electric charges send out the waves we now call radio waves. Even the sixty-cycle alternating light cir-

TABLE 36–1 ELECTROMAGNETIC SPECTRUM

NAME	WAVE LENGTH *	FREQUENCY * C.P.S.	SOURCE	METHOD OF DETECTION
60-cycle A.C. and other long electromagnetic waves	Thousands of km	60	Electric generator	Electromagnetic induction
	2×10^6 cm	1.5×10^4		
Wireless and radio			Oscillatory electric circuit	Electrical resonance
	4×10^3 cm	7.5×10^6		
Short Hertzian				
	3.5×10^{-2} cm	9×10^{11}		
Infrared, or heat			Vibrating molecules and atoms	Thermopile or Bolometer
	7×10^{-5} cm	4.3×10^{14}		
Visible light				Eye or Photography or Fluorescence effects
	4.1×10^{-5} cm	7.3×10^{14}		
Ultraviolet			Vibrating electrons in atoms	
	1.2×10^{-6} cm	2.5×10^{16}		
Extreme ultraviolet				Photography Fluorescence
	5×10^{-7} cm	6×10^{16}		
X-rays				Photography or Radiation potential
	1.2×10^{-9} cm	2.5×10^{19}		
Gamma rays			Radioisotopes Atomic explosion	Photography or Geiger counter Ionization
	5×10^{-11} cm	6×10^{20}		
	1×10^{-12} cm	3×10^{22}		
Cosmic			?	Geiger counter and Wilson cloud chamber
	1×10^{-13} cm	3×10^{23}		

* The values are approximate.

cuits in a home send out radio waves of very great wave length. About the turn of the century Guglielmo Marconi (Italy, 1874–1937) found practical application for these radio waves in wireless communication. The waves from oscillating electric charges have made radio and television networks possible, but they also, at times, have nuisance aspects. The crackling sounds from your radio, so-called "static," are also radio waves originating in the electric discharges of lightning, on the spark plugs of a passing automobile, or perhaps an arcing vacuum-cleaner or electric-shaver motor.

In 1895, Roentgen discovered the mysterious penetrating rays that have ever since been referred to by the term Roentgen himself used, namely, X-rays. Eventually these also were shown to be electromagnetic waves with wave lengths as short as 5×10^{-7} cm and frequencies as high as 6×10^{16} cycles per second. The tubes now used to produce X-rays still employ Roentgen's method of bombarding a metal target with a stream of fast-moving electrons. The improvements have been in the direction of increasing the number and the velocity or kinetic energy of the electrons which hit the target. In the modern Coolidge X-ray tube (Figure 22–1) the electrons are obtained from a white-hot filament heated by electricity. The tube must be highly evacuated. At the same time a very high potential (150,000 volts) is applied across the filament and the tungsten target, which is made positive. X-rays possess so much energy that they penetrate many forms of matter opaque to visible light and thus can be used to reveal hidden defects in metal castings, locate foreign objects in the body, study breaks in bone structure, or locate diseased areas in the body (as in the lungs, liver, or teeth).

All electromagnetic waves have certain common characteristics:

1. They are all produced by rapidly oscillating systems of an electrical nature (refer to Table 36–1).

2. They all travel with the velocity of light, 3×10^{10} cm/sec.

3. They all represent energy.

4. They all undergo reflection, refraction, diffraction, interference and reinforcement, and the Doppler effect.

5. All except visible light require some form of instrumentation to detect their presence.

The enormous quantity of energy received from the sun is radiated largely as infrared rays, visible light, and ultraviolet rays as transverse waves with a velocity of 3×10^{10} cm/sec. This type of energy is often called *radiant energy*. Infrared rays become ordinary heat when absorbed.

The common vacuum bottle is effective in keeping liquids hot or cold primarily because it prevents the loss or entrance of radiant energy. The vacuum bottle itself is constructed with an inner and outer wall of thin glass. The inside of the inner and outer walls is then carefully silvered, after which the air between the two walls is evacuated with an efficient air pump and the bottle sealed to keep out the air. Such a vessel will keep liquids hot or cold for many hours. The vacuum prevents heat from passing through the double wall by convection. Loss of heat by radiation is made very small by the silver lining which prevents the escape and entrance of infrared rays by the process of reflection.

Infrared rays can be intercepted and brought to a focus just as can visible light. Range finders – which locate invisible war vessels or "see" bombing planes through clouds or in the dark – can operate by intercepting and focusing the infrared rays from firing guns or hot airplane engines. Infrared rays have also made night photography possible.

APPLICATIONS

It is worthy of note that most of these radiations now have many important applications. Only a few of their characteristics and uses can be mentioned here.

1. *Radio waves.* These are produced by any rapidly oscillating electric current obtained with a specially designed vacuum tube. The dial on a radio set indicates that by *resonance* it is able to pick up waves with

frequencies varying from 550 to 1500 kilocycles, which correspond to lengths of 547.5 to 200 meters from crest to crest. Television makes use of radio waves of even greater frequencies in the range of 54 to 216 megacycles.

2. *Infrared.* These are ordinary heat waves which are best absorbed by dark unpolished surfaces. Greenhouses are often heated in winter only by infrared rays from the sun which pass through the glass to be absorbed by the dark soil within the greenhouse. Every warm object radiates infrared rays. Photographic film is now available which is sensitive to infrared, making photography possible even in the dark.

3. *Ultraviolet.* These rays are present in large amounts in sunlight and in the light from a mercury-vapor or carbon arc lamp. They have a great physiological significance, for certain vitamins are formed in the human body only when the skin is exposed directly to sunlight or ultraviolet light. One reason for a higher incidence of certain vitamin deficiency diseases in the winter time is the reduced possibility of bodily exposure to sunlight, for ordinary window glass does not transmit the ultraviolet. Mercury-vapor lamps are enclosed in quartz, which transmits ultraviolet readily.

4. *X-rays.* The manner of producing X-rays and some of their applications were mentioned on page 347. These rays are of great significance also because they serve as the basis for many useful tools in science. They have made possible, for example, the determination of the atomic numbers of the elements by the method of Moseley (refer to page 359,) and the crystal structure (crystal lattice) of true solids.

5. *Gamma rays.* Radioactive substances such as radium-226 and cobalt-60 spontaneously disintegrate to form simpler substances. In this process they release energy as gamma rays. These disintegrations are beyond the control of man. The gamma rays are electromagnetic radiation with frequencies somewhat greater than for X-rays. They behave similarly to X-rays but have greater energy.

The curative properties of many radioactive substances are due to gamma rays. Thus radioactive substances such as radium-226, cobalt-60, and iodine-131 are very useful in combatting certain diseases or diseased tissues — tumors or cancers — because of the gamma rays that they form as they disintegrate. The controlled use of gamma rays in the treatment of disease is studied in the science of *radiology.*

Another growing application of gamma rays is as a substitute for X-rays in examining materials for flaws or breaks. An intense cobalt-60 source, for example, has many advantages over an X-ray outfit in examining metal castings, for example, for flaws. Other radioactive substances used for this purpose are cesium-137 and iridium-192. These techniques are a part of the science of *radiography.* Gamma rays are also used to produce mutants in biological forms.

6. *Cosmic rays.* The last addition to the list of very penetrating radiations, cosmic rays are the most penetrating radiation known and the least understood. The phenomena associated with them are highly complex. Cosmic rays, for example, help to account for the ions which are always present in the atmosphere. It is these ions which cause even the best-insulated electroscopes slowly to lose their charge. Cosmic radiations are so energetic that they penetrate even into deep mines.

It appears that cosmic rays are of two types, primary and secondary. The former are positively charged bodies from outer space — probably protons. When these high-speed particles collide with atoms in the atmosphere, secondary cosmic rays, energetic gamma rays, or photons are formed. The actual collision processes are complex, because particles other than gamma rays are also formed — electrons, positrons, and neutrons. Cosmic rays illustrate the duality of very energetic particles or waves. As protons, cosmic rays must be particles. Since cosmic rays are able to penetrate deep bodies of water and deep mines, they seem to have the characteristics of very energetic electromagnetic waves. For this reason they are included in Table 36–1. The study of these particles is deferred to Chapter 38.

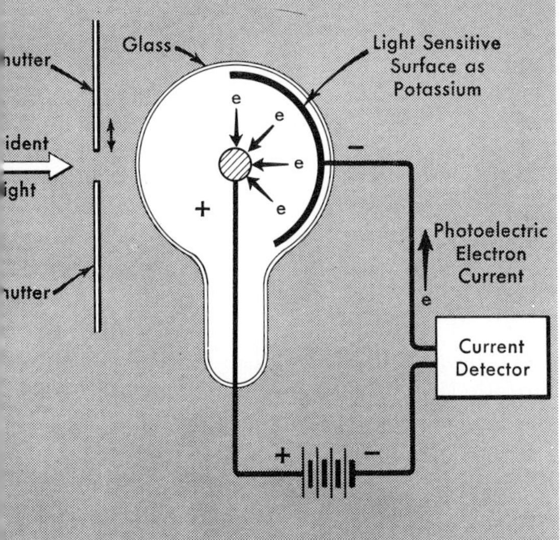

Fig. 36–1 *Essential parts of a photoelectric cell.*

LIMITATIONS OF MAXWELL'S THEORY OF RADIATION

It was Hertz in 1887, with his discovery of radio waves, who gave impetus to the general acceptance of Maxwell's electromagnetic theory of light. It was Hertz also, in 1887, who discovered the effect that led eventually to a revival in a changed form of the corpuscular theory of light. The effect referred to is the *photoelectric effect.* The term means the production of electricity by the use of light. The photoelectric effect is used in an exceedingly common and important scientific gadget, the photoelectric cell. This light-electricity cell finds myriad uses. The exit doors to some supermarkets automatically open when the shopper loaded down with bundles interrupts a light beam to a photoelectric cell in front of the door. Traffic counts on busy highways are made with photoelectric devices. The sound track on motion picture film becomes sound because of an application of photoelectric tubes. The wave theory of light failed to account for the photoelectric effect and led eventually to the wide acceptance of the quantum or photon theory of radiation.

PRINCIPLE OF THE PHOTO-ELECTRIC CELL

The essential parts of a photoelectric cell are shown in Figure 36–1. The cell is usually constructed of glass. The cathode has a large surface and consists of some light-sensitive metal such as potassium, rubidium, or cesium. The cell also contains a positive electrode. It is highly evacuated to prevent oxidation of the metal surface in the cathode. When the shutter is set to prevent entrance of light no current flows in the external circuit. Just as soon as the shutter is open, light strikes the metal surface to eject electrons, so-called photoelectrons. These are attracted and collect on the positive electrode. In effect there is a flow of electrons from the metal surface to the positive electrode which varies as the intensity and frequency of the incident light. The applications of a photoelectric cell depend on how this output current is used. It may after amplification operate a counter, operate an alarm, open or close a switch, or even produce sound in a loudspeaker.

The operation of a photoelectric cell depends on the *kind* of light which strikes it — that is, its frequency or wave length — not merely on the amount of light. (Refer to Figure 36–3.) The carbon arc serves as a convenient intense light source. The polished zinc plate and electroscope are charged positively until the leaves diverge. If the glass plate is inserted in the beam of light, the electroscope does *not* discharge. If the glass plate is removed, however, the leaves of the electroscope quickly collapse. The explanation is that a component of the light, ultraviolet rays, causes the ejection of

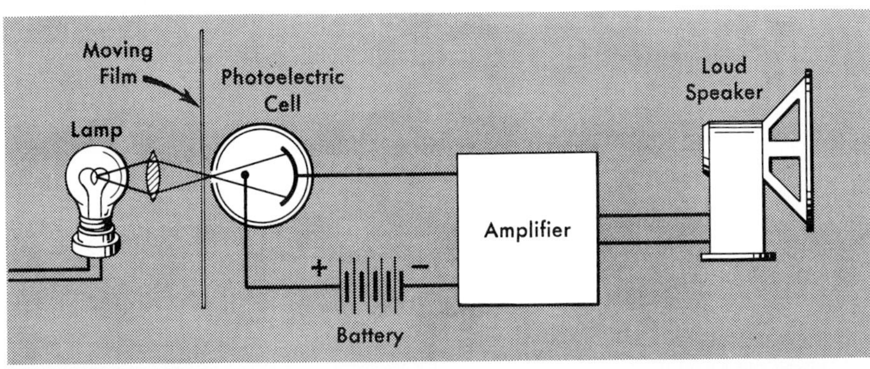

Fig. 36–2 *Application of photoelectric cell to convert recorded sound on film to sound.*

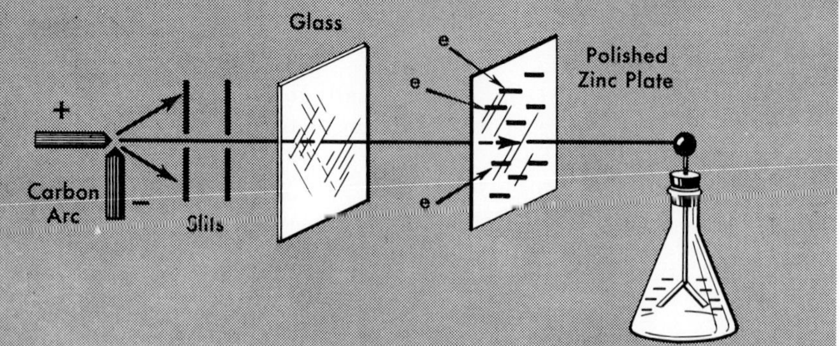

Fig. 36–3 *The photoelectric effect depends upon the kind of light.*

electrons which is shown by the discharge of the electroscope. Ultraviolet light cannot pass through common glass.

PHOTON THEORY OF RADIATION

According to the wave theory, the light-sensitive metal in a photoelectric tube receives energy whenever light waves strike it. When enough energy has been transmitted to the electrons in the metal, they should become photoelectrons. Furthermore, increasing the intensity of light might be expected to increase the rate of transference of radiant energy to electrons and thus the rate of emission of electrons. Experimentally, however, this proved untrue. The ejection of electrons depended upon the *color* or *frequency* of the light. Refer to Figure 36–3. For example, photoelectrons from zinc require ultraviolet light. Even intense light sources without ultraviolet light do not cause photoelectrons. Furthermore, in the case of ultraviolet light on zinc, there was no time lag involved in ejecting electrons as called for by the wave theory. Even low-intensity sources of ultraviolet light would cause an immediate ejection of electrons, and the electrons liberated by low-intensity light would have just as much energy as those liberated by high-intensity light.

The wave theory failed utterly to account for the photoelectric effect. It appeared instead that light consisted of bundles or packets of energy called *quanta* or *photons.* In the case of zinc only the photons in ultraviolet light had enough energy to kick out photoelectrons. This same effect was observed with other metals – the emission of electrons and the velocity of the electrons depended very definitely upon the color or frequency of the light which was used.

Eventually it was shown that the energy of the photoelectron was directly proportional to the exciting frequency. This is what the scientist calls a "straight-line relationship." (Refer to Figure 36–4.) The frequency f_0 is the "threshold frequency." Light with frequencies below this cannot eject photoelectrons. Thus yellow light is needed for the photoelectric effect with rubidium, green light for potassium, and blue light for sodium. Note from Figure 36–4 that the energies of the electrons from rubidium, potassium, and sodium are in the same order. In other words,

E(nergy) of photoelectron depends upon f, or

$$E = h \times f. \qquad (\textit{Equation 36–1})$$

Fig. 36–4 *Relation between energy of photoelectron and the exciting frequency.*

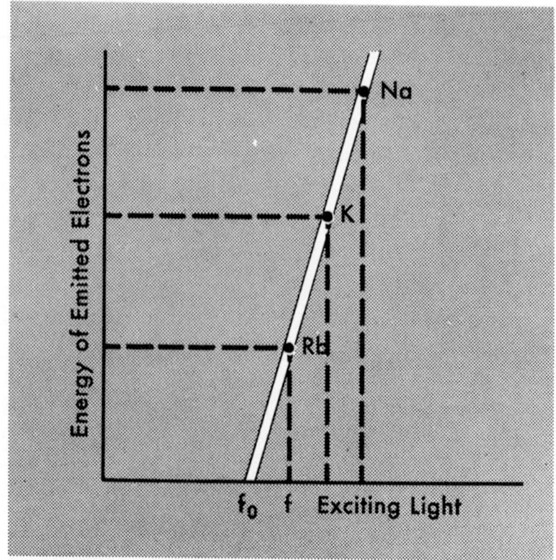

The use of this fundamental equation of the quantum (photon) theory for the photoelectric effect is due to Albert Einstein (Germany and United States, 1879–1955). The application of the quantum theory to account for some properties of light where the wave theory failed, was the work of Max Planck (Germany, 1858–1947). The constant h is known as *Planck's constant;* it is one of the important constants of nature and of science. It has the value 6.62×10^{-27} erg-sec.

MAGNITUDE OF ENERGY QUANTA

Planck's constant has many uses in science. We can make use of it to show how various forms of radiation differ in their energy content. For example, blue light has greater energy per photon than red light. The frequencies for blue and red light are 7.3×10^{14} cycles/sec and 4.3×10^{14} cycles/sec. (Refer to page 589.) Hence,

$$E \text{ of blue photon} = 6.62 \times 10^{-27} \text{ erg-sec} \times 7.3 \times 10^{14} \frac{1}{\text{sec}} = 48.4 \times 10^{-13} \text{ ergs}$$

$$E \text{ of red photon} = 6.62 \times 10^{-27} \text{ erg-sec} \times 4.3 \times 10^{14} \frac{1}{\text{sec}} = 28.5 \times 10^{-13} \text{ ergs.}$$

Thus each blue photon has nearly twice as much energy as a red photon.

In Table 36–2, some types of radiation are compared. The energy content relative to that of visible light is shown in the last column. Notice the large amount of energy associated with X-rays. This is the reason that X-rays will penetrate matter which is opaque to visible light. Gamma rays (refer to Chapter 22) which come from many radioactive substances are even more energetic than X-rays. This is the basis for the use of radium and similar materials for treating malignant diseases.

One of the most interesting recent applications of high-energy radio waves is radar, a development of World War II. The widespread use of the airplane made it necessary to detect airplanes in the dark or in the clouds while still many miles from their objectives. Radio waves of extremely short wave lengths, about one centimeter, are used for this purpose. A wave length of one centimeter means a frequency of about 3×10^{10} cycles, which is much greater than the frequency of ordinary radio waves. These ultra-high-frequency radio signals are sent out by the detector stations. When the waves strike an airplane which may be fifty or more miles away, partial reflection occurs. The small part of the original signal which is reflected back to a detector station can be picked up and amplified. The reflected waves will be picked up by more than one detector station, and each station can determine the direction of the plane which reflected the waves. Using data obtained from more than one station, it is a simple task by triangulation to locate an approaching airplane. (Refer to page 179.) Airplane detector stations can detect the approach of enemy airplanes while they are still many miles away.

TABLE 36–2

FREQUENCY AND ENERGY OF SOME COMMON TYPES OF RADIATION

TYPE OF RADIATION	MEAN VALUE OF FREQUENCY (f)	ENERGY IN ERGS (hf)	ENERGY RELATIVE TO THAT OF VISIBLE LIGHT
Radio waves	1×10^{6}	6.55×10^{-21}	2×10^{-9}
Infrared	3×10^{13}	19.7×10^{-14}	5×10^{-2}
Visible light	6×10^{14}	39.3×10^{-13}	1
X-rays	3×10^{18}	2.0×10^{-8}	5×10^{3}
Gamma rays	3×10^{19}	2.0×10^{-7}	5×10^{4}
Cosmic rays	3×10^{22}	2.0×10^{-4}	5×10^{7}

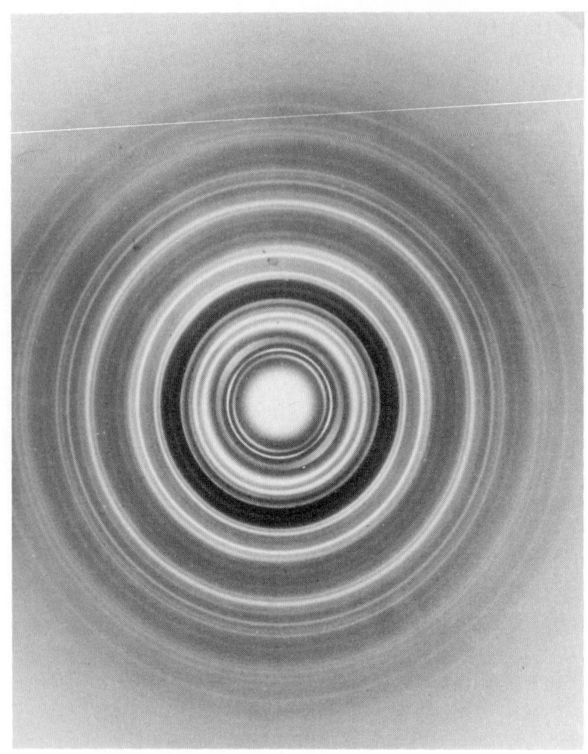

Fig. 36–5 *Diffraction pattern obtained by passing a thin pencil of electrons through thin copper-gold alloy foil. A pencil of visible light shining through a small hole forms a similar pattern. Thus high velocity electrons must have wave-like properties as does light.* (*Dr. L. H. Germer, Bell Telephone Laboratories*)

ELECTRONS CAN ACT AS WAVES

In 1927 two Americans, L. H. Germer and C. Davisson, performed an experiment which confused scientists. They shot a fast stream of electrons through metal foils and were able to photograph beautiful diffraction patterns. (Refer to Figure 36–5.) Diffraction patterns result from waves. Hence a stream of electrons, which we know are particles, have a dual nature. They behave both as particles and as waves of wave length shorter than that of light. Fundamental discoveries like this frequently lead to new discoveries. This discovery of Germer and Davisson led to the electron microscope, which far exceeds the optical microscope in its magnification of small objects. The ordinary microscope employs visible light and can be used only to examine objects relatively much larger than the wave length of light. The optical microscope can see only objects that cast sharp shadows. Thus, in Figure 36–6, the image is revealed by the light that passes by the object *AB*. Light rays passing the ends of the object *AB* must undergo bending or diffraction. When the length of *AB* is very short, the diffracted light originating at *A* and *B* will fuse in the same region at *A′B′* to form an indistinct image. This effect and a number of other factors set a practical limit of magnification of about two thousand for the best microscope with glass lenses. The amount of diffraction, of course, is a function of the wave length of the light; that is, as the wave length decreases, the amount of bending (diffraction) also decreases. This is the basis for the electron microscope. (Refer to Figures 36–7 and 36–8.) Electrons are many times smaller than light waves and when traveling as waves have wave lengths considerably shorter than those of visible light. Thus diffraction effects around the edges of an object are reduced to such an extent that magnifications as large as fifty thousand are possible in the electron microscope. Under this magnification an object with a diameter

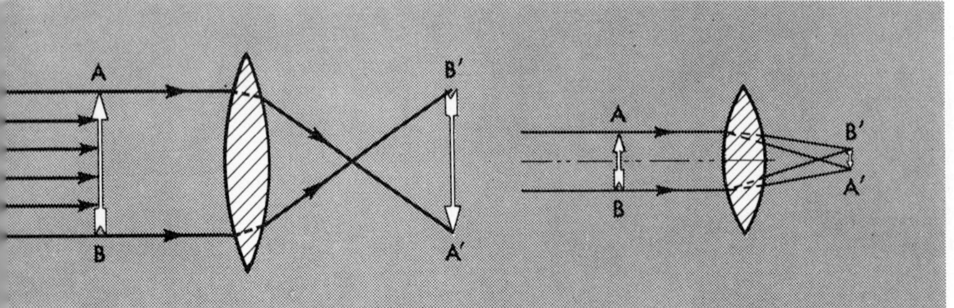

Fig. 36–6 *Very small images tend to blur. The blurring effect is reduced by using the longer wave lengths of an electron stream.*

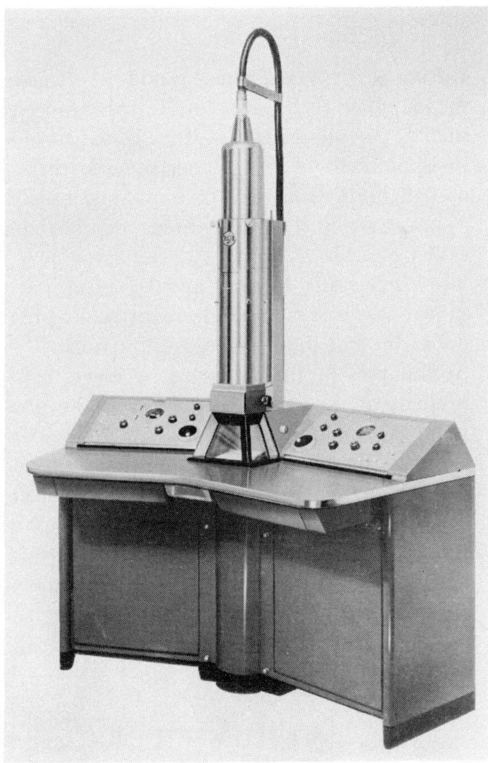

Fig. 36–7 *The electron microscope. This instrument uses the wave-like properties of fast-moving electrons in place of visible light to reveal details of structures invisible in ordinary microscopes. Particles smaller than one 10-millionth of an inch in diameter can be photographed with an electron microscope. (Radio Corporation of America)*

of one micron (10^{-4} cm) would appear to have a diameter of five centimeters. In an electron microscope the "light" consists of electrons from a heated filament given a high speed by the application of a high potential. The "lenses" for directing the path of the electrons are properly spaced in appropriate intense magnetic and electric fields. After traversing the objects and producing shadows, the electron waves are brought to a focus on a photographic plate.

WHAT IS LIGHT?

We can raise the question again, what is light? The answer is that no one knows. Some experiments indicate that light travels as transverse waves without a medium. Others show that light consists of particles, as when it is perceived by the eye, or falls on a photographic plate, or manifests itself in a photoelectric cell. Moreover, streams of certain particles, such as electrons and protons, exhibit the behavior of waves. Radiations of very short wave lengths, or of high frequencies, seem to consist predominantly of photons. A complete answer to our question must await further experimentation.

The difficulties are but further incentives. Both the wave and photon theories have

Fig. 36–8 *Photographs made with an electron microscope. The apparently structureless particles of zinc oxide smoke, left, and magnesium oxide smoke, right, are shown to exist as definite geometrical shapes under a magnification of 25,000*x. *(Battelle Memorial Institute)*

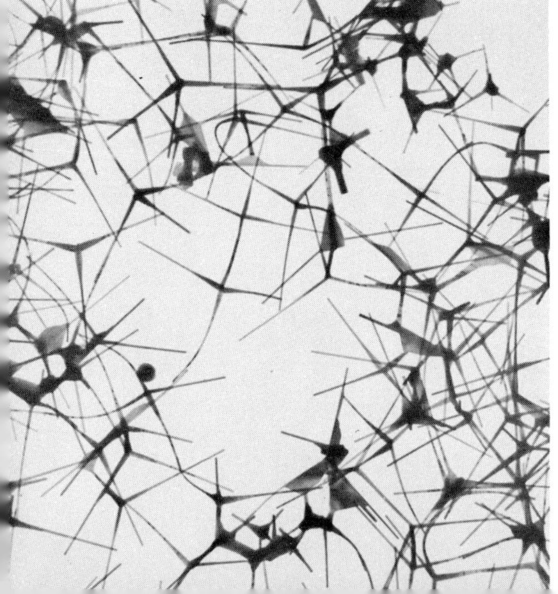

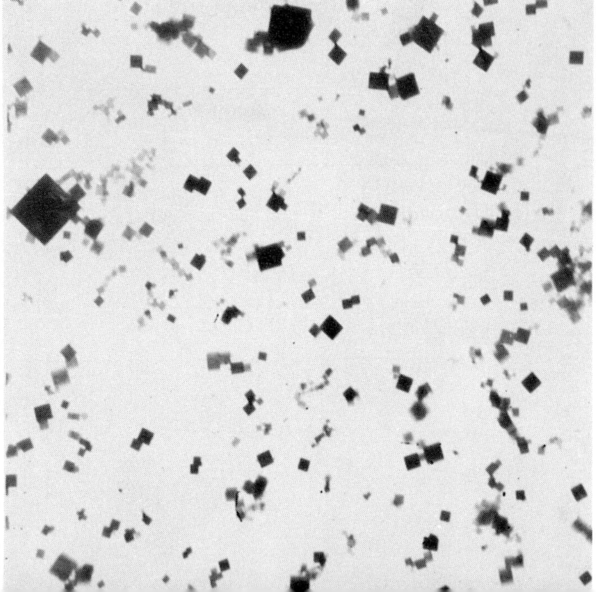

been useful in leading to many new discoveries. Eventually scientists hope to reconcile the two theories. The discoverer of the electron, J. J. Thomson, at the conclusion of a lecture (1909) pointing to some of the mysteries of nature stated, "The new discoveries in physics . . . and the ideas and potentialities suggested by them, have had an effect upon the workers in that subject akin to that produced in literature by the Renaissance. In the distance tower still higher peaks, which will yield to those who ascend them still wider prospects, and deepen the feeling, whose truth is emphasized by every advance in science, that 'Great are the Works of the Lord.' "

SUMMARY

1. Visible light is but a very small part of the total electromagnetic spectrum of radiation.
2. Radio waves, infrared rays, ultraviolet rays, X-rays, gamma rays, and cosmic rays are forms of electromagnetic waves which differ from visible light in frequency and wave length and in their applications.
3. Electromagnetic waves have three common characteristics: (*a*) they are produced by rapidly oscillating systems electrical in nature, (*b*) they all travel with the velocity of light, and (*c*) they all undergo the various phenomena characteristic of wave motion — reflection, refraction, diffraction, interference and reinforcement, and the Doppler effect.
4. All the various forms of electromagnetic waves with the exception of cosmic rays have many important applications.
5. The energy associated with electromagnetic waves is directly proportional to the frequency.
6. During recent years, Einstein and others have shown that there are certain phenomena, such as the photoelectric effect, which cannot be explained by the electromagnetic theory of light, but which can be explained on the assumption that light consists of particles called photons.
7. Two Americans, Germer and Davisson, have shown that fast-moving electrons behave like waves in that they undergo diffraction.
8. At the present time there is no single comprehensive theory of light. Most light phenomena can be explained by using the electromagnetic theory of light, but certain other phenomena, such as the photoelectric effect, can be explained only on the basis of photons or quanta of energy. Further, certain rapidly moving particles show phenomena associated with both waves and particles.

STUDY EXERCISES

1. Electromagnetic radiations have definite characteristics as to velocity, frequency, wave length, and energy content. In the table at the bottom of the page, indicate by number (1 to 6) the order of magnitude of the characteristics listed for the different kinds of radiation.
2. Items $a - n$ list certain experimental methods which can be used to produce, detect, or utilize various kinds of radiations. Indicate by number, from the following list, which kind of radiation(s) is (are) involved in each.

1. Radio waves
2. Ultraviolet
3. Infrared
4. Gamma rays
5. X-rays
6. Visible red
7. Visible violet

	Frequency Lowest = 1	Wave Length Longest = 1	Velocity	Energy Content Smallest = 1
Radio waves	....	....	....	....
Ultraviolet	....	....	....	....
X-rays	....	....	....	....
Infrared	....	....	....	....
Gamma rays	....	....	....	....
Visible light	....	....	....	....

a. Produced by a rapidly oscillating electric current. ....
b. An ordinary electric flatiron is a rich source of ....
c. Is present in direct sunlight and in the light from a mercury "sun lamp." ......
d. Produced by the impact of a rapid stream of electrons on a metal target in an evacuated tube of special design. ....
e. Are easily detected by the eye. ....
f. Will readily affect a photographic plate. ....
g. Readily penetrate many opaque materials, making photography of such materials possible. ....
h. Are used for danger signals because they are refracted less than other forms of visible light and more readily penetrate haze. ....
i. Originate in the disintegration of radioactive elements. ....
j. Responsible for sunburn. ....
k. Can be used to ionize air to operate a Geiger counter. ....
l. Can be detected by "tuning" a second electric current to oscillate with the same frequency as the radiation itself. ....
m. Originate in the coals of a camp fire. ....
n. Can be used to make photographs in the dark. ....

3. A certain radio station operates on a frequency of 670 kilocycles. What is the wave length of its radio wave in meters? NOTE: Take $v = 3 \times 10^{10}$ cm/sec.
4. A certain radio station sends out a wave with a length of 517.5 meters. What is the frequency?

FOR FURTHER READING

1. HOLTON, GERALD, *Introduction to Concepts and Theories in Physical Science.* Cambridge, Mass.: Addison-Wesley Press, 1952.
   Chapter 23 discusses the photoelectric effect and quantum theory of radiation.
2. BRAGG, WILLIAM, *The Universe of Light.* New York: The Macmillan Company, 1934.
   The author, a Nobel prize winner, presents the subject in nontechnical language; a very readable book. The electromagnetic spectrum and the experimental evidence for both the wave and corpuscular theories of light are presented in Chapters VII and IX.

37

THE EYES OF SCIENCE

MUCH OF THE INFORMATION that has been collected concerning the universe has been obtained by the sense of sight. But it is also true that much of our present information has been accumulated because man has learned to build instruments which can reveal objects too small or too distant to be seen by the naked eye and which can even penetrate into astronomical space. Then, too, objects in space emit many wave lengths of radiation that the eye cannot see. Without the telescope, for example, our knowledge of even the closer planets would be meager indeed, for they would then be mere bits of light in the heavens, bright enough only to reveal their movements along the ecliptic. The planets beyond Saturn would still be undiscovered; the rings of Saturn and the polar cap of Mars could not be seen. The only satellite that we should know very much about would be our moon. We should, in fact, still have a very meager conception of the nature of the universe. And where would we be without the microscope or the electron miscroscope? These instruments are indispensable to reveal structures that the eye cannot see, as in the study of plant and animal tissue, bacteria, textiles, rocks and minerals, and metals and their alloys. In addition, we have a large group of optical instruments, including cameras, field-glasses, rangefinders, and motion-picture machines, which are possible because of our present knowledge of lenses. It will be the purpose of this chapter to discuss certain laws and phenomena concerning light which have important applications in the construction of various optical instruments.

GLASS REFRACTS LIGHT

Light rays, in passing obliquely from one transparent substance into another transparent substance of different density, always undergo a change in velocity and a change in direction. This phenomenon, as we have seen, is called *refraction*. Thus, the light rays that traverse a piece of plate glass are definitely displaced. As shown in Figure 34–6 (page 554), the light ray *AO* on entering the glass is bent toward the perpendicular; the emergent ray *ER* is bent away from the perpendicular *PO′*. If the sides of the glass are parallel, the ray *ER* is also parallel to *AO*.

Any optical instrument depends upon the effect of lenses on light. The functioning of a common lens can be explained by consid-

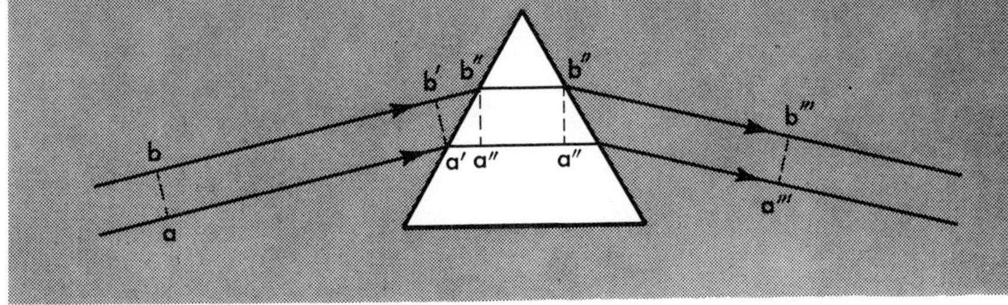

Fig. 37–1 *Bending of light rays passing through a prism.*

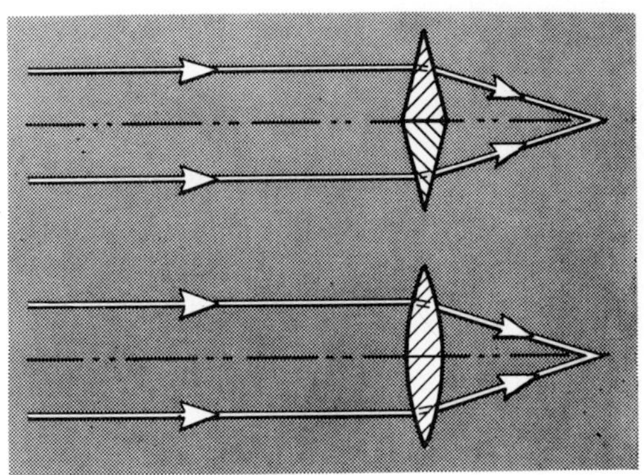

Fig. 37–2 *Comparison of two prisms with a bi-convex lens.*

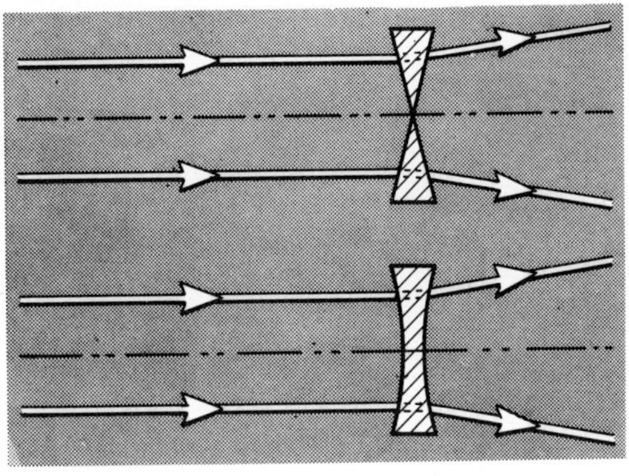

Fig. 37–3 *Comparison of two prisms with a bi-concave lens.*

ering the refraction of light through a glass prism. (Refer to Figure 37–1.) Thus, light originating at *ab* will travel in parallel paths to the prism. Here one side of the wave front, *a′*, will enter the glass first and will then travel more slowly, because of the effect of the denser medium. The part of the beam still in air, *b′*, will travel relatively faster. Hence, the wave front changes its direction of travel as it enters the prism. The student can verify for himself that the light rays are bent toward a perpendicular to the glass surface as they enter the glass. The side of the wave front *b″* will be the first to emerge into air at the other side of the prism; it then begins to travel faster. Hence, while the wave front *a″b″* is emerging into air, there will again be a change in direction of the wave front *a‴b‴*. The significant observation here is that the light undergoes two changes in direction and that it is bent toward the base of the prism.

If the above experiment is performed with two prisms base to base, the light rays can be made to *converge* (Figure 37–2). Parallel light rays may be made to *diverge* if the two prisms are placed apex to apex (Figure 37–3). The lenses which are such an essential part of many optical instruments function either by diverging or converging light rays.

There are six types of spherical lenses, three converging and three diverging (Figure 37–4). Converging lenses are invariably thinner at the edges than in the center, whereas diverging lenses are always thicker at the edges than in the center. The effect of a converging lens on a beam of light is shown in Figure 37–5; the effect of a diverging lens on a beam of light is shown in Figure 37–6.

Note that in Figures 37–2 and 37–5 the light rays are brought to focus at a point. This is called the *principal focus.* The distance of the principal focus from the lens, called the *focal length,* is an important characteristic of a lens. The numerical value of this constant for any lens is determined by the nature of the glass and the curvature of its surfaces.

Bi-convex lenses have two principal uses: (1) to produce a real image of some object on a screen, on the retina of the eye, or on a photographic film; and (2) to function

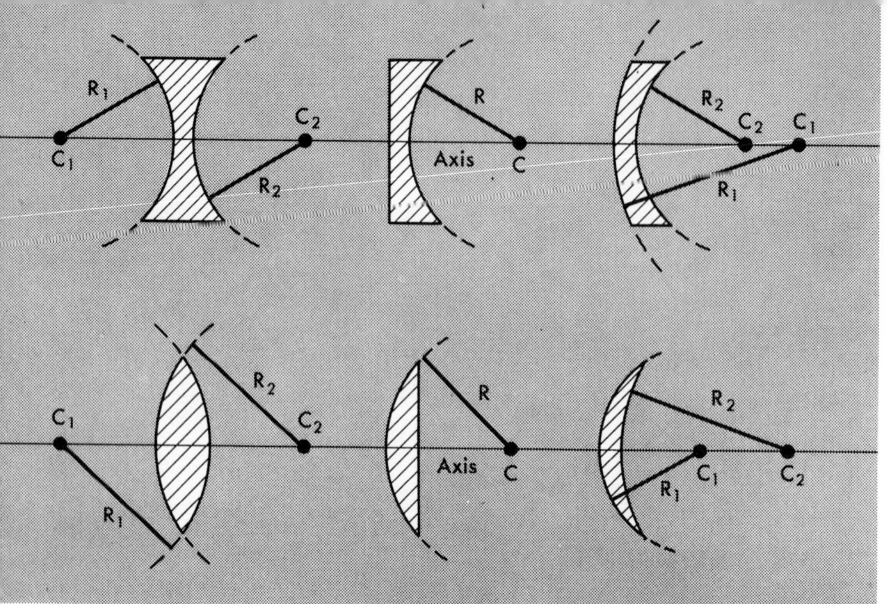

Fig. 37–4 *Diverging lenses: double concave, plane-concave, convex-concave. Converging lenses: double convex, plane-convex, concave-convex.*

Fig. 37–5 *Converging a beam of light with a convex (converging) lens.*

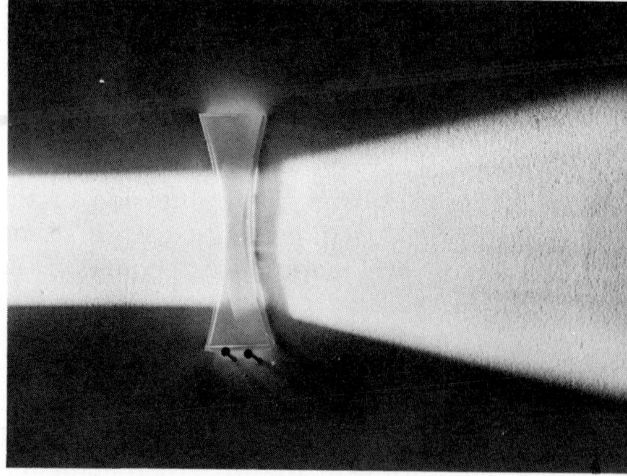

Fig. 37–6 *Parallel rays of light diverge with a concave (diverging) lens.*

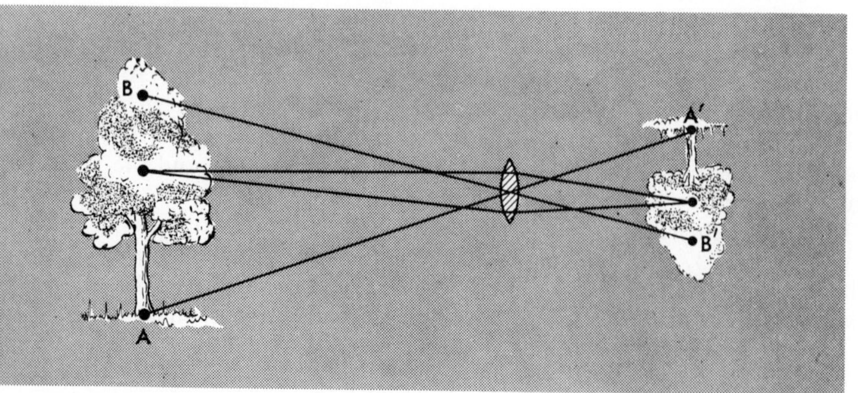

Fig. 37–7 *The principle of the lens.*

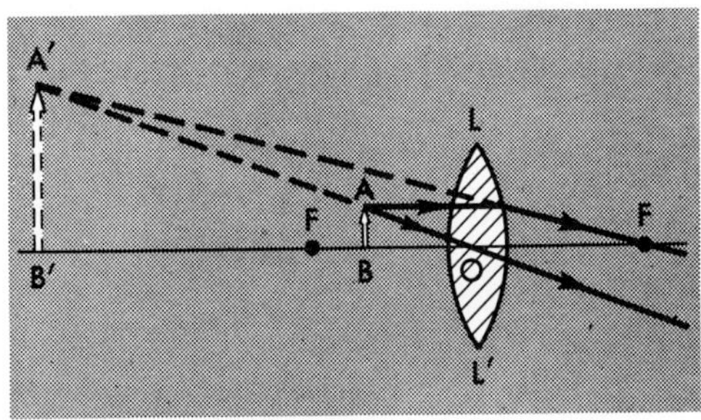

Fig. 37–8 *Principle of the magnifying glass. The object distance is less than OF. The image is virtual, not real.*

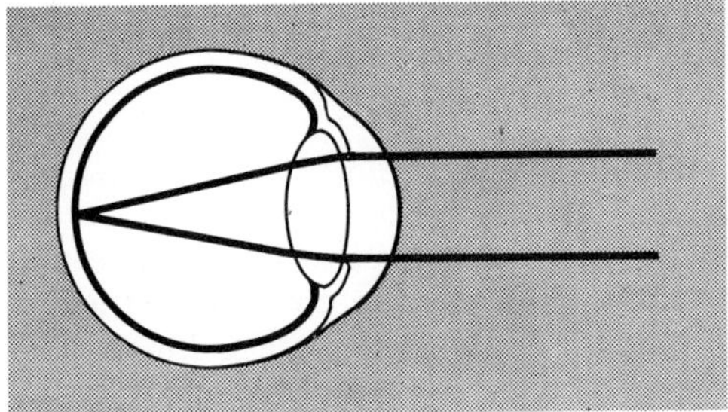

Fig. 37–9 *A normal eye.*

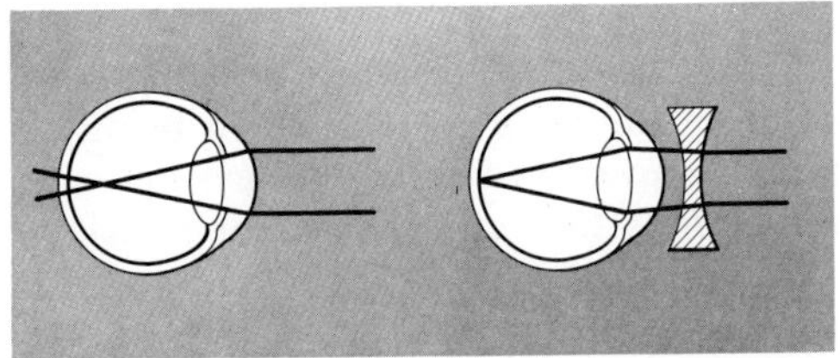

Fig. 37–10 *A near-sighted eye corrected by a diverging lens.*

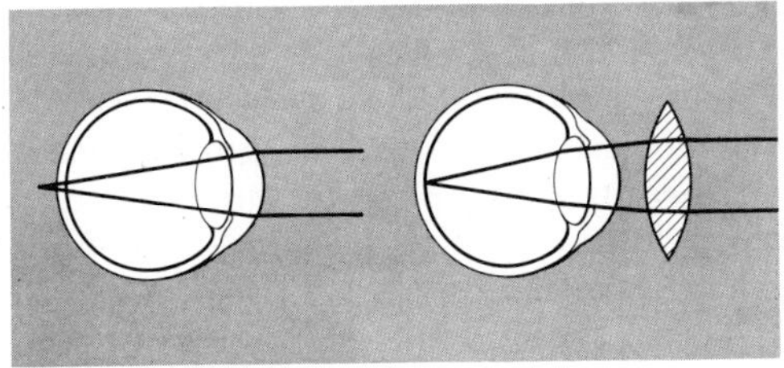

Fig. 37–11 *A far-sighted eye corrected by a converging lens.*

as a magnifying glass. Figure 37–7 illustrates the use of a bi-convex lens to produce a real image. Here the object *AB* must be located at a distance greater than the focal length of the lens. The light rays from *AB,* after passing through the lens, are made to converge to form a real image at *A′B′*, which is *inverted.* It is called a *real image* because it can be viewed on a screen or recorded on a photographic plate. The images obtained with the eye, the lens of a camera, motion-picture projector, and telescope are real images and are inverted. The image on a motion picture screen is right side up because the film is inverted in the machine.

The principles involved in the common magnifying glass are shown in Figure 37–8. *AB* represents any object so close to the lens *L* that it is inside the principal focus *F.* The image must be viewed with the eye close to the lens. It appears at *A′B′* as an *enlarged, erect* image. This kind of image must be seen with the eye through the lens, since it cannot be projected on a screen. It is called a *virtual image.* The use of a bi-convex lens to produce a real image and as a magnifying glass can be demonstrated with a common reading glass. If printed material is viewed through the glass with the eye relatively far from the lens, the type will appear inverted. When the eye approaches sufficiently close to the glass, the type will appear erect and enlarged. The erect image is a virtual image. The inverted image is a real image. A better conception of a real image is obtained by holding a reading glass two or three feet from an electric light bulb. By carefully bringing up a sheet of paper on the side of the reading glass opposite the bulb, the inverted image of the light bulb can be brought to a focus on the paper.

A very common application of converging and diverging lenses is found in ordinary spectacles. A near-sighted person, for example, cannot see distant objects clearly because the lens of the eye brings the image in focus in front of the retina. This defect is corrected by a diverging lens. (Refer to Figures 37–9 and 37–10.) A far-sighted person cannot see distinctly objects near at

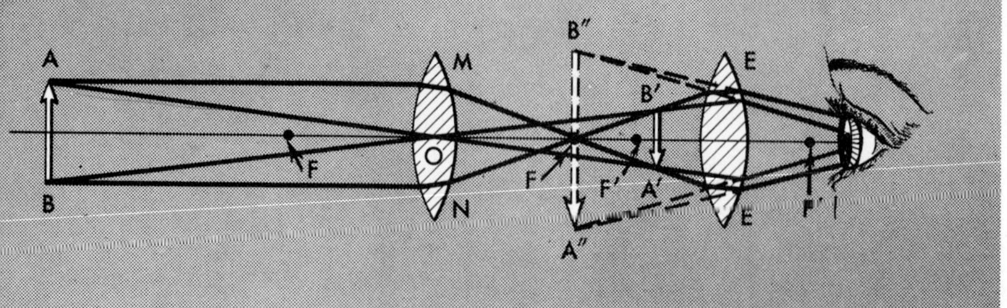

Fig. 37–12 *The functioning of a refracting telescope.*

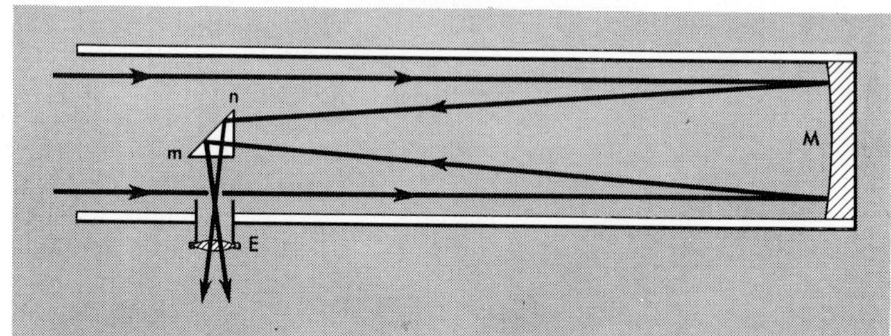

Fig. 37–13 *A diagram of a reflecting telescope.*

hand because the lens of the eye brings the image in focus behind the retina. This condition can be corrected with a converging lens. (Refer to Figures 37–9 and 37–11.)

Very important applications of lenses are found in the telescope and the microscope. The principle of the *refracting telescope* is shown in Figure 37–12. The objective lens *MN* is in one end of a tube of such length that the light rays entering it are brought to a focus at *A′B′* inside the principal focus of the eyepiece *E*. This image is real, inverted, and reduced in size. Both the objective and the eyepiece are convex (converging) lenses. The eyepiece *E* functions as a common magnifying glass and enlarges the real image, *B′A′*, to produce the final image *B″A″*, which is inverted and enlarged. However, the object is always at a great distance, and hence the image must always be smaller than the object. In order to get the image as large as possible, the focal length of the objective lens must be made as large as possible. This, of course, means that the objective lens must be mounted in a relatively long tube, a requirement that leads to mechanical difficulties. But there is a second difficulty: in order to observe a distant object, it is necessary to get as much light as possible, and this can be done only by increasing the diameter of the objective lens. These two factors combined make powerful refractors very difficult and expensive to build. The refractor of the Yerkes Observatory is the largest ever built; it has an objective lens forty inches in diameter and a focal length of sixty-four feet. The photograph of the moon shown on page 241 was taken with the Yerkes refractor.

Astronomical telescopes now being built are *reflecting* telescopes. Light in being reflected from curved surfaces obeys the same law of reflection as from a plane surface. (Refer to page 553.) Light rays can be made to converge with a concave mirror. The principle of one design of reflecting telescope is shown in Figure 37–13. The light rays from a distant object are made to converge to a focus by a concave parabolic mirror *M*. A right angle prism *mn* turns the light through an angle of ninety degrees and as in the refracting telescope produces a real image inside the principal focus of the eyepiece *E*. Further magnification is obtained by the eyepiece *E*. This particular design for a reflecting telescope is another of the contributions of Sir Isaac Newton. A second type of reflecting telescope, the Cassegrainian, uses a mirror to reflect the focused rays back through a small opening in the middle of the mirror itself, to the viewing eyepiece. (Refer to Figure 37–14.)

The microscope is essentially a train of two converging lenses. (Refer to Figure 37–15.) The object is placed beyond the principal focus of the objective lens *O*, and the image from the first lens is formed inside the principal focus of the eyepiece *E*. This image is enlarged, inverted, and real. The lens *E* produces a second image *B″A″*, further enlarged and virtual. The second image is inverted because the first real image was inverted. The object lens *O*, then, serves to produce a real inverted image *A′B′*. The eyepiece E serves as a simple magnifying glass to produce an enlarged virtual image *A″B″* of the first image. Modern microscopes of high power always consist of more than one lens in the objective, and this is likewise true of the eyepiece. (Refer to Figure 37–16.) By a suitable combination of objective lenses and eyepieces a magnifying power as great as two thousand may be obtained. The modern miscroscope finds many applications in medicine. Thus, the organisms which cause certain diseases, such as typhoid, anthrax, diphtheria, cholera, and tuberculosis, although invisible to the unaided eye, are readily identified under the microscope. Similarly, the chemist finds the microscope indispensable in the study of textiles and of metals and their alloys. The geologist uses it to study rocks and minerals.

Fig. 37–14 *Observer at Cassegrain focus of one-hundred-inch telescope of Mount Wilson Observatory. (Mt. Wilson and Palomar Observatories)*

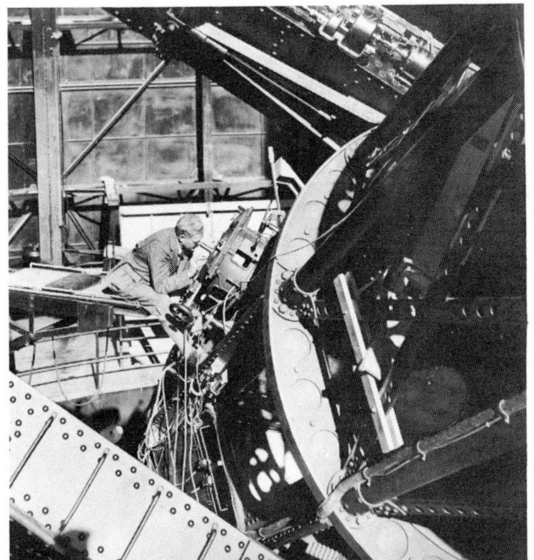

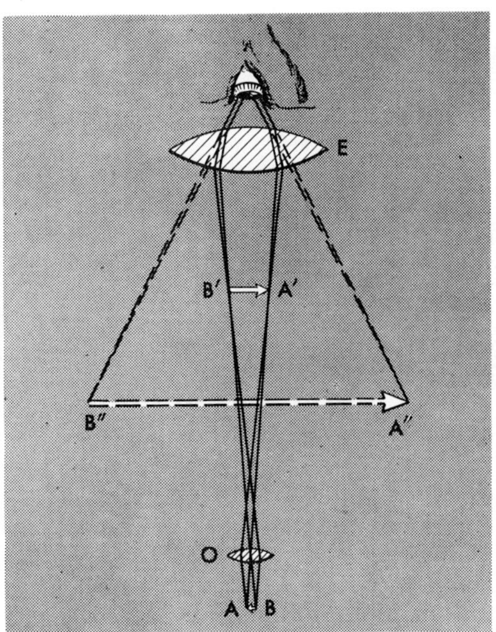

Fig. 37–15 *A diagram of a compound microscope.*

Fig. 37–16 *The optics of a compound microscope. (American Optical Company, Instrument Division, Buffalo, New York)*

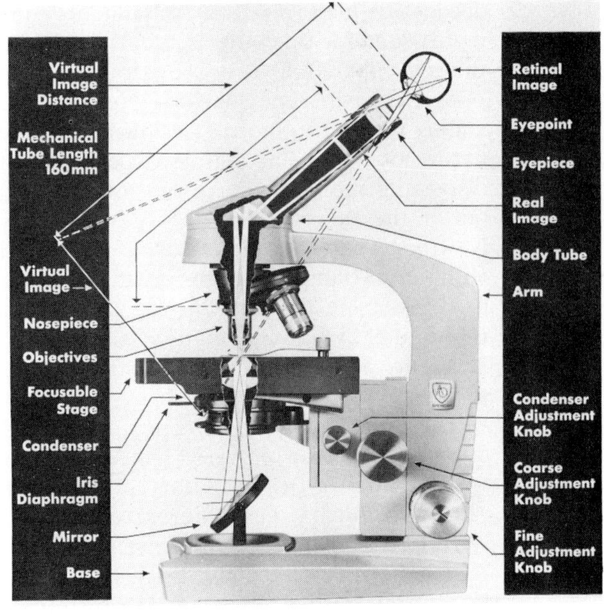

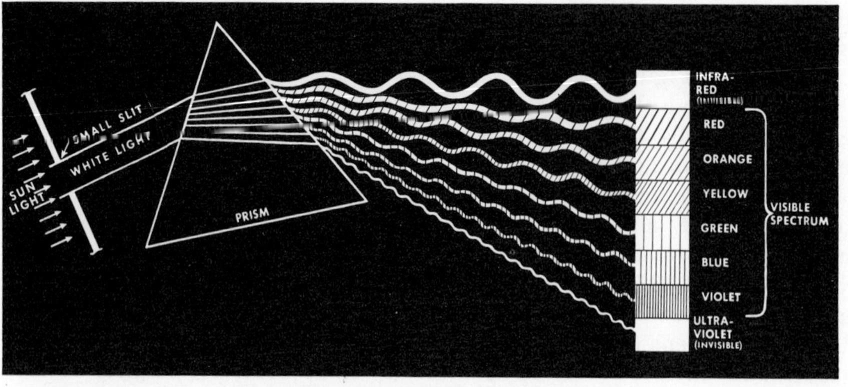

Fig. 37–17 *Formation of a spectrum by refraction of white light with a prism.*

SPECTROSCOPES AND SPECTRA

Helium, an important inert gas, was first discovered in the sun in 1868 by Janssen and Lockyer while observing a total eclipse of the sun. A period of nearly thirty years elapsed before Ramsay in England found that helium exists on the earth. The achievement of Janssen and Lockyer was possible because of their ability to decode a message of light from the sun. Thus, events are continually happening throughout the universe which are announced on the earth by streams of radiant energy, if man will but intercept those waves and decode the messages. The instruments commonly used for this purpose are the camera, the telescope, and the spectroscope.

As we have seen, Sir Isaac Newton was among the first to inquire seriously into the nature of light. The simple experiment of dispersing the light of the sun into the colors of the rainbow was first described by Newton. The experiment can be performed with any triangular glass prism. Newton used rays from the sun, but the same effect is obtained by light from any glowing solid. In Figure 37–17 light from the sun is made to pass through a prism.

The light emerges as a continuous band of color. Newton inferred correctly that white light is a fusion of the colors of the rainbow which suffer different degrees of refraction as they enter and leave the prism. Red light is refracted the least, and violet light is refracted the most. This continuous band of color is called a *continuous spectrum.* Newton confirmed his conclusion concerning the nature of white light by recombining colored light to form white light. (Refer to Figure 37–18). Light from *S* forms a color spectrum as it emerges from prism *A*. This is revealed by placing a white screen *S* between the two prisms. This band of colors is then made to pass through prism *B* turned opposite to prism *A*, and the rays converge again as white light at *D*. White light, therefore, is a composite light consisting of all the colors of the visible spectrum — *red, orange, yellow, green, blue, indigo,* and *violet.*

A continuous spectrum is obtained if light from any glowing solid — white-hot carbon, red-hot iron, a glowing tungsten filament in a light bulb — or from an incandescent liquid, or from an incandescent gas under high pressure, is passed through a prism in a spectroscope. We now describe spectrum colors in terms of their frequency and wave length. (Refer to Figure 37–19.) Thus, blue light has a wave length of 45×10^{-6} cm and a frequency of 670 million mil-

Fig. 37–18 *Recombination of spectrum colors to form white light.*

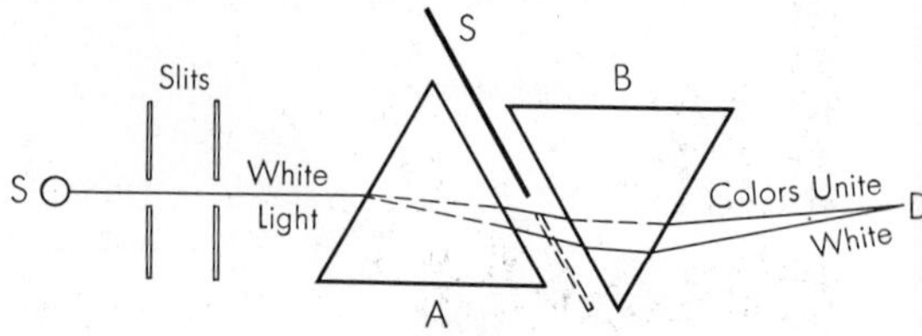

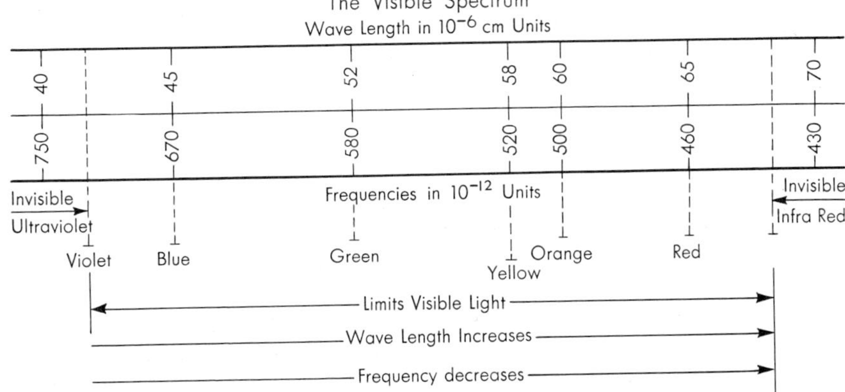

Fig. 37–19 *Frequencies and wave lengths of visible light.*

lion cycles per second (670 × 10^{12} v.p.s.). The frequency of visible light is related to the wave length by the fundamental wave equation, $v = fl$. Hence,

$$f = \frac{v}{l} = \frac{3 \times 10^{10} \text{ cm/sec}}{l}.$$

Thus, blue light with a wave length of 45 × 10^{-6} cm has a frequency, f, or

$$f = \frac{3 \times 10^{10} \text{ cm/sec}}{45 \times 10^{-6} \text{ cm/cyc}} = 670 \times 10^{12} \text{ cyc/sec.}$$

Carefully note that the borderline between the last visible red and the invisible infrared is at a wave length of about 70 × 10^{-6} cm (f = 430 × 10^{12}), and the borderline between the visible violet and the ultraviolet is at a wave length of a little more than 40 × 10^{-6} cm (f = 750 × 10^{12}). These figures, which on first thought might seem fantastic, are based upon precise physical measurements.

The dispersive action of a prism on light is utilized in the spectroscope, one of the most important instruments used to decode the messages from the stars. (Refer to Figure 37–20.) At the left is any source of light. *AB* represents a metal tube with a narrow vertical slit at *A* and a common bi-convex lens at *B*. The tube is adjustable for length so that the slit *A* can be placed at a distance from *B* corresponding to the focal length of lens *B*. On page 601 it was shown that parallel rays of light which pass through a bi-convex lens are made to converge at the principal focus. In the spectroscope, the reverse effect occurs; that is, diverging light rays from the slit are rendered parallel after passing through the lens *B*. These parallel light rays then undergo refraction in the prism *C* as in Newton's experiment. The refracted rays are then made to pass through another bi-convex

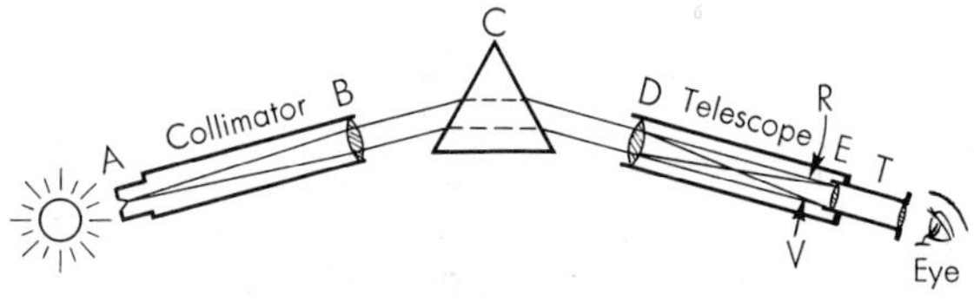

Fig. 37–20 *Essential parts of a spectroscope.*

lens *D*, which brings the light rays to a focus at the point *E*, where they may be observed with the eye or recorded on a photographic plate. The triangular prism *C* is usually made of glass or quartz. Glass readily transmits the visible spectrum but absorbs the ultraviolet. In order to transmit ultraviolet light, a quartz prism must therefore be used, since it is transparent to the ultraviolet. To study infrared radiation, the prism can be made of common salt – sodium chloride. If one looks down the length of the tube *AB* with the lens *B* and the prism *C* removed, one will see a single line – the illuminated slit *A*. When the eye looks into *T* – the prism and lens having been replaced – *many* lines will be seen. These lines are images of the slit in different colors. For example, red light from the source will form a slit image (line) at R, and blue light from the source will form a line at V, since it is refracted to a much greater extent. Thus, each separate color in light from the source will be revealed by a different so-called *spectral line* when viewed at T. In connection with the use of the spectroscope, it is worthy of note that the eye is a very imperfect device for studying the spectrum, since it readily tires and is not sensitive to either the infrared or the ultraviolet. The light-sensitive silver halide (emulsion) of the modern photographic plate is sensitive to both the infrared and the ultraviolet as well as the visible spectrum. Furthermore, the effects are accumulative and are recorded permanently. That is, spectra which cannot be seen are often photographed simply by prolonging the exposure.

KINDS OF SPECTRA

Continuous Spectra. All materials at high temperatures, whether incandescent solids, liquids, or compressed gases, emit a continuous spectrum similar to that of the sun. This is believed to be due to the rapid oscillation of electrons within the body and does not depend upon the nature of the substance heated. In the previous chapter, we learned that any oscillating electrical system emits electromagnetic radiation. The only differences are in the relative amounts of colored light which are present, and these are definitely related to the temperature of the body emitting the spectrum. Thus, a piece of hot iron not quite visibly glowing gives off its maximum radiation in the region of the infrared. When visibly red-hot, there is an abundance of radiation in the visible red. At white heat, the shorter wave lengths — green and blue — are increased in quantity, thus giving the total white effect. At the most intense temperature, found in some stars, blue radiation and even the ultraviolet predominate. The spectrum of a star thus reveals its temperature.

Bright-line Spectra. Incandescent gases at low pressures, if not highly ionized, give a spectrum consisting of fine colored lines instead of a continuous band of color. These line patterns are called *bright-line spectra.* (Refer to Figure 37–21.) Suppose, for example, common salt — sodium chloride — is vaporized in a hot flame in front of the vertical slit. The slit observed with the eye at T reveals *two* yellow slits very close together. These are called the *double spectral lines* of sodium in the yellow part of the spectrum (Figure 37–21). If light from glowing hydrogen is used to illuminate the slit, the eye at T (Figure 37–20) will observe four images of the slit — one red, one blue, and two in the violet part of the spectrum. These are the four prominent spectral lines of hydrogen (Figure 37–21).

It is now customary to record bright-line spectra on photographic plates. The spectral patterns of no two elements are ever the same; they differ in the *number, location,* and *intensity* of the lines on the photographic plate. The line spectra of sodium and hydrogen are relatively simple. The spectrum of neon, on the other hand, consists of about eighteen lines in the red, two in the yellow, and about nine in the green-blue end of the spectrum; and the spectrum of iron vapor consists literally of thousands of lines.

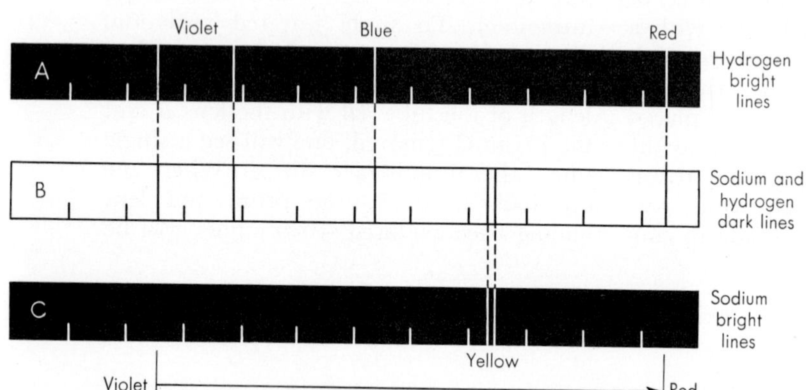

Fig. 37–21 *Bright-line and dark-line spectra.*

The scientist has found the spectroscope an indispensable instrument for studying the composition of matter, whether in the laboratory or in a star, when ordinary chemical methods of analysis fail. It was the spectroscope that made it possible for Janssen and Lockyer in 1868 to discover helium in the sun. Later, when Ramsay found helium in the earth, he proved that it was the element first found in the sun by showing that the spectral patterns were identical. The chemist has found the spectroscope an indispensable instrument for studying matter both on the earth and in space. Helium, argon, neon, krypton, rubidium, and cesium are but a few of the elements that were discovered by the use of the spectroscope.

Dark-line Spectra. In the early part of the nineteenth century, Fraunhofer, a Bavarian scientist, observed that a careful inspection of the continuous spectrum of the sun revealed many dark lines. These lines have ever since been referred to as *Fraunhofer lines.* Fifty years later, Kirchhoff, another German scientist, observed that the positions of the dark lines coincided exactly with those of a bright-line spectrum. (Refer to Figure 37–21.) The explanation was soon found. Any gaseous body under low pressure and at high temperature, as in a star, sends forth a bright-line spectrum. The outer gaseous envelope of the star is at a lower temperature, and this cooler vapor absorbs the particular frequencies of colored light – the cause of the spectral lines – which are emitted by the same gas at a higher temperature. Thus, the dark and bright lines must coincide in bright- and dark-line spectra. Since the bright lines disappear because of absorption in the cooler outer vapor, dark-line spectra are also called *absorption spectra.*

Most of the spectrographs obtained from various heavenly bodies are dark-line spectra which are checked against bright-line spectra from sources on the earth. For example, if an astronomer wishes to determine the presence or absence of calcium in a certain star, with the aid of a spectroscope he will photograph the light from the star. Then, on the same photographic plate, he will photograph the spectrum emitted by a calcium compound volatilized in the laboratory. If the two sets of spectral lines coincide when one photograph is placed above the other, then calcium must be present in the star being studied. With the spectroscope, astrophysicists have been able to prove that over sixty known elements exist in the sun.

The spectroscope is also used to determine the motions of heavenly bodies. In an earlier chapter we studied the Doppler effect (refer to page 563). If a body emitting any form of wave motion is approaching the observer, there is an apparent decrease in the wave length. We have seen that light is a wave motion. Therefore, when a source of light is approaching the observer, the wave length apparently decreases, and if the source of light recedes, there is an apparent increase in the wave length. As shown by a spectral photograph, this means that there is a shift in the position of the spectral lines – a shift toward the red end of the spectrum if the light source is receding, or a shift toward the violet end of the spectrum if the light source is approaching the earth, for red light has a longer wave length than violet light. (Refer to Figure 37–22.) The bright-line spectrum at the top and bottom is the reference spectrum from a laboratory source, in this case, sodium. The dark-line spectrum in the middle is from a comet and definitely proves that sodium lines are present. The slight shift in the position of the lines is also noticeable – in this case, a shift toward the red end of the spectrum. This indicates

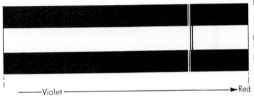

Fig. 37–22 *The Doppler effect due to motion of light source.*

that there is relative motion which results in an increase in the wave length of the light, and either that the comet was receding from the earth or that the earth was receding from the comet. Which of these alternatives is the true explanation of the shift must be settled by interpreting other observational data. In the same way, it is easy to prove that the sun is rotating. All that need be done is to take spectrographs of light from opposite sides of the sun. From one side of the sun the spectral lines are shifted toward the violet, while from the other the lines are shifted toward the red. This, of course, proves that one side of the sun is moving earthward, while the other side is moving away from the earth. This means rotation of the sun. It is possible by measuring the degree of shift of the lines to compute the actual velocity of approach or recession.

COMPOSITION OF THE SUN

Our knowledge of the chemical composition of the sun is due entirely to the spectroscope. The spectra of about eighty of the known elements on the earth are definitely known. Upwards of sixty of these elements are certainly present in the sun. Hydrogen, helium, and oxygen exist in relatively enormous quantities. The American astronomer, Henry Norris Russell, estimates that nearly half of the sun by weight is hydrogen. Approximately a fourth of the mass of the sun is due to oxygen, and helium and certain metals account for about one-sixteenth and one-fourth of the mass, respectively. In the sun, only the elements carbon, boron, and nitrogen are in the form of compounds. Free electrons exist there in large amounts. It is the presence of large quantities of hydrogen and electrons that leads scientists to believe that protons — atoms of hydrogen which have lost one electron — and electrons are converted into helium and the heavier elements as the hot gaseous body cools with a liberation of energy. (See Chapter 38.) The metals that are definitely known to exist in appreciable quantities in the sun in order of abundance are: magnesium, iron, silicon, sodium, potassium, calcium, aluminum, nickel, manganese, chromium, cobalt, titanium, copper, vanadium, and zinc.

PHOTOCELLS

Our present picture of the universe would be very different if information about the objects in distant space still had to be obtained by the human eye and the photographic plate aided by modern telescopes. It is very probable that telescopes cannot be further improved in their ability to see into space. For this reason astronomers do not plan to build instruments larger than the 200-inch reflector on Mount Palomar in California. There are other scientific devices that also enable astronomers to see into distant space. Among these instruments is the photocell. (Refer to page 593.) Since its invention, the photocell has come to be an indispensable instrument in studying the objects in distant space — stars, planets, and galaxies.

The sensitivity of photocells has been enormously increased by the device known as a photomultiplier tube. The light-sensitive substance in the cell shown in Figure 36–1 is called a photoelectric cathode. A number of these can be placed within a single tube. (Refer to Figure 37–23.) The electrons emitted by the light on the first photocathode are directed to a second photocathode *A* where the effect is multiplied. This process can be repeated at suc-

Fig. 37–23 *Principle of the photomultiplier tube.*

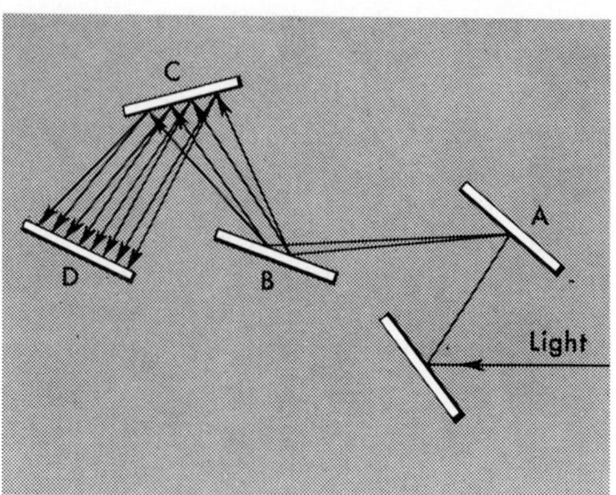

cessive photocathodes *B, C,* and *D.* In this manner the current obtained on the first photocathode can be multiplied as much as a hundred million times. The light from a star is comparable to the light of a candle at a distance of one mile. A photocell can easily detect the light of a candle at a distance of a hundred miles. The important contribution of the photocell, however, is not to detect faint light sources but to measure *differences* in brightness. This can be done with photocells much more precisely than with the human eye or a photographic plate.

INFORMATION OBTAINED WITH PHOTOCELLS

In astronomy photocells find their greatest applications in measuring changes in the brightness of astronomical objects. With a photocell, it can be shown that many so-called variable stars are actually binaries, a pair of stars rotating about a common center. In these systems each star periodically gets in front of the other. At this time there is a decrease in the brightness. Studies with photocells easily detect the differences in brightness with respect to time and from the relative brightness of each star the period of rotation can be determined.

An important class of variable stars is the Cepheid variables. These are huge stars which actually change in size periodically by as much as 5 or 10 per cent. They also vary in brightness in a regular manner which is easily followed with a photocell. As shown on page 261, the importance of these stars lies in the fact that the time that elapses from maximum to minimum brightness gives information as to their absolute magnitude of brightness, and from this information, their distances from the earth are computed. Many Cepheid variables are at distances of a million light-years!

The temperatures of stars are indicated by their color, which is readily determined with photocells. Thus the temperature of the outside of the sun is known to be about 6000 degrees Centigrade. The bright object in the sky known as Sirius has a surface temperature of 11,000 degrees Centigrade. Dull red stars have relatively low temperatures. Even the temperature of cold objects such as the moon can be determined with photocells.

RADIO ASTRONOMY

The latest method for studying the universe is to intercept radio waves from outer space. This is the basis of radio astronomy, a science only twenty-five years old. This science is now advancing our knowledge more rapidly than any other scientific technique available to astronomers. The development and applications of radio astronomy are outstanding examples of the methods and importance of science. Radio astronomy is the result of the innate curiosity that impels scientists to explore the unknown — to find information for its own sake. Furthermore, modern societies through their governments are committed to the same policy, for radio astronomy would not be possible without the expenditure of many millions of dollars to build radio astronomy installations. These expenditures cannot be justified in the name of furthering "practical discoveries", but only on the basis of the importance of learning new truths about our environment even though that environment extends millions of light-years into the outer space of the universe and then on to island universes or galaxies beyond!

During the early nineteen-thirties a communications physicist, Dr. Karl G. Jansky, was studying the often troublesome noises in radio reception called "static." Most of this static was found to be due to terrestrial causes such as electrical storms. But some could be accounted for only on the assumption of extra-terrestrial causes. In April, 1933, Dr. Jansky published his paper on "Electrical Disturbances Apparently of Extra-terrestrial Origin," which is now considered a scientific classic and is recognized as the beginning of the science of radio astronomy. In this paper, Dr. Jansky stated

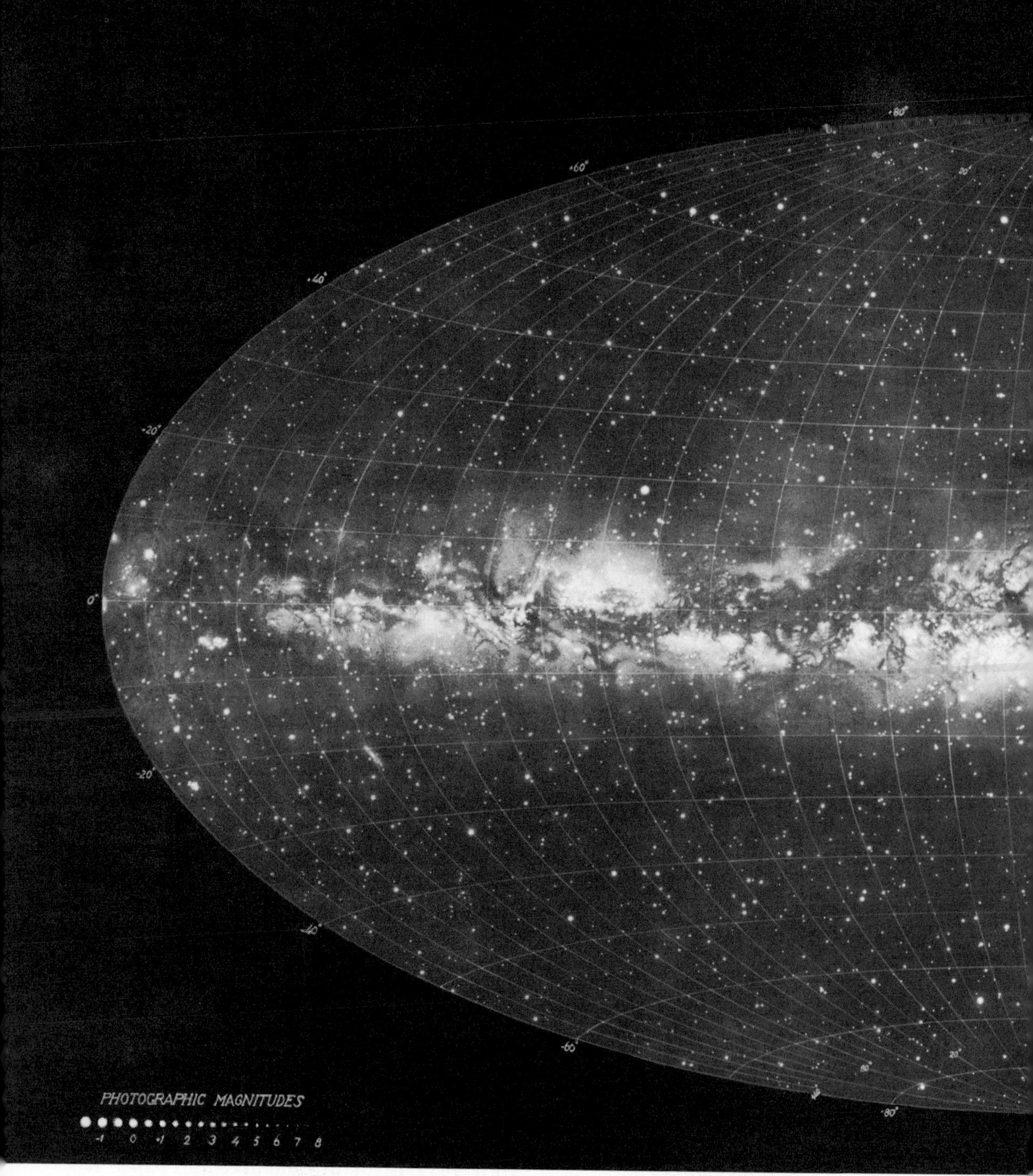

Fig. 37–24 *The photographic Milky Way. The coordinates refer to the center of the galaxy and its axis. The bright patches of light "toward five o'clock" from the center of the Milky Way are the Small and Large Magellanic Clouds. These are both galaxies.* (*Lund Observatory*)

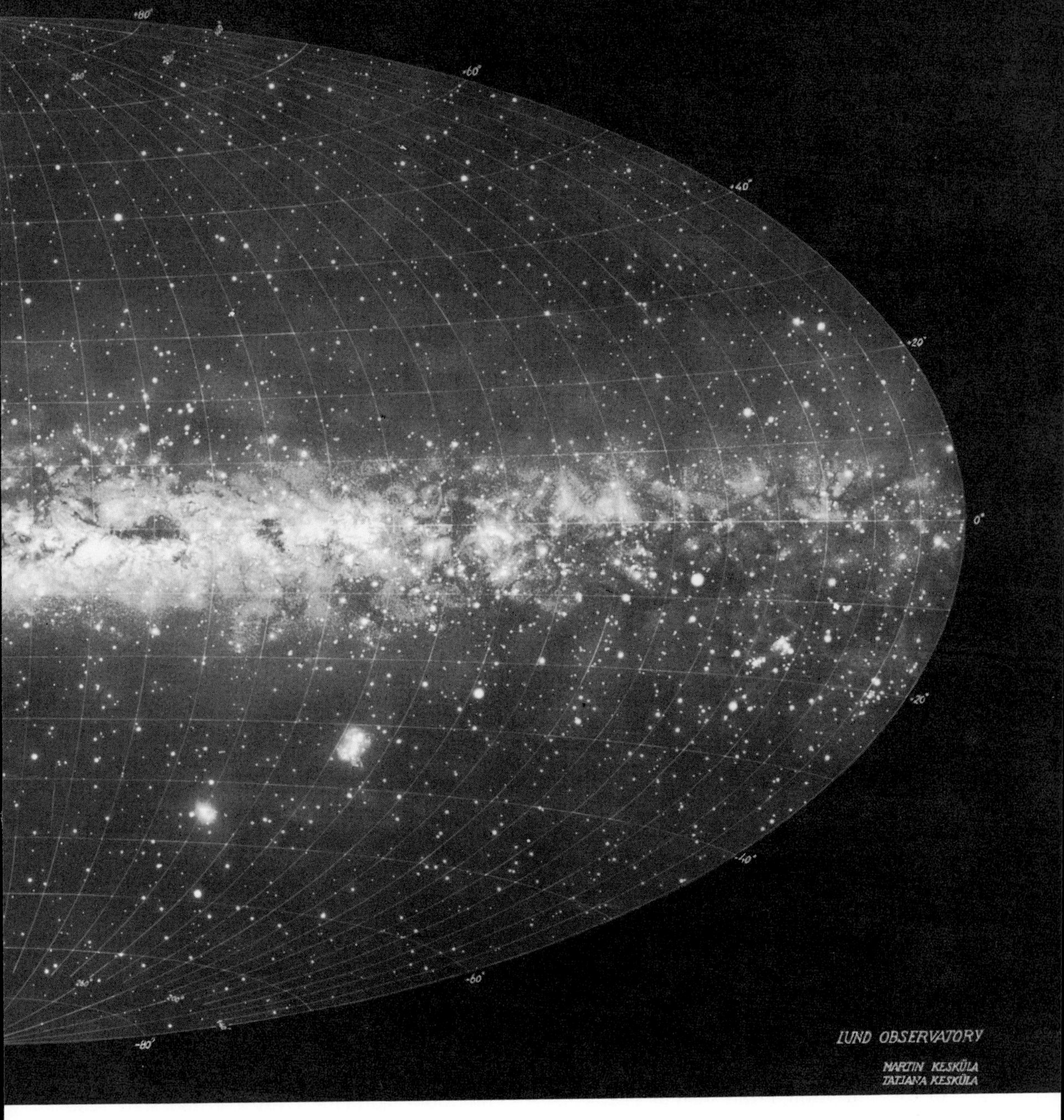
LUND OBSERVATORY
MARTIN KESKÜLA
TATJANA KESKÜLA

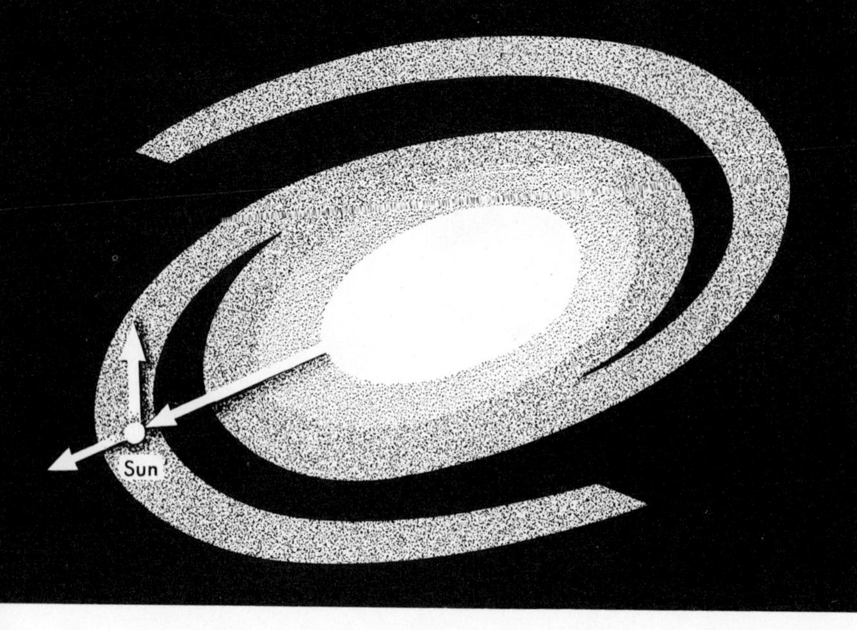

Fig. 37–25 *Our solar system is off-center with respect to our galaxy.*

that "data have been presented which show the existence of electromagnetic waves which apparently come from a direction that is fixed in space." It was soon shown that these waves were true radio waves, with wave lengths in the range of 1 centimeter to 200 meters, and that the longer wave lengths would penetrate space that would absorb visible light. The ratio of the longest to the shortest wave lengths is as much as 20,000 to one. The ratio of the wave lengths of visible red to visible blue is only two to one. Hence the range of information that can be picked up by these extra-terrestrial radio waves is much greater than can be picked up with ordinary visual telescopes.

The radio picture picked up from outer space is very different from that picked up by visual means. Ordinary stars, with the exception of the sun, send out no radio waves. On the other hand, there are many radio stars which are invisible in a telescope. They represent dark objects in space capable of sending out radio signals. There is reason to believe that there are as many of these invisible radio stars as visible stars.

Occasionally stars literally explode in outer space, forming an intense visible light source in regions previously dark. These are called *supernovae.* They rapidly decrease in size and finally become invisible. Such supernovae were observed in A.D. 1054, 1572, and 1604. Each of the places in outer space formerly occupied by these supernovae is now the location of a radio star. Hence, it is assumed that the remains left by a great stellar explosion are capable of sending out intense radio waves.

Our solar system is but a small part of a single galaxy, and is off-center with respect to the galaxy. (Refer to Figure 37–25.) When we look into the sky we observe the belt of stars known as the Milky Way. It is composed of millions of stars grouped as a disc which turns as a great wheel in space. Visually the Milky Way appears as in Figure 37–24. This photograph shows the entire Milky Way as revealed on photographic plates with a telescope.

The Milky Way as revealed by a radio map appears very different. (Refer to Figure 37–26.) The dotted line indicates the galactic equator. Radio signals have the greatest intensity near the galactic equator and decrease in intensity as the latitude increases above and below this equator. Many radio stars are found within the Milky Way but none coincide with a visual star. The nucleus of our galaxy is indicated by the very high intensity of the radio signals from that region. The antenna of the radio telescope used to get the data to prepare the radio map in Figure 37–26 is shown in

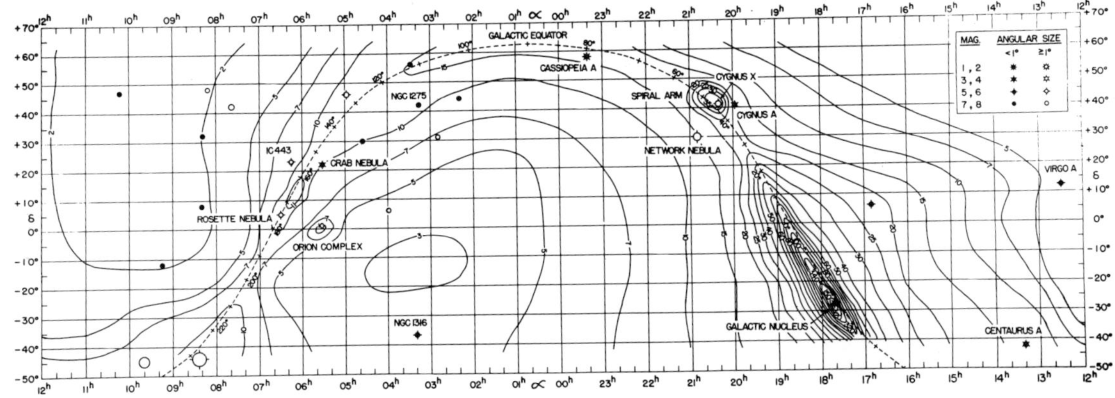

Fig. 37–26 *A radio map of the sky along a part of the axis of the Milky Way. The contours show the radio brightness (radio signal intensity) while the small circles indicate discrete sources or radio stars. (John D. Kraus, Ohio State University)*

Figure 37–27. Our galaxy is about 100,000 light-years in diameter.

The fact that radio signals come from all parts of the Milky Way indicates the presence of something able to emit energy as electromagnetic invisible radiation. It is now believed that the source of much of this radiation is hydrogen atoms. The protons and electrons in atoms spin on their own axes. These spins can be *parallel* or *anti-parallel,* the energy associated with the spin being greater when they are parallel (Figure 37–28). From many points of view the primordial element in the universe is hydrogen. It is abundant in the sun, in stars, and in all extra-terrestrial space. Even the least dense parts of the universe contain at least one atom of hydrogen per cubic centimeter. When two atoms in a higher energy state because their spins are parallel collide, they can form momentarily a "collision complex." When the two protons emerge from this complex, the spins can be anti-parallel and thus in a lower energy state. (Refer to Figure 37–28.) If this happens, the lost energy is radiated into space with a radio wave length of 21 centimeters or 1420 megacycles. A scientist in Holland, H. C. van de Hulst, in 1944 was the first to predict that energy from hydrogen atoms with an energy corresponding to a wave length of 21 centimeters should be reaching the earth. Experimental verification was not found until 1951. The time lag was the time needed to develop and build radio receiving apparatus for these very weak signals. Many measurements from hydrogen clouds have been made since that time from within our galactic system. These measurements have likewise been extended to other

Fig. 37–27 *A part of the radio telescope — the antenna — used to make the radio map shown in Fig. 37–26. (John D. Kraus, Ohio State University)*

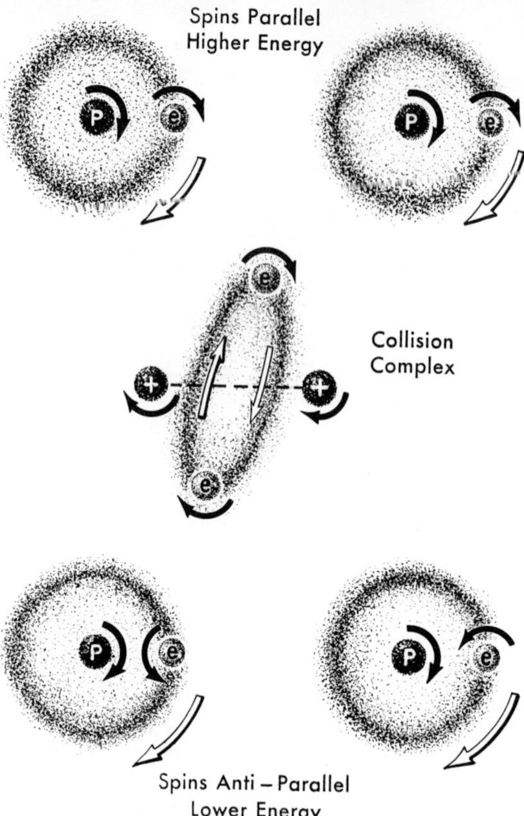

Fig. 37–28 *The two-spin focus of atomic hydrogen. Atoms with anti-parallel spins have lower energy content.*

galactic systems outside our Milky Way, such as the Large and Small Magellanic Clouds. (Refer to Figure 37–24.) These are two galactic systems entirely outside our galaxy at a distance of about 100,000 light-years.

SUMMARY

1. A virtual image is one that can be seen with the eye, but cannot be projected upon a screen; it is erect.
2. In passing from one substance into another at an angle other than 90° to the surface, light rays always undergo a change in velocity and direction. The velocity is less in the denser medium. This phenomenon is called refraction.
3. Light, in passing from a less dense into a more dense medium, is bent toward a perpendicular to the surface between the two mediums. The converse is true for light passing from a more dense to a less dense medium.
4. In passing through a triangular prism, light rays are deviated toward the base of the prism.
5. Converging lenses are used to bend parallel light rays toward each other.
6. Diverging lenses are used to bend parallel light rays apart.
7. A real image is one that can be projected upon a screen; it is inverted.
8. A converging lens brings parallel light rays to a point called the principal focus. The distance of the principal focus from the lens is called the focal length.
9. A converging lens is used (*a*) to produce a real inverted image and (*b*) to function as a magnifying glass. When used to produce a real image, the object must be located beyond the principal focus. When used as a magnifying glass, the object must be inside the principal focus, and the image is always erect, enlarged, and virtual.
10. The following facts concerning refracting telescopes are significant: (*a*) the objective lens produces an inverted real image of the object at or inside the principal focus of the eyepiece; (*b*) the eyepiece functions as a common magnifying glass and enlarges the real image produced by the objective lens; (*c*) mechanical and engineering difficulties set a limit to the size of refracting telescopes.
11. Reflecting telescopes are of two principal types: (*a*) Newtonian, and (*b*) Cassegrainian. The light rays are brought to a focus with a parabolic mirror. Reflecting telescopes can be made in much larger sizes than refracting telescopes.
12. Microscopes have a train of two converging lenses. The object is placed beyond the principal focus of the objective lens, which produces a real image, and this is thrown at or inside the principal focus of the eyepiece, which functions as a magnifying glass. The image is always enlarged.
13. The spectroscope is a principal instrument used to obtain information about luminous bodies in outer space. This instrument re-

veals light of varying frequencies (colors) as a spectrum of "lines" or bands from red to violet. These can be recorded photographically.

14. The pattern of spectral lines from any particular element is known as a spectrum. The spectra of different elements differ as to the number, location (frequency), and intensity of the lines. Spectra, therefore, can be used to identify elements.
15. Spectra are of three principal kinds: (*a*) continuous, (*b*) bright-line, and (*c*) dark-line.
16. Spectroscopes are used to determine the composition and motions of luminous bodies in outer space.
17. Our knowledge of the far reaches of the universe depends upon information collected and interpreted by the use of telescopes, spectroscopes, photocells, and radio telescopes.
18. The new science of radio astronomy is rapidly extending our knowledge of the universe.

STUDY EXERCISES

1. An astronomer made the statement that the sun can really be seen before it gets above the horizon. What did he mean? What property of light is involved? Explain.
2. Make a drawing showing the relative positions of the sun, earth, and moon during the first quarter. Indicate the path of the light from sun to observer which causes the new crescent moon. Likewise indicate the path of the light which makes visible the part of the moon which is not directly illuminated by the sun. This exercise illustrates what characteristic property of visible light?
3. Hold a pencil before a sheet of paper and close to an electric light. Hold the pencil close enough to give a sharp shadow. Verify the fact that the shadow gets less distinct as the paper is moved farther from the pencil. Is this due to reflection, refraction, diffraction, or interference of light? Explain.
4. Consider an ordinary magnifying or reading glass. Is it a concave or convex lens?

   Hold the glass at right angles to the rays from the sun in front of a piece of paper. Move the paper back and forth until the rays of the sun are concentrated in a fine point. How do you account for the result? What term is applied to this unique distance from the lens?

   If the glass is held close to a printed page, describe the image as to the following characteristics: enlarged or reduced, real or virtual, erect or inverted.

   Hold the glass about five inches from a printed page and describe the image as to the following characteristics: enlarged or reduced, real or virtual, erect or inverted.

FOR FURTHER READING

1. BRAGG, WILLIAM, *The Universe of Light.* New York: The Macmillan Company, 1934.

   Chapter II is concerned with optical instruments, including the eye.
2. WHITE, HARVEY E., *Classical and Modern Physics.* New York: D. Van Nostrand Company, 1940.

   Some common optical instruments including the eye, the camera, the telescope, and the microscope are discussed on pages 354–362.
3. LOVELL, B., and J. A. CLEGG, *Radio Astronomy.* New York: John Wiley and Sons, 1952.

   Able presentation of the new science of radio astronomy. Chapters 1 and 2 review some fundamentals of astronomy; Chapter 3 reviews electromagnetic waves; Chapters 15, 16, 17, and 18 discuss the origins of the radio signals from outer space.
4. Paperback: THE EDITORS OF SCIENTIFIC AMERICAN, *The New Astronomy.* Simon and Schuster. $1.45.

   The new science of radio astronomy is discussed in two very readable articles: "Radio Stars," by A. C. B. Lovell; and "Radio Waves from Interstellar Space."

38

THE NUCLEI OF ATOMS AND NUCLEAR ENERGY

IN PREVIOUS CHAPTERS we have discussed the properties of atoms dependent upon electronic structure. Their chemical properties depend entirely upon the character of the electron orbits. It has also been shown that the identity of an atom depends upon its atomic number or nuclear charge – the number of protons in the nucleus. With the exception of hydrogen, all atomic nuclei contain neutrons. Thus, both atoms and nuclei are complex. Much is known about the nucleus, but our understanding of it is far from complete. This should not be surprising. We are concerned with complex particles about 1×10^{-12} centimeters in diameter. Atoms are small but nuclei are only about 1/10,000 as large. Even such a fundamental question as the nature of the forces which hold the nucleus together has not been definitively answered. In Chapter 31 we learned that like charges of electricity repel each other with a force which depends upon the product of the charges and upon the distance between the charges, *decreasing inversely* as the *square* of the distance. An atom of chlorine, for example, contains 17 positively charged protons which are very close together. Why shouldn't the forces of repulsion cause the nucleus to explode? Obviously, there must be some restraining forces.

Since 1945 the world has come to talk, think, and write about a new age, the Nuclear Age: that is, the era which has come to rely on nuclear energy. The new age actually began on December 2, 1942, in Chicago, when it was demonstrated for the first time that a self-sustaining reaction for the steady release of nuclear energy was possible with uranium. The reaction is like an atomic fire always under control in which the uranium isotope U-235 is the fuel. The experiment with the uranium pile proved indisputably that the energy which lights the sun and stars had been harnessed by man and was under control. This knowledge made the Nuclear Age possible. The process of releasing the atomic energy of U-235 and plutonium is called atomic fission or fission. The discovery of atomic fission – the conversion of matter into energy by conversion of certain heavy atoms into smaller atoms – is one of the outstanding achievements of the human race.

In the decade since 1945, a second and perhaps more important process has been developed to obtain energy from nuclei of atoms — the fusion process, in which certain small atoms are converted into larger atoms. Both fission and fusion reactions result in the release of nuclear energy. The potentialities for large-scale energy supplies by fusion processes far transcend those by fission. It is the purpose of this chapter to contrast nuclear energy with conventional forms of energy and to present the story of the expansion of our knowledge of the nuclei of atoms. Finally, a presentation will be made of the enormous potentialities that controlled nuclear changes have for the good of mankind.

NUCLEAR ENERGY A RESULT OF FUNDAMENTAL RESEARCH

The large-scale use of nuclear energy has been the culmination of a sequence of events that started with the discoveries of Becquerel and Roentgen in 1895–97 and of the Curies in 1898. It is an error to believe that this discovery is something that came suddenly and unexpectedly as a result of World War II. In the first edition (1942) of the present book, for example, there occurs the following paragraph:

> As a possible energy source there is one recent development (1939–40) of great promise. One of the forms of uranium (U-235) has been found to split into barium and krypton atoms with the release of enormous quantities of energy. One pound of U-235 would liberate energy equivalent to 2,600,000 pounds of coal and would be equivalent as an explosive to fifteen thousand tons of TNT. The problem on which scientists in this country and abroad are now working (1940–41) is to find a method of separating U-235 from the other forms of uranium.

Wartime research merely carried out, on a scale never dreamed of before, theories of matter already known to scientists the world over. What had been done in university laboratories on an infinitesimal scale was now done on a factory scale.

THE EQUIVALENCE OF MATTER AND ENERGY

In the physical science of Galileo and Newton, matter and energy were separate entities. In quantum mechanics matter and energy are equivalent to each other. In other words, *matter is energy*. Under many conditions matter as such disappears and energy in an equivalent amount appears. Similarly, under some circumstances, energy disappears but matter in an equivalent amount appears. Matter and energy cannot be destroyed though they are convertible into each other. This is the law of equivalence of matter and energy.

This law was first stated in principle and mathematical form in 1905 by Albert Einstein, as follows:

Change in E(nergy) $\propto$ Change in m(ass),

or $$E = k\,m \qquad (\textit{Equation 38–1})$$

If the energy is measured in ergs and the mass in grams, Equation 38–1 takes the form,

$$E = c^2 \cdot m, \qquad (\textit{Equation 38–2})$$

TABLE 38–1

VALUES FOR k IN THE EINSTEIN EQUATION

UNITS FOR MASS	UNITS FOR ENERGY	k
grams	ergs	9×10^{20} ergs/gram
grams	calories	2.15×10^{13} calories/gram
pounds	kilowatt-hours	1.10×10^{10} kilowatt-hrs/pound
atomic mass units*	ergs*	1.49×10^{-3} ergs/amu
atomic mass units*	Mev (million electron-volts)*	931 Mev/amu

* The starred units are those usually used.

where c is the velocity of light (3×10^{10} cm/sec). This equation shows that a fantastic amount of energy appears when matter disappears. What, for example, is the energy formed when a gram of matter disappears?

$$E = c^2 \cdot m = (3 \cdot 10^{10}\ \text{cm/sec})^2\ (1\ \text{g})$$
$$= 9 \cdot 10^{20} \frac{\text{g cm}^2}{\text{sec}^2} = 9 \times 10^{20}\ \text{erg}$$

This energy is equivalent to that obtained by burning over 3000 tons of coal! The equation, $E = mc^2$, has become commonplace and is often referred to as "the Einstein equation." The value of the constant of proportionality in the Einstein equation depends upon the units used to measure the energy and the mass. (Refer to Table 38–1.)

Rutherford made the first transmutation of an element in 1919. The correct interpretation of what happened in the reaction

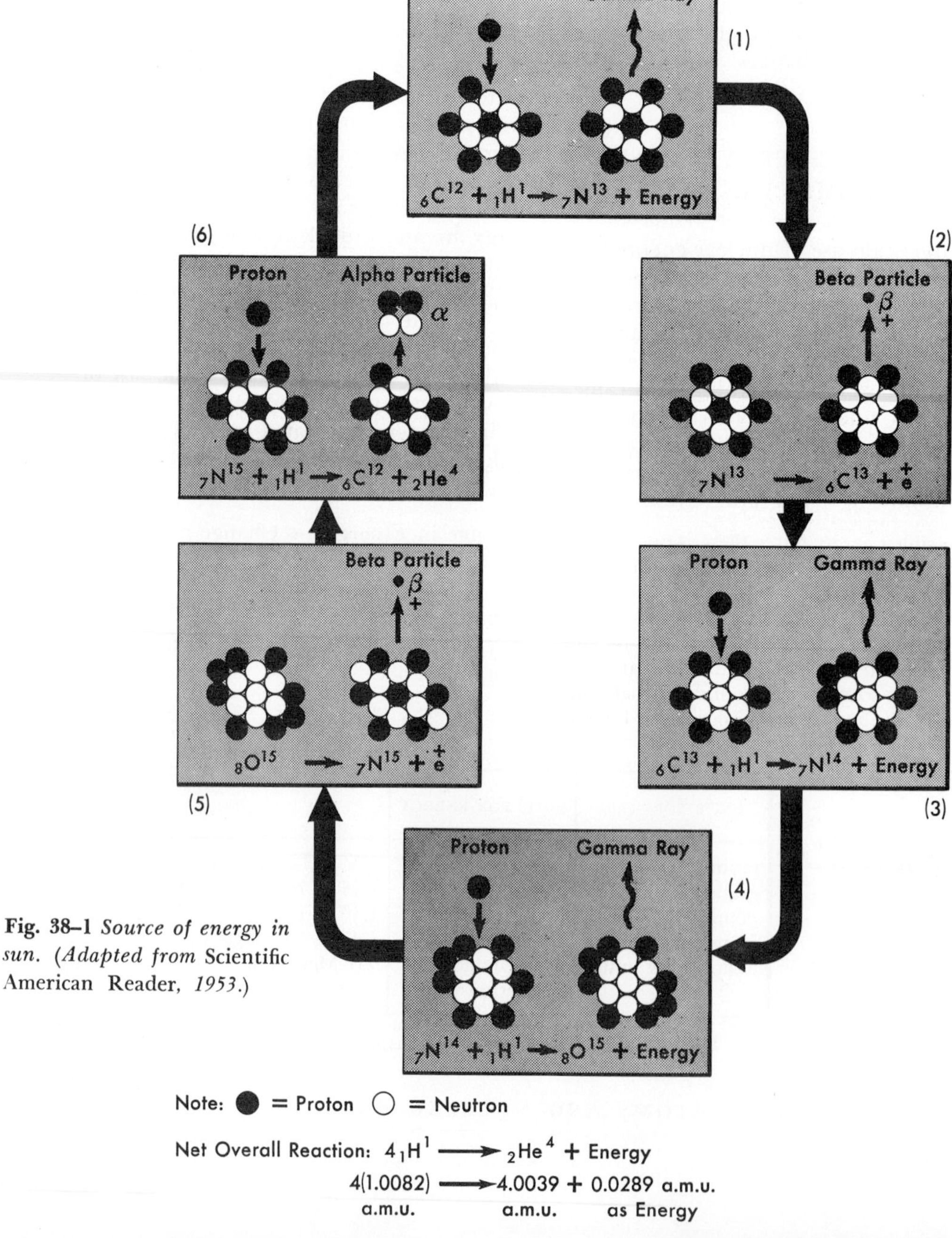

Fig. 38–1 *Source of energy in sun.* (*Adapted from* Scientific American Reader, *1953.*)

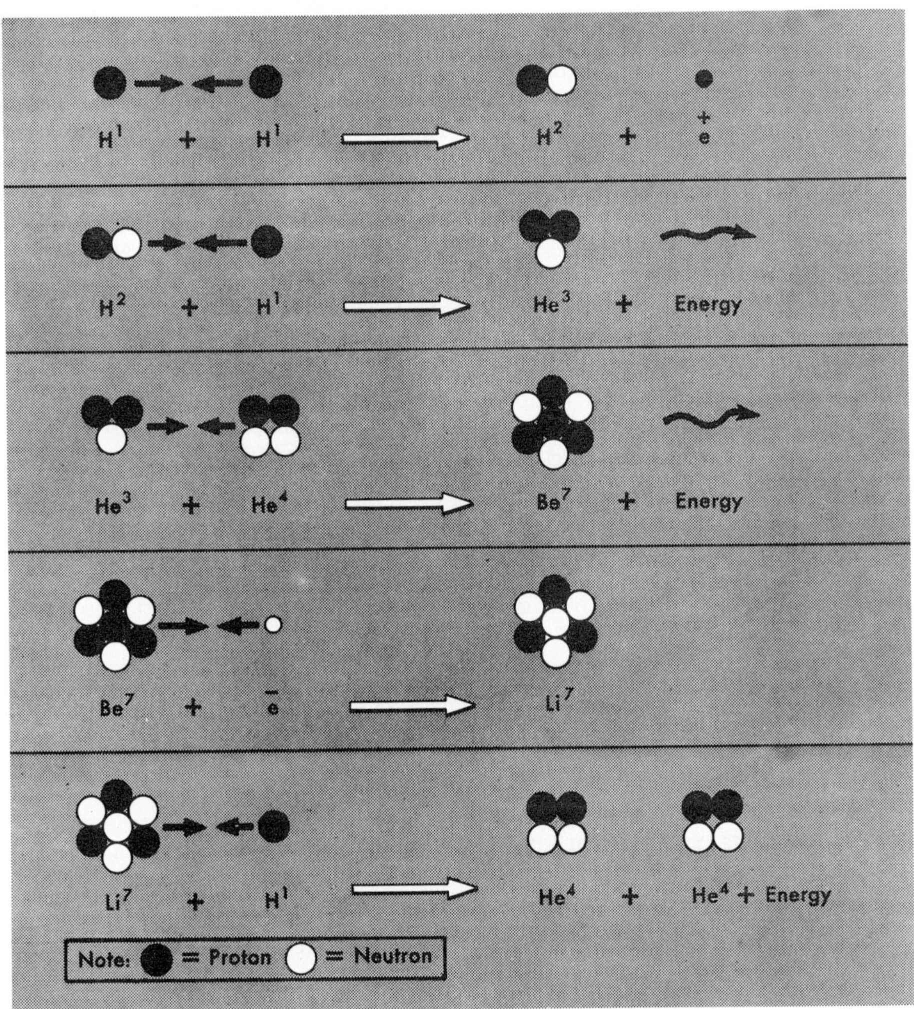

Fig. 38–2 *A primary source of cosmic energy.* (*Adapted from* Scientific American Reader, *1953.*)

required an application of the Einstein equation. Rutherford was able to show that the sum of the masses of the nitrogen and alpha particles plus their energy before the collision was greater than the sum of the masses of the oxygen and the protons after the collision. Hence, some energy was liberated as kinetic energy associated with the two product particles.

Table 38–1 illustrates the magnitude of nuclear energy. For example, the daily energy requirements of a city of 40,000 people is about 250,000 kilowatt-hours. The nuclear energy of a pound of matter could supply the daily energy requirement of 40,000 cities each with a population of 40,000!

SOURCE OF ENERGY OF THE SUN – A FUSION REACTION

An important question that has tried the skill of the greatest scientists is, what is the source of energy of the sun? The energy liberated by the sun each second is staggering in its magnitude. It streams out into space in all directions and only a very small part of it is intercepted by the earth. Just recall that the diameter of the sun is 108 times the diameter of the earth, and that its surface temperature is over 6000° C. The earth is at least three billion years old (refer to Chapter 39); and during all these years energy from the sun has been streaming out into space as radiant energy. Moreover, there is nothing to indicate that this rate is appreciably decreasing. Of course the question of the ultimate fate of the earth and sun is linked to the question of the source of the energy of the sun.

The energy of the sun is not the result of an ordinary process of combustion. Strange though it may seem, the sun is much too hot for ordinary combustion. Hypothesis after hypothesis has been invented to account for the sun's energy, but each in turn has had to be discarded because it could not account for all known facts pertaining to the sun. Finally, H. A. Bethe, an American scientist, proposed (1939) a theory which is currently accepted by scientists. He postulated as occurring in the sun the series of nuclear reactions shown in Figure 38–1. Reactions (2) and (5) are radioactive changes which liberate positrons ($e+$). The positron is a particle similar in mass to the electron but with one positive charge. In each of these six reactions there is conservation of mass and energy according to the Einstein equation ($E = mc^2$). The intermediate products, such as carbon-13, do not have permanent existence, and the carbon-12, needed for the reactions, is regenerated. The net effect of the six successive reactions is the transformation of hydrogen, plentiful in the sun, into helium, with a loss of matter and a release of energy.

Another fusion reaction which is now believed to account for most of the energy of the cosmos is outlined in stepwise fashion in Figure 38–2. It is to be noted that the net effect of these reactions is the conversion of ordinary hydrogen into helium by a fusion process:

$$4\,{}^1_1\text{H} \rightarrow {}^4_2\text{He} + \text{energy}$$

The mass of the helium produced (4.0039 a.m.u.) is *less* than that of the hydrogen (4[1.0081] = 4.0324 a.m.u.) used in its production. The energy liberated is about 1.5×10^{11} calories per gram of helium produced. The heat liberated in the formation of only a gram of helium is enough to convert over *three hundred tons* of water to steam.

The carbon cycle of Bethe and the proton-proton cycle are now generally accepted to account for solar energy. Astronomers believe that these transformations occur in all stars. The theory indicates that the final fate of the sun will depend upon the amount of hydrogen in the sun. When all the hydrogen has been converted into the more stable helium, the sun will commence to cool off and the earth will then be destined for death. This is not a matter of immediate concern, however, for it is estimated that it will take 30 billion years to consume all the hydrogen in the sun.

NUCLEAR FORCES

We have already studied Coulomb's law of electrical repulsion: the force between two like electrical charges is directly proportional to the product of the charges and inversely proportional to the square of the distance between the charges. Thus, we can write:

$$F \propto \frac{q_1 q_2}{d^2} \qquad \textit{(Equation 38–3)}$$

Considering the effect of distance alone, we can write:

$$\frac{F_2}{F_1} = \left(\frac{d_1}{d_2}\right)^2 \qquad \textit{(Equation 38–4)}$$

The effect of decreasing the distance has the effect of enormously increasing the force of repulsion between like charges. Assume that two like charges separated by a distance of one centimeter exert a force of one dyne upon each other. What is the force if the distance is only a millionth of one centimeter? Equation 38–4 predicts that

$$F_2 = 1 \text{ dyne} \times \left[\frac{1 \text{ cm}}{10^{-6} \text{ cm}}\right]^2 = 10^{12} \text{ dynes.}$$

This is equivalent to over 1000 *tons* of force. The nuclei of atoms contain protons. The radius of the nucleus is about 1×10^{-12} centimeters. The forces of repulsion between these protons should be truly enormous. Why then does the nucleus exist? Why

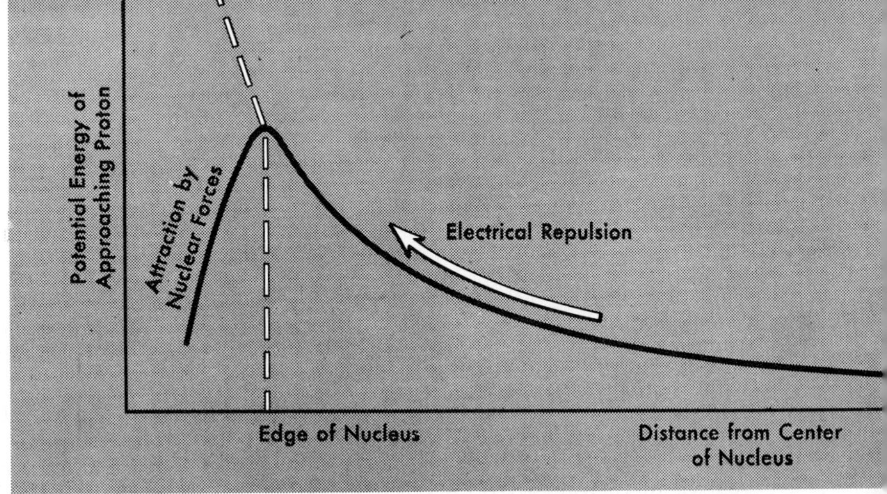

Fig. 38–3 *The attractive forces within nuclei.*

doesn't it literally fly apart? Obviously, there must be opposing forces. (Refer to Figure 38–3.) Consider a proton approaching the nucleus of the atom. As it reaches the edge of the nucleus it comes under the influence of a very large electrical force of repulsion. When the proton penetrates *inside* the edge of the nucleus it comes under the influence of even greater attractive forces — called nuclear forces — and the proton is retained within the nucleus.

Scientists *hypothesize* the existence of three kinds of forces within the nuclei of atoms. Consider the nucleus of an atom of helium (Figure 38–4.) Protons normally repel each other, but in the nucleus this force of repulsion is overcome by greater forces of attraction. They are frequently called "short-range forces." There are proton-proton (p–p) forces, proton-neutron (p–n) forces, and neutron-neutron (n–n) forces. Little is known about their magnitude, though there is reason to believe that the (p–n) forces are the greatest of the three. In the case of the lighter elements, the maximum stability of an atom results when the n/p ratio is unity. It is noteworthy that 80 per cent of the earth's crust is made up of elements ${}_{8}O^{16}$, ${}_{12}Mg^{24}$, ${}_{14}Si^{28}$, and ${}_{20}Ca^{40}$, all of which have an n/p ratio of unity.

Fig. 38–4 *Nucleus of helium atom.*

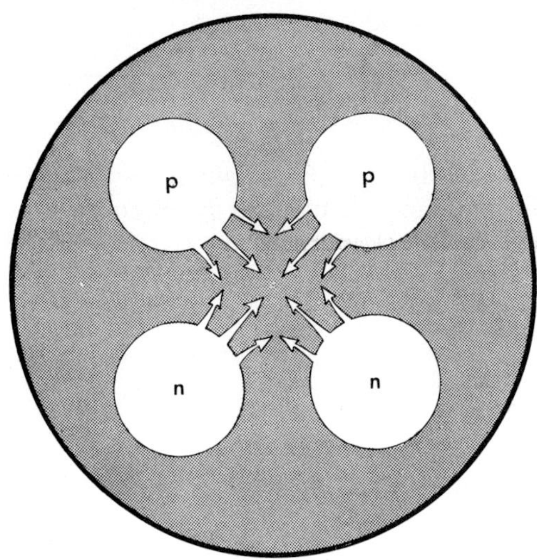

THE STABILITY OF ATOMS AND n/p RATIO

The law of the equivalency of matter and energy leads to a simple explanation of why some atoms are stable and some are unstable or radioactive. The property of radioactivity is direct evidence that atoms differ in their stability. The first radioactive elements to be studied were all of large atomic number and mass. But it is necessary to avoid the conclusion that radioactivity is due to instability in atomic nuclei merely because of large numbers of protons and neutrons. Some elements of high mass and atomic number, such as lead-206, are very stable. Also some elements of low mass and atomic number are unstable. Thus hydrogen-3 is radioactive. It disintegrates as follows:

$${}_{1}H^{3} \rightarrow {}_{2}He^{3} + {}_{-}\beta^{0}$$

The helium-3 which is formed is stable.

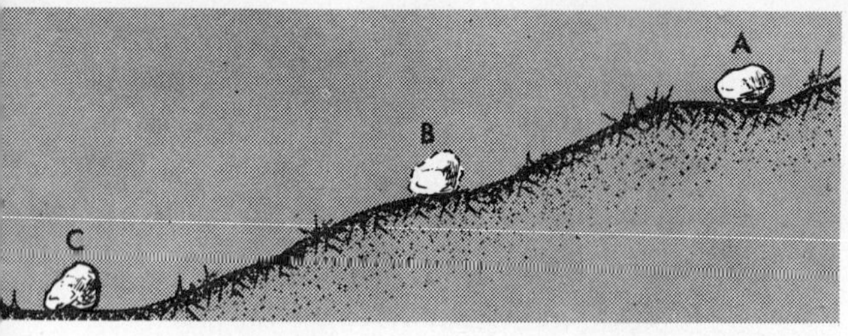

Fig. 38–5 *A system with potential energy tends to lose it.*

The beta particle ($_{-}\beta^{0}$) is a high-velocity and thus energetic negative electron which came from the hydrogen-3 nucleus.

The second law of thermodynamics, discussed in Chapter 18, points out that in any natural process only a part of the energy is converted to a useful form. The rest becomes unavailable. Consider a stone on a hillside (Figure 38–5). The stone in position *A* possesses potential energy with respect to positions *B* and *C*. It can be said to be unstable with respect to positions *B* and *C*. If given a slight push it can roll spontaneously to position *B*. If given another push, it can roll to position *C*. The kinetic energy it possesses as it nears the bottom is dissipated as heat to the surroundings. In this sense, the energy it originally possessed at position *A* becomes unavailable for further use. A measure of the stability of the stone in position *C* is the amount of energy *dissipated* in rolling from *A* to *C*.

The second law of thermodynamics can be stated in this manner: In any spontaneous process of change, there is always degradation of energy. (Refer to page 311.)

Consider the energy change involved in the formation of an atom of carbon from its constituents,

$$6\,p \;+\; 6\,n \;+\; 6\,e^{-} \;\rightarrow\; {}_{6}C^{12} \;+\; \Delta m$$

Mass of reactants:

$$\begin{aligned} 6\,p &= 6(1.007575) = 6.04545 \\ 6\,n &= 6(1.00893) \;\;= 6.05358 \\ 6\,e^{-} &= 6(0.000543) = 0.00329 \\ \text{Total} &\qquad\qquad\quad = 12.10232 \\ \text{Mass of product:} &\qquad\qquad\quad = 12.00386 \\ \text{Loss of mass} &\qquad\qquad\quad = 0.09846\text{amu} \end{aligned}$$

Hence, $\Delta m = 0.09846$ atomic mass units. This quantity in atomic mass units (amu) is a loss of mass which is converted into energy in accordance with Einstein's law. (Refer to Table 38–1.)

$$\Delta E = \Delta mk = 9.85 \times 10^{-2}\text{ amu} \times 931\ \frac{\text{Mev}}{\text{amu}}$$
$$= 91.6\text{ Mev}$$

The *same amount of energy* would be required to break up an atom of carbon into its constituent particles. We will refer to this as the *unbinding energy*. It is the amount of energy that is needed to change the nucleus back into its component parts: neutrons, protons, and electrons. It can be taken as a measure of the stability of an atom. The larger the unbinding energy, the more stable the atom; and vice versa.[1]

In working with nuclear reactions it is customary to express the energy change in electron-volts (ev) or million electron-volts (Mev), rather than in calories or joules. The electron-volt is a unit of energy – the energy possessed by one electron falling through an electric field of one volt. The Mev and calorie are definitely related. Recall that the volt means that a joule of energy must be used to transfer one coulomb of electricity (page 502). Using then the charge on the electron in coulombs,

$$\begin{aligned} 1\text{ Mev} &= 10^{6}\,e^{-} \times 1.59 \times 10^{-19}\,\frac{\text{coulomb}}{e^{-}} \times 1\text{ volt} \\ &= 10^{6}\,e^{-} \times 1.59 \times 10^{-19}\,\frac{\text{coulomb}}{e^{-}} \times 1\,\frac{\text{joule}}{\text{coulomb}} \\ &= 1.59 \times 10^{-13}\text{ joule} \\ &= 1.59 \times 10^{-13} \times \frac{1\text{ cal}}{4.185\text{ joule}} \\ &= 3.80 \times 10^{-14}\text{ calorie.} \end{aligned}$$

At first thought this might seem to be an insignificant quantity. It is, of course, the energy associated with an electron which has a mass of 9×10^{-28} gram which has "fallen through" a million volts. The energy as

[1] The term "binding energy" is also used, though with a different connotation. The term "unbinding energy" is more meaningful.

TABLE 38–2 COMBINING ENERGIES OF THE CARBON ISOTOPES

(1) ISOTOPE	(2) COMPOSITION OF NUCLEUS	(3) n/p	(4) TOTAL UNBINDING ENERGY (Δm)	(ΔE)	(5) UNBINDING ENERGY PER PARTICLE (Mev/particle)
$_6C^{11}$	6 p 5 n	0.83	−0.07844 amu	+73.0 Mev	+6.64
$_6C^{12}$	6 p 6 n	1.00	−0.09864 amu	91.6 Mev	7.65
$_6C^{14}$	6 p 8 n	1.33	−0.11248 amu	105.0 Mev	7.59

sociated with a gram of electrons would be 4.25×10^{13} calories. This is enough heat to raise the temperature of over 400,000 tons of water from the freezing point to the boiling point.

The comparison of the unbinding energies for C-11, C-12, and C-14 are given in Table 38–2. The unbinding energies per particle (nucleon) are given in column (5). The term *nucleon* applies to any nuclear particle, proton or neutron. Note that the unbinding energy for C-12, in which the n/p ratio is unity, is the largest and that it is the most stable. Where the n/p ratio is either significantly *less or greater than unity,* the unbinding energy per particle decreases, and the atom becomes more unstable. Both C-11 and C-14 are unstable and radioactive. It is noteworthy that the unbinding energy of C-11 is significantly less than that of C-14. It is not surprising then to find that C-11 is much less stable than C-14. It has a half-life of about twenty minutes, while C-14 has a half-life of over 5000 years.

MEANING OF HALF-LIFE

The degree of instability of a radioactive isotope is indicated by its *half-life* — the time needed for one-half of a sample of a radioactive substance to disappear. (Refer to page 352.) In general, the half-life of a radioactive element *decreases* as the element becomes more unstable and the n/p values depart from the value found in the stable isotope. For example, consider the isotopes Ca-40, Ca-45, and Ca-47. Their n/p ratios and half-life values are given in Table 38–3. It is apparent that Ca-47, with an n/p ratio most removed from the value in stable Ca-40, is the most unstable as indicated by the shortest half-life value. Thus the half-life values depend upon the stability of the nucleus or the n/p ratio. The half-life of any radioactive element cannot be slowed down or speeded up by any known process.

TABLE 38–3 HALF-LIFE VALUES OF CALCIUM ISOTOPES

ISOTOPE	n/p RATIO	$T_{\frac{1}{2}}$ VALUE
$_{20}Ca^{40}$	20/20	Stable
$_{20}Ca^{45}$	25/20	152 days
$_{20}Ca^{47}$	27/20	5.8 days

The character of the decay curve of any radioactive substance is shown in Figure 38–6. This is an exponential curve.

The relation between the number of elapsed half-lives and the total percentage of the radioactive substance which has disappeared is shown in Table 38–4. Thus it

Fig. 38–6 *Decay of a radioactive substance.*

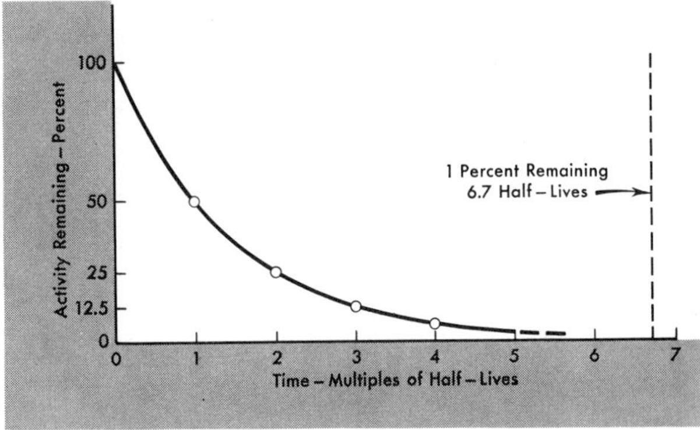

TABLE 38–4 FRACTION OF RADIOACTIVE SUBSTANCE DISAPPEARING IN RELATION TO ELAPSED TIME IN HALF-LIVES

NUMBER OF HALF-LIVES	PER CENT DISAPPEARED DURING EACH HALF-LIFE	TOTAL PER CENT DISAPPEARED
0	0	0
1	50	50
2	25	75
3	12.5	87.5
4	6.25	93.85
5	3.13	95.4
6	1.57	97.0
6.7	1.00	99.0

takes 6.7 half-lives for 99 per cent of any given sample of a radioactive substance to disappear.

UNBINDING ENERGY CURVE OF THE ELEMENTS

The unbinding energy per nucleon for the stable forms of all the elements is shown in Figure 38–7 as a function of the mass number (*A*). Two general observations can be made, namely:

1. The most stable elements have mass numbers in the range of about 40 to 120. The atomic numbers range from about 20 (calcium) to 56 (barium). Iron, for example ($_{26}Fe$), is an element with unusually great stability.

2. The very heavy elements and the very light elements are intrinsically less stable than the elements of intermediate mass number. These can achieve greater stability by undergoing nuclear changes to form either lighter or heavier elements. This topic will be discussed later.

For the lighter elements, the maximum stability of nuclei is achieved when the n/p ratio is unity. Figure 38–8 clearly shows, however, that as the number of protons in the nucleus increases there is a gradual increase in the number of neutrons. That is, the n/p ratio gradually increases. It finally reaches values as high as 1.5 for elements of very high atomic number. Just as a stone on a hill achieves greater stability by rolling to a lower position and thus spontaneously losing energy, unstable elements achieve greater stability by losing some mass and changing their n/p ratios. We have learned that neutrons can become protons by ejecting a negative beta particle $_{-}\beta^{0}$. (See Figure 38–9.) These beta particles are energetic electrons, but they do not exist as such inside the nucleus. When a negative beta particle is emitted from a nucleus, the n/p ratio decreases. The n/p ratio increases, however, upon the loss of a positron ($_{+}\beta^{0}$).

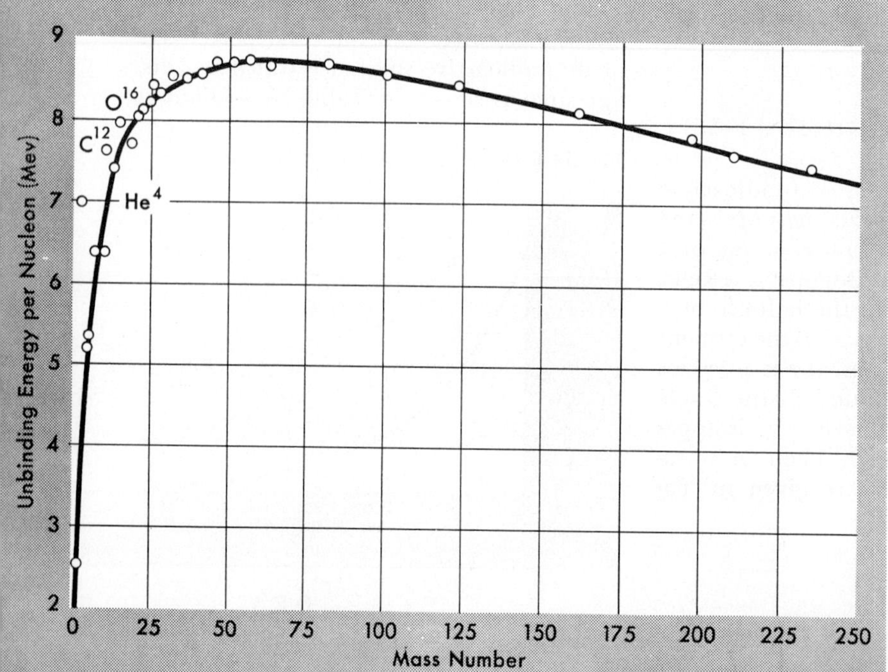

Fig. 38–7 *Unbinding energy per nucleon for the stable elements. (From Dr. Samuel Glasstone,* Sourcebook on Atomic Energy, *D. Van Nostrand Co., Inc. Copyright U. S. Atomic Energy Commission.)*

Fig. 38–8 *Relation of neutrons to protons in the stable elements. (From Dr. Samuel Glasstone,* Sourcebook on Atomic Energy, *D. Van Nostrand Co., Inc. Copyright U. S. Atomic Energy Commission.)*

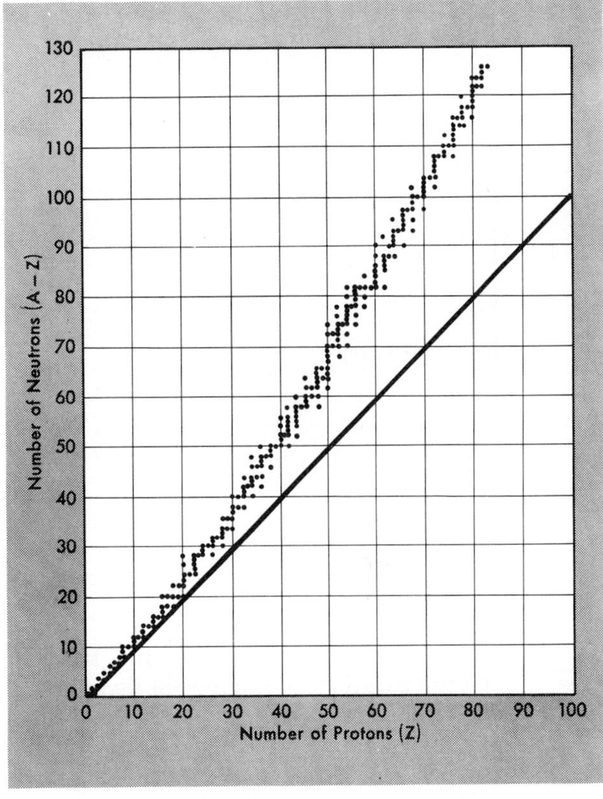

Examples of elements achieving greater stability by radioactive or nuclear changes are oxygen-19, which emits negative electrons, and neon-19, which emits positrons. They can be compared with flourine-19, which is stable. (Refer to Table 38–5 and Figure 38–10.) Note that the unbinding energy per particle is less for both oxygen-19 and neon-19 than for flourine-19, and that these are both unstable and radioactive.

As disintegration proceeds the n/p ratio changes to approach the value 1.11 and the unbinding energies per particle increase. The radioactive change in the case of $_{10}Ne^{19}$ is as follows,

$$_{10}Ne^{19} \longrightarrow {}_{9}F^{19} + {}_{+}\beta^{0}$$

TABLE 38–5 COMPARISON OF SOME UNBINDING ENERGIES

ELEMENT	COMPOSITION OF NUCLEUS (n)	(p)	n/p RATIO	UNBINDING ENERGY (Mev)	BEHAVIOR
$_{8}O^{19}$	11	8	1.37	7.31	Radioactive; $_{-}\beta^{0}$ emitter
$_{9}F^{19}$	10	9	1.11	7.74	Stable
$_{10}Ne^{19}$	9	10	0.90	7.51	Radioactive; $_{+}\beta^{0}$ emitter

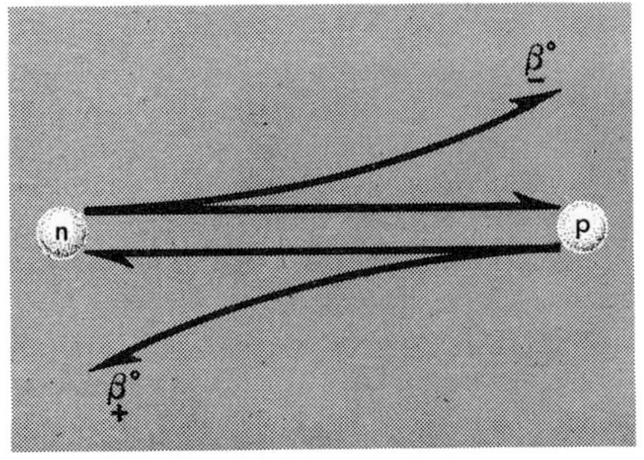

Fig. 38–9 *Apparent relation of a neutron to a proton, and vice versa.*

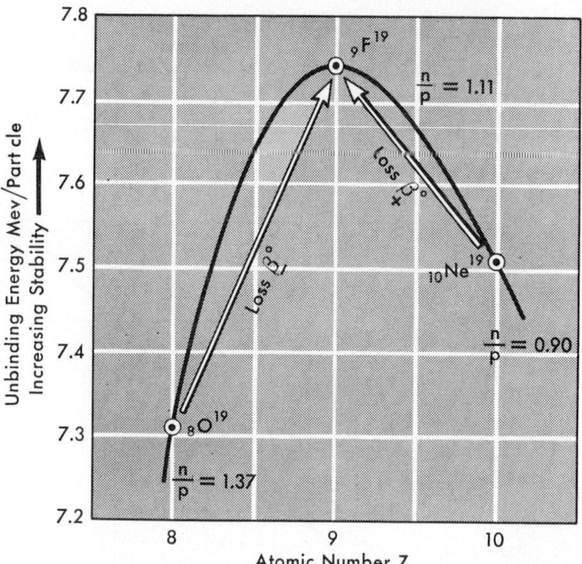

Fig. 38–10 *Radioactive O^{19} and Ne^{19} disintegrate to become stable F^{19}.*

The student is urged to determine for himself the nature of the change in the nucleus, the kind of change in the mass, the change in the n/p ratio, and the unbinding energy per particle. (Refer to Table 38–5 and Figure 38–10.)

Radioactivity, then, is not the mysterious, unpredictable property of atoms that it was once considered to be. While there is much yet to learn about energy levels within the nuclei of atoms, scientists possess a "rationale" which enables them to predict with a high degree of certainty the radioactive properties of radioisotopes.

ARTIFICIAL RADIOACTIVITY

In 1935 a daughter of Madame Curie, Irène Joliot-Curie, jointly with her husband, Frédéric Joliot, was awarded the Nobel prize in chemistry. Interestingly enough, the award was made to the second generation for the discovery of artificial radioactivity, a discovery which has been as productive of new discoveries as was that of natural radioactivity forty years earlier, and one which ranks high among the noteworthy achievements of this century.

One of the first instances of artificial radioactivity studied by the team of Joliot-Curie was that observed when aluminum foil was bombarded with alpha particles. A sample of polonium placed at the end of a small round channel in a large block of lead produced a beam of alpha particles. These were completely absorbed by a sheet of aluminum foil, and neutrons were produced in the process. (Refer to Figure 38–11.) The neutrons were detected by being absorbed in a thick block of paraffin. In this process protons were produced which were easily detected with a Geiger counter. The changes that occurred in the aluminum are more concisely represented as follows:

$$^{27}_{13}\mathrm{Al} + {}^{4}_{2}\mathrm{He} \rightarrow {}^{30}_{15}\mathrm{P} + {}_{0}\mathrm{n}^{1}$$

Thus the aluminum was converted to an element with atomic number 15 which is an isotope of ordinary phosphorus. It was radioactive. That is, it in turn emitted charged particles (positrons) which were easily detected with a Geiger counter. Furthermore, the rate of emission of charged particles tapered off comparatively rapidly to give the exponential rate curve characteristic of any radioactive substance. It was established that an isotope of phosphorus was produced of atomic weight 30, which was half gone in $2\frac{1}{2}$ minutes. The change which occurred in the radioactive phosphorus was this:

$$^{30}_{15}\mathrm{P} \rightarrow {}^{30}_{14}\mathrm{Si} + {}_{+}\beta^{0}$$

Positrons were emitted, and the stable substance which remained was an isotope of silicon within the aluminum foil. The great significance of this discovery was that for the first time a true radioactive substance in measurable quantities was produced artificially. During the same year the Joliot-Curie team also produced synthetic radioactive carbon-13 and sulfur-29. Their discovery stimulated work in laboratories all over the world.

The production of radioisotopes is now commonplace. Many particles, such as protons, deuterons, alpha particles, and neu-

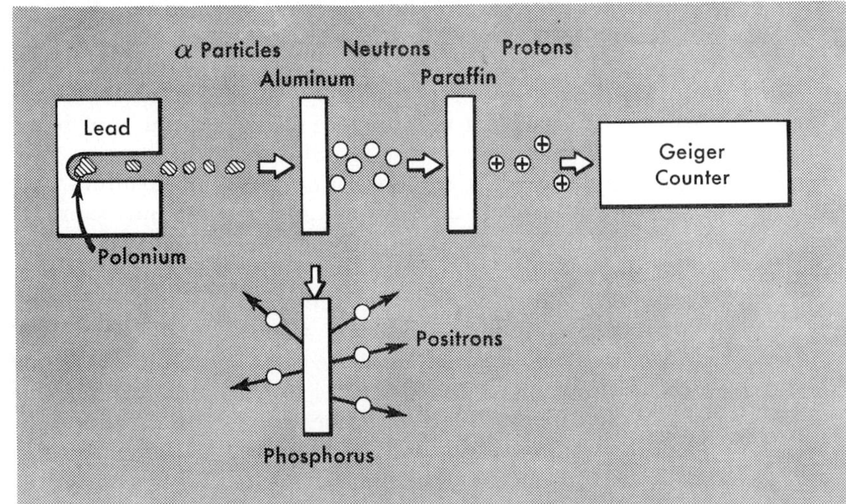

Fig. 38–11 *Conversion of aluminum to radioactive phosphorus.*

trons, if they have sufficient energy, can be made into projectiles to shoot into the nuclei of atoms and thus bring about nuclear changes. (Refer to page 355.) The products are frequently radioactive. The reactions can be summarized:

Atoms of A + Energetic particles →
{ Alpha particles, Protons, Deuterons, Neutrons, Gamma photons }
Atoms of B (or A) + Less energetic particles
{ Protons, Gamma photons, Neutrons }

When the bombarding particles are neutrons, the products are atoms of A but of higher mass.

To illustrate typical nuclear changes, consider the production of Na-24 with deuterons and with neutrons. With deuterons bombarding ordinary sodium, the change occurs as shown in Figure 38–12. With neutrons, the change that occurs is as shown in Figure 38–13. These reactions demonstrate how the same radioactive element can be synthesized by two quite dissimilar reactions. In both cases there is a decrease in mass. The mass that disappears is equivalent to the energy of the gamma rays which are emitted.

Sodium-24 has proven to be a very useful radioisotope. It disintegrates with a half-life of 14.8 hours, as follows,

$$^{24}_{11}\text{Na} \rightarrow {}^{24}_{12}\text{Mg} + {}_{-}\beta^{0} + \gamma$$

The medical uses of this radioisotope will be discussed later.

Fig. 38–12 *The production of sodium-24 with deuterons.*

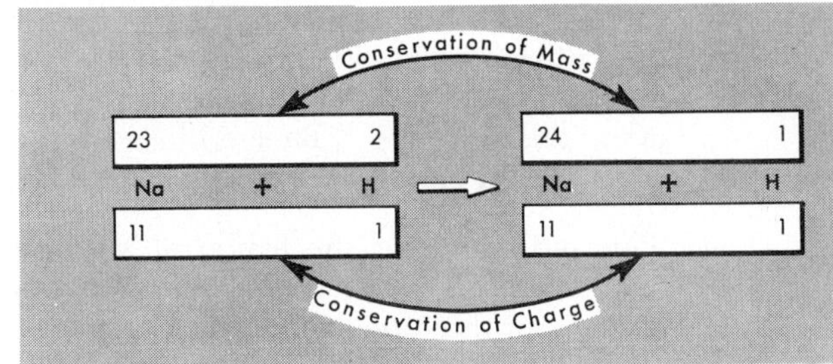

Fig. 38–13 *The production of sodium-24 with neutrons.*

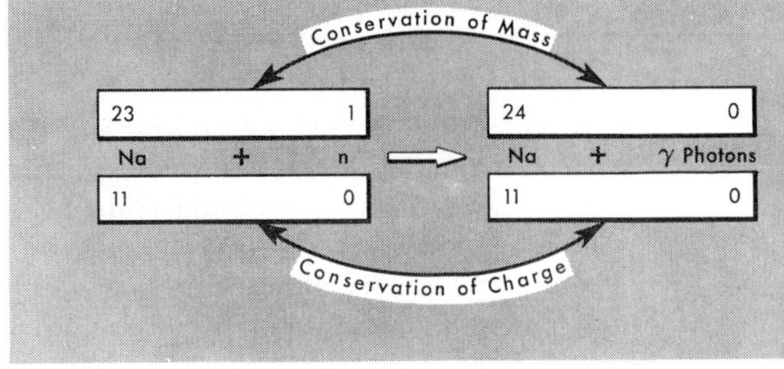

THE DISCOVERY OF FISSION

The most spectacular consequence of the knowledge that accumulated so rapidly during the nineteen thirties concerning the atom was the atomic bomb. In January, 1939, Hahn and Strassman in Germany reported the presence of barium in the disintegration products of uranium subjected to neutron bombardment. Barium, atomic number 56, is near the middle of the stability curve shown in Figure 38–7. The world was ready for the next suggestion, for which no one person can claim full credit. The idea of fission came to many nuclear scientists at about the same time, January and February, 1939, in Germany, Denmark, France, and the United States. The unusual behavior of uranium in the presence of neutrons was a splitting of the atom of uranium into two simpler elements with the simultaneous release of one to three neutrons and an enormous amount of energy. The general process is called *atomic fission*. The term *fission* means the division of a parent atom into two simpler atoms.

The fission reaction has been intensively studied since 1939. An example of fission is the following:

$$_0n^1 + {}^{235}_{92}U \rightarrow {}^{90}_{36}Kr + {}^{142}_{56}Ba + 3\,{}_0n^1 + \text{energy (200 Mev)}$$

This indicates that the fission of an atom of U-235 produces an atom of krypton, one of barium, three neutrons, and energy corresponding to the loss in mass. The fission reaction is actually very complicated. As many as thirty-four different elements have been found among the fission products. A more generalized statement for fission is:

$$_0n^1 + {}^{235}_{92}U \rightarrow {}^{85-100}_{36-42}A + {}^{130-150}_{52-62}B + (1\text{–}3)\,{}_0n^1 + \text{Energy}$$

Experimentally, it has been found that the elements that predominate in the portion A have mass numbers ranging from 85 to 100 (atomic numbers 36 to 42), while those in the portion B have mass numbers of 130 to 150 (atomic numbers 52 to 62). The atomic masses of A and B are in the ratio of about 2 : 3. The portion A has been found to contain elements such as zirconium, molybdenum, and ruthenium, while the portion B consists of elements such as neodymium, barium, xenon, cerium, and cesium. Significantly, the elements of these atomic numbers fall in the central portion of the curve shown in Figure 38–7 – an indication that the fission products are eventually very stable. Thus fission is an example of a transition of a heavy element into lighter elements to achieve greater atomic stability.

The first pair of fission products are usually radioactive. Thus, krypton-90, mentioned above, decays as

$${}^{90}_{36}Kr \xrightarrow{-\beta^0} {}^{90}_{37}Rb \xrightarrow{-\beta^0} {}^{90}_{38}Sr \text{ (relatively stable)},$$

while Ba-142 decays as

$${}^{142}_{56}Ba \xrightarrow{-\beta^0} {}^{142}_{57}La \xrightarrow{-\beta^0} {}^{142}_{58}Ce \text{ (stable)}.$$

It is characteristic of the fission products that they continue to disintegrate until such stable atom forms are produced as strontium-90 and cerium-142. The strontium-90 actually is radioactive, having a half-life of about 25 years. Its presence in the fission products makes it dangerous.

An invariable product of fission is the formation of one to three neutrons which in large enough masses of U-235 can produce more fission reactions. The whole sequence is then referred to as a *chain reaction*. The significance of this release of neutrons during fission will be discussed below.

An unusual aspect of the fission reaction is the disappearance of enough mass to produce enormous amounts of energy. Energy from ordinary combustion processes is puny by comparison. Thus our most important source of heat energy is the combustion of carbon as coal. The reaction is

$$C + O_2 \rightarrow CO_2 + 4 \text{ ev of heat per atom.}$$

The fission of one atom of U-235 produces 200 Mev of energy or 50 million times more! This is the import of nuclear energy. We may anticipate that much of the energy of the future will be produced by fission reaction.

SYNTHETIC FISSIONABLE MATERIAL

It was early demonstrated that atomic fission occurred with only one of the natural isotopes of uranium, U-235. This isotope occurs only to the extent of 0.70 per cent in ordinary uranium. To make an atomic bomb of U-235 would require the separation of that isotope from the relatively abundant and stable U-238, which is very difficult to fission. The separation of U-235 from U-238 by a gaseous diffusion process was accomplished at Oak Ridge, Tennessee, and our facilities for the production of U-235 have been enormously increased since 1946.

A second fissionable material, plutonium-239, is a synthetic element made from U-238. Fermi and others had shown that U-238, by neutron capture, could be converted into two new synthetic elements of atomic numbers 93 and 94. The reactions were as follows:

$$^{238}_{92}U + {}_0n^1 \rightarrow {}^{239}_{92}U + \gamma$$

This isotope had a half-life of only 23 minutes; and by emission of an electron it formed a new element which was named neptunium.

$$^{239}_{92}U \rightarrow {}^{239}_{93}Np + {}_{-}\beta^0$$

This likewise was short-lived, with a half-life of 2.3 days, but it formed the relatively stable plutonium-239 with a half-life of 24,000 years. This is fissionable by low-energy neutrons.

$$^{239}_{93}Np \rightarrow {}^{239}_{94}Pu + {}_{-}\beta^0 + \gamma$$

Plutonium-239 is a second isotope which has played an important part in making possible the atomic bomb. Like U-235 it undergoes atomic fission. Note that this series of reactions (given above) changes U-238 which is ordinarily not fissionable into plutonium-239 which is fissionable. This synthetic element will have important uses; as of 1958 our government was in the process of expanding its facilities for the production of plutonium.

NUCLEAR ENERGY BY FUSION OF LIGHT ELEMENTS

The fission reaction is an example of a heavy unstable element becoming more stable by forming lighter elements. Figure 38–7 indicates that fusion reactions of light elements are also possible, with greater stability resulting as the lighter elements become heavier. The conversion of four atoms of hydrogen to form one atom of helium in the sun, discussed on page 621, is a fusion reaction. There is a decrease in mass which becomes energy.

The much publicized H-bombs are fusion bombs. For reasons of national security the exact materials used in H-bombs have not been disclosed, but there are many possibilities for fusion reactions which might serve as the basis for H-bombs. Here are two hypothetical reactions using deuterium and tritium.

REACTION 1:

$$_1H^2 + {}_1H^2 \rightarrow {}_2He^4 + \Delta m$$

$$\underbrace{2.014708 + 2.014708}_{4.02942} \rightarrow 4.00390 + \Delta m$$

$$4.02942 \rightarrow 4.00390 + \Delta m$$

$$\Delta m = 0.02852 \text{ amu} = 26.6 \text{ Mev}$$

REACTION 2:

$$_1H^3 + {}_1H^1 \rightarrow {}_2He^4 + \Delta m$$

$$\underbrace{3.01702 + 1.008123}_{4.02514} \rightarrow 4.00390 + \Delta m$$

$$4.02514 \rightarrow 4.00390 + \Delta m$$

$$\Delta m = 0.02124 \text{ amu} = 19.8 \text{ Mev}$$

Note that in both reactions there is a conversion of hydrogen isotopes into helium. The loss of mass in this process (about 0.6 per cent) is relatively large. The loss of mass in the fission reaction is much less – about 0.10 per cent. The fusion reaction takes place only at very high temperatures. For this reason H-bombs are often referred to as *thermonuclear* devices, which require the detonation of an A-bomb to initiate the reaction. Hence, an H-bomb in reality is a fission-fusion bomb. The bomb is triggered with U-235.

H-bombs have a distinct difference from A-bombs, in that there is *no upper limit* to their energy, as in the case of an A-bomb. A standard A-bomb is equivalent in energy to 20,000 tons of TNT. It is a 20-kiloton bomb. H-bombs can be of the order of 2 megatons (2,000,000 tons of TNT equivalent), or even larger. The size of the H-bomb is limited only by the amounts of the fuel that can be put into it.

The same effects which accompany the detonation of an A-bomb will be observed in the explosion of any H-bomb but on an enormously greater scale. Such a weapon can destroy cities like New York, London, Paris, and Moscow with a single bomb. While a 20-kiloton A-bomb will completely destroy or seriously damage buildings out to a distance of 1.6 miles from ground zero, a 20-megaton H-bomb will do the same out to a distance of 20 miles. The area of destruction is about 8 square miles in the first case; about 1250 square miles in the second.

NUCLEAR ENERGY IN THE SERVICE OF MAN

While statesmen try to control production and use of atomic weapons scientists continue their research. In fact, more than 800 isotopes of artificial radioactive elements are now known. Radioactive forms of all the known elements have actually been produced. Research in nuclear energy during the last decade has resulted in vastly superior methods for the production of these isotopes. Many of the most useful ones are now being produced in relatively large quantities and at comparatively low cost. Experimentation with these materials has been enormously accelerated. Many persons believe that the greatest benefits to humanity from our growing knowledge of atomic energy will come from the solution of baffling problems in medicine, biology, industry, agriculture, metallurgy, physics, chemistry, entomology, and many other fields, by the widespread use of radioactive isotopes rather than from potentially abundant power.

The first radioisotope to be used in medicine was radium. It was the principal one to be used until synthetic radioisotopes were made. Radium is a long-lived element (half-life of 1622 years) which liberates gamma rays and a whole series of disintegration products, which also liberate gamma rays, until eventually the stable lead-206 is formed and all activity ceases. It is the very energetic gamma rays that destroy certain diseased tissue (so-called carcinomatous tissue), but that also destroy normal tissue. The use of gamma rays to control and cure disease has led to the science of radiology that is, the determination of the controlled dosage of gamma rays to produce a maximum effect on diseased tissue or disease organisms and a minimum effect on normal tissue.

Though radium still has important uses in medicine, it also has some serious limitations, not the least of which is its relatively great cost. Also its long half-life (1622 years) makes it very dangerous. If stray radium salts should enter the body, they are a real hazard, for their half-life far exceeds the normal human life-span. Because of

TABLE 38–6

SOME RADIOACTIVE ISOTOPES USED IN MEDICINE

RADIOACTIVE ISOTOPE	HALF-LIFE	TYPICAL USES: Treatment of —
${}_{15}P^{32}$	14.3 days	Bone diseases
${}_{26}Fe^{59}$	46.3 days	Blood diseases
${}_{53}I^{131}$	8.0 days	Thyroid disease
${}_{27}Co^{60}$	5.3 years	Deep-seated tubercular infections
${}_{79}Au^{198}$	2.69 days	Deep-seated tumors
${}_{11}Na^{24}$	14.8 hours	Edema in congestive heart disease
${}_{38}Sr^{89}$	53.0 days	Bone diseases

Fig. 38–14A *The loading side of the Oak Ridge graphite reactor. Each of the 1248 channel openings contains slugs of uranium metal. In this operation the workmen are pushing out uranium slugs for replacement.* (*U. S. Atomic Energy Commission*)

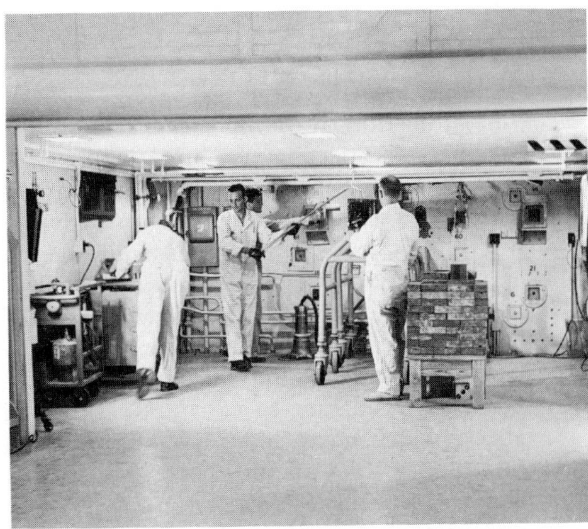

Fig. 38–14B *Removing irradiated material from the graphite reactor. This material had been in a tray which could be placed in the interior of the pile where there is high neutron density. Operator holds vial of "hot" material with tongs.* (*U. S. Atomic Energy Commission*)

their dangerous character radium salts are always used in small sealed metal tubes or needles to aid in their recovery and to prevent absorption of the radium by the patient. Furthermore, radium needles are difficult or impossible to use in the case of deep-seated infections, and the dosage is difficult to regulate. Radioactive sodium-24, on the other hand, is free of these limitations. It disintegrates as follows:

$$^{24}_{11}\text{Na} \rightarrow {}^{24}_{12}\text{Mg} + {}_{-}\beta^0 + \gamma \text{ rays}$$

It can be produced for a small fraction of the cost of radium and can be used as a solution of sodium-24 chloride. Its half-life is comparatively short – 14.8 hours. This means that 99 per cent of any sample placed in the body will disappear in 6.7 half-lives or in about 100 hours or 4 days. It also emits energetic gamma rays to form a harmless magnesium salt. As a specific example of its use in medicine, it has provided the first rational treatment to relieve edema (blood accumulation) in congestive heart attacks.

Radioactive isotopes now frequently used in medicine for their curative gamma rays are listed in Table 38–6. Note that the half-lives are all comparatively short as compared with radium and they are all the product of neutron absorption in a nuclear reactor. In the United States, this is done at Oak Ridge, Tennessee. (See Figure 38–14.) Thus, ordinary phosphorus becomes P-32 in a nuclear reactor:

$${}_{15}\text{P}^{31} + {}_{0}\text{n}^1 \rightarrow {}_{15}\text{P}^{32} + \gamma$$

Deep-seated bone infections, for example, which are very difficult to cure, often are treated by some form of radioactive phosphorus. It disintegrates in this manner:

$${}_{15}\text{P}^{32} \rightarrow {}_{16}\text{S}^{32} + {}_{-}\beta^0$$

Experimentation has shown conclusively that radioactive phosphorus is quickly deposited largely in the skeletal structure and especially in the bone marrow, the seat of origin for white blood corpuscles. In leukemia, a disease in which the white blood corpuscles multiply too rapidly, patients have shown improvement when treated with phosphorus-32.

Another approach to diseases within the bones is by the use of radioactive strontium produced with neutrons from the most abundant isotope of strontium.

$$^{88}_{38}Sr + {}_0n^1 \rightarrow {}^{89}_{38}Sr + \gamma \text{ rays}$$

Since infection of the bone marrow (osteomyelitis) is deep-seated, treatment with radium on the surface of the body is ineffective. As bone tissue is largely calcium phosphate, an ideal treatment would be the administration of radioactive calcium. Unfortunately, a suitable radioactive form of calcium is not readily available. But strontium phosphate, because of the known similarity of strontium to calcium, should be able to function in bone tissue as calcium phosphate. Experiments have shown that when a soluble form of strontium-89 is administered internally, it is very quickly deposited uniformly throughout the bony structure. It then disintegrates slowly – it has a half-life of 53 days — to give off its radioactive curative rays within the diseased area.[1]

RADIOISOTOPES AS TRACERS

There is reason to believe that one of the greatest social contributions of atomic energy will be the production of a great variety of radioisotopes for experimental use as *tracer elements*. These have been found instrumental in solving numerous problems in biology, physiology, chemistry, physics, engineering, and technology. Chemists, for example, can "tag" molecules and follow them through complex changes in either plant or animal life. Many problems involving life processes could not have been solved without the use of radioisotopes as tracers. The work with tracer atoms has been so fruitful that some biologists and medical men say that the use of radioactive tracers is "probably the most useful tool for research since the discovery of the microscope."

[1] Strontium–89 (half-life 55 days) should not be confused with strontium–90 (half-life 25 years). Strontium–89 is a product of irradiation of ordinary strontium with neutrons. Strontium–90 is formed during the detonations of A- and H-bombs. It is dangerous because it is absorbed by the skeletal structure and because it has such a long half-life.

Consider, for example, the problem of the volume of blood in the human body – a problem once thought to be without solution. Today, however, a small amount of a solution of radiosodium ($^{24}_{11}NaCl$) can be injected into the blood stream and, after a short wait for thorough mixing, a small sample of blood can be removed for analysis with a Geiger counter. From the change in the Geiger count the total dilution of the radiosodium solution and the total volume of blood are easily calculated.

The principle involved in the use of tracer elements is that the chemical properties of isotopes of the same element are essentially the same, but that radioactive isotopes are always sending out charged particles or gamma rays which tell the researcher with a Geiger counter of their presence. Thus, P-31 and P-32 are chemically similar, but the latter is radioactive. Phosphorus is necessary for the bony structure of the body. The rate of absorption of P-32 for assimilation in the bones can be determined experimentally, for example, either with photographic plates or with a Geiger-Müller counter. (Refer to Figure 38–15.)

A common disease of the aged is arteriosclerosis, a contraction in the size of certain blood vessels due to a deposition of a fat-like substance, cholesterol, on the walls of the blood vessels. Students of the disease are concerned as to the source of the cholesterol. Does it come from cholesterol-rich foods, like eggs, or is it synthesized by the body? Experimenters have recently shown that cholesterol can be synthesized in the aorta – the main trunk of the arterial system. This was done by introducing sodium acetate "labeled" with carbon-14 into an experimental animal and proving that cholesterol containing radioactive C-14 appeared in the aorta. Thus, cholesterol synthesis in the blood stream may be an important factor in the development of arteriosclerosis.

Thiamin is a vitamin that contains sulfur in its molecule. What is the fate of thiamin in the body? By using thiamin containing radioactive sulfur-35, the rate of elimination of the vitamin from the body is easily followed with a Geiger-Müller counter. Studies of the mechanism of photosynthesis are being carried on by growing plants in atmospheres containing carbon dioxide made with radioactive carbon-14. The radioactivity of the leaves, for example, indicates the absorption of carbon-14.

These examples illustrate a few of the many uses of radioisotopes as tag or tracer elements. Faster than ever before they are making it possible to push back the curtain of the unknown.

RADIOISOTOPES FOR GAMMA RAYS AS SUBSTITUTES FOR X-RAYS

Imperfections in many solid objects, such as steel castings, can be revealed by the use of X-rays. But X-ray machines are very expensive and not readily portable. A recent development is to substitute gamma rays as detectors by using large samples of cobalt-60 or cesium-137, which have half-lives of 5.3 and 33 years, respectively. These sources are relatively small as compared with an X-ray machine, require no manipulative skills, and are simple to use. The gamma rays are intensive enough to substitute for X-rays.

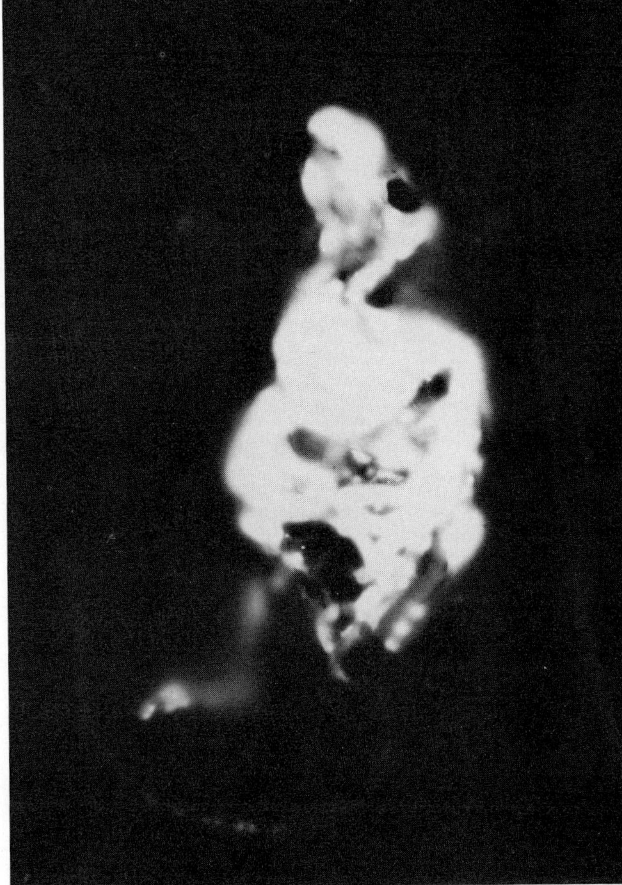

Fig. 38–15 *Radioactive phosphorus in a rat. In four and a half hours after injection, the radioactive phosphorus had gone to nearly all parts of the rat's anatomy including vertebrae in the tail. Photograph was made by laying the rat on a photographic plate.* (*By* Life *photographer Fritz Goro. Copyright* Time *Inc.*)

NUCLEAR ENERGY FOR POWER

Coal is our principal source of energy to turn the wheels of the machines of our economy, but our supply of coal is not inexhaustible. Coal in order to be used must be economically recoverable. It is not feasible to mine thin veins – and much of the world's coal is in veins too thin for economical recovery. Another factor in our world power problem is that large areas of the earth's surface have few or no coal deposits. This is true, for example, of Spain, Italy, Sweden, and much of Africa. If our American economy is to continue to expand, and if industry is to develop in many parts of the world, it will be increasingly necessary to have a better source of energy and power than coal. The best hope for the world lies in nuclear energy.

There is no doubt that in the near future energy from fissionable materials will become more important and eventually indispensable. Reference has already been made (page 630) to the enormous difference in the amounts of energy available from uranium-235 and from an atom of carbon – the important component of coal. Compare the two reactions, one a nuclear reaction and the other the chemical reaction that occurs in the burning of all carbonaceous fuels:

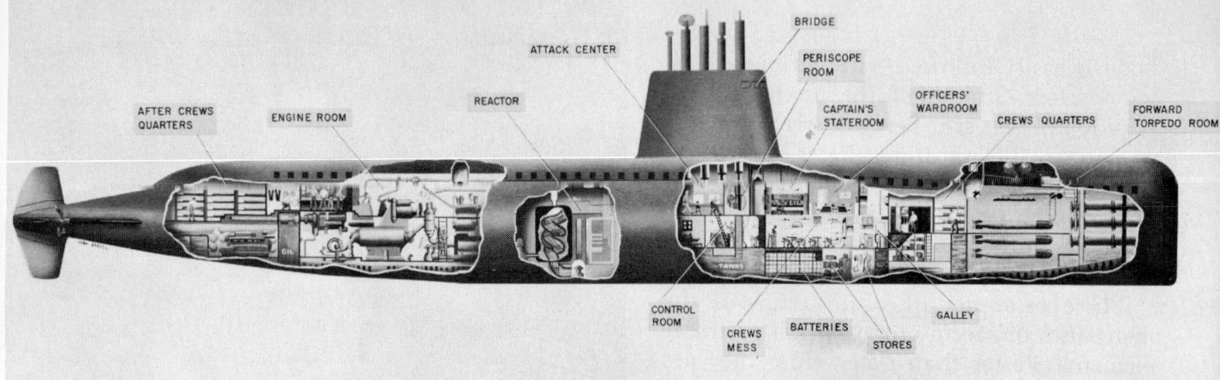

Fig. 38–16 *The submarine* Nautilus *operates on nuclear fuels.*

$$U^{235} + {}_0n^1 \rightarrow \text{fission products} + 3\ {}_0n^1 + 200{,}000{,}000 \text{ ev of energy}$$

$$C + O_2 \rightarrow CO_2 + 4 \text{ ev of energy}$$

Thus, the fissioning of one atom of U-235 releases 50 million times as much energy as the oxidation of one atom of carbon.

NUCLEAR REACTORS

It is appropriate to ask if this energy can be used to operate the machines of our modern society. The answer is, emphatically, yes. The successful trials at sea of the submarine *Nautilus,* the first nuclear-powered vessel, is but one augury for the future (Figure 38–16). A device that permits the controlled release of nuclear energy for the production of electrical energy is called a nuclear reactor. Reactors are of many designs, but in general they possess the following features or components: (1) fuel — enriched U-235 or natural uranium — and fuel chamber; (2) moderator with or without a neutron reflector; (3) heat transfer medium; (4) heat exchanger to produce steam; (5) shielding; and (6) control rods and control mechanism.

Assume that the fuel in the form of metal rods is uranium enriched in U-235. We have already learned that there is a production of about three neutrons per fission. These neutrons disappear in three principal ways: they are lost to the surroundings, they can cause fission in other atoms of U-235, or they can be captured by U-238 to form U-239, as indicated in the equation,

$${}_{92}U^{238} + {}_0n^1 \rightarrow {}_{92}U^{239} + \gamma \text{ rays.}$$

The U-239 eventually becomes plutonium-239, which is another fissionable element.

The Concept of Critical Mass. Ordinary uranium, the mixture of one atom of U-235 to 140 atoms of U-238, or small masses of U-235 are not dangerous because the "critical size" for U-235 has not been reached. The critical size is defined as the size of a mass of U-235 in which the number of neutrons produced by fission just balance those lost by escape to the surroundings and by capture of atoms of U-235, U-238, or impurities. In a small piece of uranium, the ratio of the surface to the mass is so large that neutrons escape to the surroundings before they can cause fission in other atoms of U-235 or before capture by U-238. The mass of uranium is then harmless. As the size of the uranium pile increases, a point will be reached where neutrons will cause fission in other atoms of U-235 at the same rate or even a little faster than neutrons are being produced.

The pile is then said to be "critical." It will now operate with a steady production of heat. In this second possibility, the rate of fissioning is just equal to or only slightly greater than the rate of escape. There is now a steady release of heat energy. If the mass is made still larger, a point will be reached where the rate of fissioning produces two or more neutrons for each

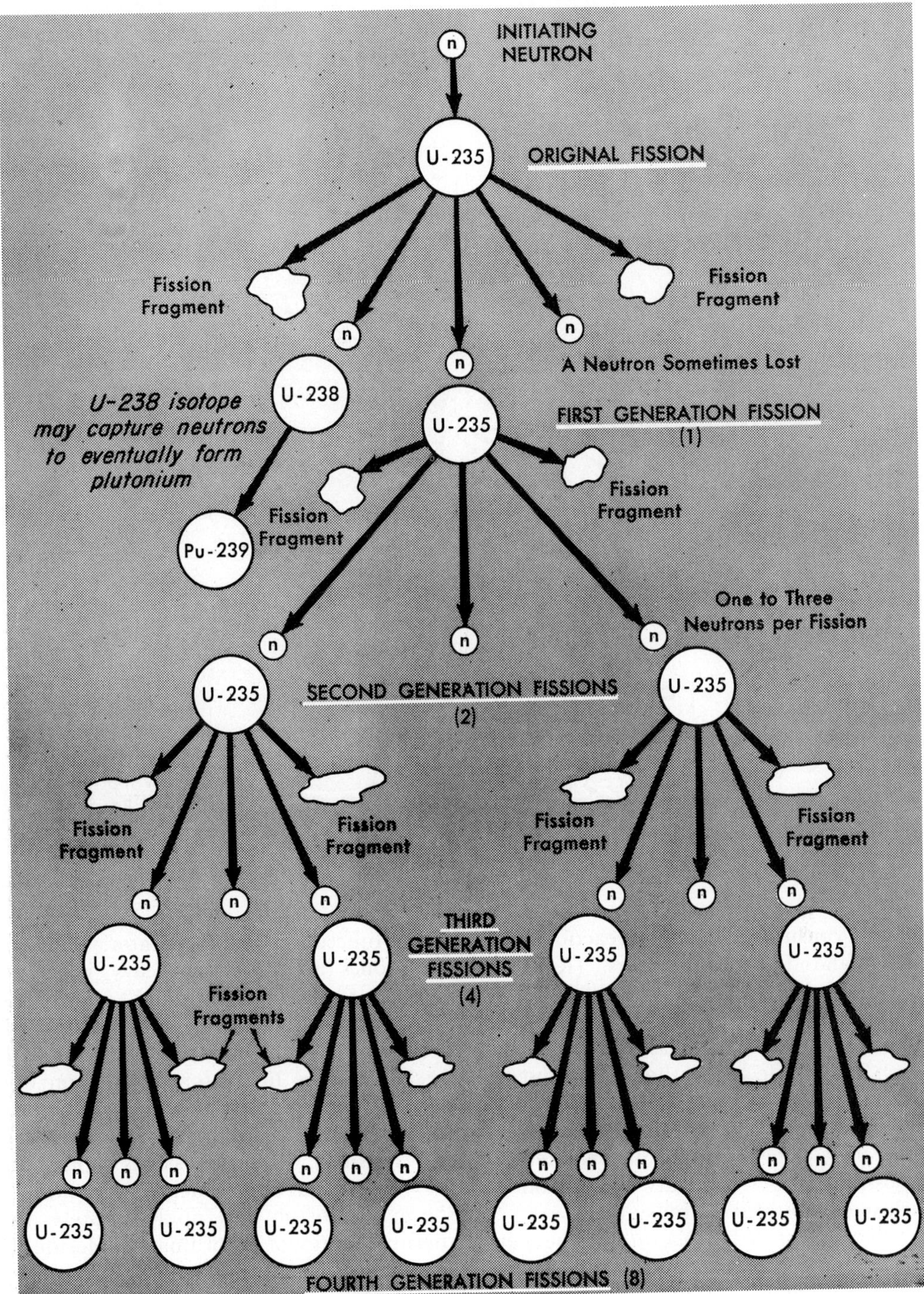

Fig. 38–17 *A chain reaction uranium-235. 1 to 3 neutrons are released per fission. If two of these cause other fissions and this process is repeated during each generation of neutrons, a chain reaction occurs. Thus in the above diagram, the fifth generation of neutrons could mean 16 fissions, the sixth generation could mean 32 fissions, etc.*

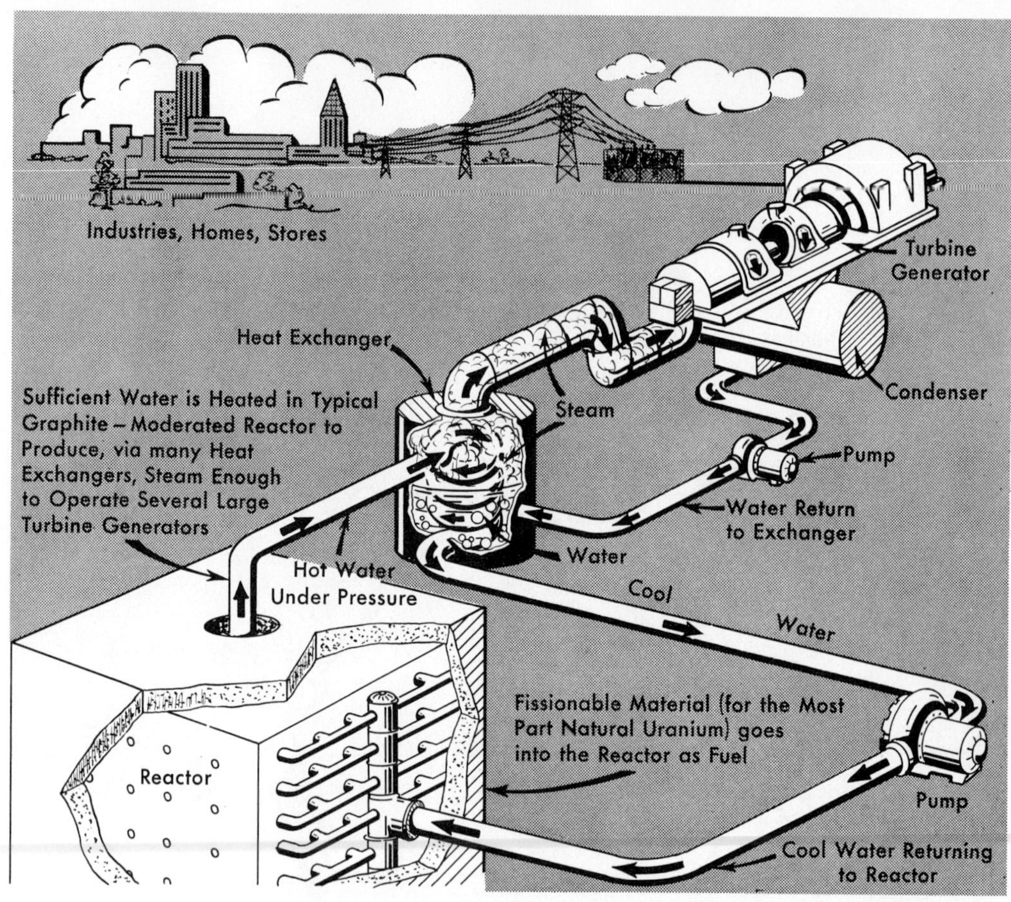

Fig. 38–18 *Electric power from nuclear energy.*

neutron consumed. A chain reaction then follows and detonation occurs. (Refer to Figure 38–17.) Masses of U-235 large enough to undergo a chain reaction have exceeded the "critical mass" for this material. The whole secret, then, of producing heat for power purposes from U-235 is to hold a mass of U-235 in a fuel chamber in the second stage outlined above. Here it is possible to get a steady conversion of nuclear energy into ordinary heat.

Purpose of the Moderator. The neutrons coming from a fission reaction are exceedingly energetic neutrons, or "fast neutrons." They are too energetic to be easily captured by U-235 nuclei and hence do not produce fission as readily as slow neutrons. For easy capture they must be made into "slow" or thermal neutrons. This is the function of the moderator. The common ones are graphite, heavy water, or ordinary water; all contain light atoms. The fast neutrons, then, in passing through these materials have many collisions with nuclei of these light atoms, and soon lose most of their energy through elastic collisions. (Refer to Figure 38–19.) In about 100 collisions, the neutron loses enough energy to become a slow neutron. A slow or thermal neutron has approximately the thermal energy of an ordinary molecule. It can then be captured by U-235 to cause fission. The moderator, whether a solid or a liquid, surrounds the uranium slugs. It is necessary to keep as many of the neutrons within the fuel chamber as possible. Various materials which serve as reflectors surround the fuel chamber and moderator.

Heat Transfer Medium. The interior of the fuel chambers can attain very high temperatures. This heat is absorbed by a circulating liquid, such as a gas, water, or melted sodium. The hot liquid passes into a heat interchanger where this heat is used to produce steam. The circulating water for steam is in a coiled pipe arrangement so the two liquids do not mix. The steam from the exit side of the turbine passes to a condenser where it becomes liquid water which is then circulated back to the heat interchanger. (Refer to Figure 38–18.)

Turbine and Generator. This part of a nuclear power plant is conventional and like any other steam turbine-electric generator combination. Refer to page 542, on heat engines which employ steam.

Shielding. Both U-235 and U-238 are radioactive. The fission reaction produces great quantities of neutrons. The radiation outside the fuel chamber then is at a very high level and dangerous. Shielding of the entire reactor is an essential procedure. The usual material for this purpose is concrete or large masses of water. This is a very practical material for a power-house reactor. However, for a reactor on board ship or in an airplane materials such as lead or iron must be used. In the case of ship or airplane propulsion, the problem of shielding all personnel from radiation from the reactor is a very difficult one.

The Control of a Nuclear Reactor. Any nuclear reactor is potentially a bomb. The

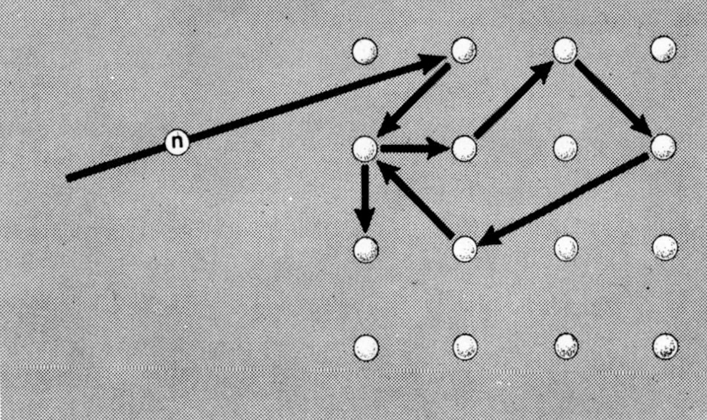

Fig. 38–19 *Loss of energy by a fast neutron through elastic collisions.*

rate of heat production must be controlled. This is the function of the control system, which is an ensemble of cadmium or boron-rich rods which readily absorb neutrons. The operation of a control system restrains the multiplying process of fissioning reactions. When a single neutron causes a fission, we get several new neutrons. If losses are kept low by use of neutron reflectors and moderators, two or more neutrons are available for new fissions. At this rate the next generation will have 4 neutrons, the next 8, the next 16, and so on. At such a reproduction rate (2 for 1), the neutron population would reach staggering figures in only a few generations. This would be an uncontrolled chain reaction. In a remarkably short time, detonation would occur.

This multiplying factor is expressed by a factor, k, which is the ratio of the num-

Fig. 38–20 *Effect of various* k *values on neutron population or power level.*

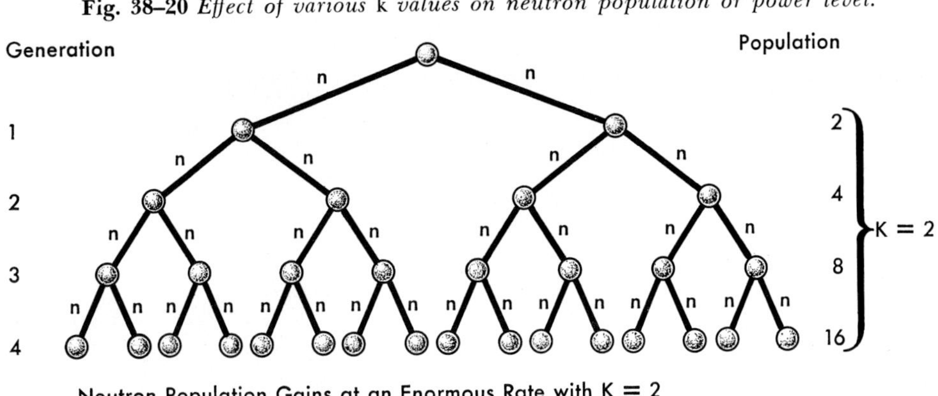

ber of neutrons in one generation to the number in the preceding generation. If k is greater than 1, the neutron population grows. If it is less than 1, the neutron population dies out. If it is just 1, the number of neutrons remains constant. Moving the control rods regulates the value of k in an operating reactor.

The power level or heat output, then, of a reactor depends upon the neutron population. (Refer to Figure 38–20.) When $k = 1$, the reactor is said to be "critical." Slowly pulling out the control rods will permit k slowly to increase to permit a higher power level. For example, if k is made 1.05, the neutron population and thus the operating power level will be doubled in about fourteen generations. In terms of time, this is a very short interval. The rate of power production, then, is dependent upon the neutron population within the reactor. The rate of build-up to any particular power level depends upon the operating value of k. When a desired power level is reached, k is reduced to unity. The reactor will then produce heat energy at a constant rate.

FUTURE OF NUCLEAR POWER

Our ultimate source of energy is the sun. Scientists believe that eventually it is going to be possible to supply the energy demands of civilizations by direct use of the sun's energy. However, this must lie in the uncertain future. Until then, our demands for energy must be supplied by our fossil fuels (gas, oil, and coal) and fissionable materials, U-233, U-235, or Pu-239. There is no reason whatever to doubt that a constantly growing share of our power needs will be based upon nuclear reactors. The first commercial power plant operating on fissionable material in the United States went into operation in 1957.

Construction of large-scale electric power plants operating on nuclear energy is now an assured fact. By 1960 it is believed that the installed capacity will be over 800,000 kilowatts. By 1964 dollar expenditures for plants to convert nuclear energy to electricity are expected to reach 1.5 billion. At that time, it is estimated that the atomic energy program in this country will need from 30,000 to 40,000 professional personnel versed in nuclear science and engineering. During the next decade, then, we shall see another revolution in our power civilization based upon the fundamental research of the decade 1945–1955 in the field of nuclear energy.

Nuclear energy plants will differ radically in appearance from our present coal-fed generator plants. (Refer to Figure 38–21.) They will be much smaller; there will be no huge storage piles of coal; there will be no smoke or ash nuisance, though the disposal of nuclear wastes is very difficult because they are dangerously radioactive for a long period. For safety and shielding purposes the reactor will probably be housed in a huge sphere as shown in Figure 38–21.

Fig. 38–21 *A power plant of the future.* (*General Electric Company*)

THE TRANSURANIUM ELEMENTS

The story of synthetic elements 93 and 94, neptunium and plutonium, has already been told in this chapter. Other transuranium elements, 95 and 96, were also discovered during the early nineteen-forties, and these were all artificially made. One of the group, plutonium, has since been found in nature, in mere traces with uranium, one part in 10^{14} parts. Element 95 was discovered after bombarding U-238 with alpha particles in a cyclotron. It was found to have chemical properties and a structure similar to the element europium. It has been named americium, or Am, after the Americas. It is a comparatively short-lived element. Plutonium-239, when bombarded in a cyclotron with alpha particles, produced element 96, which was named curium after the Curies. Its symbol is Cm. This element has a number of isotopes with half-lives as short as one month. Hence it is easy to see why it is not found in nature. The newest synthetic elements are berkelium (symbol Bk, atomic number 97) and californium (symbol Cf, atomic number 98), produced in 1949 and 1950 with the giant cyclotron at the University of California. Elements 99 and 100 were first found in the debris of an H-bomb explosion in the South Pacific. They have since been made in the laboratory. Element 99 has been named einsteinium, symbol Es, and element 100 is fermium, symbol Fm. Element 101, first produced in May 1956, has been named mendelevium (symbol Md). The last of the transuranium elements, nobelium (element 102, symbol No), was produced and studied in the summer of 1957.

Thus all the synthetic, transuranium elements have been named for regions, planets, or great scientists. These elements often have several isotopic forms and seldom have very long half-lives. Hence, one would not expect them to be found abundantly in nature nor to be very significant, except for Pu-239, which has a long half-life and is stable. They can be considered as symbols of man's great advance in understanding the nature of matter.

RADIATION AND MAN

We cannot escape radiation. There is natural radioactivity in most soils, and the earth is being continuously bombarded by cosmic rays. Radiation originating from these sources is called "background radiation." Every wrist watch with a luminous dial is a source of radiation. In every dental or chest X-ray, there is exposure to radiation. With the continued production and use of radioisotopes, the dangers of increased exposure to radiation, at least for certain persons, become greater. Radiation is a broad term used to cover both electromagnetic radiations, such as X-rays and gamma rays, and the ionizing particles given off by radioactive substances, such as alpha and beta particles. The latter particles and gamma rays originate in nuclei of radioactive atoms. They are a form of nuclear energy, collectively referred to as ionizing radiation. They are physiologically dangerous because they produce ionization within the cells in body tissue. (Refer to page 642.) Tissues are specialized populations of cells. The effect of ionizing radiation may extend to the cells themselves or cause destruction of essential liquid components within the cells, such as enzymes, which are necessary for proper cell functioning. Thus cells may be damaged or destroyed. Such damage is especially harmful if the cells responsible for hereditary characteristics, genetic cells, are destroyed or modified.

One of the characteristic effects of ionizing radiation is the frequent long delay between the time of exposure and the recognition of tissue damage. This time interval is referred to as the *latent period* and may extend over many years. There is reason to believe that radiation injury to cells is permanent and can be responsible for such effects as eye cataracts, skin or body cancers, reduction of the life span, and genetic changes.

The Roentgen. The unit which has been devised to measure amounts of radiation absorbed by body tissues is the *roentgen* or the *r* unit: an absorption of 93 ergs of radiant energy per gram of tissue. Instruments employing Geiger-Müller tubes or specially constructed electroscopes are used for making radiation measurements. (Refer to pages 348 and 349.) They are so designed that the radiation absorbed in roentgens (r) or milliroentgens (mr) is readily determined.

Physiological Effects of Radiation. Exposure to all radiation is potentially dangerous. Whole body exposure to large doses leads to various forms of "radiation sickness," serious injury, or death. For example, 50 per cent of persons who receive a dose of 400 to 450 roentgens will suffer death. Small dosages usually leave no immediate noticeable effect. However, undesirable latent effects may be present. Hence a good rule to follow is always to avoid unnecessary exposure to any form of ionizing radiation. During the last decade the so-called "tolerance dose" has been steadily lowered. As a working guide this is taken to be not over 0.3 roentgen per week and not over 3.9 roentgens during any 13-week period. Furthermore, the accumulated dose in roentgens at any age should not exceed five times the number of years past the age of 18. It is the part of prudence to record the amount of radiation received as administered by a competent radiologist.

Another aspect of radiation should be mentioned. In this nuclear age, with all its promise for good, there is an imminent danger. In every atomic explosion radioactive debris is released. When fissionable materials are used, many of the radioactive particles rapidly rise to great heights where high altitude winds carry them "down wind" to settle over large areas. This "fallout" is dangerous to all forms of life. It is imperative, then, that discoveries and advances in science be intelligently applied. The application that is made is the decision of man himself.

There have always been and always will be two opposing forces at work in the world — good against evil. Our hopes for the future lie in the expectation and the belief that man will seek and strive for that which is good.

SUMMARY

1. Matter and energy under certain circumstances are interconvertible in accordance with the relationship expressed in Einstein's law, $E = km$ (the units for k depend upon the units used to measure the energy and mass).
2. The atomic weight of an atom is not precisely the sum of the masses of the protons, neutrons, and electrons in the atom. The difference in mass represents matter converted into energy.
3. The mass loss involved in the formation of an atom becomes its unbinding energy. This amounts to 9×10^{20} ergs (2×10^{13} calories) per gram loss in mass. This amount of energy is equivalent to the heat obtained in burning 3000 tons of a high-grade coal.
4. The most stable elements are those of intermediate atomic number. Elements of low atomic number have a tendency to become more stable by undergoing changes which result in an increase in atomic number. Elements of high atomic number have a tendency to become more stable by disintegrating to form elements of lower atomic number.
5. The forces that exist within the nucleus of an atom to keep the nucleus intact are collectively referred to as "nuclear forces." These increase with the increase in unbinding energy.
6. In the lighter elements, the greatest nuclear stability results when the neutron-proton (n/p) ratio is unity.
7. Elements with too large an n/p ratio are unstable (radioactive) and achieve greater stability by emitting beta and gamma rays.
8. Elements with too small an n/p ratio are radioactive and achieve greater stability by emitting positrons and gamma rays.
9. Artificial transmutation of elements is achieved by changing the composition of the nucleus with energetic particles such as alpha particles, neutrons, deutrons, and protons. In these transformations there is conservation of the combination of mass and energy.
10. An important example of a light-to-heavier transformation of an element is the conver-

sion of hydrogen into helium in the presence of carbon as it is believed to occur in the sun. This is a *fusion* reaction.

11. The transformation of heavy-to-lighter elements is the cause of natural radioactivity. In radioactive changes, disintegration may form two or more of the following kinds of particles: alpha particles, beta particles, positrons, and neutrons, as well as gamma rays.
12. The transformation of an element into a radioactive form by bombardment with high energy particles (deuterons, protons, alpha particles, or neutrons) results in synthetic radioactive elements or artificial radioactivity.
13. Radioactive forms of practically all elements can be produced. Many of these are now utilized as tracer elements in the new science of tracer chemistry or radiochemistry, and in medicine.
14. Certain elements of high atomic number and odd atomic mass, notably uranium-235, plutonium-239, and uranium-233, undergo *fission*. In this process there are formed two simpler elements (which are initially radioactive), one to three neutrons, and a very large amount of energy.
15. Fissionable material, if subjected to neutrons in masses which exceed a certain critical size, disintegrates in a chain reaction of explosive violence. This is the basis for the atomic bomb.
16. The synthetic production of radioisotopes is now an important industry. These isotopes find use in medicine as therapeutic agents, in science as tracer elements, and in power production as sources of energy.
17. A rapidly increasing application of the energy of the nuclei of atoms is the production of electrical energy using fissionable materials. There is reason to believe that this will have enormous impact upon economies and upon nations.
18. The transuranium elements are the following:

93. Neptunium	(Np)
94. Plutonium	(Pu)
95. Americium	(Am)
96. Curium	(Cm)
97. Berkelium	(Bk)
98. Californium	(Cf)
99. Einsteinium	(Es)
100. Fermium	(Fm)
101. Mendelevium	(Md)
102. Nobelium	(No)

These are all synthetic elements.

19. The known elements now total 102 in number. These elements occur in approximately a thousand different forms called isotopes. The elements of very high atomic number have with few exceptions very short half-lives. For this reason it is not very probable that elements with atomic numbers above 94 will be found to occur in significant amounts in nature.

STUDY EXERCISES

1. Consider a hypothetical element of atomic number 89 and mass 230. Prepare a table similar to the following one and then indicate what would happen to the mass and the atomic number if it disintegrates with a loss of the kind of particles (one particle per atom) indicated below:

Particle Lost	Atomic Number	Atomic Mass
a. Neutron	....	....
b. Alpha	....	....
c. Beta	....	....
d. Positron	....	....
e. Alpha and beta	....	....

2. What is the currently accepted hypothesis for the source of the energy from the sun?
3. *a.* Indicate the nature of the changes that occur when ordinary salt, which contains sodium-23, is (1) bombarded with high-velocity deuterons and (2) exposed to slow neutrons.
   b. Indicate the nature of the radioactive change that occurs in radioactive sodium.
   c. What advantages does therapy with radioactive sodium have over radium therapy?
4. Make clear the distinction between atomic fission and a uranium or plutonium chain reaction.
5. What are some of the intrinsic difficulties in the production of power by the process of atomic fission?
6. What are some of the beneficent uses of atomic energy?

7. Radioactive sodium has a period of half-life of 14.8 hours. Imagine you were the possessor of 0.001 mg of radioactive sodium. What weight of radioactive sodium would you possess at the end of 75 hours?
8. *a.* Ordinary nitrogen when treated with slow neutrons forms an unstable product which disintegrates with the formation of protons. What radioactive element must result from this series of changes?
   b. One of the isotopes of boron ($^{11}_{5}B$) when bombarded with alpha particles forms two kinds of particles, one of which is a proton. What radioactive element must result from this series of changes?
9. If 0.001 gram of mass could be made to disappear, how much energy in ergs would be created? How many calories of heat would be liberated? NOTE: 4.185×10^7 ergs = 1 calorie.
10. Below you are given the masses in atomic mass units of some common particles:

$_1H^2$	2.01471	$_{13}Al^{27}$	26.9899
$_2He^4$	4.00390	$_{15}P^{30}$	29.9873
$_{15}P^{32}$	31.9827	$_{15}P^{31}$	30.9843
$_0n^1$	1.00893	$_8O^{17}$	17.00450
$^4_2\alpha^{++}$	4.00276		

Apply the Einstein law to predict whether or not the following changes are very probable:

$$_{13}Al^{27} + {}^4_2\alpha^{++} \rightarrow {}_0n^1 + {}_{15}P^{30}$$
$$_{15}P^{31} + {}_0n^1 \rightarrow {}_{15}P^{32} + \gamma \text{ rays}$$
$$_8O^{16} + {}_0n^1 \rightarrow {}_8O^{17} + \gamma \text{ rays}$$
$$_1H^2 + {}_1H^2 \rightarrow {}_2He^4 + \text{energy}$$

FOR FURTHER READING

1. SMYTH, H. D., *Atomic Energy for Military Purposes.* Princeton, N.J.: Princeton University Press, 1946. May also be obtained from the Government Printing Office, Washington, D.C.
   This is the famous official War Department report on the development of the atomic bomb under the auspices of the United States Government, 1940–45. Chapter I, which deals with the history of our understanding of matter, is especially recommended. Chapter II deals with atomic fission and the problems involved in the production of plutonium.
2. SCHUBERT, J., and R. E. LAPP, *Radiation.* New York: Viking Press, 1957.
   Very readable account in nontechnical language of the significance and dangers of radiation.
3. POLLARD, E. C., and W. L. DAVIDSON, *Applied Nuclear Physics.* New York: John Wiley and Sons, 1951.
   The following chapters will challenge the student who becomes more than casually interested in nuclear changes: Chapter 6, Radioactivity; Chapter 8, Artificial Radioactivity in Practice; Chapter 10, Nuclear Fission; Chapter 11, Nuclear Chain Reactions.
4. FRISCH, O. K., *Meet the Atom.* New York: A. A. Wyn, 1947.
   A popular nontechnical account of modern nuclear science. Compact and very readable.
5. HECHT, SELIG, *Explaining the Atom.* New York: The Viking Press, 1947.
   Atomic fission is discussed in Chapters V to VIII.
6. HEISENBERG, W., *Nuclear Physics.* New York: Philosophical Library, 1952.
   This little volume is by one of the world's leaders in nuclear science — a short report on the developments in nuclear science in nontechnical language. The following chapters are especially recommended: 3. The Building Blocks of the Nucleus; 4. The Normal States of Atomic Nuclei; 5. The Nuclear Forces; 6. Nuclear Reactions; 8. Practical Applications of Nuclear Science. The last chapter treats of the potentialities for good of radioisotopes as tracers, in chemistry, in biology, and in medicine.
7. GLASSTONE, SAMUEL, *Sourcebook of Atomic Energy.* New York: D. Van Nostrand Company, 1950.
   A very comprehensive presentation of nuclear science in not too complicated language. The discussions of the following topics are especially recommended: nuclear forces, stability of nuclei in terms of n/p ratios, and unbinding energy (here called binding energy) in Chapter XII; nuclear fission in Chapter XIII; utilization of nuclear energy in Chapter XIV; the new transuranium elements in Chapter XV; and the uses of radioisotopes in Chapter XVI.
8. HOPKINS, JOHN JAY, *World-wide Industrial Role of Nuclear Energy.* New York: General Dynamics Corporation, 1956.
   The subject of power from nuclear energy, together with its potentialities for future world peace, is reliably reported.

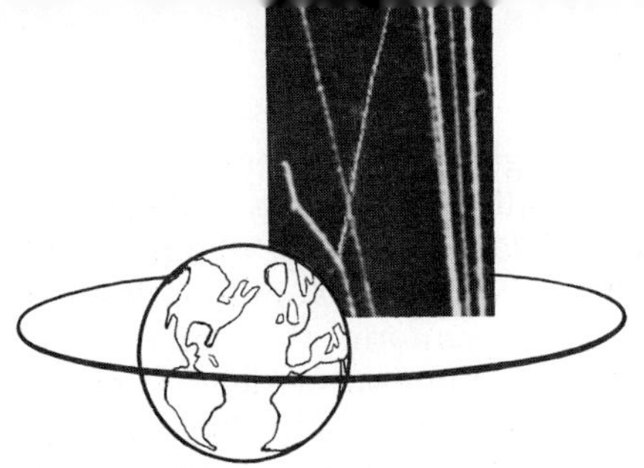

39

THE LARGER PERSPECTIVE: COSMOGONY

UP TO THE PRESENT our story of the physical world has been primarily one of matter and energy. We have seen how man, with his inherent desire to know, to understand, and to use, has gradually developed the sciences. He has designed instruments and techniques which have greatly widened his field of observation, especially during the past few hundred years. With these tools the earth with its matter and its energies has been closely examined. Telescopes have been turned toward our neighbors in the solar system and toward the more distant bodies, the stars and galaxies. The knowledge thus obtained has been evaluated and classified; laws and principles, hypotheses and theories have been formulated by the rigorous application of the scientific method.

But we are not satisfied to know something of the nature of matter, the forms of energy, and the laws which govern the universe. We ask, how and when did it all start? And what took place on the earth during that long sweep of time before man appeared and developed sufficiently so that he could leave some record of his observations? We shall therefore close our story with an endeavor to answer these questions in so far as science can supply answers. In this chapter we shall review the methods that have been used to estimate the age of the earth and consider some of the speculations concerning the origin of our solar system.

The human mind is interested in origins – the origin of life, of man, and of the astronomical bodies. So universal is this interest that every culture and clan has its legend or tradition of creation. However, no plausible attempts to formulate a scientific hypothesis concerning the origin of the earth and the solar system were made or could be made until accurate observational and mathematical astronomy was developed in the eighteenth century. But before we present pertinent facts of astronomy, geology, and certain physical principles which any hypothesis on the origin of the solar system must explain, we should point out that such hypotheses do not attempt to establish ultimate origins. If our solar system was born of the sun, or of a dust cloud, then where did the sun originate? If the sun or cloud is an offspring of one of the galaxies, we must ultimately encounter what the philosophers call the first cause or the uncaused cause. Either the solar system has always existed as it is at present, or at some time in the remote past it was quite different from its existing state. All theories that deal with a *cosmogony* — the origin of the solar system — assume that the latter postulate is true and that the sun is either the parent body or of common origin. Our first problem is to attempt to determine how long the solar system has existed, and for the answer to this question we obviously turn to the earth.

HOW OLD IS THE EARTH?

In attempting to determine the age of the earth one must seek some process of change which may be assumed to have continued at a constant rate without interruption since the present crust of the earth has been in place. Many methods — all based upon our knowledge and observation of changes which are taking place and which have taken place in the recent past — have been employed. Most of them are not even approximately quantitative and serve to indicate only that the earth is very old. We shall consider several of these methods.

1. *The rate of deposit of sedimentary rocks.* In 1854, the base of a large statue of Rameses II was found under about nine feet of sediment deposited by the Nile River. The statue is at least three thousand years old, so that the average rate of deposit for that period and place is three-tenths of a foot per hundred years. At this rate, which is certainly not typical of the rate of sedimentation over the entire surface of the earth, the formation of the estimated hundred-mile covering of sedimentary rock required more than 150 million years. Banded shales (consolidated clays), like those in the Green River deposits of Colorado and Wyoming, show seasonal markings which permit a more accurate and direct estimate of the time required for their deposition. A half-mile of such material is thought to have been deposited in six and a half million years. At this rate the sedimentary covering of the earth would have required 1300 million years of constant and uniform deposition. This method has a number of defects for, although it is useful in computing the time required for the deposition of certain specific sedimentary formations, it is inadequate to serve for all geological time. Deposition did not begin when the earth was formed, for the process requires seas and atmosphere which appeared later. Nor is deposition a continuous process. There have been times when rocks were uplifted and eroded as shown by unconformities — the gaps in geological history.

2. *The rate of erosion of the continents.* Estimates of the yearly amount of material carried into the ocean, both in solution and in suspension, indicate that in ten thousand years a one-foot layer of the surface of the North American continent is removed. In the past the continents have been successively elevated and submerged. Rather recently they have been elevated; and the present rate of erosion is therefore higher than average, but we have no way of finding how much higher. Our estimate of the age of the earth on the basis of this variable process can yield only conjectural results.

3. *The salt in the sea.* In the process of erosion and weathering, soluble salts are formed and these ultimately are carried to the oceans where they remain in solution. The volume of the ocean water can be estimated and thus the total salt content determined. By dividing the salt content by the estimated annual increase, a figure of at least 1500 million years is obtained. As with the preceding estimate, the process must have been a highly variable one, and man's observations extend over too short a period to be used as an average for geological time.

4. *Tidal effects.* The tidal effect of the moon (see page 223) has been shown to brake the earth and slowly retard its rotation. The moon moves farther and farther away from the earth. This effect and motion have been mathematically traced back-

ward in time to the period when the moon was so near the earth that it was at the point of falling into it. The earth-moon system and the seas on the earth have existed, according to the computations based on the assumption of constant tidal friction, not more than 4000 million years.

5. *Radioactivity*. We have seen (Chapter 22) that the very heavy radioactive elements disintegrate, expelling alpha particles (He^{++}), beta particles (electrons), and gamma radiation at a constant rate irrespective of conditions of temperature and pressure. No physical agency can speed or retard this disintegration in the slightest degree. The end product of the radioactive decay is lead and a by-product is helium. In a sample of uranium (half-life 4.51×10^9 years), about one sixty-seventh of its atoms would decompose in 100 million years and an equal number of atoms of lead would result as the end product. The lead so obtained has an atomic weight of 206, while that of ordinary lead is 207.2. Thorium, another radioactive element (half-life 1.39×10^{10} years), yields lead of an atomic weight of 208. An isotopic analysis of a sample of uranium-bearing rock tells us the amount of uranium present and the amounts of the different forms of lead.

It is of course necessary to know the amount of lead originally present in the rock. Lead occurs in four isotopic forms, lead-204, 206, 207, and 208. Lead-206 originates in uranium-238; 207 is a daughter of uranium-235; and 208 is a daughter of thorium-232. Fortunately, lead-204 is a stable material, and the amount of this isotope (so-called primeval lead) is an indication of the original amount of lead present in the rock. Thus, to determine the age of a rock by the uranium-lead ratio, it is necessary to use also a mass spectrograph to obtain the amounts of the four lead isotopes present. This leads then to a knowledge of the uranium-lead-206 ratio, which is used to calculate the age of the rock, the half-life of uranium being known.

The oldest surface rocks on the North American continent are those exposed in the Canadian Shield (page 146). The uranium-lead-206 ratio indicates an age of two billion years for these rocks. Some rocks are known to be even older. Scientists working in the area have arrived at the conclusion that the probable age of the earth is about 3.35 billion years. The earth as a planet must be older. Similar studies on meteorites indicate that they were possibly formed 4.5 billion years ago.

Speculations on the age of the earth raise many questions. What do we mean? The time that marks the begining of pre-Cambrian time? The time when the earth evolved from outer space? The time of the birth of our solar system? There are many questions, and there are many speculative answers. But it seems unchallengeable that our planet is at least two billion years old, that it may be over three billion years old; and that the birth of our solar system, based on astronomical evidence, may go back to five billion years ago.

RELEVANT FACTS CONCERNING THE SOLAR SYSTEM

There are a number of features of the solar system which must be explained or embodied in any theory of its origin. The system is *complex,* consisting of the sun, nine major planets, thirty-one satellites which revolve about six of the planets, about fifteen hundred planetoids whose orbits are known and tens of thousands of others, about a thousand known comets and probably thousands more, and an immense number of meteors. The system is somewhat *isolated,* as, indeed, other stars and possible systems appear to be. The time required for light to travel from the nearest star (Proxima Centauri) to the sun or earth is 4.2 years; but less than $5\frac{1}{2}$ hours are required for it to travel from the sun to the outermost planet, Pluto.

Regularities. For all its complexity, there is a regularity and an organization among the major bodies of the solar system which cannot be due merely to chance. The regularities, some of which are discussed in Chapter 15, are:

1. The planets and nearly all the planetoids revolve around the sun in the same direction and with their orbits all in practically the same plane. The orbits of the planets are ellipses of low eccentricities (nearly circular), with the exception of those of Mercury and Pluto. Some of the planetoids move in highly eccentric orbits and in planes which are greatly inclined to the plane of the planetary orbits.

2. The sun rotates in the same direction as that in which the planets revolve, and the plane of its equator nearly coincides with the planes of the planetary orbits.

3. The mean distances of the planets from the sun, with some exceptions, follow the Titus-Bode law. This regularity may be approximately shown by listing a series of 4's, and adding successively the numbers 0, 3, 6, 12—each number after the second being twice the preceding one. The result divided by 10 gives the mean distance of the planet from the sun in astronomical units:

Mercury	*Venus*	*Earth*	*Mars*	*Asteroids*
4	4	4	4	4
0	3	6	12	24
4	7	10	16	28
0.4	0.7	1.0	1.6	2.8

Jupiter	*Saturn*	*Uranus*	*Neptune*	*Pluto*
4	4	4		4
48	96	192		384
52	100	196	—	388
5.2	10.0	19.6		38.8

The ninth term of the series represents the mean distance of Pluto rather than that of Neptune, while the fifth term gives the average distance of the asteroids. The relative distances calculated by the Titus-Bode law are in fairly close agreement with the observed values:

0.39	0.72	1.00	1.52	2.80
5.20	9.54	19.19	30.07	39.5

4. The satellites revolve about the planets in the direction in which the planets rotate, except for four moons of Jupiter, one of Saturn, and that of Neptune, which revolve in a retrograde direction. Their orbits are nearly circular and in most cases lie in or very close to the plane of the planet's equator.

5. The four inner planets are separated from the outer planets in space and differ from the latter in that they are smaller, possess fewer satellites, have lower velocity of rotation, and have higher densities.

Distribution of Mass and Angular Momentum. It will be shown later that a number of hypotheses have been abandoned because they failed to explain the distribution of the angular momentum in the solar system. For a body revolving about a point, this quantity, also called moment of momentum, is the product of the mass of the body, the velocity, and the distance from the body to the point around which it is moving. If the motion is a circle, this distance is the radius.

$$\text{Angular Momentum} = m(\text{ass}) \times v(\text{elocity}) \times d(\text{istance})$$

or $$M = mvd$$

The angular momentum of a planet due to its revolution, therefore, is equal to its mass times its orbital velocity times its distance from the sun, if we assume a circular orbit with the sun at the center. The angular momentum due to rotation is the sum of the momenta of all of the particles in the body.

In the solar system the sun possesses 99.9 per cent of the mass of the system, but less than 3 per cent of its angular momentum. The planets with less than 0.14 per cent of the mass have more than 97 per cent of the angular momentum, and of this total Jupiter has nearly 60 per cent. In any isolated system—that is, a system which cannot be acted upon by some external force—the angular momentum is conserved and is therefore a constant. If, for example, a rotating body should shrink, it would rotate faster. To illustrate this principle, one may hold weights or heavy objects in each extended hand and be rotated on a turn table (Figure 39–1*a*). When the hands with the weights are dropped to the side, the rota-

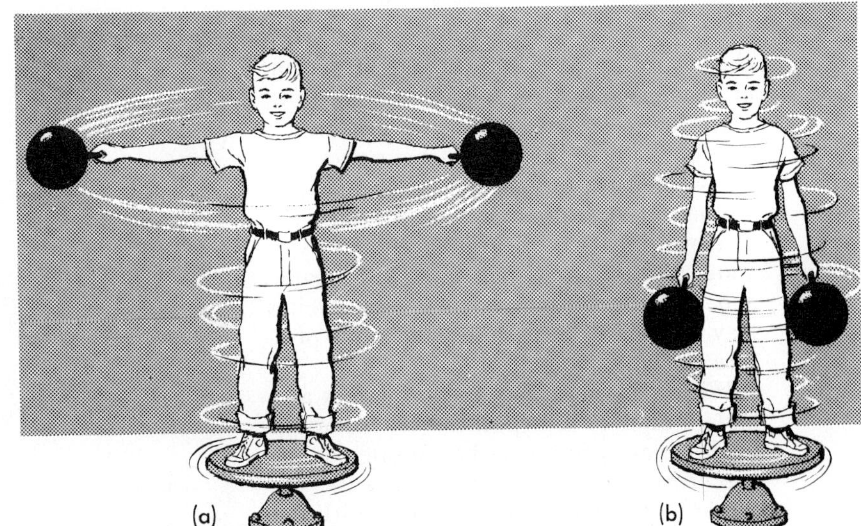

Fig. 39–1 *Conservation of angular momentum (mvd). When the arms are dropped on both sides, d is decreased and a corresponding increase in the velocity of rotation (v) is noted.*

tion becomes faster (Figure 39–1*b*). Since mvd (with hands extended) $= mv_1d_1$ (hands at side), $vd = v_1d_1$ and $v/v_1 = d_1/d$, or the velocity of rotation becomes greater as the average distance, or radius of rotation, becomes less. For a revolving body the principle may be illustrated simply by whirling a weight on a string so that the string winds around a finger (Figure 39–2). As the string becomes shorter (d becomes less), the weight revolves faster (v becomes greater), and the quantity mvd remains constant.

Chemical Constitution. It was formerly believed that the sun and other stars were composed of the same proportions of chemical elements as the earth. However, more recent estimates, based on extensive spectroscopic data, indicate that the common elements which form the body of the earth constitute only about one per cent of the mass of the sun. The rest of the sun is composed almost entirely of hydrogen and helium. It is also known that in interstellar space there are great clouds of fine dust and gas, very diffuse and of less density than the highest vacuum which has been produced on the earth. So great is the interstellar space, that the total mass of this material is probably equal to that of all of the stars. This material consists almost entirely of hydrogen and helium, with a small fraction of the heavier terrestrial elements.

Fig. 39–2 *Conservation of angular momentum in a revolving body. As the string wraps itself around the finger the weight moves faster and faster.*

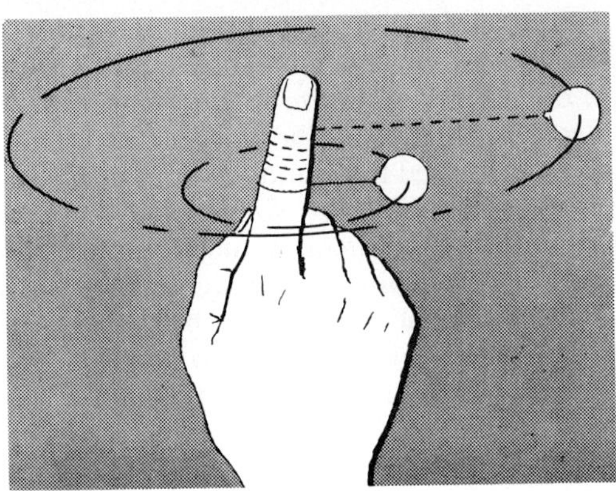

On the other hand, it has been shown that the gaseous elements (hydrogen, helium, and the other inert gases) are less abundant in the earth than one would expect from the above data. The faster moving hydrogen and helium molecules could have evaded gravitational capture by the earth, or, if on the earth, could have escaped at temperatures of a few hundred degrees. The low abundance of the heavier gases can be explained only by assuming that the earth was at one time of considerably less mass than at present.

The material of the earth is stratified (pages 120–121) with a very dense core and the stratification may have been caused by chemical changes leading to the formation of heavier substances, and to plastic flow, both due to the enormous pressures in the interior. It is therefore no longer necessary to assume that the earth was at one time molten. It has also been shown that the meteoritic matter in the solar system is of about the same composition as the earth and that the substances in the meteorites may well have been under the high pressure of a planet's interior.

With the above facts and principles as a basis, a number of hypotheses on the origin of the solar system may be considered. All hypotheses on cosmogony start with the sun or with a gas dust cloud from which the sun and the planets were formed. They may be divided into two classes: the *dualistic* or catastrophic hypotheses, which assume interaction of the sun with other stars or celestial bodies; and *monistic* or uniformitarian, which assume that the solar system developed as a closed system, isolated from other similar groups in the universe.

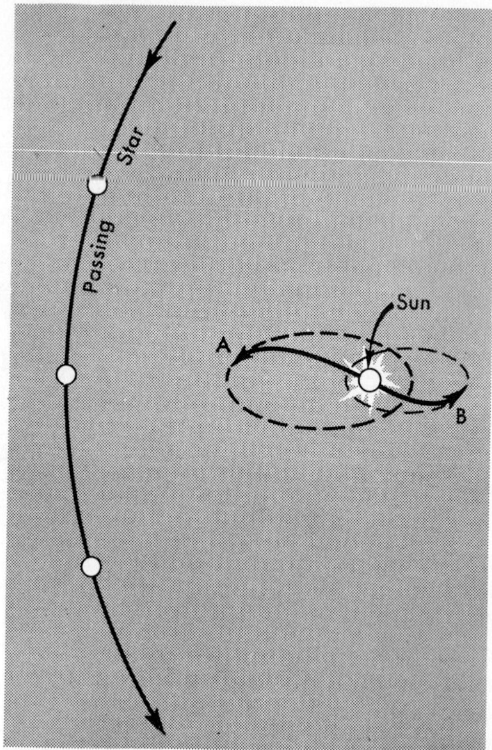

Fig. 39–3 *The planetesimal hypothesis. A passing star drew successive bolts or masses from the sun as the two bodies passed each other. Diagram shows the progress of the tidal disruption to produce mass A which became an outer planet and mass B which became a terrestrial planet.*

DUALISTIC HYPOTHESES

Hypotheses in this class, which at present are *not* generally accepted, start with the sun and postulate a close encounter or collision of another body with the sun. It was thought by those who speculated along this line that the unequal distribution of angular momentum (page 648) in the solar system could be accounted for only by assuming that a second star passed near by or sideswiped or collided with the sun. Matter was thus pulled or knocked from the sun, given momentum, and later somehow was condensed or gathered together in masses which became planets.

The idea of interaction with an outside body was proposed in 1749 by George-Louis Leclerc, Comte de Buffon, a French naturalist, who suggested that a comet may have collided with the sun, tearing from it the planetary material. This idea received little attention at that time. In 1900 T. C. Chamberlin and F. R. Moulton, both of the University of Chicago, announced the *planetesimal hypothesis,* which postulates that a star moving in a curved path came very close to the sun.

Gravitational pull, aided by great disruptive forces within the sun, caused the ejection of material from the latter in successive bolts, on the side near the star as well as on the side opposite to the passing star. (See Figure 39–3.) The hot solar material then condensed into solid particles or planetesimals of different sizes which moved around the sun in a common plane and in elliptical orbits. The more massive bodies swept up the smaller ones by their greater gravitational attraction to become the planets. Variations of this hypothesis, involving the collision of as many as three stars, were later proposed by Sir James

Jeans and Harold Jeffreys, H. N. Russell, R. A. Lyttleton, and others.

The principal defect of the collision or near-collision hypotheses was shown by Lyman Spitzer in 1939. The hot gaseous material of the sun is held together by enormous gravitational forces due to the sun's great mass and is prevented from collapsing into a more dense mass by its temperature (40 million degrees at the center). Spitzer showed mathematically that if some of this material were suddenly removed from the sun and thereby released from the enormous gravitational forces, it would expand with terrific force and most of it would escape from the region now occupied by the planets. It is unlikely that the material remaining would condense and coalesce into masses of planetary size.

MONISTIC HYPOTHESES

Hypotheses in this category start with a rotating gaseous nebula, either with a sun surrounded by a rotating gaseous cloud, or with a cloud of gas and dust particles, and assume that the solar system developed without any interaction with other celestial bodies. The troublesome distribution of angular momentum must therefore be explained by processes which take place in a closed system. After it was shown by Spitzer and others that the two or three star hypotheses were no longer satisfactory, an idea developed by Immanuel Kant in 1755 and a little later extended by Laplace was revived.

Kant, inspired by Thomas Wright's theory of the Milky Way, developed deductively the hypothesis that the solar system evolved from a great mass of gas or nebula. This mass occupied the entire volume of the present solar system, and because of gravitational attraction the heavier particles or molecules attracted and absorbed the lighter ones. The collisions of these particles generated heat and motion, so that the nebula began to rotate. As the speed of rotation increased, splashes of matter were thrown from the equatorial region, forming rings which finally condensed to form the planets. Although Kant's idea was not accepted at the time, due to certain dynamical defects, it has recently been revived on a more scientific basis. Kant also made a number of assumptions regarding Saturn's rings, the zodiacal light, and the tidal effects of the moon, which later received confirmation.

THE NEBULAR HYPOTHESIS

The renowned French mathematical astronomer, Laplace (Figure 39–4), formulated on a more scientific basis an hypothesis very similar to the idea developed by Kant. The *nebular hypothesis,* as it was called, was outlined briefly in a popular book on astronomy, *Exposition du Système du Monde* (1796). The idea attracted considerable attention, both because of the great prestige of Laplace and because it was introduced during a period of great social and scientific revolution. Widely accepted for more than a hundred years, it stirred the imagination and was the stimulus to other theories of evolution, particularly in the biological sciences.

Fig. 39–4 *Pierre-Simon, Marquis de Laplace, 1749–1827.* *(Brown Brothers)*

The nebular hypothesis assumed that the material which now comprises the solar system was once an extensive gaseous body or nebula (see Kant's hypothesis) which was originally at a high temperature, and which rotated on its axis. As it lost heat by radiation, it contracted, and by the principle of conservation of angular momentum, the mass rotated faster and faster. So great was the speed of rotation that an equatorial bulge developed; when the centrifugal force at the equator became equal to the gravitational attraction a ring of matter, bulging in one place, was left behind. As the remaining mass contracted further, the process was repeated, and more rings were successively shed (Figure 39–5) with long time intervals between. In all, ten such rings were lost, and the remaining material comprised the sun. The matter in each of nine rings in some manner gathered together or coalesced around the bulge to form a planet. One ring broke up to form the planetoids, which, for the most part, are in the space between Mars and Jupiter. The planets, still in the gaseous state, rotated, and some of them shed more rings which coalesced to form the satellites. Ultimately, the matter in the planets condensed and solidified.

The hypothesis accounts for the direction of rotation of the planets and their satellites, which is the same as the rotation of the sun, and for their nearly circular orbits, the planes of which closely coincide with the equatorial plane of the sun. It received support also because of the existence of nebulae which at that time were not known to be so extensive as to contain the mass of millions of suns, and which appeared to be replicas of the hypothetical parent gaseous mass. The rings of Saturn, which we now know are stable and apparently permanent, were cited as similar to the rings postulated by Laplace.

However, the nebular hypothesis does not account for the retrograde motions of certain satellites; nor does it explain how a satellite may revolve faster than its principal rotates, as does Phobos, a satellite of Mars. The chief objection to the hypothesis was that it did not explain how the sun, with most of the mass of the system, had so little of the angular momentum. It should, according to the hypothesis, rotate very rapidly, and continue to shed rings, or at least have an equatorial bulge; instead it rotates only once in twenty-eight days. Yet, if the sun had all of the mass and angular momentum of the solar system, it would be less flattened at the poles than some of the planets. Clerk Maxwell, who gave the hypothesis a mathematical treatment, showed that the rings thrown out from the sun would remain permanent like the rings of Saturn.

ALFVÉN'S HYPOTHESIS

A Swedish physicist, H. Alfvén, proposed in 1942 a cosmogony which takes into account the magnetic field around the sun, an idea which previously had been suggested by Birkeland in Norway and by H. P. Berlage, a Danish meteorologist. The sun's magnetic field exerts a greater force on electrically charged matter in the regions of the solar system than that due to the gravitational pull of the sun. Alfvén suggested that at one time the sun was surrounded by an interstellar gas cloud. Attracted by the gravitational force of the sun, the atoms in the cloud fell toward the sun with increasing velocities. At high speeds some of the atoms became ionized by

Fig. 39–5 *The nebular hypothesis. A great rotating nebula successively shed gaseous rings which condensed into the planets. Some of the planets lost smaller rings, which became satellites.*

collision with others. As soon as an ion was formed, its fall toward the sun was retarded and it moved along the magnetic field of the sun to an equilibrium position. By this mechanism a great amount of matter was concentrated in the equatorial plane of the sun. This matter condensed to form the planets. This process may possibly explain the formation of the outer planets, but not the inner ones. Ionization took place at too great a distance from the sun to permit a concentration of matter in the regions where the inner planets now exist. Alfvén suggested that the sun may have encountered a smoke cloud of small solid particles which vaporized when near the sun. The resulting atoms may similarly have become ionized, and by the same mechanism described above, matter might have been concentrated nearer the sun to form the inner planets.

In criticism of this interesting possibility, it has been shown that if enough matter were concentrated in a gaseous cloud around the sun to form the planets, the free movement of the atoms would be so retarded that very little ionization would take place.

THE DUST CLOUD HYPOTHESIS

In 1948 Fred L. Whipple of Harvard University introduced a new idea to account for the origin of the stars and planets. He suggested that the sun and planets were formed from a great cloud of dust and gas. That such clouds exist today is shown by the scattering of light of distant stars which passes through them. Lyman Spitzer has suggested that the feeble pressure exerted by light forced the dust particles into clouds just as it forces the fine material in the tail of a comet away from its head and from the sun. Two dust particles may be drawn together because of the lower light pressure in the shadow between them (Figure 39–6), forming a larger particle which casts a greater shadow. A small cloud may form, and, because of the larger shadow, draw in the smaller particles around it, finally growing to such a mass that its gravitational effect is greater than the light pressure. A dust cloud of the same mass as the sun and with the two forces balanced would have a diameter of about 6×10^{12} miles.

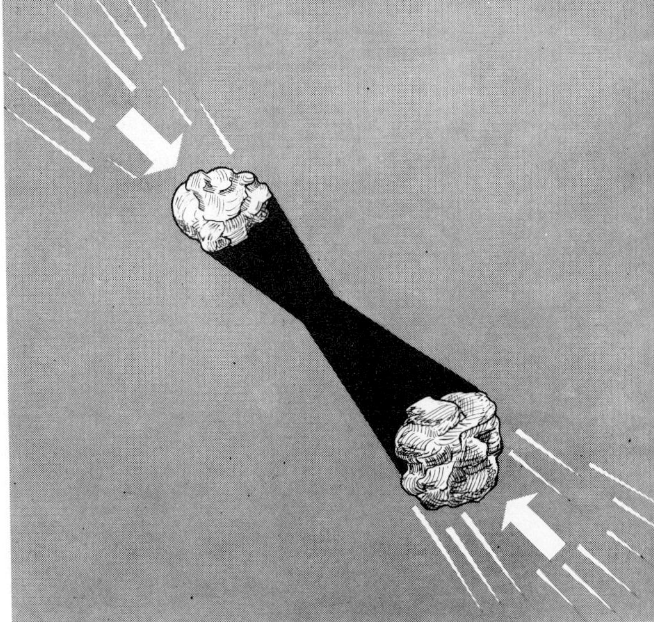

Fig. 39–6 *Radiation pressure.*

As suggested by Whipple, such a cloud, which may have acquired more mass, began to condense under its own gravity. While the material in the cloud had some random turbulence, the mass as a whole had practically no rotation nor angular momentum. It contracted, slowly at first because of the motions of the streams of dust within it, but in the course of some millions of years these motions were arrested by friction and collision. As it became smaller, its density increased, and consequently the force of gravity within it became greater. It finally collapsed at a very rapid rate, the temperature increasing due to the pressure within the cloud, until it reached millions of degrees – enough to initiate the chain of nuclear reactions with helium, hydrogen, and carbon. In this manner the hot radiating sun was formed.

The planets evolved from the same great cloud during the shrinking processes which resulted in the formation of the incandes-

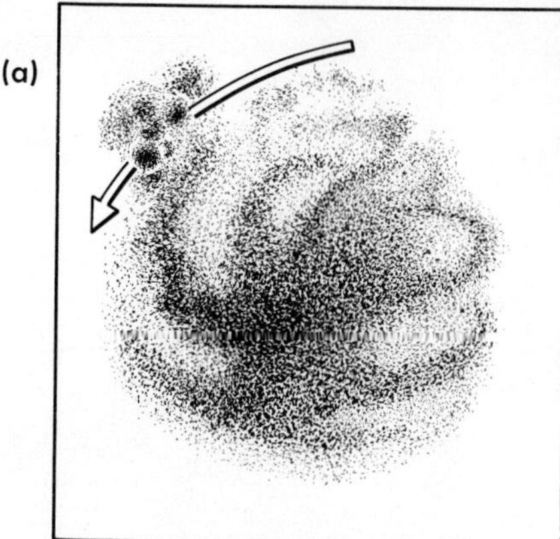

cent sun. The process is represented in Figure 39–7. (*a*) During the very early stages of contraction, streams of dust developed in the cloud. The dust became very dense and concentrated in the largest stream, where it condensed into smaller clouds which moved along with the main body. (*b*) The smaller clouds grew by gathering up the less concentrated material and became *proto-planets,* moving in toward the center of the large cloud. (*c*) These masses of a variety of sizes and speeds began to spiral toward the center of gravity of the system. Some of them may have reached the center of the mass to become part of the sun. (*d*) But in the meantime the stage of rapid collapse described above was reached, and a number of the proto-planets were left moving in orbits around the sun. These masses condensed to form the planets, but as they had less mass than the big cloud, they did not attain by contraction a sufficiently high temperature to initiate the nuclear reaction. In a similar manner the satellites may have been formed by condensation of the outer cloud of material which remained when a proto-planet collapsed to form a planet. This assumption is supported by the fact that with the exception of the earth-moon system each planet has a very much greater mass than that of all its satellites.

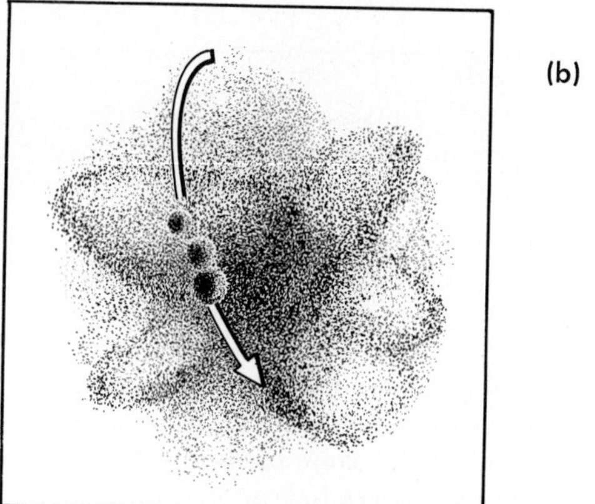

Many of the properties of the solar system are accounted for by the dust-cloud hypothesis. The newly formed planets were initially very hot and some were probably molten; this would account for the density stratification in the earth. The slow rotation of the sun and the large angular momentum of the planets is explained by the lack of rotation in the original great cloud and the spiral-like motions of the dust streams which formed the planets. As in a number of hypotheses, the chemical constitution of the system is accounted for by the failure of the less massive planets to hold by gravitational attraction very much of the light gases (hydrogen and helium) which pervaded the dust cloud.

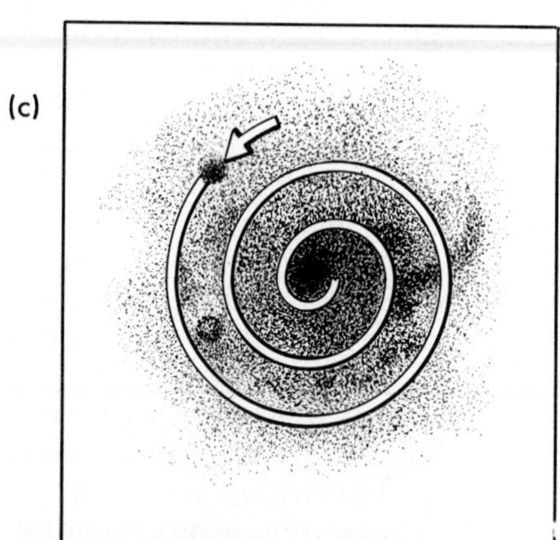

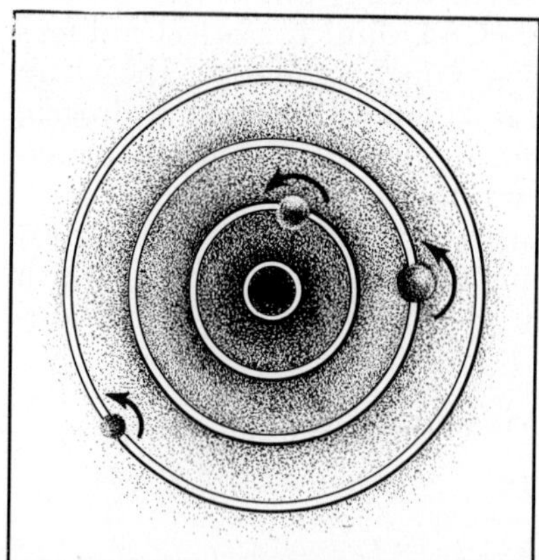

Fig. 39–7 *Stages in the formation of planets from a dust cloud.* (*Scientific American*)

The regularities of the solar system, with the exception of the Titus-Bode law, are explained satisfactorily. The path of the original stream of dust determined the direction and the plane of revolution of the planets. That the nearly circular orbits of planets are the result of the initial spiral motion, assumed in this hypothesis, is in accord with mathematical theory. The rotation of the planets is due to the increasing density of the condensing cloud into which they spiraled. The cloud was more dense toward the center, and as a proto-planet moved in, it encountered more material on the inner side, which became heavier and was slowed up. The outer side moved faster and the whole body thus acquired a forward spin or rotation. The larger planets had a greater difference in the density of the medium on their inner and outer sides, and therefore acquired greater rotational speed. The small sizes and the fewer satellites of the inner planets are due to their close proximity to the sun. They were probably within the outer fringes of the hot condensing sun, and the material which might have formed satellites was evaporated away. They were also perhaps smaller to begin with and, unlike the more massive and less dense outer planets, unable to hold the lighter gases by gravitational attraction.

The asteroids which move in the region between Mars and Jupiter are probably pieces of a broken planet which may have collided with another planet moving in a highly eccentric orbit. It has been calculated that the planet was about the size of Mars.

The explanation for the retrograde motion of several satellites is the same as that offered in the gaseous tidal hypothesis — they may have been captured from one planet by another.

The dust cloud hypothesis is compatible with most of the facts, but shares a serious weakness with a number of other hypotheses of this group. It is difficult to explain how a nucleus may form in a very rare gas dust cloud and hold itself together in the early stages and then acquire sufficient mass to attract other material by gravity.

VON WEIZSÄCKER NEBULAR CLOUD HYPOTHESIS

Astronomical space contains many nebular clouds of enormous magnitudes. The nebular clouds are interstellar in size and consist of gas and dust particles. The German astrophysicist C. F. von Weizsäcker hypothesized that our solar system started when our sun plunged into a nebular cloud. Due to the gravitational pull of the sun, great quantities of nebular material were drawn into a vast solar envelope. This envelope developed slowly into a disc-like system with a diameter comparable to the present diameter of the solar system. It is from condensations in this nebular disc that the planets are supposed to have been formed. The hypothesis quite successfully accounts for the distribution of the planets and for the variations in their composition as influenced by their distances from the sun. It has not yet had wide acceptance.

The hypothesis of von Weizsäcker leads to a very interesting conclusion. The passage of stars through nebular clouds must not be a very unusual event. If our solar system came into existence by a sequence of developments following the passage of our sun into a nebular cloud, then there must be many solar systems similar to ours in the universe.

NOVA HYPOTHESIS OF HOYLE

A nova or new star is a star which suddenly blazes up to become, for a brief period, an unusually bright star in the heavens. Some nova have been so bright that they could be seen even in daylight. After a short period of shining with great splendor, they fade and soon become insignificant again. A nova outburst is believed to be due to some intense nuclear reaction suddenly occurring in the atoms within the star. They might be, in effect, super-colossal hydrogen bombs. After the reaction is complete, fading occurs very rapidly. In 1945, F. Hoyle (Britain, 1915–   ) put forth the hypothesis that our sun was once

Fig. 39–8 *Our solar system may have come from a nova.*

a part of a binary star system separated by a distance comparable to that between the planet Jupiter and the sun. The companion star, possibly 4 or 5 billion years ago, suddenly became a nova. The assumption is made (refer to Figure 39–8) that the explosion was off-center within the nova, throwing a great mass of star material in the direction *AB*. A part of this material was captured by the sun to form our planets. The explosive force of the nova is assumed to have carried the remains of the dying nova into outer space away from the sun. The hypothesis of Hoyle explains why most of the angular momentum of the solar system is in the planets. It still, however, has not yet been sufficiently tested to gain wide acceptance.

WHAT CAN WE CONCLUDE?

When we consider our universe we must describe systems of matter and energy ranging in size from the diameter of the nucleus of an atom (1×10^{-12} cm) to the diameter of our solar system (1×10^{15} cm). From one extreme to the other we observe great orderliness and significant relationships. As we study these systems, we are impressed with the mass of information tabulated and made useful by modern science at the same time that we realize there are questions which have not been or cannot now be answered. Science, however, gives man the courage to hope that many more answers are yet to be found. As we are impressed by the intricacies of atom systems on the one hand and the grandeur of our solar system on the other, by a realization of the much we know and the much still unknown, we should come to a reassessment of our human position. With the poet Thomas Hardy we can say,

> Let me enjoy the earth no less
> Because the all-enacting Might
> That fashioned forth its loveliness
> Had other aims than my delight.

SUMMARY

1. Science is concerned with the origin of the solar system which, while speculative, involves a strict use of the scientific method.
2. The age of the earth is estimated by several methods:
   a. The rate of deposit of sedimentary rocks.
   b. The rate of erosion of the continents.
   c. The quantity of salt in the oceans.
   d. Retracing mathematically the motion of the moon to a position very close to the earth.
   e. The rate of radioactive decay – the most accurate method. The age of the earth is thought to be somewhat over three billion years.
3. The properties and relevant facts of the solar system are:
   a. Isolation in astronomical space.
   b. Complexity, yet a regularity and organization.
   c. All members, except some of the planetoids, lie in approximately the same plane, which is that of the sun's equator.
   d. All the planets revolve in nearly circular orbits, and some of them rotate in this plane, all in the same direction, and at distances which are widely separated, but

which are in accord with the Titus-Bode Law.

e. The satellites revolve in this same plane, but several move in a retrograde direction.

f. Most of the angular momentum of the system is possessed by the planets, which comprise less than one-seventh of one per cent of the total mass of the system.

g. The common elements which form the body of the earth constitute only about one per cent of the sun, which is composed mostly of hydrogen and helium. Great clouds of dust and gas of extremely low density exist in interstellar space.

4. Dualistic hypotheses initiated by Buffon and developed by Moulton and Chamberlin, Jeans and Jeffreys, Lyttleton, and others assume a collision or near collision with another star or with the sun or companion star. They were abandoned when it was shown that a hot filament drawn from the sun would expand into a cloud rather than condense to form the planets.

5. Monistic hypotheses, initiated by Kant, all postulate the birth of the solar system from a great cloud of gas and dust particles.

a. According to the *nebular hypothesis* (Laplace) a rotating gaseous nebula shed rings of gas, each of which (with one exception) condensed and gathered together to form a planet. This hypothesis, long accepted, explains most of the properties of the system but does not account for the distribution of angular momentum, the formation of the planets from rings of gaseous material, and the retrograde motions of certain satellites.

b. Alfvén's theory assumes ionization of gas atoms drawn to the sun from a cloud and a subsequent ionization and a concentration of the ions in the region of the sun's magnetic equator followed by condensation.

c. The *dust-cloud hypothesis* (Whipple) starts with a cloud of gas and dust particles, the latter collecting under the influence of light pressure. The cloud contracted, slowly at first, but finally at a very rapid rate, to form the sun and the planets. The nuclear reactions taking place in the sun were initiated at the high temperatures reached in the contraction. The planets were formed in a stream in the cloud from great masses (proto-planets) which spiraled around the sun. The satellites were similarly formed from the outer cloud of material remaining around a planet. The original cloud did not rotate; the high angular momentum of the planets is the result of the spiral-like motion of the dust stream from which they were formed. The hypothesis explains most of the regularities and properties of the system except the Titus-Bode law. The initial formation of the nucleus in the rare dust gas cloud is not satisfactorily explained.

d. In the *von Weizsäcker hypothesis* it is assumed that the sun, formed by the condensation of interstellar matter, was enveloped by a cloud of gas and dust. In the cloud, which assumed a disc-like shape, viscous forces caused the inner parts to be decelerated and move toward the sun and the outer parts to be accelerated and move out into space, thus transferring angular momentum to the outer part of the system. The material escaping was of low atomic weight. The fine dust particles grew at first by collision and then by gravitation attraction. The motions of the particles became organized and the growth of the planets occurred at the junction of rings of vortices, spaced in a geometrical progression. The satellites were formed in a similar manner from dust clouds around the planets. The hypothesis removes some of the objections of the Kant-Laplace hypothesis and gives an explanation for the Titus-Bode law, the distribution of angular momentum, and the differences in chemical composition between the planets and the sun.

e. The *nova hypothesis* of Hoyle postulates that our sun was once a binary star system. The companion star suddenly became a nova and exploded unsymmetrically to form masses which by the gravitational pull of the sun became our solar system. The hypothesis is successful in accounting for the large angular momentum of the planets; less so in accounting for the rotation of the planets and for the satellites.

STUDY EXERCISES

1. Write a brief statement to show how each of the following methods used to estimate the age of the earth may be inadequate.
   a. The rate of deposit of sedimentary rocks.
   b. The rate of erosion of the continents.
   c. The quantity of salt in the sea.
   d. The gradual movement of the moon away from the earth as caused by tidal friction.
2. The chemical and isotopic content of rocks bearing naturally radioactive elements gives a more accurate method for measuring the age of the earth, for (check each correct statement):
   .... radioactive disintegration proceeds at a constant rate which is not influenced by conditions.
   .... radioactive decay could have begun only after the material which now comprises the earth had been drawn from the sun.
   .... radioactive decay dates not from the formation of the earth but from the time of formation of radioactive substances, whereas the permanent deposit of the end products in the same minerals probably dates from the solidification of the rock in which it is found.
   .... radioactive decay is continuous and suffers no interruptions, once started.
3. Prepare a list of facts or properties of the solar system
   a. which may be regarded as a part of a regularity or organization.
   b. which may be regarded as irregular or exceptional.
4. Assume that a tenth planet is discovered beyond Pluto. Assuming the Titus-Bode law holds, calculate its probable distance in astronomical units.
5. Assume that a body is completely isolated and is rotating. Check each of the statements below if correct.
   .... If the body shrinks but retains the same mass, it should rotate at the same rate.
   .... If the body shrinks it should rotate faster but retain the same quantity of angular momentum.
   .... If the body sheds a ring of dust and gas, the total angular momentum of the system remains constant.
6. Mark each statement as follows: *D,* if true only of the dualistic hypothesis; *M,* if true only of the monistic hypothesis; and *B,* if true of both.
   .... The sun in somewhat the same form as at present was the parent body.
   .... The sun was either quite different from its present state or was formed from a nebula as the first major step in the evolution of the solar system.
   .... The earth was originally gaseous and hot.
   .... The system was always isolated and with a constant angular momentum.
   .... The present distribution of angular momentum in the system was the result of a close encounter or collision of the sun with another star.
   .... The nearly circular orbits of the planets were due to constant impacts with other bodies.
7. Discuss briefly the main reason why the dualistic hypotheses were abandoned.
8. Mark *A,* if true only of the nebular hypothesis; *B,* if true only of the von Weizsäcker hypothesis; *C,* if true only of the dust-cloud hypothesis; and *D,* if true of all three:
   .... The solar system originated from a nebula.
   .... The planets were formed from gaseous rings shed by the rotating nebula.
   .... The planets were formed from a dust stream in the dust-gas cloud.
   .... The planets were formed by accretion from the dust particles along the rings of vortices.
   .... The distribution of angular momentum is explained by the loss into space of the material which had most of the angular momentum and the acquisition by the sun of the material for which this value was zero.
   .... The distribution of angular momentum is explained by the assumption that the original whole nebula had no

rotary motion and the motion of the planets was due to the spiral-like motion of the dust stream from which they were formed.

.... The explanation for the distribution of angular momentum was not satisfactory and contributed to the abandonment of the hypothesis.

.... Utilizes the idea of light or radiation pressure.

.... Explains most satisfactorily the Titus-Bode law.

9. Write a short essay in which you show how the world was prepared for the reception of the nebular hypothesis, and what great influence it long exerted on thought.
10. Discuss the possibilities for the development of an hypothesis on the origin of the solar system which might ultimately become a theory.

FOR FURTHER READING

1. Smart, W. M., *The Origin of the Earth.* Cambridge, England: Cambridge University Press, 1951. Also available in a paperback edition: Penguin, 65¢.

   A very well written description of the earth, whence it came and when, and how our solar system might have come into existence. Includes a good account of the nebular hypothesis of Laplace and why it had to be discarded, the tidal theory of Jeans and Jeffreys, the planetesimal theory of Chamberlin-Moulton, the binary star hypothesis, the nebular cloud hypothesis of von Weizsäcker, and the nova theory of Hoyle. Very interesting reading.
2. Whipple, Fred L., "The Solar System and Its Origin," page 103 in H. Shapley, H. Wright, and S. Rapport, *Readings in the Physical Sciences* (New York: Appleton-Century-Crofts, 1948).

40

A LOOK AT THE FUTURE

> It is a telling comment that the hall of fame in science contains the names of few men who discovered facts, but a host who made facts significant by pervasive and integrating explanation.
>
> — HENRY MARGENAU

THIS BOOK has been concerned primarily with the story of the physical sciences, but there has been no intent to magnify the physical sciences to the disparagement of other sciences or other branches of learning. The fundamental aim of all education is wisdom. True wisdom can come only through training in the study of man — the humanities — and the sciences. The great hopes, faiths, and aspirations of the human race have come down to us through the branches of learning represented by the humanities. Man defines his goals by the humanities; he achieves them through science. Now, more than ever, he has the knowledge to achieve great goals. Will these goals be good or bad? The answer is up to man.

The capabilities of science have expanded enormously during the last generation. A new era has already begun — the nuclear era — bringing with it great hope for the good of mankind, but also, whether we like it or not, tremendous power for destruction, a problem facing all civilization. Science is where it is today because scientists and society have the simple faith that it is man's mission to understand the forces in the universe around us and that the advances of science should benefit all. The Nobel prize winner William Faulkner has said, "Our privacy has been slowly and steadily and increasingly invaded until now our very dream of civilization is in danger. Who will save us but the scientist and the humanitarian? Yes, the humanitarian in science, and the scientist in the humanity of man."

Mankind faces many problems. The advances of science and technology have created a world community in which many tensions exist between the "have" and the "have-not" nations. There is an imbalance in the world populations for such reasons as the uneven distribution of cheap fuels, of metal resources, of fertile soils, of rainfall, and of ground water supplies. The "have" nations possess adequate amounts of the above-mentioned resources; the "have-not" nations have an inadequate supply. These inequalities can be relieved only by modern science.

SOME WORLD PROBLEMS THAT REQUIRE SOLUTION

1. *The problem of cheap fuels.* The fossil fuel reserves, coal, petroleum, and natural gas, are very unevenly distributed over the earth. Only Poland, Russia, China, South Africa, and the United States, for example, are in a position to export coal to other countries, and even these minable reserves of coal are definitely limited. The present population of the United States is about 172 million, and there is reason to believe that there will be a 35 per cent increase in the next twenty years, and a 100 per cent increase in the next forty years. Consequently, our demand for power to operate our homes and our economy will increase at even a greater rate. Our present installed power capacity is about 100 million kilowatts, and it is estimated that this will increase to at least 300 million kilowatts by 1980. While our nation is fortunate in the large size of its reserves of coal, petroleum, and natural gas, even these reserves of cheap fuels will not permit tripling their production in the next twenty years. Hence, we *must* turn to nuclear energy. (Refer to Chapter 38.) The science and technology of obtaining electrical energy from fissionable materials have already advanced to a point where industry is investing many millions of dollars in nuclear power. Already there are some large commercial electrical power plants operating on fissionable material in Britain and the United States. Improvements in the status of "have-not" nations can be expected as they gradually expand their economies upon a base of nuclear energy. Many nations can raise their standards of living only by moving in the direction of an industrial economy, which requires relatively cheap fuel. Nuclear energy can make this development possible in many regions now deficient in cheap energy supplies. In this coming era, coal will be reserved for use as a rich essential source for many organic chemicals.

2. *The problem of energy from the sun.* There will be a period in which we must depend upon power plants operating on fissionable materials. But we know that the ideal source of energy is the sun. Its energy supply is practically inexhaustible. The sun shines over the entire earth, and its rays (when shining perpendicularly to the earth) deliver 1.92 calories per minute per square centimeter of surface. This is the so-called *solar constant* which means that the earth receives power from the sun at the rate of nearly 3,600,000 kilowatts per square mile. This power in the form of electricity could take care of the energy needs of a typical American city of 560,000 people.

Scientists eventually hope to be able to harness the radiant energy of the sun for conversion to electrical energy. Sun engines, however, will be very inefficient if they are merely heat traps to operate present types of heat engines. Scientists working in this area, therefore, are looking for some novel way of utilizing the relatively low temperatures available in direct sunlight. Already they have achieved some successes, as shown by the solar battery which even now is finding application in the operation of telephone systems. (Refer to Figure 34–1.) The great difficulties involved in this problem are serving as a stimulus to research.

3. *The problem of adequate water supplies.* As populations increase, the problem of adequate water supplies becomes more and more acute. Water is needed for drinking and for sanitation, but growing populations also need more food, which in turn requires more water for its growth. Rainfall over many regions is irregular or virtually nonexistent. When rainfall is inadequate, other sources must be found, such as inland bodies of fresh water or wells. In many regions, the demand for water has increased to such an extent that it is being pumped out of the soil faster than it is being replenished. This is true, for example, on Long Island and in certain parts of California. The steady lowering of the water table is a matter of growing concern to many localities. If the water table in lands close to the oceans is lowered too much, sea water flows into the wells and ruins them.

All agricultural and industrial activities require large amounts of water. It takes, for example, 65,000 gallons to make a ton of steel, 50,000 gallons to produce a ton of paper, 7500 gallons to grow a bushel of wheat, and five gallons to produce a gallon of milk. On an average, each person in the United States uses about 145 gallons of water per day. If industrial and farm uses are considered, we need 1200 gallons of water daily for every man, woman, and child. Fundamentally, this water comes from the oceans as atmospheric moisture which reaches the earth again as rain or snow. Over large areas of the United States we are not now getting enough water. Furthermore, we have not learned to conserve adequately the rain water that we get. In the eastern states, for example, it is estimated that 92 per cent of the rainfall runs unused back into the oceans. The complexities of our shortage of water will be enormously increased by the rapid rate of the population increase in the United States, which indicates that by 1975 our population will total about 230,000,000.

The food supply of the world could be greatly increased if water could be brought to regions with good soils but inadequate water supplies. This problem is such a a complicated one that it will require more than one solution, such as combining the more careful use of water with the re-use of water by industry and the prevention of run-off to the oceans. Our greatest potential source of water is the oceans. Three-fourths of the earth's surface is covered by water to an average depth of a mile. But this water contains salt which makes it unsuitable for direct use in agriculture and for the support of animal life. Nature de-salts sea water on an enormous scale through the functioning of the water cycle, which depends upon the energy of the sun. It appears, then, that one solution to the problem of increasing our water supplies lies in finding a cheap process of removing salt from ocean waters either by evaporation with subsequent condensation or by a chemical process. Both schemes are now in operation but the present costs are prohibitive. All current researches on obtaining fresh water from ocean water are aimed at perfecting a process which will make it possible to produce rainfall quantities of water at low cost. This is another problem for the scientists of the future.

4. *The problem of food supplies.* Large masses of the world's population must subsist on diets substandard both in amount and in dietary adequacy. The average daily per capita intake of food in India is only 1650 calories, as contrasted with 3120 calories in the United States. This, of course, is a reflection on mankind itself. It is known that the yield of food crops in many regions could be very largely increased through improved modern scientific methods of soil and water management, by the use of appropriate fertilizers, by selection of improved plant strains, and by the use of power machinery. Food production in the United States averages 10,400 calories per capita per day, compared with only 2200 calories per capita per day in India, where greater efficiency of food production is desperately needed.

The four- to five-fold greater production of food in the United States as compared with India reflects the operation of such factors as the following:

	U.S.	*India*
Fertilizer, in pounds applied, per person per year	61	0.5
Coal production, in tons, per person per year	2.3	0.1
Petroleum production, in barrels, per person per year	17	0.1
Electricity used, in kilowatt-hours, per person per year	2900	21

One important way of increasing food supplies is through improved plant strains. Thus, the Iowa corn farmer using hybrid corn strains developed by plant biologists, and using modern fertilizers and culture methods with power machinery, produces three to five times as much corn per acre as did his grandfather. By contrast, the peasant in the Nile Valley today grows his crops by methods that have not changed for thousands of years.

The total arable land of the earth and our known potential for growing food could provide for a world population of 50,000,000,000 persons. The present world population is more than 2,500,000,000. Supplying food for this expanding population is limited not by the earth's potential for providing food, but rather by the inability of many nations to put modern methods of food production into practice. Societies acting through governments must solve the problems of raising the educational level of those engaged in agriculture and providing for them more adequate sources of energy.

It is interesting to note that some scientists consider the oceans, especially in the warmer latitudes, as future sources of food. The production of plant food through the process of photosynthesis calls for carbon dioxide, and the concentration of carbon dioxide in the oceans is over sixty times greater than in the air. Refer to page 445. There is evidence that 90 per cent of all photosynthetic processes occur in the seas. Here, then, is a significant area for research looking to increased food supplies.

SOME PROBABLE FUTURE DEVELOPMENTS IN SCIENCE

Scientists are always curious about any phenomenon which is not clearly understood. This curiosity leads to so-called *fundamental research,* research carried out to gain new knowledge for the sake of the knowledge itself and without any regard for the usefulness of the new knowledge. Oersted's discovery in 1819 of a magnetic field about an electrical conductor and Faraday's discovery in 1831 that magnetic fields produce electric currents in conductors are good examples of fundamental research (pages 511 and 520). These two discoveries underlie all the developments of our modern electrical age, yet their many applications could not be foreseen at the time they were made.

Biochemistry and Biophysics. Of many areas where scientists are today engaged in fundamental research with unforeseeable potentialities for the good of man, we may single out for special note the work being done in pushing back the frontiers of the biological sciences. These are now passing from a period when they were largely descriptive and factual to one where scientists are concerning themselves with biological processes in terms of the chemical changes and the role of energy in the life processes of plants and animals. In essence, biological scientists are now no longer content merely to describe life processes but are concerned with the nature of life itself from the point of view of chemistry and physics.

Forms of life may be very simple or very complex but all show at least three common characteristics. The first is the ability of the life form to reproduce itself. Secondly, life forms take in various substances called foods, and ingest them by various chemical reactions to gain energy for carrying on life processes; the sum of these chemical changes is what we have called *metabolism.* Thirdly, all living plants and animals have the ability to respond to various stimuli from their environment. Thus a sunflower daily turns toward the sun, and a person drops an object if it is too hot to hold. The modern biological scientist is definitely making progress in answering questions as to the nature of life. This progress is possible because he has learned to study the relationship of cause to effect and of effect back to cause in terms of reactions involving many kinds of molecules and particles.

It is estimated that the total number of cells in the human body is about 10^{14}. These cells are themselves minute energy systems consisting, in the main, of many kinds of molecules and ions. Some of the particles in these cells are relatively simple molecules such as water (H_2O), carbon dioxide (CO_2), or glucose ($C_6H_{12}O_6$), but many are very large with enormous molecular weights. Thus hemoglobin, an essential component in all red blood cells, has been shown to have a molecular weight of about 68,000. Biochemists have made remarkable strides in identifying the specific molecular forms which are essential to the human body and in finding out their functions. Insulin, for example, a secretion in the pancreas of many animals which is essential in the oxidation of sugar by the body to obtain energy, has been shown to be a protein with a molecular weight of 12,000, and consists of a pattern or sequence of amino acids which is now known. During recent years, too, the structure of many vitamins has been determined. They serve as essential catalysts for many body processes. Some are effective in amounts as low as one microgram (1×10^{-6} g) per day. The structure of that remarkably effective antibiotic, penicillin, has also been determined. Some of the viruses, moreover, that cause diseases in plants and animals have been shown to be giant molecules with a definite molecular structure. The photograph reproduced as Figure 40–1 shows a virus having a molecular arrangement which is cubic close packing of essentially spherical molecular particles of diameter of about 230 angstrom units. The edge length of the unit cube containing four of these molecules is about 325 angstroms. The union of chemistry with biology (biochemistry) and the union of physics with biology (biophysics) are active areas of fundamental scientific research today. The rate of making fundamental discoveries in the biological sciences has increased sharply during the last decade, and there is every reason to believe that the rate will continue to increase. This development augurs well for the future well-being of mankind.

Fig. 40–1 *Electron micrograph of the southern bean mosaic virus protein. Magnification 75,000x. (Courtesy, Dr. Ralph W. G. Wyckoff, National Institute of Arthritis and Metabolic Diseases, Bethesda, Maryland.)*

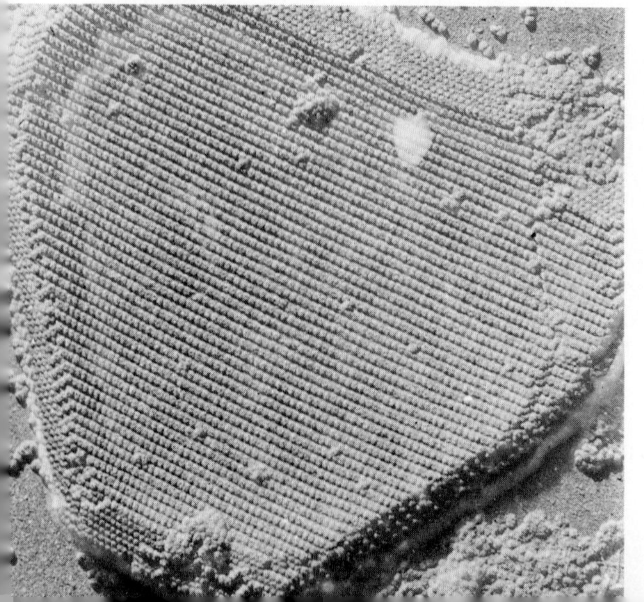

Instruments of Detection. Another area in which rapid progress is being made in pushing back the curtain of the unknown is in the procedures for revealing to the human eye very small particles. The discovery and perfection of the microscope by Leeuwenhoek (Netherlands, 1632–1723) was a fundamental discovery of vast significance. The microscope made it possible to see and photograph particles of the size of red blood cells and many bacteria. We often forget the difficulties that have had to be overcome to arrive at our present state of knowledge. We accept the fact that many diseases are caused by specific forms of bacteria, for example, and forget that there once was a germ hypothesis for disease that had to be proved. The notion that many diseases are caused by minute forms of life called germs was initially a working guess that had to be stoutly defended by experiments to which the microscope was indispensable. When Loeffler (Germany, 1852–1915) demonstrated that all persons suffering from diphtheria harbored an organism with a dumbbell shape, he was on his way to proving that *Bacillus Loeffler* was the causative organism of that disease. The microscope has been used over and over to relate specific diseases to microorganisms.

The microscope of today is a vast improvement over the original instrument of Leeuwenhoek. The science of optics has made it possible to develop microscopes with magnifying powers up to the theoretical limit of magnification – about 2000 times. This is ample, for instance, to reveal a red blood cell, which has a diameter of about 0.0008 cm or 80,000 angstrom units. The science of optics shows that objects smaller than the wave length of visible light (about 5000 Å) cannot be revealed by a microscope. Even the largest molecules are smaller than light waves and cannot, therefore, be seen by optical microscopes.

The first instrument to exceed the optical microscope in magnification was the *electron miscroscope* which was perfected about two decades ago. Very small energetic particles have been found to act as waves, and the wave lengths of energetic electrons are roughly one-thousandth the wave length of visible light. In an electron microscope objects are revealed on a photographic plate using fast-moving electrons instead of visible light. Magnifications in the range of 50,000 to 200,000 are possible with electron microscopes, approximately 50 to 200 times greater than with an ordinary microscope. Thus, a particle 1000 angstrom units in diameter can be photographed to produce an image 2 centimeters in diameter on a photographic plate. It is possible to see objects as small as 25 Å (25×10^{-8} cms) with an electron microscope. While ordinary molecules cannot be seen, the largest molecules, so-called "giant" molecules, are readily made visible.

The electron microscope has many uses for studying particles from 10^{-4} to 10^{-6} centimeters (10,000 to 100 Å). Using the microscope, medical scientists were never able to demonstrate that certain diseases, such as smallpox and spinal meningitis, were caused by minute organisms. The evidence for the existence of minute causative organisms, however, was overwhelming, Organisms too small to be revealed by ordinary microscopes were suspected, but there was no objective proof until the electron microscope could be applied. This definitely revealed the presence of *viruses,* organisms too small to be seen by microscopes, but easily visible in the electron microscope because of its much greater magnification.

The most recent technique for revealing very minute particles is known as *electric field emission microscopy.* This technique has pushed magnifying power 1 to 10 million times. With this technique even atoms and molecules can be photographed. (Refer to Figure 40–2, which reveals the atoms in the atom lattice in crystals of tungsten.) The power of this technique is shown by the fact that, with a magnification of 10 million, an atom with a diameter of 2 Å is revealed on a photographic plate as an image 2 millimeters in diameter. The development of electric field emission microscopy is truly an extraordinary scientific achievement. It demonstrates the enormous strides science has made since Avogadro in the early nineteenth century guessed at the existence of molecules. We now can photograph the atoms and molecules themselves!

The technique of field emission microscopy is so new that it does not yet have the ready applicability of the electron microscope. The technique is being studied and developed, and we can look for rapid developments in this field.

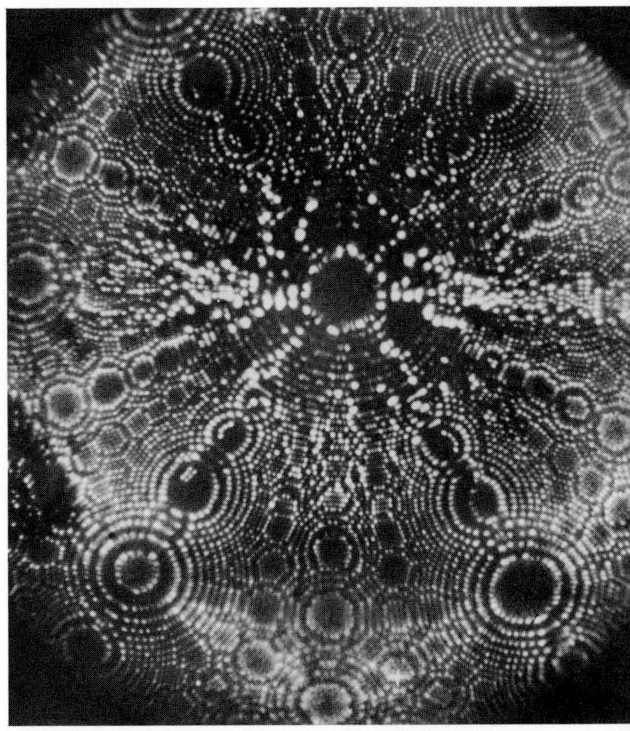

Fig. 40–2 *Central part of a tiny hemispherical tungsten crystal as revealed with a field ion microscope. Magnification 1,600,000*x. *(Photograph by E. W. Muller, Pennsylvania State University)*

SCIENCE AND SOCIETY

It would be tragic to accept complacently the achievements of present-day science. For knowledge alone and the ability to solve problems do not of themselves guarantee that this knowledge and ability will be used to benefit mankind. We have learned to increase the production of food, yet there is overproduction in some areas of the world while in other areas millions subsist on substandard diets. We pride ourselves on our ability to cross continents and oceans in a matter of hours and thus save valuable time. But time saved for what purpose? We have marvelous media for mass communication, but much of the material that travels by these electromagnetic waves is trivial. Worse, we have seen how control of these media by the unscrupulous can be used to distort the thinking of man.

Many hold science responsible for the world's present ills. Yet science is neutral. It is man and societies of men who must choose how scientific knowledge is to be used. Science may furnish a means of welding societies together, but only if human beings, thinking and working constructively, *will* it so. A true scientist is not one who compartmentalizes his knowledge and restricts his scientific thinking to his own field. On the contrary, he applies the rigor and definiteness of scientific thinking wherever it is appropriate. We have seen how the scientific method has pushed back frontiers in such traditional scientific fields as physics and chemistry. Today we are witnessing an increasing tendency to apply the methods of scientific thinking on the social and behavioral fronts also. Research scientists, engineers, and technologists can solve scientific problems and devise practical applications of scientific knowledge, but they alone cannot solve the problems of the world. Every one of us has a part to perform. The world imperatively needs persons who have a real appreciation of the power of science, of its interconnection with human society, and of the value of scientific thinking in working out a union between science and society that will further man's greater good.

Science has largely shaped our present way of life. Yet in our eagerness to benefit from the "useful" or "practical" applications of science, we are apt to forget that desirable and necessary changes in our way of life will ultimately come about from the discoveries that result from systematic fundamental research. Such research takes money. The annual budget of the United States Government runs to many scores of billions. This includes only about one billion dollars for research and development, of which only about $47,000,000 (about 5 per cent) is at present devoted to fundamental research. Again, the American public in 1955 spent $282,000,000 for chewing gum, but less than $15,000,000 for research in the medical sciences. Yet fundamental research "pays off" in many ways – in a declining death rate, for example – even though the usefulness or applicability of a discovery may not be immediately evident. Fundamental research is essential to the development of our society, and it must have a wider base of support if we are to keep faith with our future.

CONCLUSION

Man is unique. A few simple forms of plant and animal life exist today in essentially the same form as when they evolved many millions of years ago. Some existing forms represent relatively recent varieties of life in an evolutionary sense – perhaps 100,000 generations. But man has arrived at his present state in perhaps only 300 generations. He has learned to control and change his environment. He has learned to have faith in the belief that it is worth while to go on to yet greater control over his environment to free himself for greater things. "In his uniqueness, he [man] is capable of attaining heights far greater than his most magnificent cultural achievements of the past." [1] And one of the most important factors for change and for human achievement in our culture is science.

[1] G. W. Beadle, former president of the American Association for the Advancement of Science.

FOR FURTHER READING

1. AYRES, E., and C. A. SCARLATT, *Energy Sources — The Wealth of the World*. New York: McGraw-Hill Book Company, 1952.

   Discusses the world reserves of energy and points out how energy sources which are not now very important, such as nuclear and solar energy, must be more important in the future.

2. PUTNAM, P. S., *Energy in the Future*. New York: D. Van Nostrand Company, 1953.

   Very comprehensive survey of present uses of energy, present energy resources, and probable trends in consumption of energy in the future. Nuclear fuels will be extensively used by A.D. *2000, but the only long-time hope for relatively cheap energy is solar energy.*

3. Paperback: EDITORS OF SCIENTIFIC AMERICAN, *The Physics and Chemistry of Life*. Simon and Schuster, $1.45.

   Excellent articles on life as a physical process. The questions raised about the nature of life are the kind that can be answered within the disciplines (chemistry and physics) that explain the behavior of nonliving atoms and molecules. The sections dealing with the origin of life, the molecules of life (complex proteins), and the molecule of heredity (desoxyribonucleic acid, or DNA) are recommended.

INDEX

Italic page numbers refer to Figures.